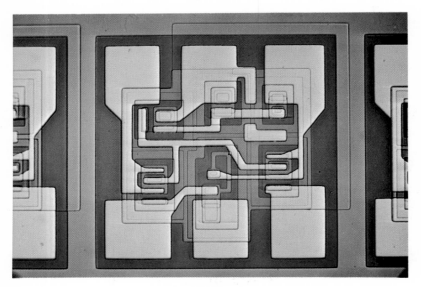

PLATE I

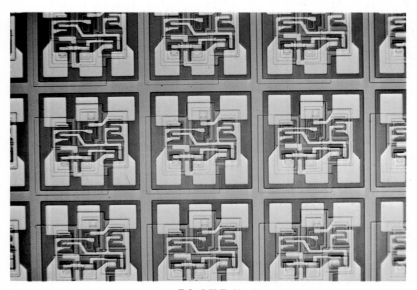

PLATE II

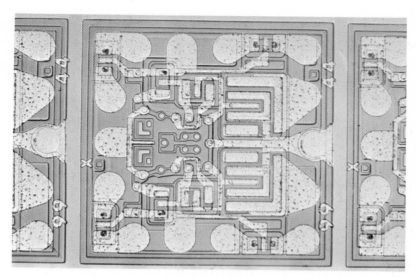

PLATE III

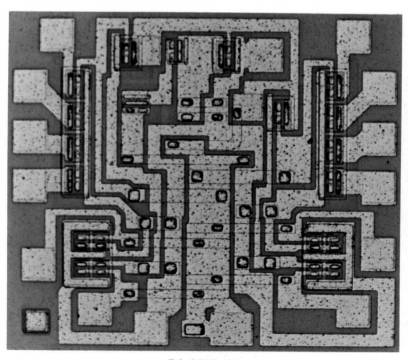

PLATE IV

ELECTRONIC PRINCIPLES

BY THE SAME AUTHORS

Introduction to Electronics, 1967
P. E. Gray

SEMICONDUCTOR ELECTRONICS EDUCATION COMMITTEE BOOKS

Vol. 2 *Physical Electronics and Circuit Models of Transistors*, 1964
P. E. Gray, D. DeWitt, A. R. Boothroyd, and J. F. Gibbons
Vol. 3 *Elementary Circuit Properties of Transistors*, 1964
C. L. Searle, A. R. Boothroyd, E. J. Angelo, Jr.,
P. E. Gray, and D. O. Pederson
Vol. 4 *Characteristics and Limitations of Transistors*, 1966
R. D. Thornton, D. DeWitt, P. E. Gray, and E. R. Chenette
Vol. 5 *Multistage Transistor Circuits*, 1965
R. D. Thornton, C. L. Searle, D. O. Pederson, R. B. Adler, and E. J. Angelo, Jr.
Vol. 6 *Digital Transistor Circuits*, 1966
J. N. Harris, P. E. Gray, and C. L. Searle
Vol. 7 *Handbook of Basic Transistor Circuits and Measurements*, 1966
R. D. Thornton, J. G. Linvill, E. R. Chenette, H. L. Ablin,
J. N. Harris, A. R. Boothroyd, J. Willis, and C. L. Searle

ELECTRONIC PRINCIPLES
Physics, Models, and Circuits

Paul E. Gray

AND

Campbell L. Searle

Massachusetts Institute of Technology

JOHN WILEY & SONS, INC.
New York • London • Sydney • Toronto

We gratefully acknowledge the reproduction, with the permission of the manufacturer, of color slides and photographs of integrated circuits. The cover illustration, and plates I, II and III were provided by Fairchild Semiconductor, Mountain View, California; Plate IV was provided by Motorola Semiconductor Products, Inc., Phoenix, Arizona.

20 19 18 17 16 15 14 13 12 11

Library of Congress Catalogue Card Number: 78–107884
ISBN 471 32398 5

Printed in the United States of America

To our teachers and our students.

Now separated by two generations, their joint influence on the creation
of this book defies measure or acknowledgement.

PREFACE

The trend toward the use of integrated circuits in electronic systems, which started in the early 1960's, is now firmly established. This revolutionary change in the conceptualization and fabrication of electronic systems has almost obliterated the traditional boundaries between the three disciplines of device or component design, circuit design, and system design. Instead, two broadly defined disciplines are emerging from the areas of activity that encompass electronics from devices through systems. The first of these disciplines is concerned with the general area of devices and circuits; the second is concerned with circuits and systems.

The devices-and-circuits area is primarily the province of those who design and manufacture integrated circuits, discrete semiconductor devices, and other "components" of modern electronics. Engineers who work in this area of activity must be knowledgeable in semiconductor fabrication technology, in the physical electronics and circuit modeling of semiconductor components, and in the methods and techniques of circuit analysis and design; their activity is subject to the constraints and opportunities of both device technology and circuit theory. In addition, the device-and-circuits engineer must have a sufficient knowledge of systems engineering to enable him to communicate with the users of his products who work at the systems design level.

The engineers who design electronic systems must be competent in a broad area that includes circuits as well as systems, because this task involves both the exploitation of integrated-circuit functional blocks, such as operational amplifiers, logic gates, and memory elements, and the use of passive components and discrete transistors in "interfaces" between integrated assemblies. In addition to being thoroughly familiar with both circuit theory and system theory, these engineers should have some knowledge of device structure and behavior to facilitate communication with those who work in the devices-and-circuits area and to facilitate the intelligent design of circuits that make use of semiconductor components.

During the same time that semiconductor integrated circuits have come to the fore in electronics, there has occurred an explosive growth both in the use of high-speed computational methods in engineering design and in the availability of computational facilities on university campuses and at industrial laboratories. As a result, it is now commonplace to undertake the analysis of circuits and systems that are orders of magnitude more complex than those that could be studied only a few years ago.

This book has been shaped to meet the educational needs implied by the dominance of integrated circuits in electronic technology and by the use of digital computers in engineering design. Thus the book begins with the physical principles that are involved in the operation of semiconductor components, proceeds through the physical electronics, modeling, and circuit characteristics of these components, and engages the questions and problems that arise in the computer-aided design of complex multistage amplifiers and functional assemblies of the type found in modern integrated-circuit packages.

The book covers five principal areas:

An introduction to electronics
Semiconductor physics
Device physical electronics, models, and properties
Multistage circuits in which transistors are used as linear amplifiers
Multistage circuits in which transistors are used as switches

Chapter 1 serves as an introduction by illustrating the nature and use of an electronic control valve. Many of the device and circuit issues that are studied in detail later are introduced in this chapter. The semiconductor active device that is used as a vehicle in this introductory motivational development is the metal-oxide-semiconductor-field-effect transistor—the MOSFET. It was chosen because its physical operation is, at the qualitative level, relatively transparent. For those users of this book who prefer to employ vacuum tubes as the vehicle, Appendix A provides a parallel development of the introductory material in which the vacuum triode is used as a representative control valve. Those who wish to develop the physical electronics of vacuum tubes beyond the qualitative level will find the material in Appendix B appropriate for that purpose.

Chapters 2 through 5 provide a self-contained treatment of those aspects of the electrical properties of semiconductors, the physical electronics of *pn* junctions, and semiconductor-device-fabrication technology that are essential to an understanding, at the quantitative level, of the behavior of semiconductor active devices and integrated circuits. Although familiarity with elementary electrostatics and with the general concepts of the structure of atoms and of solids is assumed, no quantitative background in modern physics or in quantum theory is assumed or expected.

The fundamental features of electrical conduction in semiconductors, which involves the flow of two independent, oppositely charged carriers—holes and conduction electrons—are made plausible by use of the qualitative valence-bond model of a semiconductor. The dynamical features of charge carriers—drift, diffusion, and recombination—are introduced as postulates amply supported by direct experimental evidence. Following this development of the pertinent features of semiconductor behavior, the internal physical behavior of *pn* junction structures is developed in quantitative terms.

We have chosen to introduce the electrical behavior of semiconductors in this way rather than in terms of elementary wave mechanics, quantization in the hydrogen atom, and the energy-band model of a semiconductor, for two reasons. First, there is generally not enough time available in a first course in electronics to do justice, in quantitative terms, to the energy-band model of a semiconductor. Consequently, most efforts to introduce these concepts at this level in the undergraduate curriculum amount only to the establishment of a vocabulary; they develop very little real understanding or facility with the quantitative capabilities of the model. Second, it has been our experience that the level of development of the electrical aspects of semiconductor physics presented in this book is entirely adequate as a basis for the detailed quantitative development of the physical electronics of semiconductor active devices.

Chapters 6 through 14 deal with the physical electronics, circuit modeling, and circuit properties of the most important semiconductor components, including junction diodes, bipolar junction transistors, unipolar (field-effect) junction transistors, and metal-oxide-semiconductor unipolar or field-effect transistors. Throughout this development the emphasis is on the establishment of a framework of internal physical behavior, a framework that supports and relates a hierarchy of circuit models. For example, the picture of the distribution and flow of excess carriers in the base region of the bipolar transistor provides a basis for the Ebers-Moll total-variable static model, the charge-control total-variable dynamic model, and the hybrid-pi linear incremental model. In exploring the elementary circuit properties of transistors we have emphasized the importance of choosing a circuit model that is appropriate to the circuit issues of concern.

Chapters 15 through 20 are concerned with multistage applications of transistors, in which the active devices are used as linear control valves. The important topic of feedback in linear amplifier is considered in detail. Throughout this portion of the text, extensive use is made of automatic-computational methods for the analysis of complex circuits. However, such computations rarely provide the insight required for good circuit design; hence simple approximate design methods are also developed, and their limitations and ranges of validity are explored.

Chapters 21 through 24 deal with application of the transistor as a switch. The emphasis is on multiple-component circuits that are used for the processing of information in digital form. Once again, automatic-computational methods are used extensively in circuit analysis to indicate the nature and limitations of approximate methods of analysis.

The material in this book can be covered in two or three semesters, depending on the amount of classroom time devoted to the many worked-out examples that are included in the text. More of such examples have been included than would normally be used in one particular year, to provide the instructor with more flexibility in his teaching. We have taught essentially all of this material to undergraduates in the Department of Electrical Engineering at M.I.T. at least twice, in the following sequence:

Second term, sophomore year (the first course in electronics): Chapters 1 through 7, selected topics from Chapters 8 through 11.

First and second terms, junior year (an elective in semiconductor electronics): Chapters 12 through 22, Chapter 24, selected topics from Chapter 23.

Obviously we have arranged the twenty-four chapters in the order in which we believe they are best taught. Nevertheless, in an effort to meet the diverse needs of other users we have organized the book in a flexible format, and other orderings of the chapters are possible. For example, Chapter 8, on the active-region charge-control model can be delayed until after Chapter 20 without loss of continuity. Alternatively, the four chapters on digital circuits, Chapters 21 through 24, can be moved to a much earlier point, for example, ahead of the multistage linear amplifier discussion starting with Chapter 15. On a smaller scale, many sections (marked with an asterisk) throughout the book can be delayed or omitted entirely without loss of continuity.

We have, in teaching this material over a period of many years, made intensive use of lecture demonstrations to reinforce concepts presented in the classroom. Such demonstrations allow the students to see, in graphic sequential terms, the consequences of the variation of a particular parameter. Also, demonstrations provide a forceful tie to the "real world," a tie that is of great value to both student and teacher: on more than one occasion a discussion or a lecture has been revised to conform more closely to the final arbiter—the reality of an experiment. Whatever the reason, there is no denying that lecture demonstrations are a profoundly effective teaching tool. We have, therefore, included suggested demonstrations at the end of many chapters. These should not be allowed to limit the individual instructor; rather, they should serve as a point of departure for the imagination and interests of the teacher and student. The only nonstandard equipment required is a television camera ($300 to $400), with an $f/1.6$ close-up lens ($165) and one or two 23-inch television monitors.

In teaching this material we have found it possible to make effective use of open-ended design problems, problems that emphasize the interdependent roles of experience, intuition, and analysis in the development of new solutions to real problems. For example, the presentation of the instructional sequence on multistage amplifiers culminates in a two-week take-home quiz that requires the students to design a video amplifier with a voltage gain magnitude of 3000 and a bandwidth of 10 MHz. Computer verification of the design has been required, and in many cases students also checked their amplifiers experimentally in the laboratory. Students have been uniformly enthusiastic about such design problems. They find it exciting and challenging to work on their own designs, rather than regurgitating some material already predigested by the instructor. In 65 solutions received during one recent semester, there were 14 topologically different designs, and of course no two of the 65 solutions were completely alike. The designs submitted ranged all the way from a three-stage common-emitter cascade to a six-transistor amplifier made up of a cascade of three cascode (common-emitter, common-base) circuits. Such a level of sophistication is well beyond what had been taught in class in previous years, let alone generated by students.

During the past eight years about 1200 M.I.T. undergraduate students have studied from portions of the material presented here. They have thus left their marks on this book, through their critical questions, their constructive criticism, and their insistent pressure for understanding in depth.

A few of our students have devoted substantial time to this effort outside the classroom: L. W. Banks, S. G. Finn, M. E. Jernigan, G. K. Montress, W. H. Ryder, R. K. Stockwell, and R. C. Walleigh. We gratefully acknowledge their efforts in proofreading manuscript and preparing computer solutions. The computer programs listed in the appendices were written by Robert Voit and William Ohm. Most of the lecture demonstrations were prepared by Michael Monet.

It will be clear to any reader who is familiar with the Semiconductor Electronics Education Committee texts that we have drawn heavily on our experience on that Committee in writing this text. We wish to acknowledge the indirect help of the members of that Committee. In addition, we wish to acknowledge the contributions made to this book by Professors R. B. Adler, R. D. Thornton, and B. D. Wedlock through many discussions in the course of teaching this material at M.I.T.

Most of the manuscript typing was done by Mrs. Donna T. Spencer and Miss Jean Gorrasi: their help and good humor in the face of impossible time schedules is gratefully acknowledged.

During both the initial and the final stages of preparation, the manuscript was reviewed in detail by professors from ten universities representing a broad spectrum of approaches to the teaching of semiconductor electronics. We wish to acknowledge the valuable advice provided by these reviewers, and hope that we have been responsive to their suggestions.

Cambridge, Mass.   *Paul E. Gray*
June 1969   *Campbell L. Searle*

CONTENTS

List of Frequently used Symbols

a	Gain of the amplifier in a feedback block diagram.
a_o	Mid-frequency value of a.
b	Imaginary part of an admittance.
A	Junction area.
C	Capacitance.
C_b	Incremental base-charging capacitance.
C_{gs}	Incremental gate-to-source capacitance.
C_{gd}	Incremental gate-to-drain capacitance.
C_j	Incremental junction space-charge-layer-capacitance.
C_{jc}	Incremental capacitance of the collector junction.
C_{je}	Incremental capacitance of the emitter junction.
C_μ	Incremental feedback capacitance in a bipolar transistor.
C_π	Incremental capacitance $(C_b + C_{je})$ in the hybrid-pi model.
D	Charge-carrier diffusion coefficient.[1]
$\mathscr{E}$	Electric field.
$\mathscr{E}_o$	Oxide-layer electric field in an MOS transistor.
$\mathscr{E}_0$	Electric field at the metallurgical boundary of a pn junction.
f	Gain of the feedback network in a feedback block diagram.
f_o	Mid-frequency value of f.
f_T	The frequency at which the magnitude of the incremental short-circuit common-emitter current gain extrapolates to unity.
G, g	Conductance, real part of an admittance.
g_m	Incremental transconductance of a transistor.
g_o	Incremental output conductance.
g_x	Incremental base conductance.

[1] In designating diffusion coefficients and mobilities, the subscripts e and h are generally used to denote that the parameters describe the dynamical properties of electrons or holes, respectively. With reference to *bipolar* transistors, the subscripts e, b, and c are used to indicate that the parameter applies to the minority carriers in the emitter, base and collector regions. In the few cases where majority-carrier diffusion coefficients or mobilities are used, double subscripts are employed if there is a possibility of confusion.

g_π — Incremental conductance in the hybrid-pi model.

h — Two-port incremental h parameter.[2]

I, i — Electric current.[3]

I_{CBO}, I_{CO} — The collector-junction saturation current of a transistor with the emitter open.

I_{CS} — The collector-junction saturation current of a transistor with the emitter shorted to the base.

I_{EO} — The emitter-junction saturation current of a transistor with the collector open.

I_{ES} — The emitter-junction saturation current of a transistor with the collector shorted to the base.

I_s — Saturation current of an idealized junction diode.

J — Electric current density. Subscripts h and e denote hole and electron current densities.

k — Boltzmann's constant.

K_E, K_C — Parameters that relate the emitter and collector space-charge-layer charges to the junction voltages.

[2] The h, y, and z two-port parameters are identified with a double-subscript notation. The *first* subscript denotes the *function* of the parameter:

    i Input driving-point parameter
    o Output driving-point parameter
    f Forward transfer parameter
    r Reverse transfer parameter

When these parameters are used to describe transistor properties the *second* subscript denotes the *configuration*:

    e Common emitter s Common-source
    b Common-base g Common-gate
    c Common-collector d Common-drain

When these parameters are used to describe the components of a feedback connection, the second subscript is either a (which applies to the basic amplifier) or f (which applies to the feedback network).

[3] Currents and voltages at the terminals of diodes and transistors are designated in the following manner: Subscripts are used to indicate the terminal at which a current flows (reference direction is *in* at the terminal) or the terminal pair at which a voltage appears (reference direction is defined by the order of the subscripts; the plus sign is associated with the terminal identified by the first subscript). Variables of four types are defined:

    D-c or operating-point variables—upper-case symbols with upper-case subscripts
    Total instantaneous variables—lower-case symbols with upper-case subscripts
    Incremental instantaneous variables—lower-case symbols with lower-case subscripts
    Complex amplitudes of incremental components—upper-case symbols with lower-case subscripts

A voltage v or V next to a node is assumed to be measured with respect to ground, i.e. it is a node-to-datum voltage. Unless otherwise marked, the reference direction is such that the node is positive with respect to ground when v or V is positive.

L	Channel length in a field-effect transistor; excess-carrier diffusion length.
l	Total width of the depletion layer at a junction.
l_n	Width of the portion of the depletion layer lying in the n-type material.
l_p	Width of the portion of the depletion layer lying in the p-type material.
M	Avalanche multiplication ratio; rate of surface generation of excess carriers (per unit time, per unit area).
N	Net impurity concentration, i.e., excess of donor concentration over acceptor concentration.
N_a	Acceptor impurity concentration.
N_A	Acceptor concentration on the p-type side of an abrupt pn junction.
N_d	Donor impurity concentration.
N_D	Donor concentration on the n-type side of an abrupt pn junction.
n	Electron concentration.[4]
n'	Excess electron concentration.[4]
$n_i, n_i(T)$	Intrinsic carrier concentration.
p	Hole concentration.[4]
p'	Excess hole concentration.[4]
q	Magnitude of the electronic charge.
q_B	Total excess charge stored in the base of a bipolar transistor.
q_F	Forward component of the excess charge stored in the base of a bipolar transistor.
q_R	Reverse component of the excess charge stored in the base of a bipolar transistor.
q_S	Saturation charge stored in the base of a transistor.
q_V	Charge in either half of the dipole layer in a junction-space-charge region, measured with respect to the charge at $V = 0$.
q_{VE}	Emitter junction space-charge-layer charge.
q_{VC}	Collector junction space-charge-layer charge.
Q	Quality factor of a complex pole pair.
Q_{FO}, Q_{RO}	Parameters that relate the forward and reverse components of the excess base region charge to the junction voltages.
R, r	Resistance.
r_x	Incremental base resistance.
$\mathscr{R}$	Rate of recombination (per unit time, per unit volume) of excess carriers.
r_π	Incremental resistance in the hybrid-pi model.

---

[4] In designating carrier concentrations in junction devices, the semiconductor region is indicated by a subscript n or p for a diode or e, b, or c for a bipolar transistor. The use of a second subscript o denotes the thermal-equilibrium value of the corresponding concentration.

s	Complex frequency variable.
t_d	Delay time.
t_f	Fall time.
t_r	Rise time.
t_{sd}	Storage-delay time.
T	Absolute temperature.
V, v	Terminal-pair voltage (see footnote 3, *supra*).
V_i	Junction voltage, i.e., the change in the height of the potential barrier at a junction.
V_p	Pinch-off voltage of a field-effect transistor.
W	Width of the neutral base region in a transistor or thin-region diode.
y	Two-port incremental y or admittance parameter (see footnote 2, *supra*).
z	Two-port incremental z or impedance parameter.
α	Incremental common-base short-circuit current gain.
α_F	Large-signal forward-injection common-base short-circuit current gain.
α_R	Large-signal reverse-injection common-base short-circuit current gain.
β	Incremental common-emitter short-circuit current gain.
β_o	Low-frequency value of β.
β_F	Large-signal forward-injection common-emitter short-circuit current gain.
β_R	Large-signal reverse-injection common-emitter short-circuit current gain.
γ_s	Surface charge density.
Δ	Designates a small change when used in front of a variable; a determinant.
∇	Denotes *gradient* of a function.
δ	Recombination defect.
ϵ	Absolute dielectric permittivity.
μ	Charge carrier mobility (see footnote 1, *supra*).
ρ	Space-charge concentration.
σ	Electrical conductivity.
τ	Time constant; lifetime of excess charge carriers.
τ_{BF}	Effective base-region lifetime with forward injection.
τ_{BR}	Effective base-region lifetime with reverse injection.
τ_F	Forward injection charge-control parameter.
τ_{jo}	Time constant associated with capacitor j with all other capacitors open-circuited.
τ_{js}	Time constant associated with capacitor j with all other capacitors shorted.
τ_R	Reverse injection charge-control parameter.

τ_S Saturation region charge-control parameter.

ψ Electrostatic potential.

ψ_0 Thermal equilibrium electrostatic potential barrier at a *pn* junction (contact potential).

ω Angular frequency.

ω_b Transverse cutoff frequency.

ω_h The frequency above the midfrequency range at which the gain magnitude has dropped to 0.707 of its midfrequency value.

ω_l The frequency below the midfrequency range at which the gain magnitude has dropped to 0.707 of its midfrequency values.

ω_T Angular frequency at which the magnitude of the incremental short-circuit common-emitter current gain extrapolates to unity.

ELECTRONIC PRINCIPLES

CHAPTER ONE

Electronic Circuits, Devices, and Models

1.1 Introduction

The engineer's stock in trade is the ability to develop technological solutions to problems that grow out of social and economic needs. Familiar examples of such problems can be found in the broadly defined areas of communications, information processing, distribution and control of energy, and the monitoring and control of natural and industrial processes.

Much of the technological activity that concerns electrical engineers relates to *electric circuits*. In general, circuits are interconnections of circuit *components* such as resistors, capacitors, semiconductor devices, vacuum tubes, and relays, which perform required functions in engineering systems. Of course, the family of generic types of circuit components is enormous, and so is the range of application of circuit techniques.

The technical concerns of the circuit engineer often center in the problem of *circuit design*. That is, the engineer is presented with the desired functional behavior of a required piece of equipment or subsystem and is expected to devise specific interconnections of specific components in such a way that the complete assembly will have the prescribed characteristics. Circuit design is a creative activity that requires not only experience and skill but intuition and luck as well; it also calls for an intimate knowledge of the circuit properties of available components, as well as the ability to predict the behavior of circuits comprised of interconnections of these components. Thus circuit design is based on a blend of two complementary aspects of electric circuits. The first relates to the electrical description of the components used in circuits and is called *modeling*. The second relates to the mathematical description of interconnections of models of components and is called *circuit theory* or *network theory*.

Device modeling begins with a description of a component in physical and structural terms, and arrives, both by processes of approximation and analysis of the internal mechanisms of operation and by interpretation of measurements, at a description of the electrical behavior of that component as viewed at its terminals. These descriptions or models are usually expressed in terms of simple idealized circuit abstractions or *elements*.

Circuit theory, on the other hand, begins with statements, in circuit terms, of the laws of conservation of charge and conservation of energy, and develops techniques and points of view that are useful in expressing, in mathematical terms, the behavior of topological arrangements of models of circuit components. The emphasis in circuit theory is on the development of insights that have broad applicability to circuits comprised of the simple idealized circuit elements used to construct models.

This book introduces the study of electronic circuits and of the electronic components, such as transistors, that endow these circuits with useful special properties. The development of the material here assumes a knowledge of elementary circuit theory.[1] Our treatment of electronics differs from that in traditional introductory studies of circuit theory in three principal respects. First, it is concerned with the general class of circuit components known as *active devices* or *control valves*. Second, it deals at length with the *modeling*, or characterization in circuit terms, of the properties of these devices. Third, it emphasizes the analysis and design of the relatively complex circuits in which active electronic devices are used. Before turning to specific examples of electronic circuits and components as illustrations of the scope of our concerns, we discuss the peculiar attributes of the class of components known as active devices and consider some of the implications of our concern for models and the modeling process.

1.1.1   Power Control and Active Devices

Introductory studies of circuit theory are usually restricted to simple *passive* circuit components and to *independent sources*. Passive circuit components are dissipative elements and are incapable of *controlling* the flow of energy in a circuit. Furthermore, most have only *two terminals* or points of connection to a circuit (transformers are exceptions; although they have three or more terminals, they are passive components). Resistors, capacitors, and inductors are the simplest and most familiar examples of passive circuit components. All are incapable of controlling the flow of energy in a circuit. This feature is obvious in resistors, which can only absorb energy when connected in a circuit. Although capacitors and inductors can store energy, they cannot return to a circuit more energy than was previously supplied to them. In fact, all inductors and capacitors are imperfect stores of energy because of residual loss mechanisms, which cause them to dissipate some of the energy supplied to them. Independent sources are components that generate prescribed signals and are capable of delivering electric power to a circuit on a sustained basis. Common examples are batteries and sine-wave sources of alternating current.

Circuits comprised only of passive components and energized by independent sources have important uses. For example, tuned or resonant circuits comprised of inductors and capacitors can be used as selective filters. Many communications systems use such *LC* filters to select, on the basis of frequency, one signal out of many. The most common examples are found in radio and television receivers. Circuits comprised of passive components can also be used to perform certain linear operations, such as differentiation or integration, in signal-processing applications.

Nevertheless, circuits that have only passive components are incapable of performing one of the most vital operations expected of electronic circuits—

---

[1] Any one of References 1.1 through 1.13 provides appropriate coverage.

amplification. As an example of the function of amplification, consider the transmission of speech over long distances by wire. Because of losses in the telephone cables, the waveform that conveys the information is gradually attenuated as the length of the cable is increased. Consequently, repeaters or amplifiers, powered by local sources of energy (batteries or the power line), are required at regular intervals to amplify the signal. Their action results in control by the input signal of the flow of energy from the local energy source to the outgoing cable so that the output signal is a scaled-up or amplified replica of the input signal, as shown in Fig. 1.1*a*. The essential features of this operation are represented in block-diagram form in Fig. 1.1*b*. The flow of energy from the source to the "load", that is, to the outgoing cable, is controlled in some prescribed manner by the input signal. Furthermore, this control is accomplished with the expenditure of relatively little power at the input. That is, the system has the property of *power gain* or *power amplification.*

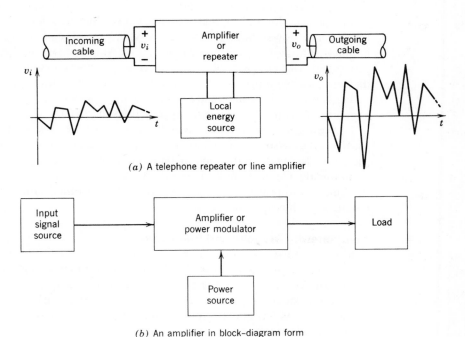

(*a*) A telephone repeater or line amplifier

(*b*) An amplifier in block–diagram form

Figure 1.1 An illustration of the need for active devices.

There are many other familiar examples of the requirement for the control of power in electronic systems. Thus signals that are of nanowatt intensity at the antenna terminals of a receiver must be amplified to control power levels of the order of watts so as to operate output transducers such as loudspeakers and cathode-ray-tube deflection coils. Such requirements for amplification or power gain obviously cannot be met by circuits comprised solely of passive components; the power dissipation that is intrinsic to passive components results in a *loss* of signal power instead of a gain.

The requirement for amplification or power gain in circuits is met by components of the class known as active devices or control valves. Transistors and vacuum tubes are the most familiar electronic examples. These devices can control or modulate the flow of energy in a circuit. Most active devices have three or more terminals and are constructed so that the electrical conditions at one pair of terminals control the flow of energy in a circuit connected at another pair of terminals. If the device is to be useful as a power modulator, the energy controlled by the device must be appreciably larger than the energy required to actuate the device or to exercise control. One of the simplest active devices is the electrical relay. In this active device the magnetic forces produced by current in an actuator coil cause the contacts to be open or closed. The relay is designed so that the contacts can control much more power than is required to energize the coil that actuates the contacts. Thus a relay can have power gain. Although we shall primarily be concerned with active devices that exercise continuous control rather than discrete binary control, and depend on the behavior of electrons in solids rather than on electromagnetic forces for their action, the relay provides a very simple example of the general principles involved.

The concept of *power gain*, involving control of the flow of energy from a local source to some output load in response to an input signal, provides the most satisfactory distinction between passive components and active components. Circuits containing *only* passive components are incapable of the function of power gain. Active devices, on the other hand, can endow a circuit with the capability of power gain.

1.1.2   Components, Models, and Elements

Before we can intelligently use any component in a circuit, be it a simple passive device like a resistor or a relatively complex active device like a transistor, we must have some characterization or description of the electrical behavior of the device. Any description of the electrical behavior of a device, as viewed at its terminals or points of connection to a circuit, constitutes a *circuit model* for that device.

There are, of course, many different models for any device. One approach to the modeling of a component involves the measurement of the electrical behavior of the device at its terminals and the direct use of these measured properties as a model for the device. The measured properties may be presented in tabular form, in graphical form, or in terms of empirically derived functional relationships.

As a general technique, sole reliance on measurements as a device model creates several formidable difficulties. First, the measurements must be made under appropriate environmental and operating conditions. The observed behavior provides, in itself, no basis for understanding the behavior of the device if the environmental or operating conditions are changed. Since the engineer has no theoretical basis for extrapolation of the old measurements to a new domain of interest, his only recourse is to obtain measurements that are relevant under the new conditions. Thus if the characteristics of the device are observed to depend, for example, on the environmental temperature, the measurements must be made at the temperature at which the device will be operated in the intended application. If some of the electrical variables at the terminals are observed to depend not only on the instantaneous values of the other variables but also on their rates of change, the measurements must be made under dynamic conditions that correspond closely to the actual conditions under which the device will operate. Characterization of a device solely on the basis of measurements, therefore, generally produces a large atlas of information that is not structured and may be difficult to use in situations not envisioned by the person who compiles the atlas.

These difficulties are so troublesome that every serious effort to model the behavior of *every* device is guided by some understanding of the internal physical behavior of that device. If we understand, at almost any level, how a device is constructed and how it behaves, in terms of the basic internal physical mechanisms, we are guided in its characterization in at least two respects. First, we are better able to select terminal measurements that will yield significant device parameters applicable over wide ranges of operation. Second, we can develop a theoretical framework that gives structure and coherence to the measurements. This theoretical framework also provides a basis for extrapolation of measured parameters to new domains of applicability. Of course, the more we know about the internal physical behavior of a device, the greater is our leverage both in specifying the critical measurements that should be made to characterize the device and in assembling a model that is compact, precise, and of broad applicability.

The immediate result of this process of theoretical analysis of physical behavior and interpretation of measurements is a description of electrical behavior consisting of a set of functional relationships in which the terminal voltages and currents (and their rates of change) are the pertinent variables. Such a model is less than satisfactory for many applications because it requires that the behavior of a circuit that uses the device be investigated by means of numerical (or perhaps graphical) techniques of analysis. Thus we are prevented from making use of the repertoire of analytical methods and points of view developed in the study of passive linear circuits. To partially circumvent this limitation, we seek a model for a component in which the required functional relationships are manifested by an appropriate inter-connection of idealized *circuit elements*. These are mathematically defined abstractions that express simple, widely useful relationships among currents and voltages (or their rates of change).

It is necessary to distinguish very carefully between circuit *components* or devices and circuit *elements*. We designate the physical devices or hardware used in circuits as *components*. In contrast, the idealized abstractions of which models are built, and which form the basis of circuit theory, are called *elements*. Thus a resistor, a transistor, and a battery are components, whereas a resistance (defined by $e = Ri$), an inductance (defined by $e = L\,di/dt$), and a voltage source [defined by $e = f(t)$] are elements. Elements appear in the differential equations of circuit theory; components appear on parts lists and in purchase orders.

In modeling a component, the number and type of elements used and the complexity of the model that results depend both on the complexity of the component and on the precision of the description. In many cases extremely simple models suffice. Consider, for example, the electrical behavior of a simple tubular capacitor. This device is made by rolling into cylindrical form a sandwich comprised of two metal foils and a dielectric (which may be paper or a plastic film), as shown in Fig. 1.2a. The simplest possible model

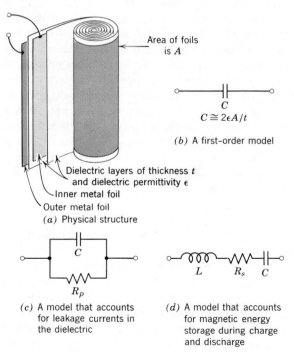

Area of foils
is A

C

$C \cong 2\epsilon A/t$

(*b*) A first-order model

Dielectric layers of thickness t
and dielectric permittivity ϵ

Inner metal foil

Outer metal foil

(*a*) Physical structure

C

R_p

(*c*) A model that accounts
for leakage currents in
the dielectric

L R_s C

(*d*) A model that accounts
for magnetic energy
storage during charge
and discharge

Figure 1.2   Physical structure and models for a capacitor.

for this device consists of a single capacitance, as shown in Fig. 1.2*b*. If the capacitor is used to store energy for an extended period, this minimal model is inadequate; a charge placed on the capacitor decays with time even when the capacitor leads are open-circuited. This decay, which results from leakage currents in the dielectric, can be accounted for by adding a resistance to the model, as shown in Fig. 1.2*c*. Other applications may require other extensions of the model. For example, if the capacitor is charged and then discharged by shorting the terminals together, the discharge current may have a damped oscillatory character. This behavior, which is concerned with the storage of energy in the magnetic field associated with the discharge current, can be accounted for by adding an inductance and a series resistance to the model, as shown in Fig. 1.2*d*.

We have introduced this brief and incomplete example of the modeling of a passive component to illustrate the way in which a component can be represented by a mathematical abstraction called a model, which consists of an interconnection of idealized elements. In fact, most passive components can be represented by models that use only a few elements of the *RLC* variety; for many purposes a capacitor is adequately modeled by a single capacitance, as in Fig. 1.2*b*. Consequently, modeling issues usually are suppressed in introductory studies of circuit theory, and idealized elements are postulated at the outset, without reference to physical components.

The modeling of active devices is different in two important respects. First, the variety of common, widely applied active devices is so great that no simple generalized model is adequate, even for the purposes of crude first-order estimates of performance. Second, active devices are nonlinear, and characterization of these nonlinearities requires a larger repertoire of elements than resistance, capacitance, and inductance. Thus we shall find it necessary to define several nonlinear elements as we develop circuit models for active devices. Of course, the presence of nonlinear elements in models —elements that are unfamiliar from a study of linear circuit theory—requires that we extend our techniques of circuit analysis accordingly.

The process of modeling active electronic devices is one of the principal themes of this book. Four thoughts are vital to this issue, and are applicable whether the device to be characterized is a transistor, a vacuum tube, or any other circuit component.

1. The modeling process depends, essentially, on measurements. Although analysis of the internal physical behavior of the device guides the modeling process and leads to the specification of a topological arrangement of idealized elements as characteristic of the behavior of the device, the engineer ultimately depends on measurements as the basis for numerical specification of the models. Some of these measurements may be of electrical behavior at the terminals; others may be of internal structure and parameters.

2. Any model can represent the behavior of a component only under appropriately limited operating conditions. For circuit models of electrical devices, these limits usually apply to the terminal currents and voltages and to their rates of change. For example, a resistor can be modeled for many purposes by means of the ideal circuit element called resistance. Such a model can be quite accurate and has broad utility. It ceases to be useful, however, when the current through the resistor is large enough to cause appreciable heating, when the rates of change of the terminal variables are so large that the power required to change the energy stored in the electromagnetic fields associated with the resistor becomes comparable to the power dissipated, or when the signals applied to the resistor are so small that the random thermal noise generated within the resistor itself is significant. Although models can be developed to account for each of these effects in a resistor, a *single* model that accounts for all these effects would be too complicated to be useful to the circuit engineer. Furthermore, there is no single application in which all of these effects are important. It is much more reasonable to devise a family of models for a resistor, each of which applies under appropriately limited operating conditions. The same is true of models for control valves.

3. Even after a model appropriate to the operating conditions has been selected, there remains the issue of precision. The precision with which a model describes a device need only be adequate for the application under consideration. There is little virtue in devising a model that will characterize the behavior of a component with errors that are less than 0.1% of the values of the variables if the circuit that uses the component contains other components having 20% tolerances. In general, increased accuracy in a model requires increased complexity which, in turn, implies greater difficulty in analysis of the circuit in which the model is used. Thus it is important to choose a model that is no more powerful than demanded by the nature of the application and the accuracy of description. Modeling and the analysis of circuits that contain active devices inevitably require a compromise between accuracy and completeness, on the one hand, and complexity and analytical difficulty, on the other hand. It is essential to recognize the need for this compromise and to make it consciously, after considering both the operating conditions of interest and the accuracy required.

4. When a model that is adequate in terms of accuracy and operating conditions has been devised, it is important to avoid extrapolation of the results predicated on that model to regions of operation or to levels of accuracy that are not justified by the model itself. Although this need for self-consistency in the application of models may seem obvious, it is not difficult to find examples of incorrect or misleading analytical conclusions that have resulted from overextension of the applicability of a circuit model.

1.2   A Solid-State Active Device

As our first example of an active device, and as a vehicle for an introduction to the issues that arise in electronic circuits, we consider a type of solid-state device known as a *metal-oxide-semiconductor (MOS) transistor*. We consider this device because its structure is simple and its mode of operation can easily be understood, at least at the qualitative level.

1.2.1   Physical Structure

The structure of a typical MOS transistor is illustrated in Fig. 1.3. The device is made on a *substrate* of a *semiconductor*, such as silicon. When we study the electrical properties of semiconductors in detail in Chapter 2, we shall find that these materials are distinguished by the property that electrical conductivity can be varied over extremely wide ranges by controlling precisely the chemical composition of the material. Electrical conduction in any substance is, of course, a consequence of the ordered motion of charged particles, such as electrons, called *charge carriers*. It turns out that the concentration or volume density of the charge carriers in a semiconductor can be varied by controlling the impurity content, that is, the concentrations

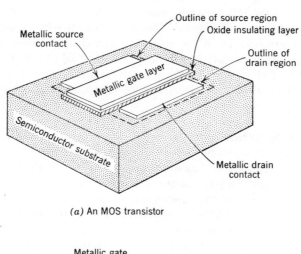

(*a*) An MOS transistor

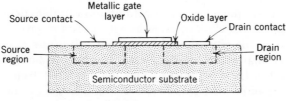

(*b*) Cross section

Figure 1.3   The MOS transistor consists of a sandwich of metal, insulator, and semiconductor layers.

of certain trace impurities. The semiconductor substrate used in the MOS transistor we are describing is chosen and processed so that it has very few electrons available as charge carriers. Thus it is a poor conductor of electricity and behaves almost as an insulator.

The two semiconductor regions denoted in Fig. 1.3 as the *source* and the *drain* differ from the substrate in that the concentration of electrons in these regions is large—many orders of magnitude larger than in the substrate region. We shall see in Chapter 5 that such regions, characterized by electrical properties quite different from those of the substrate, can be made by the selective introduction of impurities in these regions.

The portion of the substrate that lies between the source and drain regions is called the *channel*. The reasons for this name, as well as for the descriptions "source" and "drain," will become clear when we describe the operation of the device. The *channel* region is covered with a thin layer of insulating material, which is usually an oxide. A thin layer of metal film is deposited (usually by evaporation of a metal in a vacuum) on top of the oxide layer that covers the channel. This metal electrode is called the *gate*. Also, metal films are deposited over the source and drain regions for the purpose of making electrical contact to these regions. Wires are bonded to the three metal films and are used to connect the device in a circuit. Because there are three terminals, this device is called a *triode*.

The metal and insulating films have thicknesses ranging from several hundred angstroms to a few microns.[2] The spacing between the source and drain regions is usually in the range of 10 to 20 μ, and the length of these electrodes may be about 10^3 μ (i.e., about a millimeter). Thus the device is extremely small and occupies a total substrate area of only a few square millimeters.

1.2.2 Mode of Operation

We consider first the behavior observed at the source and drain terminals when the gate electrode has nothing connected to it, that is, when it is open-circuited. There is a path from the source region to the gate region through the channel region of the semiconductor. However, since the semiconductor substrate contains very few electronic charge carriers, this path has a very low conductance (or high resistance), and little current results at the source or drain terminals in response to an externally imposed drain-to-source voltage. In terms of the reference directions and variables defined in Fig. 1.4, we have i_D approximately zero even though v_{DS} is nonzero.

Consider now the situation when the gate electrode is connected to a voltage source that makes it *positive* with respect to both the source and drain regions. For the present we assume that v_{DS} is small enough compared with either the impressed gate-to-source voltage v_{GS} or the gate-to-drain

---

[2] An angstrom (Å) is 10^{-8} cm; a micron (μ) is 10^{-4} cm.

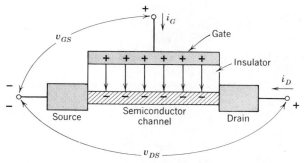

Figure 1.4 Schematic representation of an MOS transistor. The arrows in the insulator show the direction of the field for positive values of gate voltage, that is, for $v_{GS} > 0$. This field originates on positive charge in the gate and terminates on negative charge (electrons) in the channel.

voltage to allow us to neglect the variation of potential along the channel. That is, we assume that the potential variation along the channel produced by v_{DS} is small compared with the potential differences between the gate and the channel produced by v_{GS}. Clearly the gate-insulator-channel sandwich resembles a capacitor. The positive gate-to-source voltage produces an electric field in the insulator. The electric field originates on positive charge distributed along the inner surface of the gate electrode and terminates on negative charge that must be similarly distributed along the channel. This negative channel charge consists of *electrons* that flow into the channel from the metallic source and drain regions. Although the channel itself has few electrons, it is in intimate contact with the two semiconductor regions that are capable of supplying electrons in large quantities. Thus electrons are drawn into the channel by a positive gate-to-channel voltage; once in the channel, they provide the negative charge on which the electric field in the insulator terminates, as suggested in Fig. 1.4.

Note, however, that these extra electrons in the channel are free to move in response to an electric field directed along the channel, that is, from source to drain. Thus these electrons provide a mechanism of conduction in the channel between source and drain and *enhance* the conductivity of that path. The degree of enhancement depends on the value of gate voltage v_{GS}. As v_{GS} increases, the electric field in the insulator increases, the amount of electronic charge required in the channel for termination of that field increases, and the conductance of the channel increases correspondingly. This dependence is illustrated in Fig. 1.5, where channel conductance is shown as a function of the gate-to-source voltage (the source-to-drain voltage is assumed to be small, as discussed previously).

If the gate-to-source voltage has the other polarity, that is, if it is *negative*, the electric field in the insulator has a different distribution and does not

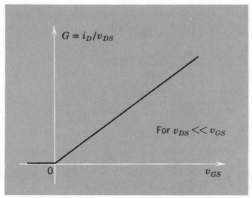

Figure 1.5 The conductance of the channel increases as the gate-to-source voltage increases because the channel charge is enhanced.

increase the channel conductance, as we shall see in Chapter 9. Thus in Fig. 1.5, G is negligible for _negative_ values of v_{GS}.

The dependence of channel conductance on gate voltage can also be displayed by plotting the drain current as a function of the drain-to-source voltage, as shown in Fig. 1.6. The gate-to-source voltage is a parameter in this family of curves; larger values of v_{GS} correspond to increased conductance and thus to greater slopes on the curves of i_D versus v_{GS}. These curves are referred to as the _output_ or _drain characteristics_ of the transistor.

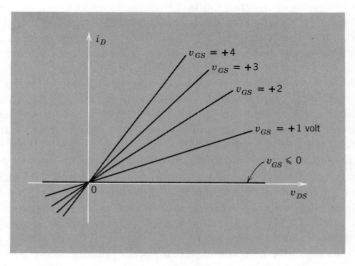

Figure 1.6 Drain characteristics for small values of drain-to-source voltage.

The output characteristics show that this device is active and can function as a control valve. Consider, for example, the simple circuit of Fig. 1.7 in

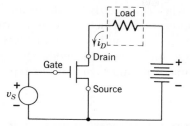

Figure 1.7   A circuit in which an MOS transistor functions as an active device.

which the drain-to-source path (the channel) forms part of a series circuit which contains also a battery and a resistor. The symbol introduced in this sketch is widely used as a "shorthand" notation for an *MOS transistor*. The gate-to-source voltage is controlled directly by the voltage source v_S. When v_S is less than or equal to zero, the channel conductance is negligibly small and there is no drain current; all of the battery voltage appears across the transistor and no power is delivered to the resistor. If v_S is made positive, the nonzero channel conductance that results permits drain current to flow. Thus the battery supplies power, some of which is dissipated in the resistive load and some of which is dissipated in the transistor. Hence in this circuit the transistor controls the flow of power from the battery to the load. Furthermore, this control is accomplished with the expenditure of very little power at the gate terminal. That is, the signal source v_S supplies very little power because there is negligible gate current; the gate current that results from leakage in the insulating film is usually less than a picoampere (10^{-12} amp).

The physical behavior and electrical characteristics of the MOS transistor change significantly when the drain-to-source voltage becomes large enough to make the variations in potential along the channel important. To illustrate these changes, we consider the consequences of positive values of v_{DS}, which is the polarity of drain-to-source voltage with which the device is normally operated. Note that positive values of v_{DS} correspond to positive values of drain current i_D; the physical mechanism that accounts for this drain current is the flow of electrons along the channel from the source to the drain, which explains the origin of these names.

The effect of increased drain-to-source voltage is to *reduce* the voltage across the insulating film near the drain end of the channel. While the voltage across the insulator is v_{GS} at the source end of the channel, it is only $v_{GS} - v_{DS}$ at the drain end of the channel. Consequently, the density of channel charge (of electrons that terminate the field in the insulator) must decrease as we move along the channel from source to drain. Because of this nonuniform distribution of channel charge, the drain current depends nonlinearly on the drain-to-source voltage and increases less rapidly than at smaller values of v_{DS}. In fact, when v_{DS} exceeds v_{GS}, the drain current *saturates* or reaches a definite maximum value, which depends, of course, on v_{GS}, and does not increase further as v_{DS} continues to increase. The drain characteristics that accompany this saturated mode of operation are illustrated in Fig. 1.8. The numerical values shown are representative of practical MOS transistors.

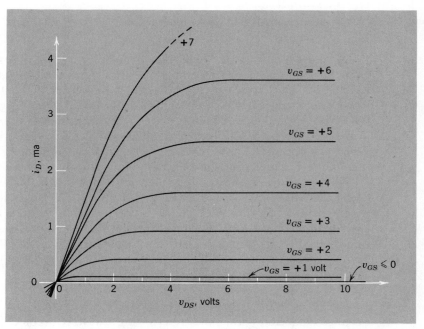

Figure 1.8   Drain characteristics that show the effect of saturation. In the flat portions of the curves the drain voltage exceeds the gate voltage.

The device we have described is an example of a broad class of solid-state active devices known as *field-effect transistors* or *FETs*. This name reflects the essential operating principle of these devices, which involves the modulation of the conductance of a material (the semiconductor) by the effect of an electric field in an adjacent insulator.

1.2.3   A Circuit Model
The description of the electrical behavior of the *FET* given in the preceding section constitutes a useful model for the device. The curves of Fig. 1.8

present the functional relationship

$$i_D = i_D(v_{DS}, v_{GS}) \tag{1.1a}$$

and for the gate current we have

$$i_G \simeq 0 \tag{1.1b}$$

These equations express two of the three terminal currents in terms of two of the three terminal-pair voltages. This is, in fact, a complete description, since Kirchhoff's current law ensures that the third terminal current (i_S) can be expressed in terms of the two given by Eqs. 1.1 and Kirchhoff's voltage law ensures that the third terminal-pair voltage (v_{GD}) can be expressed in terms of the two that appear as independent variables in Eqs. 1.1. That is,

$$i_S = -(i_D + i_G) \tag{1.2a}$$

$$v_{GD} = v_{GS} - v_{DS} \tag{1.2b}$$

Of course, this model (Eqs. 1.1) is limited to a restricted range of operating conditions. Specifically, this model is valid only if the terminal variables are static or changing slowly. If the terminal-pair voltages change rapidly, internal dynamic effects become important, and the currents are found to depend not only on the voltages but on their rates of change as well. We explore the question of dynamic models for FETs and other transistors later.

1.3 An Elementary Amplifier

We shall illustrate the principal performance features of circuits that contain active devices by studying the simple FET circuit shown in Fig. 1.9. This

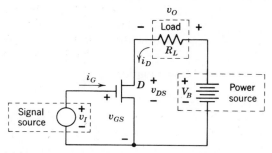

Figure 1.9 A simple triode amplifier circuit.

circuit uses an MOS transistor to control the flow of power from a source (characterized here as a voltage source of value V_B) to a load (characterized by a resistance R_L). This characterization of the load by a resistance would be applicable, under appropriate limiting conditions, for a load such as a loud-speaker, an electromechanical actuator, or a transmission line. The input of the active device—the gate-to-source voltage—is set by a signal source (characterized here by the variable voltage source v_I). Our objective is to determine the dependence of the current i_D in the load (or, equivalently, the voltage v_O across the load) on the signal-source voltage v_I.

From a network point of view, this circuit contains two meshes or loops. The *input* mesh includes the gate-source path in the triode as well as the signal source. The *output* mesh includes the drain-source path in the triode (i.e., the channel), the power source, and the load.

The physical nature of the FET is such that there is negligible gate current. Furthermore, the gate-to-source voltage is directly constrained by the signal source. Thus for the input mesh we may write

$$i_G \simeq 0 \tag{1.3a}$$

$$v_{GS} = v_I \tag{1.3b}$$

Application of Kirchhoff's voltage law to the output mesh yields

$$V_B = v_O + v_{DS} \tag{1.4}$$

or, equivalently,

$$V_B = i_D R_L + v_{DS} \tag{1.5a}$$

The transistor imposes a constraint on i_D and v_{DS}, which is of the form

$$i_D = i_D(v_{GS}, v_{DS}) \tag{1.5b}$$

This constraint can be expressed in graphical form by output characteristics such as those shown in Fig. 1.8.

Since we wish to determine the dependence of the drain current i_D on the signal-source voltage v_I, all that is required is to eliminate v_{GS} and v_{DS} from Eqs. 1.3b, 1.5a, and 1.5b. The problem, of course, is that Eq. 1.5b is nonlinear. At this point in the discussion the only model we have available for the FET is a graphical one, such as Fig. 1.8. Consequently, we turn to graphical methods for the solution of these equations.

1.3.1 Graphical Analysis

We assume for the purposes of this illustration that the FET used in the circuit of Fig. 1.9 is described by the output characteristics of Fig. 1.8. These curves present the *driving-point characteristics* of the transistor at the output terminal pair. That is, they display the dependence of a current at a terminal pair on the voltage at the same terminal pair. Of course, these are parametric curves—the parameter is the voltage at the input terminal pair.

The constraint imposed by the power source and load (Eq. 1.5a) constitutes a linear relationship between the current and voltage variables at the output terminal pair. That is, Eq. 1.5a expresses a linear relationship between i_D and v_{DS}. Consequently, this constraint can be plotted as a *straight line* on the driving-point characteristics at the output terminal pair, that is, on the output or drain characteristics of Fig. 1.8. The straight line that corresponds to the constraint of Eq. 1.5a is called the *load line*.

The intercepts of the load line are, from Eq. 1.5a:

$$\text{when } v_{DS} = 0, \qquad i_D = \frac{V_B}{R_L} \qquad\qquad (1.6a)$$

$$\text{when } i_D = 0, \qquad v_{DS} = V_B \qquad\qquad (1.6b)$$

Thus the load line has a slope, on the i_D versus v_{DS} coordinates:

$$\text{slope} = -\frac{1}{R_L} \qquad\qquad (1.6c)$$

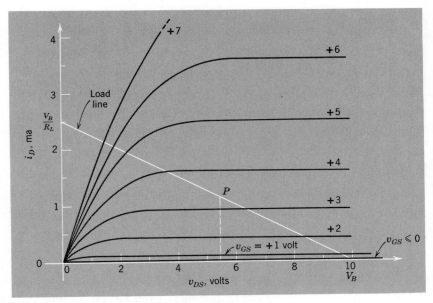

Figure 1.10 Output characteristics with the load line superimposed.

The load-line construction is shown in Fig. 1.10. The parameter values used in making this construction are

$$V_B = 10 \text{ volts}$$

$$R_L = 4 \times 10^3 \text{ ohms} = 4 \text{ kohm}$$

The values of i_D and v_{DS} at which the circuit operates for any particular value of $v_I (= v_{GS})$ correspond to the coordinates of the point of intersection of the load line and the output-characteristic curve for that value of v_{GS}. For example, if $v_I = +3.5$ volts, the state of the circuit is defined by the point P. Thus we have solved the two simultaneous equations (Eqs. 1.5) by graphical analysis.

The manner in which the input voltage v_I controls the load or output voltage v_O can be summarized graphically by means of the voltage *transfer characteristic* shown in Fig. 1.11. The characteristic is generated by

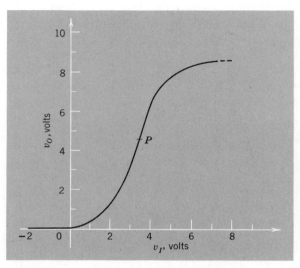

Figure 1.11   Transfer characteristic for the circuit of Fig. 1.9.

considering the set of intersections of the load line with the output characteristics for various values of v_I. For any value of v_I ($= v_{GS}$) the output voltage v_O can be calculated from the value of i_D found from the graph (1.15 ma for point P) and the relation

$$v_O = i_D R_L$$

Hence v_O at point P is $1.15 \times 4 = 4.6$ volts as indicated in Fig. 1.11. Alternatively, we can determine v_O from Eq. 1.4. We find v_{DS} from the graph (5.4 volts for point P) and subtract this from $V_B = 10$ volts to obtain 4.6 volts as before.

The transfer characteristic flattens for negative values of v_I because the triode does not conduct in this region. The characteristic flattens for large positive values of v_I because the curves of the output family become crowded together for small values of v_{DS}. In this region nearly all the supply voltage appears across the load resistor.

1.3.2   Energy Flow

The capability of a transistor to act as a control valve or power modulator is evident from the transfer characteristics of Fig. 1.11. As v_I increases above zero, the voltage v_O and thus the power delivered to the load also increase.

The details of energy flow in this simple triode circuit are important because they illustrate a fundamental property. To investigate the power distribution in the output mesh (there is *no* power developed in the input mesh because we assume that i_G is zero), we multiply Eq. 1.5a, which expresses Kirchhoff's voltage law in that mesh, by i_D, the current in that mesh. The result, slightly rearranged, is

$$i_D{}^2 R_L = V_B i_D - v_{DS} i_D \qquad (1.7)$$

This equation has a simple interpretation. The power delivered to the load is $i_D{}^2 R_L$; the power supplied by the source is $V_B i_D$; the power dissipated as heat in the transistor is $v_{DS} i_D$. Thus Eq. 1.7 states that the power delivered to the load is equal to the power supplied by the energy source reduced by the power dissipated in the active device. The active device, in this case the FET, controls the flow of energy from the source to the load and, in the process, consumes some power itself (unless v_{DS} or i_D is zero).

The transistor in this circuit is considered to have *power gain* because it can control more power than is required at its input terminals. Since the gate current is exceedingly small, the power gain is in this case very large.

1.3.3 Graphical Methods in More Complex Circuits

The load-line construction developed in the preceding section can be adapted to any circuit situation in which a device described in terms of a driving-point characteristic at a terminal pair is embedded in a network consisting solely of sources and linear elements. Any such situation can be analyzed by forming the Thévenin or Norton equivalent network of the linear portion of the circuit and then describing this equivalent network by a load line on the nonlinear characteristics.

As a specific example of such a construction, consider the circuit of Fig. 1.12a. The portion of the network to the right of the terminals labeled *aa'* can be replaced by a Thévenin equivalent network as shown in Fig. 1.12b.

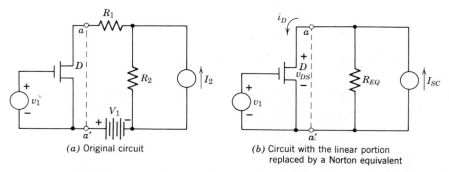

(a) Original circuit

(b) Circuit with the linear portion replaced by a Norton equivalent

Figure 1.12 A transistor circuit in which the linear portion of the network contains several elements.

The elements in this equivalent network are obtained by inspection of the original circuit. The equivalent source resistance R_{EQ} is determined by disconnecting the independent current source I_2 and replacing the independent voltage source V_1 by a short circuit. Thus

$$R_{EQ} = R_1 + R_2 \qquad (1.8a)$$

The open-circuit voltage at the terminals aa' is obviously

$$V_{OC} = I_2 R_2 - V_1 \qquad (1.8b)$$

Thus the short-circuit current at the terminals aa' is

$$I_{SC} = \frac{V_{OC}}{R_{EQ}} = \frac{I_2 R_2 - V_1}{R_1 + R_2} \qquad (1.8c)$$

Consequently, the intercepts of the load line on the output driving-point characteristics of the transistor, which are plotted on the $i_D - i_{DS}$ plane, are:

$$\text{when} \quad i_D = 0, \qquad v_{DS} = V_{OC}$$

$$\text{when} \quad v_{DS} = 0, \qquad i_D = I_{SC}$$

The slope of the load line is, of course, $-1/R_{EQ}$.

The circuit of Fig. 1.13 provides another example of graphical analysis. Because the input and output meshes are coupled by a resistance in the source lead, the gate-to-source voltage is no longer equal to the input signal source voltage as it was in the previous examples.

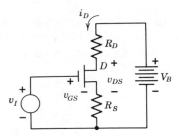

Figure 1.13   A circuit in which the input and output meshes share a common resistance.

Since the gate current is negligible, the current in the common source resistance is just equal to the drain current. Consequently, application of Kirchhoff's voltage law to the two meshes yields:

$$\text{input mesh}: \quad v_I = v_{GS} + i_D R_S \qquad (1.9a)$$

$$\text{output mesh}: \quad V_B = v_{DS} + (R_D + R_S) i_D \qquad (1.9b)$$

The second of these equations defines a load line on the output characteristics of the transistor. The intercepts are:

$$\text{for}\quad i_D = 0,\quad v_{DS} = V_B$$

$$\text{for}\quad v_{DS} = 0,\quad i_D = \frac{V_B}{R_D + R_S}$$

This load line can be used to generate a transfer characteristic which relates the drain current i_D to the gate-to-source voltage v_{GS}. Once this relationship between i_D and v_{GS} has been determined, Eq. 1.9a can be used to relate the signal-source voltage v_I to i_D. Thus the desired relationship that shows the dependence of i_D on v_I is obtained by working "in both directions" from v_{GS}.

1.3.4   Linear Amplification

As we have seen in Fig. 1.1, many applications of electronics present a requirement for linear amplification, that is, for the replication of a signal or waveform at a higher power level. The basic field-effect transistor circuit of Fig. 1.9 can meet this requirement. However, the voltage transfer characteristic of Fig. 1.11 shows clearly that it is not possible to simply connect the input signal at the gate-to-source terminals if linear amplification is desired; the transfer characteristic is nonlinear, and the voltage across the load will in no sense be a scaled-up or amplified replica of the input voltage. If, however, the input signal is limited in its range of excursion, and if it is added to an appropriately chosen dc voltage, a linear relationship between output and input can be obtained. This is possible because there is a portion of the transfer characteristic, in the neighborhood of the point P, in which the output voltage is responsive to changes in the input voltage *and* in which changes in these voltages are approximately linearly related. Thus linear operation can be achieved if the circuit is operated on the portion of the characteristic near P.

A circuit that permits operation near P is shown in Fig. 1.14. Note that the drain power source is not shown explicitly; it is understood to be connected between the terminal labeled $+V_B$ and the "ground" or reference

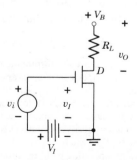

Figure 1.14   A triode circuit in which linear amplification is obtained.

point symbolized by $\perp$. This circuit differs from that discussed in connection with Fig. 1.9 only in that the input voltage v_I, which appears between the gate and the source of the FET, consists of the sum of two component voltages. That is,

$$v_I = V_I + v_i \qquad (1.10)$$

The dc voltage V_I is provided by a fixed voltage source, symbolized by the battery. The signal that is to be amplified is denoted by v_i.[3]

The dc component of the input voltage (V_I) must be chosen so that the circuit operates on a linear portion of the transfer characteristic. We shall arbitrarily assume that the input signal (v_i) has equal positive and negative excursions, and choose V_I so that when the signal voltage is zero, the circuit operates in the middle of the linear region.[4] The point P in Fig. 1.11 is more or less in the middle of the linear portion of the characteristic. This point corresponds to $v_I = +3.5$ volts. Thus we set V_I at this value:

$$V_I = +3.5 \text{ volts}$$

The action of the circuit as a linear amplifier is shown in Fig. 1.15. For the purposes of this illustration, the signal voltage v_i is assumed to be a sine wave of amplitude 0.5 volt. The instantaneous output voltage is determined by projecting the instantaneous input voltage onto the transfer characteristic to find the corresponding value of v_O. This construction is shown for a specific time t_1 by the dotted lines.

The construction of Fig. 1.15 shows clearly that the output voltage has a component that is an amplified replica of the signal component of the input voltage. This sine-wave component is superimposed on a dc component which corresponds, of course, to the value of v_O at the point P. Thus the instantaneous output voltage v_O may be written as

$$v_O = V_O + v_o \qquad (1.11)$$

where V_O is a dc component having a value of about $+4.6$ volts and v_o is the signal component; it is approximated by a sine wave having an amplitude of about 1.5 volts.

---

[3] The notation introduced here is standard for electronic circuits. Instantaneous total variables are set in lower case with uppercase subscripts (v_I). Fixed or dc components appear in upper case with uppercase subscripts (V_I). Instantaneous signal components appear in lower case with lowercase subscripts (v_i). We shall later use uppercase variables with lowercase subscripts to denote complex amplitudes. Although this notation may, at this point, seem cumbersome or unnecessary, some convention is absolutely essential to reduce confusion. This notation has the important advantage of displaying at a glance the type of variable under consideration.

[4] If v_i had unequal positive and negative swings, an operating point toward an extreme of the linear region would be a better choice.

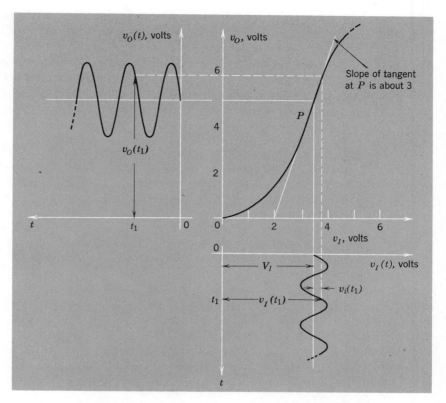

Figure 1.15 If the operating point is properly chosen, and if the range of excursion of the input voltage is limited, linear amplification is obtained.

If we focus attention on the *signal components* v_i and v_o, we find that these are approximately linearly related, as desired. Specifically

$$v_o(t) \simeq 3v_i(t) \qquad (1.12)$$

The *voltage amplification* or *voltage gain* of 3 corresponds to the slope of the transfer characteristic in the region of operation; a tangent to the curve of v_O versus v_I at the point P has a slope of about 3.

This circuit has the property of *power amplification* or *power gain* as well. The average ac power dissipated in the 4 kohm load resistor is

$$P_{AV} = \frac{(1.5)^2}{2 \times 4 \times 10^3}$$

$$\simeq 0.3 \text{ mw}$$

while the power that must be supplied at the input terminals by the signal-voltage source v_i might be as small as a few nanowatts. Thus the power gain can be as large as 10^5 or 10^6.

It is important to recognize that the property we call power gain, which, after all, is what distinguishes this active circuit from a passive transformer with voltage gain, is a manifestation of a controlled transfer of power from the drain power source (V_B) to the load. The transistor simply controls the

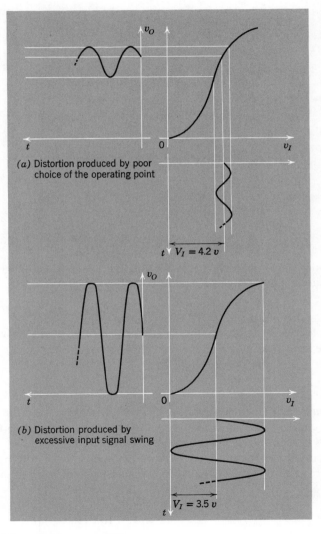

(a) Distortion produced by poor choice of the operating point

(b) Distortion produced by excessive input signal swing

Figure 1.16 Distortion in an amplifier.

flow of power from the source to the load so that the desired replica of the input signal is obtained.

The construction of Fig. 1.15 shows that two conditions must be met if the signal component of the output is to be linearly related to the signal component of the input. First, the dc component of the input voltage must be chosen so that the circuit operates in a linear portion of the transfer characteristic in which there is gain. That is, the *operating point* or *quiescent point* must be properly chosen. The battery that establishes the operating point is often called the *bias source*. Second, the excursion of the input signal must be limited appropriately. If the circuit is improperly biased, or if the input signal voltage is too large, *distortion* will occur as the relationship between the signal components becomes nonlinear, that is, as the instantaneous point of operation moves into a portion of the transfer characteristic where the curvature matters. The effect of distortion on the output signal is illustrated in Fig. 1.16.

1.3.5 Coupling and Bias Circuits

As a practical amplifier, the circuit of Fig. 1.14 has two disadvantages:

1. The input signal source v_i must be connected in series with the bias source V_I. Thus the dc characteristics of an actual signal source might disturb the operating point.

2. The output signal is superimposed on a dc component.

An amplifier circuit in which the input and output terminals are referenced to ground and isolated from the dc power source (V_B) is shown in Fig. 1.17. Since the capacitors block direct current, they isolate the portions

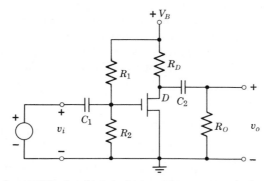

Figure 1.17 An amplifier in which the input and output terminals are isolated from the power source by capacitors.

of the circuit connected to the power source from the terminals. Thus the circuit that governs the operating point of the transistor consists only of R_1, R_2, R_D, and the MOS transistor, as shown in Fig. 1.18. The dc value of

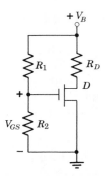

Figure 1.18   Circuit used in determining the operating point of the transistor in Fig. 1.17.

the gate-to-source voltage is governed by the voltage divider comprised of R_1 and R_2:

$$V_{GS} = V_B \frac{R_2}{R_1 + R_2}$$ (1.13)

Thus if we take $V_B = 10$ volts, $R_D = 4$ kohm, $R_1 = 650$ kohm, and $R_2 = 350$ kohm, the dc gate-to-source voltage is 3.5 volts and the operating point is the same as in the circuit of Fig. 1.9; the graphical load-line construction is shown in Fig. 1.10.

Because of the capacitors in the circuit of Fig. 1.17, the output voltage v_o is zero when the input voltage v_i is zero. The input capacitor C_1 charges up to a voltage of V_{GS}, whereas the output capacitor charges to a voltage of V_{DS}, the dc drain-to-source voltage at the operating point.

The capacitors serve to couple the ac input signal (v_i) to the gate and to couple ac components of the drain-to-source voltage to the output terminals, that is, to v_o. If the capacitors are large enough in value so that the changes in the voltages across them are negligible during the time intervals of interest, the *signal component* of the gate-to-source voltage v_{gs} is equal to the input voltage v_i, and the output voltage v_o is equal to the *signal component* of the drain-to-source voltage. That is,

$$v_i = v_{gs}$$ (1.14a)

$$v_o = v_{ds}$$ (1.14b)

Note, however, that when nonzero values of v_i cause the instantaneous point of operation of the transistor to shift away from the quiescent point (P in Fig. 1.10), the motion is *not* along the load line used in determining the operating point. Because the voltage across C_2 does not change, but remains fixed at the value it has when v_i is zero, a change in drain voltage appears across *both* R_D and R_O, and the corresponding change in the drain current is the sum of the changes in the currents in these two resistors. Consequently, the load line that governs ac or signal-produced changes from the operating point has a slope, not of $-1/R_D$, but of[5]

$$\text{slope} = -\frac{1}{R_D \| R_O} = -\frac{R_D + R_O}{R_D R_O} \tag{1.15}$$

The locus of operation, which is called the *ac load line*, has a slope greater than the *dc load line*, as shown in Fig. 1.19, because the ac load resistance

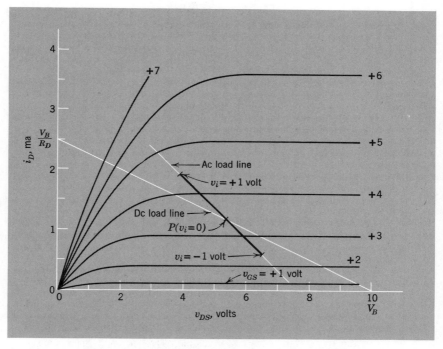

Figure 1.19 The ac load line, which passes through the quiescent operating point, shows the locus of operation for ac signals.

$R_D \| R_O$ is smaller than the dc load resistance (the sketch is drawn for $R_O = R_D$). The darkened portion of the ac load line shows the excursion of the state of the circuit that accompanies an input signal excursion of ± 1 volt. The ac component of the drain-to-source voltage, which can be determined simply by projecting the operating-point excursion along the ac load line onto the voltage axis, is equal to v_o. In this way an *ac transfer characteristic* can be constructed.

An alternative circuit that uses a transformer to separate the output signal voltage from the dc component of the drain voltage and to isolate the

[5] The notation $\|$ is used to denote the parallel combination of resistances.

load resistance R_L from the power source is shown in Fig. 1.20a. The transformer does not, of course, transform the direct current. A model for the transformer that reflects this fact is shown in Fig. 1.20b. The inductance

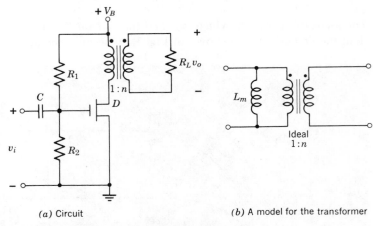

(a) Circuit   (b) A model for the transformer

Figure 1.20   A circuit in which the load is transformer-coupled.

L_m, which is called the *magnetizing inductance*, shorts out the ideal transformer at dc. If L_m is large enough, the current through it does not change appreciably during the time intervals of interest when signals are present, and it can then be ignored.

The ac and dc load lines for this circuit are shown in Fig. 1.21. The dc load line is vertical because there is no dc voltage drop across the transformer.[6]

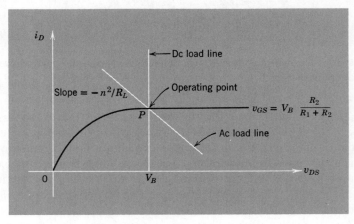

Figure 1.21   Load lines for the circuit of Fig. 1.20.

[6] A more realistic transformer model would allow for winding resistance. The dc load line would then be steep but not vertical.

The quiescent operating point P is set by R_1 and R_2, which govern the dc gate-to-source voltage. The ac load line goes through the operating point with a slope of $-1/(R_L/n^2)$, since the transformed load resistance seen on the primary of the transformer is R_L/n^2. The ac component of the drain-to-source voltage is determined, as in Fig. 1.19, by projecting the variation of the instantaneous operating point on the ac load line onto the voltage axis. This ac voltage is, of course, n times smaller than the ac output voltage v_o. Note that the instantaneous drain-to-source voltage may be larger than V_B in this circuit.

The capacitors used in the two amplifier circuits discussed in this section block dc currents and couple ac signals into (or out of) the amplifier. Thus they are known either as *coupling capacitors* or *blocking capacitors* and are selected so that the signal voltage drops across them are negligible.

1.4   Modeling and Analysis of Linear Active Circuits

As we have seen, amplifiers that employ active devices are often operated in such a way that linear input-output relationships are obtained. This is accomplished by so restricting the range of variation of the currents and voltages at the terminals of the active device that the nonlinearities in its characteristics are not perceived. When this is the case, the signal components of the variables, which measure the departures from a quiescent operating point, are approximately linearly related.

We can make use of the fact that the signal components of the variables are linearly related for small enough excursions to obtain an algebraic description of the behavior of the device. Such a description provides an alternative to the graphical models we have so far considered and makes it possible to bring the powerful tools of linear circuit theory to bear on the analysis of active circuits. We once again employ the MOS field-effect transistor to illustrate this technique.

1.4.1   An Incremental Model

The physical nature of the FET is such that it is sensible to regard the terminal-pair voltages as independent variables and the terminal currents as dependent variables. Thus a formal description of the electrical behavior of the device has the form of Eqs. 1.1, which are repeated here:

$$i_D = i_D(v_{DS}, v_{GS}) \tag{1.16a}$$

$$i_G \simeq 0 \tag{1.16b}$$

We regard each of the terminal variables as comprised of a *quiescent* or dc component and a *signal* component. The quiescent components define the dc operating point; the signal components measure departures from that operating point. Hence, the four instantaneous total variables that appear in Eqs. 1.16 can be written as follows:

$$v_{DS} = V_{DS} + v_{ds} \tag{1.17a}$$

$$v_{GS} = V_{GS} + v_{gs} \tag{1.17b}$$

$$i_D = I_D + i_d \tag{1.17c}$$

$$i_G = I_G + i_g \tag{1.17d}$$

The notation is that introduced in Section 1.3.4; the first terms on the right sides of these equations are the dc components and the second terms are the signal components.

A formal representation of the relationship between the signal components can be obtained by expanding, in Taylor's series about the quiescent state, the functional relationships implied by Eqs. 1.16. Expansion of Eq. 1.16a yields

$$
\begin{aligned}
i_D = i_D|_Q &+ \left.\frac{\partial i_D}{\partial v_{DS}}\right|_Q v_{ds} + \left.\frac{\partial i_D}{\partial v_{GS}}\right|_Q v_{gs} \\
&+ \frac{1}{2!}\left.\frac{\partial^2 i_D}{\partial v_{DS}^2}\right|_Q v_{ds}^2 + \frac{1}{2!}\left.\frac{\partial^2 i_D}{\partial v_{GS}^2}\right|_Q v_{gs}^2 + \left.\frac{\partial^2 i_D}{\partial v_{GS}\,\partial v_{DS}}\right|_Q v_{ds} v_{gs}
\end{aligned}
\tag{1.18}
$$

$$+ \text{ higher-order terms}$$

The notation $i_D|_Q$ or $\partial i_D/\partial v_{DS}|_Q$ indicates that the function or partial derivative is to be evaluated at the quiescent operating point, that is, the point $v_{DS} = V_{DS}$, $v_{GS} = V_{GS}$. Now, if the signal variables are small enough for the instantaneous drain current to be approximately linear in these variables, the expansion can be approximated by the truncated series that is obtained when *all* terms that are second-order and higher are neglected. Thus

$$i_D \simeq i_D|_Q + \left.\frac{\partial i_D}{\partial v_{DS}}\right|_Q v_{ds} + \left.\frac{\partial i_D}{\partial v_{GS}}\right|_Q v_{gs} \tag{1.19a}$$

If we express the drain current in terms of its dc and signal components, using Eq. 1.17c, Eq. 1.19a becomes

$$I_D + i_d = i_D|_Q + \left.\frac{\partial i_D}{\partial v_{DS}}\right|_Q v_{ds} + \left.\frac{\partial i_D}{\partial v_{GS}}\right|_Q v_{gs} \tag{1.19b}$$

Since the incremental components are independent of the quiescent components, they may be set equal to zero without affecting the quiescent state of the device. In this case Eq. 1.19b becomes

$$I_D = i_D|_Q \tag{1.20a}$$

Finally, if this quiescent relationship is subtracted from Eq. 1.19b, we are left with a relationship among the incremental components:

$$i_d = \left.\frac{\partial i_D}{\partial v_{DS}}\right|_Q v_{ds} + \left.\frac{\partial i_D}{\partial v_{GS}}\right|_Q v_{gs} \tag{1.20b}$$

There is nothing new in Eq. 1.20a, which states simply that the quiescent drain current is related to the quiescent terminal-pair voltages by the functional relationship of Eq. 1.16a evaluated at the operating point. The second equation (Eq. 1.20b) is a *linear* relationship among the *signal* components. The coefficients of this linear relationship are derivatives of the total-variable relationship evaluated at the quiescent operating point.

The fact that the gate current is approximately zero means that a formal expansion of Eq. 1.16b is not required. Rather, we have

$$i_G \simeq 0 \tag{1.21a}$$

$$i_g \simeq 0 \tag{1.21b}$$

Of course, a nonzero functional relationship for the total gate current could be expanded in precisely the same manner as was illustrated for i_D.

The results of the drain-current expansion, given by Eq. 1.20b, constitute a model that relates the signal components and is linear in those components. This model is called a *small-signal model* or an *incremental model*. The signal variables that it relates are often called *incremental variables*. These names emphasize that the model applies only for restricted ranges of variation of the signal or incremental variables.

The incremental model can be expressed in terms of an arrangement of idealized circuit elements. Toward this end we write Eq. 1.20b as

$$i_d = g_o v_{ds} + g_m v_{gs} \tag{1.22a}$$

where

$$g_o = \left.\frac{\partial i_D}{\partial v_{DS}}\right|_Q \tag{1.22b}$$

is known as the *incremental output conductance* and

$$g_m = \left.\frac{\partial i_D}{\partial v_{GS}}\right|_Q \tag{1.22c}$$

is called the *incremental forward transfer conductance* or simply the *incremental transconductance*. In terms of this notation the incremental model can be represented as shown in Fig. 1.22. This circuit model is equivalent to the description of Eqs. 1.20b and 1.21b because the node equations of the circuit correspond exactly to these algebraic descriptions.

Of course, the incremental circuit model of Fig. 1.22 is only a formal representation of the relationships among the incremental variables; it is not

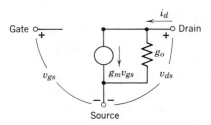

Figure 1.22   An incremental circuit model for the MOS transistor.

complete until the coefficients g_o and g_m are determined. Analysis of the physical electronics of the transistor would provide us with a specific algebraic relationship having the form of Eq. 1.16a. This device description could then be used as a basis for specifying the incremental parameters directly, in accordance with Eqs. 1.22b and 1.22c. We shall illustrate this procedure in Chapter 11, after we have analyzed the physics of this and other active devices in quantitative detail. For the present, we evaluate the incremental coefficients by noting their relationship to a graphical description of the device.

The incremental coefficients g_o and g_m are related to the slopes and spacings of the static output characteristics. The definition of Eq. 1.22b shows that g_o can be written as

$$g_o \simeq \frac{\Delta i_D}{\Delta v_{DS}} \bigg|_{\substack{v_{GS}=V_{GS} \\ v_{DS}=V_{DS}}} \tag{1.23a}$$

In other words, the incremental output conductance is equal to the slope at the operating point of the curve of drain current versus drain-to-source voltage for fixed gate-to-source voltage. Similarly, the incremental transconductance can be written as

$$g_m \simeq \frac{\Delta i_D}{\Delta v_{GS}} \bigg|_{\substack{v_{GS}=V_{GS} \\ v_{DS}=V_{DS}}} \tag{1.23b}$$

This coefficient is equal to the per-unit spacing at the operating point of the curves of drain current. These relationships are illustrated in Fig. 1.23.

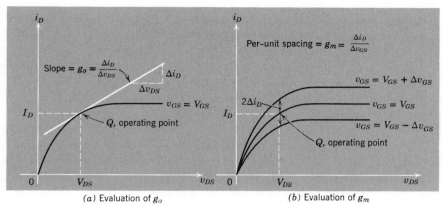

(a) Evaluation of g_o (b) Evaluation of g_m

Figure 1.23   Evaluation of incremental coefficients from characteristic curves.

1.4.2   Incremental Analysis of an Amplifier

To illustrate the application of incremental circuit models we consider once again the simple amplifier of Fig. 1.14. The constraint that the power source and the load resistance impose on the transistor is given by Eq. 1.5a, which is repeated here:

$$V_B = i_D R_L + v_{DS} \tag{1.24}$$

When the drain current and drain-to-source voltage are expressed in terms of their dc and signal components, we obtain

$$V_B = (I_D R_L + V_{DS}) + (i_d R_L + v_{ds}) \tag{1.25}$$

Since the quiescent and incremental components are independent, this equation may be separated into two parts:

$$V_B = I_D R_L + V_{DS} \tag{1.26a}$$

$$0 = i_d R_L + v_{ds} \tag{1.26b}$$

Equation 1.26a relates the dc components and has nothing new in it. Equation 1.26b relates the incremental components. The left side is zero because the power source voltage is fixed in value and has no incremental component.

Equation 1.26b is the constraint that the circuit imposes on the incremental variables at the drain-source terminals of the transistor. Consequently, this constraint can be represented together with the incremental model of the device as shown in Fig. 1.24. The effect of what we have done is to replace each component by its incremental model. The incremental model of the battery, or of any *fixed* voltage source, is a short circuit. Had there been a fixed current source in the complete circuit, it would have been replaced by an open circuit. Thus the gate-source terminals are connected directly to v_i,

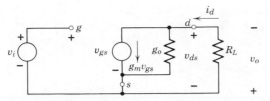

Figure 1.24   Incremental model for the amplifier of Fig. 1.14.

the signal component of the input voltage; the corresponding dc component V_I (which sets the operating point) does not appear in this incremental network.

The circuit model of Fig. 1.24 can be used to evaluate the dependence of v_o on v_i. Specifically, we have

$$v_o = (g_m v_{gs}) R_L \| \left(\frac{1}{g_o} \right) \tag{1.27a}$$

or, equivalently,

$$v_o = g_m \frac{R_L r_o}{R_L + r_o} v_{gs} \tag{1.27b}$$

where r_o denotes the reciprocal of g_o. Finally, since $v_{gs} = v_i$, we find

$$\frac{v_o}{v_i} = g_m \frac{R_L r_o}{R_L + r_o} \tag{1.27c}$$

This ratio of incremental variables is the *forward incremental voltage transfer ratio* (which, of course, must be equal to the slope at the operating point of the voltage transfer characteristic shown in Fig. 1.15).

To check, let us evaluate g_m and g_o from Fig. 1.10 and calculate v_o/v_i. The operating point is shown on the output characteristics in Fig. 1.10. In accordance with Eqs. 1.22, we find for this operating point

$$g_o \simeq 0$$

$$g_m \simeq 0.7 \text{ mmho}$$

For $R_L = 4$ kohm we find $v_o/v_i \simeq 2.8$, which, to the accuracy of these sketches, is the same as the slope of the transfer characteristic.

In more complex circuits, linear incremental models such as that employed in this example offer important advantages when compared with graphical techniques of analysis. This is particularly apparent when the circuits of interest contain energy-storage elements and when the dynamics of the active devices must be considered. In such cases the use of linear incremental models permits us to employ all the analysis tools, viewpoints, and intuition developed in the study of the dynamics of linear passive circuits. For example, techniques that consider exponential excitations and focus on the natural frequencies of the system can often be used very profitably.

Three aspects of incremental models and incremental analysis deserve special emphasis. First, the coefficients of these models depend explicitly on the operating point. Consequently, it is meaningless to specify the parameters of an incremental model without also specifying the operating point at which those parameters apply. Second, incremental analysis suppresses all evidence of the inherently nonlinear nature of active devices. Such models cannot be used to evaluate distortion in an amplifier; they do not even suggest the existence of distortion-producing nonlinearities. Thus it is necessary to bear in mind that incremental analysis is valid only for limited excursions of the variables, and to make use of other points of view in determining the appropriate limits. Third, the incremental model applies *only* to the incremental or signal components of the variables and cannot be used to explore relationships among the quiescent components of the variables or among the total variables. In fact, all dc sources must be suppressed when the incremental circuit is formed. That is, dc voltage sources must be replaced by short circuits (as in Fig. 1.24) and dc current sources must be replaced by open circuits.

1.5 Development of the Subject

The illustrations in this chapter have shown how active devices can be used as control valves and how electronic circuits can be used for amplification. In addition, the modeling of an active device has been considered and graphical techniques for circuit analysis have been introduced. These brief examples of electronic device and circuit applications provide some perspective for a more detailed study of electronics.

Thus in the next chapter we turn to a more detailed study of the physical electronics, modeling, and circuit applications of a variety of semiconductor active devices. We restrict our attention to semiconductor active devices in view of their dominance in the class of electronic circuit applications considered in an introduction to the field. A brief overview of the physical electronics and modeling of vacuum tubes is included in Appendices A and B.

REFERENCES

1.1 E. A. Guillemin, *Introductory Circuit Theory*, Wiley, New York, 1953.

1.2 A. G. Bose and K. N. Stevens, *Introductory Network Theory*, Harper and Row, New York, 1965.

1.3 H. H. Skilling, *Electrical Engineering Circuits*, Wiley, New York, 1965.

1.4 L. A. Manning, *Electrical Circuits*, McGraw-Hill, New York, 1965.

1.5 M. E. Van Valkenburg, *Network Analysis*, 2nd Ed., Prentice-Hall, Englewood Cliffs, N.J., 1964.

1.6 C. M. Close, *The Analysis of Linear Circuits*, Harcourt, Brace & World, New York, 1968.

1.7 R. E. Scott, *Elements of Linear Circuits*, Addison-Wesley, Reading, Mass., 1965.
1.8 R. E. Scott, *Linear Circuits*, Parts I and II, Addison-Wesley, Reading, Mass., 1960.
1.9 J. B. Cruz and M. E. Van Valkenburg, *Introductory Signals and Circuits*, Blaisdell Publishing Company, Waltham, Mass., 1967.
1.10 N. Balabanian, *Fundamentals of Circuit Theory*, Allyn & Bacon, Boston, 1961.
1.11 R. J. Smith, *Circuits, Devices and Systems*, Wiley, New York, 1966.
1.12 S. I. Pearson and G. J. Maler, *Introductory Circuit Analysis*, Wiley, New York, 1965.
1.13 W. L. Cassell, *Linear Electric Circuits*, Wiley, New York, 1964.

PROBLEMS

P1.1 The MOS transistor characteristics of Fig. 1.8 are a graphical presentation of the functional relationship

$$i_D = i_D(v_{GS}, v_{DS})$$

in which v_{GS} is taken as a parameter and i_D is plotted against v_{DS}. Alternatively, we could display this relationship by taking v_{DS} as a parameter and plotting i_D versus v_{GS}. The resulting family of curves is called the *forward transfer characteristics* of the triode.

(*a*) Use the data of Fig. 1.8 to generate this family of curves. Plot the three curves that correspond to $v_{DS} = 2$ volts, 4 volts, and 6 volts.

(*b*) Can a load-line construction analogous to that illustrated in Fig. 1.10 be used with this family of curves?

P1.2 The FET whose drain characteristics are shown in Fig. 1.8 is connected in the circuit of Fig. 1.9. The drain supply voltage is $V_B = 8$ volts and the load resistance is $R_L = 3$ kohm. Find the point of operation of the circuit for $v_I = +4$ volts, that is, evaluate v_{DS} and i_D for this value of v_I.

P1.3 The FET whose drain characteristics appear in Fig. 1.8 is connected in the circuits shown in Fig. 1.25. For each circuit sketch and dimension the

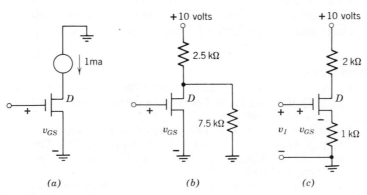

(*a*)   (*b*)   (*c*)

Figure 1.25 Transistor circuits.

load line (in the $i_D - v_{DS}$ plane) imposed on the transistor by the external circuit, and find the operating point when $v_{GS} = +4$ volts.

P1.4 Determine the operating point of the transistor whose characteristics are shown in Fig. 1.8 when it is connected in the circuit of Fig. 1.25c and when $v_I = +6$ volts. Note that $v_I \neq v_{GS}$. Devise a graphical method that can be used to determine the operating point for any fixed value of v_I. (*Suggestion.* Notice that v_I and i_D fix v_{GS}. Express v_{GS} in terms of v_I and i_D and plot this relationship, for fixed v_I, on the drain characteristics. Is this curve linear?)

P1.5 The transistor whose characteristics are shown in Fig. 1.8 is connected in the circuit of Fig. 1.17. The following parameter values apply:

$$
\begin{aligned}
V_B &= 15 \text{ volts} \\
R_1 &= 22 \text{ kohm} \\
R_2 &= 8 \text{ kohm} \\
R_D &= 5 \text{ kohm} \\
R_O &= 2 \text{ kohm}
\end{aligned}
$$

(a) Determine the quiescent operating point of the circuit.

(b) Sketch the ac load line on the drain characteristics and determine the ac transfer characteristic that relates v_o to v_i. Assume that C_1 and C_2 remain charged to the voltages that exist under quiescent conditions.

(c) What is the largest excursion of v_i for which the amplifier is reasonably linear, that is, for which gross distortion is avoided?

P1.6 The incremental parameters defined in Eqs. 1.22 can also be evaluated from the forward transfer characteristics of the transistor in which i_D is plotted versus v_{GS} with v_{DS} as a parameter (see Problem P1.1). Prepare sketches, analogous to those of Fig. 1.23, that show how g_o and g_m are evaluated directly from the forward characteristics.

P1.7 Evaluate g_m and g_o for the transistor whose characteristics are shown in Fig. 1.8 for the following operating points:
(1) $v_{DS} = +2$ volts, $v_{GS} = +4$ volts
(2) $v_{DS} = +8$ volts, $v_{GS} = +5$ volts

P1.8 Determine, sketch, and label a linear circuit that can be used in calculating the incremental voltage transfer ratio of the circuit of Fig. 1.17. Making use of the parameter values specified in Problem P1.5, and using the operating point found there, evaluate the incremental voltage transfer ratio.

P1.9 Determine, sketch, and label a linear circuit that can be used in calculating the incremental voltage transfer ratio of the circuit of Fig. 1.20a. Use the transformer model of Fig. 1.20b. Derive a literal expression for the incremental voltage transfer ratio v_o/v_i. Assume that the rates of change of the incremental signal are large enough so that there is negligible incremental current in the inductance and negligible incremental voltage drop across the coupling capacitance.

P1.10   The transistor whose characteristics appear in Fig. 1.8 is used in the circuit of Fig. 1.9, with $V_B = 8$ volts and $R_L = 2$ kohm. Use graphical techniques to determine, sketch, and label the transfer characteristic that relates i_D to v_I for v_I in the range $-2 < v_I < +6$ volts.

P1.11   An incrementally linear three-terminal device can be characterized by the following pair of equations, which are written in terms of the variables defined in Fig. 1.26:

$$i_i = gv_i + c(dv_i/dt)$$

$$v_o = \alpha v_i + ri_o$$

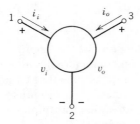

Figure 1.26   An incrementally linear three-terminal device.

Devise a network model comprised of ideal passive circuit elements and dependent sources which represents this behavior. Label the terminals clearly.

CHAPTER TWO

Conduction Mechanisms in Semiconductors

2.1 Metals and Semiconductors

Most solid conductors of electricity can be classified as either metals or semiconductors. Since current is a manifestation of the motion of charge within a material, it is necessary to examine the origin and behavior of the charge that is capable of motion in order to understand the conduction process in a material. Semiconductors (silicon and germanium are the most familiar examples) differ from metals in several respects. The most fundamental and significant difference is that at the microscopic level semiconductors conduct electric current by means of two distinct and independent modes of motion of electrons. Although one of these modes can be described at the macroscopic level in terms of the flow of negative charges, the other mode must be described in terms of the flow of *positive* charges. Metals, in comparison, conduct by means of mobile *negative* charge carriers alone; there are no mobile carriers of positive charge in a metal. This distinction lies at the root of the operation of most semiconductor junction devices, including diodes and bipolar transistors.

2.1.1 Charge Carriers in Metals

Most metals are good conductors of electricity; they have electrical conductivities that are larger (often by many orders of magnitude) than the conductivities of nonmetallic solids, liquids, and gases. Metals conduct well because they contain *free* or *mobile* electrons in large concentrations. The electrons are mobile in the sense that they are not bound to the metal atoms but are free to move throughout the volume of the metal. In many metals these free electrons can be regarded, for most purposes, as a uniformly distributed "gas" or "free electron sea" which permeates the volume of the metal. Usually each atom of the metal contributes only one or two electrons (the valence electrons) to this electron gas. The other electrons of the atom are not free to move throughout the specimen, but are constrained to remain associated with ("bound to") particular nuclei. The atoms of any solid have a volume concentration that is of the order of Avogadro's number—about 6×10^{23} cm^{-3}. Consequently, the free electrons of a metal have a volume concentration of the order of 10^{23} electrons per cubic centimeter.

A metal is electrically neutral because the negative charge on the free electrons is exactly balanced by the net positive charge associated with the nuclei and bound electrons of the metal atoms. When an atom contributes an electron to the electron gas, the atom remains fixed in position as a positive ion, with a charge equal in value but opposite in sign to the electronic charge. Although the metal ions constitute a "background" of positive charge, the positive-charge distribution makes *no* contribution to electrical conduction, because these charges are *immobile*, that is, not free to move about in the metal. Conduction in metals is, therefore, a *single-carrier process* involving only negative charges.

2.1.2 The Hall Effect

The fact that electrical conduction in metals is a consequence of the motion of *negative* charges can be confirmed by a simple classical experiment. This experiment, illustrated in Fig. 2.1, is known as the *Hall effect*. The charge carriers that comprise the current I in the metallic conductor, which is portrayed as a bar of rectangular cross section, move between the pole faces

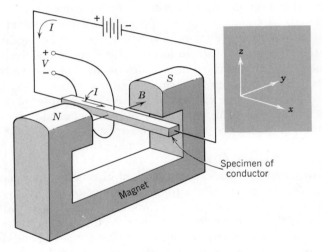

(*a*) Experimental arrangement; the axis of the points at which V is measured is orthogonal to both the magnetic field B and the current I

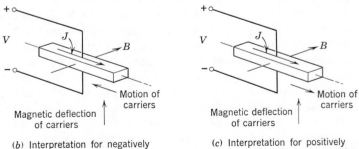

(*b*) Interpretation for negatively charged carriers: V is negative

(*c*) Interpretation for positively charged carriers: V is positive

Figure 2.1   The Hall voltage V appears when charge carriers move in, and are deflected by, a transverse magnetic field. The polarity of the Hall voltage reveals the sign of the charge on the carriers.

of a magnet. These charge carriers therefore experience a force of magnetic origin, which displaces them *transversely* in the z direction. This displacement of the charge carriers produces a transverse voltage drop, which is known as the *Hall voltage*. The polarity of this voltage provides unambiguous evidence of the *sign* of the charge carriers.

To determine the relationship between the polarity of the Hall voltage and the sign of the charge carrier, we consider the effect of the force of magnetic origin, which is called the Lorentz force. The Lorentz force that acts on particles of charge q moving with velocity $\mathbf{v}$ in a magnetic field $\mathbf{B}$ is

$$\mathbf{F} = q(\mathbf{v} \times \mathbf{B}) \tag{2.1a}$$

The multiplication denoted is the cross product of two vectors.

The moving charge carriers produce an electric current. To investigate the relationship between this current and the carrier velocity $\mathbf{v}$, we consider the boxlike volume element shown in Fig. 2.2 and evaluate the current crossing

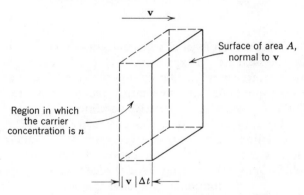

Figure 2.2 The relationship between drift velocity and particle flux.

the surface of area A, normal to $\mathbf{v}$. Consider a time interval of duration Δt. In this interval, *all* of the charge carriers in the element of thickness $|\mathbf{v}| \, \Delta t$ cross the surface A. Thus if these carriers have a density or volume concentration of n and carry charge q, the charge that crosses A in Δt is simply $qn|\mathbf{v}| \, \Delta t A$. Consequently the corresponding current is $qn|\mathbf{v}| \, A$ and the *current density* is

$$\mathbf{J} = qn\mathbf{v} \tag{2.1b}$$

If Eq. 2.1b is used to express $\mathbf{v}$ in terms of $\mathbf{J}$, Eq. 2.1a becomes

$$\mathbf{F} = \frac{1}{n}(\mathbf{J} \times \mathbf{B}) \tag{2.1c}$$

Note that when the Lorentz force is expressed in this manner, it is independent of the polarity of the charge carried by the moving particles; q does not appear in Eq. 2.1c.

For the experimental arrangement shown in Fig. 2.1, the current density and the magnetic field are orthogonal. The Lorentz force, which is normal to both, deflects the charge carriers toward the *upper* surface of the specimen. This transverse deflection of carriers causes an accumulation of charge carriers on the upper surface and a depletion of charge carriers on the lower surface. These small charge imbalances give rise to a transverse electric field, which *opposes* the magnetic deflection. Of course, the direction of this field and the polarity of the transverse Hall voltage associated with it depend on the sign of the charge carriers.

The situation for negative charge carriers is shown in Fig. 2.1b; the transverse Hall voltage is negative. If the charge carriers were postulated to have positive charge, the Hall voltage would have the opposite polarity, as shown in Fig. 2.1c.

Observation of the Hall effect in most metals yields the polarity of the transverse voltage shown in Fig. 2.1b, thus demonstrating that metallic conduction is the result of motion of negative charges.[1]

2.1.3   Charge Neutrality

Metals invariably exhibit *local* charge neutrality as well as gross neutrality. That is, the charge density is approximately zero at every point within the metal;[2] gross neutrality requires only that the sum of the negative charges be equal to the sum of the positive charges, regardless of the distribution of either, and this is a much less restrictive condition.

There is no appreciable space-charge density in a metal because any significant deviation from local charge neutrality would produce large internal electric fields, and the conduction currents associated with the internal fields would quickly remove the charge that was responsible for the field. To illustrate this situation in lumped terms, we model a small region of the metal as a leaky "parallel plate capacitor" as shown in Fig. 2.3a. The metal "dielectric" of this capacitor is described by a conductivity σ and a dielectric permittivity ϵ. Consequently the physical structure can be modeled by the parallel RC network shown in Fig. 2.3b. The capacitance C has the value

$$C = \frac{\epsilon A}{d} \tag{2.2a}$$

[1] Many metals, including the alkali metals (lithium, sodium, potassium, etc.), and the good conductors like copper, silver, gold, and aluminum, have a polarity of Hall voltage which indicates conduction by negative charges, as in Fig. 2.1b. Some metals, including iron, zinc, and bismuth, exhibit the opposite polarity of the Hall voltage, thus indicating conduction by means of *positive* charge carriers. This anomalous situation, which can be understood only in terms of a detailed quantum-mechanical description of these metals, occurs because these metals are not accurately described by the "electron gas" model we have introduced. Specifically, the electrons in these metals interact strongly with the electrostatic forces associated with the ions, and this interaction influences their behavior in a major way.

[2] Provided, of course, that we do not look on a scale comparable to distance between atoms, which is the order of 10^{-8} cm.

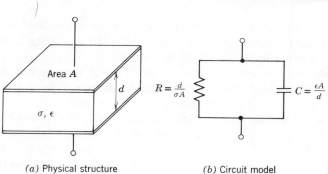

(a) Physical structure   (b) Circuit model

Figure 2.3   Charge within a conductor decays with a time constant given by ϵ/σ.

and the resistance R has the value

$$R = \frac{d}{\sigma A} \quad (2.2b)$$

If charge is placed on the plates of this structure, it decays exponentially with time. That is, the charge at time t is

$$Q(t) = Q_0 e^{-t/\tau_d} \quad (2.3)$$

where Q_0 denotes the charge at $t = 0$ and τ_d is the time constant of the parallel RC network. In accordance with Eqs. 2.2, this time constant has a value

$$\tau_d = RC$$

$$= \frac{\epsilon}{\sigma} \quad (2.4)$$

The time constant, which is known as the *dielectric relaxation time,* is exceedingly small. For example, metals such as copper and aluminum have conductivities of the order of 10^6 mhos/cm and dielectric permittivities of the order of 10^{-12} farads/cm. These parameter values yield a dielectric relaxation time of 10^{-18} sec. Thus in a metal any deviation from charge neutrality disappears in an extremely short time (about 10^{-17} sec). Any charge imbalance produces an internal electric field, and this field gives rise to conduction currents that eliminate the charge imbalance.

Although we have based this discussion on a structure in which the charges that produce the field reside on the *surface* of the conductor, the conclusion applies to an *internal* charge distribution as well. Any unneutralized charge distribution produces, as a consequence of Gauss's law, an electric field that radiates from the charge distribution. That is,

$$\oint_S \mathscr{E}_n \, dS = \frac{Q}{\epsilon} \quad (2.5)$$

Here Q denotes the net unneutralized charge, ϵ the dielectric permittivity, and $\mathscr{E}_n$ the normal component of the electric field crossing a closed surface S, which surrounds the charge Q. Because the metal has a large conductivity σ, this field produces conduction currents that remove the internal charge imbalance. The decay is characterized by the dielectric relaxation time defined by Eq. 2.4 (see Problem P2.1).

The distribution of the positive charge associated with the ions of a metal is uniform throughout the volume of the metal. Consequently, to avoid space charge, *the free electrons also must be uniformly distributed.* That is, the free-electron concentration must be equal to the positive-ion concentration and thus must be independent of position within the metal.

Our simple physical picture of the charge carriers in a metal is summarized in Fig. 2.4, which is a two-dimensional representation of the actual three-dimensional situation. Electrons that are free to move are distributed *uniformly* through the metal (provided, once again, that we do not look on a distance scale on the order of the interatomic spacing). The negative charge carried by the electrons is neutralized by the positive charge of the immobile metal ions. The electron concentration is governed solely by the volume concentration of the atoms in the metal.

Figure 2.4   The electron-gas model of a metal. This sketch, which presents in two dimensions the important features of the three-dimensional situation, is drawn for ions having a net charge (excess of nuclear charge over bound electrons) of $+2q$; each atom contributes two electrons to the electron gas.

The pictorial representation of the electron gas model of a metal shown in Fig. 2.4 is misleading in an important respect: it ascribes a "size" or spatial extent to the electrons which is far too small. In reality, the quantum-mechanical nature of electrons and other atomic particles limit the degree to which a free electron can be localized in a metal crystal. As a result, it is not meaningful to speak of determining the position of an electron with an uncertainty that is less than about 30 times the distance between atoms. We make use of Fig. 2.4 in spite of this gross inadequacy because it emphasizes that the "electron gas" is uniformly distributed through a neutralizing background of immobile positive charge.

2.1.4   Charge Carriers in Semiconductors

The valence electrons of the atoms of a semiconductor (such as silicon) are not, for the most part, free to move throughout the volume of a semiconductor. Instead, they participate in the *covalent bonds* that hold the assembly of semiconductor atoms together in a periodic crystalline arrangement. The general form of the crystalline structure of the elemental semiconductors silicon and germanium is shown in Fig. 2.5. Each atom in the crystal has four nearest neighbors, and shares its valence electrons with those neighbors. The rods that connect the atoms in Fig. 2.5 may be thought of as indicative of the spacial location of these valence electrons.

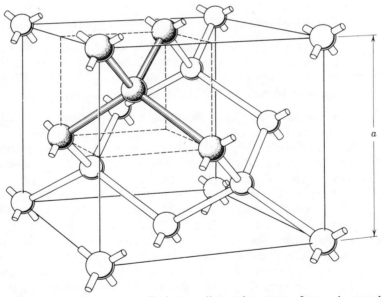

Figure 2.5   The diamond crystal structure. Each atom lies at the center of a regular tetrahedron and has four equidistant nearest neighbors. The dimension *a* is 5.4 and.5.7 Å (10^{-8} cm) for silicon and germanium respectively. (Adapted from R. B. Adler et al., *Introduction to Semiconductor Physics*, Wiley, New York, 1964.)

We can represent the essential features of this crystalline structure in *two-dimensional* form as shown in Fig. 2.6a. This representation, which is known as the *two-dimensional bond model* of a semiconductor, describes the

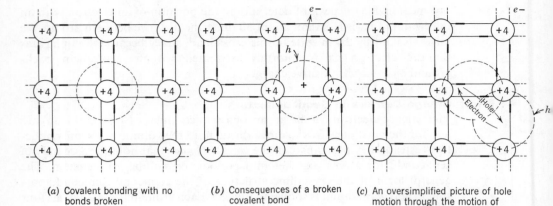

(a) Covalent bonding with no bonds broken

(b) Consequences of a broken covalent bond

(c) An oversimplified picture of hole motion through the motion of bound valence electrons

Figure 2.6   The two-dimensional covalent-bond model of a semiconductor. Each ion or core has a net charge of $+4q$. (Adapted from R. B. Adler et al., *Introduction to Semiconductor Physics*, Wiley, New York, 1964.)

actual three-dimensional situation in two important respects:

    1. Each atom is surrounded by four equidistant neighbors.

    2. The valence electrons, which number four per atom, are shared equally with the four nearest neighbors. Consequently, each bond between an atom and one of its nearest neighbors contains two electrons.

    When all the valence electrons are constrained in covalent bonds, as illustrated in Fig. 2.6a, electrical conduction is not possible because there are no charge carriers that are free to move. Consequently, a material having this electronic arrangement behaves as an insulator. Diamond, the crystalline form of carbon, is such a material.

    The actual distribution of the valence electrons in a semiconductor differs in one important respect from that illustrated in Fig. 2.6a—at all temperatures above absolute zero a few covalent bonds are incomplete. The electrons missing from these bonds are no longer confined to the region of the bond, but are free to move. This situation is illustrated in Fig. 2.6b. The sketch is not intended to be descriptive with respect to scale; as in the electron gas model of a metal described in Section 2.1.3, the electron and the broken bond are localized far too much.

    The few broken bonds that occur at normal temperatures result from the random thermal vibration of the valence electrons. A few valence electrons acquire enough energy to "shake loose" from the bonds and become free. The fraction of the valence electrons that are disengaged from covalent bonds is exceedingly small. For example, in germanium at room temperature (about 300°K), there are about 10^{13} broken bonds per cubic centimeter. Since there are about 10^{23} atoms per cubic centimeter, only about one atom out of every *ten billion* has a broken bond. Nevertheless, these events, rare as they are, have an enormous effect on the electrical properties of the semiconductor; they make conduction possible by providing charge carriers in a situation where otherwise there would be none. The material is considered to be a semiconductor, rather than an insulator like diamond, when the number of broken bonds is on the order of one in 10^{15}, or about 10^8 per cubic centimeter.

As a consequence of broken covalent bonds, there exist two distinct and independent groups of charge carriers that can support electric currents in semiconductors. The mobile electrons that are produced when a valence electron "shakes loose" from a bond constitute one class of charge carrier. These *conduction electrons*, which carry a charge of $-q$, can move about within the semiconductor, thereby producing current in the same manner that the free electrons in a metal produce current.[3]

The other charge carrier is associated with the valence electrons that remain tied up in covalent bonds. Clearly, a broken bond is associated with a localized region of *positive* charge; in the neighborhood of the broken bond there is an excess of positive ionic charge over negative electronic charge, and the excess amounts to $+q$. This region of positive charge is called a *hole* because it results from a defect or vacancy in the bond structure.

It is perhaps not so obvious that the hole can move about in the semiconductor independently of the conduction electrons. Motion of the localized positive charge does occur because a valence electron in a bond *near* the broken bond (i.e., near the hole) can fill the vacancy, thus causing the hole to move in the opposite direction. The valence electrons can move in this manner from bond to bond without even acquiring enough energy to become free of the bond structure. Therefore, the hole can move throughout the material without involving in any way the conduction electrons. The process is illustrated in Fig. 2.6c.

Although this description of the motion of the hole in terms of the motion of bound electrons is helpful, it has important limitations. First, the hole cannot be localized nearly so much as this mechanistic. classical picture suggests; fundamental quantum-mechanical considerations limit the localization of the hole to a volume comparable to a sphere having a diameter of about 30 times the distance between atoms. Second, we must *not* assume that the organized motion of holes (such as would be associated with an electric current) can be described by a sequence of events in which holes and specific bound electrons simply change places. In fact, if we pursue this erroneous idea of hole motion to its logical conclusion, and equate hole motion to the simple retrograde motion of individual bound electrons, we are led to a contradiction when we consider the Hall effect in a semiconductor in which

---

[3] The symbol q denotes the magnitude of the electronic charge; $q \simeq 1.6 \times 10^{-19}$ coulomb.

current is carried by holes. This paradox is discussed further in Section 2.1.6.

In essence, the concept of the hole as a mobile carrier of positive charge is an artifice that allows us to describe, in a simple and elegant way, the relatively complex motion of the bound valence electrons. Some of this simplification results solely from the numbers; it is easier to account for the motion of the exceedingly small fraction of the bonds that are broken than it is to describe the motion of all the rest of the complete bonds. Furthermore, it turns out that the motion of the hole can be described in terms of classical mechanics in which the hole is regarded simply as a particle that carries positive charge. A comparable description of the motion of the bound electrons is not possible; they must be treated quantum-mechanically rather than classically. When this treatment is pursued in detail, it is found that some of the valence or bound electrons behave as particles in the classical sense. However, others behave as particles whose dynamic behavior can be explained only if they are assigned a *negative* mass. Consequently, our intuitive notion of the behavior of classical particles goes awry when we try to apply it to the bound electrons. If, however, we focus clearly and unambiguously on the *defects* in the bond structure, that is, on the holes, the same detailed analysis shows that the holes do behave as particles with a positive mass that obey the familiar laws of classical mechanics and do not betray our intuition.

It is possible to understand, in considerable detail, the physical behavior and electrical characteristics of semiconductor devices if we are willing to accept (essentially as postulates or as a model of the conduction process) the concepts of holes and conduction electrons (hereafter usually referred to simply as "electrons"). Both the holes and the electrons may be regarded, in terms of their contributions to electrical conduction, as independent mobile carriers with charges of the opposite sign.

As we proceed, it will be necessary to postulate three other characteristics of holes and electrons; these assumptions will be introduced as they are required.

The only alternative to proceeding on the basis of these postulates involves the study, in quantum-mechanical terms, of the electronic properties of semiconductors. This study, in which the quantization of energy in atomic structures is accounted for, leads to a description of semiconductors known as the *energy band model*. Analysis of the band model supports the picture of electrical behavior that we have postulated on the basis of the valence bond model. Specifically, conduction occurs as a consequence of two modes of electronic motion—modes that can be described in the classical terms we introduced to describe the behavior of holes and conduction electrons. All of these matters are described in Reference 2.1, which gives an excellent introductory account of the electronic behavior of semiconductors and introduces the energy band model.

2.1.5   Impurities in Semiconductors

The model of a semiconductor that we have introduced requires that the holes and conduction electrons be present in exactly equal numbers. Each of these charge carriers is the result of a broken covalent bond; therefore, holes and electrons are produced in pairs when bonds are broken and disappear in pairs when electrons and holes get together to form complete bonds.

Holes and electrons usually are *not* present in equal numbers in a semiconductor, and we must extend our model to explain an imbalance in the hole and electron concentrations. The relative concentrations of the holes and electrons are strongly influenced by minute amounts of *impurities*, which are added to a semiconductor when it is fabricated. These impurities or *dopants* are of the following two classes.

1. *Donor impurities* are elements that have *five* valence electrons rather than the four valence electrons that characterize silicon or germanium. Phosphorus, arsenic, and antimony are commonly used as donor impurities in semiconductor devices. Atoms of these dopants fit readily into the regular crystalline structure of the host semiconductor. However, because donor impurities have five valence electrons rather than four, one valence electron is "left over" after the covalent bonds that bind the impurity atom to its four nearest neighbors are formed. Because it is not needed to complete a valence bond, this extra electron is only loosely bound to the impurity atom; in the temperature range in which semiconductor devices commonly operate, the extra electron becomes dissociated from the impurity atom and moves about through the semiconductor as a conduction electron. That is, the impurity atom *ionizes*. The impurity atom ion, which has a charge of $+5q$ rather than $+4q$ (because the nucleus contains one more proton than does the nucleus of a semiconductor ion), represents a localized *immobile* positive charge. This situation is illustrated in Fig. 2.7*a*, in which the two-dimensional bond model introduced in Fig. 2.6 is modified to account for donor impurities. The key point is that ionization of a donor-impurity atom produces a single conduction electron and a single *immobile* positive ionic charge; no valence bonds are broken. Consequently donor impurities contribute conduction electrons to the semiconductor *without* contributing holes. Each donor-impurity atom, by *donating* its extra valence electron to the ensemble of conduction electrons, augments by one the mobile-electron population.

2. *Acceptor impurities* are elements that have *three* valence electrons rather than four, such as boron, indium, or aluminum. These atoms fit into the periodic crystalline structure of the host semiconductor, but they have one valence electron less than required to complete the covalent bonds. Thus there is a vacancy in the bond structure, or a *hole* associated with each acceptor atom. This hole is loosely bound to the acceptor atom so that at

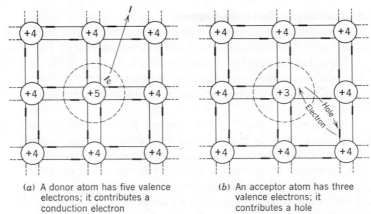

(a) A donor atom has five valence
electrons; it contributes a
conduction electron

(b) An acceptor atom has three
valence electrons; it
contributes a hole

Figure 2.7   Schematic representation of impurities in the two-dimensional covalent-bound model. (Adapted from R. B. Adler et al., *Introduction to Semiconductor Physics*, Wiley, New York, 1964.)

normal temperatures it becomes dissociated from the acceptor atom and is free to move throughout the semiconductor.[4] The acceptor ion then constitutes a local immobile negative charge; it lacks one nuclear proton of the number needed to balance the negative charge of the bound electrons. This situation is illustrated in Fig. 2.7b. The key point here is that an ionized acceptor-impurity atom produces a single mobile hole and a single *immobile* negative charge without breaking valence bonds; acceptor impurities contribute holes to the semiconductor *without* contributing electrons. By *accepting* a bound electron to complete its covalent bond structure, each acceptor-impurity atom augments by one the hole population.

In summary, semiconductors, unlike metals, conduct electricity as a consequence of the independent motion of *two* oppositely charged classes of mobile charge carriers: holes and electrons. These charge carriers can be created in a semiconductor by three distinct processes:

1. A very small fraction of the covalent bonds are broken as a result of thermal agitation of the valence electrons. This process alone produces equal numbers of holes and electrons; that is, holes and electrons are produced in pairs when a bond is broken and disappear in pairs when an incomplete bond is reconstructed.

2. Donor-impurity atoms contribute only electrons when they ionize. Although there is a localized positive charge associated with the donor ion, this charge is immobile and does *not* participate in conduction.

3. Acceptor-impurity atoms contribute only holes when they ionize.

---

[4] In terms of electrons, the impurity atom accepts a valence electron from elsewhere in the crystal; this produces a displacement of the vacancy in the bond structure.

Although there is a localized negative charge associated with the acceptor ion, this charge is immobile and does *not* participate in conduction.

If a semiconductor contains negligible quantities of either donor or acceptor impurities, the hole and electron concentrations are equal. The semiconductor is then called *intrinsic* because its electrical properties are intrinsic to the semiconductor material and are not a result of impurities. If, on the other hand, a semiconductor contains a significant quantity of donor atoms (and no acceptors), it has more electrons than holes and is known as an *n-type* semiconductor because the dominant charge carrier is negative. If there is a significant quantity of acceptor atoms, rather than donors, there will be more holes than electrons, and the material is known as *p-type* because the dominant charge carrier is positive.

Both *n*-type and *p*-type materials are called *extrinsic* semiconductors because their electrical properties are governed more by the impurities than by the semiconductor itself.

The carrier that has the larger concentration is called the *majority carrier*, and the less populous carrier is called the *minority carrier*. Thus in an *n*-type extrinsic semiconductor the majority carriers are electrons and the minority carriers are holes; the opposite is true in *p*-type material.

2.1.6 Experimental Evidence for the Two-Carrier Model

The existence of two types of semiconductor, which differ in the sign of the dominant or majority charge carrier, can be demonstrated by observing the polarities of the Hall voltages, as discussed in connection with Fig. 2.1.[5] Extrinsic semiconductors that have been doped with donor impurities behave as shown in Fig. 2.1b, which proves that conduction in *n*-type materials is dominated by negatively-charged carriers: the conduction electrons. On the other hand, extrinsic semiconductors that have been doped with acceptor impurities behave as shown in Fig. 2.1c. Conduction in these *p*-type materials is dominated by the positively-charged holes.

The Hall effect in a *p*-type semiconductor provides a simple illustration of the difficulty of describing conduction in such a material in terms of the motion of the bound electrons rather than in terms of the fictitious, but well-behaved, holes. If we focus on the bound electrons, ascribe the electric current to their motion, and *assume* that they move in response to the Lorentz force (Eq. 2.1c) as a classical particle should, we immediately conclude that the Hall voltage should have a polarity opposite to that which is observed. That is, Fig. 2.1b should apply, but we observe the polarity shown in Fig. 2.1c. The problem here is that the bound electrons do *not* behave simply as negatively-charged particles; the bound electrons whose motion governs the

---

[5] The Hall effect in semiconductors can be developed easily into a simple lecture demonstration or into an experiment for a student laboratory. The details of this experiment, and of the other experiments described in this chapter, are given in the section following the problems.

Hall voltage behave as though they had *negative mass* as well as negative charge.

An independent, although somewhat less direct, experimental confirmation of the existence of two different conductivity types is provided by measurement of the thermal emf or thermoelectric voltage produced by a heated electrode, as illustrated in Fig. 2.8. When the hot electrode or probe is placed on the semiconductor, a voltage V appears between the probe and the specimen. For small differences in temperature this voltage is proportional to the temperature difference.

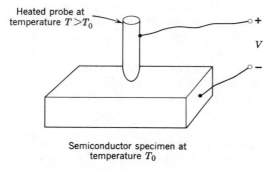

Heated probe at temperature $T > T_0$

V

Semiconductor specimen at temperature T_0

Figure 2.8   The hot-probe experiment in which the polarity of the thermal emf is observed to depend on the conductivity type of the specimen.

The polarity of this voltage is dependent on the sign of the charge on the majority carrier. Mobile carriers tend to flow away from the hot region of the semiconductor toward the cold regions. This flow is one of the mechanisms by which heat is removed from the hot region; the carriers transport the thermal energy that is associated with this motion away from the hot region. Because the mobile carriers tend to flow away from the hot region toward the cooler regions, the hot probe acquires a charge *opposite* to that of the mobile *majority* carriers. Thus a potential difference appears between the hot probe and the cooler portions of the semiconductor. If the semiconductor is *n*-type, the migration of electrons away from the hot probe leaves it positively charged; the voltage V defined in Fig. 2.8 is positive. If the semiconductor is *p*-type, holes migrate away from the hot probe and V is negative. A steady state is reached in either case when the internal field associated with V balances the flow tendencies produced by the temperature differential, thus reducing the net flow of carriers to zero.

This observation of the polarity of the thermal emf provides a simple way of identifying the sign of the majority carrier (the conductivity type) of a semiconductor. The hot-probe technique is often used for this purpose in the laboratory, since nothing more than a soldering iron and a high-resistance dc voltmeter are necessary.[6]

It should be noted that both the Hall effect and the thermal emf become complicated in intrinsic or near-intrinsic material, in which we must account for the motion of *both* charge carriers.

2.2 Carrier Concentrations

We now consider the constraints placed on the numerical values of the carrier concentrations in a semiconductor. That is, we wish to determine the manner in which the hole and electron concentrations depend on the donor and acceptor concentrations and on other parameters of the semiconductor. We first consider the situation at equilibrium when a semiconductor is undisturbed in its thermal environment. Under equilibrium conditions there must be no currents and no net flows of either holes or electrons.

2.2.1 Equilibrium Carrier Concentrations

We have observed that there are four classes of charged particles in a semiconductor:

Particles that have $\begin{cases} 1.\ \text{Mobile holes, } p \\ 2.\ \text{Immobile donor ions, } N_d \end{cases}$
positive charge

Particles that have $\begin{cases} 1.\ \text{Mobile electrons, } n \\ 2.\ \text{Immobile acceptor ions, } N_a \end{cases}$
negative charge

In each case the symbol shown represents the *volume concentration* of the corresponding charged particle.[7] Each of these types of charged particles carries a charge of magnitude q, the electronic charge. Therefore, the local charge density ρ can be written as

$$\rho = q(p + N_d - n - N_a) \tag{2.6}$$

In a homogeneous or uniformly-doped semiconductor the space-charge density must vanish at every point; local neutrality is required as a consequence of Gauss's law, just as in a metal.[8] The situation with respect to space charge in a homogeneous semiconductor differs from that in the metal only in that the dielectric relaxation time (Eq. 2.4) may be several orders of magnitude larger; the conductivity of a semiconductor is typically several orders of magnitude smaller than that of a metal. Nevertheless, internal

---

[6] For details, see the section on demonstrations at the end of the chapter.

[7] In this book, as in most writing on semiconductors, the dimensions of particle concentration are per cubic centimeter, or cm^{-3}.

[8] We shall see, in Chapter 4, that nonzero space charge can exist in an inhomogeneous semiconductor in regions where the impurity concentration changes rapidly. The issue there is that we must account for current which is independent of the electric field but which results from the nonuniform carrier concentrations that exist when the impurity concentration varies. That is, $\mathbf{J} = \sigma \mathscr{E}$ must be modified to account for diffusion currents.

deviations from neutrality can persist for only very short times, of the order of picoseconds (1 psec $= 10^{-12}$ sec), before the charge that produces the imbalance is transported to the surface of the semiconductor by the conduction currents. Therefore, the concentrations of the several charged particles must satisfy the following condition, which is obtained by setting $\rho = 0$ in Eq. 2.6:

$$n - p = N_d - N_a \tag{2.7}$$

The impurity concentrations N_d and N_a are determined solely by the fabrication and subsequent processing of the semiconductor. Therefore, Eq. 2.7 can be regarded as one constraint on the concentrations p and n of the mobile carriers. A second constraint can be obtained from detailed consideration, on a quantum-statistical basis, of the hole and electron concentrations in a semiconductor. The result, which we introduce as a postulate, is quite simple: the *equilibrium* hole and electron concentrations are coupled in such a way that for any particular semiconductor (e.g., silicon) in equilibrium the *product* of the hole and electron concentrations is a function of temperature alone and is independent of the concentrations of donor and acceptor impurities. That is,

$$np = f(T)$$

where T denotes the absolute temperature and $f(T)$ is independent of the concentrations of the impurities. By common convention, the equilibrium np product is denoted by $n_i^2(T)$:

$$np = n_i^2(T) \tag{2.8}$$

The notation originated from the special case of an intrinsic semiconductor that contains negligible concentrations of impurities. As we have seen, the hole and electron concentrations are equal in an intrinsic semiconductor because carriers are produced and disappear in pairs by the breaking or completing of covalent bonds. These equal hole and electron concentrations are commonly denoted by n_i, the *intrinsic* carrier concentration:

$$n = p = n_i \quad \text{for intrinsic material}$$

Since the np product is independent of the impurity concentration, it can be written as n_i^2, as shown in Eq. 2.8.

The fact that the np product in a semiconductor *at equilibrium* is independent of the impurity concentrations (and dependent only on the temperature and fundamental crystalline characteristics of the particular semiconductor of concern) can be understood in terms of the processes by which carriers are produced or disappear in pairs. Several distinct processes operate in each direction. For example, a hole-electron pair can be produced by a process in which some of the thermal energy manifested by the random motion of the atoms and bound electrons is channeled into a bound electron, liberating it from the bond and producing a hole-electron pair. Carriers can also be produced by the absorption of a photon that possesses sufficient energy to break a bond, as well as by multiple-step processes that involve defects in the crystal structure. On the other hand, there is a recombination mechanism that acts as the inverse of each of these generation mechanisms. A pair can disappear by a process in which the energy released when the free electron becomes bound goes into the thermal system as vibrational energy, or a process in which the energy is taken up by a photon, or by the multiple-step processes associated with crystalline defects.

Now it is obvious that in equilibrium the sum of the pair-generation rates characteristic of these separately-identifiable generation mechanisms must equal the sum of the pair-recombination rates characteristic of the several inverse mechanisms by which pairs are annihilated. That is, generation and recombination must be in balance. But we can make a stronger statement: this balance must occur as the result of the *separate balancing* of each of the generation mechanisms with its own inverse recombination mechanism. For example, the rate at which pairs are produced by thermal breaking of a bond must be equal, on the average (i.e., ignoring statistical fluctuations), to the rate at which pairs disappear by the process in which their energy is released to the thermal system. That is, each identifiable physical process (of generation, in this case) must proceed, under equilibrium conditions, at the same *average* rate as its own inverse. This requirement that the processes self-balance is known as *the principle of detailed balance*; it is a consequence of the second law of thermodynamics. In fact, we can illustrate the need for the principle of detailed balance by showing that the second law would be violated if this principle did not hold.

Consider, for example, an equilibrium situation in a semiconductor in which we assume that the various generation-recombination mechanisms do not self-balance; e.g. generation is dominated by a thermal process, whereas recombination is dominated by the process in which the energy released when the free electron becomes bound is carried off by a photon. This light produced by pair recombination can be collected and prevented from returning to the crystal. If these opposing rates are equal, the hole and electron concentrations will *not* change with time, but the semiconductor will cool off, and the emitted light can be made to do useful work, such as operating a photovoltaic cell. A situation of this type, in which useful work is done at the expense of a decrease in the temperature of an isothermal system, constitutes a violation of the second law of thermodynamics; it is tantamount to a perpetual-motion machine. *Any* violation of the principle of detailed balance can be shown to be a violation of the second law.

If we use the fact that the various generation-recombination mechanisms must self-balance in pairs, and focus on the *thermal* generation mechanism and its inverse, we can show that the *np* product of a specific semiconductor should be independent of the impurity concentration in that material. The thermal generation rate is dependent on the dynamics of the process by which a bond is broken to create a hole-electron pair, and on the temperature, which is a measure of the thermal energy. Furthermore, this generation rate is essentially independent of the impurity content as long as the fractional impurity concentrations are small enough not to disturb appreciably the bond structure or the thermal environment. The corresponding recombination rate is, to first order, proportional to the product of the number of electrons and the number of holes; that is, this rate varies as np because the probability of a chance encounter between an electron and a hole increases as n and p increase. Furthermore, the constant of proportionality, which is governed by the dynamics of the recombination process and the chance that a hole and electron get together, is independent of the impurity content. In equilibrium these two mechanisms, one of generation and one of recombination, must self-balance. Thus the np product must, for a specific semiconductor, be independent of the impurity concentrations and be only a function of temperature, as given by Eq. 2.8.

The equilibrium carrier concentrations in a semiconductor are governed by Eqs. 2.7 and 2.8 which relate n and p to n_i, a property of the semiconductor, and to the impurity concentrations N_d and N_a. These equations can be solved for n and p explicitly. However, in many practical circumstances the impurity concentrations are large enough compared with the intrinsic concentration n_i to make simple approximate solutions quite accurate. For example, consider a specimen of n-type material in which $N_a = 0$ and $N_d \gg n_i$. The constancy of the np product suggests that p will be much less than n because n is pushed up by the donors and p is correspondingly depressed. Thus an approximate solution to Eqs. 2.7 and 2.8 in this case is, using Eq. 2.7,

$$n \simeq N_d \tag{2.9a}$$

and, using Eq. 2.8,

$$p \simeq \frac{n_i^2}{N_d} \tag{2.9b}$$

Investigation of the exact solution shows that these approximations are accurate within about 5% if the impurity concentration is greater than about $5n_i$. Of course, analogous approximations hold for p-type material.

Because the np product of a specific material is constant for any fixed temperature, and because the intrinsic-carrier concentration n_i is small (expressed as a fraction of the atomic concentration), relatively small impurity concentrations suffice to unbalance the concentrations of the mobile carriers by large amounts. For example, silicon has, at room temperature, an np product of about 10^{20} cm^{-6}. An impurity concentration of 10^{15} donor atoms per cubic centimeter (and a negligible concentration of acceptors) yields, from Eqs. 2.9:

$$n \simeq 10^{15} \text{ cm}^{-3}$$

$$p \simeq 10^5 \text{ cm}^{-3}$$

Thus the equilibrium carrier concentrations differ by ten orders of magnitude.

It is of some importance that the fractional concentration of impurities necessary to make a semiconductor extrinsic is, by normal chemical or metallurgical standards, exceedingly small. In a silicon crystal the concentration of silicon atoms is about 10^{23} cm^{-3}. Consequently, a donor-impurity concentration of 10^{15} cm^{-3}, as in the example above, corresponds to one impurity atom per 100 million silicon atoms, or to an impurity fraction of 10 parts per billion. Although such minute concentrations have no perceptible effects on the chemical or mechanical properties of the semiconductor, they have an enormous effect on the concentrations of the mobile carriers and thus on the electrical properties of the material.

2.2.2 Temperature Dependence of Equilibrium Carrier Concentrations

The intrinsic-carrier concentration n_i increases as the temperature increases; this is illustrated in Fig. 2.9a, which shows the temperature dependence of n_i for silicon over the range of temperatures in which semiconductor electronic devices normally operate. Note that the rate of increase of n_i with temperature is large; near room temperature (300°K) a temperature change of 25°K produces almost an order of magnitude change in n_i.

The strong temperature dependence shown in Fig. 2.9a is employed in a class of temperature-dependent resistors known commercially as *thermistors*. A thermistor is simply a piece of intrinsic semiconductor to which leads are attached to make a two-terminal resistor. Since this resistor has a large temperature coefficient, it can be used as a temperature sensor, either for temperature measurement or for temperature compensation.

We conclude this discussion of equilibrium carrier concentrations by investigating the temperature dependence of the carrier concentrations in a *doped* semiconductor. As an example we consider an *n*-type specimen of silicon in which the donor concentration is

$$N_d = 10^{13} \text{ cm}^{-3}$$

If the intrinsic-carrier concentration is *small* compared with the donor concentration, the minority-carrier concentration will be much less than the majority-carrier concentration, which will be approximately constant and equal to N_d; this is the situation described by Eqs. 2.9. The graph of Fig. 2.9a shows that n_i is small compared with $N_d = 10^{13} \text{ cm}^{-3}$ for temperatures less than about 375°K. This is known as the *extrinsic temperature range*. The carrier concentrations have the form shown in Fig. 2.9b in which the hole

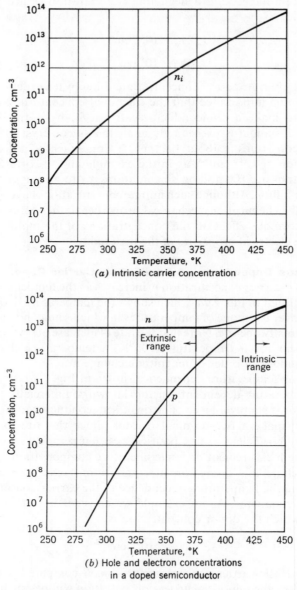

Figure 2.9 Temperature dependence of equilibrium carrier concentrations in silicon.

and electron concentrations given by Eqs. 2.9 have been plotted. As expected from Eqs. 2.9, the majority-carrier concentration n is constant and the minority-carrier concentration p has a large positive temperature coefficient.

If, on the other hand, the intrinsic-carrier concentration is *large* compared with the donor concentration, Eqs. 2.7 and 2.8 show that the hole and electron concentrations are approximately equal to n_i. That is,

$$n \simeq p \simeq n_i$$

The condition holds in the present example for temperatures in excess of about 425°K. This is known as the *intrinsic temperature range*; the intrinsic-carrier concentration is so large that the impurities have no appreciable effect on the carrier concentrations. Clearly, any extrinsic semiconductor can be made to exhibit intrinsic behavior simply by increasing the temperature.

The curves of Fig. 2.9*b* show that over an interval of about 50°K this specimen of semiconductor is neither intrinsic nor extrinsic. In the intermediate range Eqs. 2.7 and 2.8 must be solved without approximation to determine the hole and electron concentrations.

2.2.3   Nonequilibrium Situations—Excess Carriers

Under equilibrium conditions, the concentrations of the mobile charge carriers—the holes and electrons— are determined solely by the impurity concentrations and the temperature [through $n_i^2(T)$]. However, the mobile-carrier concentrations can be changed significantly when equilibrium is disturbed. The equilibrium can be disturbed in several ways. For example, holes or electrons can be introduced into the semiconductor by means of a metal contact or a semiconductor contact. Processes of this kind are fundamental to the operation of junction devices such as diodes and transistors. We shall consider them in detail in Chapter 4. On the other hand, *pairs* of holes and electrons can be produced by illuminating the semiconductor with light of appropriate wavelength; the photons transfer their energy to some of the valence electrons, thereby breaking bonds and producing conduction electrons and holes.

Apart from the specific mechanism by which the carrier concentrations are disturbed, *the useful properties of semiconductor devices all depend on the fact that the carrier concentrations can be disturbed locally without producing significant deviations from electrical neutrality.* Because there are two kinds of mobile charge carriers, having complementary charges, *equal changes* in p and n will not produce a local charge density, in accordance with Eq. 2.6.

In considering nonequilibrium situations, it is convenient to regard each of the mobile-charge-carrier concentrations as comprised of two components. One component, which is identified by the subscript o, is the *equilibrium value* of the corresponding carrier concentration. The other component, which is distinguished from the total concentration by a prime and which describes the deviation from equilibrium, is called the *excess concentration*.

$$p = p_o + p' \tag{2.10a}$$

$$n = n_o + n' \tag{2.10b}$$

If we use these definitions of the excess concentrations in Eq. 2.6, the space charge density can be written

$$\rho = q(p_o + N_d - n_o - N_a) + q(p' - n') \tag{2.11}$$

The first term on the right is the *equilibrium* space charge; it vanishes in homogeneous semiconductors for the reasons discussed in connection with Eq. 2.5. The second term on the right is the space charge that results from *excess* carriers. It is very small if the excess hole and electron concentrations are approximately equal. That is, approximate electrical neutrality can be preserved, even with excess carriers present, if

$$n' \simeq p' \tag{2.12}$$

We describe this condition as *quasi-neutrality*; a semiconductor in which the excess concentrations are nearly equal is said to be *quasi-neutral*. As long as the concentrations of the excess holes and electrons are nearly equal, that is, the *difference* $n' - p'$ is small compared with either n' or p', the concentrations of the mobile carriers can be disturbed without producing the electric fields and restoring currents associated with large deviations from electrical neutrality. This freedom to disturb the mobile-carrier concentrations, which differs sharply from the situation in a metal and which underlies the distinguishing features of semiconductors, is a direct consequence of the presence of two oppositely-charged classes of *mobile* charge carriers.

Since the *excess* hole and electron concentrations are nearly equal in a semiconductor, we shall often refer simply to the excess concentration, thus meaning either the excess-electron concentration or the excess-hole concentration.

It should be noted that whereas Eq. 2.7 applies even when there are nonzero excess-carrier concentrations (since $\rho \simeq 0$, even out of equilibrium), Eq. 2.8 does not apply except in equilibrium. *That is, the np product is constant and equal to n_i^2 only under equilibrium conditions.* If, when the equilibrium is disturbed, n increases, p must increase by a similar amount, so that np will be greater than n_i^2; if, on the other hand, n decreases, p also decreases, so that np will be less than n_i^2. In order to emphasize that Eq. 2.8 applies *only* under equilibrium conditions, we shall henceforth write it as

$$n_o p_o = n_i^2(T)$$

2.3   Recombination and Generation of Excess Carriers

In view of the fact that nonzero excess-carrier concentrations represent a deviation from equilibrium conditions, there arise physical mechanisms that endeavor to restore the equilibrium state. More precisely, whenever n' and p' are positive, corresponding to total carrier concentrations greater than the equilibrium values, there is a tendency for the excess carriers to *recombine* or to disappear by mutual annihilation; conduction electrons fall back into vacancies in the bond structure, thereby removing both themselves and an equal number of holes from circulation. If, on the other hand, n' and p' are negative, as they will be if the total concentrations are caused to be less than the corresponding equilibrium values, there is a tendency for excess carriers to appear or to be *generated* in pairs by the breaking of covalent bonds.

The recombination-generation process that comes into operation when the equilibrium is disturbed can be described in terms of a local *rate of recombination* $\mathcal{R}$, which has the dimensions of pairs per cubic centimeter per second. In general, $\mathcal{R}$ is a homogeneous function of the excess-carrier concentrations. When n' and p' are positive, $\mathcal{R}$ is positive, corresponding to the disappearance or recombination of carriers; when n' and p' are negative, $\mathcal{R}$ is negative, corresponding to the production or generation of carriers.

For many situations of practical significance the rate of recombination can be approximated as a linear homogeneous function of the excess-carrier concentrations:

$$\mathcal{R} = an' + bp' \tag{2.13}$$

where a and b are constants that do not depend on n' and p'. Since we are concerned with quasi-neutral situations, the recombination rate can be written as

$$\mathcal{R} = (a + b)n'$$

or

$$\mathcal{R} = (a + b)p'$$

That is, the recombination rate is a linear homogeneous function of the excess-carrier concentration $n' \simeq p'$. Often this relationship is written as

$$\mathcal{R} = \frac{n'}{\tau} \tag{2.14a}$$

or

$$\mathcal{R} = \frac{p'}{\tau} \tag{2.14b}$$

The parameter τ, which has the dimensions of time, is called the *lifetime* of the excess carriers. The lifetime depends strongly on the chemical and metallurgical nature of the particular semiconductor specimen, and is in no sense a constant parameter that characterizes a certain type of semiconductor. It is seldom larger than 500 microseconds (1 μsec $= 10^{-6}$ sec) and is usually not less than a few nanoseconds (1 nsec $= 10^{-9}$ sec).

The recombination of excess carriers can be demonstrated by means of the simple experiment illustrated in Fig. 2.10. A bar of semiconductor is

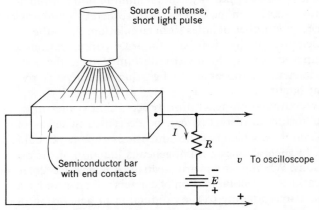

Figure 2.10   Apparatus for observation of photoconductivity and excess carrier recombination.

connected to a battery E and a large series resistor R. If R is much larger than the resistance of the bar the current I is constant:

$$I \simeq \frac{E}{R}$$

For constant current, the voltage drop v across the bar, which can be displayed on the oscilloscope, provides a direct measure of the *conductance G* of the bar. That is,

$$v = I\left(\frac{1}{G}\right) \tag{2.15}$$

A source of short-duration, high-intensity light pulses, such as a xenon flashtube, is used to illuminate the central portion of the semiconductor. Many of the photons contained in this light pulse have sufficient energy to liberate an electron from a covalent bond, thus producing hole-electron pairs in the bar.[9] These excess holes and electrons contribute to the electrical

---

[9] For silicon and germanium the photons of visible light have sufficient energy to break bonds. In fact, any radiation having wavelengths less than the near-infrared range will be absorbed, and thus will provide pairs, in these materials. If the wavelength of the radiation is longer, that is, infrared and beyond, no pairs are produced and no absorption occurs, that is, silicon and germanium are transparent for long wavelengths. Actually, silicon has been used as a lens material in infrared optical systems because it combines a very high index of refraction with high transmission for these long wavelengths.

conductivity and increase the conductance G of the semiconductor. In accordance with Eq. 2.15, the conductance increase is manifested as a drop in the voltage v, which occurs in synchronism with the light pulse, as shown in Fig. 2.11a. The voltage recovers its original value relatively slowly after the light pulse has ended. This gradual increase in the voltage, which corresponds to a *decrease* in conductance (see Eq. 2.15), is a manifestation of the recombination of the excess carriers produced by the pulse of ionizing radiation. We shall later find (see Problem P2.16) that the excess-carrier concentrations decay *exponentially* with time, and shall show that the time constant that governs this decay of the photoconductivity is simply the excess-carrier lifetime, defined in Eqs. 2.14. The exponential nature of the decay is shown in Fig. 2.11b, in which the conductance *change*, which is proportional to the excess-carrier concentration, is replotted as a function of time on semilogarithmic coordinates. This observation of photoconductive decay is frequently used for a simple and quick determination of the excess-carrier lifetime of a semiconductor (see *Notes on Demonstrations*).

Semiconductor devices in which the conductance of a material is sensitive to the quantity or wavelength of the light falling on the device are in wide use. These devices, known as *photoresistors* or *photoconductive cells*, usually employ compound semiconductors such as cadmium sulfide or cadmium selenide. They are used for light-operated controls and for the measurement of light intensity. Many modern photographic exposure meters use a photoresistor to vary the current in a simple series circuit in response to light intensity.

2.4 Transport of Electric Current

The mobile charge carriers in a semiconductor are in constant motion, even under thermal equilibrium conditions. This motion is a manifestation of the random thermal energy of atoms and electrons that comprise the semiconductor. The motion of an individual hole or electron is tortuous and erratic; the charge carrier has frequent collisions with the atoms, including impurities, of the semiconductor. The direction of motion of the charge carrier usually changes as a consequence of these collisions. In addition, there is usually some change in the kinetic energy of the particle; in some encounters the kinetic energy of the particle increases, while in other collisions it decreases.

Because of the exceedingly large number of particles present in a specimen of material, it is necessary to employ statistical methods in describing the random thermal motion of these particles. In statistical terms, the holes and electrons in a semiconductor are characterized (near room temperature) by mean thermal speeds of the order of 10^7 cm/sec and by collision frequencies of about 10^{10} or 10^{12} sec^{-1}. Under equilibrium conditions, no average electric current results from this random thermal motion; the group of carriers that comprise the population in any volume element has no average

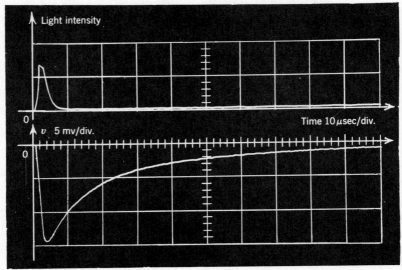

(a) Photograph of the waveforms of
light pulse intensity and of the
voltage v across the
semiconductor bar

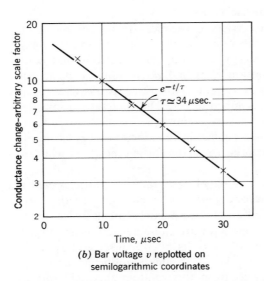

(b) Bar voltage v replotted on
semilogarithmic coordinates

Figure 2.11 The voltage across the bar drops suddenly when the light pulse occurs and recovers exponentially. The recovery time constant is the lifetime of the excess carriers.

velocity because this group contains as many carriers moving in any given direction as carriers moving in the opposite direction.[10]

The equilibrium situation can be disturbed in two ways:

1. An electric field can be applied
2. The carrier distributions can be made nonuniform

In both of these cases gross motion of the charge carriers results, thus producing electric currents.

2.4.1   Drift in an Electric Field

An electric field affects the random thermal motion of charge carriers in the intervals between collisions by imparting a small but uniform acceleration to all the carriers exposed to the field. Although, for any carrier, the velocity increment produced by this acceleration is wiped out by the collisions that the carrier has with its environment, the electric field has a net effect simply because the velocity increments that it imparts to carriers are all directed along the field. This net effect is called *drift*.

The net effect of the collisions and the intervals of acceleration between collisions can be described by assigning to a group of carriers a *drift velocity* that is proportional to the electric field. Thus the group of holes that populate a volume element have a velocity $\mathbf{v}_h$, given by

$$\mathbf{v}_h = \mu_h \mathscr{E} \tag{2.16a}$$

where the parameter μ_h, which is independent of the electric field, is called the *hole mobility*. Similarly, the drift velocity of the electrons in a volume element is

$$\mathbf{v}_e = -\mu_e \mathscr{E} \tag{2.16b}$$

where μ_e is the *electron mobility*. The minus sign appears here because the electrons, having negative charge, are accelerated in a direction opposite to the field.[11] In both silicon and germanium the carrier mobilities are of the order of 10^3 cm/sec per volt/cm.

It is important to recognize that the drift velocity of either carrier *cannot* be ascribed, at any instant of time, to a particular carrier. More precisely, the probability that a hole, or a group of holes for example, has velocity $\mathbf{v}_h$, as given by Eq. 2.16a, is extremely small. Individual carriers are moving in random directions with thermal speeds much larger than $|\mathbf{v}_h|$. Nevertheless, all of these carriers have their trajectories between collisions distorted by the force associated with the field. The *net effect* of these distortions, averaged over many carriers, can be represented by imagining that the random

---

[10] Although there is no *average* current, there is *instantaneous* current as a result of the random carrier motions. These current fluctuations are the source of the thermal or Johnson noise associated with the random thermal motion of carriers.

[11] Note that by definition both μ_e and μ_h are positive.

thermal motion, which gives rise to *no* current itself, is suppressed and that each carrier in the group has a velocity $\mathbf{v}_h$.

The drift of charge carriers in an electric field is, in a phenomenological sense, not unlike the motion through a viscous fluid of particles in a gravitational field; the velocity is proportional to the field strength in each case. In a conductor the "viscous drag" is produced by the collisions of the carriers with their environment.

The electric currents associated with drift are related to the drift velocity in accordance with Eq. 2.1b (see Fig. 2.2). Thus the hole current density is

$$\mathbf{J}_h = qp\mu_h\mathscr{E} \tag{2.17a}$$

The electron current density is

$$\mathbf{J}_e = qn\mu_e\mathscr{E} \tag{2.17b}$$

The electron current density has the same direction as the electric field because, while the electrons move opposite to the field, they carry negative charge; the two minus signs cancel.

The total electric current produced by an electric field in a semiconductor is the sum of the currents carried by the holes and electrons. Thus we have, for the total current density $\mathbf{J}$,

$$\mathbf{J} = q(\mu_h p + \mu_e n)\mathscr{E} \tag{2.18}$$

The coefficient of $\mathscr{E}$ in this result is simply the electrical *conductivity* σ of the semiconductor:[12]

$$\sigma = q(\mu_h p + \mu_e n) \tag{2.19}$$

2.4.2 Diffusion in a Concentration Gradient

Diffusion is a manifestation of the random thermal motion of particles; it shows up as a particle current that appears whenever mobile particles are nonuniformly distributed in a system. We base our discussion of diffusion on the sketch of Fig. 2.12a showing the concentration of the carriers, taken to be holes for this development, as a function of the position coordinate x in a one-dimensional semiconductor bar. Consider a surface normal to the x coordinate at x_0. For the hole distribution shown in Fig. 2.12a, there is a diffusive flow of holes across this surface in the $+x$ direction. This diffusive flow arises simply because the hole concentration to the left of x_0 is greater than the hole concentration to the right of x_0.

We illustrate the dependence of the diffusive flow of carriers on the concentration imbalance by focusing on the carriers in the two boxlike volume elements of cross-sectional area A and width δ which lie on either

---

[12] Equation 2.18 is a statement of Ohm's law in terms of the current density and field vectors. This correspondence to a basic physical law that has wide applicability provides justification for the "viscous flow model" introduced in Eqs. 2.16.

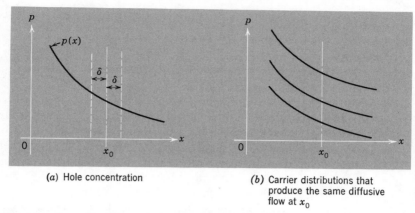

(a) Hole concentration

(b) Carrier distributions that produce the same diffusive flow at x_0

Figure 2.12   Diffusion arises when the carrier distribution is nonuniform.

side of the plane at x_0. In unit time some fraction of the carriers in the volume element to the left of x_0 flow in the $+x$ direction across the plane at x_0 as a result of their random thermal motion. In the same time interval the *same* fraction of the carriers in the volume element to the right of x_0 flow in the $-x$ direction across the plane at x_0. The fractions are the same because the volume elements are in the same thermal environment and are symmetrically defined.

There is a net flow of carriers from left to right because there are *more carriers* in the left volume element than in the right one. The net rate of flow of holes is proportional to the concentration imbalance. More precisely, if p_- denotes the hole concentration in the left volume element and p_+ the concentration in the right volume element, the rate at which holes cross the boundary at x_0 is

$$\text{hole flux} = (\text{constant})[p_- - p_+] \qquad (2.20a)$$

In the limit, as δ approaches zero, this rate is proportional to the first derivative of the concentration at x_0. That is,

$$\text{hole flux} = -D_h\left(\frac{dp}{dx}\right)_{x_0} \qquad (2.20b)$$

The constant of proportionality is called the *diffusion coefficient* for holes. The minus sign appears because carriers flow *down* the concentration slope from regions of high concentration to regions of lower concentration.

The hole current density associated with diffusion is

$$J_h = -qD_h\frac{dp}{dx} \qquad (2.21)$$

This proportionality is usually written, for three-dimensional concentration variations, as[13]

$$\mathbf{J}_h = -qD_h \, \nabla p \tag{2.22a}$$

The corresponding relationship for electrons, which carry *negative* charge, is

$$\mathbf{J}_e = qD_e \, \nabla n \tag{2.22b}$$

Diffusive flow is in no sense a cooperative process, and it has nothing to do with the fact that the diffusing carriers are charged. It occurs simply because the *number of carriers* that (as a result of random thermal motion) have velocity components directed from the region of high concentration toward a region of lower concentration is greater than the *number of carriers* that have oppositely-directed velocity components.

It is important to notice that the particle flux density that results from diffusion depends on the carrier-concentration *gradient* and *not* on the concentration itself; it is the concentration imbalance that matters, not the value of the concentration. Thus all three carrier distributions shown in Fig. 2.12b will produce the *same* diffusive flux density at x_0.

Diffusion, which forms the basis of the physical behavior of many semiconductor devices, does not contribute significantly to charge flow in metals. As discussed in Section 2.1.3, because there can be no appreciable concentration gradient of the single mobile carrier in a metal, diffusion is negligible.

2.4.3 Flow with Both Drift and Diffusion

In many situations, an electric field and carrier-concentration gradients are simultaneously present in a semiconductor. For small disturbances from equilibrium, it is reasonable to regard the total hole or electron current density as a linear combination of two component current densities, one generated by drift and the other by diffusion. Thus the net hole current density can be written (using Eqs. 2.17a and 2.22a) as

$$\mathbf{J}_h = q(p\mu_h \mathscr{E} - D_h \, \nabla p) \tag{2.23a}$$

and the net electron current density can be written as

$$\mathbf{J}_e = q(n\mu_e \mathscr{E} + D_e \, \nabla n) \tag{2.23b}$$

This description of hole and electron motion in nonequilibrium situations in terms of drift and diffusion can be justified in detail in terms of statistical-mechanical concepts and techniques. In keeping with our prior assumptions, we shall adopt, as a postulate, the description of hole and electron currents presented above, including the definitions of mobility and of diffusion coefficient.

---

[13] The symbol ∇p denotes the gradient of p. In one dimension, $\nabla p = \mathbf{a}_x \, dp/dx$ where $\mathbf{a}_x$ is a unit vector in the x direction.

2.4.4 The Einstein Relations

Drift and diffusion are both manifestations of the random thermal motion of the carriers. Consequently, the mobility μ and the diffusion coefficient D are not independent. More precisely, they are related as follows:

$$\frac{D_h}{\mu_h} = \frac{kT}{q} \tag{2.24a}$$

$$\frac{D_e}{\mu_e} = \frac{kT}{q} \tag{2.24b}$$

These equations are known as *Einstein relations*. The proportionality constant kT/q, which has the dimensions of voltage, is called the *thermal voltage*. The factors that appear in the thermal voltage are: k, Boltzmann's constant; q, the electronic charge; and T, the absolute temperature. Near room temperature the thermal voltage is about 25 mv ($kT/q = 25$ mv for $T = 290°K$ or $17°C$).

The Einstein relations can be justified fully by considering the statistical-mechanical implications of the equilibrium situation in a semiconductor that is not uniformly doped. In accordance with our previous position, we adopt these relations as postulates.

REFERENCES

2.1 R. B. Adler, A. C. Smith, and R. L. Longini, *Introduction to Semiconductor Physics*, Wiley, New York, 1964.

2.2 F. W. Sears, *An Introduction to Thermodynamics, the Kinetic Theory of Gases, and Statistical Mechanics*, Addison-Wesley, Reading, Mass., 1950 (see, in particular, Chapter 13).

PROBLEMS

P2.1 This problem is concerned with the requirement for space-charge neutrality in the interior of a good conductor. The electric field produced by an unneutralized charge distribution is related to the total charge by Gauss's law, given by Eq. 2.5. This field gives rise to a conduction current $\mathbf{J} = \sigma\mathscr{E}$, where σ is the electrical conductivity. The net current crossing the surface S is related to the total charge Q by the law of conservation of charge:

$$\oint_S J_n \, dS = -\frac{dQ}{dt}$$

where J_n denotes the normal component of the current density crossing the surface S.

Derive a first-order linear differential equation for Q and show that the expression for $Q(t)$ given by Eq. 2.3 is a solution of this differential equation.

P2.2   Semiconductors have interesting electrical properties principally because they conduct by means of two independent classes of mobile carriers, holes, and electrons. The existence of holes and electrons can be understood qualitatively in terms of the valence-bond model of a semiconductor, which is discussed in Section 2.1.4. Explain briefly, in terms of this model, the following statements:

(a) Both charge and mass are conserved when holes and electrons are annihilated in pairs by recombination or are produced in pairs by thermal generation.

(b) Hole motion does not involve the conduction electrons.

(c) Ionization of an acceptor-impurity atom produces a mobile hole *but* neutrality is preserved.

P2.3   One constraint on the hole and electron concentrations in a semi-conductor is given by Eq. 2.7:

$$n - p = N_d - N_a$$

where N_d and N_a are the donor and acceptor concentrations, respectively. In the text, this equation was obtained by observing that the local space-charge density in a homogeneous semiconductor must be zero. Show that the same result can be obtained as follows.

(a) Assume that the mobile carriers are uniformly distributed.

(b) Equate, on a per unit volume basis, the number of electrons produced by the breaking of covalent bonds to the number of holes similarly produced.

P2.4   Near room temperature (290°K) silicon has an intrinsic-carrier concentration of $n_i = 10^{10}$ cm^{-3}.

(a) Estimate the hole and electron concentrations in silicon at this temperature if the material contains acceptor impurities at a concentration of $N_a = 2 \times 10^{14}$ cm^{-3} and a negligible quantity of donor impurities. Is this material intrinsic at 290°K?

(b) If the temperature is increased to 573°K (300°C), the intrinsic-carrier concentration increases to approximately 3×10^{15} cm^{-3}. Assuming the same impurity concentrations as in (a), estimate the hole and electron concentrations. Is this material intrinsic or extrinsic at this temperature (573°K)?

Answers. (a) $p_o \simeq 2 \times 10^{14}$ cm^{-3}, $n_o \simeq 5 \times 10^5$ cm^{-3}; (b) $n_o \simeq p_o \simeq 3 \times 10^{15}$ cm^{-3}.

P2.5   A specimen of germanium is uniformly doped with aluminum atoms to produce an impurity concentration of 5×10^{16} cm^{-3}. At 300°K the intrinsic-carrier concentration is approximately $n_i^2 = 2 \times 10^{13}$ cm^{-3}.

(a) Calculate the approximate hole and electron concentrations in this semiconductor.

(b) As the temperature increases, the imbalance between the carrier concentrations decreases. At what temperature is the minority-carrier concentration approximately 1% of the majority-carrier concentration? Assume that the intrinsic-carrier concentration increases exponentially with temperature at a fractional rate of 6%/°K.

Answers. (*b*) $T \simeq 350°$K.

P2.6 A semiconductor has, under equilibrium conditions, a hole concentration of 10^{14} cm^{-3} and an electron concentration of 2×10^{13} cm^{-3}.

(*a*) Determine the net impurity concentration.

(*b*) What type of impurity dominates?

(*c*) Determine the intrinsic-carrier concentration.

P2.7 This problem is concerned with the equilibrium carrier concentrations in a semiconductor.

(*a*) Derive expressions for p_o and n_o, the hole and electron concentrations, in terms of the *net* impurity concentration $N = N_d - N_a$ and the intrinsic-carrier concentration n_i.

(*b*) In *n*-type material, the net impurity concentration N is positive ($N_d > N_a$). Show that if N/n_i is large enough, the expressions that you obtained in (*a*) reduce to

$$\left. \begin{array}{l} n_o = N + \dfrac{n_i{}^2}{N} \\[3mm] p_o = \dfrac{n_i{}^2}{N} \end{array} \right\} \quad N \gg n_i ; \text{ } n\text{-type material}$$

(*c*) In *p*-type material, N is negative. Show that if $-N/n_i$ is large enough, the equations for p_o and n_o reduce to

$$\left. \begin{array}{l} n_o = \dfrac{n_i{}^2}{-N} \\[3mm] p_o = -N + \dfrac{n_i{}^2}{-N} \end{array} \right\} \quad -N \gg n_i ; \text{ } p\text{-type material}$$

(*d*) How large must $|N|/n_i$ be to ensure that the errors introduced by these approximate expressions for n_o and p_o are less than 5%?

[*Suggestion.* Express the radicals in your results for (*a*) in the form

$$\sqrt{1 + (2n_i/N)^2}$$

and expand those radicals in Taylor's series in $(2n_i/N)^2$ about $(2n_i/N)^2 = 0$.]

Notice that the approximate expressions for n_o and p_o are reasonably accurate over an extremely wide range of dopings; these results are useful even for near-intrinsic conditions.

(*e*) If the material is strongly extrinsic the *second terms* in the approximate expressions for the majority-carrier concentrations developed in (*b*) and (*c*) are negligible compared with the first terms. How large must $|N|/n_i$ be to ensure that the errors made by neglecting the *second terms* in the *majority-carrier* expressions are less than 1%?

P2.8   At room temperature the intrinsic-carrier concentration of germanium is approximately 2×10^{13} cm^{-3}. Consider a germanium specimen that has a *donor* concentration of $N_d = 5 \times 10^{14}$ cm^{-3} and no acceptors.

(*a*) Estimate the equilibrium hole and electron concentrations.

Acceptor impurities can be added to the specimen by *solid-state diffusion*. This is a process in which impurity atoms diffuse or migrate into the specimen at high temperatures. We assume that the net result of this diffusion is a uniform distribution of acceptors in the specimen.

(*b*) Compute, sketch, and dimension the hole and electron concentrations as functions of the normalized *added* acceptor concentration N_a/n_i. Use logarithmic scales for both axes and consider acceptor concentrations in the range $0.1 < N_a/n_i < 100$.

Notice that the addition of acceptor impurities converts the material from *n*-type to intrinsic to *p*-type. This process is known as *compensation*. It is a manifestation of the fact that only the *net* impurity concentration matters in determining the equilibrium carrier concentrations (see Eq. 2.7).

Answers. (*a*) $n_o = 5 \times 10^{14}$ cm^{-3}, $p_o = 8 \times 10^{11}$ cm^{-3}.

P2.9   The intrinsic-carrier concentration n_i depends strongly on temperature, as shown in Fig. 2.9. *For limited ranges of temperature variation near room temperature* this dependence is approximately *exponential* for both silicon and germanium (an exponential variation plots as a straight line on the coordinates of Fig. 2.9). In silicon n_i increases by a factor of about 2.5 for a temperature increase of 10°C, that is

$$n_i(T) = n_i(T_o)2.5^{(T - T_o)/10} \qquad T, T_o \text{ in } °C$$

The corresponding factor in germanium is about 1.8. The room temperature (300°K) values of n_i in silicon and germanium are approximately 10^{10} cm^{-3} and 2×10^{13} cm^3, respectively.

(*a*) Plot, on separate but identical semilogarithmic coordinates, $n_i(T)$ for silicon and germanium. Use the *exponential approximation* discussed above. Consider temperatures, which are plotted on the linear axis, over the range of 300 to 450°K. The logarithmic scale should be chosen to span about 10 decades. Note that linear graph paper can be used for these sketches; the ordinate scale can be chosen so that major divisions correspond to decades of concentration, that is, 10^{10}, 10^{11}, and so on. Note also that two points suffice to determine the curves.

Both the silicon and germanium specimens contain donor concentrations of 10^{15} cm^{-3} and negligible concentrations of acceptors. Thus the two specimens have nearly equal majority-carrier (electron) concentrations in the region of temperature for which the specimens are extrinsic.

(b) Using your results for Problem P2.7, compute, sketch, and dimension n_o and p_o as functions of temperature for both specimens. Your results should be plotted on the same coordinates used in (a). Note that all asymptotes are straight lines.

(c) Compare the temperatures at which the silicon and germanium specimens become *intrinsic* ($n_o \simeq p_o$). Inasmuch as extrinsic materials are required for semiconductor junction devices, this difference in temperature dependence is the principal reason why silicon devices are useful at higher temperatures than germanium devices.

P2.10   A specimen of silicon has a uniform acceptor concentration of $2 \times 10^{16} \, \text{cm}^{-3}$ and a uniform donor concentration of $5 \times 10^{15} \, \text{cm}^{-3}$. At $T = 300°\text{K}$, n_i is approximately $10^{10} \, \text{cm}^{-3}$.

(a) Is this specimen p-type or n-type at 300°K?

(b) At about what temperature does this specimen become intrinsic?

(c) What type impurity should be added to this specimen to reduce the difference between the majority- and the minority-carrier concentrations? What should be the concentration of this added impurity to make $n_o = p_o$?

Answers. (b) $T \simeq 460°\text{K}$; (c) $N_d = 1.5 \times 10^{16} \, \text{cm}^{-3}$.

P2.11   This problem is concerned with the Hall effect in extrinsic semiconductors; it leads to an evaluation of the Hall voltage and a derivation of the Hall constant. Refer to Fig. 2.1a for a sketch of the physical arrangement. As discussed on page 45, the transverse deflection of charge carriers causes a transverse electric field to exist. This field exerts a transverse force on the carriers, which must be added to the Lorentz force given by Eq. 2.1c in formulating the equation of motion for transverse carrier motion. Thus the transverse component of Eq. 2.1c becomes

$$F_z = \pm q \mathscr{E}_z + \frac{1}{c}(J_x B_y)$$

in which the subscripts denote components of the vectors in the right-hand coordinate system defined in Fig. 2.1a. The carrier concentration is denoted by c; the plus sign applies for holes, the minus sign for electrons.

Consider first a p-type semiconductor with $c = p_o$.

(a) In equilibrium there must be no transverse (z) component of current. What must F_z be in equilibrium?

(b) If the bar has a width along the transverse axis (a distance between the contacts at which V is defined) of W, express the Hall voltage V in terms of q, p_o, W, J_x, and B_y.

(c) The *Hall constant R* is, by definition,

$$R = \frac{\mathscr{E}_z}{J_x B_y}$$

Evaluate the Hall constant for p-type material. Note that it provides a measure of the majority-carrier concentration.

(d) Repeat (b) and (c) for n-type material with $c = n_o$.

(e) What is the magnitude of the Hall voltage in a semiconductor having a majority-carrier concentration of 10^{16} cm^{-3} if $W = 1$ mm, $B_y = 0.1$ weber/ m^2 (1 kgauss), and the bar carries a current of 10 ma through a cross-sectional area of 10^{-2} cm^2? Be consistent in your choice of units.

Answers. (e) $|V| \simeq 0.6$ mv.

P2.12 A thermistor which is made of intrinsic silicon (see Fig. 2.9a) has a resistance of 500 ohms at 290°K. In answering the following questions *assume* that the carrier mobilities do *not* vary appreciably with temperature.

(a) What is the temperature coefficient of the resistance of this thermistor at 290°K? Express your result in percent per degree Kelvin. What is the corresponding value at 400°K?

(b) What is the approximate resistance of the thermistor at 325°K? At 250°K?

Answers. (a) 9.2% per °K at 290°K ; (b) 50 ohms at 325°K.

P2.13 Because of the large difference between n_o and p_o in an extrinsic semiconductor, excess carriers may change the total minority-carrier concentration enormously, while having negligible effect on the total majority-carrier concentration. Consider an n-type semiconductor in which $n_o = 10^6 p_o$.

(a) Express n and p, the total concentrations, in terms of the *injection ratio* p'/p_o.

(b) What is the value of p'/p_o for which the majority-carrier concentration is disturbed from its equilibrium value by 10%? What is the corresponding percentage increase of minority-carrier concentration?

P2.14 This problem and the one that follows are concerned with carrier conservation laws that are quite general and are extremely important in understanding the physical behavior of transistors. Consider a region V of a semiconductor in which there are excess carriers. Assume that:

1. No excess carriers enter or leave the region, that is, there is no flow of carriers across the surface that encloses the region.

2. The generation and recombination of the excess carriers is described completely by a linear recombination law, that is, the net rate (per unit volume, per unit time) of recombination of excess carriers is $\mathcal{R} = p'/\tau = n'/\tau$, where τ, the lifetime, is a *constant*.

(a) Note that the total number of excess carriers within the region can change *only* as a consequence of recombination or generation. Prove that the following conservation relation holds true:

$$\frac{dQ_h}{dt} + \frac{Q_h}{\tau} = 0$$

where

$$Q_h = q \int_v p' \, dV$$

denotes the total charge of excess holes in the region. That is, Q_h is the excess hole charge stored in the region; it is frequently called the *hole store*. Note that this language does *not* imply a net volume space charge because p' is at every point balanced by an $n' = p'$ so that there is no *net* unbalanced charge.

(b) Assume that the hole store at $t = 0$ is $Q_h(0)$, and determine $Q_h(t)$ for $t > 0$ by solving the differential equation for the stored charge. Use your result to give a physical interpretation of the lifetime τ.

The differential equation obtained in (a) constitutes a conservation law for total hole charge in V. In general, it cannot be used to make inferences about the time dependence of the local concentration p'. If, however, there is no hole current within V, that is, if $J_h = 0$ throughout V, the time dependence obtained in (b) applies to $p'(\mathbf{r}, t)$ for all $\mathbf{r}$ in V. We shall see that such a situation exists for the excess majority carriers in the base region of a transistor.

P2.15 A more general treatment of the type developed in Problem 2.14 would account for the flow of excess carriers *into or out of* the region V. In general, both holes and electrons may flow across the surface that encloses V.

(a) Denote the *net* electric current that flows *into* V as a consequence of the flow of *holes into* V by I_h. Prove that the following conservation relation holds true:

$$\frac{dQ_h}{dt} + \frac{Q_h}{\tau} = I_h$$

where Q_h denotes the store of excess holes, as defined in Problem P2.14.

(b) Give physical interpretations to the two terms on the left side of this differential equation, which is a conservation law for holes.

(c) Formulate an analogous differential equation that relates the excess *electron store*

$$Q_e = -q \int_v n' \, dV$$

to the electric current I_e into V that is associated with the flow of *electrons* (electrons entering V transport negative charge in, which is equivalent to the flow of positive charge out, and thus is described by a negative value of I_e).

(d) Show that the conservation laws formulated in (a) and (b) are equivalent. (*Suggestion.* Note that the law of conservation of charge requires that $I_h + I_e = 0$. Why?)

P2.16 This problem is concerned with the photoconductive-decay experiment discussed in connection with Figs. 2.10 and 2.11. It makes use of the conservation equation for the total charge Q_h developed in Problem P2.14 to show that the conductance *change* decays exponentially with time. Consider the rectangular bar of semiconductor shown in Fig. 2.13 and assume

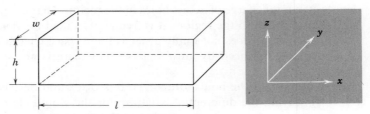

Figure 2.13 A rectangular bar of semiconductor.

that electrical contacts are applied to the ends of the bar (the ends are the surfaces of area wh). Assume also that the bar is uniformly doped.

(*a*) Show that the total current passing through the bar is

$$I = \int_A \sigma \mathscr{E}_x \, ds$$

where $\mathscr{E}_x$ is the x-directed electric field, σ is the conductivity, and the surface integral is taken over the cross-sectional area A of the bar.

(*b*) In equilibrium the field $\mathscr{E}_x$ is uniform and equal to V/l where V is the voltage across the bar. When excess carriers are injected into the bar, the conductivity changes and the electric field changes also. However, if the conductivity change is *small*, the corresponding change in the electric field can be ignored, in evaluating the integral in (*a*). Assume that $\mathscr{E}_x$ is *constant* at its equilibrium value and that neutrality holds ($n' = p'$) and show that the conductance of the bar can be written as

$$G = G_o + \Delta G$$

where

$$G_o = \frac{\sigma_o wh}{l}$$

and

$$\Delta G = \frac{q(\mu_h + \mu_e)}{l} \int_o^l \int_A p' \, ds \, dx$$

In these equations σ_o denotes the equilibrium conductivity $[q(\mu_h p_o + \mu_e n_o)]$ and p' denotes the excess-hole concentration.

(*c*) Note that the integral in ΔG above gives the *total* number of excess holes in the bar, independent of their detailed distribution. Use this fact, together with the result of Problem P2.14, to show that the conductance change ΔG decays exponentially with time following a short pulse of ionizing radiation. Show also that the time constant of this decay is the excess-carrier lifetime.

(*d*) Considering the circuit of Fig. 2.10, show that the change in the voltage v is, for small changes in G, proportional to ΔG.

P2.17 A germanium bar has the shape illustrated in Fig. 2.13 with dimensions

$$l = 1 \text{ cm}$$

$$h = w = 0.1 \text{ cm}$$

The hole and electron mobilities are 2×10^3 and 4×10^3 cm²/(volt)(sec), respectively.

(*a*) If the bar is *intrinsic* ($n_o = p_o = n_i \simeq 2 \times 10^{13}$ cm⁻³ at $T = 300°K$), find the conductivity σ and the resistance measured between the ends of the bar (the ends are the surfaces of area wh).

(*b*) If the bar is known to be n type and has a resistance (measured between the ends) of 10 ohms, what is the donor concentration?

$$\textit{Answers. (a) } R = 5.2 \text{ kohm}; \text{ (b) } N_d = 1.5 \times 10^{16} \text{ cm}^{-3}$$

P2.18 A silicon sample is uniformly doped with phosphorus atoms at a concentration of 10^{13} cm⁻³. At the temperature of interest the intrinsic carrier concentration is 2×10^{12} cm⁻³ and the mobilities are $\mu_e = 800$ cm²/(volt)(sec) and $\mu_h = 300$ cm²/(volt)(sec).

(*a*) Determine the hole and electron concentrations.

(*b*) Determine the electrical conductivity.

(*c*) What fraction of the current produced by an electric field is carried by holes?

(*d*) Neglecting the temperature dependence of the carrier mobilities, how do you expect the conductivity of this specimen to vary as the temperature is lowered 75°K? As it is raised 75°K?

$$\textit{Answers. (b) } \sigma \simeq 1.4 \times 10^{-3} \text{ mho/cm}; \text{ (c) } 1.4\%.$$

P2.19 Copper has an electron concentration of about 10^{23} cm⁻³. The electrical conductivity of copper is about 10^6 mhos/cm.

(*a*) Estimate the mobility of the free electrons in copper.

(*b*) A 100-meter length of copper wire that is 10^{-2} cm in diameter is connected across a 1-volt battery. Estimate the current and the electric field in the wire. What is the corresponding drift velocity of the electrons?

(*c*) How long does it take an electron to drift from one end of the wire to the other end if it drifts with the velocity established in (*b*)? Reconcile this with the experimental fact that the current in the wire reaches its steady-state value in less than 1 μsec when the wire is connected to the battery.

$$\textit{Answers. (a) } \mu = 60 \text{ cm}^2/(\text{volt})(\text{sec}); \text{ (c) } 1.6 \times 10^6 \text{ sec.}$$

NOTES ON DEMONSTRATIONS

Each of the three experiments described in this chapter can serve as a simple and effective demonstration. The Hall effect and the hot probe–thermal emf observation provide direct experimental evidence for the existence of two classes of semiconductors, *p*-type and *n*-type, which differ in the sign of the charge on the dominant charge carrier. The photoconductive decay experiment demonstrates the optical injection of excess carriers and also reveals the dynamics of excess-carrier recombination.

All three of these experiments can be performed conveniently using small bars of *p*-type and *n*-type germanium. Specimens of 1 to 5 ohm-cm resistivity, about 1 to 2 cm in length and having square cross sections 1 to 2 mm on a side are satisfactory.[14] For the Hall effect and photoconductive-decay demonstrations, wire contacts must be soldered to these bars. These connections can be made with a pencil-type soldering iron if coreless solder and a suitable flux are used.[15] The area to which the contact is to be made should be roughened with fine emery paper and wetted with the flux before the solder is applied with the iron. If too large an area is tinned, the excess solder

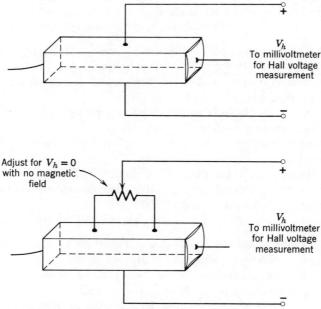

Figure 2.14   Samples for observation of the Hall voltage.

[14] Suitable samples of germanium can be obtained from Semimetals, Inc., 172 Spruce Street, Westbury, New York (AAPT set, about $1), or from the Central Scientific Company, 1700 Irving Park Road, Chicago, Illinois (Semiconductor Demonstration Kit).

[15] Coreless lead-tin solder which contains 50 to 60% lead is suitable. A satisfactory commercial flux, called Polyflux, is made by Industrial Craftsmen, Inc., 39 Stevens Road, Needham, Massachusetts.

can be removed by polishing with fine emery cloth. Care is necessary; germanium is quite brittle and can easily be broken by nonuniform pressure during polishing.

Hall Effect. Four contacts should be soldered to the germanium bars as shown in Fig. 2.14. Note that the transverse contacts between which the Hall voltage appears must be aligned carefully. If these contacts are offset along the axis of the bar, there will be a voltage between them when the magnetic field is zero because of the voltage drops associated with the longitudinal current. Small offsets can be often compensated for by trimming the tinned areas of the transverse faces of the bar with a razor blade. If the offset voltage cannot be made small compared with the Hall voltage by care in contact placement, three contacts and a balancing potentiometer can be used, as shown in Fig. 2.14*b*. If the magnetic field is nearly uniform over the region that includes the contacts on the lateral faces, the Hall voltage will be the same at all cross sections. Thus the potentiometer can be used to reduce the zero-magnetic-field voltage to zero without affecting the Hall voltage.

Magnetron magnets having fields of the order of 1 kgauss are suitable for Hall effect demonstrations. With such a field, and with a longitudinal current of the order of 10 ma, the Hall voltage is in the range of a few mv.

A method of mounting samples that is convenient for classroom demonstration of the Hall effect is shown in Fig. 2.15. Similarly mounted specimens are available commercially.[16]

Figure 2.15 Hall effect demonstration.

[16] Ealing General Corporation, 2225 Massachusetts Avenue, Cambridge, Massachusetts (N and P Hall Effect Semiconductors).

Hot Probe. No soldered contacts are necessary for this experiment. The thermoelectric voltage can be observed between a heated electrode, such as a soldering iron operated at reduced voltage, and an electrode that contacts a cool region of the semiconductor bar. With a temperature difference of about 100°C, the thermal emf is in the range of 10 mv.

Photoconductive Decay. It is necessary to treat the surfaces of the semiconductor bar to reduce the rate of recombination of carriers at the surfaces. If the surfaces are not prepared to minimize defects and contamination, the loss of excess carriers will be dominated by surface processes, and it will be difficult to observe the lifetime that is characteristic of bulk recombination.

The first step in preparation of the bars for this experiment is tinning of the end faces. This is done so that wires can later be soldered to these faces. Next, the four lateral faces of the bar must be polished until all visible scratches are removed and until these surfaces are smooth and mirrorlike. This can be accomplished by polishing the bar with Linde type A lapping powder against a glass plate.[17] Once again, care is needed to avoid breaking the brittle germanium sample. After the desired finish is obtained, the bar is washed in water to remove the powder, and then in acetone to remove any grease that may be present. Finally, the bar is boiled in 3% hydrogen peroxide for several minutes, rinsed in water, and dried. The bar should be handled with plastic tweezers and should *not* be touched with the fingers after these cleaning operations are completed.

Connecting wires should be soldered to the tinned end faces, and the bar should be connected as shown in Fig. 2.10. A dc current of 10 to 20 ma suffices for this experiment.

The light source should be of high intensity and should have a light-pulse duration not in excess of a few microseconds. The time dependence of the photoconductivity is simple to interpret only if the pulse duration is short compared with the excess-carrier lifetime, which should be at least 15 μsec if the surfaces are properly prepared.[18] The ends of the bar should be shielded from the light so that excess carriers are not produced near the ends where they can be swept to the contact before having time to recombine. Only the middle half or third of the bar should be illuminated.

The light intensity should be adjusted (by changing the distance between the source and the bar) so that the conductance change (as measured by the change in the voltage across the bar) is not in excess of a few percentage points.

[17] This lapping powder is available from the Linde Company, Crystal Products Division of Union Carbide, 300 First Street, Needham, Massachusetts.

[18] The General Radio type 1531 Strobotac has a light pulse duration of about 1 μsec when used on the high-speed range. The pulse duration is greater on the lower-speed ranges.

CHAPTER THREE

The Distribution and Flow of Charge Carriers in Semiconductors

3.1 Introduction

As we have seen in Chapter 2, electric current can flow in a semiconductor through the motion of *two* independent classes of charge carriers, holes and electrons or, more precisely, holes and *conduction* electrons. Furthermore, each of these classes of charge carriers can develop the gross motion associated with a current as a result of *two* independent mechanisms of charge-carrier flow: drift, which is produced by an electric field, and diffusion, which is produced by a concentration gradient. Finally, holes and electrons recombine or disappear in pairs in regions where the local carrier concentrations are greater than the corresponding equilibrium values, and are generated or appear in pairs in regions where the local carrier concentrations are less than the corresponding equilibrium values.

The carriers in the semiconductor devices that we wish to study are moved by both drift and diffusion, and excess carriers recombine, affecting the physical behavior of these devices. We shall, therefore, examine the consequences of drift, diffusion, and recombination by investigating the distribution and flow of holes and electrons in a semiconductor in which the equilibrium is disturbed in some way. This behavior can be explored if we focus attention on appropriate *continuity relationships* or *conservation laws* for holes and electrons. The fundamental relationships can be derived by accounting for the existence of all carriers of each type in the semiconductor volume of interest, and relating these carrier populations to the dynamic mechanisms of drift, diffusion, and recombination. For example, if we find that the concentration of the holes in a certain volume element is increasing, the increase must result from either of the following imbalances or from some combination of them.

1. An imbalance between the rate at which holes flow *into* the volume element (by drift or diffusion or both) and the rate at which holes flow *out of* the volume element.

2. An imbalance between the rate at which holes are generated within that volume element and the rate at which they recombine.

Rather than formulating these conservation laws for holes and electrons in quite general terms, we shall treat a sequence of special simple cases, which illustrate essentially all of the important physical considerations and provide a basis for our subsequent study of diodes and transistors without requiring complicated mathematical developments.[1] The examples all conform to several assumptions about the physical situation:

[1] The general case is considered in Chapter 4 of Reference 2.1.

1. The system is one-dimensional; that is, the carrier-concentration distributions are uniform on planes that are normal to the single coordinate of interest (which we denote as the x coordinate) and carriers flow only parallel to that coordinate.

2. The carrier distributions are *static* and the carrier flows are *steady-state*; that is, the distributions and the currents do not change with time. Although we shall later study device behavior in which the carrier concentrations and the currents change with time, we shall find that this dynamic behavior can often be approximated as a succession of static distributions.

3. The semiconductor, which is electrically neutral in equilibrium, remains approximately neutral when the carrier concentrations are disturbed. That is, neutrality is preserved, even though the excess-carrier concentrations are nonzero. As we found in Section 2.2.3, neutrality will be maintained in the presence of injection if the excess concentrations are equal, that is, if $p' = n'$. Actually, small deviations from neutrality exist, so that the excess concentrations are only *approximately* equal; that is, $p' \simeq n'$. We describe this situation as *quasi-neutrality*.

4. The total hole and electron concentrations are grossly unbalanced and remain so under all operating conditions of interest. Specifically, the *minority-carrier concentration is small compared with the majority-carrier concentration.* This condition can be expressed in terms of two requirements:

(*a*) The semiconductor is *extrinsic*, so that the equilibrium concentrations are unbalanced.

(*b*) The excess concentration $p' \simeq n'$ is small compared with the *equilibrium majority-carrier* concentration. This requirement, which is usually described as the *low-level injection condition*, ensures that the majority-carrier concentration is not appreciably disturbed by excess-carrier injection. Thus under low-level injection conditions in an extrinsic material the minority-carrier concentration remains small compared with the majority-carrier concentration.

3.2   Optical Injection into a Region with No Recombination

As our first example of evaluation of the static distribution and steady-state flow of carriers in a semiconductor, we consider the situation shown in Fig. 3.1. The uniformly-doped extrinsic semiconductor is taken to be *n*-type; the discussion that follows could just as well have been phrased in terms of a *p*-type extrinsic semiconductor. Although the doping is uniform throughout the bar of semiconductor, we assume that the excess-carrier lifetime that characterizes the recombination mechanism is *not* uniform. Specifically, region 1, which extends from the surface at $x = 0$ to the plane at $x = W$, is assumed to have such a large lifetime τ_1 that recombination there is negligible. Since the recombination rate $\mathscr{R}$ in this region is equal to p'/τ_1, large values of τ_1 imply very small rates of recombination, even if p' is large. On the other hand, region 2, which extends from the plane at $x = W$ to the end of the bar,

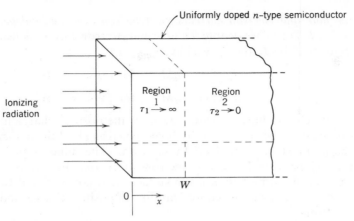

Figure 3.1   Optical injection into a one-dimensional structure.

is assumed to have such a *small* lifetime τ_2 that the excess-carrier concentration there is negligible.

We assume that the semiconductor face at $x = 0$ is illuminated with ionizing radiation that is absorbed at the surface and produces hole-electron pairs in a skin of negligible thickness. We describe this pair-generation process as *excess-carrier injection* and characterize it in terms of a *surface generation rate M*. Thus the ionizing radiation produces *both* holes and electrons at a rate of M carriers per unit time per unit area. Consequently, positive charge is liberated in the skin at the rate qM (amperes per unit area), as is negative charge. Of course, the rate at which *net* charge is produced at the surface is identically zero, for holes and electrons are liberated in pairs.

Because of pair production at the surface, the hole and electron concentrations there are increased above the corresponding equilibrium values; the excess concentrations are positive. Thus both carriers tend to diffuse into the semiconductor bar. Since there is negligible recombination in region 1, all of these carriers survive their transit across region 1 and flow into region 2. However, the very small lifetime of region 2 ensures that these excess carriers recombine with ease, so that the holes and electrons that were produced at the surface by the radiation disappear by mutual annihilation in region 2 near the plane at $x = W$. The excess-carrier concentration at $x = W$ must be nearly zero because the lifetime in region 2 is so small.

We now wish to evaluate the hole and electron concentrations and currents in the semiconductor. To do this we must formulate explicit conservation laws for the carriers in region 1. The key to these conservation laws lies in the fact that there is negligible recombination in this region of the semiconductor. If we consider any volume element of thickness Δx in this region, the rate at which carriers enter the element must equal the rate at which they leave because there is negligible recombination in this element. It follows that *the hole and electron currents must be constant (i.e., independent of x) in region 1.* Thus if we denote the hole and electron current densities (which are x-directed) by J_h and J_e, we have

$$J_h(x) = \quad qM \qquad \text{for} \quad 0 < x < W \tag{3.1a}$$

$$J_e(x) = -qM \qquad \text{for} \quad 0 < x < W \tag{3.1b}$$

These relationships indicate that all of the positive charge liberated at the surface must be carried off by holes, whereas all of the associated negative charge must be carried off by electrons. The minus sign is necessary in Eq. 3.1b because the flow of electrons *away from* the surface corresponds to an electron current *toward* the surface; it is conventional to describe any current in terms of the equivalent flow of positive charge, and the reference direction is $+x$.

The total current J, is given by

$$J = J_h + J_e \tag{3.2}$$

is, of course, identically zero. There can be no *net* current in this particular example because the holes and electrons are generated *in pairs* (at $x = 0$) and recombine *in pairs* (at $x = W$).

3.2.1 Concentration and Current Distributions

If we use Eqs. 2.23 to express the hole and electron currents of Eqs. 3.1 in terms of their drift and diffusion components, we obtain

$$J_h = \quad qM = q\left(\mu_h p \mathscr{E}_x - D_h \frac{dp}{dx} \right) \tag{3.3a}$$

$$J_e = -qM = q\left(\mu_e n \mathscr{E}_x + D_e \frac{dn}{dx} \right) \tag{3.3b}$$

The diffusion terms are not independent because of our limitation to homogeneous material and our assumption that quasi-neutrality holds. Specifically, the hole and electron concentrations p and n can be written as

$$p = p_o + p'$$

$$n = n_o + n'$$

However, quasi-neutrality requires that

$$p' \simeq n' \tag{3.4}$$

Thus the hole and electron concentrations can be written as

$$p = p_o + p' \tag{3.5a}$$

$$n = n_o + p' \tag{3.5b}$$

If we substitute these expressions into the *diffusion* terms in Eqs. 3.3, and recognize that n_o and p_o are independent of x, the two conservation laws given by Eqs. 3.3 become

$$\text{(hole current)} \qquad qM = q\left(\mu_h p \mathscr{E}_x - D_h \frac{dp'}{dx}\right) \left.\begin{matrix} \\ \\ \\ \end{matrix}\right\} \qquad (3.6a)$$

$$\qquad\qquad\qquad\qquad\qquad\qquad\qquad\qquad\qquad 0 < x < W$$

$$\text{(electron current)} \qquad -qM = q\left(\mu_e n \mathscr{E}_x + D_e \frac{dp'}{dx}\right) \qquad (3.6b)$$

Equations 3.5 and 3.6 involve four variables: n, p, p', and $\mathscr{E}_x$. Thus these equations constitute four equations in four unknowns and can be solved for these variables. Once this has been done, we know the distributions of the hole and electron concentrations and of the electric field.

Elimination of the electric field between Eqs. 3.6 yields

$$\frac{dp'}{dx} = -M\frac{\mu_e n + \mu_h p}{\mu_e n D_h + \mu_h p D_e} \qquad 0 < x < W \qquad (3.7)$$

Since both n and p can be expressed in terms of p' (see Eqs. 3.5), this relationship is a first-order differential equation for p'; it can be solved to yield $p'(x)$ in region 1. The constant of integration that arises in its solution can be evaluated by using the condition that $p'(x)$ vanishes at the boundary between the regions

$$p'(W) = 0 \qquad (3.8)$$

This boundary condition occurs because the very small lifetime in region 2 demands that p' be very small there.

Elimination of dp'/dx from Eqs. 3.6 yields

$$\mathscr{E}_x = M\frac{D_e - D_h}{\mu_e n D_h + \mu_h p D_e} \qquad 0 < x < W \qquad (3.9)$$

Thus the electric field can be evaluated once the carrier-concentration distributions are known, that is, once $p'(x)$ has been determined.

Instead of solving this problem in detail, as outlined above, we shall make a simplifying approximation that is consistent with the assumptions set forth in Section 3.1. Specifically we assume that the minority-carrier concentration is much less than the majority-carrier concentration. Since the hole and electron mobilities are of the same order of magnitude, and since p is assumed to be much less than n, Eq. 3.7 can be simplified as follows:

$$\frac{dp'}{dx} \simeq -\frac{M}{D_h} \qquad \begin{cases} 0 < x < W \\ p \ll n \end{cases} \qquad (3.10)$$

This first-order differential equation is easily integrated. The result is

$$p'(x) = -\frac{M}{D_h}x + C \qquad 0 < x < W \qquad (3.11a)$$

where C is a constant of integration. This constant can be evaluated by making use of the fact that the excess-carrier concentration vanishes at the edge of the high-recombination region (Eq. 3.8). Thus we find that

$$C = \frac{M}{D_h}W \tag{3.11b}$$

and the excess-carrier concentration can be written as

$$p'(x) = \frac{M}{D_h}(W - x) \qquad 0 < x < W \tag{3.12}$$

This result indicates that the *excess-carrier concentration decreases linearly* from a maximum at the surface where the optical generation of pairs occurs to zero at the edge of region 2 where these pairs disappear by recombination. This result is shown in Fig. 3.2, in which the total hole and electron concentrations are also indicated. The excess concentration is zero everywhere in

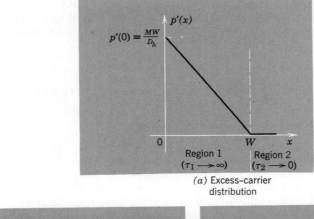

(a) Excess–carrier
distribution

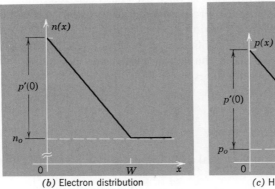

(b) Electron distribution

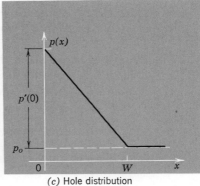

(c) Hole distribution

Figure 3.2   Carrier distributions in the device of Fig. 3.1.

region 2, and the hole and electron concentrations are equal to their respective equilibrium values there, because all the injected carriers recombine as soon as they enter region 2; none survive to flow into this region of high recombination.

It is important to note that the zero is suppressed on the vertical coordinate on which the majority-carrier electron concentration is plotted in Fig. 3.2b. The equilibrium majority-carrier concentration n_o is much larger (often by many orders of magnitude) than the equilibrium minority-carrier concentration p_o. Thus if the hole and electron concentrations are plotted to the same scale, as in Fig. 3.2, it is necessary to suppress the origin on the majority-carrier plot. Recall also that p' is everywhere much less than n_o; this is implicit in our assumption that the minority-carrier concentration is much less than the majority-carrier concentration. Consequently, the fractional change in the majority-carrier concentration displayed in Fig. 3.2 is very small. On the other hand, the fractional change in the minority-carrier concentration may be enormous, since p' can be much larger than p_o.

A numerical example may help to illustrate these differences. Consider a surface generation rate M of 10^{17} pairs per square centimeter per second; this corresponds roughly to the generation rate produced by sunlight in silicon. Assume that the other pertinent parameters are:

$$\left.\begin{array}{l} n_o = 10^{16} \text{ cm}^{-3} \\ p_o = 10^4 \ \text{ cm}^{-3} \end{array}\right\} \quad n_i = 10^{10} \text{ cm}^{-3}$$

$$D_h = 10 \text{ cm}^2/\text{sec}$$

$$W = 10^{-2} \text{ cm}$$

The current (of either holes or electrons) developed by the surface generation is, from Eqs. 3.1,

$$J_h = -J_e = qM$$

$$= 16 \text{ ma/cm}^2$$

The excess concentration at the surface ($x = 0$) is, from Eq. 3.12,

$$p'(0) = \frac{MW}{D_h} = 10^{14} \text{ cm}^{-3}$$

This value of excess concentration should be compared with the equilibrium concentrations. It corresponds to a 1% change in majority-carrier concentration. That is, the majority-carrier concentration at the surface is

$$n(0) = n_o + p'(0) = 1.01 \times 10^{16} \text{ cm}^{-3}$$

On the other hand, $p'(0)$ is *ten* orders of magnitude larger than p_o. Thus the minority-carrier concentration at the surface is

$$p(0) = p_o + p'(0) \simeq 10^{14} \text{ cm}^{-3}$$

Note that p is much less than n everywhere, so that the assumption we used in arriving at Eq. 3.10 is valid. Of course, if M were increased (corresponding to increased light intensity), p' would eventually become comparable to n_o and this approximate analysis would be invalid. Under such conditions it would be necessary to solve Eqs. 3.6 *without* assuming $p \ll n$.

The current distributions that accompany the carrier-concentration distributions discussed above are shown in Fig. 3.3. The currents are constant in region 1 because no recombination occurs there; for the one-dimensional static situation of concern here the lack of recombination or generation requires that the currents be constant. The currents drop to zero at the edge of the high-recombination region because carriers die there in pairs. The currents are zero in region 2 because no carriers survive to flow there.

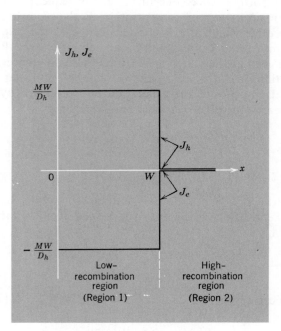

Figure 3.3   Current distributions in the device of Fig. 3.1.

3.2.2   The Role of the Electric Field

We use Eq. 3.9 to evaluate the electric field and assume once again that n is much greater than p. Since the majority-carrier concentration is not changed much by the excess carriers, we may replace n by n_o. Equation 3.9 then becomes

$$\mathscr{E}_x = M\frac{(D_e/D_h) - 1}{\mu_e n_o} \qquad \begin{cases} 0 < x < W \\ p \ll n \end{cases} \qquad (3.13)$$

Thus the electric field is independent of x in region 1. It is, of course, zero in region 2 where there are no excess carriers and where no flow occurs. If D_e is greater than D_h, which happens to be the case in both silicon and germanium, the electric field is positive, that is, it is directed from the surface at $x = 0$ toward the high-recombination region. For the numerical values introduced in Section 3.2.1, and for $D_e/D_h = 2$, the field has a value of about 1.2×10^{-2} volt/cm.

In order to explore the consequences of this electric field in more detail, we substitute it into the hole and electron current expressions of Eqs. 3.3. At the same time we use Eq. 3.10 to replace dp'/dx in these expressions. The following approximate equations result:

$$J_h \simeq qM \frac{p}{n_o} \frac{\mu_h}{\mu_e}\left(\frac{D_e}{D_h} - 1\right) + qM \tag{3.14a}$$

$$J_e \simeq qM\left(\frac{D_e}{D_h} - 1\right) - qM\frac{D_e}{D_h} \tag{3.14b}$$

The first terms on the right sides of these equations are the drift currents; the second terms are the diffusion currents. It is evident that the diffusion components of the hole and electron currents are comparable and differ only because the diffusion coefficients are not equal. The gradients are equal, and this forces the diffusion currents to differ only by the ratio of diffusion coefficients.

The drift components of the hole and electron currents are *not* comparable. More precisely, the minority-carrier hole drift current contains the factor p/n_o, which must be small if our analysis is to be valid. Thus the drift component of the minority-carrier current is much less than the drift component of the majority-carrier current. Equation 3.14a also shows that the drift component of the minority-carrier current is much less than the diffusion component of the same current. In other words, *the minority-carrier current is not appreciably influenced by the electric field; it is dominated by diffusion.*

The majority-carrier current is strongly influenced by the electric field. In fact, the drift term is usually comparable to the diffusion term. The physical explanation is quite simple. If there were no field, the hole and electron currents would be unequal because their diffusion components are unequal. Thus *the electric field modifies the flow of majority carriers so that the physical conditions (i.e., the boundary conditions) to which the majority-carrier current must conform are satisfied.* In this example the majority-carrier current must be the negative of the minority-carrier current (in order that the total current may vanish), and the electric field opposes the diffusion of majority carriers, thus slowing them down, without appreciably affecting the flow of minority carriers, in order to satisfy this condition.

A numerical example may help to make this clear. Consider a situation in which $D_e = 2D_h$, and, because of the Einstein relation, $\mu_e = 2\mu_h$. Equation

3.14b shows that for the *majority* carriers the drift term (first on the right) is half as large as the diffusion term (second on the right). On the other hand, for an assumed carrier-concentration ratio of $p/n = 10^{-2}$ (which corresponds to the situation just inside the surface with the value of M used earlier), Eq. 3.14a shows that for the *minority* carriers the drift term is only 1/200 of the diffusion term.

It is important to understand the nature of the charge distributions on which the electric field originates and terminates. We consider the case in which D_e exceeds D_h, so that the field is in the x direction. The optical injection of hole-electron pairs produces a linear distribution of excess carriers, as shown in Fig. 3.2, in which the minority carriers move by diffusion alone. If there were no field, diffusion alone would tend to remove more electrons than holes from the surface; D_e is greater than D_h, and the constant gradient is the same for holes and electrons. Since carriers are generated in pairs, greater removal of electrons than holes will leave the surface at $x = 0$ with net *positive* charge while the boundary between the regions at $x = W$ will accumulate *negative* charge. The dipole layer of surface charge, which results from this imbalance in flows, establishes an electric field that impedes the flow of the majority carriers just enough to balance the currents.

Although this example has been phrased in terms of a specific physical model, several aspects of the solutions developed here are quite general and apply to a broad range of physical situations in semiconductors, as long as the assumptions set forth in Section 3.1 hold true:

1. Injection of excess carriers in extrinsic material gives rise to a very small electric field. This injection-produced field influences the flow of the *majority* carriers to satisfy the physical conditions imposed by the structure.

2. In all situations in which the minority-carrier current is significant compared with the majority-carrier current (i.e., whenever minority-carrier flow contributes significantly to the *total* current), the minority carriers flow by diffusion. In these cases the injection-produced field has a negligible effect on the flow of the minority carriers. This general conclusion can be understood by examination of Eqs. 2.23, in which the hole and electron currents are expressed in terms of their drift and diffusion components:

$$J_h = q\left(\mu_h p \mathscr{E}_x - D_h \frac{dp}{dx}\right)$$

$$J_e = q\left(\mu_e n \mathscr{E}_x + D_e \frac{dn}{dx}\right)$$

Clearly, the minority and majority diffusion currents are comparable because the gradients are approximately equal and the diffusion coefficients are normally of the same order of magnitude. However, the drift currents are *not* comparable; the minority-carrier drift current is less than the majority-carrier drift current by the ratio of minority-to-majority-carrier concentrations. Consequently, the only way in which the minority-carrier current can be comparable in magnitude to the majority-carrier current is for it to be dominated by diffusion.

3.3 The Effect of Recombination on Flow

Our analysis in the preceding section of the distribution and flow of carriers in the structure of Fig. 3.1 was based on the assumption that all the recombination occurred in region 2, and that *no* recombination of excess carriers occurred in region 1, as a consequence of the large lifetime there. We now wish to relax this assumption and to investigate the consequences of a finite lifetime in region 1. Two questions arise:

1. How small can the lifetime be before the analysis of Section 3.2 becomes invalid?

2. How can the analysis be modified to account for significant recombination in region 1?

3.3.1 Evaluation of the Current Lost by Recombination

If the lifetime in region 1 is large enough, nearly all of the optically generated carriers will diffuse across this region without recombination. Thus we shall assume that essentially all carriers make it across, so that the gradient is nearly constant at the value given by Eq. 3.10 and so that the excess-carrier distribution is given by Eq. 3.12, and shall then proceed to evaluate the fraction of the injected carriers that recombine along the way. If this fraction is very small, we are assured that we have introduced little error by basing our evaluation of this fraction on a result that assumes no recombination. Thus this development constitutes a check on the assumption of negligible recombination that we made in Section 3.2.

The local rate of recombination in region 1 is, from Eqs. 2.14,

$$\mathcal{R} = \frac{p'}{\tau_1}$$

Clearly, the recombination rate is greatest near the surface at which injection occurs and least near the interface with region 2 at $x = W$. The *total* number of pairs lost, per unit cross-sectional area and per unit time, to recombination in region 1 is

$$\int_0^W \frac{p'}{\tau_1} \, dx$$

Thus the total hole current per unit area that is absorbed by recombination in region 1 is

$$J_R = q \int_0^W \frac{p'}{\tau_1} \, dx \tag{3.15}$$

This "recombination current" per unit area is the difference between the hole current density that enters this region at $x = 0$ and the hole current density that flows out of this region at $x = W$; it is the component of the optically-produced hole current that feeds recombination in region 1.

The integral of Eq. 3.15 can be evaluated by making use of the excess-carrier distribution of Eq. 3.12. Since the distribution is linear, evaluation of the integral involves evaluating the area of a triangle of height $p'(0) = MW/D_h$ and of the base W. The result is

$$J_R = \left(\frac{W^2}{2D_h\tau_1}\right)qM$$

The product $D_h\tau_1$ has dimensions of length squared. Its square root is called the *minority-carrier diffusion length* and is denoted by L_h. Thus the current per unit area that is absorbed by recombination can be written as

$$J_R = \frac{1}{2}\left(\frac{W}{L_h}\right)^2 qM \tag{3.16}$$

However, the factor qM describes the hole current density that flows into the region from the skin at $x = 0$ where pairs are produced (see Eq. 3.1a). Thus the *fraction* δ_R of the injected hole current that is lost by recombination in region 1 is

$$\delta_R = \frac{J_R}{J_h(0)} = \frac{1}{2}\left(\frac{W}{L_h}\right)^2 \tag{3.17}$$

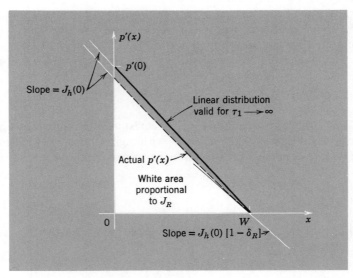

Figure 3.4   Illustration of the effect of recombination on the excess-carrier distribution.

This result shows that the fraction of the injected carriers that die in region 1 is determined by the relationship between the width W of this region and the corresponding diffusion length L_h. The diffusion length may range from a few tenths of a centimeter down to a few microns. If the width W of region 1 is small compared with the diffusion length L_h, the fraction of carriers lost by recombination in region 1 will be negligible. In this case both the approximate analysis developed in Section 3.2.1, and the approximate evaluation of J_R presented here will be valid, since the carrier distribution deviates very little from the linear relationship of Eq. 3.12, and the integral of Eq. 3.15 is not sensitive to small changes in the form of $p'(x)$. This situation is illustrated in Fig. 3.4. Although we have not yet evaluated the actual form of $p'(x)$, shown in this sketch as dashed, we know that it must have the following general features:

1. The slope at $x = 0$ must be such that the associated diffusion current is $J_h(0) = qM$.
2. The slope at $x = W$ must be smaller, since the diffusion current there is less by the factor $1 - \delta_R$.
3. The excess concentration must be zero at $x = W$ because the very small lifetime of region 2 prevents the establishment of any significant quantity of excess carriers there.

The current per unit area lost by recombination J_R is proportional to an *area* under the excess-carrier distribution, as shown by the white area in Fig. 3.4. Clearly this area is only insignificantly different from the area of the triangle of base W and of height $p'(0)$ *if δ_R is small.*

If W is one-fifth a diffusion length, Eq. 3.17 shows that only 2% of the injected current is lost to recombination in region 1. Under such conditions we would conclude that the analysis of Section 3.2 is valid, to a high order of accuracy, and that our assessment of the recombination current is reasonably accurate. If, on the other hand, the width of region 1 is equal to the diffusion length, Eq. 3.17 suggests that 50% of the carriers die in region 1. Under such conditions the analysis of Section 3.2 does not apply, the result for δ_R of 50% is significantly in error, and we must account for the recombination in our formulation of the continuity relationship or conservation law.

3.3.2   A Modified Conservation Law

We now formulate a conservation law for carriers in a semiconductor in which recombination has a first-order effect on the hole and electron currents. Because the minority carriers are *not* influenced by any injection-produced electric field, but flow by diffusion alone, we focus attention on the minority carriers and formulate a conservation law for them. To be consistent, we again base this discussion on an extrinsic n-type semiconductor.

Consider a boxlike volume element of unit cross-sectional area and of thickness Δx, as shown in Fig. 3.5. The hole concentration within this element

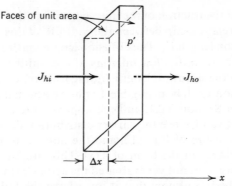

Faces of unit area

p'

J_{hi}

J_{ho}

Δx

x

Figure 3.5 The conservation law accounts for the flow and recombination of carriers in the volume element.

is not changing with time, that is, it is static. Thus the difference between the rate at which holes flow into the element and the rate at which they flow out must just be balanced by the hole recombination that occurs within the element. We denote the rate at which hole charge enters the element across the left face by J_{hi} and the rate at which hole charge leaves the element across the right face by J_{ho}. The element is taken to be thin enough for the excess-hole concentration throughout its extent to be reasonably approximated by p' at its center. Consequently, the total rate (per unit area) at which holes are lost by recombination is $p'\,\Delta x/\tau$, where τ denotes the excess-carrier lifetime. In terms of these symbols the conservation law for holes becomes

$$\frac{1}{q}(J_{hi} - J_{ho}) = \frac{p'}{\tau}\,\Delta x \tag{3.18}$$

If we divide through by Δx, proceed to the limit as Δx becomes very small, and recognize that

$$\lim_{\Delta x \to 0} \frac{J_{hi} - J_{ho}}{\Delta x} = -\frac{dJ_h}{dx}$$

we obtain

$$-\frac{1}{q}\frac{dJ_h}{dx} = \frac{p'}{\tau} \tag{3.19}$$

This conservation law for holes relates the hole current J_h to p'/τ the local recombination rate.[2]

[2] Note that if we consider the case in which the lifetime is very large, Eq. 3.19 reduces to

$$\frac{dJ_h}{dx} \simeq 0$$

or, equivalently, to

$$J_h = \text{constant}$$

which is the conservation law we applied in Section 3.2.

We can use Eq. 3.19 to evaluate the excess-carrier distribution simply by expressing the hole current density in terms of the excess concentration. Since the minority-carrier hole current flows principally by diffusion and is not appreciably influenced by the injection-produced electric field, we may write

$$J_h \simeq -qD_h \frac{dp'}{dx} \tag{3.20}$$

Thus the conservation law Eq. 3.19 becomes

$$D_h \frac{d^2 p'}{dx^2} = \frac{p'}{\tau} \tag{3.21}$$

This linear second-order differential equation has exponential solutions in which the characteristic length is the diffusion length L_h;

$$L_h = \sqrt{D_h \tau} \tag{3.22}$$

That is, the general solution of Eq. 3.21 is of the form

$$p'(x) = C_1 e^{-x/L_h} + C_2 e^{+x/L_h} \tag{3.23}$$

in which C_1 and C_2 are constants of integration. The correctness of this solution can be confirmed by direct substitution into Eq. 3.21.

We illustrate the nature of the carrier and current distributions in the presence of substantial recombination by considering the structure of Fig. 3.6. This structure differs from that studied in Section 3.2 only in that the lifetime is finite and uniform throughout. Carriers are produced at the surface, flow into the uniformly-doped bar by diffusion, and ultimately die by recombination. In the present case, however, recombination is distributed uniformly throughout the bar rather than concentrated, as it was in the structure of Fig. 3.1.

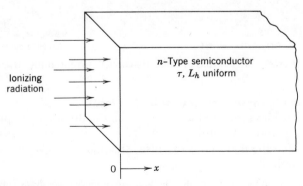

Figure 3.6   Optical injection into a semi-infinite bar.

The general form of the excess-hole distribution is given by Eq. 3.23. Thus the hole current distribution is, using Eq. 3.20,

$$J_h = \frac{qD_h}{L_h}C_1 e^{-x/L_h} - \frac{qD_h}{L_h}C_2 e^{+x/L_h} \qquad (3.24)$$

Clearly both the excess-hole concentration and the hole current must vanish for large values of x. Thus the term in which the exponential grows with distance must vanish:

$$C_2 = 0 \qquad (3.25)$$

Furthermore, the hole current at $x = 0$ must be equal to qM—the rate at which hole charge is generated optically. Thus

$$C_1 = \frac{ML_h}{D_h} \qquad (3.26)$$

and the excess-carrier distribution and the hole current are

$$p'(x) = \frac{ML_h}{D_h}e^{-x/L_h} \qquad (3.27a)$$

$$J_h(x) = qMe^{-x/L_h} \qquad (3.27b)$$

These distributions are sketched in Fig. 3.7.

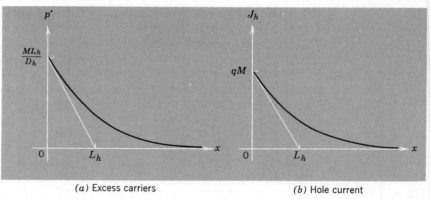

(a) Excess carriers   (b) Hole current

Figure 3.7   Distributions of excess carriers and of minority-carrier current in the structure of Fig. 3.6.

3.4   Graded Semiconductors and Built-in Fields

We now consider semiconductors in which the doping or impurity distribution is *not uniform*. We still limit ourselves to static one-dimensional situations in which the material is extrinsic, the injection level is low, and quasi-neutrality holds.[3]

[3] Although nonuniform impurity distributions can produce *major* deviations from neutrality, we postpone consideration of these cases until Chapter 4.

3.4.1   The Equilibrium Situation

If the impurity concentrations vary along the length of a semiconductor bar, the equilibrium hole and electron concentrations will also vary, in accordance with Eqs. 2.9. As we shall see, these concentration variations are associated with an internal electric field and with an electrostatic potential that varies from point to point within the semiconductor. We now study this situation in some detail with the dual objective of relating the internal electric field to the impurity distribution and of determining the dependence of the carrier concentrations on the equilibrium electrostatic potential distribution.

To satisfy the principle of detailed balance, which was introduced in Section 2.2.1, the hole and electron currents must vanish *separately* under equilibrium conditions. The spatial variation of the impurity concentration in an inhomogeneous semiconductor implies that there are concentration gradients, hence diffusion currents, of *both* carriers. Consequently, there must be a "built-in" electric field that produces drift currents which balance these diffusion currents, in order that the net currents may vanish. This equilibrium balance of drift and diffusion can be expressed with the aid of Eqs. 2.23:

$$\text{(hole current)} \qquad 0 = \mu_h p_o \mathscr{E}_x - D_h \frac{dp_o}{dx} \tag{3.28a}$$

$$\text{(electron current)} \qquad 0 = \mu_e n_o \mathscr{E}_x + D_e \frac{dn_o}{dx} \tag{3.28b}$$

Solution of these equations for the electric field, and use of the Einstein relations (Eqs. 2.24), yields

$$\mathscr{E}_x = \frac{kT}{q} \frac{1}{p_o} \frac{dp_o}{dx} \tag{3.29a}$$

and

$$\mathscr{E}_x = -\frac{kT}{q} \frac{1}{n_o} \frac{dn_o}{dx} \tag{3.29b}$$

The equations relate the built-in electric field to the equilibrium carrier concentrations and thus to the doping distribution. These expressions for the built-in field are not independent because n and p are not independent in equilibrium. Specifically, Eq. 2.8 requires that

$$n_o p_o = n_i^2$$

Therefore, we may express dp_o/dx in terms of dn_o/dx:

$$\frac{dp_o}{dx} = -\frac{n_i^2}{n_o^2} \frac{dn_o}{dx} \tag{3.30a}$$

or, equivalently,

$$\frac{1}{p_o} \frac{dp_o}{dx} = -\frac{1}{n_o} \frac{dn_o}{dx} \tag{3.30b}$$

Clearly Eq. 3.29b yields the same value of $\mathscr{E}_x$ as does Eq. 3.29a. Consider, for example, an *n*-type *extrinsic* semiconductor with a donor distribution $N_d(x)$. We have, from Eq. 2.9a,

$$n_o \simeq N_d(x)$$

and, using Eq. 3.29b, we obtain

$$\mathscr{E}_x \simeq -\frac{kT}{q}\frac{1}{N_d(x)}\frac{dN_d(x)}{dx} \tag{3.31}$$

The electric field is associated with an electrostatic potential ψ in the following manner:

$$\mathscr{E}_x = -\frac{d\psi}{dx} \tag{3.32}$$

Consequently, Eqs. 3.29 may be written as

$$d\psi = -\frac{kT}{q}\frac{dp_o}{p_o} \tag{3.33a}$$

and

$$d\psi = \frac{kT}{q}\frac{dn_o}{n_o} \tag{3.33b}$$

Finally, these equations can be integrated to obtain explicit relationships between the equilibrium carrier concentrations and the electrostatic potential. The results are

$$\psi = -\frac{kT}{q}\ln\frac{p_o}{p_c} \tag{3.34a}$$

and

$$\psi = \frac{kT}{q}\ln\frac{n_o}{n_c} \tag{3.34b}$$

in which p_c and n_c are constants of integration. These constants depend on the choice of the reference level of the electrostatic potential. It is convenient to *define* the potential to be zero in *intrinsic* material. That is, $\psi = 0$ when $n_o = p_o = n_i$. This specification of reference level requires, from Eqs. 3.34, that

$$p_c = n_c = n_i$$

Consequently, Eqs. 3.34 may be written as

$$\psi = -\frac{kT}{q}\ln\frac{p_o}{n_i} \tag{3.35a}$$

and

$$\psi = \frac{kT}{q}\ln\frac{n_o}{n_i} \tag{3.35b}$$

These equations, which relate the *equilibrium* electrostatic potential to the carrier concentrations, will be used in Chapter 4 in inverted form:

$$p_o = n_i e^{-q\psi/kT} \tag{3.36a}$$

$$n_o = n_i e^{q\psi/kT} \tag{3.36b}$$

The electrostatic potential differences associated with the built-in field depend on the carrier-concentration differences that are established by the grading. For example, consider an *n*-type semiconductor in which the doping is graded so that the electron concentration varies from 10^{14} cm^{-3} at one place to 10^{17} cm^{-3} at another place. The potential difference between these places is, in accordance with Eq. 3.34b,

$$\Delta\psi = \frac{kT}{q} \ln\frac{10^{17}}{10^{14}} \simeq 6.9\frac{kT}{q}$$

Since kT/q is approximately 25 mv near room temperature, this potential difference is about 0.17 volt.

The potential difference between two planes depends only on the concentrations at those planes and *not* on the distance between them or on the details of the impurity variation between them. The electric field, on the other hand, depends on the rate of change of the impurity distribution, as emphasized by Eq. 3.31.

An electric field that has a spatial variation requires, as a consequence of Gauss's law, local space charge. There must be deviations from neutrality to support the internal equilibrium electric field. A careful study of this situation, which is itself more of a diversion than we wish to undertake, shows that the deviations from neutrality are quite small *provided* that the spatial rate of change of the impurity concentration is not too large.[4] That is, quasi-neutrality is a reasonable approximation if the grading of the impurity concentration is limited.

The kinds of impurity distributions that can be obtained in practical semiconductors are severely limited by fabrication technology. It is possible to fabricate materials whose impurity concentration variation can be approximated by an exponential in position over several decades of concentration. The electric field that results is *uniform*, as can be seen in Eq. 3.31.

As an example consider an *n*-type semiconductor in which the donor density over some range of x is

$$N_d = N_0 e^{x/a}$$

The electric field, using Eq. 3.31, is,

$$\mathscr{E}_x = -\frac{kT}{qa}$$

---

[4] See Chapter 4 of Reference 2.1 for further development of this issue.

The characteristic length a is the distance over which the carrier concentration changes by a factor of $e \simeq 2.7$. If we consider a value of this parameter of 10^{-3} cm, the built-in field has a value of 25 volts/cm.

3.4.2 Minority-Carrier Flow*

We now consider the flow of injected excess carriers in a material in which impurity grading has produced a built-in electric field. Excess carriers can be introduced by a variety of mechanisms; for example, by optical injection as in Fig. 3.6. It is no longer true that the minority carriers flow by diffusion alone.

For this development it is necessary to distinguish clearly between the equilibrium electric field, which we denote by $\mathscr{E}_{xo}$, and perturbations in that field, produced by injection, which we denote by $\mathscr{E}_{xi}$. Thus the total field is

$$\mathscr{E}_x = \mathscr{E}_{xo} + \mathscr{E}_{xi} \tag{3.37}$$

We employ the usual notation for equilibrium and excess-carrier concentrations and note that *both* are position-dependent in this case.

Using Eqs. 2.23 and the notation introduced above, we can write the hole and electron currents in n-type material as

$$J_h = q\mu_h(p_o + p')(\mathscr{E}_{xo} + \mathscr{E}_{xi}) - qD_h\left(\frac{dp_o}{dx} + \frac{dp'}{dx}\right) \tag{3.38a}$$

$$J_e = q\mu_e n_o(\mathscr{E}_{xo} + \mathscr{E}_{xi}) + qD_e\left(\frac{dn_o}{dx} + \frac{dp'}{dx}\right) \tag{3.38b}$$

In writing these we have made use of the conditions of quasi-neutrality ($p' \simeq n'$) and of low-level injection ($n \simeq n_o$). The balance of *equilibrium* drift and diffusion terms expressed by Eqs. 3.28 (written now with the notation p_o, n_o, and $\mathscr{E}_{xo}$) can be subtracted from the right side of Eqs. 3.38, leaving

$$J_h = q\mu_h(p_o + p')\mathscr{E}_{xi} + q\mu_h p'\mathscr{E}_{xo} - qD_h\frac{dp'}{dx} \tag{3.39a}$$

$$J_e = q\mu_e n_o\mathscr{E}_{xi} + qD_e\frac{dp'}{dx} \tag{3.39b}$$

Clearly, the last terms in these equations, which account for the diffusive flow of *excess* carriers, are comparable; the gradients are identical, and the hole and electron diffusion coefficients are not grossly different. The first terms in these equations, which account for the portion of the drift of holes and electrons that is created by the *injection-produced* field, are grossly different. The minority-carrier drift term is much less than the majority-carrier drift term because p is much less than n_o. We are interested in situations in which the minority-carrier current is significant compared with the

---

*This section may be omitted in an introductory study without loss of continuity.

majority-carrier current, or with the total injected current. It follows from this discussion that if the minority-carrier current is to be significant, it must be so because that current is dominated by some combination of the second and third terms in Eq. 3.39a. In other words, *the injection-produced field $\mathscr{E}_{xi}$ has a negligible effect on minority-carrier flow.* The built-in field $\mathscr{E}_{xo}$ may have a major effect on minority-carrier flow, as shown by the second term in Eq. 3.39a.

Hence the minority-carrier current that results from injection can be written as

$$J_h \simeq q\mu_h p' \mathscr{E}_{xo} - qD_h \frac{dp'}{dx} \tag{3.40}$$

Thus even though minority-carrier drift is important, the current is linearly dependent on the excess-carrier concentration p'. Consequently, when this flow relationship is substituted into the conservation law of Eq. 3.19, a linear differential equation results.

Although we have based the developments of this section on a graded semiconductor having a built-in field, the principal conclusions are applicable to a homogeneous semiconductor in which an electric field is established by charges outside the semiconductor. For example, an electric field will exist in a semiconductor bar if current is made to flow in that bar as a consequence of a potential difference applied between contacts at the ends. If excess carriers are injected into this semiconductor (e.g., optically) *minority*-carrier flow will be negligibly influenced by the perturbation of the field produced by injection. The current carried by the minority carriers can be evaluated by assuming that they diffuse, and *drift in the field that was present before injection.*[5]

3.5 An Overview of Flow Considerations

Two themes have been developed in the chapter. Both are central to the discussion of semiconductor device behavior that follows.

First, the analysis of any problem that involves the distribution and flow of excess carriers must begin with an explicit statement of a continuity relationship or conservation law for these excess carriers. For one-dimensional situations in which the distributions are *static*, and the flow is *steady-state*, the conservation law simply expresses a balance between carrier flow and recombination. If there is a net flow into a region, it must be balanced by recombination in that region. If there is negligible recombination in a one-dimensional situation, the flow must be uniform, that is, the current must be constant.

---

[5] These matters are illustrated by a classic semiconductor experiment—the Haynes–Shockley Experiment. This experiment is developed in a 16-mm sound film entitled "Minority Carriers in Semiconductors". The film, which was prepared by the Semiconductor Electronics Education Committee, is available (purchase or loan) from the Education Development Center, Chapel Street, Newton, Massachusetts.

Second, in all situations in which the material is *extrinsic*, the *injection level is low*, and *quasi-neutrality* holds, there is an enormous practical advantage in focusing on the *minority carriers* when the conservation law is formulated. This premium arises because injection of excess carriers invariably produces an electric field or disturbs an existing field. Such perturbations are necessary to modify the flow of *majority* carriers to conform to the physical situation. However, the flow of *minority* carriers is not appreciably influenced by these injection-produced field disturbances, and minority carriers flow as though the field were fixed at the value it had prior to injection of excess carriers.

Once the excess-carrier distribution has been determined by focusing on the minority-carrier conservation law, the complete solution of the problem unfolds. The excess-carrier distribution leads directly to the hole and electron distributions and to the minority-carrier current. The physical constraints imposed by the structure then lead to evaluation of the majority-carrier current and of the electric field.

PROBLEMS

P3.1 Verify Eqs. 3.7 and 3.9.

P3.2 Using the numerical values introduced in Section 3.2.1, and assuming $D_e = 3D_h$, evaluate *at the front surface* $(x = 0)$ numerically the separate terms in the numerators and denominators of Eqs. 3.7 and 3.9 and show that the approximate forms given by Eqs. 3.10 and 3.13 are valid.

P3.3 A structure similar to that sketched in Fig. 3.1 is uniformly doped with *acceptors* and has an equilibrium majority-carrier concentration of 10^{17} cm^{-3}. The *electron* diffusion coefficient is 50 cm^2/sec and the width of the low-recombination region is 5×10^{-3} cm.

(a) What is the maximum value of the surface generation rate M for which the majority-carrier concentration is disturbed not more than 1%? Specify units.

(b) What is the corresponding value of the electron or hole current density at the surface? Specify units.

(c) If the radiation that produces this injection is monochromatic with a photon energy of 1.4 ev and is entirely absorbed, what is the corresponding radiant power density? Specify units.

(d) If $D_h/D_e = \frac{1}{2}$, what is the corresponding value of the electrostatic potential difference between the illuminated front face and the interface at $x = W$? Assume $kT/q = 25$ mv.

Answers. (a) 10^{19} cm^{-2} sec^{-1}; (d) 0.25 mv.

P3.4 A structure similar to that shown in Fig. 3.1 is uniformly doped with donors at a concentration of 10^{16} cm^{-3}. The minority-carrier diffusion coefficient is $D_h = 10$ cm^2/sec, and the width of the low-recombination region is $W = 5 \times 10^{-3}$ cm. The optically-produced hole-current density is 50 ma/cm^2.

(*a*) What is the rate (per unit area) at which pairs are produced at the surface? If we assume that pair production occurs in skin having a depth of 10^{-5} cm, approximately what fraction of the covalent bonds in this skin are broken to produce pairs every second?

(*b*) What is the corresponding excess concentration at the surface?

(*c*) What is the fractional change in the majority-carrier concentration at the surface? In the minority-carrier concentration? (Assume $n_i = 10^{10}$ cm^{-3}.)

Answers. (*a*) $M \simeq 3 \times 10^{17}$ cm^{-2} sec^{-1}; (*b*) $p'(0) \simeq 1.5 \times 10^{14}$ cm^{-3}.

P.35 The low-recombination region of the three-layer, uniformly-doped structure shown in Fig. 3.8 is illuminated *off center* by a thin collimated beam of ionizing radiation. Assume that this radiation injects pairs *uniformly* over the plane at $x = x_1$, and denote the generation rate by M (pairs per unit area per unit time).

(*a*) Compute, sketch, and dimension the excess-carrier concentration $p'(x)$ for $0 < x < 2a + W$. Introduce (and define) whatever physical parameters are required for this analysis.

(*b*) Using your result for (*a*), sketch and dimension the hole and electron concentrations.

(*c*) Compute, sketch, and dimension the hole and electron current densities over the entire length of the bar.

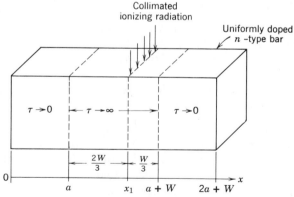

Figure 3.8 A three-layer structure.

P3.6 Derive a conservation law for *majority* carriers which is analogous to Eq. 3.19 (consider *n*-type material).

P3.7 This problem is concerned with a structure similar to that shown in Fig. 3.1. It differs only in that the lifetime τ_1 in region 1 is finite. Thus the conservation law in this region is given by Eq. 3.21, and the corresponding general solution for the excess-carrier concentration is given by Eq. 3.23.

(a) What is the boundary condition at $x = 0$?

(b) What is the boundary condition at $x = W$?

(c) Show that the excess-carrier concentration in region 1 is of the form

$$p'(x) = A \sinh\left(\frac{W - x}{L_h}\right) \qquad L_h = \sqrt{D_h \tau_1}$$

and evaluate A. Sketch and dimension this result.

(d) Show that the result obtained in (c) reduces to the linear dependence of Eq. 3.12 as τ_1 becomes very large.

P3.8   This problem is concerned with a structure similar to that shown in Fig. 3.1. It differs only in that the lifetime τ_2 in region 2 is nonzero. Consequently, the conservation law in this region is given by Eq. 3.21, and the corresponding general solution for the excess-carrier concentration is given by Eqs. 3.23.

(a) What is the boundary condition for large x? What condition does this impose on the constants of integration in Eq. 3.23?

(b) Show that the hole current density crossing the plane at $x = W$ is proportional to the excess-carrier concentration there and evaluate the constant of proportionality.

(c) Show that if τ_2 becomes very small, the relationship derived in (b) reduces to $p'(0) = 0$.

P3.9   This problem, which builds on the results of Problems P3.7 and P.3.8, is concerned with the structure of Fig. 3.1. Assume that *both* regions are characterized by the *same* minority-carrier diffusion coefficient D_h but have *different* (finite, nonzero) lifetimes τ_1 and τ_2.

(a) Specify the general form of the excess-carrier concentration in each region.

(b) Set up the boundary conditions that determine the constants in these general forms. Do *not* solve for the constants.

P3.10   A homogeneous p-type semiconductor bar is illuminated by a collimated beam of ionizing radiation, as shown in Fig. 3.9. The bar is characterized by a minority-carrier diffusion coefficient D_e and a diffusion length L_e. Assume that pairs are generated *uniformly* over the plane at $x = 0$ at rate M (pairs per unit area per unit time). Assume also that the bar is many diffusion lengths long.

(a) Determine the excess-carrier distribution in the bar. Sketch and dimension your results.

(b) Determine the hole and electron current-density distributions. Sketch and dimension your results.

P3.11   This problem is concerned with the structure introduced in Problem P3.10 and illustrated in Fig. 3.9. Assume that a voltage is applied between

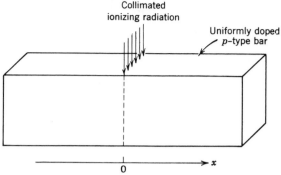

Collimated
ionizing radiation

Uniformly doped
p-type bar

0

x

Figure 3.9 A homogeneous *n*-type bar with optical generation.

contacts at the ends of the bar, thus developing an *x*-directed uniform electric field of magnitude $\mathscr{E}_{xo}$. All other conditions are as specified in Problem P3.9. Repeat (*a*) and (*b*) with the electric field present.

P3.12 This problem is concerned with the structure introduced in Fig. 3.1. Region 1 has negligible recombination ($\tau_1 \to \infty$) and region 2 has such a small lifetime ($\tau_2 \to 0$) that the excess-carrier concentrations there are zero. Instead of being uniformly doped, the bar has an *exponential* impurity distribution over *all* of region 1, of the form

$$N_d = N_0 e^{-x/a}$$

Excess carriers are injected in pairs at $x = 0$ at a rate characterized by *M* (pairs per unit per unit time).

(*a*) What is the equilibrium electric field in region 1?

(*b*) Determine the excess-carrier distribution in region 1. Sketch and dimension your results.

(*c*) Assume that region 1 has a large but finite lifetime τ_1. What fraction of the injected carriers recombine in region 1? Compare this result with that of Eq. 3.17, which applies for uniform doping.

P3.13 This problem is concerned with the development of a conservation law that applies when the excess-carrier concentrations are changing with time. Consider a *one-dimensional* situation in which the *injection level is low*, so that the *minority carriers* are not influenced by the injection-produced field.

(*a*) Note that the net rate (per unit area) at which the hole population in a slice of thickness Δx increases is $(dp'/dt)\Delta x$, and derive a conservation law analogous to Eq. 3.18.

(*b*) Show that this conservation law reduces, as Δx goes to zero, to

$$-\frac{1}{q}\frac{\partial J_h}{\partial x} = \frac{p'}{\tau} + \frac{dp'}{dt}$$

CHAPTER FOUR

Junction Diode Physical Electronics

4.1   Introduction

The majority of semiconductor active devices have one or more *pn junctions,* that is, regions of semiconductor in which a nonuniform distribution of impurities produces an essentially abrupt change from *p*-type material to *n*-type material. The physical structure of a *pn* junction is shown in Fig. 4.1*a*. Acceptor impurities in the *p*-type region cause the hole concentration there to exceed the electron concentration. Donor impurities in the *n*-type region cause the electron concentration to dominate there. Consequently, there are concentration gradients of holes and electrons near the junction plane. These gradients are oriented so that holes tend to diffuse from the *p*-type region to the *n*-type region, whereas electrons tend to diffuse the other way. However, in equilibrium, holes and electrons do *not* flow steadily across the junction, because there is a potential difference or *potential barrier* near the junction plane, as shown in Fig. 4.1*b*. The electric field associated with the potential barrier is directed from the *n*-type region to the *p*-type region; thus it opposes the diffusive tendencies associated with the concentration gradients and prevents (in equilibrium) the flow of *both* holes and electrons.

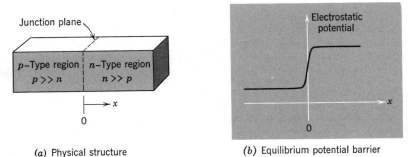

(*a*) Physical structure   (*b*) Equilibrium potential barrier

Figure 4.1   The carrier-concentration imbalances associated with a *pn* junction give rise to an electrostatic potential barrier at the junction.

We can think of the potential barrier as arising from the charge imbalance caused by the diffusive flow of carriers across the junction plane, so that the *n*-type region becomes positively charged with respect to the *p*-type region. The resulting charge imbalance must be accompanied by a potential difference between the regions, and it is this potential difference or potential barrier that reduces the net charge flow to zero when equilibrium is reached. Thus the diffusion of carriers across the junction from the side on which they are in the majority to that in which they are in the minority is a self-limiting process.

We now examine the situation when a voltage is applied across the junction terminals. We consider first a polarity of applied voltage which makes the *n*-type region *more positive* than the *p*-type region, that is, *increases* the height of the potential barrier. A voltage that increases the barrier height is said to be of *reverse polarity*. The junction conducts very poorly in the reverse direction, first, because holes from the *p*-type side and electrons from the *n*-type side where they are respectively majority carriers are unable to surmount the increased potential barrier and, second, because there are very few minority carriers available from the two regions to move in the opposite directions, *down* the barrier. Therefore, the current flow in the external circuit through which the voltage is applied is negligible, and the junction can be approximated by an open circuit.

An external voltage of the polarity opposite to that discussed above is called a *forward* voltage. A voltage of forward polarity makes the *n*-type region less positive than the *p*-type region, hence *reduces* the height of the potential barrier at the junction. This reduction in the potential barrier permits carriers to flow from the regions where they are in the majority to the regions where they are in the minority. These flows are sustained by the generation of carriers at the contacts applied to the regions where these carriers are in the majority and by the recombination of these carriers where they are in the minority. The junction conducts well in the forward direction because there are many carriers available to support current flow in that direction.

This asymmetry of electrical behavior, and the internal carrier distributions and flows associated with it, form the basis of almost all of the properties of junction diodes that make them useful as circuit components. Therefore, we now examine this basic structure in more detail. Our objectives are twofold. First, we wish to understand the internal physical behavior of junction diodes.[1] Second, we wish to describe their terminal behavior and to develop circuit models that embody this kind of behavior. We shall postpone a discussion of the methods of fabrication of both *pn* junctions and the devices that embody them and shall focus on the properties of the junction itself.

4.2   The *pn* Junction

A *pn* junction occurs whenever the impurity concentration changes from a predominance of donors to a predominance of acceptors over a sufficiently small distance. Under such conditions a region develops in which the mobile-carrier concentrations are much smaller than the immobile-impurity concentrations and there are local deviations from electrical neutrality, accompanied by intense electric fields. The characteristic behavior associated with *pn* junctions is a consequence of these deviations from neutrality. In

---

[1] The physical electronics of junction diodes is developed in more detail in References 4.1 and 4.2.

silicon and germanium, this change must occur over a distance not significantly greater than about 10^{-5} cm to produce a *pn* junction. If the change in impurity concentration occurs more gradually, there will be no substantial deviation from neutrality, and the structure will behave simply as a two-carrier conductor in which the carrier concentrations vary from point to point. Flow in such graded structures was discussed in Section 3.4.

We consider a somewhat idealized *pn* junction in which the change in impurity concentration occurs *abruptly*, as shown in Fig. 4.2a. In this sketch we have plotted versus distance the *net* impurity concentration N, which is defined as

$$N = N_d - N_a \qquad (4.1)$$

In accordance with this definition, N is positive in *n*-type material ($N_d > N_a$) and negative in *p*-type material ($N_d < N_a$). The net immobile impurity charge is simply qN. We denote the value of the net impurity concentration in the homogeneous *p*-type and *n*-type regions by $-N_A$ and N_D, respectively.

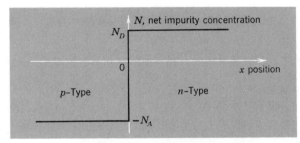

(a) Impurity distribution at an abrupt function

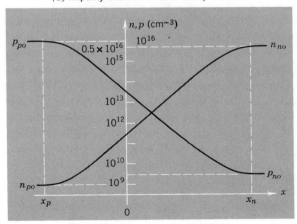

(b) Equilibrium carrier concentrations

Figure 4.2   Impurity concentrations and carrier concentrations near a *pn* junction in equilibrium. The position coordinate is normal to the plane on which the impurity concentration changes.

4.2.1 Equilibrium Conditions

In the *p*-type region well away from the junction, the equilibrium hole concentration p_{po} is much greater than the corresponding equilibrium electron concentration n_{po}. For typical values of N_A, the ratio p_{po}/n_{po} may be as large as 10^8 or 10^{10}, as we saw in Chapter 2. Similarly, in the *n*-type region well way from the junction the ratio of majority-carrier concentration to minority-carrier concentration, n_{no}/p_{no}, may also be very large. Clearly, near the junction both carrier concentrations must change grossly, as illustrated in Fig. 4.2*b* (notice that the ordinate axis has a logarithmic scale). The numerical values of this sketch apply to a semiconductor in which $n_i^2 = 10^{25}$ cm^{-6}, $N_D = 5 \times 10^{15}$ cm^{-3}, and $N_A = 10^{16}$ cm^{-3}.

In equilibrium the hole and electron currents are separately zero.[2] The carrier-concentration gradients associated with the transition from *p*-type to *n*-type are "balanced" with respect to the flow of carriers by an electric field, which is directed toward the *p*-type region. In terms of Eqs. 2.23, the electric field and the concentration gradients are related by

$$\text{(hole current)} \qquad \mu_h p \mathscr{E}_x - D_h \frac{dp}{dx} = 0 \qquad (4.2a)$$

$$\text{(electron current)} \qquad \mu_e n \mathscr{E}_x + D_e \frac{dn}{dx} = 0 \qquad (4.2b)$$

because the current densities $\mathbf{J}_h$ and $\mathbf{J}_e$ must be zero *everywhere* under equilibrium conditions.

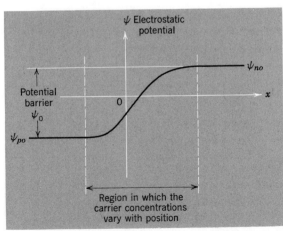

Figure 4.3 Electrostatic potential distribution near a *pn* junction in equilibrium

[2] Notice that it is not sufficient for the total current $\mathbf{J} = \mathbf{J}_h + \mathbf{J}_e$ to vanish in equilibrium; the hole and electron currents must vanish separately. This requirement follows from the principle of detailed balance, which demands that every identifiable physical process (i.e., hole flow and electron flow) must self-balance independently in equilibrium, as discussed in Section 2.2.1.

As discussed in Section 4.1, the electric field near the junction is associated with an electrostatic potential barrier. The potential distribution, which has a negative gradient equal to the electric field, is such that the n-type region is at a positive potential with respect to the p-type region, as shown in Fig. 4.3. In equilibrium, this potential barrier prevents the flows of holes and electrons from the regions where they are in the majority to the regions where they are in the minority.

As in the discussion of the equilibrium situation in a inhomogeneous semiconductor presented in Section 3.4.1, the magnitude of the potential barrier can be calculated with the aid of Eqs. 4.2, which express the equilibrium between drift and diffusion. Specifically, introduction of the electrostatic potential ψ through Eq. 3.32 and integration of the resulting equations yield Eqs. 3.36, which couple the carrier concentrations at a point to the electrostatic potential at the same point:

$$p_o = n_i e^{-q\psi/kT} \tag{4.3a}$$

$$n_o = n_i e^{+q\psi/kT} \tag{4.3b}$$

We have denoted the equilibrium carrier concentrations on the n-type side by n_{no} and p_{no}; the corresponding potential, which is positive, is ψ_{no}. The concentrations on the p-type side are p_{po} and n_{po}, and the potential, which is negative, is ψ_{po}. Thus if we denote the height of the potential barrier by ψ_0, as shown in Fig. 4.3, and recognize that ψ_0 is

$$\psi_0 = \psi_{no} - \psi_{po} \tag{4.4}$$

we have, from Eqs. 4.3,

$$\frac{p_{no}}{p_{po}} = e^{-q\psi_0/kT} \tag{4.5a}$$

and

$$\frac{n_{po}}{n_{no}} = e^{-q\psi_0/kT} \tag{4.5b}$$

For typical values of impurity concentration and intrinsic-carrier concentration, the equilibrium potential barrier height is of the order of a few tenths of a volt.

The equilibrium situation associated with the potential barrier can also be thought of in terms of the distributions in kinetic energy of the carriers on both sides of the barrier. These carriers, which are in thermal equilibrium with their environment, have kinetic energies that fluctuate randomly. The average energy of the ensemble of carriers is a definite quantity, which is proportional to the temperature. This *mean thermal energy* can be computed with the methods of statistical mechanics. Some of the carriers have, at any instant of time, kinetic energies greater than the mean thermal energy; others have kinetic energies that are less than the mean thermal energy. The fraction that have energies between any prescribed limits is a definite quantity, which can be determined from statistical mechanics.

If we now focus on, for example, the holes, all of the minority-carrier holes in the *n*-type region find it energetically favorable to flow down the potential barrier to the *p*-type region; the potential energy is lower there. On the other hand, the majority-carrier holes in the *p*-type region find it energetically unfavorable to flow up the potential barrier, and only a small fraction of these holes have sufficient energy to surmount the barrier, interchanging their kinetic energy for potential energy in the process. The greater the height of the barrier, the smaller is the fraction of the majority-carrier holes that have sufficient energy to surmount it. Under equilibrium conditions the height ψ_0 of the potential barrier has just the right value so that the concentration of majority-carrier holes having sufficient kinetic energy to surmount the barrier is exactly equal to the concentration of minority-carrier holes on the other side of the junction. Thus a balance exists, and there is no net flow of holes across the junction. A similar balance holds simultaneously for the electrons.[3]

The energy distributions that apply in this situation are called *Maxwell–Boltzmann* distributions.[4] Since Eqs. 4.4 can be derived directly from these energy distributions, the carrier-concentration ratios are often called the *Boltzmann relations.*

The equilibrium potential barrier height, ψ_0, is also referred to as the *contact potential* associated with the junction of the dissimilar semiconductors. Contact potentials arise whenever dissimilar conductors are in contact; they serve to inhibit the diffusion of majority carriers across the junction thus formed.

A closer examination of Fig. 4.2 shows that there is a region of nonzero space charge near a *pn* junction in equilibrium. In particular, if the carrier-concentration variations shown in Fig. 4.2*b* are plotted on coordinates in which the ordinate scale is linear (Fig. 4.4*a*), it is clear that over most of the region between the planes denoted by $-l_p$ and $+l_n$ *both* the hole and the electron concentrations are small compared with the magnitude of the net impurity concentration N. Therefore, there is a space-charge density in this region, which is approximately qN. The general form of the charge distribution is shown by the solid curve in Fig. 4.4*b*. The gradual transitions to $\rho = 0$ on both sides of the distribution result from the contributions of the mobile charge carriers. The region in which there is significant space charge is usually called the *space-charge layer.*

---

[3] Simultaneous balance, which is required by the principle of detailed balance, is possible because the holes and electrons obey the same statistical-mechanical laws and have the same form of distribution in energy.

[4] See, for example, Reference 2.2.

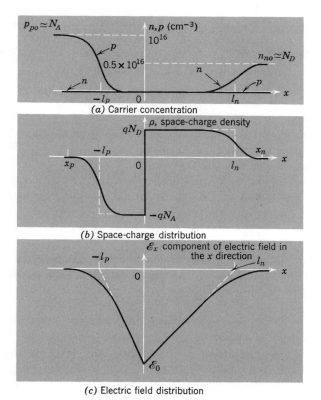

$p_{po} \simeq N_A$

n,p (cm^{-3})

10^{16}

p

0.5×10^{16}

$n_{no} \simeq N_D$

n

n

p

$-l_p$ 0 l_n x

(a) Carrier concentration

qN_D ρ, space-charge density

$-l_p$ x_n

x_p 0 l_n x

$-qN_A$

(b) Space-charge distribution

$\mathscr{E}_x$ component of electric field in the x direction

$-l_p$ l_n

0   x

$\mathscr{E}_0$

(c) Electric field distribution

Figure 4.4 Distributions of carrier concentration, space charge, and electric field at an abrupt *pn* junction.

The distribution of space charge at a *pn* junction is a *dipole layer*; that is, the amount of unneutralized negative charge in the portion of the distribution that lies on the *p*-type side is just equal to the positive charge that lies on the *n*-type side. This is required because the electric field vanishes *outside* the region of nonzero space charge, where the concentrations are constant. The electric field originates on the positive charge in the portion of the dipole layer lying on the *n*-type side, and terminates on the negative charge in the other half of the dipole layer, as shown in Fig. 4.4c.

The space charge and the electric field are related through Gauss's law, which can be written in integral form as

$$\int_V \frac{\rho}{\epsilon} \, dV = \oint_S \mathscr{E}_n \, dS \tag{4.6a}$$

where S denotes the surface that encloses the volume V, ϵ denotes the dielectric permittivity of the semiconductor, and $\mathscr{E}_n$ denotes the normal component (outwardly directed) of the electric field crossing S. In accordance with our previous notation, ρ denotes the charge density inside the volume V. Gauss's law can be put in simple form for the one-dimensional abrupt junction structure because $\mathscr{E}_n$ has only an x component and is zero outside the space-charge layer (see Fig. 4.4). Thus Eq. 4.6a may be written as

$$A \int_{x_p}^{x} \frac{\rho(x')}{\epsilon} dx' = A\mathscr{E}_x(x) \tag{4.6b}$$

where A is the cross-sectional area of the junction, x' is a dummy variable, and x_p denotes the plane in the p-type region where the buildup of space charge ρ begins (see Fig. 4.2b or Fig. 4.4b).

Furthermore, the electric field $\mathscr{E}_x$ is given by the negative gradient of the electrostatic potential ψ. Thus the potential at x can be written

$$\psi(x) = -\int_{x_p}^{x} \mathscr{E}_x(x') \, dx' + \psi_{po} \tag{4.6c}$$

in which ψ_{po} denotes the potential in the p-type region to the left of the space-charge layer (i.e., to the left of x_p). Therefore, the electrostatic potential barrier height ψ_0 is, in accordance with Eq. 4.4,

$$\psi_0 = -\int_{x_p}^{x_n} \mathscr{E}_x(x') \, dx' \tag{4.6d}$$

where x_n denotes the extent of the space-charge layer on the n-type side. Equations 4.6b and 4.6c provide relationships among charge density, the electric field, and the electrostatic potential in the space-charge layer.

In some pn junctions the portions of the space-charge layer over which ρ is intermediate in value between qN and zero are very thin in comparison with the region in which $\rho \simeq qN$. In such cases, it is reasonable to neglect the mobile charge carriers entirely and to assume $\rho = qN$ *throughout* the space-charge layer, that is, for $-l_p < x < l_n$. This assumption implies a space-charge distribution for an abrupt junction that is rectangular, as shown by the dashed curve in Fig. 4.4b. The corresponding electric field distribution (Fig. 4.4c) is triangular. This model for the space-charge layer is known as the *depletion approximation* because it assumes that the entire space-charge layer is depleted of mobile carriers. The depletion approximation is helpful, for it reduces the solution of Eqs. 4.6b and 4.6c to a trivial double integration in which the form of $\rho(x)$ *is known at the outset.*

To illustrate the use of the depletion approximation in the analysis of the space-charge layer, we consider the situation illustrated in Fig. 4.4. The dipole layer of charge, shown by the dashed lines in Fig. 4.4b, extends from $-l_p$ to l_n. The peak electric field, that is, the field at $x = 0$, which we denote by $\mathscr{E}_0$, is, from Eq. 4.6b,

$$\mathscr{E}_0 = -\frac{q}{\epsilon} N_A l_p \tag{4.7a}$$

The depletion approximation reduces evaluation of the integral of Eq. 4.6b to the determination of the area of a rectangle of height $-qN_A$ and of base l_p. Since the field is zero again at $x = l_n$, we have, applying Eq. 4.5b once again,

$$N_A l_p = N_D l_n \tag{4.7b}$$

Finally, Eq. 4.6d (in which the limits are now $-l_p$ and l_n) yields the contact potential as the area of a triangle of height $\mathscr{E}_0$ and base $l_p + l_n$:

$$\psi_0 = -\tfrac{1}{2}\mathscr{E}_0(l_p + l_n) \tag{4.7c}$$

These three equations (4.7a, b, c) can be solved to yield the extent of the space-charge layer (l_p, l_n) and the peak electric field $\mathscr{E}_0$ in terms of the impurity concentrations N_A and N_D and the contact potential (which itself depends on the impurity concentrations through Eqs. 4.5). (See Problems P4.1 and P4.2.) If the depletion approximation were not made, it would be necessary to express the charge density ρ in terms of the electrostatic potential, using Eqs. 4.3, and to solve a *nonlinear* differential equation for the potential (see Problem 4.4).

Although the depletion approximation is a real convenience in the analysis of electrical behavior in the space-charge layer, it is *not* universally applicable. Under certain conditions, which are favored by a relatively large intrinsic-carrier concentration, and by having one side of the junction doped much more heavily than the other (such a junction is referred to as *asymmetrically doped*) the contribution of the mobile carriers to the space charge cannot be ignored. Such a situation is illustrated in Fig. 4.5, which should be compared with Fig. 4.4. Although the space-charge distribution shown in Fig. 4.5b is a dipole layer, the mobile carriers are by no means negligible. In fact, depletion exists over only the portion of the n-type side contained between the dashed lines. Not only is the p-type side not depleted, but also the mobile holes make a substantial contribution, shown by the white area, to the positive charge in that half of the dipole layer which lies on the n-type side. Clearly, analysis of the electrical conditions in this space-charge layer must be based on a formulation of the problem that accounts for the contribution of the mobile carriers, particularly the holes, to the space charge. Nevertheless, we shall see that even for such a junction the depletion approximation is useful for *reverse biases* much larger than ψ_0.

4.2.2   Nonequilibrium Conditions at a pn Junction

We now wish to study the internal physical behavior of a pn junction when the equilibrium situation described in the preceding section is disturbed. Specifically, we consider the consequences of a change in the height of the junction potential barrier. We shall see later that such a change can be produced by applying a voltage to contacts or terminals applied to the p-type and n-type regions. A voltage that makes the contact applied to the

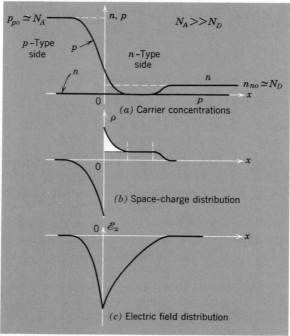

Figure 4.5   In an asymmetrically doped junction ($N_A \gg N_D$) the distributions of carrier concentration, space charge, and electric field are such that the depletion approximation is invalid.

p-type region positive with respect to the contact applied to the n-type region *reduces* the height of the potential barrier as shown in Fig. 4.6a. It is called a forward voltage, and it *forward-biases* the junction. On the other hand, a voltage of the opposite polarity *increases* the height of the potential barrier (Fig. 4.6b). Voltage of this polarity *reverse-biases* the junction.

Any change in the height of the junction potential barrier upsets the balance that exists when the junction is in equilibrium. The reduction in barrier height that accompanies a *forward* voltage increases the fraction of the majority carriers that can surmount the barrier. Thus holes flow from the p-type region to the n-type region, where they augment the minority-carrier (hole) concentration. This process is referred to as *minority-carrier injection*. These injected holes flow, principally by diffusion, away from the junction deeper into the n-type region where they eventually recombine with the majority-carrier electrons. Similarly, electrons flow from the n-type region to the p-type region, where they cause the minority-carrier (electron) concentration to increase. These injected electrons diffuse deeper into the p-type region, where they are eventually annihilated by recombination with the majority-carrier holes.

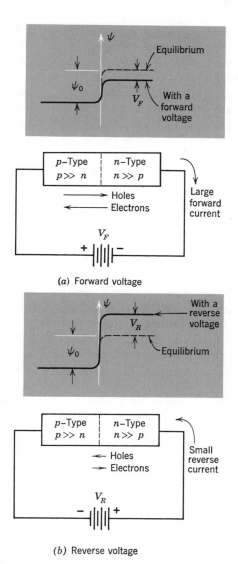

(a) Forward voltage

(b) Reverse voltage

Figure 4.6 Illustration of forward and reverse voltages and currents in a junction diode.

Many carriers are available to support minority-carrier injection; the majority carriers that flow across the junction to become injected minority carriers are in copious supply and are replenished by generation mechanisms at the contacts. Consequently, a forward-biased junction conducts well; large current densities are produced by small voltages, and the current increases sharply as the forward voltage increases.

The situation with a *reverse* voltage is completely different. The increase in barrier height *decreases* the fraction of the majority carriers that can surmount the barrier. Reverse voltages of only a few tenths of a volt suffice to make this fraction so small that majority-carrier flow across the junction is effectively blocked. Although carriers do flow across the junction from the regions in which they are in the minority, the magnitude of this flow is restricted by the relative scarcity of minority carriers. Consequently, the reverse current of a junction is small, and the diode conducts poorly when it is reverse-biased. The small reverse current that exists is limited by the rate of generation of minority carriers and is essentially independent of the reverse voltage.

The minority-carrier concentrations near the junction are depressed below the corresponding equilibrium values when a reverse voltage is applied. This reduction, which is referred to as *minority-carrier extraction*, occurs because all of the available minority carriers flow down the barrier, thereby depleting the population of these carriers near the junction.

On the basis of the discussion above, it is clear that the current-voltage characteristic of a *pn* junction must have the general form shown in Fig. 4.7. The rapid increase of current with voltage in the forward direction results from the availability of large numbers of majority carriers, which can flow up the reduced potential barrier at the junction. The small, nearly constant, reverse current results from the limited number of minority carriers available to flow down the increased potential barrier, which blocks the flow of majority carriers.

To determine the analytical expression for the current-voltage characteristic of the *pn* junction, we must examine in detail the effects of a change in the height of the potential barrier. We define the *change* in barrier height, produced by an externally applied voltage, as V_j, the junction voltage. Thus

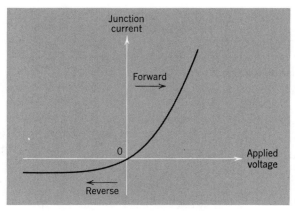

Figure 4.7   The current-voltage characteristic of a *pn* junction.

application of a junction voltage causes the height of the potential barrier to change from ψ_0, its equilibrium value, to $\psi_0 - V_j$. Note that positive values of V_j correspond to forward bias.

The effect of a change in the barrier height on the distributions of space charge, electric field, and electrostatic potential in the space charge layers can be determined by replacing ψ_0 by $\psi_0 - V_j$ in the analysis of Sec. 4.2.1. Thus, Eq. 4.6d becomes

$$\psi_0 - V_j = -\int_{x_p}^{x_n} \mathscr{E}_x(x')\,dx'$$

and Eq. 4.7c becomes

$$\psi_0 - V_j = -\tfrac{1}{2}\mathscr{E}_0(l_p + l_n)$$

Although the junction voltage V_j disturbs the carrier concentrations in the vicinity of the junction, electrical neutrality is preserved over most of the semiconductor volume, so that we can still regard the device as comprised of a nonneutral dipole layer of space charge sandwiched between neutral regions of negligible space charge. Even though we cannot justify this viewpoint a priori, we shall assume its validity. The behavior that follows is in agreement with observed junction characteristics and can be shown to be self-consistent with the assumption.

4.2.3   Current Flow in the pn Junction

The junction current flows through the space-charge layer as well as through the neutral regions. In general, the current could be governed either by the flow mechanisms in the space-charge layer or by the flow mechanisms in the neutral regions. In other words, the "bottleneck" that determines the flow of carriers could be either in the space-charge layer or in the neutral regions (or, possibly, distributed between the two regions). The analytical approach that we employ depends quite strongly on where the flow is limited.

Since this issue is central to our analysis of the junction diode, we digress to consider a simple hydraulic analogy, illustrated in Fig. 4.8a. The apparatus consists of two tanks, one of which contains a set of perforated baffle plates. The tanks are connected by a flexible tube and an adjustable valve. The entire system is about half-filled with a liquid. We consider the consequences of lifting the left-hand tank, thus establishing a pressure differential and causing flow from the left-hand tank to the right-hand tank, which contains the baffle plates. The flow rate is governed by several parameters of the system, including the viscosity of the fluid, the magnitude of the "head," the setting of the valve, and the "porosity" of the baffle plates. We consider two extreme or limiting situations.

The first, shown in Fig. 4.8b, is the case for which the rate of fluid flow between the tanks is determined not by the valve setting, but by the flow through the baffles within the tank toward which the flow is directed. Note

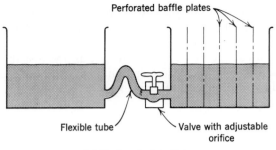

Perforated baffle plates

Flexible tube   Valve with adjustable
orifice

(a) The two–tank system

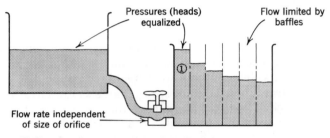

Pressures (heads)   Flow limited by
equalized   baffles

Flow rate independent
of size of orifice

(b) Flow governed by mechanisms (baffles) in the tank

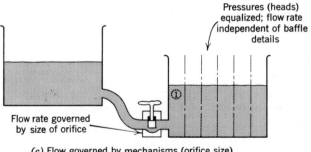

Pressures (heads)
equalized; flow rate
independent of baffle
details

Flow rate governed
by size of orifice

(c) Flow governed by mechanisms (orifice size)
in the connecting tube

Figure 4.8   A hydraulic analogy that illustrates the issue of the location of the "bottleneck" in a junction diode.

that the first cell in this tank (cell 1 in Fig. 4.8*b*) is "in equilibrium" with the left-hand reservoir; the fluid is at the same level in both. The various cells within the right-hand tank are not in equilibrium, however; there is a pressure differential across each baffle, and the flow rate is governed *solely* by the properties of the baffles. In particular, the flow rate is, within limits, independent of the setting of the valve. Opening the valve further does not increase the rate of flow; decreasing the valve opening or orifice does not decrease the rate of flow, provided that the orifice is greater than some lower bound, below which cell 1 does not remain in equilibrium with the reservoir.

The second extreme case is shown in Fig. 4.8c. Here the rate of flow between the tanks is determined not by the details of the baffles but by the size of the valve opening. Note that the cells in the right-hand tank are in equilibrium with each other; there are no pressure differentials across the baffles. The interconnection is not in equilibrium, however, because there is a difference in level between the reservoir and cell 1. Under these conditions the flow rate is governed solely by the size of the opening in the valve. The flow rate is not affected by changes in the porosity of the baffles. Decreasing their resistance to flow clearly has no effect; increasing their flow resistance also has no effect unless the baffles are made so resistant to flow that pressure differentials begin to develop across them (see *Notes on Demonstrations*).

The situations pictured are extreme cases. There obviously exist inter-mediate cases in which the flow rate depends on *both* valve setting and baffle resistance.

This hydraulic analogy obviously differs from the junction diode situation in several respects: it "runs down" and flow eventually stops, whereas flow in a diode continues because generation mechanisms at the contacts supply majority carriers continuously and recombination mechanisms absorb minority carriers continuously. Nevertheless, it does help to clarify what is meant by locating the "bottleneck" in a flow situation. In this analogy the "bottleneck" that limits flow may, in one extreme, be in the tank itself (Fig. 4.8b) or, in the other extreme, in the interconnection between the tanks (Fig. 4.8c).[5]

In the case of the junction diode the "bottleneck" that governs flow can be either in the neutral regions or in the space-charge layer that "intercon-nects" the neutral regions. We shall *assume* that carriers flow freely across the space-charge layer and that the junction current is limited by the flow processes in the neutral regions outside the space-charge layer. Once again, we cannot make an a priori justification of this assumption. However, the assumption yields results that explain observed junction behavior, and we can show, in retrospect, that the approximations embodied in the assumption are justified by the results that are derived from it.

4.2.4 Carrier Concentrations at the Edges of the Space-Charge Layer

Since we assume that the junction current is limited by the mechanisms governing flow in the neutral regions, we are assured that the current which

[5] A second analogous situation arises in a vacuum diode, where the current can be governed either by emission of electrons at the hot cathode (emission-limited or temperature-limited flow) or by flow through the cloud of space charge that surrounds the cathode (space-charge-limited flow). The analysis that must be employed is quite different for these two limiting situations, and the current-voltage characteristics that result when the "bottleneck" is at the cathode are quite different from the characteristics that result when the bottleneck is in the cloud of space charge. See Appendix A.

the space-charge layer is called upon to supply to the neutral regions is always much smaller than that which it is capable of supplying. That is, the equilibrium state of the space-charge layer, which as we have seen results from a balance between oppositely-direct currents, is not seriously disturbed by the need to supply some current to the neutral region. In other words, the oppositely-directed drift and diffusion currents are large enough compared with the net junction current to remain *approximately* in balance. Therefore, Eqs. 4.2, which are exact in equilibrium, must hold true as well, in an approximate sense, out of equilibrium when the height of the potential barrier is $\psi_0 - V_j$ rather than ψ_0. Solving Eqs. 4.2 under these conditions, we obtain

$$\frac{p_n(0)}{p_p(0)} = e^{-q(\psi_0 - V_j)/kT} \tag{4.8a}$$

$$\frac{n_p(0)}{n_n(0)} = e^{-q(\psi_0 - V_j)/kT} \tag{4.8b}$$

The notation $p_n(0)$, and so on, emphasizes that these are the carrier concentrations at the *edges* of the space-charge layer, that is, at the planes that differ in electrostatic potential by $(\psi_0 - V_j)$. The concentrations are identified in Fig. 4.9. If Eqs. 4.5 are used to eliminate ψ_0, Eqs. 4.8 can be written as

$$\frac{p_n(0)}{p_p(0)} = \frac{p_{no}}{p_{po}} e^{qV_j/kT} \tag{4.9a}$$

$$\frac{n_p(0)}{n_n(0)} = \frac{n_{po}}{n_{no}} e^{qV_j/kT} \tag{4.9b}$$

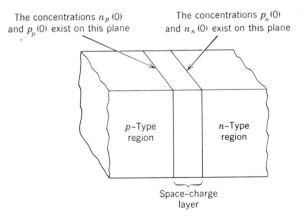

The concentrations $n_p(0)$ and $p_p(0)$ exist on this plane

The concentrations $p_n(0)$ and $n_n(0)$ exist on this plane

p-Type region

n-Type region

Space-charge layer

Figure 4.9   Definition of carrier concentrations at the space-charge-layer edges. Notice that the "origin" implicit in $p_n(0)$ and $n_n(0)$ is not the same as the "origin" implicit in $n_p(0)$ and $p_p(0)$.

These equations show that for forward junction voltages ($V_j > 0$), the ratios at the space-charge-layer edges of minority-carrier concentration to majority-carrier concentration increase. Because electrical neutrality is preserved outside the space-charge layer, the increases in these ratios must be accomplished by *equal* increases of *both* the minority- and majority-carrier concentrations; that is, the *excess* hole and electron concentrations outside the space-charge layer must be equal. Since the minority-carrier concentration is orders of magnitude smaller than the majority-carrier concentration under equilibrium conditions, equal changes of both carrier concentrations will affect the minority-carrier concentration much more than the majority-carrier concentration. For example, if the majority-carrier concentration is 10^{16} cm^{-3} and the minority-carrier concentration is 10^9 cm^{-3}, excess hole and electron concentrations of 10^{14} cm^{-3} increase the *minority*-carrier concentration by a factor of 10^5 while increasing the *majority*-carrier concentration by only 1%.

It follows that there is a range of junction voltage V_j for which the majority-carrier concentrations at the space-charge layer edges are essentially undisturbed even though the minority-carrier concentrations may have increased by many orders of magnitude. This domain of operation is called the domain of *low-level injection*. To simplify the ensuing analysis, we restrict our investigation of junction behavior to this domain. On this basis, the majority-carrier concentrations at the space-charge-layer edges are

$$p_p(0) \simeq p_{po} \tag{4.10a}$$

$$n_n(0) \simeq n_{no} \tag{4.10b}$$

Consequently, Eqs. 4.9 yield the following expressions for the minority-carrier concentrations at the space-charge-layer edges:

$$p_n(0) = p_{no}e^{qV_j/kT} \tag{4.11a}$$

$$n_p(0) = n_{po}e^{qV_j/kT} \tag{4.11b}$$

The expressions can also be written in terms of the excess concentrations:

$$p'_n(0) = p_n(0) - p_{no}$$
$$= p_{no}(e^{qV_j/kT} - 1) \tag{4.12a}$$

$$n'_p(0) = n_p(0) - n_{po}$$
$$= n_{po}(e^{qV_j/kT} - 1) \tag{4.12b}$$

These equations summarize the physical behavior of the space-charge layer. A change in the height of the potential barrier of amount V_j causes the excess-carrier concentrations at the edges of the space-charge layer to change. For positive V_j, the excess concentrations increase rapidly with voltage; a V_j of only 0.1 volt (approximately $4\,kT/q$ at room temperature) produces excess concentrations nearly two orders of magnitude greater than the equilibrium minority-carrier concentrations. On the other hand, for negative V_j, the excess hole and electron concentrations rapidly reduce to $-p_{no}$ and $-n_{po}$, respectively, which correspond to $p_n(0) \simeq 0$ and to $n_p(0) \simeq 0$. These excess concentrations are essentially independent of V_j for all voltages more negative than a few kT/q.

We now turn to the mechanisms of flow of the injected carriers in the neutral regions outside the space-charge layer; these flow mechanisms govern the junction current. First, however, we must be more explicit about the physical structure of the *pn* junction.

4.3 A Physical Model for a *pn* Junction

To continue our analysis of *pn* junction behavior developed in the preceding section, it is necessary to focus attention on a specific physical junction structure. We base our analysis on the asymmetric *pn* junction structure shown in Fig. 4.10. This structure has the following features:

1. The *p*-type region is doped much more heavily than the *n*-type regions. Consequently, the equilibrium majority-carrier hole concentration p_{po} in the *p*-type region is much larger than the equilibrium electron concentration n_{no} in the *n*-type regions. Thus the hole current that flows across the junction when the equilibrium is disturbed is much larger than the electron current.

2. There are two adjacent *n*-type regions, designated as n_1 and n_2 in Fig. 4.10. These regions have the same impurity concentration, but they have quite different lifetimes. Specifically, the lifetime in region 1 (which is called the *base* and which is adjacent to the *p*-type region) is so large that negligible recombination occurs there, while the lifetime in region 2 is so small that the excess-carrier concentrations there are constrained to be negligible in comparison with the corresponding equilibrium concentrations.

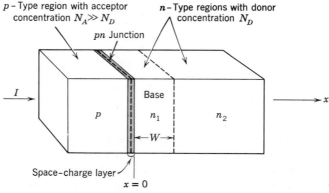

Figure 4.10 Asymmetric thin-base junction diode.

The diode structure shown in Fig. 4.10 is called a *thin-base diode*, reflecting the fact that the base region (region 1) must be thin if the recombination that occurs there can be safely neglected. This characterization is chosen not because it conforms to the physical structure of most *pn* junction diodes, but because it places in evidence most of the features of the physical electronics of most junction devices with a minimum of physical and mathematical complexity. We shall see that the conclusions we reach on the basis of this model can be extended to a wide variety of junction devices. Moreover, we shall find in Chapter 7 that the physical behavior of this diode structure is quite relevant to that of bipolar junction transistors.

The distribution of recombination on the *n*-type side of the thin-base diode is, in detail, the same as that postulated for the first structure that we studied in Chapter 3, which is shown in Fig. 3.1. Consequently, the conclusions we reached there concerning the conservation law and the principal features of the distribution and flow of excess carriers will be applicable to the diode structure introduced here.

There is, of course, one important difference. In the uniformly-doped structure of Fig. 3.1, excess carriers were injected into the *n*-type region at $x = 0$ *in pairs*; each absorbed photon produced *both* a minority-carrier hole *and* a majority-carrier electron. Although in that structure both carriers flow into the *n*-type material, there is no *net* current. We shall see that application of forward bias to the diode structure causes excess minority carriers (holes) to be injected into the *n*-type region at $x = 0$. However, there is negligible *majority*-carrier flow at this point. Thus minority-carrier injection produces, in the diode structure, a net current, equal to the injected hole current at $x = 0$.

4.3.1   Minority-Carrier Distribution and Flow

Our junction model is asymmetrically doped. Specifically, the acceptor concentration N_A in the *p*-type region is much larger than the donor concentration N_D in the *n*-type regions. Consequently, there is a correspondingly large imbalance of the equilibrium carrier concentrations, which can be expressed either in terms of majority-carrier concentrations as

$$(p_{po} \simeq N_A) \gg (n_{no} \simeq N_D)$$

or in terms of minority-carrier concentrations as

$$n_{po} \ll p_{no}$$

since $n_{po}p_{po} = n_{no}p_{no} = n_i^2$. It follows from Eqs. 4.11 that for this structure $p_n(0)$ is much greater than $n_p(0)$ for all values of V_j. Although it is not obvious at this point, this asymmetry of the carrier concentrations causes the current crossing the space-charge layer to be comprised *primarily* of holes, that is, of the carriers that are dominant on the heavily-doped side. Therefore, we now focus on the *n*-type region, where there may exist large concentrations of excess holes, and investigate the factors that govern the hole flow there. We later return to electron flow on the heavily-doped side and justify our assumption that the junction current is dominated by hole flow.

When the junction voltage V_j is positive, the excess-carrier concentration at the space-charge-layer edge of the n-type neutral region is positive (see Eq. 4.12a) and minority-carrier holes flow into the low-recombination base region. Since negligible recombination occurs in the base, *all* of the injected holes flow across the base and enter the high-recombination region at $x = W$. These injected holes are annihilated in the high-recombination region (near $x = W$) by recombination with majority-carrier electrons. Electrons flow in the high-recombination region *toward* the junction to feed the recombination of the injected holes.

Since there is negligible recombination in the base region, the hole current density must be *constant*, that is, independent of x, in the base. This condition on the hole current density amounts to a conservation law for the minority carriers; this law is entirely analogous to that discussed in Section 3.2 (see Eq. 3.1a). Because we are restricting the excess concentration (and thus the junction voltage) to the domain of *low-level injection*, the flow of injected minority carriers is not significantly influenced by the electric field that may be produced by injection. That is, *the minority-carrier holes flow in the base by diffusion alone*. Consequently, we may express the hole current density in the following form:

$$J_h = -qD_h \frac{dp'_n}{dx} \qquad 0 < x < W \qquad (4.13)$$

Since the current J_h is constant throughout the base region, this differential equation for $p'_n(x)$ can be integrated directly to yield

$$p'_n(x) = -\frac{J_h}{qD_h} x + C \qquad 0 < x < W \qquad (4.14)$$

where C is a constant of integration, which can be evaluated using the boundary condition imposed by the high-recombination region. At $x = W$, the excess-carrier concentration must vanish because the remote n-type region has an extremely small lifetime or, equivalently, an extremely high rate of recombination. Thus

$$p'_n = 0 \qquad \text{at } x = W \qquad (4.15)$$

When this constraint is applied to the solution of Eq. 4.14, we find

$$C = \frac{J_h}{qD_h} W$$

so that

$$p'_n(x) = \frac{J_h}{qD_h}(W - x) \qquad 0 < x < W \qquad (4.16)$$

That is, the excess concentration decreases linearly from a maximum at $x = 0$ to zero at $x = W$.

The excess concentration at the space-charge-layer edge is, of course, governed by the junction voltage in accordance with Eq. 4.12a. This relationship provides the final link between the hole current density and the junction voltage. Using Eqs. 4.12a and 4.16, we obtain

$$p_{no}(e^{qV_j/kT} - 1) = \frac{J_h W}{q D_h} \tag{4.17}$$

Thus, in summary, we have

$$J_h = \frac{q D_h}{W} p_n'(0) \tag{4.18a}$$

$$p_n'(x) = p_n'(0)\left(1 - \frac{x}{W}\right) \tag{4.18b}$$

$$p_n'(0) = p_{no}(e^{qV_j/kT} - 1) \tag{4.18c}$$

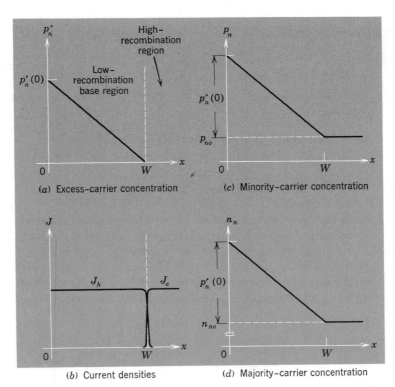

(a) Excess-carrier concentration

(b) Current densities

(c) Minority-carrier concentration

(d) Majority-carrier concentration

Figure 4.11 Distributions of carrier concentrations and currents in the low-recombination n-type base region of the asymmetric diode shown in Fig. 4.10 (for a forward voltage).

The variations in position of the hole and electron concentrations and of the current densities for positive V_j are shown in Fig. 4.11. The physical operation of the device is illustrated in these sketches. Holes are injected across the space-charge layer into the n-type region; the concentration $p'_n(0)$ is determined by the junction voltage V_j (Eq. 4.18c). The excess concentration is zero at $x = W$ because of the high recombination rate in the remote region. Consequently, holes move through the base region by diffusion and recombine at the boundary of the region of high recombination. The hole current is *uniform* throughout the base region, because there is negligible recombination in that area and all holes that enter must leave. The linear variation of hole concentration is consistent with the uniform diffusion current. The electron current is constant through the high-recombination region and is equal to J_h. This electron current corresponds to a flow of electrons to the boundary of the base region where the electrons recombine with the holes and thus disappear.

The total hole and electron concentrations increase by equal amounts in the base region. Consequently, electrical neutrality is preserved, even though the excess-carrier concentration may be large compared with the equilibrium minority-carrier concentration.

The distribution of Eq. 4.18b should be compared with the corresponding result for the uniformly-doped structure with optical generation, studied in Section 3.2 (Eq. 3.12). Also, the sketches showing carrier and current distributions in Fig. 4.11 should be compared with those in Figs. 3.2 and 3.3. The structure of Section 3.2 and the thin-base diode are essentially identical insofar as minority-carrier flow is concerned. Although the boundary conditions at $x = 0$ differ (in one case the carrier concentration is fixed, in the other case its slope is fixed), the distributions are the same in form.

4.3.2 Junction Diode Current-Voltage Characteristics

The total current carried by the *pn* junction is proportional to the sum of the hole and electron current densities at any plane in the structure. It is convenient to evaluate this sum at the space-charge layer. In the asymmetric structure of concern here the electron current injected into the p-type region is negligible compared with the hole current injected into the n-type side. If we assume that there is *negligible generation or recombination of carriers in the space-charge layer*, the diode current I is simply

$$I = AJ_h \tag{4.19}$$

where A denotes the cross-sectional area of the junction, and J_h is the density of the hole current injected in the base (Eq. 4.18a). Thus the current-voltage relationship of this *pn* junction is

$$I = I_s(e^{qV_j/kT} - 1) \tag{4.20a}$$

where

$$I_s = qA \frac{D_h p_{no}}{W} \tag{4.20b}$$

The coefficient I_s is called the *saturation current* of the diode. The exponential current-voltage relationship of Eq. 4.20a is frequently designated as the *idealized pn junction diode equation*. It is fundamental to all semiconductor junction-device behavior. Although we have derived the idealized diode equation in terms of a specific physical model for a junction diode, the result applies to other diode structures if the form of the coefficient I_s is modified appropriately (see Problems 4.12 and 4.13). The physical conditions to which the diode equation corresponds are clear from Eq. 4.13: the electric field has a negligible effect under low-injection conditions, and the minority carriers flow solely by diffusion.

Our evaluation of the static excess-carrier distribution in the low-recombination *n*-type region has been greatly facilitated by our assumption that recombination in this region is of no consequence. This assumption permitted us to regard the hole current density as constant through this region, making possible formulation and direct integration of Eq. 4.13. If we had considered instead the case in which a significant fraction of the holes that are injected at $x = 0$ die by recombination before reaching the region of high recombination at $x = W$, it would have been necessary to formulate a different conservation law in which the effect of recombination on the minority-carrier current density was accounted for. We studied an example of this type in Section 3.3, and the conservation law developed there, expressed by Eq. 3.19, is applicable here. Of course, the resulting carrier-concentration distributions will no longer be linear in x.

It is easy to evaluate the fraction of the hole current that disappears in the base region if that fraction is small enough to be regarded as a perturbation having a negligible effect on the distribution. Specifically, we assume that excess-carrier distribution in the base is identical to that which would exist if there were no recombination, and we use this simple triangular distribution to evaluate the recombination that occurs when we characterize the base region by a finite lifetime τ_1. This calculation was developed in Section 3.3.1, and the result, which is expressed in Eq. 3.17 as the *fraction* of the injected minority-carrier current that is lost by recombination in the base between $x = 0$ and $x = W$, is applicable here. The fraction δ_R, which is often called the *recombination defect*, will be small if the base width W is small compared with the diffusion length L_h.

The analysis developed above embodies the assumption that the electron current associated with injection into the heavily-doped *p*-type region is negligible. Thus Eq. 4.19 contains only the hole current density. We now evaluate the neglected electron current density and check the validity of the assumption.

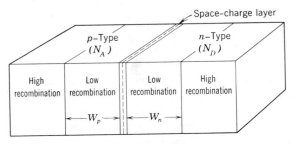

Figure 4.12   An alternative *pn*-junction diode structure.

We consider the diode structure shown in Fig. 4.12. This structure has a thin low-recombination base region on *each* side of the space-charge layer. When the junction is forward-biased, electrons are injected into the *p*-type region, thus contributing a component of junction current that has the *same* polarity as the injected hole current given by Eq. 4.18a. The polarities are the same because the motion of the electrons toward the *p*-type region is equivalent to the flow of positive charge toward the *n*-type region. The calculation of the excess-carrier distribution and of the injected electron current is *exactly* analogous to that developed in Section 4.3.1. The resulting electron current density in the *p*-type base region is

$$J_e = \frac{qD_e}{W_p} n_p'(0) \tag{4.21}$$

where D_e is the diffusion coefficient for minority-carrier electrons in the *p*-type region and W_p is the width of the low-recombination *p*-type region. This expression for the electron current density should be compared with Eq. 4.18a, for the corresponding hole current density. The ratio of these currents is

$$\frac{J_e}{J_h} = \frac{D_e W_n}{D_h W_p} \frac{n_p'(0)}{p_n'(0)} \tag{4.22a}$$

where W_n denotes the width of the low-recombination *n*-type region. If Eqs. 4.12 are used to express the dependence of the excess concentrations on junction voltage, the voltage-dependent factors cancel, and we have

$$\frac{J_e}{J_h} = \frac{D_e W_n}{D_h W_p} \frac{n_{po}}{p_{no}} \tag{4.22b}$$

or, equivalently,

$$\frac{J_e}{J_h} = \frac{D_e W_n}{D_h W_p} \frac{n_{no}}{p_{po}} \tag{4.22c}$$

This result shows that the electron current will be small compared with the hole current if the impurity concentration in the *p*-type region ($N_A \simeq p_{po}$)

is much larger than the corresponding impurity concentration in the n-type region ($N_D \simeq n_{no}$). Thus our initial assumption is justified if, as we stated, $N_A \gg N_D$.

If, on the other hand, the impurity concentrations on the two sides are not grossly imbalanced, the hole and electron currents may be comparable, and *both* must be considered in formulating the junction current-voltage characteristic. Since both currents have the same voltage dependence (through Eqs. 4.12), only the value of the saturation current I_s in Eq. 4.20a is affected.

The distributions of the hole and electron current densities are shown in Fig. 4.13 for a two-sided junction having the structure shown in Fig. 4.12 in which the injected electron current is assumed to be one-third of the injected hole current (and in which there is no recombination in the space-charge layer). The sum of the hole and electron currents is, of course, independent of x. In evaluating the total current initially it is, however, necessary to form their sum at the space-charge layer, where the injected (minority-carrier) hole and electron currents are known explicitly (see Problems P4.13 and P4.14).

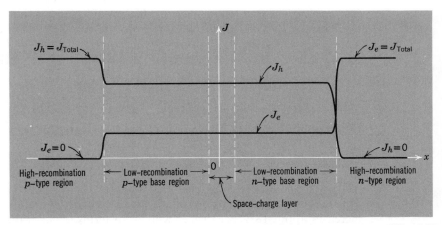

Figure 4.13 Distributions of hole and electron current in the two-sided thin-base structure of Fig. 4.12.

4.3.3 Temperature Dependence of the Idealized Diode Equation

The idealized diode law of Eq. 4.20a is influenced by temperature in two ways:

1. The equilibrium minority-carrier concentration, which appears in the saturation current (Eq. 4.20b), is proportional to n_i^2. Therefore, it increases strongly with temperature, as discussed in Section 2.2.2.

2. The thermal voltage kT/q, which appears in the argument of the exponential, is linearly dependent on temperature.

The temperature dependence of the diffusion coefficient, which appears in the saturation current, can usually be neglected in comparison with the strong dependence of the minority-carrier concentration on temperature.

To explore the consequences of these thermal effects further, we approximate the temperature dependence of the intrinsic carrier concentration by an exponential[6] (see Problem P.2.9). That is, we assume that:

$$n_i^2(T) \simeq n_i^2(T_0)e^{a(T-T_0)} \tag{4.23a}$$

The factor a is equal to the *fractional* rate of change of n_i^2 with respect to temperature:

$$a = \frac{1}{n_i^2}\frac{d(n_i^2)}{dT} \tag{4.23b}$$

For germanium near room temperature a is about 0.12 per degree Kelvin ($12\%/°K$). The corresponding value for silicon is about 0.18 per degree Kelvin.

We now consider three temperature coefficients commonly associated with the idealized junction diode, and express each in terms of the relevant parameters. The first temperature coefficient of interest is that of the saturation current I_s. This coefficient applies to the reverse current of the diode, since $I \simeq -I_s$ when V_j is more negative than a few kT/q. The fractional temperature coefficient of the saturation current is, by definition,

$$\frac{1}{I_s}\frac{dI_s}{dT}$$

Differentiation of Eq. 4.20b and use of Eq. 4.23b as well as $p_{no} = n_i^2/N_D$ yield

$$\frac{1}{I_s}\frac{dI_s}{dT} = a \tag{4.24}$$

Thus the saturation current of an idealized silicon diode, for example, increases about 18% per degree Kelvin. In terms of the frame of reference provided by other electronic components such as resistors, capacitors, and vacuum tubes, such a temperature coefficient is extraordinarily large. We shall see that its effects must be recognized when junction devices are employed in circuits.

Next we consider the temperature dependence of the junction current with forward bias applied. We assume that the forward bias is large enough

---

[6] The actual temperature dependence of n_i^2 is of the form $T^3e^{-\beta/T}$ where β is a constant. For silicon, β is of the order of 7000°K, whereas in germanium it is approximately 4500°K. For temperatures within $\pm75°K$ of room temperature, it is difficult to discern the differences between the $T^3e^{-\beta/T}$ dependence and the $e^{a\Delta T}$ approximation that we have employed. We have used the $e^{a\Delta T}$ approximation because it is accurate near room temperature and because it simplifies the algebra.

for the exponential in the diode equation to be large compared to unity. Thus the diode equation can be approximated by

$$I \simeq I_s e^{qV_j/kT} \tag{4.25}$$

Differentiation with respect to T (with V_j held constant) yields

$$\left(\frac{dI}{dT}\right)_{V_j} = \frac{dI_s}{dT} e^{qV_j/kT} - \frac{1}{T}\frac{qV_j}{kT} I_s e^{qV_j/kT}$$

Thus the *fractional* temperature coefficient of the forward current with fixed voltage is

$$\left(\frac{1}{I}\frac{dI}{dT}\right)_{V_j} = a - \frac{1}{T}\frac{qV_j}{kT} \tag{4.26}$$

Clearly, the temperature coefficient of the forward current is smaller than that of the saturation current. For a silicon device at $T = 300°K$ and with $V_j = 30(kT/q)$, about 0.76 volt, this coefficient has a value of about $8\%/°K$. The coefficients of Eqs. 4.24 and 4.26 show that for small temperature changes (small compared with the absolute temperature T) the saturation current and the forward current with fixed voltage increase exponentially with temperature.

Finally, we evaluate the temperature dependence of the diode voltage for fixed forward current. Solving Eq. 4.25 for V_j and differentiating with respect to T (with I held constant), we obtain

$$\left(\frac{dV_j}{dT}\right)_I = -\frac{kT}{q} a + \frac{V_j}{T} \tag{4.27}$$

Using the numbers introduced above for a silicon device at 300°K (with a forward voltage of 0.76 volt) gives a value of about -2 mv/°K. For temperature changes that are small compared with the absolute temperature the forward voltage with fixed current decreases linearly with temperature.

4.4 Dynamic Behavior of a pn Junction

All of the analysis of the *pn* junction presented thus far is limited to essentially static situations—conditions for which the junction voltage, the carrier concentrations, and all carrier flow processes are changing very slowly, if at all; that is, the treatment has been limited to the dc steady-state situation. We now wish to consider the consequences of more rapid changes in the electrical variables and the carrier concentrations. In general, we should expect the current-voltage relationship developed in Section 4.3.2 to be in error whenever the internal charge distributions change rapidly enough to require charging currents that are comparable to the static conduction currents we have evaluated. We must look in two places for changing charge distributions: in the space-charge layer and in the neutral regions.

4.4.1 Charge Stores in the Space-Charge Layer

As we have seen in Section 4.2.1, there is a dipole layer of charge that straddles the plane at which the impurity concentration changes. This dipole layer is shown in Figs. 4.4b and 4.5b. The magnitude of the charge in either half of the space-charge layer depends on the electrostatic potential drop across the space-charge layer. This drop is equal to the contact potential ψ_0 under equilibrium conditions; it changes to $\psi_0 - V_j$ when a junction voltage V_j is applied.

To investigate the consequences of changes in this dipole layer, we must determine the relationship between the charge and the junction voltage. The dependence of the amount of charge in the dipole layer on the potential drop can be inferred from Eqs. 4.6b and c (page 122). Using Eq. 4.6c, the total potential drop, which is equal to $\psi_0 - V_j$, can be written as

$$\psi_0 - V_j = - \int_{x_p}^{x_n} \mathscr{E}_x(x')\, dx' \tag{4.28}$$

Recall that the limits x_n and x_p are chosen to include the entire space-charge layer. However, since $\mathscr{E}_x$ is zero for large values of $|x|$, we can change the lower limit to $-\infty$ and the upper limit to $+\infty$ without changing the value of the integral. We make these changes in the following analysis to emphasize that the change in the barrier height produced by V_j requires a change in the *integrand*, that is, in $\mathscr{E}_x$.

Integration of Eq. 4.28 by parts yields

$$\psi_0 - V_j = - x' \mathscr{E}_x(x') \Big|_{-\infty}^{\infty} + \int_{-\infty}^{\infty} x' \frac{d\mathscr{E}_x(x')}{dx'} dx'$$

The first term on the right vanishes, since the electric field is zero outside the space-charge layer. The second term can be simplified by differentiating Eq. 4.6b to obtain $d\mathscr{E}_x(x')/dx'$. That is,

$$\frac{d\mathscr{E}_x(x')}{dx'} = \frac{\rho(x')}{\epsilon} \tag{4.29}$$

Thus the relationship between the potential drop across the space-charge layer and the space-charge density is

$$\psi_0 - V_j = \frac{1}{\epsilon} \int_{-\infty}^{\infty} x' \rho(x')\, dx' \tag{4.30}$$

The magnitude Q_j of the charge stored in either half of the dipole layer is

$$Q_j = A \int_{0}^{\infty} \rho(x')\, dx' \tag{4.31a}$$

or, equivalently,

$$Q_j = -A \int_{-\infty}^{0} \rho(x')\, dx' \tag{4.31b}$$

where A is the junction area.

This analysis shows that the height of the potential barrier is proportional to the *first moment* of the charge distribution, whereas the magnitude of the dipole charge is proportional to the *integral* of the charge distribution. Consequently, changes in V_j, which require a change in the first moment of the charge distribution, lead, in general, to changes in its integral as well, thus changing Q_j.

This situation is illustrated in Fig. 4.14a, which shows the space-charge distribution for two values of junction voltage. The sketch applies to a junction in which the mobile-carrier concentrations are negligible over most of the space-charge layer, that is, to a junction in which the depletion approxi-

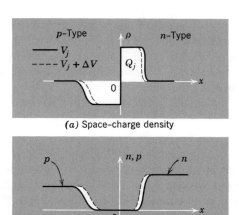

(a) Space–charge density

(b) Mobile–carrier distributions

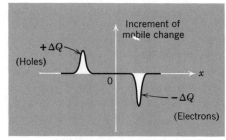

(c) Increment of mobile charge

Figure 4.14   Space-charge distributions for two values of junction voltage in a junction that is depleted over most of its extent.

mation discussed in Section 4.2.1 is applicable. The corresponding mobile-carrier distributions are shown in Fig. 4.14b. When the junction voltage increases from V_j to $V_j + \Delta V$, the space-charge layer shrinks slightly, thus decreasing both the first moment and the charge in either half of the dipole layer. Majority carriers flow in on both sides to neutralize some additional impurity charge. The quantities of holes and electrons required to accommodate the change ΔV are proportional to the white areas shown in Fig. 4.14b. These increments appear, in terms of the charge carried by these mobile carriers, in Fig. 4.14c. The charges ΔQ indicated in Fig. 4.14c represent majority-carrier charges that must flow into the space-charge layer to accommodate the increase ΔV in the junction voltage.

If the voltage change ΔV is small enough, the charge change ΔQ is proportional to ΔV. Thus an *incremental junction space-charge* capacitance C_j can be defined as

$$C_j = \lim_{\Delta V \to 0} \frac{\Delta Q}{\Delta V} = \frac{dQ}{dV} \tag{4.32a}$$

This incremental capacitance is, of course, dependent on the height of the potential barrier. It can be used to describe the dynamic component of the junction current that changes the space-charge-layer charge store. If the incremental *ac* component of the junction voltage is v, the corresponding incremental ac component of the junction current is just

$$i = C_j \frac{dv}{dt} \tag{4.32b}$$

If, as in Fig. 4.14, the depletion approximation is applicable, the charge change ΔQ associated with a change in junction voltage can be expressed in terms of the charge stored in either half of the dipole layer. We designate by q_V the difference between the stored charge in equilibrium and the stored charge at any voltage. That is,

$$q_V(V_j) = Q_j(0) - Q_j(V_j) \tag{4.33a}$$

Note that q_V is positive for forward bias [when $Q_j(V_j) < Q_j(0)$] and negative for reverse bias. *Thus q_V corresponds to the majority-carrier charge that must be added to each side of the dipole layer when the voltage changes from zero to V_j.* Consequently $\Delta Q = \Delta q_V$, and we have

$$C_j = \frac{dq_V}{dV_j} \tag{4.33b}$$

If we use the depletion approximation as in Section 4.2.1, we can use Eqs. 4.31 and 4.33b to evaluate the incremental junction capacitance of an *abrupt* junction directly. We assume that the space-charge distribution is

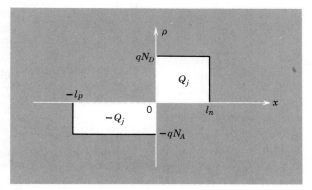

Figure 4.15   Approximate space-charge distribution used in evaluating the incremental capacitance of a junction in which the depletion approximation applies.

rectangular, as shown in Fig. 4.15. The application of Eq. 4.30 to this distribution yields

$$\psi_0 - V_j = \frac{1}{\epsilon}\left(-qN_A \int_{-l_p}^{0} x\,dx + qN_D \int_{0}^{l_n} x\,dx\right)$$

or, equivalently,

$$\psi_0 - V_j = \frac{q}{2\epsilon}(N_A l_p{}^2 + N_D l_n{}^2) \tag{4.34a}$$

Similarly, Eqs. 4.31 yield

$$Q_j = AqN_D l_n \tag{4.34b}$$

and

$$Q_j = AqN_A l_p \tag{4.34c}$$

Elimination of l_n and l_p from the last three equations yields

$$Q_j = K_a(\psi_0 - V_j)^{\frac{1}{2}} \tag{4.35a}$$

where the constant K_a is given by

$$K_a = A\left[(2\epsilon q)\frac{N_A N_D}{N_A + N_D}\right]^{\frac{1}{2}} \tag{4.35b}$$

The charge q_V, defined by Eq. 4.33a, is

$$q_V = K_a[\psi_0{}^{\frac{1}{2}} - (\psi_0 - V_j)^{\frac{1}{2}}] \tag{4.36}$$

and the incremental junction capacitance is

$$C_j = \frac{K_a}{2}(\psi_0 - V_j)^{-\frac{1}{2}} \tag{4.37}$$

Clearly, the incremental space-charge-layer capacitance depends on the junction voltage, increasing as the junction voltage increases.

We can express C_j in a different algebraic form, which is helpful in relating the capacitance to the physical situation. If Q_j is eliminated from among Eqs. 4.34, we can obtain expressions for l_n and l_p. The *total* width $l = l_n + l_p$ of the space-change layer is found to be

$$l = \left[\left(\frac{2\epsilon}{q} \right) \frac{N_A + N_D}{N_A N_D} \right]^{1/2} (\psi_0 - V_j)^{1/2} = \frac{2\epsilon}{AK_a} (\psi_0 - V_j)^{1/2} \tag{4.38}$$

Comparison of Eq. 4.38 with the expression for the incremental capacitance in Eq. 4.37 shows that C_j can be written as

$$C_j = \frac{\epsilon A}{l} \tag{4.39}$$

which is, of course, the capacitance of a parallel-plate capacitor of area A and plate spacing l, having a dielectric with a permittivity of ϵ. The incremental capacitance has this form because charge is added to and removed from the space-charge layer *at the edges* when the voltage changes, as shown in Fig. 4.14.

Although we have illustrated the evaluation of the incremental capacitance for an abrupt junction, the definitions of Eqs. 4.33 and the result of Eq. 4.39 apply to any junction in which the depletion approximation is valid. Of course, the dependence of q_V on V_j will be different for different impurity profiles. For example, in a linearly-graded junction, the space-charge layer charge q_V has the form

$$q_V = K_g[\psi_0^{2/3} - (\psi_0 - V_j)^{2/3}] \tag{4.40a}$$

where K_g is a constant dependent on the junction area and the rate of change of the impurity distribution (see Problem P4.17). In this case the incremental space-charge-layer capacitance has the following voltage dependence:

$$C_j = \frac{2K_g}{3} (\psi_0 - V_j)^{-1/3} \tag{4.40b}$$

The voltage dependence of q_V is shown in Fig. 4.16 for both abrupt and linearly graded junctions (the two curves are drawn for junctions that have the same incremental capacitance at $V_j = -10$ volt).

It should be emphasized that although the incremental space-charge-layer capacitance, as defined by Eq. 4.32 and Fig. 4.14, is a concept that is meaningful in all *pn* junctions, *Eq. 4.33b, which expresses the capacitance in terms of the charge stored in either half of the dipole layer, is valid only if the junction is depleted of mobile carriers near $x = 0$.* To illustrate this limitation, we consider an asymmetric junction that is not depleted of mobile carriers near the metallurgical junction. The space-charge distribution for this case

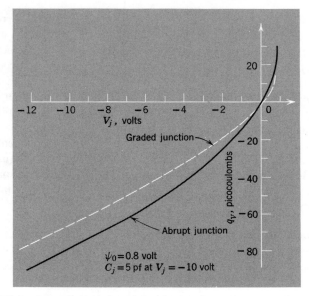

Figure 4.16   The voltage dependence of the charge qV.

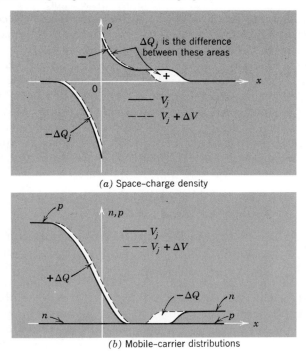

(a) Space-charge density

(b) Mobile-carrier distributions

Figure 4.17   The space-charge layer in a junction in which the depletion approximation does *not* apply.

is shown in Fig. 4.17a for two values of junction voltage. The corresponding mobile-carrier distributions are shown in Fig. 4.17b; the equal white areas here represent the quantities of majority-carrier holes and electrons that must be supplied to cause the space-charge layer to shrink to accommodate ΔV. Obviously the associated charge changes, which we have defined to be ΔQ, are *not* equal to the changes in the charge stored in either half of the dipole layer, which changes are denoted by the white areas in Fig. 4.17a and are defined as ΔQ_j. Thus in any junction in which either mobile-carrier concentration is significant (compared with the impurity concentration) at the metallurgical junction ($x = 0$ in our model), ΔQ is *not* equal to Δq_V, and Eq. 4.33b is *not* a valid definition of the incremental space-charge capacitance. Of course, Eqs. 4.36, 4.38 and 4.40 are similarly inapplicable in such cases.

4.4.2   Charge Stores in the Neutral Regions

We have seen that excess carriers appear in the neutral regions outside the space-charge layer when a forward junction voltage is applied (see Fig. 4.11). Clearly, excess carriers must be removed or supplied in order to change the excess-carrier distributions. Because the holes and the electrons are generally supplied from different places in the structure, these changes in excess-carrier distributions require dynamic charging currents that must be accounted for. We now consider the nature and origin of the dynamic currents associated with changes in these *excess-carrier charge stores*.

The excess-carrier distributions in the thin-base diode studied in Section 4.3 are shown in Fig. 4.18a for two values of the junction voltage. An increase in the junction voltage from V_j to $V_j + \Delta V$ causes the injection of more excess carriers. Thus the charge associated with excess holes, which we call the *hole store*, denote by Q_h, and illustrate in Fig. 4.18b, must increase; similarly the *electron store*, shown in Fig. 4.18c, increases by an equal amount. Since the holes and electrons carry opposite charges and change by equal amounts, neutrality is preserved; that is,

$$\Delta Q = \Delta Q_h + \Delta Q_e$$

$$= 0$$

We might think that because ΔQ is zero, there is no charging current associated with this change in the excess-carrier charge stores. However, this is not the case, because the holes and electrons required to change the corresponding stores *come from opposite terminals*. Specifically, the holes are injected from the p-type side, across the space-charge layer, into the base region. The electrons, on the other hand, flow into the base from the high-recombination n-type material (region 2) across the plane at $x = W$. Consequently, the charging currents associated with dynamic changes in these charge stores must be *added* to the static current manifested by the exponential idealized junction diode equation (Eq. 4.20a).

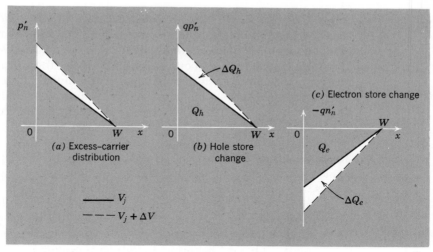

Figure 4.18 Excess-carrier charge stores in a thin-base diode with forward bias.

If the junction voltage change ΔV is small enough, the change in either excess-carrier store is proportional to ΔV. It is tempting to define an *incremental charge-store capacitance* as

$$C_D = \lim_{\Delta V \to 0} \frac{\Delta Q_h}{\Delta V} \tag{4.41a}$$

or as

$$C_D = \lim_{\Delta V \to 0} \frac{-\Delta Q_e}{\Delta V} \tag{4.41b}$$

and to use this capacitance as the basis for a description of the relationship between the dynamic charging current and changing junction voltages. Such an approach is of limited usefulness in a junction diode for two reasons:

1. When the time rates of change involved are large enough to be interesting for a junction diode, the excess-carrier distribution is no longer linear, but may exhibit considerable curvature. This curvature arises because the hole current (which, remember, is proportional to the *slope* of the distribution) has different values at different values of x, since some portion of this current is causing the changes in the hole store. Consequently, a capacitance based on the triangular distributions of Fig. 4.18 will be in error.

2. It is not possible to separate cleanly the static conduction current from the dynamic charging or displacement current. Some of the holes that are required to change the hole store can be supplied by transient imbalances in the conduction current. Thus not all of the current that "charges" C_D must be supplied across the space-charge layer; some of the charging current is supplied by delayed buildup of the hole current that flows *out* of the low-recombination region at $x = W$.

Detailed analysis of these dynamic effects in junction diodes requires consideration of time-dependent conservation laws, which are expressed as partial differential equations, and this we do not undertake. We shall return to this problem, however, in our study of the bipolar transistor in Chapter 7, where we find, surprisingly enough, that *neither* of the difficulties described above presents a serious limitation for the transistor situation, and where we shall introduce a charge-storage capacitance defined in accordance with Eqs. 4.39.

4.5   Junction Diode Structures

Semiconductor devices that embody *pn* junctions are of practical interest because of their usefulness as circuit components. Thus to complete the development of this chapter we must consider the way in which *contacts* or *terminals* are added to the *pn* junction structures that we have studied, and we must relate the current-voltage characteristics observed *at the terminals* to the internal physical behavior that we have explored.

4.5.1   Contacts and Metal-Semiconductor Junctions

Contacts are necessary in order to couple the junction voltage changes and the junction currents discussed earlier to "the outside world." These electrical connections can be made to the *p*-type and *n*-type regions in several ways. The semiconductor can be soldered to a metal, which then constitutes a terminal of the device. Or a thin metal film can be evaporated onto the surface of the semiconductor. Wires can then be soldered or bonded by a combination of heat and pressure ("thermocompression bonding") to this metal film to provide the contact. In either case we can obtain a structure similar to that shown in Fig. 4.19, which should be compared with Fig. 4.10. We denote the terminal voltage by *V*. The terminal current is, of course, just equal to the junction current *I*, since all the current that crosses the space-charge layer must flow in the terminal circuit.

Under equilibrium conditions, there is obviously no voltage across the terminals of an isolated junction diode. If there were a voltage, current could be made to flow in a load connected to the terminals; such a situation would

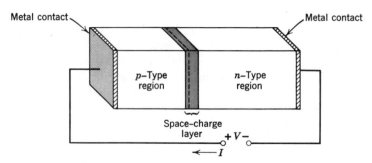

Figure 4.19   A junction diode with contacts.

clearly violate the general laws of thermodynamics, which state, in part, that an isothermal system in *equilibrium with its environment* cannot deliver work (second law). It should be clear from our discussion in Section 4.2.1 that there is an electrostatic potential difference between the *n*-type and *p*-type regions of the structure. This potential difference is the contact potential that arises at the junction of the dissimilar semiconductors. It serves, in equilibrium, to oppose the tendency of mobile carriers to diffuse into the regions where they are less populous. How is the existence of a contact potential at the junction consistent with the requirement that the voltage at the open-circuited terminals be zero? The answer lies in the recognition that the path through the device contains two metal-semiconductor junctions as well as a *pn* junction. The algebraic sum of the contact potentials of these three junctions must be identically zero to satisfy the thermodynamic constraint referred to above.

Metal-semiconductor (MS) junctions differ, in terms of their electrical behavior, from the *pn* junction in two important respects:

1. The MS junctions conduct current well in both directions. To do so, they must facilitate a free interchange of charge between the charge carrier in the metal (electrons) and the charge carriers in the semiconductor (holes in *p*-type material, conduction electrons in *n*-type material).

2. The potential barrier at an MS junction does not change in height significantly when current flows through the junction. Therefore, the excess-carrier concentration in the semiconductor immediately adjacent to the contact is zero, even in the presence of current.

These physical properties can be produced in an MS junction either by choosing the metal so that the space-charge layer that is formed at the junction produces an enhancement rather than a depletion of mobile carriers or by making the lifetime in the semiconductor adjacent to the junction exceedingly small. Metal-semiconductor contacts that have these properties are referred to as *nonrectifying* or *ohmic*.[7]

4.5.2 Static Voltage-Current Characteristics

Since the metal-semiconductor contacts in a junction diode are fabricated in such a way that they are ohmic, the voltage V at the terminals of the diode can differ from the junction voltage V_j only insofar as there are electrostatic potential drops in the neutral semiconductor regions. These potential drops may arise as a result of the flow of current through these regions, which have significant electrical resistivity.[8] Under low-injection conditions, such that

---

[7] Not all MS junctions are ohmic; some are rectifying and have current-voltage characteristics not unlike those of a *pn* junction. Point contact "crystal detectors," used in the early days of radio communications, are examples of nonohmic MS contacts. For further discussion of these complicated matters, see Chapter 4 of Reference 4.3.

[8] The doped semiconductors used in junction devices commonly have resistivities that are 2 to 6 orders of magnitude larger than the resistivity of good metallic conductors, such as silver.

the majority-carrier concentrations and thus the resistivity are negligibly affected by the excess carriers, the electrostatic potential drops in the neutral regions are ohmic (i.e., they are proportional to the junction current I) and can be represented by means of a series resistance R_S. Hence, the total terminal voltage V can be written as

$$V = R_S I + \frac{kT}{q} \ln\left(\frac{I}{I_s} + 1\right) \tag{4.42}$$

The second term is the junction voltage V_j, which is obtained by inverting Eq. 4.20a. The series resistance R_S is invariably small enough so that for low currents V is dominated by the junction voltage. Thus for low current, that is, for reverse bias and moderate forward bias, the voltage-current (V–I) characteristic of a junction diode should have the form of the idealized *pn* junction diode equation.[9] Behavior of this kind is shown in Fig. 4.20a. The saturation current shown in Fig. 4.20a is larger than that which occurs in most diodes. This parameter may range, at room temperature, from microamperes down to picoamperes (10^{-12} amp).

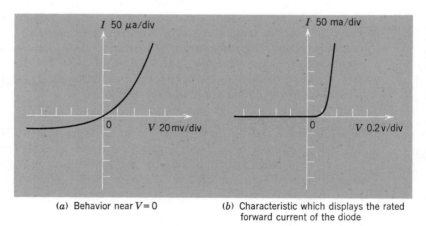

(a) Behavior near $V=0$ (b) Characteristic which displays the rated forward current of the diode

Figure 4.20   Static junction diode V–I characteristics.

The curve of Fig. 4.20a is plotted on scales that display the reverse or saturation current. If the scales are changed so that typical forward currents can be displayed, the reverse current generally cannot be seen (Fig. 4.20b). Furthermore, the small size of the saturation current compared with typical forward currents, coupled with the strong voltage dependence implicit in the exponential diode equation, leads to an apparent *voltage threshold* below which there is little forward current and above which the forward current

---

[9] A variety of other physical effects, which we shall not discuss here, may cause significant deviations from the idealized diode equation at low currents. See Chapter 4 of Reference 4.1.

increases strongly with voltage. The voltage threshold shown in Fig. 4.20*b* is about 0.2 volt. This characteristic voltage commonly lies in the range from about 0.2 volt (for germanium diodes with large saturation currents) to about 0.7 volt (for silicon diodes with small saturation currents).

As the forward diode current increases, the ohmic term in Eq. 4.42 ultimately increases faster than the logarithmic term, and the terminal voltage is dominated by drops in the neutral regions. In this region the diode characteristic becomes approximately linear.

4.6 Junction Photodiodes

In all of the *pn* junction structures studied so far, excess carriers have resulted from either injection or extraction across a junction. It is, of course, possible to produce excess carriers by other means, such as optical injection. To illustrate another application of the *pn* junction physical electronics developed in this chapter, we now consider a simple junction photodiode, in which optically-generated excess carriers provide a means for converting radiant energy to electrical energy.

Once again, we study a simple, idealized physical structure, which has been chosen to minimize analytical difficulties. The structure, which is shown in Fig. 4.21, has the following characteristics:

1. The diode is asymmetrically doped: the *p*-type region is doped much more heavily than the *n*-type region. Consequently, the current across the space-charge layer is comprised almost entirely of hole flow.

2. The *n*-type region has a large lifetime; hence the excess-carrier diffusion length there is *large* compared with the width *W*.

3. Both semiconductor regions are provided with metal contacts. The contact to the *p*-type region is placed so that it does not interfere with photon absorption on the plane that is parallel to the junction.

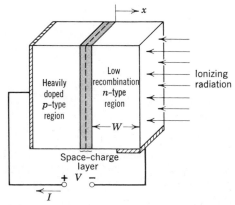

Figure 4.21 A junction photodiode structure.

We assume that the face of the n-type region at $x = W$ is *uniformly* illuminated with ionizing radiation, so that pairs are produced at this surface at a rate of G pairs per unit area per unit time. Consequently, the excess-carrier concentration at $x = W$ is positive. These optically-generated minority carriers flow, by diffusion (when the injection level is low), toward the space-charge layer, where they are collected and swept into the p-type region by the electric field associated with the potential barrier. The optically-generated majority carriers cannot, on the other hand, flow through the space-charge layer; the field there opposes their flow. The majority carriers flow transversely in the n-type region and exit through the contact, thus supporting current flow in the external circuit.

The magnitude of the current that is developed depends, of course, on the terminal voltage V. We consider two important special cases: short-circuit conditions, when $V = 0$, and open-circuit conditions, when $I = 0$.

When the diode is short-circuited, the junction voltage V_j is zero and the potential barrier is at its equilibrium value.[10] Therefore, the excess-carrier concentration at the space-charge-layer edge ($x = 0$) of the n-type region is zero, in accordance with Eq. 4.12a. Since the width W of this region is much less than a diffusion length, the diffusive hole current is nearly independent of x, and the excess-carrier distribution has the form shown in Fig. 4.22a. The distribution is linear because the hole current is constant *and* diffusive, so that the gradient or slope must be constant.

The rate at which hole current is generated (per unit area) is qG. Consequently, the corresponding junction current is simply

$$I = -qAG \quad \text{for} \quad V = 0 \tag{4.43a}$$

where the minus sign is required to satisfy the reference direction for I indicated in Fig. 4.21. The excess hole concentration $p_n'(W)$ at the illuminated face can be related to the hole generation rate G by recognizing that the optically-generated holes flow to the junction by diffusion. Thus we have

$$qG = qD_h \frac{p_n'(W)}{W} \tag{4.43b}$$

so that

$$p_n'(W) = \frac{GW}{D_h} \tag{4.43c}$$

When the diode is open-circuited, the current I is zero. The junction is forward-biased, however, to just such degree that the slope of the hole distribution is zero at the space-charge-layer edge, as shown in Fig. 4.22b.

---

[10] Assuming once again that electrostatic potential drops in the neutral regions are negligible.

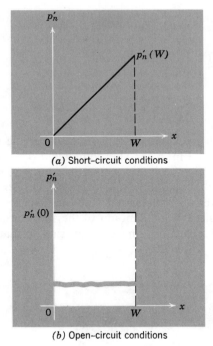

(a) Short-circuit conditions

(b) Open-circuit conditions

Figure 4.22   Excess-carrier distributions in the photodiode of Fig. 4.20.

That is, the forward bias is just sufficient to block the flow of the optically-generated minority carriers across the junction. The vertical scale is broken in this sketch because $p'_n(0)$ is likely to be much larger than the excess concentration under short-circuit conditions. In fact, the nearly uniform concentration in the n-type region builds up to just such a value that the net rate of recombination in that region, which is proportional to the white area in Fig. 4.22b, is equal to the generation rate. If we denote the lifetime in the n-type region by τ, the local recombination rate per unit volume is simply p'_n/τ. Thus for the distribution of Fig. 4.22b the total rate of recombination (per unit area per unit time) is

$$\frac{p'_n(0)W}{\tau}$$

This recombination rate must be equal to the surface generation rate of holes G. Thus we have

$$p'_n(0) = \frac{G\tau}{W} \tag{4.44a}$$

Finally, the terminal voltage, which is equal to the junction voltage, is, using Eq. 4.12a,

$$V = \frac{kT}{q} \ln\left[\frac{p'_n(0)}{p_{no}} + 1\right]$$

$$= \frac{kT}{q} \ln\left(\frac{G\tau}{Wp_{no}} + 1\right) \qquad \text{for} \quad I = 0 \qquad (4.44b)$$

We have thus obtained two points on the *I–V* characteristic of the photodiode. These are shown in Fig. 4.23. The complete *I–V* characteristic is easily obtained by determining the excess-carrier distribution for an arbitrary junction voltage; we leave the details of this for a problem (Problem P4.19). It is worth noting, however, that the actual *I–V* characteristic is simply an exponential diode law shifted by the amount of the short-circuited current. After all, with no light we have an ordinary *pn* junction so that

$$I = I_s(e^{qV/kT} - 1)$$

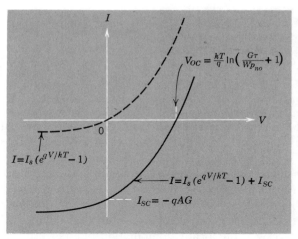

Figure 4.23   Current-voltage characteristic of a photodiode.

The physical principles illustrated in this example form the basis of the operation of essentially all photovoltaic junction devices, including light detectors and solar cells for energy conversion. The pairs produced by the absorption of radiation are, in every case, separated by the one-way nature of a space-charge layer and thus made to flow in an external circuit. When illuminated by sunlight, silicon photovoltaic cells develop short-circuit currents of the order of 1 to 10 ma/cm² of illuminated surface and have open-circuit voltages of a few tenths of a volt. As energy converters they develop output powers of about 10 mw/cm². The *I-V* characteristics of a typical silicon photodiode are shown in Fig. 4.24*a*. The linear dependence of the short-circuit current on light intensity is shown in Fig. 4.24*b*, while the logarithmic dependence of the open-circuit voltage on light intensity is shown in Fig. 4.24*c*.

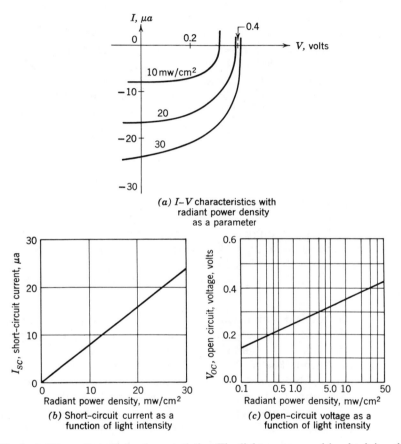

(a) *I–V* characteristics with radiant power density as a parameter

(b) Short–circuit current as a function of light intensity

(c) Open–circuit voltage as a function of light intensity

Figure 4.24   Typical silicon photodiode characteristics. The light source used in obtaining these data was a tungsten-filament lamp operating at a color temperature of 2800°K.

REFERENCES

4.1   P. E. Gray, D. DeWitt, A. R. Boothroyd, and J. F. Gibbons, *Physical Electronics and Circuit Models of Transistors*, Wiley, New York, 1964.

4.2   A. K. Jonscher, *Principles of Semiconductor Device Operation*, Wiley, New York, 1960.

4.3   E. Spenke, *Electronic Semiconductors*, McGraw-Hill, New York, 1958.

PROBLEMS

P4.1 This problem is concerned with the electrical behavior of the space-charge layer at an *abrupt pn* junction. The analysis is based on the depletion approximation, which requires a rectangular charge distribution, as shown by the dashed lines in Fig. 4.4b.

(a) Derive expressions for the electric field in the space-charge layer. Consider the regions $-l_p < x < 0$ and $0 < x < l_n$ separately.

(b) Derive expressions for the electrostatic potential in the space-charge layer. Again consider the two halves of the space-charge layer separately.

(c) Solve for the peak electric field $\mathcal{E}_0$ and the total width of the space-charge layer $l = l_p + l_n$ in terms of ψ_0, ϵ, q, and the impurity concentrations.

Although this analysis has been for equilibrium conditions, it applies as well when the junction is biased. It is necessary only to replace ψ_0 by $\psi_0 - V_j$.

P4.2 An abrupt silicon *pn* junction has impurity concentrations:

$$N_A = 10^{15} \text{ cm}^{-3}$$

$$N_D = 2 \times 10^{17} \text{ cm}^{-3}$$

(a) Evaluate the contact potential ψ_0 at room temperature where $n_i \simeq 10^{10} \text{ cm}^{-3}$.

(b) Evaluate, using the depletion approximation, the width l of the space-charge layer and the peak electric field $\mathcal{E}_0$ for $V_j = 0$ and for $V_j = -10$ volt. Assume $\epsilon = 10^{-12}$ farad/cm.

Answers. (a) $\psi_0 \simeq 0.71$ volt; (b) $l = 9.5 \times 10^{-5}$ cm, $\mathcal{E}_0 = 1.5 \times 10^4$ volts/cm for $V_j = 0$.

P4.3 Consider an asymmetrically-doped abrupt *pn* junction in which the intrinsic-carrier concentration is small enough so that the depletion approximation applies. Assume $N_A = 100 N_D$.

(a) Sketch the distributions of space charge, electric field, and electrostatic potential. Note that the penetration of the space-charge layer into the heavily-doped *p*-type material is much less than into the *n*-type material. Consequently, most of the potential variation occurs on the *n*-type side.

(b) Assume that *all* of the potential variation occurs on the lightly-doped side and derive an approximate expression for the width of the space-charge layer in terms of q, ϵ, N_D, and $\psi_0 - V_j$. Check your result by evaluating the limit of your result to Problem P4.1c for $N_A \gg N_D$.

P4.4 This problem is concerned with electrical conditions within the space-charge layer of a one-dimensional junction to which the depletion approximation does *not* apply.

(a) Express the space-charge density ρ in terms of the electrostatic potential. Note that both immobile charge *and* mobile charge contribute to ρ.

(b) Using Gauss's law applied to a differential volume element in the space-charge layer, derive a second-order nonlinear differential equation in the potential ψ which describes $\psi(x)$ in the space-charge layer.

(c) Show that your result can be expressed in the form

$$\frac{d^2\phi}{dy^2} = \sinh\phi - \frac{N}{2n_i}$$

where $\phi = q\psi/kT$ is a normalized potential
$y = x/L_D$ is a normalized position coordinate

$$L_D = \sqrt{\frac{\epsilon kT}{2q^2 n_i}}$$ is called the *Debye length*

This nonlinear differential equation has no closed-form solution; it must be solved numerically to obtain $\phi(y)$ and thus $\psi(x)$, $n(x)$, and $p(x)$ in the space-charge layer. The characteristic length that governs the position dependence of the solution is the Debye length L_D. In silicon at $300°K$ it has a value of about 3×10^{-3} cm.

P4.5 The equilibrium situation at a *pn* junction can be viewed as the result of a balance between drift and diffusion within the space-charge layer (see Eqs. 4.2). Consider a *symmetrically-doped* abrupt *pn* junction ($N_D = N_A$) and derive an expression for either the hole flow due to *drift* ($\mu_h p \mathscr{E}_x$) or the hole flow due to diffusion ($D_h dp/dx$) at the plane where the impurity concentration changes ($x = 0$ in Fig. 4.4). Assume that the depletion approximation holds. (*Suggestion*. Notice that the ratio of the hole concentrations at any two planes can be related to the potential difference between those planes by an equation similar to Eq. 4.5.) Evaluate the electric current density at $x = 0$ due to either drift or diffusion for $N_D = N_A = 10^{16}$ cm^{-3}, $n_i = 10^{13}$ cm^{-3}, and $D_h = 50$ cm^2/sec.

P4.6 This problem is concerned with the space-charge layer of a *graded pn* junction, that is, one in which the change of impurity concentration from *p*-type to *n*-type is gradual rather than abrupt. This situation is illustrated in Fig. 4.25. As in the case of the abrupt junction, the dipole layer of space charge develops because there is a region in which the mobile-carrier concentrations are negligible compared with the impurity concentration. The electric field distribution is the integral of the space-charge distribution, and the potential distribution is the integral of the field distribution, in accordance with Eqs. 4.6b and c.

Consider a junction in which the net impurity concentration varies *linearly*, that is,

$$N(x) = -ax$$

where a is a positive constant. Compute, sketch, and dimension $\rho(x)$, $\mathscr{E}(x)$, and $\psi(x)$ on the basis of the *depletion approximation*.

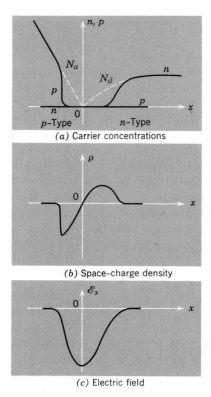

(a) Carrier concentrations

(b) Space–charge density

(c) Electric field

Figure 4.25   Electrical conditions in the space-charge layer of a graded *pn* junction.

P4.7   A germanium junction diode, which has the structure illustrated in Fig. 4.10, has the following parameters:

impurity concentrations $\begin{cases} N_A = 10^{18} \text{ cm}^{-3} \\ N_D = 10^{16} \text{ cm}^{-3} \end{cases}$

cross-sectional area $A = 10^{-3} \text{ cm}^2$

width of low-recombination base region $W = 10^{-3} \text{ cm}$

hole diffusion coefficient in the *n*-type region $D_h = 40 \text{ cm}^2/\text{sec}$

intrinsic-carrier concentration at 300°K $n_i = 2 \times 10^{13} \text{ cm}^{-3}$

(a) Determine the *equilibrium* carrier concentrations on both sides of the space-charge layer (at 300°K).

(b) Evaluate, at 300°K, the contact potential ψ_0.

(c) Evaluate, at 300°K, the saturation current I_s that appears in Eq. 4.20a.

(d) For what range of values of injected excess-carrier concentration $p_n'(0)$ is the low-injection-level approximation satisfied? Assume that the domain of low-level injection ends when the majority-carrier concentration at the edge of the space-charge layer is increased 10% by injection, and consider $T = 300°K$.

(*e*) Evaluate, for $T = 300°K$, the junction current I, and the junction voltage V_j, at the upper boundary of the low-injection domain.

Answers. (*b*) $\psi_0 \simeq 0.43$ volt; (*c*) $I_s \simeq 250$ na; (*e*) $V \simeq 0.25$ volt, $I \simeq 6.4$ ma.

P4.8 Compute, sketch, and dimension the excess-carrier distribution, the current-density distributions, and both $p_n(x)$ and $n_n(x)$ for *reverse bias* applied to the diode structure of Section 4.3. Assume $V_j \ll -kT/q$ (i.e., V_j is negative and $|V_j|$ is much greater than kT/q). In essence, this problem asks you to redraw Fig. 4.11 for reverse bias. Explain the origin of the junction current and account for the flow of both holes and electrons.

P4.9 This problem is concerned with minority-carrier flow in the base region of the thin-base diode shown in Fig. 4.10. Because of the asymmetry of the doping and of the lack of substantive recombination in the base region, the *majority-carrier* (*electron*) *current density in the base is negligible*.

(*a*) Use the fact that $J_{ex} \simeq 0$ to evaluate $\mathscr{E}_x$ in the base. Express $\mathscr{E}_x$ in terms of dp_n'/dx, n_n, and kT/q.

(*b*) Prove that the drift component of the minority-carrier (hole) current density is negligible compared with the corresponding diffusion component for low injection levels.

P4.10 The analysis of Section 2.1.3 demonstrates that the space-charge density in the interior of a metal must, under static conditions, vanish; internal charges are carried to the surfaces by conduction currents associated with the high conductivity of a metal. This analysis is obviously invalid in the space-charge layer of a *pn* junction, where there is significant space charge, even though the conductivity of a semiconductor is only a few orders of magnitude smaller than that of a metal. Reconcile this apparent discrepancy. Detailed analysis is not necessary; a clear explanation is sufficient.

P4.11 A diode that has the structure illustrated in Fig. 4.10 has a base region (region 1) of width $W = 25 \mu$ in which the diffusion coefficient for holes is $D_h = 40$ cm^2/sec. What is the *minimum* value for the lifetime in the base region if not less than 95% of the holes injected into the base are to diffuse across to the region of high recombination without recombining?

Answer. $\tau > 1.5 \mu$sec.

P4.12 Consider a one-dimensional asymmetrically-doped *pn* junction in which the lightly-doped *n*-type side has a *uniform* lifetime τ and thus a uniform diffusion length L_h. Make use of the conservation law and solutions developed in Section 3.3.2.

(*a*) Compute, sketch, and dimension the excess minority-carrier concentration on the *n*-type side (assume that V_j is positive).

(*b*) Compute, sketch, and dimension the corresponding minority-carrier current density.

(c) Compute the junction current I and derive an expression for the saturation current I_s in the exponential diode equation (Eq. 4.20a).

(d) Sketch, on the same coordinates used in (a), the *majority*-carrier current density on the *n*-type side.

P4.13 This problem is concerned with a *pn* junction structure in which both the *n*-type and the *p*-type regions have uniform lifetime (see Problem P4.12). The relative doping of the two sides is such that the hole and electron currents at the space-charge layer are comparable. Construct a sketch analogous to Fig. 4.13 showing the distributions of the hole and electron currents in the space-charge layer and in the neutral regions. *Assume* that

(a) The junction is forward-biased.

(b) The injected hole current at the *n*-type edge of the space-charge layer is twice the injected electron current at the *p*-type edge.

(c) The diffusion length in the *n*-type region is twice the diffusion length in the *p*-type region.

P4.14 Consider a *pn* junction diode that differs from the one described in Problem P4.13 only in that *there is significant recombination of carriers in the space-charge layer*. In addition to (a), (b), and (c) above, *assume* that the net rate at which pairs recombine in the space-charge layer is equal to *half* the net rate at which electrons recombine in the *p*-type region. Construct a sketch showing the distributions of the hole and electron currents in the space-charge layer and in the neutral regions. Demonstrate that the total diode current can be obtained by adding a term that describes the space-charge-layer-recombination current to the injected current given by Eq. 4.20a (modified to account for electron injection).

P4.15 This problem is concerned with a two-sided one-dimensional diode such as that shown in Fig. 4.12. Assume $D_e = D_h$, $W_p = 2W_n$, and $N_A = 3N_D$ and derive an expression for the saturation current of this diode. Note that *both* hole and electron currents must be considered when the junction current is evaluated.

P4.16 A silicon *pn* junction diode that is used as a thermometer is biased in the forward direction by a fixed current. At 27°C the forward voltage is 700 mv.

(a) Calculate the temperature coefficient of the diode voltage at this temperature and current.

(b) The temperature increases to 80°C. How much does the diode voltage change?

Answers. (a) -2.2 mv/°K ; (b) V decreases 115 mv.

P4.17 Making use of the results of Problem P4.6, derive an expression for the incremental space-charge-layer capacitance of a linearly-graded *pn* junction in which the depletion approximation applies. Show that the capacitance can be written in the same form as Eq. 4.39.

P4.18 An abrupt *pn* junction has the following parameters:

$$n_i = 10^{10} \text{ cm}^{-3}$$
$$N_A = 10^{18} \text{ cm}^{-3}$$
$$N_D = 10^{16} \text{ cm}^{-3}$$
$$\epsilon = 10^{-12} \text{ farad/cm}$$

(a) Evaluate the incremental space-charge-layer capacitance at zero bias $(V_j = 0)$. Express your result as a capacitance per square centimeter of junction area. Assume $kT/q = 25$ mv.

(b) Repeat (a) for a reverse bias of 20 volts ($V_j = -20$ volt).

Answers. (a) $C_j \simeq 3.2 \times 10^4$ pf/cm^2; (b) $C_j \simeq 6.2 \times 10^3$ pf/cm^2.

P4.19 The problem is concerned with the photodiode structure shown in Fig. 4.21 and discussed in Section 4.6.

(a) Consider first the case in which there is no illumination so that $G = 0$. When the diode is forward-biased, the junction current is determined by the small but nonzero amount of recombination that occurs in the *n*-type region. Assume that the diffusion length L_h is much greater than W and derive an expression for the saturation current of this diode by equating the injected hole current to the recombination current.

(b) Now consider the situation with illumination and derive an expression for the *I–V* characteristic of the photodiode. Put your result in the form

$$I = I_s(e^{qV/kT} - 1) + I_{sc}$$

and evaluate I_s and I_{sc}.

P4.20 A junction photodiode having a saturation current of 1 μa develops a short-circuit current under illumination of 25 ma. The temperature is 290°K.

(a) What is the open-circuit voltage of this diode under the same conditions of illumination?

(b) Determine the maximum power that this diode can deliver to a load.

(c) What value of load resistance is required to achieve this condition of maximum output power?

Answers. (a) $V_{oc} \simeq 0.25$ v; (b) 4.5 mw; (c) 8.7 kohm.

NOTES ON DEMONSTRATIONS

The hydraulic analogy discussed in Section 4.2.3 can be employed in an effective lecture demonstration to illustrate alternative locations of the "bottleneck" in flow situations. Suitable apparatus is shown in Fig. 4.26. The tanks in this apparatus are cemented together; the sections are cut from $\frac{1}{8}$-in. polystyrene sheet. The tanks are connected with a length of $\frac{5}{8}$-in. i.d. flexible tubing, which can be constricted with a hose clamp. The baffles are made of $\frac{1}{8}$-in. plates perforated with a single $\frac{1}{8}$-in. hole near the bottom of each baffle. The tank is used with water dyed with ink. A pressure differential is established by raising one tank about 3 in.

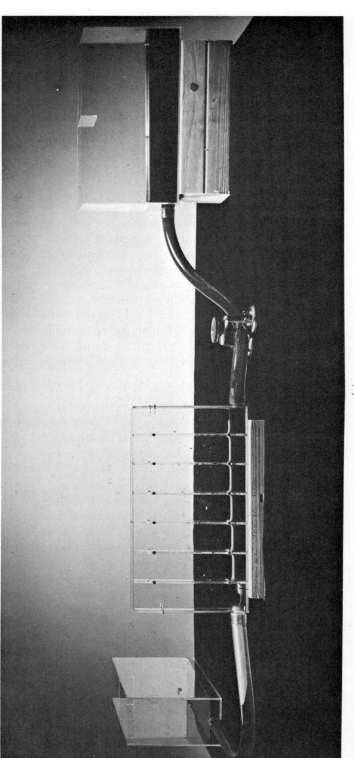

(a)

Figure 4.26 Apparatus used in demonstrating alternative locations of the bottleneck in a fluid-flow situation (see Fig. 4.8).

(a) General view showing, from left to right, source tank, adjustable clamp, baffle tank, and receiver tank.

(b) Source and baffle tanks showing *steady-state* behavior when the clamp is released so that the bottleneck to flow is in the baffles.

(c) Source and baffle tanks showing steady-state behavior when the clamp is tightened down to provide the major bottleneck to flow.

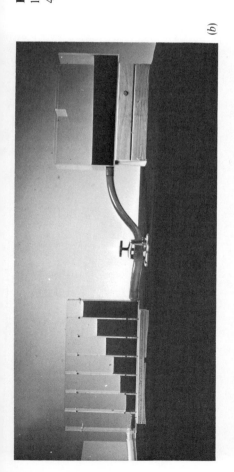

(b)

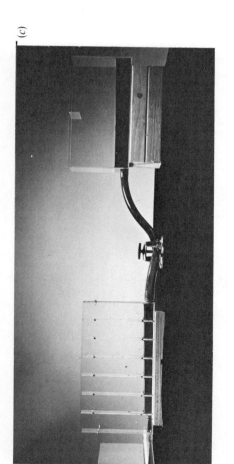

(c)

CHAPTER FIVE

Semiconductor Device Structure and Fabrication

5.1 Introduction

We have so far investigated the physical and electrical behavior of semi-conductors, *pn* junctions, and junction diodes without paying much attention to the structure of these devices. The structure of actual semiconductor devices is, of course, strongly influenced by the techniques that are employed in the fabrication of these devices. Consequently, we must give some attention to semiconductor technology and to the methods employed in making semiconductor devices.

The field of semiconductor technology has gone through a period of rapid and revolutionary development in the decade of the 1960's, during which several fundamental principles and techniques in semiconductor device fabrication technology have emerged. We emphasize fundamental ideas without considering technological details, because the latter are often proprietary and frequently quite transient.

5.2 Fabrication of Semiconductor Structures

Just as the first decade (the 1950's) of the exploitation of semiconductor electronics was dominated by germanium technology, the second decade has been dominated by silicon technology. Silicon devices are superior to germanium devices in several compelling respects, so that the emphasis will continue to be placed on the former. Most of the silicon devices that are made rely on a set of techniques often summarized in the description: *planar diffusion technology*. These techniques provide the means for creating, in pieces of silicon that were originally homogeneous, *pn* junctions and regions of different conductivity of controlled extent, and means of connecting these regions to contacts or terminals. We now describe briefly the principal features of the several techniques that are part of the technology of planar diffused devices.

5.2.1 Compensation and Solid-State Diffusion

The equilibrium hole and electron concentrations in a semiconductor are governed by the intrinsic concentration n_i and by the impurity concentrations N_a (acceptors) and N_d (donors). As we have seen (Section 2.2.1), only the *net* impurity concentration N, which is the *difference* between the donor and acceptor concentrations, matters. That is, the equilibrium concentrations are determined by the difference

$$N = N_d - N_a$$

and *not* by N_d and N_a separately. If donors predominate, that is, if N_d exceeds

N_a, the semiconductor is *n*-type. In this case N is positive. If, on the other hand, acceptors predominate, the semiconductor is *p*-type and N is negative.

Since the conductivity type is governed only by the net impurity concentration, a piece of semiconductor can be converted from one conductivity type to the other by the introduction of the appropriate impurity. For example, a *p*-type semiconductor can be converted to an *n*-type semiconductor by adding donor impurities in a quantity sufficient to change the sign of the net impurity concentration. If the material originally contained an acceptor concentration of, say, 10^{16} cm^{-3}, added donors having a concentration of 2×10^{16} cm^{-3} will convert the material to *n*-type (and will exactly invert the numerical hole and electron concentrations). This method of changing the conductivity type by adding impurities is called *compensation*; it is fundamental to semiconductor device technology.

Impurity atoms can be added to a semiconductor by the mechanism of solid-state diffusion. Essentially all of the trivalent and pentavalent impurities that are of interest in the control of conductivity dissolve in silicon in small quantities. Although the solid solubilities, which limit the concentrations of

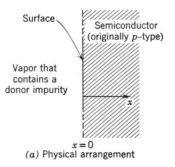

(a) Physical arrangement

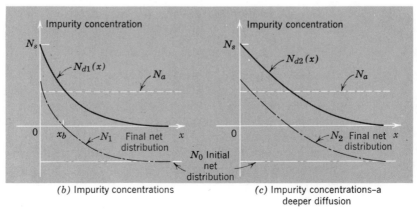

(b) Impurity concentrations

(c) Impurity concentrations–a deeper diffusion

Figure 5.1   Production of a *pn* junction by diffusion of donor impurities from a constant vapor source into a *p*-type semiconductor.

the dissolved impurities, are small, impurity concentrations up to 10^{18} or 10^{20} cm^{-3} can be obtained (recall that these correspond to impurity fractions that are exceedingly small, being of the order of 0.001 to 0.1%). These dissolved impurities enter the crystalline structure of the semiconductor *substitutionally*. That is, they tend to be located at host-atom lattice sites, where they replace the silicon atoms. Consequently, the covalent-bond model of impurity conduction discussed in Section 2.1.5 applies.

Impurity atoms can move within the semiconductor by solid-state diffusion. The diffusion coefficients that govern this motion are extremely temperature dependent, increasing as the temperature increases. Thus the desired distribution of impurities can be obtained by raising the temperature of the semiconductor to the neighborhood of 1000°C for periods of the order of tens of minutes. When the temperature is lowered, the diffusion coefficient decreases, and the impurity atoms are immobilized or "frozen in" with the new distribution.

Compensating impurities are thus introduced into a homogeneous semiconductor by diffusion through the surfaces. This situation is illustrated in Fig. 5.1, which shows the dependence of the net impurity concentration on the distance from the surface for several conditions. Originally, the semiconductor was homogeneous and *p*-type, as indicated by the uniform acceptor concentration N_a, shown by the dashed line. The corresponding original *net* impurity concentration is denoted by N_0.

Consider the consequences of placing this semiconductor in a vapor that contains a compound having donor-impurity atoms as one of its constituents. This compound is chosen so that it reacts with the silicon at the surface, thus releasing the donor impurities and establishing at the surface a concentration of donor impurities which we denote by N_s. This surface concentration depends on the concentration of impurities in the vapor and on the temperature. We assume that the temperature of this system is high enough so that the impurities diffuse from the surface where they are liberated into the semiconductor. The resulting profile of donor impurities depends on the time the high temperature is maintained; the longer the time the deeper the penetration of the donors. Two profiles are shown in Figs. 5.1*b* and *c*. The profile labeled $N_{d2}(x)$ results from a longer diffusion time than that which yields $N_{d1}(x)$.

The net impurity concentration that results after the diffusion that yields $N_{d1}(x)$ is shown in Fig. 5.1*b*. It is simply

$$N_1(x) = N_{d1}(x) - N_a$$

Note that the net impurity concentration changes sign at $x = x_b$ so that a *pn* junction is formed at this plane.[1] The semiconductor between the surface

---

[1] A junction results only if the gradient of $N_2(x)$ is large enough near x_b. Gradients of sufficient magnitude are easy to obtain by appropriate selection of surface concentration, temperature, and time.

and the parallel plane at x_b has been converted from p-type to n-type; the diffused-in donors have compensated the acceptors present in the starting material. The semiconductor beyond x_b, the *substrate region*, is still p-type (although it is no longer uniform near x_b).

The situation illustrated in Fig. 5.1 is called *constant-source diffusion* because the surface concentration of the diffusant is held constant by the "infinite" source of donors provided by the vapor. As time goes on more and more donors enter the semiconductor, but the surface concentration remains constant at a value determined by the vapor pressure of the gas that contains the donors.

A slightly different technique for diffusing impurities into a semiconductor is shown in Fig. 5.2. In this case a layer of donor atoms is deposited on the

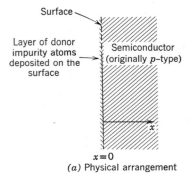

x=0
(a) Physical arrangement

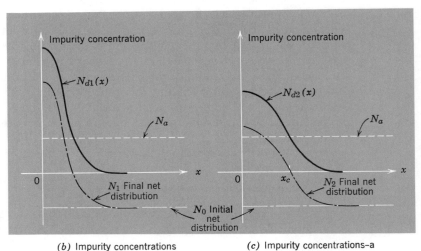

(b) Impurity concentrations

(c) Impurity concentrations–a deeper diffusion

Figure 5.2   Production of a *pn* junction by diffusion from a limited source of impurities.

surface of the semiconductor at a lower temperature than that at which the solid-state diffusion will take place. This layer of atoms constitutes a source of diffusant which has a fixed quantity of impurity atoms. Consequently, the surface concentration that exists following the diffusion depends on the duration of the diffusion. The deeper impurity penetration, which results from longer diffusion times, results in a surface concentration that is less than that for shorter diffusion times. Two donor profiles are shown in Figs. 5.2b and c. The profile labeled $N_{d2}(x)$ results from a longer diffusion time than that which yields $N_{d1}(x)$. These two profiles have the property that their areas, which are proportional to the total number of donor atoms introduced into the semiconductor, are equal, since both profiles resulted from the same number of donors deposited on the surface. This technique is called *limited-source diffusion.*[2]

The net impurity concentration that results after the diffusion that yields $N_{d2}(x)$ is also shown in Fig. 5.2c. It is designated as N_2. Once again a *pn* junction has been formed, with a junction plane at $x = x_c$.

The technique of solid-state diffusion of compensating impurities is not limited to a single diffusion or to the production of a single junction. Two or three diffusions can be done in sequence to produce multiple-layer structures, as illustrated in Fig. 5.3. In this case a piece of *p*-type semiconductor has been subjected, in turn, to two diffusions. The first introduces donor impurities and generates the donor profile designated by N_{d1}. It produces a junction plane at $x = x_1$ and converts the portion of the semiconductor between $x = 0$ and $x = x_1$ to *n*-type. The second diffusion, which is shallower, introduces acceptor impurities and generates the profile of *added* acceptors denoted by N_{a2}. Since the second diffusion has a higher surface concentration and is shallower than the first, a region of material near the surface is compensated back to *p*-type, thus producing a *second* junction at x_2.[3] The final net impurity concentration is

$$N_2 = N_0 + N_{d1} - N_{a2}$$

The result of these two sequential diffusions is shown in Fig. 5.4. A three-layer, two-junction structure has been produced. The junction depths,

[2] Limited-source diffusion can be carried out in one step rather than in two steps. Initially the surface is exposed to a source of donor atoms, which diffuse in a very limited distance. Then the source of donor atoms is removed, and the final number of impurities then present is redistributed by a longer diffusion, which may be at a different temperature as well.

[3] As Fig. 5.3 is drawn, the second, shallow diffusion does not penetrate to the plane of the first junction (at x_1). Thus the location of the first junction is unchanged by the second diffusion. A slightly deeper second diffusion would cause the first junction to move toward the surface. Also, we have shown the profile produced by the first diffusion as unchanged after the second diffusion. In reality N_{d1} will flatten somewhat (maintaining the same area) when the semiconductor is reheated to diffusion temperatures. This change in the first profile during the second diffusion can be minimized by selecting impurities such that the second impurity has a larger diffusion coefficient.

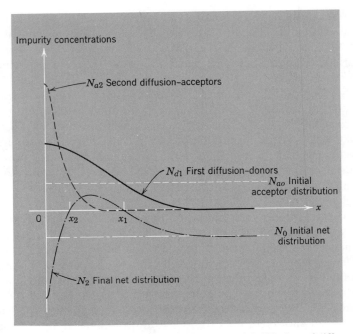

Figure 5.3   Multilayer structures can be produced by sequential diffusion of different impurities.

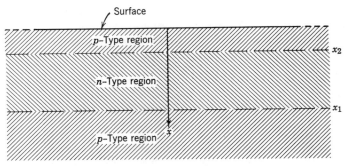

Figure 5.4   Structure that results from the two diffusions illustrated in Fig. 5.3.

denoted by x_1 and x_2, can be controlled by the choice of diffusants and the conditions of the diffusions. These depths may range in practice from a fraction of a micron ($1\,\mu = 10^{-6}$ meter) to about $10\,\mu$. The net impurity concentrations in the diffused layers, and thus the equilibrium carrier concentrations there, can be controlled in the same manner. Note, however, that these diffused layers are not uniform, but are graded in the x direction.

The practical limit on the number of sequential diffusions that can be employed to make multiple-layer structures is about three. This limit arises because the *total* (not net) impurity concentration near the surface becomes very large when compensation is carried out several times. Thus it may become impossible to compensate the material once again because the impurity concentration has reached the upper limit set by the solid solubility of the impurity in silicon. Usually other effects limit the number of sequential diffusions even before the solubility limit is reached. Specifically, the very large total concentration of impurities under the surface reduces the hole and electron diffusion coefficients (and thus mobilities) by providing many opportunities for scattering collisions, and reduces the excess-carrier lifetime by contaminating the crystalline structure. For these reasons, practical device structures are limited to not more than three diffused layers.

5.2.2 Oxide Layers and Area Selection

To make useful semiconductor devices, it is necessary to limit the spatial regions over which the conductivity type is changed by diffusion of compensating impurities. The key to control of the surface areas through which solid-state diffusion occurs lies in the use of silicon dioxide (SiO_2) as a mask that prevents the diffusion of impurities. Silicon dioxide is a form of glass. It serves as an electrical insulator and it shields the semiconductor beneath it from the impurities. That is, the diffusion coefficients of the impurities in the silicon dioxide are so small that no impurities penetrate the oxide layer.

A skin of silicon dioxide which is the order of a micron in thickness can be grown on a clean silicon surface simply by exposing the silicon to an oxidizing atmosphere (oxygen or oxygen and steam) at high temperatures. This skin of silicon dioxide prevents the diffusion of impurities into the semiconductor that it covers; the diffusion coefficients of impurities in the oxide are exceedingly small. Consequently, if it is desired to diffuse an impurity into a semiconductor over only a single prescribed area and not elsewhere, it is simply necessary to remove the oxide layer over the desired area, leaving it undisturbed elsewhere, so that impurities will enter the semiconductor only through the aperture or "window" created by oxide removal. This procedure is illustrated in Fig. 5.5. The oxide initially covers the entire surface, as shown in Fig. 5.5a. A hole or window is cut in the oxide layer by dissolving the oxide with hydrofluoric acid (HF) over the area where it is desired to make a *pn* junction (Fig. 5.5b). Then the semiconductor under the window is converted to *n*-type by diffusion of a donor impurity into the *p*-type semiconductor. After this diffusion the chip appears as shown in Fig. 5.5c. Impurities have compensated the semiconductor under the window, thus producing an *n*-type region, but have not penetrated into the material that is covered by the oxide layer. There is, of course, some lateral or side diffusion of the impurities under the edge of the oxide as well as down into the semiconductor.

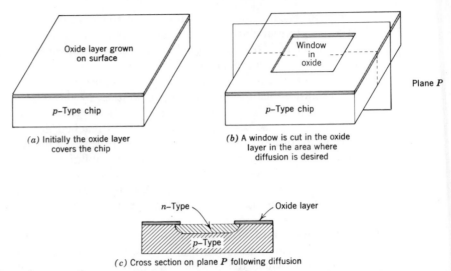

(a) Initially the oxide layer covers the chip

(b) A window is cut in the oxide layer in the area where diffusion is desired

(c) Cross section on plane *P* following diffusion

Figure 5.5   Silicon dioxide can be used as a mask to limit the diffusion of impurities to selected areas. Depths are not to scale.

Consequently, the place at which the space-charge-layer comes to the surface of the chip is *under* the oxide layer, and the edge of the space-charge-layer is never exposed to external contaminants. The fact that the space-charge-layer is not exposed to contamination because of the oxide-layer shield that is present even before the junction is formed is of considerable practical importance, and is one of the principal features of the planar-diffused process.

The sketches in Fig. 5.5 are not to scale. In practice, difficulty in handling small chips sets the minimum size of the semiconductor chip at about 0.5 mm by 0.5 mm by about 0.1 mm (100 μ) in thickness. By comparison, the oxide layer is seldom more than a micron thick, and the depth of the diffused layer is seldom more than a few microns.

Since the oxide layer can easily be regrown following a diffusion, it is possible to produce more complex structures by a sequence of window-cutting, impurity-diffusion operations. For example, the structure that resulted from the operations shown in Fig. 5.5 can be made into a three-layer, two-junction structure by following the sequence of events illustrated in Fig. 5.6.

The oxide layer serves a second purpose apart from its usefulness as a means of limiting the area of diffusions. Since it is impervious to most contaminants that might influence the characteristics of a semiconductor or cause those characteristics to change gradually in time, the oxide layer serves as a protection for the semiconductor surface after fabrication is completed. The oxide layer is said to *passivate* the semiconductor surface.

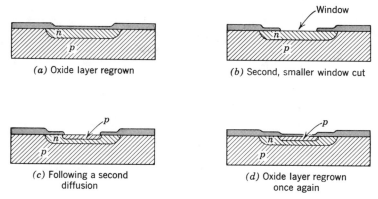

(a) Oxide layer regrown

(b) Second, smaller window cut

(c) Following a second
diffusion

(d) Oxide layer regrown
once again

Figure 5.6   Development of a three-layer structure from the structure shown in Fig. 5.5c.

For this reason the oxide layer is regrown following each diffusion so that the semiconductor surface is completely covered by a layer of glass, as shown in Fig. 5.6d.[4]

The areas in which the oxide layer is to be removed by dissolving it in acid are defined by a masking technique that uses photographic methods. These methods are based on a photosensitive liquid known as a *photoresist*. The photoresist is first spread uniformly across the surface of the oxide layer, as shown in Fig. 5.7a and allowed to dry. This film is then exposed to ultraviolet light through a photographic mask that permits the light to fall only on those areas in which the oxide layer is to be preserved. The exposure of the photoresist causes the areas that are illuminated to polymerize or to change structure, as shown in Fig. 5.7b, while the film that covers the darkened areas remains unchanged.

The unexposed film is next washed away from the surface of the chip, leaving a solid film of photoresist in the areas that were exposed, as shown in Fig. 5.7c. When the chip is etched in hydrofluoric acid, the oxide layer is removed in the unprotected areas, but is unaffected under the photoresist. Finally, the hardened photoresist is removed with an organic solvent, leaving only the oxide layer with windows in the areas through which it is desired to diffuse impurities into the semiconductor, as shown in Fig. 5.7d. If carefully controlled, these photographic techniques permit windows to be opened in the oxide in which the narrowest dimension is of the order of a few microns.[5]

---

[4] In fact, the oxide layer can be regrown at the same time that the diffusion is carried out by introducing oxygen into the furnace.

[5] The photographic mashing technique we have described is known as a *negative photoresist* method because the resulting pattern in the oxide layer is the negative of that in the photographic film. *Positive photoresist* methods are also used in device fabrication.

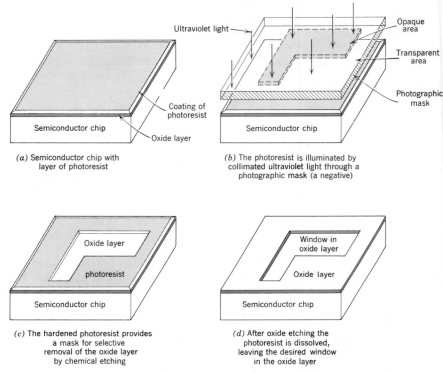

(a) Semiconductor chip with layer of photoresist

(b) The photoresist is illuminated by collimated ultraviolet light through a photographic mask (a negative)

(c) The hardened photoresist provides a mask for selective removal of the oxide layer by chemical etching

(d) After oxide etching the photoresist is dissolved, leaving the desired window in the oxide layer

Figure 5.7   The photoresist technique can be used to create patterns of apertures in the oxide layer.

5.2.3   Metallic Contacts

We have seen that the techniques of photoresist masking, oxide-layer passivation of a semiconductor surface, and solid-state diffusion can be used to create multiple-layer junction structures in a semiconductor chip that was originally homogeneous. All that remains in the fabrication of a useful semiconductor device, such as a diode, is the application of metallic contacts to the regions of interest.

Once again photographic and oxide-layer masking techniques provide a solution. Contacts can be fabricated by opening windows in the oxide layer through which a metal can be evaporated onto the semiconductor surface. Metals such as gold and aluminum provide ohmic contacts when these metals are evaporated onto clean silicon surfaces.

This technique of contact fabrication is illustrated in Fig. 5.8, in which the two-layer structure of Fig. 5.6a is used as an example. First, apertures are cut in the oxide layer over each of the semiconductor regions, as shown in Fig. 5.8a. Then a metal such as aluminum is evaporated over the *entire* surface of the chip, as shown in Fig. 5.8b. The evaporation is done in a vacuum at

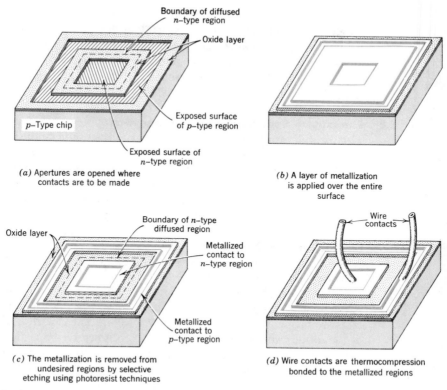

(a) Apertures are opened where contacts are to be made

Boundary of diffused n–type region

Oxide layer

p–Type chip

Exposed surface of p–type region

Exposed surface of n–type region

(b) A layer of metallization is applied over the entire surface

(c) The metallization is removed from undesired regions by selective etching using photoresist techniques

Oxide layer

Boundary of n–type diffused region

Metallized contact to n–type region

Metallized contact to p–type region

(d) Wire contacts are thermocompression bonded to the metallized regions

Wire contacts

Figure 5.8   Selective metallization is used to make metal-semiconductor contacts.

relatively low temperatures. Next, photographic techniques exactly analogous to those described in the preceding section are used to cover the regions in which the metallization is to be retained with a polymerized layer of photoresist. Then an acid that attacks the aluminum without attacking the oxide (hydrochloric and phosphoric acids meet these requirements) is used to etch away the aluminum metallization in all areas unprotected by photoresist. When the photoresist is removed by dissolving it with an organic solvent, a pattern of metallization remains, as shown in Fig. 5.8c. Each of the areas of metallization makes contact through the hole in the oxide layer with a region of the semiconductor. Finally, small wires (commonly of gold 10 to 20 μ in diameter) are "thermocompression bonded" to the metallized regions by intense pressure at a moderately high temperature, as shown in Fig. 5.8d. Alternatively, small aluminum wires can be fastened to the metallization by ultrasonic bonding techniques. These wires provide terminals for the semiconductor device. They are usually bonded to heavier wires, which protrude through the *header* on which the chip is finally mounted.

When contacts must be made to several regions of a semiconductor chip, they are all made simultaneously, as described above. Of course, the same metallization techniques can be used to connect one region of a chip to another region of the same chip simply by bridging the regions with a layer of metallization. The oxide layer insulates the bridge from the intervening regions.

5.3   Elementary Semiconductor Components

The techniques of silicon diffusion semiconductor technology can be used to make a variety of electronic components. We now illustrate the principal structural features of several of these components, without saying more about the manner in which they are made. In every case, these devices can be fabricated by sequential application of the methods of area control, diffusion, passivation, and metallization already described.

5.3.1   Semiconductor Diodes

A diode requires only a single *pn* junction and is easily fabricated by silicon diffusion technology. The completed structure may have the form shown in Fig. 5.9*a*, in which one contact is provided by the header to which the chip is bonded, or it may have the structure shown in Fig. 5.9*b*, in which both contacts are brought to the top surface of the chip. The electrical characteristics of the diode can be controlled by proper choice of the critical parameters that determine its structure. The junction area, the impurity profile, and the impurity concentrations in the two regions govern its electrical characteristics.

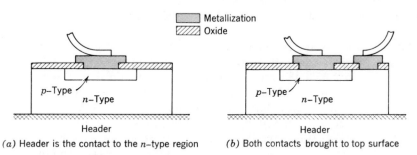

(*a*) Header is the contact to the *n*-type region   (*b*) Both contacts brought to top surface

Figure 5.9   Diffused semiconductor diodes.

The diffused diode structure shown in Fig. 5.9 obviously differs in its details from the somewhat idealized model introduced in Section 4.3 and shown in Fig. 4.10. Specifically, it does not have the region of negligible recombination characteristic of the thin-base diode. Also, it does not have an abrupt junction; rather, the doping is graded at the junction plane. Nevertheless, it preserves the essential features of the idealized structure, and its physical behavior can be analyzed in the same manner that was employed in

Chapter 4. More precisely, the diffused diode has the following characteristics in common with the idealized structure:

1. The junction is essentially planar. The dimensions of the junction parallel to the surface are 10 to 1000 times as large as the junction depth. Consequently, the curved ends of the junction (where it comes to the surface; see Fig. 5.5) can be neglected.

2. The flow of injected carriers is essentially one-dimensional. The diffusion length of excess carriers in silicon is usually in the range from 5 to 20 μ. This distance, which governs the spatial distribution of excess carriers, is usually small compared with the dimensions of the junction parallel to the junction plane. Thus the excess-carrier distribution can be regarded for most purposes as one-dimensional, with the single coordinate normal to the junction plane.

The current-voltage characteristics of diffused silicon diodes obey the idealized *pn* junction diode law (Eq. 4.20a) over a considerable range of modest *forward* voltages. Deviations occur for very small forward- and reverse-bias voltages, where carrier generation and recombination in the space-charge layer cannot be neglected, and for very large forward-bias voltages, where voltage drops in the neutral regions (particularly in the relatively thick substrate) cannot be neglected. In many cases, the neutral-region drops that accompany large forward bias and large forward currents can be modeled in terms of a resistance that is placed in series with the idealized diode model (see Eq. 4.42 and Fig. 4.20).

The effects of carrier generation and recombination in the space-charge layer show up as a reverse current which is considerably larger than the value predicted by the idealized model, and which fails to saturate as the reverse-bias voltage is increased; that is, the reverse current increases with increasing reverse voltage instead of being independent of voltage, as required by Eq. 4.20a. The modeling of these deviations requires a more detailed understanding of generation-recombination mechanisms than we have developed in this book, and we are thus unable to extend our diode model to include them.[6]

5.3.2 Capacitors

As we have seen in Section 4.4.1, a reverse-biased semiconductor diode has charge stores in the space-charge layer that depend (nonlinearly) on the reverse-bias voltage. For relatively small voltage changes, the charge-voltage relationship can be linearized, and the associated current-voltage relationship can be modeled by a capacitance—the incremental space-charge-layer capacitance. Thus any *pn* junction can be used as a capacitor if it is operated with a dc reverse voltage and if the incremental voltage swing superimposed on this dc voltage is small enough.

[6] See Reference 5.1.

Either of the *pn* junction structures shown in Fig. 5.9 can be used as a semiconductor capacitance. The capacitance depends on the junction area (see Eq. 4.39) and on the impurity profile at the junction, as well as on the bias voltage. Values in the range from 100 to 1000 pf/mm^2 can readily be obtained.

Junction capacitors have several disadvantages as circuit components:

1. Their values are rather limited; capacitance values in the hundredth microfarad range cannot be obtained because of limits on junction area.

2. These capacitors are "leaky" because of the saturation current of the reverse-biased diode. The strong temperature dependence of this current can be awkward in circuit applications.

3. The capacitors are polarized and voltage-dependent. The diode must not be allowed to become forward-biased, and the voltage swing must be limited if the operation is to be reasonably linear.

In spite of these disadvantages, junction capacitors are used in semiconductor circuits because they can be fabricated by the same steps and techniques that are used in making diodes (and, as we shall see later, active devices such as transistors). For some applications, the "disadvantages" listed above can be turned to advantage. For example, the voltage dependence of the capacitance forms the basis of operation of a class of semiconductor devices known as *varactors* (for *va*riable re*actors*).

5.3.3   Resistors

The structure of a semiconductor resistor is shown in Fig. 5.10, in which a diffused *p*-type layer is contacted at *both* ends to form a resistive path. The resistance between the metallized contacts at the ends of the path depends on the shape and doping of the *p*-type region or *channel*. Clearly, for a given impurity distribution long, thin, and shallow channels produce larger resistance values than do short, wide, and deep channels. In order for this structure

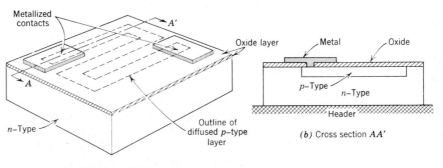

(a) A diffused layer forms
the resistive path

(b) Cross section AA'

Figure 5.10   Diffused semiconductor resistor.

to function as a resistor at all, the *pn* junction that delineates the *p*-type channel from the *n*-type substrate must be reverse-biased. This condition is met if the substrate is positive with respect to the potentials at both ends of the channel.

Diffused resistors of this type can be made with resistance values in the range from a few ohms to about 2×10^4 ohms. It is generally not possible to obtain larger resistance values in silicon structures because of the technological limits placed on resistivities and on length-to-area ratios of the diffused channels.

Diffused resistors have several disadvantages which must be kept in mind when they are used in circuits:

1. Their precision is limited severely by tolerances in the masking and diffusion technology. Although it is seldom possible to specify the value of a diffused resistor with a precision better than $\pm 20\%$, several resistors made at the same time on the same substrate usually have *relative* values that fall within $\pm 2\%$ tolerances.

2. Diffused resistors have rather large temperature coefficients of resistivity (from about 0.02 to 0.2%/°C). These coefficients, which arise from the temperature dependence of the carrier mobilities, are much larger than the temperature coefficients of more conventional carbon or metal resistors. The impact of this temperature dependence on circuit design can often be eased by recognizing that the relative values of several resistors made on the same substrate track reasonably well as the temperature changes because temperature gradients in the substrate are small (as a consequence of its extremely small size and relatively high thermal conductivity).

3. There is considerable distributed capacitance between the resistive channel and the substrate. This capacitance results from the space-charge layer of the reverse-biased *pn* junction which isolates the channel from the substrate.

5.4 Integrated Circuits

We have seen that planar diffused technology permits the fabrication of diodes, capacitors, and resistors in small chips of silicon that were originally homogeneous. Furthermore, the same techniques are used in making all three classes of components. We shall see in Chapters 7 and 9 that the same techniques can also be employed to fabricate transistors, which are active devices. Thus all the circuit components necessary to assemble many electronic circuits can be made *simultaneously, using a single set of fabrication techniques.*[7] Consequently, it is possible to make interconnected assemblies

---

[7] No satisfactory method for making an inductor using planar diffused technology has been found. The difficulty here is that it has not been possible to incorporate highly-permeable magnetic materials, which store magnetic energy with high density, into a silicon substrate. For this reason, circuit designers who wish to make use of diffused components go to extremes to avoid using inductors in their designs.

of many components on a single chip of silicon. Such assemblies of components are called *integrated circuits.*

5.4.1   A Circuit Example

To illustrate the structure and fabrication of a simple integrated circuit, we consider the network shown in Fig. 5.11, which contains three junction diodes, a resistor, and a capacitor.

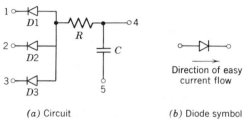

(a) Circuit   (b) Diode symbol

Figure 5.11   A simple diode network that can be made in integrated form.

In drawing this circuit, we have introduced the standard circuit symbol for a diode. By convention, the "arrow" contained in the symbol points in the direction of easy current flow, that is, from the *p*-type region to the *n*-type region. Thus the diodes in Fig. 5.11 have their *p*-type regions connected together.

The structure of an integrated form of this circuit is shown at several steps in its fabrication in Fig. 5.12. This circuit is made, for the purposes of our example, on a substrate of *n*-type material. As a first step, acceptor diffusion is used to create a *p*-type layer uniformly across the substrate, as shown in Fig. 5.12a. This diffused layer may penetrate 5 to 10 μ into the substrate.

Next a deeper donor diffusion is used to create three "islands" of *p*-type material by diffusing donors right through the *p*-type layer to the substrate, as shown in Figs. 5.12b and c.[8] The donor impurities are diffused through the *p*-type layer around the perimeter of the semiconductor chip and between the islands. These islands form the regions into which the three diodes, the resistor, and the capacitor are subsequently diffused. Note that the islands of *p*-type material serve to isolate these components from each other, *if* the substrate is always held at a potential that is positive with respect to *all* of

---

[8] It is possible to make the structure shown in Figs. 5.12b and c with only *one* diffusion of acceptors into the *n*-type substrate; the mask cut into the oxide layer would, of course, be the complement of that employed in the donor diffusion shown. We have illustrated a two-step process for creation of the *p*-type islands because in practice the islands are made by diffusing substrate-type impurities through to the substrate. This method of processing isolated islands is known as isolation by *through diffusion.* However, the material from which the islands are "cut" is usually not diffused; instead, it is grown on the substrate by a technique known as *epitaxial growth.* See References 5.2 and 5.3.

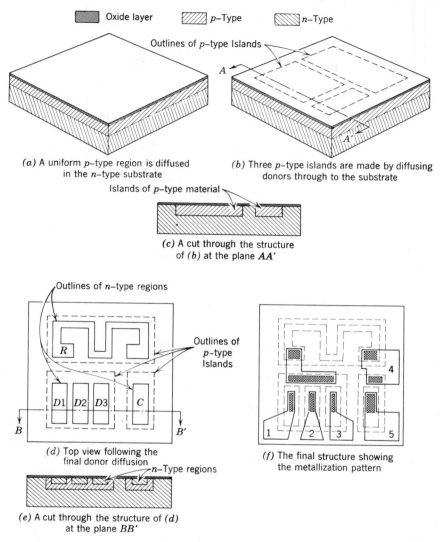

Oxide layer   *p*–Type   *n*–Type

Outlines of *p*-type Islands

A

A'

(*a*) A uniform *p*–type region is diffused in the *n*–type substrate

(*b*) Three *p*–type islands are made by diffusing donors through to the substrate

Islands of *p*-type material

(*c*) A cut through the structure of (*b*) at the plane *AA'*

Outlines of *n*–type regions

R

Outlines of *p*–type Islands

D1 D2 D3   C

B   *B'*

(*d*) Top view following the final donor diffusion

n–Type regions

(*e*) A cut through the structure of (*d*) at the plane *BB'*

4

1   2   3   5

(*f*) The final structure showing the metallization pattern

Figure 5.12   An integrated-circuit realization of the network of Fig. 5.11. Depths shown are not to scale.

the islands. For this polarity of substrate voltage the *pn* junctions that delineate the islands are always reverse-biased so that little current flows.

This method of isolating the several components of an integrated circuit is known as *junction isolation.* Of course, the degree of isolation provided is not perfect because of the leakage currents *and* the space-charge-layer capacitances of the isolating junctions. If the circuit designer pays attention to these defects in isolation in his design, adequate decoupling can, in most cases, be obtained.

The next step in the fabrication of the circuit of Fig. 5.12 involves a third (and final) diffusion in which donors are diffused into, but not through, the p-type islands to produce the desired components. The plan view of the structure after this diffusion is shown in Fig. 5.12d. A cross-sectional cut through the diodes and capacitor is shown in Fig. 5.12e.

The structure of the separate components now emerges. The diodes, which share a common p-type region, are in the lower left-hand corner. The n-type regions of the three diodes are denoted by D1, D2, and D3. The resistor is the n-type "maze" denoted by R. The capacitor is the pn junction in the lower right corner denoted by C.

All that remains is to form the pattern of metallization that makes the necessary metal-to-semiconductor contacts and provides the essential interconnections. A metallization pattern is shown in Fig. 5.12f. The metallized areas are indicated by the solid boundaries. The areas in which the oxide layer has been removed so that the metallization makes contact with the underlying semiconductor are shown by cross-hatching. The large, numbered metal pads provide the terminals of the integrated circuit. Fine wires can be bonded to these pads to make contact externally. The pad numbering corresponds to the terminal numbering on the circuit diagram of Fig. 5.11.

In drawing the metallization pattern of Fig. 5.12, we have arbitrarily chosen to connect the anode of the junction used as the capacitor to the resistor and to pad 4. Thus the circuit will function properly only if terminal 5 is positive with respect to terminal 4 (i.e., if $v_{54} > 0$). If this condition is not satisfied, the element in the lower right corner will behave not as a capacitor but as a forward-biased diode. If we had chosen to connect the cathode of the diode to the resistor, the opposite condition would apply (i.e., $v_{54} < 0$).

The integrated structure of Fig. 5.12 is by no means unique as a realization of the circuit of Fig. 5.11. Even if we restrict the structure to having an n-type substrate, other structures are possible. Nevertheless, this example serves to illustrate the concept of integrated circuits and shows how pn junctions can be used to isolate regions of the semiconductor, which then are made to perform different circuit functions. The example also emphasizes that an integrated circuit is seen, both from the point of view of structure and from the point of view of circuit operation, as a collection of discrete components that happen to be fabricated simultaneously in a monolithic structure.

5.4.2   Circuit Modeling and Parasitic Elements

In reality, the circuit diagram of Fig. 5.11 is not a complete representation of the electrical behavior of the integrated circuit shown in Fig. 5.12; it ignores the existence of the pn junctions that isolate the p-type islands shown in Fig. 5.12b. The circuit of Fig. 5.13 is more nearly correct in this regard, since it shows the junction diodes (a, b, and c) that connect these regions to the substrate, which is associated with terminal 6. This circuit also emphasizes that the capacitor C is provided by a diode (d) which has a leakage current, and shows the diode (e) which isolates the resistive channel from its p-type island. The latter coupling is, of course, distributed over the whole length of the resistive channel, so that its representation by a lumped diode is, at best, approximate.

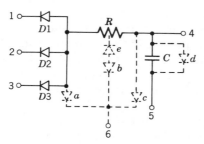

Figure 5.13 A more complete circuit diagram for the integrated circuit of Fig. 5.12.

The circuit of Fig. 5.13 emphasizes that the isolation junctions indeed isolate the components if the substrate (terminal 6) is at a potential that is more positive than any potential in the intended circuit. If this condition is met, the isolation junctions contribute only leakage currents and capacitive couplings to the system.

If the electrical conditions in a circuit that is to be fabricated in integrated-circuit form are such that the parasitic elements introduced by the isolating pn junctions cannot be tolerated, better methods of isolation are possible. For example, it is possible to develop a monolithic silicon structure in which islands of semiconductor are isolated by shells of silicon dioxide, which provides much better isolation, for both dc and ac, than does a reverse-biased junction.[9] This method, called *dielectric isolation*, requires processing on both sides of a chip, however, and is thus considerably more expensive than junction isolation. When both sides of the chip must be processed, it is necessary to measure and control chip thickness carefully, and to ensure that the opposite masking operations are in satisfactory registration; these issues increase the cost of dielectric-isolation processes.

5.4.3 Multiple-Chip Processing

The real impact of the diffused planar technology and of the integrated-circuit concept grows out of the fact that the circuits, which are extremely small, can be fabricated in large batches using only the techniques we have described. For example, the simple integrated circuit of Fig. 5.12 might have dimensions of 0.5 mm by 0.5 mm (20 mils by 20 mils) and might be built on a substrate

[9] See References 5.2 and 5.3.

0.1 mm in thickness (4 mils). Thus a circular wafer of homogeneous silicon 3 cm in diameter and 0.1-mm thick has sufficient surface area for about 2800 integrated circuits of the size shown in Fig. 5.12. Furthermore, *all* of these circuits can be fabricated simultaneously merely by making photographic masks in which the detailed patterns used to make the circuit of Fig. 5.12 are repeated in a regular two-dimensional array large enough to cover the entire wafer. All of the individual circuits would thus receive the same treatment, as the wafer is carried through the various steps of etching, oxide growth, diffusion, and metallization. Only after all these steps are complete, that is, after each of the roughly 2800 circuits is finished, would the wafer be scribed with a diamond-cutting tool and broken into separate individual integrated circuits. The circuits would then be tested electrically, bonded to headers, wired to terminals as described in Section 5.2.3, and encapsulated.

The mass production of the integrated circuits is illustrated by the photographs of Fig. 5.14. The photomicrograph of Fig. 5.14*a* shows a single integrated rf amplifier which contains five transistors and two resistors. The area occupied by this amplifier is a square 0.5 mm (20 mils) on each edge. Fig. 5.14*b* shows a portion of the silicon wafer that contains 9 such amplifiers. The silicon wafer has a diameter of about 3 cm. Consequently, approximately 2800 of these circuits are processed simultaneously on a single chip.

5.4.4 Integrated Circuits in Electronics

Integrated circuits obviously have several important advantages over circuits built of components that are physically discrete. Size is one advantage. An integrated circuit containing the equivalent of 100 to 200 discrete components can be placed in a package not much larger than one containing a transistor alone. Cost is also an advantage. An integrated circuit can be sold for less than the cost of an equivalent assembly of discrete components. Instead of handling, mounting, and wiring dozens or hundreds of discrete components, one handles only a single small chip of semiconductor or a single package. Also, integrated circuits are more reliable than assemblies of discrete components. This reliability arises largely because many fewer interconnections are required, and soldered or welded interconnections are a major source of unreliability in electronic equipment.

There are, of course, some associated disadvantages. The limited repertoire of component types and values puts some constraints on the circuit designer. Also, it is obviously not economic to use integrated-circuit technology to build a few, or even a few thousand, replicas of a single circuit; the costs involved in making photographic masks that would be used to process only one wafer would be prohibitive. Nevertheless, these disadvantages are so far overshadowed by the advantages of cost, size, and reliability that for many applications of electronic circuits, semiconductor integrated circuits dominate the field.

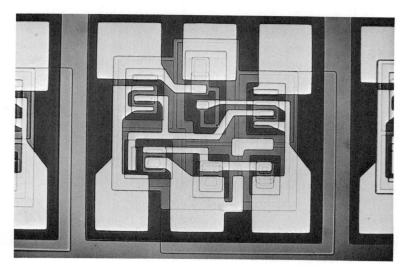

(a) Single circuit. See Plate 1.

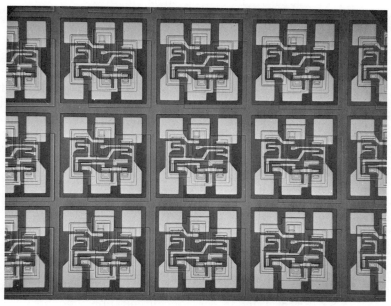

(b) Larger portion of the wafer showing 9 circuits. See Plate 2.

Figure 5.14 Many identical integrated circuits are fabricated simultaneously on a single wafer of silicon.

The integrated-circuit concept blurs greatly the dividing line between a device and its circuit applications. Thus it is no longer possible to separate rigidly the function of electronic circuit design from an understanding of the structure, physical operation, and modeling of electronic components. Even though circuit considerations are related closely to structural and physical considerations in integrated circuits, these circuits are regarded, from an analytical point of view, as collections of discrete components, some of which represent parasitic effects. Thus the circuits can be studied as lumped systems, and it is not necessary to analyze them as distributed systems.

REFERENCES

5.1   A. K. Jonscher, *Principles of Semiconductor Device Operation*, Wiley, New York, 1960.

5.2   D. L. Lynn, C. S. Meyer, and D. J. Hamilton, *Analysis and Design of Integrated Circuits* (Motorola Semiconductors, Inc.), McGraw-Hill, New York, 1967.

5.3   H. R. Camenzind, *Circuit Design for Integrated Electronics*, Addison-Wesley, Reading, Mass., 1968.

PROBLEMS

P5.1   The distribution of the added impurities that results from solid-state diffusion is governed by a partial-differential equation known as the *diffusion equation*. For diffusion in one-dimensional situations it is

$$D\frac{\partial^2 N}{\partial x^2} - \frac{\partial N}{\partial t} = 0 \tag{5.1}$$

where N denotes the concentration of the added impurity and D denotes the diffusion coefficient. The solution of this equation depends on the boundary conditions. For *constant-source* diffusion, illustrated in Fig. 5.1, the solution of the diffusion equation, assuming D constant, is

$$N(x, t) = N_s \, erfc\left(\frac{x}{2\sqrt{Dt}}\right) \tag{5.2}$$

where N_s is the fixed surface concentration (at $x = 0$) and *erfc* denotes the *complementary error function*, which has the form shown by the solid curve in Fig. 5.15.

(a) Sketch $N(x, t)/N_s$ versus x for three fixed times: t_1, $4t_1$, and $9t_1$. Assume that $\sqrt{Dt_1} = 5\,\mu$.

Phosphorus impurities are introduced into p-type silicon by a constant-source diffusion. The specimen has a uniform acceptor concentration of 5×10^{15} cm^{-3} and the surface concentration of donors during the diffusion is 10^{19} cm^{-3}. The diffusion is carried out at a temperature of 1100°C at which the diffusion coefficient D of the phosphorus in silicon is approximately 5×10^{-13} cm^2/sec.

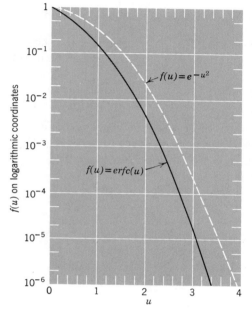

$f(u) = e^{-u^2}$

$f(u) = erfc(u)$

Figure 5.15 The complementary error function and the Gaussian function arise in solid-state diffusion.

(b) For how long should diffusion be continued under these conditions if the junction plane is to lie $5\,\mu$ under the surface?

(c) If the diffusion time is 15 hours, how far under the surface is the junction?

Answers. (b) 5.5 hours; (c) 8.2 μ.

P5.2 For *limited-source diffusion*, illustrated in Fig. 5.2, the solution of the diffusion equation given by Eq. 5.1, again assuming D constant, is

$$N(x, t) = \frac{M}{\sqrt{\pi D t}} e^{-x^2/4Dt} \tag{5.3}$$

where M denotes the initial surface concentration, in *atoms per unit surface area* (*not* per unit volume). This impurity distribution is known as the Gaussian distribution. The form of the *exponential factor* is shown by the dashed curve in Fig. 5.15.

(a) Sketch $N(x, t)/M$ versus x for three fixed times t_1, $4t_1$ and $9t_1$. Assume that $\sqrt{Dt_1} = 5\,\mu$.

Boron impurities are introduced into n-type silicon by a limited-source diffusion. The specimen has a uniform donor concentration of 5×10^{15} cm^{-3}, and the initial layer of acceptor impurities has a surface concentration (M) of 10^{16} cm^{-2}. The diffusion is carried out at a temperature of 1150°C at which the diffusion coefficient D of the boron in silicon is approximately 10^{-12} cm^2/sec.

(b) For how long should diffusion be continued (i.e., how long should the temperature be maintained at 1150°C) if the junction plane is to lie 5 μ under the surface?

(c) If the diffusion time is 1 hour, how far under the surface is the junction?

Answers. (b) approximately 1.7 hours; (c) 3.8 μ.

P5.3 Consider a thin sheet of homogeneous conductive material of thickness w. The electrical resistivity of the material is ρ. Highly conducting metallic contacts are applied to the opposite faces of a rectangular section of this sheet, as shown in Fig. 5.16.

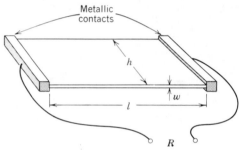

Figure 5.16 The resistance between the opposite edges of a rectangular section of a thin sheet is proportional to the sheet resistance.

(a) Derive an expression for the resistance R seen between the parallel contacts.

(b) Show that if the section is *square*, that is, if $l = h$, the resistance between the contacts is independent of the dimension of the square. The resulting resistance, which depends only on ρ and w, is called the *sheet resistance* of the conducting film or sheet. Although sheet resistance has the dimension of ohms, it is usually assigned the dimension of *ohms per square* and denoted by ohms/□.

(c) A conducting film has a sheet resistance of 1500 ohms/□. What is the resistance of a rectangular section such as that shown in Fig. 5.16 if $l = 20$ mils and $h = 2$ mils?

P5.4 This problem is concerned with the resistance of a structure in which flow is one-dimensional, but the resistivity varies with position. It is based on the rectangular block of conducting material shown in Fig. 5.17. Assume that the faces at $x = 0$ and at $x = W$ are equipotential surfaces and that a potential difference of V is applied between these faces so that current I flows in the bar.

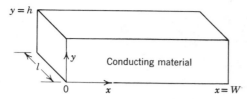

Figure 5.17 A resistor in which flow is one-dimensional.

(a) If the resistivity of the bar is uniform and has a value of ρ_a (i.e., if the bar is homogeneous), derive an expression for the resistance R_a between the end faces; that is, evaluate $R_a = V/I$.

(b) Assume now that the bar is uniform in the y direction but graded in the x direction. That is, assume that the resistivity ρ is independent of y but is a prescribed function of x, $\rho = \rho_b(x)$. Derive an expression for the resistance R_b between the end faces.

(c) Show that the equation derived in (a) can be used to express the resistance evaluated in (b) if ρ_a is replaced by an *average resistivity*:

$$\bar{\rho}_c = \frac{1}{W} \int_0^W \rho_b(x)\, dx$$

(d) Assume now that the bar is uniform in the x direction, but graded in the y direction. That is, assume that the resistivity ρ is independent of x, but is a prescribed function of y, $\rho = \rho_d(y)$. Derive an expression for the resistance R_c between the end faces.

(e) Show that the equation derived in (a) can be used to express the resistance evaluated in (d) if ρ_a is replaced by a different average resistivity:

$$\bar{\rho}_e = \frac{1}{\dfrac{1}{h} \int_0^h \dfrac{dy}{\rho_d(y)}}$$

These average resistivities are relevant to the evaluation of integrated-circuit parameters. The average defined in (c) applies when current flow is along the resistivity gradient, as in the case of evaluation of the series resistance contributed to the neutral regions of a diffused diode. On the other hand, the average defined in (e), which is simply the reciprocal of the average of the conductivity, applies when current flow is normal to the resistivity gradient, as in the case of a diffused resistor.

P5.5 This problem is concerned with the space-charge-layer capacitance of graded junctions such as those encountered in diffused structures. Consider the two profiles of *net* impurity concentration shown in Fig. 5.18; one is abrupt, one is graded. Assume that the space-charge layer is essentially depleted of mobile carriers, that is, use the *depletion approximation* in answering the questions below. Recall also:

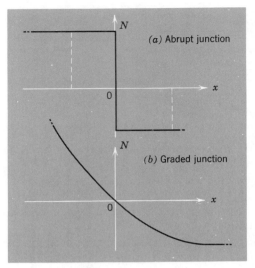

Figure 5.18 Two impurity profiles that produce different junction capacitances.

(1) The space-charge layer is a dipole layer (Eqs. 4.31).

(2) The total potential drop across the junction is proportional to the first moment of the charge distribution (Eq. 4.30).

(3) The space-charge-layer capacitance (in a depleted layer) is proportional to the reciprocal of the total space-charge-layer width (Eq. 4.39).

Assume that both junctions have the *same potential drop* and that the space-charge layer of the abrupt junction extends out to the dotted lines shown in Fig. 5.18a.

(a) Is the space-charge layer of the graded junction wider or narrower than that of the abrupt junction?

(b) Which junction has the smaller incremental capacitance?

(c) For which junction does the incremental capacitance have the stronger voltage dependence for voltage changes away from this operating point?

P5.6 Consider a diffused diode having the structure shown in Fig. 5.9a. Assume that the chip has dimensions of 0.2 mm by 0.2 mm by 0.1 mm (thickness) and that the junction covers 80% of the area of the chip. *Estimate* the series resistance introduced by the substrate if the substrate resistivity is 2 ohm-cm.

P5.7 A diffused diode can be modeled by an idealized *pn* junction diode (Eq. 4.20a) in series with a 100-ohm resistance contributed by the substrate. The idealized diode has a saturation current I_s of 1 μa.

(a) At what total forward voltage does the series resistance contribute 10% of the total voltage drop?

(b) What is the corresponding current?

P5.8 This problem is concerned with the integrated-circuit structure of Fig. 5.12. Note that the resistor, the capacitor, and the three diodes are made by the *same* donor diffusion into *p*-type islands that were produced at the same time. Thus all of these *pn* junctions have the same impurity profile and the same junction depths. Similarly, the isolation junctions have the same impurity profiles. The various regions have the following areas:

Overall chip size: 0.25 mm^2
p-type isolation islands
         diode 0.05 mm^2
         resistor 0.07 mm^2
         capacitor 0.02 mm^2
n-type diffused regions
         each diode 0.01 mm^2
         resistor channel 0.02 mm^2
         capacitor top plate 0.015 mm^2

The following measurements have been made on this chip:
(1) One of the diffused diodes is observed to have a reverse current of $0.2 \ \mu a$ and an incremental space-charge-layer capacitance of 8 pf at a reverse voltage of 3 volts.
(2) The leakage current between the *p*-type island that contains the diodes and the substrate is $0.5 \ \mu a$, and the corresponding capacitance is 5 pf when the reverse voltage is 5 volts.

Assuming that the bias voltages are the same, *estimate* the following parameter values:
(*a*) The capacitance and leakage current of the capacitor.
(*b*) The parasitic capacitance between the resistive channel of the resistor and the *substrate*. Note that the *p*-type island into which the resistor is diffused is an equipotential.
(*c*) The effective parasitic capacitance and leakage current between terminal 4 and the substrate. Assume that terminal 5 is open.
(*d*) The effective parasitic capacitance and leakage current between the interconnection of the diode anodes with the resistor and the substrate.

P5.9 The resistive element in the integrated circuit of Fig. 5.12 has an effective length of 0.6 mm and a depth to the space-charge layer of $1 \ \mu$. If the average conductance of the diffused *n*-type region is 10 mhos/cm, what is the sheet resistance? What must be the width of the channel if the resistor is to have a value of 2×10^4 ohms?

CHAPTER SIX

Diode Circuits and Models

6.1 Introduction

From the point of view of circuit analysis, the common thread that runs through essentially all applications of electronic circuit components is their *nonlinear* nature. We have already seen two examples of this—both the field-effect transistor employed as a vehicle in Chapter 1 and the junction diode studied in Chapter 4 have nonlinear volt-ampere characteristics—and we shall encounter others as we continue our study of active components. Each of these examples illustrates the fact that the study of electronic circuits differs from the study of circuits that contain only linear passive components principally in the techniques and points of view that are developed to deal with nonlinear components.

Semiconductor junction diodes, whose internal physical behavior we studied in detail in Chapter 4 and whose structure we illustrated in Chapter 5, represent the simplest class of two-terminal nonlinear circuit components. Although diodes are not active devices, and are incapable of functioning as control valves, their electrical characteristics are strongly nonlinear. Consequently, they serve as a representative vehicle for our study of the analysis of nonlinear circuits.

It should be evident from the discussion in Chapter 1 that we could base our analysis of nonlinear circuits solely on graphical techniques such as load-line constructions and transfer-characteristic curves. There are, however, several reasons for extending our analytical capabilities beyond graphical techniques. First, graphical methods become complicated and cumbersome in complex circuits, particularly those that contain more than one nonlinear component. Second, graphical methods are of limited usefulness in circuits that contain energy-storage components (inductors or capacitors) and in circuits for which dynamic aspects of the behavior of the nonlinear components become important. In such situations, the dependent variables may be governed as much by the rates of change of the independent variables as by their instantaneous values, and it becomes difficult to represent these functional relationships in graphical terms; the number of coordinates or dimensions required becomes too large for convenient graphical representation. Third, graphical methods make little use of the generalizations and points of view that are developed in the study of linear circuits. The simplifications afforded by such generalizations become vitally important in complex circuits.

Therefore, in this chapter we develop several alternative nongraphical models for junction diodes. These models are networklike in nature and are comprised, in part, of familiar linear circuit elements such as resistances and capacitances. Of course, it is necessary to extend our repertoire of idealized circuit elements to include nonlinear elements. We shall find that the new elements we define and the modeling techniques we describe are applicable to a broad range of nonlinear components; they are by no means restricted to junction diodes. Furthermore, we shall find that because these models are networklike and are comprised partially of familiar linear circuit elements, many nonlinear circuits can be studied by means of the tools of linear circuit theory. This reduction of nonlinear systems to linear terms is a simplification of enormous potential.

6.2   Piecewise-Linear Diode Models
6.2.1   Diode Characterization

Our analysis in Chapter 4 of the static electrical behavior of *pn* junction diodes can be summarized by Eq. 4.20a,

$$i = I_s(e^{qv/kT} - 1) \tag{6.1}$$

or by the characteristic curves of Fig. 4.20, which is repeated here as Fig. 6.1.

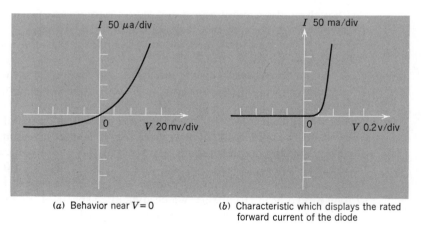

(a) Behavior near $V = 0$ (b) Characteristic which displays the rated forward current of the diode

Figure 6.1   Static junction diode *I-V* characteristics.

Even though the physical model we employed there was rather idealized, the results of that analysis are representative of the behavior of essentially all *pn* junction diodes. This behavior can be described in two complementary ways:

1. A junction diode permits large current to flow in one direction (the forward direction), but supports only a very small current in the opposite (reverse) direction. Whereas the forward current may easily be in the range of tens or hundreds of milliamperes, the reverse current is usually in the range of nanoamperes, that is, about six orders of magnitude smaller.

2. A junction diode permits a large voltage drop across its terminals of one polarity (reverse polarity), but allows only a very small drop of the opposite (forward) polarity. Whereas the reverse voltage may be as large as several hundred volts, the forward voltage is seldom more than a few tenths of a volt.

In view of these gross differences between forward and reverse behavior, an approximate characterization of a junction diode suffices for many applications. If a diode is used in a circuit in which the currents are large compared with the reverse current and the voltages are large compared with the forward voltage, the diode can be modeled by the following pair of equations:

$$v = 0 \qquad \text{for} \quad i > 0 \tag{6.2a}$$

$$i = 0 \qquad \text{for} \quad v < 0 \tag{6.2b}$$

This model neglects entirely both the forward voltage drop and the reverse current of the diode.

The diode model defined by Eqs. 6.2 is called an *ideal piecewise-linear diode*; the circuit symbol and the *I-V* characteristic of this idealized circuit element are shown in Fig. 6.2. This element is described as piecewise-linear

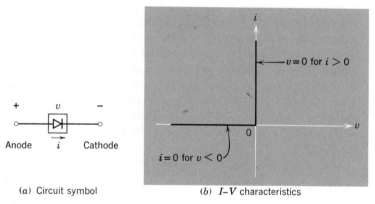

| (a) Circuit symbol | (b) *I-V* characteristics |

Figure 6.2 The ideal diode symbol and its *I-V* characteristics.

because its *I-V* characteristic is comprised of segments of straight lines. The piecewise-linear diode permits no voltage drop when the current is positive and no current when the voltage is negative. In other words, the ideal piecewise-linear diode reduces to a short circuit when the current is positive and to an open circuit when the voltage is negative. Note that the direction of easy current flow corresponds to the direction of the "arrow," which is part of the symbol. The diode terminals are called the *anode* and the *cathode*, as shown in Fig. 6.2.

6.2.2 Piecewise-Linear Circuit Analysis

Although the ideal piecewise-linear model is a fairly gross approximation to the characteristics of a *pn* junction diode, there are many situations in which the accuracy that it provides is sufficient. It is particularly useful as a "first-order" model, which can be employed when we wish to explore the general features of the performance of an unfamiliar diode circuit.

For our first example of the use of piecewise-linear diode models, we consider the circuit of Fig. 6.3. We regard the voltage v_1 as the input and the voltage v_2 as the output, and we wish to determine the relationship between v_2 and v_1. We assume that the diode is adequately modeled by an idealized piecewise-linear diode.

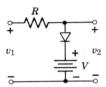

Figure 6.3 A diode limiter circuit.

The state of the diode is governed by the input voltage v_1. When v_1 is greater than the voltage V developed by the battery, the diode is forward-biased and can thus be approximated by a short circuit. On the other hand, when v_1 is less than V, the diode is reverse-biased and can be approximated by an open circuit. Thus the behavior of the *nonlinear* circuit of Fig. 6.3 can be determined by studying the two *linear* circuits shown in Fig. 6.4. The circuit of Fig. 6.4a applies when the diode is forward-biased, that is, when v_1 is greater than V, and the circuit of Fig. 6.4b applies when the diode is reverse-biased.

The analysis of the linear networks of Fig. 6.4 is trivial. From Fig. 6.4a we have

$$v_2 = V \qquad \text{for} \qquad v_1 > V \tag{6.3a}$$

and from Fig. 6.4b we have (since there is no current in R in this case)

$$v_2 = v_1 \qquad \text{for} \qquad v_1 < V \tag{6.3b}$$

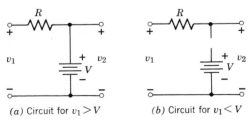

(a) Circuit for $v_1 > V$ (b) Circuit for $v_1 < V$

Figure 6.4 Linear models that are equivalent to the circuit of Fig. 6.3 for limited ranges of the input voltage.

Thus the complete transfer characteristic that relates v_2 to v_1 is comprised of two linear segments, as shown in Fig. 6.5. The point at $v_1 = v_2 = V$ where these straight lines intersect is called the *breakpoint*; it is the point at which the piecewise-linear diode changes state from *off* (no current) to *on* (no voltage drop).

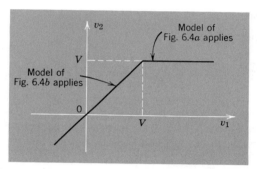

Figure 6.5   Piecewise-linear transfer characteristic for the circuit of Fig. 6.3.

The circuit of Fig. 6.3 is called a *diode limiter* because it limits the output voltage to a prescribed range, that is, to less than V for this example.

As a second example of the use of piecewise-linear analysis we consider the circuit shown in Fig. 6.6 and investigate the driving-point characteristic at the terminals aa'. That is, we wish to determine the dependence of i_a on v_a. Once again we assume that each of the junction diodes is modeled by a piecewise-linear diode.

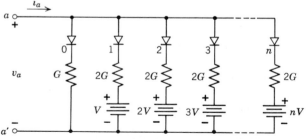

Figure 6.6   A diode circuit having a nonlinear driving-point characteristic.

As in the preceding example, the states of the diodes in this circuit are governed by the input voltage v_a. If v_a is negative, all of the diodes are reverse-biased and the current i_a is zero. If v_a is positive but less than V, only the diode labeled 0 is forward-biased and can thus be replaced by a short circuit.

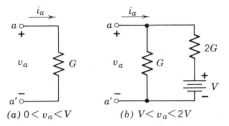

(a) $0 < v_a < V$ **(b)** $V < v_a < 2V$

Figure 6.7   Linear models for the circuit of Fig. 6.6.

Consequently, in this range of voltage the model of Fig. 6.7a applies, and we have

$$i_a = Gv_a \qquad \text{for} \quad 0 < v_a < V \tag{6.4a}$$

As v_a increases, more diodes change state from *off* to *on*. Thus if v_a is greater than V but less than $2V$, the model of Fig. 6.7b applies, and we have

$$i_a = Gv_a + 2G(v_a - V)$$
$$= 3Gv_a - 2GV \qquad \text{for} \quad V < v_a < 2V \tag{6.4b}$$

If v_a is greater than kV but less than $(k + 1)V$, the first $k + 1$ diodes are on, and we have

$$i_a = (2k + 1)Gv_a - k(k + 1)GV \qquad \text{for} \quad kV < v_a < (k + 1)V \tag{6.4c}$$

This piecewise-linear $I - V$ relationship is plotted in Fig. 6.8 for v_a up to $4V$. Clearly, the $I - V$ relationship of the circuit of Fig. 6.6 is an approximation in the first quadrant to the parabolic or square-law relationship

$$i_a = GV \left(\frac{v_a}{V} \right)^2 \tag{6.4d}$$

which is shown by the dashed line. Such a square-law relationship is useful if it is desired to generate a signal proportional to the *power* associated with another signal. Thus if v_a denotes the voltage across some *linear* load, the current i_a is proportional to the instantaneous power delivered to that load by v_a.

The degree to which the driving-point characteristic of this circuit approximates a square law is governed not only by the number of parallel branches used but also by the degree to which the junction diodes can be characterized as piecewise-linear. It is reasonable to represent the diodes by idealized piecewise-linear models if the voltage V is large compared with the forward drop of the junction diodes and if the current GV is large compared with the reverse current of the junction diodes.

The example just considered underlines the motivation for introducing a piecewise-linear model for diodes. By replacing the junction diodes in the

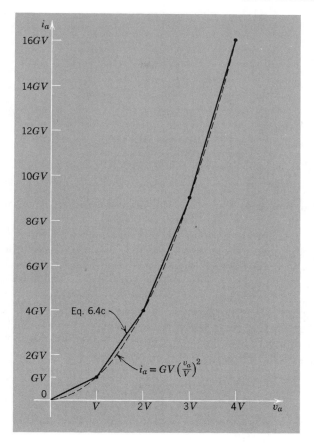

Figure 6.8   Driving-point characteristic for the circuit of Fig. 6.6.

circuit of Fig. 6.6 with idealized piecewise-linear diodes, we reduced the problem of analysis of the nonlinear network to the study of a set of *linear* networks, such as those shown in Fig. 6.7. These linear networks are analyzed with the conventional methods developed in linear circuit theory, and the resulting linear *I-V* relationships are pieced together at the diode breakpoints to generate an approximation to the complete nonlinear *I-V* characteristic. The amount of labor involved is dramatically smaller than if we had available only graphical or numerical analytical techniques.

As a final example of the analysis of simple piecewise-linear diode networks, we consider the two circuits shown in Fig. 6.9. The voltages v_1 through v_4 are regarded as the inputs in these circuits, and the voltage v_O is regarded as the output. The fixed negative voltage in Fig. 6.9a (-10 volts) is chosen to be less than the most negative of the input voltages. Similarly, the fixed positive voltage in Fig. 6.9b ($+10$ volts) is chosen to be greater than the most positive

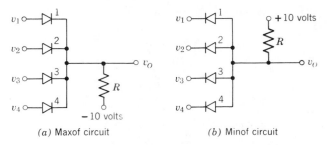

(a) Maxof circuit   (b) Minof circuit

Figure 6.9   Diode circuits that realize the Maxof and Minof functions.

of the input voltages. We model the junction diodes by piecewise-linear diodes.

Consider first the circuit of Fig. 6.9a. The diodes have their *n*-type regions or cathodes connected together. If the input voltages have different values, only the diode connected to the *largest* (the most, positive) voltage will conduct; the other diodes will be reverse-biased. Current flows through the forward-biased diode and the resistor *R* to the negative supply voltage (which is smaller than any of the input voltages). Clearly, the output voltage v_O is equal to the largest of the input voltages, to which it is connected by the single *on* diode. For this reason the circuit has been called the "Maxof circuit" and is described by the following functional notation:

$$v_O = \text{MAXOF}\,(v_1, v_2, v_3, v_4) \tag{6.5a}$$

This notation means simply that v_O is equal to the largest or maximum of the several input voltages.

The diodes in the circuit of Fig. 6.9b have their *p*-type regions or anodes connected together. Thus if the input voltages have different values, only the diode connected to the *smallest* (the most negative) input voltage will conduct; all the others will be *off*. The output voltage is thus equal to the smallest or the minimum of the several input voltages. This circuit is called the "Minof circuit" and is described by the function

$$v_O = \text{MINOF}\,(v_1, v_2, v_3, v_4) \tag{6.5b}$$

The circuits are obviously not required to have four inputs; any number can be used.

These two circuits form the basis of an important class of diode circuits known as *logic gates*, which are employed in binary systems used in digital computation. Logic gates are operated with input and output voltages that are quantized into two separate and narrow ranges of voltage. That is, the variables in these circuits cannot take on any range of values, but must have values in one or the other of two discrete ranges of voltage, as shown in Fig.

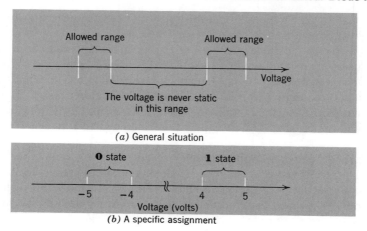

(a) General situation

(b) A specific assignment

Figure 6.10   Voltage levels in a binary system are quantized in two discrete ranges.

6.10a. The two allowed ranges correspond to the two states or values of the associated binary variable.

To illustrate the function of the Maxof and Minof circuits as gates, we shall arbitrarily require that the allowed ranges of the input voltages be from -5 to -4 volt, which we denote as the "**0** state," and from $+4$ to $+5$ volts, which we denote as the "**1** state."[1] These voltage assignments are illustrated in Fig. 6.10b.

The Maxof circuit of Fig. 6.9a will have its output voltage in the **0** state if all of the input voltages are in the **0** state. However, the output will be in the **1** state if *any one* of the input voltages is in the **1** state. Thus, for this assignment of states, the Maxof circuit is said to be an OR *gate*, since the output is in the **1** state if input 1 *or* input 2 *or* input 3 *or* input 4 is in the **1** state.

The Minof circuit has a **0**-state output if any one of the inputs is in the **0** state. The output is in the **1** state if and only if input 1 *and* input 2 *and* input 3 *and* input 4 are in the **1** state. Thus for the assignment of states used here the Minof circuit is said to be an AND *gate*.

A significant practical disadvantage of the diode logic circuits shown in Fig. 6.9 is the shift in voltage levels between input and output in each circuit. This shift is caused by the nonzero forward voltage drop of the diodes. Thus in the OR gate of Fig. 6.9a the upper output voltage level is about 0.6 volt (for a silicon diode) less than the upper input voltage level because of the drop in the *on* diode. Consequently, in a cascade of such diode logic gates the voltage levels tend to fall out of the ranges specified in Fig. 6.10b. We

---

[1] This arrangement, in which the most positive voltage range denotes the **1** state, is called *positive representation*. Assignment of the most negative range of voltages to the **1** state is called *negative representation*; its logical consequences are explored in Problem P6.4.

shall see in Chapter 23 that this problem of logic-level shift can be overcome by adding a transistor after each diode gate.

The simple diode gates of Fig. 6.9 are often fabricated in integrated form, using the techniques described in Chapter 5. Except for the output capacitor, the integrated circuit whose structure is shown in Fig. 5.12 has the same form as a three-input Minof circuit. Of course, it would be necessary to bring out a terminal from the metallization that interconnects the *p*-type diode region and the resistor *R* and to apply the fixed positive voltage at terminal 4.

6.2.3 More Accurate Diode Models

The idealized piecewise-linear diode model can be used as an element of more complex, more accurate models for junction diodes and other nonlinear devices. In fact, these nonlinear elements can be used as the basis for piecewise-linear approximations to essentially any nonlinear I–V characteristic, as suggested by the example of Fig. 6.6.

As an example of a more complex model we construct a diode model that characterizes the forward voltage drop of a *pn* junction diode with greater precision than the unadorned piecewise-linear diode of Fig. 6.2. Since the saturation current of a junction diode is usually four to eight orders of magnitude smaller than forward currents at which the diode may be operated, the exponential diode law causes the I–V characteristic to have an apparent threshold for forward conduction, as shown in Fig. 6.11. The forward

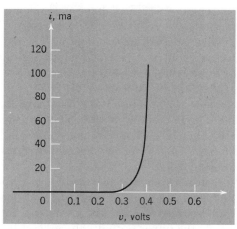

Figure 6.11 Illustration of the threshold voltage of a junction.

voltage must increase to several tenths of a volt before the current becomes perceptible. Above this threshold of conduction the forward current increases rapidly with voltage. Models that represent this threshold of conduction are shown in Figs. 6.12*a* and 6.12*b*. The threshold voltage V_O, which appears in

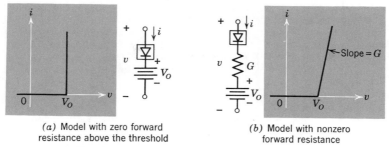

(a) Model with zero forward
resistance above the threshold

(b) Model with nonzero
forward resistance

Figure 6.12 Two circuit models that contain a threshold voltage.

these models, commonly lies in the range from 0.2 to 0.4 volt for germanium diodes and in the range from 0.5 to 0.7 volt for silicon diodes. This voltage commonly has a temperature coefficient in the range from -1 to -2 mv/°C (see Eq. 4.27). The conductance G depends upon the range of current over which the model applies. The slope of the exponential diode characteristic is, from Eq. 6.1,

$$\frac{di}{dv} = I_s e^{qv/kT}\left(\frac{q}{kT}\right) \tag{6.6a}$$

or, equivalently, for large forward currents,

$$\frac{di}{dv} \simeq \left(\frac{q}{kT}\right) i \tag{6.6b}$$

where i is the current at which the slope applies. If, for example, we are modeling the behavior of a junction diode at currents in the range of tens of milliamperes, the conductance in the model of Fig. 6.12b would be of the order of

$$G = \frac{q}{kT}(10 \text{ ma}) = 0.4 \text{ mho}$$

since $q/kT \simeq 0.04$ mho/ma at room temperature.

Before we continue, some comment on notation and circuit symbols is necessary. The diode symbol used in Figs. 6.3 and 6.6 is frequently employed to represent an idealized (exponential) *pn* junction diode or any semiconductor diode. To avoid this ambiguity we shall use the three different symbols shown in Fig. 6.13 to represent these three *I-V* characteristics. Notice that in all three cases the "arrowhead," which is part of the symbol, points in the direction of easy or forward current flow.

As an example of the use of more elaborate piecewise-linear diode models in circuit analysis, we consider the symmetrical limiter shown in Fig. 6.14.

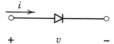

+ v −

(a) General symbol for any semiconductor diode—no
particular *V–I* characteristic implied

(b) Symbol reserved for the idealized exponential
pn junction diode. The saturation current is
denoted by I_s, which is part of the symbol

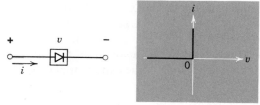

(c) Symbol used for the ideal piecewise–linear diode

Figure 6.13   Diode circuit symbols.

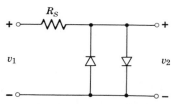

Figure 6.14   A symmetrical diode limiter.

We model the two diodes used in this circuit with the piecewise-linear model
of Fig. 6.12*b*. The network that results when the diodes in the circuit of Fig.
6.14 are replaced by this model is shown in Fig. 6.15. The analysis of this
circuit to determine the transfer characteristic v_2 versus v_1 hinges on the
observation that the states of the diodes are controlled directly by the output
voltage v_2. Specifically, both diodes do not conduct when v_2 is zero; both
are reverse-biased by V_O. A small nonzero value of v_2 decreases the magnitude
of the reverse bias on one diode while increasing it on the other. For example,
if v_2 is positive, but less than V_O, the magnitude of the reverse bias on diode 2
is reduced to $(V_O − v_2)$ while the magnitude of the reverse bias on diode 1 is
increased to $(V_O + v_2)$. When v_2 is negative, but less in magnitude than V_O,
the opposite situation holds. Clearly, when $|v_2|$ reaches V_O, one of the ideal

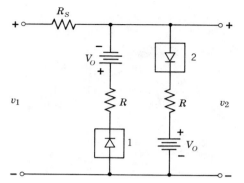

Figure 6.15   The circuit of Fig. 6.8*a* with the diodes replaced by piecewise-linear models.

diodes changes state and becomes conducting, that is, it changes state from *off* to *on*. Larger values of $|v_2|$ cause current to flow through that diode (and thus through R_S, which must supply the diode current) while increasing the magnitude of the reverse bias on the other diode.

We are thus able to identify three regions of operation of this circuit, all of which are defined in terms of the value of v_2:

Region 0, $-V_O < v_2 < V_O$. In this region both ideal diodes are reverse-biased (*off*) so that no current flows in R_S. The transfer relationship is

$$v_2 = v_1 \tag{6.7a}$$

Region +, $V_O \leqslant v_2$. Ideal diode 2 is conducting (*on*) in this region while diode 1 remains *off*. Superposition of the components of v_2 produced by V_O and by v_1 gives

$$v_2 = V_O\frac{R_S}{R_S + R} + v_1\frac{R}{R_S + R} \tag{6.7b}$$

Region −, $v_2 \leqslant -V_O$. The behavior in this region is similar to that in region + except that the roles of the diodes are interchanged, and both v_1 and v_2 have the opposite sign. Thus in this region

$$v_2 = -V_O\frac{R_S}{R_S + R} + v_1\frac{R}{R_S + R} \tag{6.7c}$$

The complete piecewise-linear transfer characteristic, which is defined in three segments by Eqs. 6.7, is sketched in Fig. 6.16. Note that for $|v_1|$ greater than V_O (i.e., in regions + and −), the transfer characteristic has the same slope as a simple voltage divider in which the resistance of the output element is R and the resistance of the input element is R_S. This equivalence follows from the fact that in these regions the network forms (except for V_O) a resistive voltage divider.

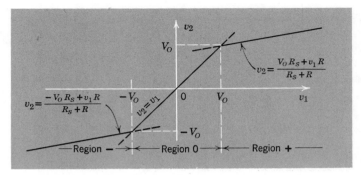

Figure 6.16   Piecewise-linear transfer characteristic for the circuit of Fig. 6.15.

If the resistance R_S is much larger than the diode forward resistance R, the transfer characteristic is nearly flat in regions $+$ and $-$. In other words, such a circuit would serve as a "hard" limiter for input voltages outside the range $\pm V_O$. This circuit could be used to protect a meter or other sensitive apparatus from unintentional overvoltages simply by inserting the limiter between the voltage source and the meter. As long as the input voltage is within the range $\pm V_O$, neither diode conducts and no limiting occurs. Of course, it is necessary to account for the voltage drop in R_S if the meter or other load draws appreciable current.

Most of the circuits that arise in the use of piecewise-linear models for nonlinear devices can be analyzed simply by inspection of the circuit. As in the examples we have considered, one seeks to identify the various states of the circuit, that is, the states of the idealized piecewise-linear diodes, and to determine the ranges of key variables that define these states. Of course, a few circuits will not yield easily to analytical methods based so casually on intuition. For these situations more formal systematic methods of analysis have been developed.[2]

6.3   Incremental Diode Models and Analysis

6.3.1   Incremental Models

All of the diode models discussed thus far preserve the gross nonlinear nature of the physical device and are therefore capable of representing a diode for both polarities of the terminal voltage. In some circuit situations we are interested only in modeling the characteristics of the device over a narrow range of currents and voltages. For example, we may seek a model for the diode characteristic of Fig. 6.17a that relates small changes in the current and voltage in the immediate neighborhood of the point whose coordinates are (V_D, I_D). If the diode current and voltage do not differ appreciably from the

---

[2] See Reference 6.3.

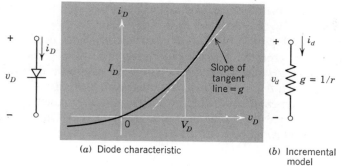

(a) Diode characteristic   (b) Incremental
                                                  model

Figure 6.17   A linear incremental model for the diode.

values at the dc *operating point*, we may write

$$v_D = V_D + v_d \qquad v_d \ll V_D \tag{6.8a}$$

and

$$i_D = I_D + i_d \qquad i_d \ll I_D \tag{6.8b}$$

where the *incremental variables* v_d and i_d, which describe the *deviations* of the total variables v_D and i_D from the operating point given by V_D and I_D, are *linearly related*. That is,

$$i_d = g v_d \tag{6.9a}$$

Here g denotes the *incremental conductance* of the diode at the operating point (V_D, I_D).[3] The graphical interpretation of this linear homogeneous relationship between the incremental variables is shown in Fig. 6.17a. The incremental conductance g is the slope of the *V-I* characteristic at the operating point.

$$g = \left.\frac{di_D}{dv_D}\right|_{v_D = V_D} \tag{6.9b}$$

Thus for small changes about an operating point, the nonlinear diode characteristic can be modeled by a resistance or conductance, which is chosen to match the slope of the *V-I* characteristic at the operating point. More precisely, the *incremental* diode current is proportional to the *incremental* diode voltage if the incremental variations are small enough; the constant of proportionality is the incremental conductance, which is equal to the

[3] The notation employed here is standard for semiconductor device description; see the comment in Chapter 1, page 24. Although this notation is cumbersome for a diode, it is introduced here because its consistent use will reduce confusion, particularly later when we are dealing with two-terminal-pair devices.

slope of the *V-I* characteristic at the operating point. A circuit model that embodies this relationship is shown in Fig. 6.17*b*.[4]

This development of a *linear incremental model* need not be tied to a graphical interpretation of the relationships between variables; the development can be based on the representation of a nonlinear algebraic relationship by means of a truncated Taylor's series, as in Section 1.4.1.

The incremental conductance of an idealized *pn* junction diode is related in a very simple way to the operating point current. Direct differentiation of the idealized *pn* junction diode equation (Eq. 6.1) yields

$$g = \frac{q}{kT}(I_D + I_s) \tag{6.10}$$

The incremental conductance is thus directly proportional to the dc operating-point current I_D for forward currents that are large compared to the saturation current. It approaches zero asymptotically as the reverse current approaches $-I_s$.

Two aspects of the incremental model for a nonlinear device deserve special emphasis. First, the parameters that characterize an incremental model (in this case, the incremental conductance or its reciprocal—the incremental resistance) depend, in general, on the operating point. Consequently, it is meaningless to specify an incremental model for a device without identifying the operating point at which it holds. Second, the incremental model cannot be used to relate either the operating-point variables (I_D and V_D) or the total variables (i_D and v_D).

In this section we have developed a linear incremental model for the junction diode from the *static V-I* relationship of the device. Therefore, the incremental model is resistive. As an alternative, we could approach the incremental model directly from the physical electronics of the diode. If this is done, and if we account for the currents required to change the internal charge distributions, we can obtain a model that contains energy-storage elements representing the effects of changing charge distributions.

If the diode operating point is in the region of forward voltage, the dynamics of the electrical behavior of the diode are dominated by the charge stores in the neutral regions. If the incremental variables change slowly enough, the effect of changes in the neutral-region charge stores can be approximated by adding a capacitance in parallel with the conductance of Fig. 6.17*b*.

If, on the other hand, the operating point is in the region of reverse voltages, the charge distributions in the neutral regions are essentially independent of the junction voltage and have a negligible effect on the incremental dynamic behavior of the diode. With a reverse voltage, the charge distribution in the space-charge layer dominates the dynamics of the diode. As we have seen in

---

[4] This discussion tacitly assumes that the incremental variables change slowly enough so that the static *V-I* relationship provides an adequate description of the relationship between the total variables v_D and i_D.

Section 4.4.1, currents associated with incremental changes in the space-charge-layer charge distributions can be modeled in terms of an incremental space-charge capacitance, given by Eq. 4.32a. This capacitance can be used alone as an approximate incremental model for a reverse-biased junction diode.

The fact that the parameters of the incremental diode model depend rather strongly on the operating point can be used in circuit applications in which an electrically-variable resistance or capacitance is required. For example, the dependence of the forward incremental conductance on dc current can be used to obtain a voltage divider whose attenuation is electrically-controlled (see Problem 6.7). Also, the dependence of the incremental space-charge capacitance on the reverse voltage can be used for electrical tuning of resonant circuits (see Problem 6.6).

6.3.2 Diode Gates

The sharp difference between the forward and reverse states of a diode makes this device useful as an electrically-controlled switch in signal-processing applications. An example of a circuit of this type is shown in Fig. 6.18a. During the intervals of time in which the gate control voltage v_G is positive, the diode is forward-biased through R_G. The output voltage v_O is equal to the forward drop of the diode, which is influenced only weakly by the signal voltage v_S. On the other hand, when the gate control voltage is negative, the diode is reverse-biased and conducts poorly. Consequently, for low frequencies at which the junction capacitance has negligible admittance, the signal voltage appears at the output terminals, attenuated by the factor $R_G/(R_G + R_S)$ and shifted by an amount $-VR_S/(R_S + R_G)$. The diode in this circuit functions as a *gate* in that it determines, in response to v_G, whether the signal voltage is coupled to the output terminals.

We can use incremental models to determine the signal component of the output voltage in each of the two states of the gate. When the control voltage v_G is positive, the diode, which is forward-biased, can be characterized for incremental components by a resistance of value r, which, in accordance with Eq. 6.10, is given by

$$r = \frac{kT}{qI_D} \tag{6.11a}$$

Here I_D denotes the dc diode current; it is approximately

$$I_D = \frac{V}{R_G} \tag{6.11b}$$

The incremental model of the circuit in this state is shown in Fig. 6.18c. Note that the voltage source that supplies the gate control voltage is replaced by a short circuit, because in this state this source develops a *fixed* voltage and thus has *zero* incremental component. This circuit can be used to compute

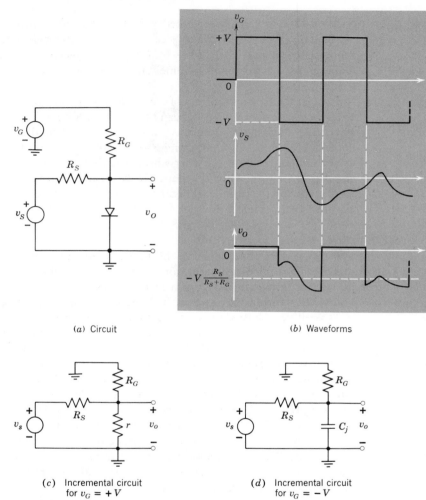

(a) Circuit   (b) Waveforms

(c) Incremental circuit
for $v_G = +V$

(d) Incremental circuit
for $v_G = -V$

Figure 6.18   A diode gate circuit.

the incremental component v_o of the output voltage v_O. Thus

$$v_o = v_s \frac{r \| R_G}{r \| R_G + R_S} \tag{6.12}$$

This voltage is very small because r is much less than R_S. The total output voltage is simply the superposition of this incremental component and the dc forward drop that corresponds to the current given by Eq. 6.11b.

When the control voltage is negative, the diode can be characterized for incremental components as a capacitance of value C_j, and the incremental model of Fig. 6.18d applies. In this case the total output voltage is the superposition of the incremental component determined from this incremental model and the dc component, which is simply $-VR_S/(R_S + R_G)$. For low frequencies the incremental component is approximately equal to v_s, and the output waveform is as shown in Fig. 6.18b.

The range of values of v_S for which the circuit functions as a gate is, of course, limited. If v_S has too large a positive value, it will cause the diode to be *on* when it should be *off*, thereby clipping off the positive extremes of the signal waveform. If v_S has too large a negative value, it will cause the diode to be *off* when it should be *on*, thereby permitting the negative extremes of the signal waveform to pass through the gate when the gate should be closed.

The simple gate circuit shown in Fig. 6.18 has the disadvantage that the output voltage is shifted from zero when the gate is open, the shift being proportional to the gate control voltage. This shift can be eliminated by using a balanced circuit, such as the one shown in Fig. 6.19. If the diodes are

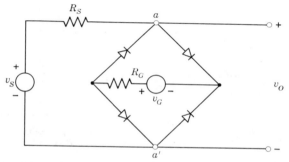

Figure 6.19 Use of four diodes in a balanced bridge.

identical, the gate control voltage v_G produces no voltage across the output terminals. When v_G is positive, all four diodes are forward-biased, so that the signal is effectively "shorted out" by the diode bridge and does not appear at the output terminals. On the other hand, when v_G is negative, all four diodes are reverse-biased (if v_S is limited appropriately) and v_S appears unattenuated at v_O.

We can use incremental models to investigate the linear signal-processing properties of this gate circuit.

We assume that the control voltage v_G takes on one of two values

$$v_G = \begin{cases} +V \\ \text{or} \\ -V \end{cases}$$

When v_G is positive, all four diodes are forward-biased. Since the diodes are assumed to be identical, the current established in each by v_G is approximately

$$I_D \simeq \frac{V}{2R_G} \qquad (6.13a)$$

This result is based on the assumption that V is much larger than the diode forward drop. If v_S is not too large, each diode can be characterized for incremental components by a resistance of value r, which is given by Eq. 6.11a. An incremental model of the circuit when v_G is positive appears in Fig. 6.20a. The symmetry of the bridge demands that the incremental current in R_G always be zero. Consequently, R_G can be removed, and the circuit can be simplified as shown in Fig. 6.20b. The incremental voltage transfer ratio is simply

$$\frac{v_o}{v_s} = \frac{r}{r + R_S} \qquad (6.13b)$$

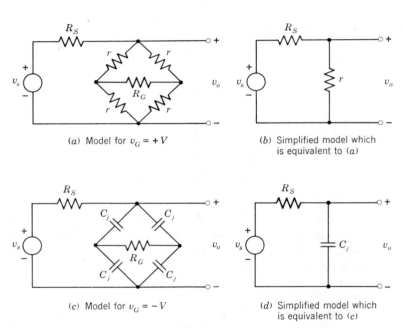

(a) Model for $v_G = +V$

(b) Simplified model which is equivalent to (a)

(c) Model for $v_G = -V$

(d) Simplified model which is equivalent to (c)

Figure 6.20   Incremental models for a balanced diode gate.

When v_G is negative, all four diodes are reverse-biased; the reverse voltage on each diode is $-V/2$. If we characterize the incremental behavior of the reverse-biased diodes by means of space-charge capacitances C_j, the incremental model of the circuit has the form shown in Fig. 6.20c. Again the incremental current in R_G is zero, so that the model can be simplified as shown in Fig. 6.20d. If the signal source voltage changes slowly, the voltage transfer ratio is approximately unity. Rapid changes in v_s produce some attenuation in v_o because the current required by C_j produces a drop in R_S.

This incremental analysis provides no information on the ranges of signal source voltages for which the gate remains open when $V_G = -V$ or remains closed when $V_G = +V$. The limits of operation can easily be investigated by evaluating the transfer characteristic from v_S to v_O in each state of the gate. Once again, piecewise-linear diode models can be used to characterize the nonlinear behavior of the diodes for the purposes of this analysis (see Problem P6.9).

6.4   Power Conversion Circuits*

There are many requirements in engineering systems for the conversion or *rectification* of alternating currents to direct currents. For example, most active electronic circuits require sources of dc power. Also, many electro-mechanical control systems use dc power to operate motors or other output transducers. In both cases the dc power can be obtained from the 60 Hz ac power lines by conversion of alternating current to direct current. Diodes, with their unidirectional behavior, can be used in this conversion process.

6.4.1   Rectifier Circuits

The simplest form of a practical power-conversion circuit is shown in Fig. 6.21a; it is called a *half-wave rectifier*. Its function with a sinusoidal input voltage is illustrated in Fig. 6.21b, where the junction diode is modeled by an ideal piecewise-linear diode. When the sinusoidal source voltage is positive,

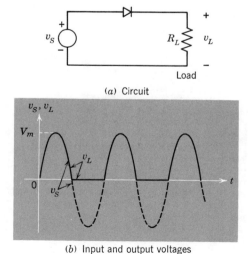

(a) Circuit

(b) Input and output voltages

Figure 6.21   A half-wave rectifier.

* This section can be omitted in an introductory study without loss of continuity.

the diode is *on* and the load voltage is equal to the source voltage. When the source voltage is negative, the diode is *off* and the load voltage is zero. Thus the load voltage follows the input voltage for one-half of the input cycle and is zero for the other half cycle. The dc component of the load voltage is simply the average value of the solid waveform in Fig. 6.21*b*. That is, the dc load voltage is

$$V_{dc} = \frac{V_m}{2\pi} \int_0^\pi \sin\theta \, d\theta$$

$$= \frac{V_m}{\pi} \qquad (6.14a)$$

where V_m is the peak value of the ac input voltage. The corresponding dc component of the load current is simply V_{dc}/R_L, where R_L is the load resistance. Thus the dc load current is

$$I_{dc} = \frac{V_m}{\pi R_L} \qquad (6.14b)$$

If the ac source has appreciable source resistance, our analysis of the half-wave rectifier must be modified to account for the voltage drop in that source resistance. A circuit that includes source resistance, and the corresponding waveforms are shown in Fig. 6.22. Once again we have modeled the diode

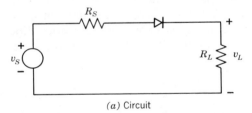

(*a*) Circuit

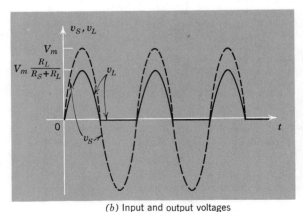

(*b*) Input and output voltages

Figure 6.22 Source resistance causes the output voltage waveform to be scaled down at all points in time.

with an ideal piecewise-linear diode in sketching the waveforms. The effect of the source resistance is to scale down the output voltage by the factor $R_L/(R_L + R_S)$. Consequently, the dc components of both the output voltage and the output current are scaled down from the values given in Eqs. 6.14 by the same factor.

When rectifier circuits are used to obtain relatively small dc voltages, it is necessary to employ a diode model that accounts for the forward voltage drop in the diode. Silicon junction diodes have a threshold voltage in the forward direction of about 0.5 to 0.7 volt. Thus it is necessary to account for this drop when the peak value of the ac voltage is less than about 10 volts. A model that accounts for the forward drop in this diode is shown in Fig. 6.23a; the diode is represented by an ideal piecewise-linear diode in series with a dc voltage source whose value, V_O, is the threshold voltage (see Section 6.2.3). The corresponding waveforms are shown in Fig. 6.23b. Since no current flows until v_S reaches V_O, the conduction interval is shortened somewhat. Of course, the peak output voltage is less than the peak input voltage by V_O. Since the output voltage is no longer comprised of half periods of a sine wave, the average given by Eq. 6.14b is no longer applicable (see Problem P6.10).

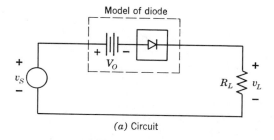

(a) Circuit

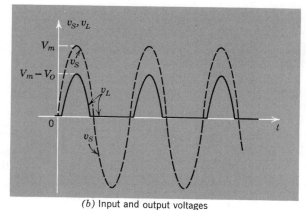

(b) Input and output voltages

Figure 6.23 The forward drop of the diode shortens the conduction interval and reduces the output voltage by a fixed amount.

The half-wave rectifier clearly yields an output voltage that has an appreciable ac component as well as the desired dc component. A slightly more complicated circuit, called a full-wave rectifier and shown in Fig. 6.24, doubles the dc component of the output voltage without increasing the peak-to-peak excursion of the ac component. The transformer in this circuit makes use of a center tap on the secondary to develop two sinusoidal voltages v_1 and v_2 that are equal in magnitude but 180° out of phase. That is

$$v_2(t) = -v_1(t)$$

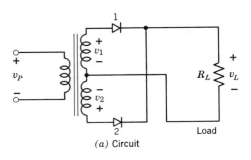

(a) Circuit

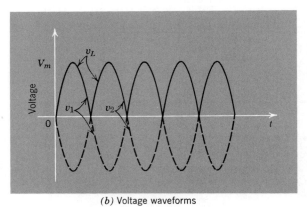

(b) Voltage waveforms

Figure 6.24   A full-wave rectifier that uses a transformer.

During the half cycle in which v_1 is positive, diode 1 conducts. If the diodes can be modeled adequately by ideal piecewise-linear diodes (as is usually the case), the output voltage v_L is equal to the input voltage during the half cycle in which v_1 is positive and diode 2 is *off*. During the other half cycle when v_1 is negative and v_2 is positive, diode 2 is *on* and the output follows v_2, as shown in Fig. 6.24b. The dc component of the load current of a full-wave rectifier is obviously twice that of a half-wave rectifier that operates with the same ac input voltage and the same load (assuming a 1:1:1 transformer).

That is, from Eq. 6.14b, we have

$$I_{dc} = \frac{2V_m}{\pi R_L} \tag{6.15}$$

This use of both phases of the input voltage can be achieved without a transformer if four diodes are used. The circuit, which is shown in Fig. 6.25, is called a *full-wave bridge rectifier*. When v_S is positive, diodes 1 and 2 are *on* and diodes 3 and 4 are *off*. Thus the upper terminal of the load is connected to the upper terminal of the source, and the load voltage follows the input voltage v_S. On the other hand, when v_S is negative, diodes 3 and 4 are *on* and diodes 1 and 2 are *off*; the upper terminal of the load is connected to the lower terminal of the source so that the load voltage follows $-v_S$.

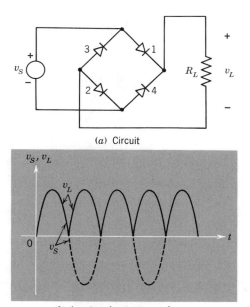

(a) Circuit

(b) Input and output waveforms

Figure 6.25   A full-wave bridge rectifier.

6.4.2 Ripple Filtering

As sources of dc power, all of the rectifier circuits we have considered are inadequate because the output or load voltage pulsates. In other words, the load voltage has a significant ac component in addition to the desired dc component. The waveforms of Figs. 6.21, 6.24, and 6.25, for which the diodes are ideal, show that the peak-to-peak value of the ac component of the output voltage is equal to the peak value of the ac input voltage.

In applications where pure direct current is required, it is necessary to modify the circuit so that the ac component is reduced in value. Figure

6.26a shows a circuit in which a capacitance is used to reduce the ac component of the output voltage of a half-wave rectifier. The capacitor charges up to peak ac input voltage V_m through the diode and discharges into the load during the interval until the diode once again turns on. As shown by the waveforms of Fig. 6.26b and c, the diode normally conducts for only a very small fraction of a half cycle. Specifically, the diode turns on (times t_0 and t_2) when the increasing ac input voltage equals the exponentially decaying voltage across the parallel RC combination, and turns off again (times t_1 and t_3) when the rate of change of the input voltage becomes more negative than the rate at which the load voltage decreases as a result of the discharge of the filter capacitance through the load resistance. If the time constant that governs the RC decay of the load voltage is large compared with the period of the input voltage, the conduction interval

$$\Delta t = t_1 - t_0 \tag{6.16a}$$

is small compared with the period.

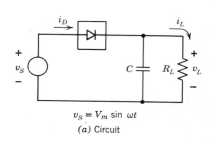

$v_S = V_m \sin \omega t$

(a) Circuit

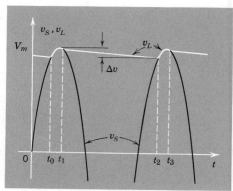

(b) Source and load voltage waveforms

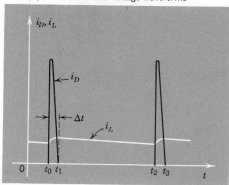

(c) Diode and load current waveforms

Figure 6.26   A half-wave rectifier with a filter capacitor used for ripple reduction. The input voltage is assumed to be a sinusoid.

The ac component of the output voltage can be characterized in terms of the *peak-to-peak ripple* Δv, which is defined in Fig. 6.26b. Obviously, small values of ripple are associated with small values of the conduction interval Δt. The ripple can be reduced by increasing the RC time constant, thereby decreasing the rate of decay of the load voltage and decreasing the duration of the conduction interval.

An approximate calculation of the ripple magnitude is not difficult. We assume that the conduction interval Δt is negligible compared with the period of the input voltage $T = 2\pi/\omega$. In this case the duration of the exponential decay of v_L is approximately equal to T, and the value of v_L at the beginning of the decay interval is approximately V_m, the peak value of the ac input voltage. Thus

$$\Delta v \simeq V_m(1 - e^{-T/R_L C}) \tag{6.16b}$$

Or, since the time constant $R_L C$ is large compared with T,

$$\Delta v \simeq V_m \frac{T}{R_L C} \tag{6.16c}$$

In practice, large values of capacitance are often required for satisfactory ripple reduction. Consider, for example, a half-wave rectifier with capacitor filter which operates from 60 Hz ac and which is intended to develop a dc output voltage of 12 volts across a resistive load that draws 10 ma. It is desired that the peak-to-peak ripple voltage be less than 0.1% of the dc output voltage, that is, less than 12 mv. What value of capacitance is required in the filter?

The load resistance is

$$R_L = \frac{12 \text{ volts}}{10 \text{ ma}} = 1200 \text{ ohms}$$

The period T is

$$T = \frac{2\pi}{\omega} = \frac{1}{f} = \frac{1}{60 \text{ Hz}} = 16.7 \text{ msec}$$

Since the fractional ripple is required to be less than 10^{-3} (0.1%), Eq. 6.16c requires that the time constant be at least 10^3 times as large as the period. Thus the minimum value of C is set by

$$R_L C = 16.7 \text{ sec}$$

or

$$C = \frac{16.7 \text{ sec}}{1200 \text{ ohms}}$$

$$\simeq 1.4 \times 10^{-2} \text{ farad}$$

It should be noted that the peak current in the diode must be many times larger than the average current in the load. All the charge removed from the capacitor during the interval when the diode is *off* (nearly a full half-cycle) must be replaced during the conduction interval Δt. For the usual case in which the ripple is small we can make a simple estimate of the magnitude of the charging current that must be carried by the diode. We assume that the diode current is approximately constant during the charging interval Δt and denote its value by i_{DP}. Since the load current is nearly constant throughout the period, the charge condition referred to above requires that

$$i_{DP} \Delta t = I_L T \tag{6.17a}$$

where I_L denotes the dc load current. Thus

$$i_{DP} = I_L \frac{T}{\Delta t} \tag{6.17b}$$

We estimate the conduction interval Δt by recognizing that this interval begins when the ac source voltage is less than V_m by Δv and ends (approximately) when the source voltage reaches V_m. Thus

$$\frac{\Delta v}{V_m} = 1 - \cos \omega \, \Delta t \tag{6.17c}$$

or, for $\omega \, \Delta t$ very small, so that $\cos \omega \, \Delta t \simeq 1 - \frac{1}{2}(\omega \, \Delta t)^2$,

$$\omega \, \Delta t \simeq \sqrt{2 \frac{\Delta v}{V_m}} \tag{6.17d}$$

Thus the peak diode current is approximated by

$$i_{DP} = I_L \frac{2\pi}{\sqrt{2\Delta v/V_m}} \tag{6.17e}$$

Clearly the diode current increases as the fractional ripple decreases, in response to larger values of capacitance.

For the numerical example introduced above, the conduction interval is, from Eq. 6.17d,

$$\omega \, \Delta t = \sqrt{2 \times 10^{-3}}$$

$$\simeq 4.5 \times 10^{-2} \text{ radian}$$

$$= 2.6 \text{ degrees}$$

The peak diode current which corresponds to the dc load current of 10 ma is, from Eq. 6.17e,

$$i_{DP} = 10^{-2} \frac{2\pi}{4.5 \times 10^{-2}}$$

$$\simeq 1.4 \text{ amp}$$

Although these estimates of peak-to-peak ripple, of conduction interval, and of peak diode current have been developed for a half-wave rectifier, they can be adapted to full-wave circuits. Because the full-wave circuits utilize two phases of the ac input voltage, the output voltage pulsates twice as fast (for the same input frequency) as in the half-wave case. Consequently the filter capacitance charges twice each cycle instead of once. Therefore, the estimate of Eqs. 6.16c and 6.17b can be adapted to full-wave circuits simply by replacing T by $T/2$. Similarly the factor of 2π in Eq. 6.17e must be replaced by π. It follows that reduction of the ripple to a prescribed level requires only half as much filter capacitance (for the same load) in a full-wave circuit compared with a half-wave circuit. Similarly, for the same fractional ripple voltage, the peak diode current is only half as large in a full-wave circuit.

This discussion of ripple filtering in power supplies has assumed that the diodes can be modeled as ideal piecewise-linear elements having no forward drop. If the dc output voltage is less than about 10 volts, the forward drop across the diodes becomes a significant fraction of the total ac input voltage and cannot be neglected. This forward drop or threshold voltage is easily accounted for in those circuits in which the filter has an input capacitance into which the diodes deposit charge. If we model the diodes by means of an ideal piecewise-linear diode in series with a fixed voltage source, equal in value to the threshold voltage, the analysis of the circuit differs only in that the peak voltage to which the capacitor charges is less than the amplitude of the ac input voltage by the threshold voltage. Thus in the circuit of Fig. 6.26 the amplitude of the ac voltage that drives the diodes must be larger than the desired dc output voltage by the threshold voltage.

6.4.3 Output Regulation

Circuits such as we have considered which convert ac power to dc power are often required to operate with variable loads. That is, the dc load current is not fixed, but may vary over a range that is often quite wide. Since these circuits are usually intended to provide a dc output voltage that is nominally constant, the degree of variation of the output voltage produced by changes in the load (or output current) is of interest. This aspect of the performance of a power supply circuit can be described by specifying the *regulation* of the circuit. The regulation is, by definition, the fractional change of output voltage for an output current (or load resistance) variation of some prescribed extent. In general, the smaller the value of the regulation, the better the power supply.

It should be noted that it is generally not possible to describe the dependence of dc output voltage on dc load current by means of a Thévenin equivalent source resistance. Because of the nonlinear nature of the rectifier circuit, the output voltage is not, in general, linearly dependent on the output current, and this relationship cannot be modeled by a linear network. Of course, it is always possible to linearize the nonlinear voltage-current relationship for currents in some suitably narrow range. In this case, the concept of an incremental Thévenin equivalent source resistance has meaning, and is often useful.

To illustrate these ideas, we evaluate the regulation of two of the rectifier circuits introduced earlier in this section. Consider first the full-wave circuit without filter that is shown in Fig. 6.24. We assume that the ac voltages developed by the transformer decrease as the current supplied to the diodes by the transformer increases, and model this dependence with source resistances, as shown in Fig. 6.27. These source resistances may represent winding resistance in the transformer, diode series resistance, or equivalent source resistance in the ac power line. Once again we use ideal piecewise-linear diode models.

The dependence of the load voltage v_L on the load current i_L is easily determined. When i_L is small, that is, when the load resistance R_L is large, there is negligible drop in R_S, and the output waveform has the form shown in Fig. 6.24b; the peak output voltage is equal to the amplitude V_m of the ac input voltage. When i_L is increased, by decreasing R_L, the voltage drops across R_S become significant and cause the output voltage to decrease. However, since i_L and v_L are proportional ($v_L = i_L R_L$), the diodes still change state when v_S passes through zero, and the output voltage waveform still has the same shape. This waveform is simply scaled down by the factor $R_L/(R_L + R_S)$, just as in the circuit of Fig. 6.22. Consequently, the output voltage and the output current (or their dc components) are, for this particular circuit, linearly related. The corresponding value of Thévenin equivalent source resistance at the output terminals is R_S. If, for example, we consider output currents that range in *peak* value from zero to I_{max}, the corresponding value of the regulation of this circuit is

$$\text{regulation} = \frac{I_{max} R_S}{V_m} \tag{6.18}$$

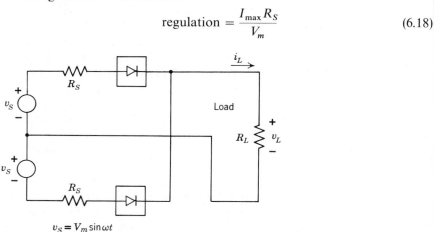

$$v_S = V_m \sin \omega t$$

Figure 6.27   A full-wave circuit without filter that accounts for source resistance.

As a second example we consider the filtered half-wave circuit of Fig. 6.28a, which differs from that shown in Fig. 6.26a only in that the ac source includes a source resistance R_S. We assume that the filter capacitance is large enough for the peak-to-peak ripple in the output voltage v_L to be negligible compared with the dc component V_L of that voltage.

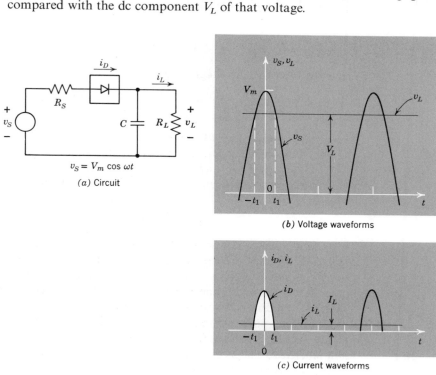

(a) Circuit

(b) Voltage waveforms

(c) Current waveforms

Figure 6.28   In a filtered circuit source resistance affects the conduction interval.

The source resistance R_S limits the rate at which charge can flow through the diode into the capacitor. Thus, as the dc output current I_L increases, the dc output voltage must drop below V_m, as shown in Fig. 6.28b, so that the diode conduction interval can increase by a sufficient amount to permit the replacement of the additional charge on C. The diode current, shown in Fig. 6.28c, is, during the conduction interval,

$$i_D(t) = \frac{v_S(t) - V_L}{R_S} \qquad -t_1 < t < t_1 \tag{6.19}$$

where the times $-t_1$ and t_1 denote the beginning and end of the conduction interval. At these times there is no drop in R_S, and $v_S(t)$ equals V_L. Thus t_1 is given by

$$V_m \cos \omega t_1 = V_L \tag{6.20}$$

We evaluate the dependence of V_L on the dc load current I_L by recognizing that the charge removed from C by the load during a full cycle must be replaced by i_D during the conduction interval. This charge is the white area in Fig. 6.28c. Equivalently, the average of $i_D(t)$ over one period must just equal I_L. This charge-balance condition requires

$$\int_{-t_1}^{t_1} i_D(t)\, dt = \frac{2\pi}{\omega} I_L \tag{6.21a}$$

Or, using Eq. 6.19 and integrating,

$$\frac{2}{R_S}\left(\frac{V_m \sin \omega t_1}{\omega} - V_L t_1\right) = \frac{2\pi}{\omega} I_L \tag{6.21b}$$

To find the dependence of V_L on I_L, we simply eliminate t_1 between Eqs. 6.20 and 6.21b. Since the conduction interval is usually short we will assume $\sin \omega t_1 \simeq \omega t_1$ and $\cos \omega t_1 \simeq 1 - \frac{1}{2}(\omega t_1)^2$. With this approximation we obtain, after some algebraic manipulation (see Problem P6.13)

$$\frac{V_L}{V_m} = 1 - \left(\frac{\pi I_L R_S}{\sqrt{2} V_m}\right)^{2/3} \tag{6.22}$$

This relationship, which is sketched in Fig. 6.29, can be used to evaluate the regulation for any prescribed range of variation of load current. If, for example, the load current varies between zero and $0.2(\sqrt{2}V_m/\pi R_S)$ as shown in the sketch, the regulation has a value of about 0.35 as indicated.

The curve of Fig. 6.29 shows that the output I-V relationship of this power supply can be approximated by a linear model for relatively wide variations in load current. Consider, for example, load currents which vary around the point labeled P. The slope of the curve at this point is about -1.1. Thus for current variations about P we may write

$$\frac{\Delta V_L}{V_m} \simeq -1.1 \frac{\pi R_S}{\sqrt{2} V_m} \Delta I_L \tag{6.23a}$$

so that the incremental Thévenin equivalent source resistance that applies near P is

$$R_{eq} = -\frac{\Delta V_L}{\Delta I_L} \simeq 1.1 \frac{\sqrt{2}}{\pi} R_S \tag{6.23b}$$

The tangent to the curve at P intersects the zero current axis at $V_L/V_m \simeq 0.87$. Thus the complete Thévenin equivalent model for this power supply has the values shown in Fig. 6.30. It is clear from the sketch that this linear model is reasonably accurate even for load currents that differ from the current at P by a factor of 2.

Although this evaluation of the regulation of a filtered power supply applies only to the specific circuit of Fig. 6.28a, the point of view we have

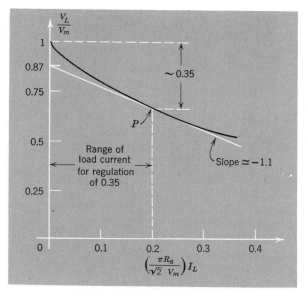

Figure 6.29   The dc output voltage is a nonlinear function of the dc load current.

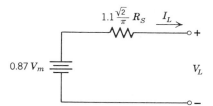

Figure 6.30   A linear Thévenin equivalent approximation for the output *I-V* relationship of the circuit of Fig. 6.28. This model is valid for load currents near $0.2\sqrt{2}V_m/\pi R_s$.

employed, namely, the charge-balance condition of Eq. 6.21a, can be adapted to other circuits as well.

6.5   Special-Purpose Semiconductor Diodes

6.5.1   Breakdown Diodes

Our discussions of semiconductor diode physical electronics and of diode circuit models have both involved the observation that the reverse current of a junction diode is small and essentially independent of the reverse voltage. In fact, this condition does not hold if the reverse voltage is made large enough. All junction diodes exhibit a region of behavior in the reverse direction in which large reverse currents can flow if the reverse voltage exceeds a value referred to as the *reverse breakdown voltage*. The breakdown voltage ranges in different practical diodes from a few volts to several hundred volts. The general shape of the diode characteristic in this region is shown in Fig. 6.31, which also shows the circuit symbol used for these diodes. The reverse breakdown voltage is denoted by V_B.

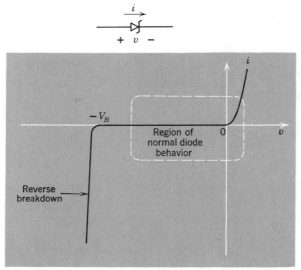

Figure 6.31   Reverse breakdown in a junction diode.

Reverse breakdown in *pn* junctions may arise from either of two mechanisms; both depend on the fact that the electric field in the space-charge layer increases as the reverse voltage increases.

One mechanism that causes reverse breakdown in *pn* junctions is *avalanche multiplication*. The carriers that constitute the normal reverse current of a junction flow across the space-charge layer from the regions where they are in the minority to the regions where they are in the majority. Thus they move down the potential barrier at the junction and are accelerated between collisions by the field there. If the field is large enough (in the range of 2×10^5 volts/cm) the energy that these carriers acquire from the field between collisions is sufficient to produce a hole-electron pair when the energy is transferred to the crystal during a collision. Thus a single carrier can produce another pair of carriers, which in turn flow out of the space-charge layer and contribute to the reverse current. These *secondary carriers* can produce other pairs or *tertiary carriers* through their own collisions with the lattice. In this way the reverse current is multiplied and can become quite large. The probability that a carrier will produce a secondary pair in a collision is strongly dependent on the electric field. This dependence accounts for the rapid increase of reverse current for reverse voltages larger than the breakdown voltage V_B, as shown in Fig. 6.31.

The second mechanism of junction breakdown is called *Zener breakdown*. If the electric field in the space-charge layer is strong enough (in the range of 5×10^5 volts/cm) the force that it exerts on bound or valence electrons is sufficient to strip some of those electrons away from the valence bonds, thereby creating hole-electron pairs that contribute to the reverse current. There is no multiplication effect involved in this mechanism; the pairs are produced directly by the field and not through the action of a primary carrier.

Silicon junction diodes that are relatively lightly doped have breakdown voltages in the range of tens or hundreds of volts. In such diodes the break-down current is produced by avalanche multiplication. Diodes that are more heavily doped have lower breakdown voltages; the space-charge layer is thinner and the electric field is larger for the same applied voltage, and avalanche multiplication sets in at lower voltages. Diodes that are very heavily doped have breakdown voltages as small as one or two volts. In such diodes the breakdown current is produced by the Zener mechanism; the electric field is very high, and the space-charge layer is so thin that carriers spend too little time in the space-charge layer to produce significant numbers of secondary carrier pairs. Diodes that break down for reverse voltages in the range of 6 to 8 volts have both mechanisms operating simultaneously.

Note that although both the avalanche and Zener mechanisms are des-cribed as "breakdown phenomena," neither is, of itself, destructive or irreversible. When the reverse voltage is reduced below the critical level, the breakdown mechanism subsides, and the junction behaves normally once again. Of course, the large currents and high voltages associated with reverse breakdown can easily cause the junction to overheat, and this can lead to irreversible destruction of the diode owing to excessively high temperatures.

The behavior of breakdown diodes is easily modeled using piecewise-linear techniques. A simple model is shown in Fig. 6.32a. Diode 1 together with

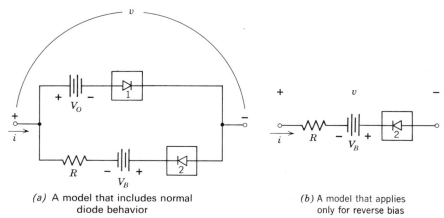

(a) A model that includes normal diode behavior

(b) A model that applies only for reverse bias

Figure 6.32   Piecewise-linear models for breakdown diodes.

the source V_O model the forward behavior and the "normal" reverse behavior; the threshold voltage V_O is usually of the order of a few tenths of a volt. Diode 2 together with the source V_B and the resistance R are added to represent the breakdown region. Clearly, this diode does not conduct until v reaches $-V_B$. Larger values of reverse voltage forward-bias this diode, thus introducing the resistance R, through which the reverse current flows. The resistance R may range in value from a few ohms to several hundred ohms. If the circuit application is such that the breakdown diode never becomes forward biased, the simpler model of Fig. 6.32b can be used.

Breakdown diodes can be used as simple voltage regulators for power supplies. As we saw in the preceding section, the dc output voltage of a power supply decreases as the load current increases. This dependence can be reduced by using a breakdown diode as shown in Fig. 6.33a. In this circuit the

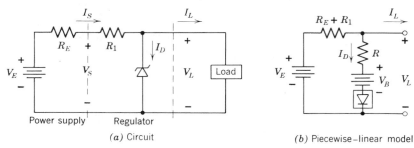

(a) Circuit   *(b)* Piecewise–linear model

Figure 6.33   A breakdown diode can be used as a voltage regulator.

basic dc power supply is modeled by the Thévenin equivalent comprised of V_E and R_E. The regulator consists of the breakdown diode and the series resistance R_1. A piecewise-linear model for this circuit is shown in Fig. 6.33b; the resistance R represents the incremental resistance of the diode in the breakdown range. The regulation of this circuit is improved by the breakdown diode because the Thévenin equivalent output resistance is reduced from R_E without the regulator to $(R_E + R_1) \| R$. The series resistance R_1 is chosen to limit the maximum diode current to a safe value. The maximum diode current occurs when the load current I_L is zero. The diode current (assuming that R is small compared to $R_E + R_1$) is then approximately

$$(I_D)_{max} = \frac{V_E - V_B}{R_E + R_1} \tag{6.24}$$

The value of R_1 is selected so that the $(I_D)_{max}$ is less than the maximum rated diode current (which is, of course, governed by power dissipation in the diode). As the load current increases, the diode current decreases. The current I_S, produced by the power supply, and the load voltage V_L are nominally constant. When the load current reaches the value given by Eq. 6.24, the diode current drops to zero, and the load voltage begins to fall, as the extra load current is supplied through R_1. Consequently, the point

$$(I_L)_{max} = \frac{V_E - V_B}{R_E + R_1} = (I_D)_{max} \tag{6.25}$$

marks the end of the regulating range.

The regulation of this circuit is not perfect for currents less than the limit given by Eq. 6.25, because the voltage across the breakdown diode is not precisely fixed, but increases slightly as the diode current increases (see Fig. 6.31). This effect has been modeled by the series resistance R, in Fig. 6.33b. Clearly, the diode in this model is at its breakpoint when the load current has the value given by Eq. 6.25. For smaller load currents the diode is *on*, and the output voltage is, using the superposition principle,

$$V_L = V_E \frac{R}{R + R_E + R_1} + V_B \frac{R_E + R_1}{R + R_E + R_1} - I_L[R\|(R_E + R_1)] \tag{6.26a}$$

$$\text{for} \quad I_L < (I_L)_{max}$$

On the other hand, when the load current is larger than $(I_L)_{max}$, the diode is *off*, and we have

$$V_L = V_E - I_L(R_E + R_1) \tag{6.26b}$$

These V–I characteristics are sketched in Fig. 6.34. For comparison the V–I characteristic of the basic power supply without the regulator is also shown. Since the resistance R of the breakdown diode is usually very small compared with R_E and $R_E + R_1$, the regulation is obviously improved.

Breakdown diodes are also useful as limiters and for the establishment of reference voltages. In this regard, the circuit of Fig. 6.33a serves to establish the level of V_L as nearly equal to V_B in spite of variations in I_L and V_E.

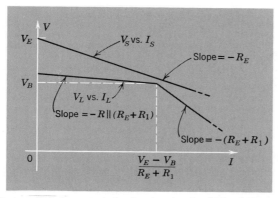

Figure 6.34 Output V-I characteristics for the circuit of Fig. 6.37.

6.5.2 Tunnel Diodes

In junctions that are very heavily doped, the phenomenon of Zener break-down can occur at very small reverse voltages. It can, in fact, occur at zero bias. A junction that is in Zener breakdown at zero bias will support large currents for a reverse voltage (which make the field bigger) and will gradually revert to normal operation as the applied voltage is made positive (which reduces the electric field). A forward voltage of one or two tenths of a volt may be enough to eliminate the Zener breakdown mechanism and to reduce the junction current. Further increases in forward voltage produce minority-carrier injection so that the current once again rises. An *I-V* characteristic that exhibits this behavior is shown in Fig. 6.35. Devices behaving in this manner are called *tunnel diodes*. The name originates from a quantum-mechanical explanation of the Zener breakdown mechanism. Tunnel diodes are useful as circuit components because they have a region of *negative* incremental conductance, that is, a region in which the *I-V* characteristic has negative slope.

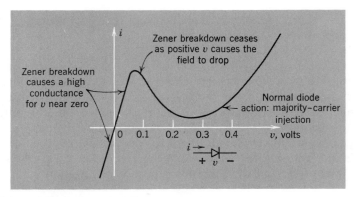

Figure 6.35 A tunnel diode characteristic.

REFERENCES

6.1 L. B. Arguimbau and R. B. Adler, *Vacuum Tube Circuits and Transistors*, Wiley, New York, 1956.

6.2 C. L. Alley and K. W. Atwood, *Electronic Engineering*, Wiley, New York, 1966.

6.3 H. J. Zimmermann and S. J. Mason, *Electronic Circuit Theory*, Wiley, New York, 1959.

PROBLEMS

P6.1 The junction diode whose *V–I* characteristics are shown in Fig. 6.11 is used in the symmetrical clipper circuit of Fig. 6.14. Using graphical methods, determine, sketch, and dimension v_2 versus v_1 for v_1 in the range $-5 < v_1 < 5$ volts. Assume $R_S = 100$ ohms.

P6.2 The diodes in the circuits of Fig. 6.36 are all ideal piecewise-linear diode elements. Evaluate, sketch, and dimension for each circuit the indicated driving-point or transfer characteristics.

P6.3 The logical operation of the gate circuits shown in Fig. 6.9 can be described in terms of a "truth table" or *table of combinations* on which all possible input states are listed along with the corresponding output states.

Assume that the input voltages are quantized in two narrow ranges as shown in Fig. 6.10 and that *positive representation* is used, that is, the more positive range of voltages corresponds to the **1** state and the other, more negative, range corresponds to the **0** state.

A table that lists the 16 possible combinations of states of the four inputs is shown below. Add two columns of 1's and 0's describing the corresponding states of the output voltages of these two circuits.

Input Variable				Output Variable	
1	2	3	4	Circuit of Fig. 6.9*a*	Circuit of Fig. 6.9*b*
0	0	0	0		
0	0	0	1		
0	0	1	0		
0	0	1	1		
0	1	0	0		
0	1	0	1		
0	1	1	0		
0	1	1	1		
1	0	0	0		
1	0	0	1		
1	0	1	0		
1	0	1	1		
1	1	0	0		
1	1	0	1		
1	1	1	0		
1	1	1	1		

P6.4 Again considering the circuits of Fig. 6.9, generate truth tables for the case in which *negative representation* is employed. That is, let the most negative range of voltages correspond to the **1** state and the other, more positive, range correspond to the **0** state.

Which of these circuits can, with this representation, be described as an AND *gate*? Which can be described as an OR *gate*? Compare with the situation that exists with positive representation.

P6.5 In choosing a model to represent the characteristics of a device, it is usually essential to specify the range of operating conditions over which the

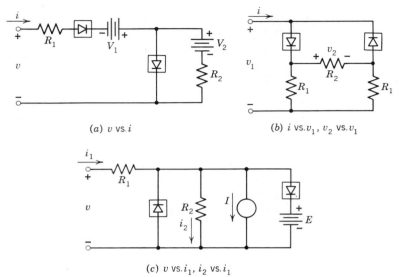

(a) v vs. i (b) i vs. v_1, v_2 vs. v_1

(c) v vs. i_1, i_2 vs. i_1

Figure 6.36   Diode networks.

model is to apply. This problem employs a semiconductor diode to illustrate this issue. Consider a diode whose static *V-I* relationship is described by

$$I = I_s(e^{qV/kT} - 1) \qquad I_s = 10^{-11} \text{ amp}$$

This value of I_s is typical of a silicon diode. Assume that $kT/q = 25$ mv.

(a) Plot, on three separate sets of linear coordinates, the *V-I* curves of this diode with the scales chosen so that the following three ranges of forward current are displayed:

$$
\begin{array}{lll}
(1) & 1 < I < 10 \; \mu\text{a} \\
(2) & 1 < I < 10 \; \text{ma} \\
(3) & 100 < I < 1000 \; \text{ma}
\end{array}
$$

We wish to approximate the *V-I* characteristics of this device with the piece-wise-linear model of Fig. 6.12*b*.

(b) Using the graphs of (a), pick reasonable values of V_O for this model for each of the three current ranges.

(c) Specify G for each of the three ranges by computing dI/dV from the exponential diode equation and evaluating this slope for a current in the middle of each range.

(d) Use the graphs of (a) to estimate values for G for each of the ranges of current by connecting the end points of the range. Compare these values of G with those determined in (c).

(e) What can you say about the dependence of V_O and G on the range of operation for which the model is devised?

P6.6 The incremental space-charge capacitance of a diode is dependent on the dc component of the junction voltage. For an abrupt-junction diode, this dependence is of the form

$$C_j(V) = \frac{C_o \psi_0^{1/2}}{(\psi_0 - V)^{1/2}}$$

where C_o is a constant and ψ_0 is the contact potential (the height of the equilibrium potential barrier). Consequently, a model for a *reverse-biased* diode that has negligible saturation current is shown in Fig. 6.37a. The voltage dependence of the incremental capacitance of a reverse-biased diode is often employed in a tuned circuit whose resonant frequency can be voltage-controlled. For example, the driving-point impedance Z of the circuit shown in Fig. 6.37b has a resonant peak at a frequency that can be changed by varying V. The blocking capacitor C is large enough so that negligible ac voltage appears across it, that is, it can be treated as a short circuit at signal frequencies. Furthermore, the resistance R is small enough so that the dc voltage across the diode is V (which is a negative quantity).

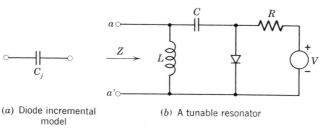

(a) Diode incremental model

(b) A tunable resonator

Figure 6.37 A varactor circuit.

(a) Represent the reverse-biased diode by a capacitance C_j and compute both the resonant frequency (the frequency where $|Z|$ is a maximum) and the half-power bandwidth of the impedance. Express your results in terms of R, L, and C_j.

(b) It is desired to vary the resonant frequency over a 2:1 range by changing V, which is negative and lies in the range

$$V_{max} > |V| > 2 \text{ volts}$$

Specify V_{max} so that the resonant frequency is variable over a 2:1 range. Assume that $\psi_0 = 1$ volt. Assume that the resonant frequency is much greater than the half-power bandwidth.

(c) Assume that $C_o = 20$ pf (20×10^{-12} farad). Specify L and R so that the smallest value of the resonant frequency is 10 MHz (10×10^6 cycles per second) and the resonant impedance is 10 kohm (10×10^3 ohms). What is the half-power bandwidth at each end of the 2:1 range of resonant frequency?

(d) *Optional*. Estimate the largest value of signal voltage that you would be willing to permit at the terminals *a-a'* without invalidating the use of a linear capacitance model as a representation for the reverse-biased diode.

Diodes used in this manner are called *varactors*, for *var*iable re*actors*.

Answers. $V_{max} = 47$ volts, $L \simeq 22\ \mu h$.

P6.7 The circuit of a variable attenuator is shown in Fig. 6.38a. The capacitors C, which couple the input signal into the diode and block the dc component of the output, have enough capacitance so that their impedance at signal frequencies of interest is negligible compared with the resistance R. Assume that the diode is characterized by

$$i = I_s(e^{qV/kT} - 1)$$

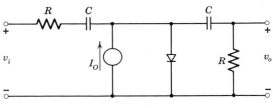

(a) Circuit of a variable attenuator

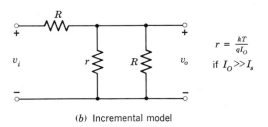

(b) Incremental model

$$r = \frac{kT}{qI_O}$$
if $I_O \gg I_s$

Figure 6.38 A diode attenuator.

If the input signal voltage v_i is small enough, the diode is incrementally linear, so that v_o is a linear homogeneous function of v_i. The incremental resistance of the diode is determined by the operating point, which is set by the dc current source I_O. As I_O changes, the operating point shifts, the incremental resistance changes, and the voltage transfer ratio v_o/v_i changes. Since this ratio is controlled by I_O, the circuit functions as an electrically controlled variable attenuator.

(a) Show that the *incremental* behavior of the circuit can be represented by the circuit of Fig. 6.38b.

(b) Compute, sketch, and dimension v_o/v_i as a function of I_o for I_o in the range $0.1\,\text{ma} < I_o < 10\,\text{ma}$. Assume that $kT/q = 25\,\text{mv}$ and $R = 100$ ohms.

(c) Estimate the maximum value of $|v_i|$ for which the circuit is incrementally linear for all values of I_o in the range defined in (b).

P6.8 The attenuator described in Problem 6.7 has the disadvantage that the resistance seen looking into the attenuator varies as I_o changes. Devise a circuit that has constant input resistance but provides a variable *transfer conductance* i_o/v_i when operated into a short circuit. (*Suggestion*. Use two diodes and note that a variable transfer conductance into a short circuit, and *not* a variable voltage-transfer ratio into an open circuit, is desired.)

P6.9 The balanced diode gate shown in Fig. 6.19 operates as described in the text only if the signal v_S is appropriately limited in range. This problem deals with the factors that determine the allowable range. Assume that

$$R_S = 1\,\text{kohm}$$

$$R_G = 5\,\text{kohm}$$

$$v_G = \begin{cases} +V \\ \text{or} \\ -V \end{cases} \quad \text{where} \quad V = 10\,\text{volts}$$

and represent the diodes by ideal piecewise-linear models.

(a) When $v_G = +V$, the diodes should be *on*. Determine the maximum value $|v_S|$ for which no diode becomes reverse-biased.

(b) When $v_G = -V$, the diodes should be *off*. Determine the maximum value of $|v_S|$ for which no diode becomes forward-biased.

P6.10 This problem is concerned with a half-wave rectifier without filter in which the voltages involved are so small that the forward drop of the diode *cannot* be neglected. The circuit is shown in Fig. 6.21a [the waveforms of (b) do *not* apply]. Assume that the diode is modeled by the circuit of Fig. 6.12b and that $v_S(t) = V_m \sin \omega t$.

(a) Derive expressions involving V_m, V_o, and ω for the times at which the diode changes state from off to on and from on to off.

(b) Sketch and dimension the waveform of the output voltage $v_L(t)$.

(c) Derive an expression for the dc component of the output voltage.

(d) Assume $R_L = 10$ ohms, the diode forward resistance $R = 1/G = 2$ ohms, and $V_o = 0.5$ volt. What must be the amplitude V_m of the ac input voltage if the dc output voltage is to be 4 volts? What is the corresponding peak value of the output voltage? What is the value of the dc component of the load current?

P6.11 The circuit of Fig. 6.26a is used to develop 10 volts of direct current across a 1000-ohm load. The filter capacitance has a value of $500\,\mu f$

$(500 \times 10^{-6}$ farad).

(a) What is the peak-to-peak ripple voltage?

(b) For what fraction of the cycle does the diode conduct?

(c) What is the average diode current?

(d) Estimate the peak diode current.

(e) What must be the amplitude of the ac input voltage?

(f) Repeat (e) for the case in which the diode has a forward drop (assumed fixed) of 0.8 volt.

P6.12   The full-wave bridge rectifier shown in Fig. 6.39 is used to develop 40 volts of direct current across a nonlinear resistive load which draws a constant current of 25 ma. The fractional ripple voltage is small, and the diodes may be assumed to be ideal.

(a) What must be the value of V_m?

(b) What value must C have if the fractional ripple is to be 1%?

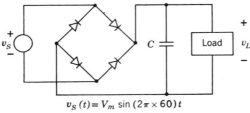

$$v_S\,(t) = V_m \sin{(2\pi \times 60)t}$$

Figure 6.39   A bridge rectifier with filter.

P6.13   This problem is concerned with the estimation of the regulation of the circuit of Fig. 6.26a.

(a) Verify Eq. 6.21b.

(b) Expand the trigonometric functions in Eqs. 6.20 and 6.21b about $\omega t_1 = 0$, retaining only the terms up to $(\omega t_1)^2$. Show that the results may be written as

$$\frac{V_m}{R_S}\left(1 - \frac{V_L}{V_m}\right)\omega t_1 = \pi I_L$$

and

$$\frac{V_L}{V_m} = 1 - \tfrac{1}{2}(\omega t_1)^2$$

(c) Verify Eq. 6.22 by eliminating ωt_1 between the equations obtained in (b).

(d) Derive, by differentiation of Eq. 6.24, expressions for the Thévenin equivalent source resistance *and* source voltage for operation near the current $I_L = I_{LP}$.

(e) What is the largest value of I_L for which you would be willing to use the result given by Eq. 6.26, that is, when do the approximations made in the truncated expansions of (b) fail?

CHAPTER SEVEN

Bipolar Junction Transistors

7.1 Junction Transistors as Control Valves

Junction transistors comprise the most widely used class of electronic control valves or power modulators. There are two general types of junction transistor: *unipolar* transistors and *bipolar* transistors. We defer discussion of unipolar transistors to Chapters 9 and 10, and concentrate here and in Chapter 8 on bipolar junction transistors.

Figure 7.1 shows one form of a *bipolar* junction transistor. This transistor contains two *pn* junctions which, in the case illustrated, share a single thin *n*-type region. In this respect, the device is a sandwich consisting of a single *n*-type layer between two *p*-type layers; it is commonly designated as a *pnp* transistor. Transistors that have complementary dopings are also widely used; these units are called *npn* transistors.

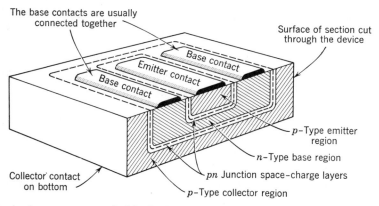

Figure 7.1   The basic components of a bipolar junction transistor (not to scale).

As indicated in Fig. 7.1, a bipolar transistor has two *pn* junctions. The semiconductor region that is common to these junctions is called the *base*. The other two regions are referred to as the *emitter* and *collector*. Although the latter two regions are of the same conductivity type, they usually have different physical and electrical properties, as well as somewhat different size, as shown in the sketch. The junction comprised of the emitter and base is called the *emitter junction*; the other is called the *collector junction*.

The basic mode of operation of the bipolar transistor as a control valve can be understood in terms of the flow of minority carriers across the thin-base region between the junctions. When the emitter junction is forward-biased, holes are injected from the emitter region, where they are majority carriers, into the base region, where they are in the minority, just as in a forward-biased diode. Most of these injected carriers diffuse across the base and reach the collector space-charge layer. That is, the fraction that dies in the base by recombining with majority-carrier electrons is small. The holes are swept into the collector region by the electric field in the collector space-charge layer. Since the collector junction is reverse-biased for normal operation, no injection occurs there, and these collected holes dominate the collector current. The device can be used as a control valve because the collector current is controlled directly by the base-to-emitter voltage, which sets the forward bias on the emitter junction. Power gain is realized because the base-to-emitter voltage and the base current are very small. This device is called a *bipolar* transistor, since it depends on the existence of *both* minority and majority carriers.

Bipolar transistors can be fabricated in silicon by applying the techniques of the planar diffusion technology described in Chapter 5. For example, the *pnp* transistor illustrated in Fig. 7.1 can be made by diffusing two junctions into a *p*-type substrate, using silicon dioxide masking techniques to define both the junction areas and the metallized contact areas. For the sake of clarity, the oxide layers are not shown in the sketches of Fig. 7.1. The planar diffused technology leads to devices in which the junctions have areas in the range from a few hundred to a few thousand square microns and lie a few microns below the surface of the semiconductor. The base width of a bipolar transistor (the width of the base layer between the junction planes in Fig. 7.1) may be as small as a few tenths of a micron.

We now study the internal physical behavior of transistors in more detail. In addition, we develop circuit models that characterize the electrical behavior of these devices, and illustrate the principal features of their behavior as circuit components. We examine first the bipolar structure, and return, in Chapter 9, to the unipolar structure.

Our development of the physical behavior of bipolar transistors is based entirely on the *pnp* form of these devices. Consequently, the models that we develop apply directly to *pnp* structures. It is important to recognize, however, that the fundamental behavior of *npn* structures is the same; only the roles of holes and electrons are interchanged. Thus all junction voltages and currents have the opposite polarity in *npn* structures. We shall see that the models that we develop can easily be adapted to *npn* structures. In the case of total-variable models, appropriate polarity changes are required; incremental models can be applied directly without change.

7.2 Operation of the Bipolar Transistor
7.2.1 Internal Physical Behavior

When a transistor is used as a control valve, the emitter junction is forward-biased and the collector junction is reverse-biased. Under these circumstances, the transistor is said to operate in the *active region*. Carriers are injected across the emitter space-charge layer (holes in one direction, electrons in the other), thereby causing the excess-carrier concentrations at the edges of the emitter space-charge layer to increase. The emitter junction is fabricated with the emitter-region doping much larger than the base-region doping. Because of the resulting asymmetry of the impurity concentrations, flow across the emitter space-charge layer is dominated by the emitter-region majority carriers (or base-region minority carriers), that is, *holes* for a *pnp* arrangement. As a consequence of the reverse-biased state of the collector junction, the carrier concentrations at the edges of the collector space-charge layer are depressed below their equilibrium values. This corresponds to negative excess-carrier concentration. If the magnitude of the reverse bias is in excess of a few kT/q, the total minority-carrier concentrations at the space-charge-layer edges are negligible in comparison with the equilibrium concentrations. Therefore, there are concentration gradients of both minority and majority carriers in the base region, as shown in Figs. 7.2a and 7.2b.

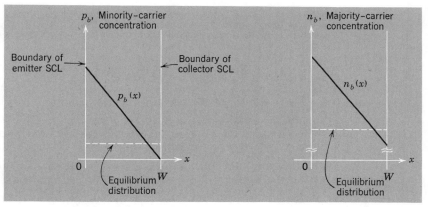

(a) Minority-carrier concentration   (b) Majority-carrier concentration

Figure 7.2 Carrier concentration distributions in the base region of a transistor operating as a control valve with forward-biased emitter and reverse-biased collector.

The position coordinate (x) in these sketches is normal to the junction planes. The current of injected minority carriers, which flows *normal* to the junction planes, is approximately the same at the collector as at the emitter, since there is very little recombination in the base, and this current is diffusive. Consequently, the excess concentrations are approximately linear in position (the gradients are independent of position). This elementary picture of transistor behavior is illustrated in Fig. 7.3.

A base current (small in comparison with the emitter and collector currents) is necessary to feed the recombination that does occur in the base and to support the injection of base-region majority carriers into the emitter. This base current can be small because the base is thin and characterized by a large lifetime and because the emitter is doped much more heavily than the base, thus minimizing reverse injection into the emitter.

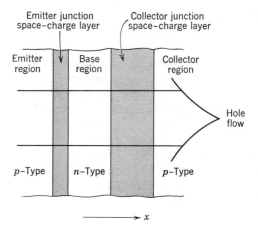

Figure 7.3   The principal current in a *pnp* transistor is that associated with the flow of base-region minority carriers across the base from emitter to collector.

The current that flows in the emitter-collector path (normal to the junctions) is under the direct control of the emitter-junction voltage and is essentially independent of the collector-junction voltage. This current, which we designate as *longitudinal,* is a strong function of the emitter-junction voltage for the same reason that the forward current of a junction diode is strongly dependent on the diode-junction voltage; small reductions in the height of the potential barrier make large numbers of majority carriers available for injection, so that the excess-carrier concentrations at the edges of the space-charge layer increase exponentially with the forward junction voltage. The longitudinal current is independent of the collector-junction voltage for the same reason that the reverse current of a junction diode is independent of the reverse voltage (for reverse voltages greater than several kT/q); the potential barrier at the collector junction is large enough to block entirely the flow of carriers from the regions in which they are in the majority to the regions in which they are in the minority, while the associated electric field sweeps carriers out of the regions in which they are in the minority. The rate at which minority carriers are swept across depends only on the rate at which minority carriers arrive at the collector edge of the base region, and is independent of the field strength. Consequently, there is no dependence of the current on the reverse voltage.[1]

---

[1] The lack of coupling between the collector current and the collector-to-base voltage is an approximation. A less restrictive physical model than the one we have chosen must include the fact that the width of the neutral base region (its extent on the longitudinal direction) depends on the collector-to-base voltage because the width of the collector space-charge layer depends on this voltage. As the space-charge layer widens in response to larger reverse voltages, the base width must shrink. This effect, called *base-width modulation,* influences the concentration gradient in the base and causes the collector current to depend weakly on the collector-to-base voltage. See Section 7.5.

    The situation described above is similar to the internal physical behavior
of the asymmetrically-doped thin-base structures introduced earlier: the
thin-base structure of Fig. 3.1, in which carriers are produced in the base by
optical injection, and the thin-base junction diode of Fig. 4.10, in which
excess carriers are injected into the base by the *pn* junction. The distribution
and flow of the excess carriers in the *n*-type base region of the *pnp* transistor
are approximately the same as the distribution and flow of the excess carriers
in both of these simpler structures. That is, the distributions of Fig. 7.2 are
similar in all important respects to those of either Fig. 3.2 or Fig. 4.11. In all
three cases there is negligible recombination in the base region, so that the
minority-carrier current produced by the injection of carriers is essentially
constant throughout the base regions and the excess-carrier distributions
are approximately linear in the base regions.
    The transistor differs in operation from the other two structures in one
important respect. This difference relates to the source of supply of the
base-region majority carriers which feed the small amount of recombination
that does occur in the base and which support the small current associated
with reverse injection into the emitter (into the *p*-type region in the diode).
In the thin-base structures studied earlier, these carriers enter the base region
from the *n*-type region of high recombination and flow in the base in opposition to the flow of injected minority carriers. That is, these majority carriers
flow *normal* to the junction plane in those thin-base structures. We have
referred to flow in this direction as *longitudinal*. In the transistor structure,
the majority-carrier electrons cannot be supplied to the base across the
collector space-charge layer because there are very few electrons available
in the *p*-type collector. Instead, they must be supplied by the base-region

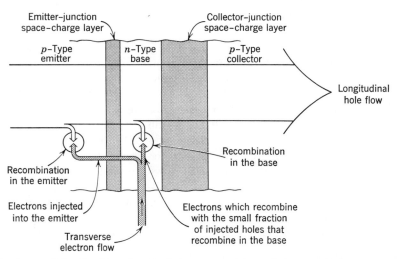

Figure 7.4   The internal flows of carriers and the composition of the terminal currents of a *pnp*
transistor.

contact and thus must flow in the base in a direction *parallel* to the junction planes. For this reason, the base-region majority-carrier current is referred to as *transverse* to distinguish its direction from that of the *longitudinal* base-region minority-carrier current. The internal currents are depicted schematically in Fig. 7.4, which is a refinement of Fig. 7.3 that accounts for the small base current.

We shall use the similarities described above, together with our previous investigation of diode behavior, as the basis for quantitative analysis of the physical behavior of transistors.

7.2.2 Transistor Circuit Symbols and Terminal Variables

Before continuing our discussion of the bipolar transistor, it is desirable to introduce a symbol and reference directions of current and voltage for the device. The standard symbol for a *pnp* bipolar transistor is shown in Fig. 7.5a. Notice that the emitter terminal is distinguished by an arrow, which points in the direction in which emitter current flows when the transistor is operated in the active region, that is, with forward-biased emitter and reverse-biased collector.

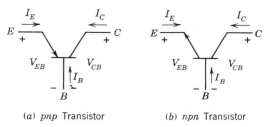

(a) *pnp* Transistor   (b) *npn* Transistor

Figure 7.5 Bipolar transistor circuit symbols and reference directions for current and voltage.

The current and voltage reference directions shown in Fig. 7.5a are standard for *both pnp* and *npn* transistors. Positive values of the terminal currents correspond to flow of positive charge *into* the associated terminal; positive values of the terminal-pair voltages V_{EB} and V_{CB} correspond to having the emitter or collector terminals positive with respect to the base.[2] The symbol for an *npn* transistor, shown in Fig. 7.5b, differs only in that the "arrow," which identifies the emitter terminal, is reversed; consequently, it again points in the direction of flow of emitter current for operation in the active region.

The notation for the terminal currents and terminal-pair voltages employed in Fig. 7.5 is standard for transistors and is an extension of the notation introduced in Section 1.3.4. The uppercase variables with uppercase

---

[2] The collector-to-emitter voltage V_{CE} is frequently used in an electrical description of the device. It is $V_{CE} = V_{CB} - V_{EB}$.

subscripts denote *static* conditions. That is, the variables I_E, V_{EB}, and so forth, either are constant or are changing so slowly that the relationship between them is essentially the same as the corresponding static relationship. Another standard notation, which is used to represent instantaneous total variables and incremental variables, will be introduced as necessary in our development.

7.2.3 The Transistor as a Control Valve

Transistor action hinges on the flow of base-region minority carriers from the emitter across the base into the collector. The collector current is only slightly smaller than the emitter current, and the base current is much smaller than either. This situation obtains so long as the collector junction is reverse-biased; and the current that flows across the base is essentially independent of the exact value of the reverse voltage on the collector junction so long as the voltage is greater than several kT/q. Consequently, *the transistor has a small emitter-base voltage, corresponding to forward bias on the emitter junction, and develops a collector current that is independent of the collector-base voltage provided that the collector junction is reverse-biased. It can be regarded, at the collector terminal, as a dependent current source that is controlled by some other variable.*

There are four points of view concerning the "control" of the dependent current source in the collector:

1. The collector current is controlled by the *emitter-base voltage* and increases strongly as the forward voltage at the emitter junction increases. On the basis of our analysis of *pn* junction diode behavior, we expect this dependence to be exponential; this expectation, which will be supported by analysis in Section 7.3.1, is substantiated by the data of Fig. 7.6a in which collector current is plotted on semilogarithmic coordinates as a function of the emitter-base voltage for a typical germanium transistor.

2. The collector current is controlled by the *excess charge in the base* and increases as the excess charge increases. It is clear from the discussion associated with Fig. 7.2, and from our study of diode behavior, that the minority-carrier current that flows across the base is accompanied by positive excess-carrier distributions. For low-injection situations, this current is proportional to the *total* excess charge associated with either the hole or electron distributions (the two distributions have equal magnitudes of total excess charge because the base region is neutral). This point of view regarding the nature of the "handle" on the control valve is powerful because excess *majority* carriers can be supplied to the base region *only* at the base terminal.[3] Consequently, the excess charge in the base region, and thus the collector current, can be controlled directly by adding or removing charge at the base terminal.

[3] Assuming that the small constant flow of majority carriers entering the base as a consequence of extraction at the reverse-biased collector is negligible. This component is neglected in Fig. 7.4.

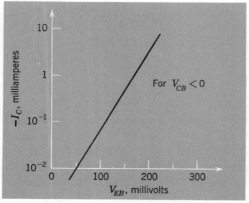

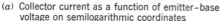

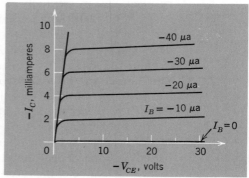

(a) Collector current as a function of emitter–base voltage on semilogarithmic coordinates

(b) Common–emitter output characteristics

Figure 7.6 Static characteristics that display the "control-valve" function of a transistor (germanium *pnp*).

3. The collector current is controlled by the *base current*. This view is really a more limited interpretation of the charge-control mechanism described above, since the base-region excess charge is governed by the past history of the base current. This viewpoint on control of the collector current forms the basis for one set of static characteristic curves for the transistor, in which collector current is plotted versus collector-to-emitter voltage with base current as a parameter. Such a family of static curves is shown in Fig. 7.6*b*; this family is commonly called the *common-emitter output characteristic*.

4. The collector current is controlled by the *emitter current*. As we have seen, the collector current is almost equal to the emitter current. This view is usually not particularly helpful in terms of an electrical description of the device for two reasons. First, in most practical transistor circuits "input signals" are applied directly to the base. This kind of situation is awkward to describe when the control variable is the emitter current. Second, since the collector and emitter currents are approximately equal, even instantaneously under dynamic conditions, this viewpoint is not amenable to a description of the internal dynamical features of transistor performance.

We have introduced the four points of view regarding the "operating mechanism" of a transistor because all of them are employed in the literature of electronic circuits and active devices and should be familiar and meaningful to everyone who professes to understand the physical electronics of transistors. In the analysis that follows we shall emphasize the first two viewpoints, in which either the emitter-base voltage or the base-region excess charge is the independent variable that controls the dependent current source at the collector.

7.3   Circuit Models for Low-Speed Active-Region Operation
7.3.1   Terminal Currents in the Active Region

We begin our detailed analysis of transistors by considering situations in which the terminal variables are either constant or changing slowly with time, that is, *static* or *low-speed* situations. More precisely, we assume that the voltages and charge distributions are changing slowly enough so that the components of the terminal currents that add to or subtract from stores of excess carriers are negligible compared with the corresponding "conduction" components. We shall see later (in Chapter 8) that this low-speed condition is often satisfied even for rather rapid changes; in many modern transistors the charge-changing components of the terminal currents are negligible for changes that occur as rapidly as in a few tenths of a microsecond.

Throughout this discussion, indeed throughout the chapter, we are considering only active-region operation, with the collector junction reverse-biased (by at least several kT/q) and the emitter junction forward-biased (again by at least several kT/q). Under these conditions, the excess-carrier distribution in the base region is approximately linear, as shown by the solid curve in Fig. 7.7. The excess concentration at the emitter edge, denoted by $p_b'(0)$, is exponentially related to the emitter-base voltage V_{EB} in accordance with the Boltzmann relation of Eq. 4.12a.[4] That is,

$$p_b'(0) = p_{bo}(e^{qV_{EB}/kT} - 1) \tag{7.1a}$$

where p_{bo} denotes the equilibrium minority-carrier concentration in the base.

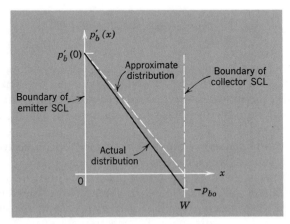

Figure 7.7   Excess-carrier distribution in the base for active-region operation.

[4] We assume that electrostatic potential drops in the neutral emitter and base regions are negligible compared with the junction voltage. This assumption is reasonable under low-injection conditions, but in transistors, just as in diodes, high injection and large currents produce significant drops in the neutral regions. See Section 11.4.3.

The excess concentration at the collector edge is negative, in accordance with Eq. 4.12a, because the collector junction is reverse-biased. That is,

$$p'_b(W) = -p_{bo} \qquad (7.1b)$$

If, as we have assumed, the forward emitter-base voltage is greater than a few kT/q, then $p'_b(0)$ is clearly much greater in magnitude than $p'_b(W)$ (We return in Section 7.3.3 to remove this restriction). Consequently, the distribution can be approximated by the dashed curve in Fig. 7.7, and the slope or gradient of the excess-carrier distribution is approximately $-p'_b(0)/W$. The gradient is independent of x because the minority-carrier current is diffusive and recombination in the thin base is, to first order, negligible. Consequently the collector current I_C is

$$I_C = qAD_b \frac{dp'_b}{dx} \qquad (7.2)$$

or, approximately,

$$I_C \simeq -qAD_b \frac{p'_b(0)}{W} \qquad (7.3)$$

Here D_b denotes the minority-carrier diffusion coefficient in the base, W the width of the neutral base region, and A the cross-sectional area of the base. If we make use of Eq. 7.1a, this expression for the collector current may be written as

$$I_C = -I_1(e^{qV_{EB}/kT} - 1) \qquad (7.4a)$$

where

$$I_1 = qA \frac{D_b p_{bo}}{W} \qquad (7.4b)$$

This I–V relationship is identical in form to Eq. 4.20a, which we derived for a thin-base diode. In fact, the result could have been written directly by analogy with the diode; we have rederived it to emphasize the linear relationship between I_C and $p'_b(0)$, the excess-hole concentration at the emitter edge of the base.

Although recombination in the base and injection of electrons into the heavily-doped emitter give rise to currents that are negligible compared with the collector current given by Eq. 7.4a, the currents must be accounted for at the *base* terminal. We first evaluate the component of base current which results from the flow of electrons into the base to support the small amount of recombination that occurs there. This component of the base current is proportional to the total number of excess carriers in the base. Since the distribution of Fig. 7.7 is roughly triangular, the total excess-hole charge q_F in the base is approximately

$$q_F = qA[\tfrac{1}{2}p'_b(0)W] \qquad (7.5)$$

Consequently, the component of base current I_{BA} that results from recombination in the base is

$$I_{BA} = -\frac{q_F}{\tau_b}$$

or

$$I_{BA} = -\frac{qAW}{2\tau_b}p_b'(0) \tag{7.6a}$$

where τ_b denotes the lifetime of excess carriers in the base. The minus sign in these equations is required because the physical effect, illustrated in Fig. 7.4, corresponds to a flow of electrons *into* the device. In our assumed frame of reference in which a positive value of base current corresponds to the flow of positive charge into the base, this flow is a *negative* current.

The second component of base current supports the injection of base-region majority carriers into the emitter. The magnitude of this current depends on the details of the emitter structure. If we assume that the emitter is a thin low-recombination region having a width of W_e, and recognize that injection levels there are surely low, since they are low in the base (the emitter is more heavily doped), this component of the base current is, by analogy with Eq. 4.18a,

$$I_{BB} = -\frac{qAD_e}{W_e}n_e'(0) \tag{7.6b}$$

where D_e denotes the minority-carrier (electron) diffusion coefficient in the base and $n_e'(0)$ is the excess-electron concentration in the emitter at the space-charge-layer edge. This excess concentration has the same voltage dependence as does $p_b'(0)$. Thus Eq. 7.6b may be written as

$$I_{BB} = -\frac{qAD_e}{W_e}\left(\frac{n_{eo}}{p_{bo}}\right)p_b'(0) \tag{7.6c}$$

where n_{eo} denotes the equilibrium minority-carrier concentration in the emitter.

The total base current $I_{BA} + I_{BB}$ is clearly proportional to $p_b'(0)$. Consequently, the base current has precisely the same dependence on the emitter-base voltage as does the collector current (and the same lack of dependence on the collector-base voltage). Since the base current and the collector current have the same dependence on $p_b'(0)$ and on V_{EB}, it is convenient to express the base current as a fraction of the collector current. That is, we write

$$I_B = \delta I_C$$
$$= -\delta I_1(e^{qV_{EB}/kT} - 1) \tag{7.7}$$

The coefficient δ, which can obviously be expressed in terms of the parameters of Eqs. 7.6a and c, is called the *base defect* (see Problems P7.1 and P7.2). This name arises because the base current originates in second-order mechanisms—base-region recombination and injection into the emitter—that may be thought of as defects in the device. They are defects in the sense that a transistor designer would avoid them entirely if it were possible. The base defect δ may range in value from about 10^{-1} to about 10^{-3}. Because it arises from second-order mechanisms, its value is difficult to control with precision in the design and fabrication of transistors. Thus a group of transistors that are nominally the same may exhibit a spread in their value of δ as large as 10 to 1.

Finally, we must evaluate the emitter current. This current can be expressed in terms of the collector and base currents by making use of Kirchhoff's current law, which requires that

$$I_E + I_B + I_C = 0 \tag{7.8}$$

Hence the emitter current is, using Eqs. 7.4a and 7.7,

$$I_E = -(I_B + I_C)$$
$$= (1 + \delta)I_1(e^{qV_{EB}/kT} - 1) \tag{7.9}$$

The terminal currents all depend on V_{EB} in the same way; this proportionality is shown by Eqs. 7.4a, 7.7, and 7.9. Since the ratios of currents are *independent* of I_1 and V_{EB}, the ratios are useful parameters of the transistor; two of them are widely used:

1. The ratio of the magnitude of the collector current to the magnitude of the emitter current is called the *short-circuit common-base current gain*, and is denoted by α_F. In accordance with Eqs. 7.4a and 7.9 it is

$$\left|\frac{I_C}{I_E}\right| = \alpha_F = \frac{1}{1 + \delta} \tag{7.10a}$$

Clearly α_F is only slightly less than unity, since δ is very small.

2. The ratio of the magnitude of the collector current to the magnitude of the base current is called the *short-circuit common-emitter current gain*, and is denoted by β_F. It has the value

$$\left|\frac{I_C}{I_B}\right| = \beta_F = \frac{1}{\delta} \tag{7.10b}$$

This current gain is quite large because δ is very small. It usually lies in the range from 10 to 10^3.

The direct relationship between these coefficients may be expressed either as

$$\alpha_F = \frac{\beta_F}{1 + \beta_F} \tag{7.11a}$$

or as

$$\beta_F = \frac{\alpha_F}{1 - \alpha_F} \tag{7.11b}$$

7.3.2   Dependent Generators and Circuit Models

The I-V relationships developed in the preceding section can be modeled in circuit terms in several ways. The relationship between the emitter current and the emitter-base voltage (Eq. 7.9) has the same form as the I-V characteristic of an idealized pn junction diode (Eq. 4.20a). Therefore, the behavior of the transistor at the emitter-base terminals can be modeled by an idealized junction diode having a saturation current of $(1 + \delta)I_1$, as shown in Fig. 7.8a. The collector current is dependent on V_{EB} in the same way, but is *independent* of the collector-base voltage. The exponential dependence of the collector current on the emitter-base voltage and its independence of the collector-base voltage can be modeled by means of a *controlled* or dependent current generator, connected as shown in Fig. 7.8b. This model is a complete representation, in terms of circuit symbols and a network, of the three relationships given by Eqs. 7.4a, 7.7, and 7.9. Note that the base current is modeled correctly as a consequence of Kirchhoff's current law.

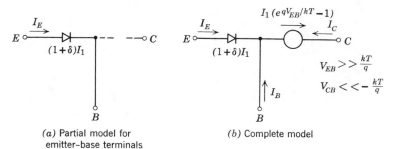

(a) Partial model for emitter–base terminals   (b) Complete model

Figure 7.8   The evolution of a circuit model that represents the static active-region behavior of a *pnp* transistor.

It is essential to understand the nature of the dependent source used in Fig. 7.8b. As we observed in Section 1.4.1, a dependent source differs from an independent source (which is a concept familiar from elementary circuit theory) only in that its value is not independently prescribed, but is governed by some other variable in the circuit. Thus the controlled current source of

Fig. 7.8*b* develops a current at the collector that is explicitly dependent on a voltage elsewhere in the circuit—specifically, at the emitter-base terminals.

The model of Fig. 7.8*b* expresses the collector current in terms of the emitter-base voltage. The choice was an arbitrary one, suggested by Eq. 7.4a; clearly other choices are possible. For example, we can use the proportionality between collector current and emitter current, as expressed by α_F, to form the model shown in Fig. 7.9*a*. Or we can use the proportionality between collector current and base current, as expressed by β_F, to form the model shown in Fig. 7.9*b*. The alternative models are fully equivalent to that shown in Fig. 7.8*b* and correspond exactly to the algebraic *I-V* relationships.

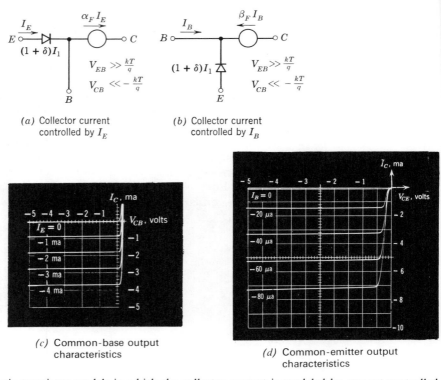

(*a*) Collector current controlled by I_E

(*b*) Collector current controlled by I_B

(*c*) Common-base output characteristics

(*d*) Common-emitter output characteristics

Figure 7.9 Static transistor models in which the collector current is modeled by current-controlled dependent generators.

If a transistor is operated with the input applied to the emitter-base terminals and the output taken from the collector-base terminals, it is considered to be connected in the *common-base* configuration. The model of Fig. 7.9*a* in which the collector current is controlled by the emitter current, shows that under these circumstances the ratio of the "output" (collector) current to the "input" (emitter) current is just α_F. A set of measured common-base output characteristic curves is shown in Fig. 7.9c. The spacing between the curves is proportional to α_F. The active region, in which the collector junction is reverse-biased, occurs in the third quadrant. Clearly the model of Fig. 7.9a with a constant α_F will have characteristics which closely match these measured curves.

A transistor can also be connected so that the emitter is common to the input and output loops; this kind of arrangement is referred to as a *common-emitter* configuration. The model of Fig. 7.9b shows that the current gain of the common-emitter connection is just β_F. A set of measured common-emitted output characteristic curves is shown in Fig. 7.9d. In this case the spacing between the curves is proportional to β_F. Once again, the third quadrant corresponds to the active region. Again the model of Fig. 7.9b with constant β_F will have characteristics which closely match these measured curves.

The circuit models developed in this section all represent the relationship between the emitter current and the emitter-base voltage as an exponential. Just as in the case of the *pn* junction diode discussed in Section 6.2.1, the detail embodied in the exponential nonlinearity is not required in some situations. In these cases, piecewise-linear diodes can be used to replace the exponential diode in the transistor circuit model. Since all of the development to this point applies *only* when the emitter junction is forward-biased (and when the collector junction is reverse-biased), the ideal piecewise-linear diodes used in these models will always be in the *on* state.

The simplest transistor model of this sort is one in which the voltage across the forward-biased emitter junction is neglected entirely. A model based on the common-emitter model of Fig. 7.9b and having this property is shown in Fig. 7.10a. A more accurate model, which includes the threshold voltage

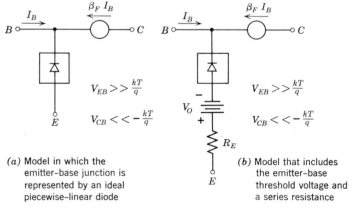

(a) Model in which the emitter–base junction is represented by an ideal piecewise–linear diode

(b) Model that includes the emitter–base threshold voltage and a series resistance

Figure 7.10   Piecewise-linear models that apply when the emitter is forward-biased and the collector is reverse-biased.

V_O associated with the emitter-base junction, and a series resistance R_E, is shown in Fig. 7.10b. These simple models, which have the advantage of containing only *linear* elements (the piecewise-linear diodes are always *on* in the active region), often suffice for an initial exploration of the properties of a transistor circuit.

7.3.3   Models that Include the Collector-Junction Saturation Current

The analysis of Section 7.3.1 and the models of Section 7.3.2 are based on the approximation that the forward emitter-base voltage is large enough so that excess-carrier concentration at the edge of the emitter space-charge layer is much larger than the equilibrium minority-carrier concentration. That is,

$$p_b'(0) \gg p_{bo}$$

It is this condition that permits us to approximate the slope of the excess-carrier distribution, shown in Fig. 7.7, by $-p_b'(0)/W$ and the area under the distribution by $\frac{1}{2}p_b'(0)W$. The first of these approximations was employed in evaluating the collector current (see Eq. 7.3); the second was used in determining the recombination component of the base current (see Eq. 7.5).

These approximations are clearly in error for relatively small forward bias on the emitter-base junction. In such cases the slope of the excess-carrier distribution is more accurately given by $-[p_b'(0) + p_{bo}]/W$, and the area is actually $\frac{1}{2}[p_b'(0) - p_{bo}]W$. Thus both the slope and the area differ from our approximate values by amounts that are independent of $p_b'(0)$, hence of V_{EB}, but are proportional to p_{bo}. It follows that all three terminal currents actually contain components that are independent of V_{EB} but are proportional to p_{bo}. Although negligible under most conditions, these components become important whenever the excess concentration at the emitter edge of the base is not large compared with the equilibrium minority-carrier concentration, that is, when the forward bias on the emitter-base junction is not large or when the temperature is high (recall that p_{bo} is exponentially dependent on temperature).

These temperature-dependent currents can be modeled as shown in Fig. 7.11a, by adding two independent current sources to the common-base model of Fig. 7.9a. The currents produced by these sources, which we have denoted by I_S and I_{CO}, are proportional to p_{bo} and independent of both junction voltages. We postpone evaluation of these currents until Chapter 21, where this matter can be reviewed in a more general context. We shall find there that these fixed currents have values of the order of I_1, the emitter-junction saturation current. Thus for a silicon transistor near room temperature they lie in the range from a nanoampere to a picoampere.

Of course, these temperature-dependent currents can also be added to the common-emitter model of Fig. 7.9b. Such a model appears in Fig. 7.11b. This model can easily be shown to be equivalent to that of Fig. 7.11a by using Kirchhoff's current law to express I_E in terms of I_B and I_C.

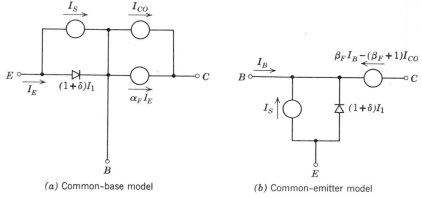

(a) Common–base model   (b) Common–emitter model

Figure 7.11   Static active-region models that include the collector saturation currents.

The current that we have denoted by I_{CO} is called the *open-circuit collector saturation current*. The origin of this name can be understood with the aid of the model shown in Fig. 7.11a. When the emitter junction is open-circuited so that $I_E = 0$, the collector current is equal to I_{CO}.

7.3.4   Limits of the Active Region

All of the discussions, analyses, and circuit models in this chapter are based on two assumptions concerning the electrical operating condition of the transistor:

1. The emitter junction is forward-biased. Except in the preceding section, we require that the forward voltage on this junction be much greater than kT/q.

2. The collector junction is reverse-biased by an amount that is much greater than kT/q.

These conditions define the boundaries of the active region; the models that we have developed are useful in circuit analysis only if the transistor is confined to the active region.

In Chapter 21 we return to a more general analysis of transistor behavior and models, and consider the details of performance outside the active region. However, we pause here to describe, in qualitative terms, the two ways in which a transistor can depart from the active region, and to introduce the models which then apply.

One way of leaving the active region is for the emitter junction to become reverse-biased. The transistor is then said to be *cut off*. In the cut-off region there is no excess carrier injection, and the terminal currents are all small (on the order of I_{CO} or I_1) and independent of the junction voltages. To first order, the electrical behavior of a cut-off transistor can be modeled in terms of an open circuit, as shown in Fig. 7.12a.

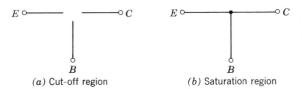

(a) Cut-off region   (b) Saturation region

Figure 7.12   Approximate models for operation in cutoff and saturation regions.

The transistor also leaves the active region if the collector junction becomes forward-biased. The device is then said to be *saturated*. In the saturation region there is injection across both junctions, and the voltages across the forward-biased junctions are small and relatively independent of the terminal currents. To first order, the electrical behavior of a *saturated* transistor can be modeled in terms of a short circuit, as shown in Fig. 7.12b.

7.3.5   Models for *npn* Transistors

Transistors having the *npn* structure differ in operation from the *pnp* device studied above only in that the roles of holes and electrons are interchanged. Thus active-region behavior in an *npn* device involves the flow of *electrons* across the base. It follows that I_E and V_{EB} are *negative* for an *npn* transistor in the active region, whereas I_B, I_C, and V_{CB} are *positive*. Thus the *npn* I-V relationships that are analogous to the *pnp* relationships given by Eqs. 7.4a, 7.7, and 7.9 are

$$I_C = I_1(e^{-qV_{EB}/kT} - 1) \tag{7.12a}$$

$$I_B = \delta I_1(e^{-qV_{EB}/kT} - 1) \tag{7.12b}$$

$$I_E = -(1 + \delta)I_1(e^{-qV_{EB}/kT} - 1) \tag{7.12c}$$

The coefficients I_1 and δ (hence α_F and β_F) are, as a matter of definition, *positive* for both *pnp* and *npn* transistors.

Circuit models for *npn* devices must reflect the polarity differences shown in Eqs. 7.12. Thus all elements that represent the exponential I-V relationship must be inverted. For example, the *pnp* model of Fig. 7.8b can be adapted to the *npn* structure by reversing both the exponential diode and the reference direction of the dependent generator (in which V_{EB} is replaced by $-V_{EB}$), as shown in Fig. 7.13a. When the current-controlled models of Fig. 7.9 are adapted to the *npn* configuration, *only* the exponential diode is reversed. This is illustrated in Fig. 7.13b, where the base-current-controlled model is analogous to that of Fig. 7.9b. Finally, in models that include junction saturation currents (Fig. 7.11) it is necessary to reverse both the exponential diodes and those portions of dependent generators that reflect saturation currents, since these fixed currents have the opposite polarity in *npn* devices. Thus the *pnp* model of Fig. 7.11b transforms to the *npn* model shown in Fig. 7.13c; both I_S and the portion of the collector current generator proportional to I_{CO} are reversed.

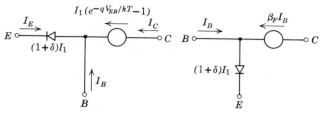

(a) Model with voltage-controlled dependent generator

(b) Model with base-current-controlled dependent generator

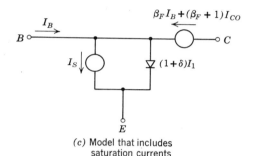

(c) Model that includes saturation currents

Figure 7.13 Circuit models for *npn* transistors. All of these models are applicable only in the active region, that is for $V_{EB} \ll -kT/q$, $V_{CB} \gg kT/q$.

7.4 Examples of Transistor Circuit Analysis

To illustrate the application of the circuit models developed in the preceding sections, we consider three simple circuits in which transistors serve as control valves.

7.4.1 A Common-Emitter Amplifier

The circuit of Fig. 7.14 shows one way in which a *pnp* bipolar transistor can be employed in a circuit as a control valve. The emitter-to-collector path through the device forms part of a loop that contains a dc power source, characterized by the fixed voltage source E_C, and a load, characterized by a

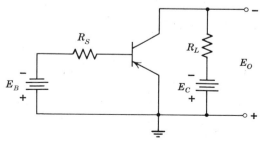

Figure 7.14 A common-emitter amplifier.

resistance R_L. The input comprised of E_B and R_S is connected at the base-emitter terminals. Since the emitter terminal is part of both the input and output loops, this circuit is illustrative of the common-emitter configuration. Although the amplifier will operate as shown, we shall see later that a slightly more complicated circuit configuration is required to ensure correct operation over a range of temperatures.

Let us find for this elementary amplifier the output voltage E_O in terms of the supply voltage E_C and the input voltage E_B. It is clear from the figure that for the indicated polarity of voltage E_B, the emitter junction will be forward-biased. The collector junction will be reverse-biased for E_C as shown, provided that the collector current is not too large. Specifically, we require that

$$-I_C R_L < E_C \tag{7.13}$$

If this condition is met, the transistor will operate in the active region; hence it is appropriate to represent the device by one of the active-region total-variable models developed in Section 7.3.2. In Fig. 7.15 the transistor

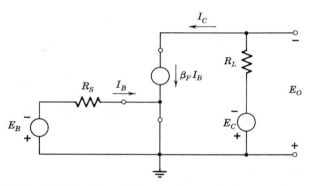

Figure 7.15 The circuit of Fig. 7.14 with the transistor replaced by the model of Fig. 7.10a.

is represented by the simple piecewise-linear model of Fig. 7.10a. Since the piecewise-linear diode is always *on*, it is shown as a short circuit. Now, with all elements expressed in electrical network terms, we can proceed with the analysis. Because of the simplicity of the circuit, the base current I_B can be calculated directly:

$$I_B = -\frac{E_B}{R_S} \tag{7.14}$$

The output relationship is also very simple:

$$E_O = E_C + I_C R_L \tag{7.15a}$$

or

$$E_O = E_C + \beta_F I_B R_L \tag{7.15b}$$

Combining Eqs. 7.14 and 7.15b, we obtain the desired relation for the output voltage

$$E_O = E_C - \beta_F \frac{R_L}{R_S} E_B \qquad (7.16)$$

This equation indicates that the amplifier output voltage E_O can be much more sensitive to changes in E_B than to those in E_C. That is,

$$\frac{\Delta E_O}{\Delta E_C}\bigg|_{E_B \text{ constant}} = 1 \qquad (7.17a)$$

whereas

$$\frac{\Delta E_O}{\Delta E_B}\bigg|_{E_C \text{ constant}} = -\beta_F \frac{R_L}{R_S} \qquad (7.17b)$$

If we assume plausible values of $R_L = R_S = 1$ kohm and $\beta_F = 100$, then E_O changes by 100 mv for every millivolt of change in E_B. Thus the circuit is said to possess the important and useful property of *voltage amplification.*

The circuit also has the property of *current amplification.* Specifically, the change in the output (collector) current produced by a change in input (base) current is

$$\frac{\Delta I_C}{\Delta I_B} = \beta_F \qquad (7.18)$$

For the numerical values introduced above, a change of 1 μa in I_B produces a change of 100 μa in I_C.

Transistors, like other control valves, are useful as circuit components not because they are capable of either voltage amplification or current amplification alone (either of which can be provided by a transformer), but because both can be accomplished in the same circuit, thereby making possible *power amplification.*

The power supplied to the circuit by the input source is simply $-E_B I_B$, or, using Eq. 7.14,

$$P_{\text{in}} = I_B{}^2 R_S$$

The flow of power in the output mesh can be exposed by multiplying Eq. 7.15a by I_C and rearranging terms to obtain

$$-E_C I_C = -E_O I_C + I_C{}^2 R_L \qquad (7.19)$$

The left side of this equation is the power supplied to the circuit by the source E_C. The first term on the right is the power delivered to the transistor (and dissipated from it as heat), and the second term on the right is the power delivered to the load resistor. The ratio of the power delivered to the load to the power supplied by the input source is

$$\frac{P_{\text{load}}}{P_{\text{in}}} = \left(\frac{I_C}{I_B}\right)^2 \frac{R_L}{R_S} \qquad (7.20a)$$

or, equivalently,

$$\frac{P_{\text{load}}}{P_{\text{in}}} = \beta_F{}^2 \frac{R_L}{R_S} \qquad (7.20b)$$

This ratio, which may be called the *power amplification* of the circuit, has a value of 10^4 for the element values used above. Note that it is the product of the voltage amplification defined by Eq. 7.17b and the current amplification defined by Eq. 7.18.

This discussion illustrates the function of the transistor as a control valve or power modulator. The power delivered to the load by the source E_C is controlled by the input variable E_B. Furthermore, this control is accomplished with the expenditure of relatively little power at the input terminals.

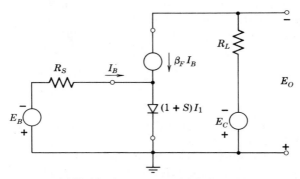

(a) Model using an exponential diode model

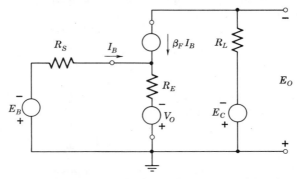

(b) Model using a piecewise-linear diode model

Figure 7.16   Circuits for the amplifier of Fig. 7.14 in which more elaborate and more accurate models are used for the transistor.

To improve the accuracy of this analysis, we can use a transistor model that includes an exponential diode to represent the emitter-base junction, as shown in Fig. 7.16*a*. Alternatively, we could use the transistor model shown in Fig. 7.16*b* in which the emitter junction has been modeled by a threshold voltage V_O and a resistor R_E.

The analysis required to find E_O in Fig. 7.16*b* is slightly more complicated than before because resistor R_E couples the input and output circuits together. The Kirchhoff's voltage-law equation for the input loop yields

$$-E_B - I_B R_S - (I_B + \beta_F I_B)R_E + V_O = 0 \tag{7.21}$$

Solving for I_B, we obtain

$$I_B = \frac{-E_B + V_O}{R_S + (\beta_F + 1)R_E} \tag{7.22}$$

The output equation, Eq. 7.15b, is unaltered by the presence of R_E, because the current source $\beta_F I_B$ sets the current through R_L regardless of other elements in the loop. By eliminating I_B from Eqs. 7.15b and 7.22, we obtain (see Problem P7.8)

$$E_O = E_C - \frac{\beta_F R_L}{R_S + (\beta_F + 1)R_E}(E_B - V_O) \tag{7.23}$$

If we assume that the circuit uses a silicon transistor and that the collector currents of interest are on the order of milliamperes, reasonable values of the new parameters are $V_O = 0.6$ volt and $R_E = 5$ ohms. Using the same resistor values as before, we find that a 1-mv change in E_B will, according to this more accurate analysis, produce a 67-mv change in E_O. Notice that V_O has no effect on the amplifying property of the circuit. However, it can adversely affect circuit performance, as we shall see in the next section.

7.4.2 A Balanced DC Amplifier

Suppose that we wish to use the circuit in Figure 7.14 as an electronic meter to measure an unknown voltage by connecting this voltage in series with E_B. Equation 7.23 indicates that the circuit would be quite unsatisfactory for this purpose. It would be possible to calibrate the "instrument" before use and thus account for E_C and the resistor values, which presumably are constant. But the voltage V_O associated with the emitter-base junction is temperature-dependent, decreasing as the temperature increases at a rate of approximately 2 mv/°C, as we saw in Section 4.3.3. (For simplicity, we ignore in this example the fact that β_F is also temperature-dependent.) Thus to build a satisfactory meter it is essential to eliminate the voltage V_O from the measurement. One particularly effective method of accomplishing this is shown in Fig. 7.17. Note that to emphasize the basic operational similarities between *npn* and *pnp* transistor circuits, we have switched in this circuit to *npn* transistors (see Problem P7.9).

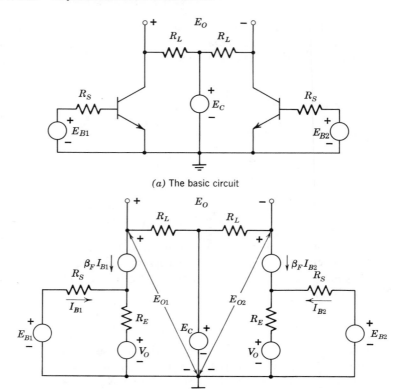

(a) The basic circuit

(b) The circuit after insertion of
models for the transistor

Figure 7.17 A balanced amplifier. Note that *npn* transistors are used.

A closer examination of the circuit in Fig. 7.17*a* discloses that it has been
constructed by placing two simple common-emitter circuits together. The
difference between the individual output voltages E_{O1} and E_{O2} is the circuit
output:

$$E_O = E_{O1} - E_{O2} \qquad (7.24)$$

Furthermore, because the only common element between the two halves of
the circuit is the fixed voltage source E_C, there is no coupling between the
two halves. Hence E_{O1} depends only on the elements in the left-hand circuit,
and the relationship is again given by Eq. 7.23.[5]

$$E_{O1} = E_C - \frac{\beta_F R_L}{R_S + (\beta_F + 1)R_E}(E_{B1} - V_O) \qquad (7.25a)$$

[5] This equation has the same form for the circuit of Fig. 7.17 even though *npn* transistors are
used, because the polarities of E_{O2}, E_{O2}, and *all* sources (including E_{B1} and E_{B2}) are inverted
(see Problem P7.9).

Similarly

$$E_{O2} = E_C - \frac{\beta_F R_L}{R_S + (\beta_F + 1)R_E}(E_{B2} - V_O) \tag{7.25b}$$

Subtracting these two voltages in accordance with Eq. 7.24, we obtain for the electronic meter output

$$E_O = \frac{\beta_F R_L}{R_S + (\beta_F + 1)R_E}(E_{B2} - E_{B1}) \tag{7.26}$$

Because of the balanced or symmetric nature of the circuit, the temperature-dependent voltage V_O has been eliminated from the meter output. A simple calibration procedure can now be used to establish the value of the multiplier constant in Eq. 7.26. First set E_{B1} equal to E_{B2}, thereby making $E_O = 0$ (for perfect circuit symmetry). Then add a small known calibrating voltage E_k in series with E_{B2}. The ratio E_O/E_k is the multiplier constant. To make the measurement, the voltage E_k is replaced by the unknown voltage.

Of course the threshold or offset voltage V_O is balanced out only to the extent that the circuit is truly symmetric and isothermal. Any asymmetry in resistor values or in β_F, or any temperature difference between the two transistors, will give rise to an output voltage that is present even when $E_{B1} = E_{B2}$ and reflects the temperature dependence of V_O. One of the important advantages of the planar diffusion process for manufacturing integrated circuits is that several transistors and associated circuitry can be produced on the same chip of silicon; this process provides both closely matched element values and good thermal contact between elements and thus is ideal for manufacturing amplifiers of this type.

In discussing the behavior of symmetrical circuits such as that of Fig. 7.17 it is convenient to regard the input voltages E_{B1} and E_{B2} as the superposition of two sets of component voltages. Specifically, we write

$$E_{B1} = (E_{BS} - E_{BD}) \tag{7.27a}$$

$$E_{B2} = (E_{BS} + E_{BD}) \tag{7.27b}$$

The component E_{BS} is called the *sum* or *common-mode* component of the input voltages. Equations 7.27 show that it is the average of the input voltages

$$E_{BS} = \frac{E_{B1} + E_{B2}}{2} \tag{7.28a}$$

The component E_{BD} is called the *difference* or *difference-mode* component of the input voltages. It is simply half the difference of these voltages:

$$E_{BD} = \frac{E_{B2} - E_{B1}}{2} \tag{7.28b}$$

Our analysis of the circuit of Fig. 7.17 shows, in Eq. 7.26, that the output voltage is a function only of the difference component of the input voltages and is independent of the sum component. For this reason the circuit is often called a *difference* or *differential amplifier*.

Although the differential amplifier circuit of Fig. 7.17a has the property that with perfect symmetry and balance the output voltage E_O depends only on the difference between the input voltages, the collector-to-ground voltages E_{O1} and E_{O2} are separately strongly dependent on E_{B1} and E_{B2}, that is, they depend on the sum component of the inputs. This dependence is shown by Eqs. 7.25. The circuit may be modified to reduce this dependence by returning the emitters to ground through a *common* current source as shown in Fig. 7.18. It is obvious from the symmetry of this circuit that the collector-to-collector voltage E_O is zero whenever the difference component of the input is zero, that is, whenever E_{B1} is equal to E_{B2} (assuming again that the elements are matched). Furthermore, the separate collector-to-ground voltages are clearly *independent* of E_{B1} and E_{B2} for equal input voltages. The collector-to-ground voltages are simply

$$E_{O1} = E_{O2} = E_C - \frac{I_A R_L}{2} \tag{7.29}$$

and are independent of E_{B1} and E_{B2}, since for balanced inputs the current I_A divides equally between the two halves of the circuit.

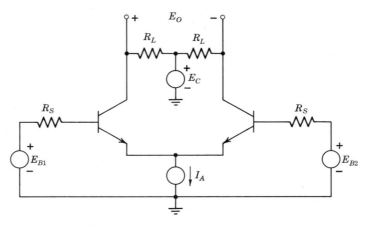

Figure 7.18　A differential amplifier in which common-mode input signals are not amplified.

The current source in the emitter lead has no effect, however, on the differential behavior of the circuit. That is, Eq. 7.26 applies to the circuit of Fig. 7.18 as well as to the circuit of Fig. 7.17a for which it was derived. The differential gain is unaffected by I_A because differential input signals cause the current in one transistor to increase by the same amount by which the current in the other transistor decreases. Thus the sum of the emitter currents is constant even in the circuit of Fig. 7.17 when differential input signals are considered, and the addition of the current source, as in Fig. 7.18, is of no consequence.

Thus addition of the current source reduces the common-mode gain of the amplifier without affecting the difference-mode gain. This makes the output voltage less sensitive to small deviations from symmetry and also suppresses any undesirable common-mode component that may be present in the input.

A more practical version of the balanced dc amplifier, which operates from a single 6-volt battery, is shown in Fig. 7.19. Resistor R_5 has approximately

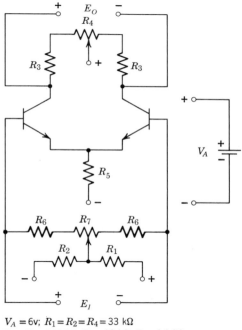

$V_A = 6v$; $R_1 = R_2 = R_4 = 33$ kΩ
$R_3 = R_5 = 100$ kΩ; $R_6 = 10$ kΩ; $R_7 = 3.3$ kΩ
Sil: $I_C = 12$ μa, $V_{CE} = 2.2$ v

Figure 7.19 A more practical differential amplifier.

half the supply voltage across it and thus develops a current that is reasonably constant if the common-mode component of the input voltages is small compared with the supply voltage. Although the common-mode gain of this circuit is not zero, it is much smaller than it would be if the common emitter resistor R_5 were not present. Potentiometers R_4 and R_7 are used to balance out any small differences in transistor characteristics or resistor values. To ensure rapid convergence of the balance controls, adjust R_4 to make $E_O = 0$ when the input terminals are shorted. Then adjust R_7 to make $E_O = 0$ when the input terminals are open-circuited.

7.4.3 A Voltage Regulator[*]

As another example of the use of transistor circuit models, let us design a voltage-regulator circuit to be used in connection with the half-wave rectifier circuit described in Section 6.4. A simple circuit of this type is illustrated in Fig. 7.20a. A single transistor is connected between the rectifier output and the resistor R_L, used here to represent the load on the system. A breakdown diode is connected to the base lead of the transistor to keep the base at a constant potential with respect to ground. Resistor R_S supplies both the current for the breakdown diode and the base current. Since the output voltage E_O differs from this fixed reference voltage only by the voltage across the forward-biased emitter-base junction, E_O is nearly constant, even though the load resistance and the ac input voltage may change. Changes in the

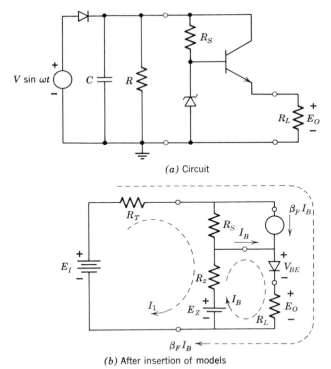

(a) Circuit

(b) After insertion of models

Figure 7.20 A transistor voltage regulator.

[*] This section may be omitted in an introductory study without loss of continuity. It should be omitted if Section 6.4.3 was omitted.

rectifier output voltage are taken up across the reverse-biased collector junction. To complete the design, we must select a suitable breakdown diode voltage and a suitable value for R_S.

For any finite value of R_L, there will be current flowing down through R_S and through the emitter-base junction of the transistor. Thus the emitter-base junction will be forward-biased. At the same time, the voltage drop across R_S ensures that the collector-base junction will always be reverse-biased. Hence for finite values of R_L the transistor will be in the forward active region and therefore can be replaced for analysis by the model of Fig. 7.13b, as shown in Fig. 7.20b. Also in this figure the half-wave rectifier and capacitor have been modeled by a voltage source E_I and a resistance R_T. The Thévenin equivalent source resistance R_T reflects the fact that increased load current causes the average capacitor voltage to decrease, as discussed in Section 6.4.3. The breakdown diode is modeled by a voltage source E_Z and a series resistance R_z. With all devices now represented by network elements, we can proceed with the analysis.

The circuit has only two independent loop currents, for the third loop current is determined by the dependent current source. Although several choices of loop variables are possible, the analysis is somewhat simplified if the identities of the currents I_B and $\beta_F I_B$ are retained. Three loop currents selected on this basis are shown dashed in Figure 7.20b. The resulting loop equations (Kirchhoff voltage law) are

$$E_I - (I_1 + \beta_F I_B)R_T - I_1 R_S - (I_1 - I_B)R_z - E_z = 0 \qquad (7.30a)$$

$$E_z - (I_B - I_1)R_z - V_{BE} - (I_B + \beta_F I_B)R_L = 0 \qquad (7.30b)$$

Collecting the terms, we have

$$E_I - E_z = I_1(R_T + R_S + R_z) + I_B(\beta_F R_T - R_z) \qquad (7.31a)$$

$$E_z - V_{BE} = -I_1 R_z + I_B[R_z + (\beta_F + 1)R_L] \qquad (7.31b)$$

(Equations 7.31 can be obtained directly by use of superposition. Equate the voltage sources around the loop to the voltage drops produced in the resistors first from I_1 acting along and then from I_B acting alone. Hereafter, all loop equations will be written on this basis.) The relation between the regulator output voltage E_O and the loop currents is

$$E_O = (\beta_F + 1)I_B R_L \qquad (7.32)$$

Hence we must solve Eqs. 7.31 for I_B.[6] By Cramer's rule,

$$I_B = \frac{(E_z - V_{BE})(R_T + R_S + R_z) + (E_I - E_z)R_z}{(R_T + R_S + R_z)[R_z + (\beta_F + 1)R_L] + R_z(\beta_F R_T - R_z)} \qquad (7.33)$$

---

[6] Note that we have tacitly assumed that V_{BE} is constant in solving these equations. In reality, V_{BE} depends on I_B. The assumption that V_{BE} is constant is equivalent to replacing the exponential diode by a piecewise-linear diode having a threshold voltage V_{BE}.

This expression, although not complicated, is at least intricate enough to obscure any first-order design information therein. To simplify, let us introduce numerical values. Assume that we are trying to design a power supply to deliver 20 volts at a maximum current of 500 ma. Thus the resistor R_L representing the load on the system has a *minimum* value of 40 ohms. If the transistor is silicon, V_{BE} will be about 0.6 volt, so that we select a 20.6 volt breakdown diode. In this voltage range, diode resistances of 5 to 10 ohms are typical, for currents greater than 1 ma. We choose the ac input voltage so that with no load current the voltage across the smoothing capacitor is 30 volts, and we somewhat arbitrarily take the power supply Thévenin resistance R_T to be 10 ohms. Assuming the above resistor values, and a value for β_F of at least 100, we can simplify Eq. 7.33 to

$$I_B \simeq \frac{(E_z - V_{BE})(R_T + R_S + R_z) + (E_I - E_z)R_z}{(R_T + R_S + R_z)[(\beta_F + 1)R_L]} \tag{7.34}$$

(The term $R_z\beta_F R_T$ has been neglected compared to $R_S\beta_F R_L$ on the basis that even though the exact value of R_S is not known, it will certainly be much bigger than R_z.) Substituting into Eq. 7.32 and simplifying, we obtain

$$E_O = E_z - V_{BE} + (E_I - E_z)\frac{R_z}{R_T + R_S + R_z} \tag{7.35}$$

A definite design criterion can now be deduced from this first-order analysis. Any changes in E_I, resulting from line voltage changes, for example, will be suppressed at the output by the ratio

$$\frac{\Delta E_O}{\Delta E_I} = \frac{R_z}{R_T + R_S + R_z} \tag{7.36}$$

Thus if R_S can be made much larger than $R_T + R_z$, then E_O will depend almost completely on $E_z - V_{BE}$ and will be nearly independent of E_I.

As mentioned above, R_S must supply the transistor base current and the breakdown diode current. Thus there is a limit to the maximum size of R_S. A little thought will show that the constraint on R_S will be most severe when the system is delivering full load current, for under this condition the rectifier output voltage is lowest (25 volts) and the base current requirement is greatest (5 ma for a β_F of 99). Thus the largest that we can make R_S, based on a 1-ma minimum diode current, is

$$R_S(\text{max}) = \frac{25 - 20.6}{5 + 1} \simeq 730 \text{ ohms}$$

For this value of R_S, Eq. 7.36 shows that changes in E_I are suppressed by a factor of 75.

To complete the design, we should check that the transistor stays in the active region and within its power-dissipation capability for all anticipated power supply loads.

It is clear from the preceding discussion, particularly from Eq. 7.36, that a very simple voltage-regulator circuit, consisting of a transistor, a breakdown diode, and a resistor, can greatly improve the performance of a power supply by making the output voltage less dependent on the characteristics of the half-wave rectifier. Other performance characteristics of the circuit, such as output ripple and effective output resistance, are much simpler to discuss in terms of increments rather than the total variables used in this chapter. Hence the calculations of these properties will be postponed until after the introduction of incremental analysis in Chapter 11.

7.5   Transistor Operation at Extremes of Collector Voltage

Throughout this chapter we have assumed that the internal physical behavior of a bipolar transistor that operates in the active region is unaffected by variations in the collector junction voltage. In reality, this assumption is not quite true; there are two mechanisms by which the collector junction voltage affects the terminal currents. These mechanisms involve the dependence of base width on collector voltage, and avalanche multiplication in the collector junction.

7.5.1   Base-Width Changes

The width W of the active base region is measured between the emitter and collector space-charge layers. Since these space-charge layers have widths that depend on the junction voltages, the base width varies as these voltages change. For operation in the active region, the collector junction, which is reverse-biased and whose width is much greater than that of the emitter space-charge layer, dominates the voltage dependence of the base width. Specifically, as the reverse voltage on the collector junction *increases*, the corresponding space-charge layer *widens*, and the width of the active base region *decreases*. As a consequence of this dependence of base width on collector-to-base voltage, both the saturation current I_1 (see Eq. 7.4b) and the base defect δ (see Eq. 7.7) are not constant but depend on V_{CB}. Though this dependence is seldom an important effect in the context of *total-variable* transistor models, such as those shown in Figs. 7.8 and 7.9, it does influence significantly the parameters that characterize the *incremental* behavior of bipolar transistors, as we shall see in Chapter 12.

The degree of dependence of the base width on the collector-to-base voltage is governed by the physical structure of the transistor, specifically by the impurity profile in the base. Transistors in which the junctions are formed by solid-state diffusion have impurity profiles similar to that shown in Fig. 7.21a, which should be compared with Fig. 5.3. The impurity concentration is greater toward the middle of the base than near the collector. Consequently, increases in the collector reverse voltage require relatively little additional penetration of the space-charge layer into the base (recall that the reverse voltage is proportional to the first moment of the space-

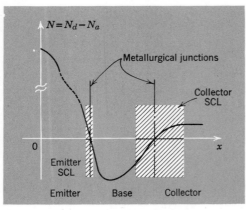

(a) Diffused junction transistor

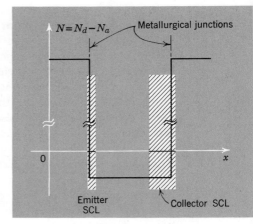

(b) Alloyed junction transistor

Figure 7.21   Impurity profiles for *npn* bipolar transistors. Note that the scale is broken on the net impurity concentration coordinate.

charge-layer charge distribution) and the base width is weakly dependent on V_{CB}. On the other hand, transistors in which the junctions are formed by alloying impurities into a homogeneous base region to form the emitter and collector regions have flat impurity profiles, as shown in Fig. 7.21*b*. In these devices it is possible for the collector space-charge layer to penetrate all the way across the active base region and to merge with the emitter space-charge layer. Such a condition is known as *punch-through*. Normal transistor action ceases as soon as punch-through occurs.[7]

Clearly, it is necessary to operate transistors well below the collector voltage at which punch-through occurs if uniform reproducible circuit performance is required. Thus the punch-through voltage constitutes a fundamental collector voltage limit on transistor operation. Because the base width varies greatly in magnitude as the collector junction voltage approaches the punch-through value, there are radical changes in those characteristics that depend on base width. For this reason it is seldom desirable to operate with V_{CB} greater than about half the punch-through voltage.

7.5.2   Avalanche Multiplication at the Collector

Transistors operated at large values of collector-base voltage have their electrical characteristics modified by avalanche multiplication of carriers in the collector space-charge layer. The physical mechanism is precisely the same as that discussed in Section 6.5.1 in the context of junction diodes; primary carriers that flow into the collector space-charge layer from the

[7] The modeling of a transistor under punch-through conditions is discussed in Reference 7.2, Chapter 1.

base region produce hole-electron pairs by the process of impact ionization of covalent bonds. The resulting secondary carriers flow out of the collector space-charge layer and contribute to the collector current.

For operation in the common-base configuration, the consequences of this avalanche multiplication are straightforward. The collector current is simply multiplied by M, the avalanche multiplication factor, which is defined as the ratio of the total current crossing the junction to the primary current produced *outside* the junction. This factor rises sharply and without apparent limit as the collector-base voltage approaches the avalanche breakdown voltage V_a. Figure 7.22, which shows the common-base collector characteristics of an *npn* transistor, illustrates the consequences of avalanche multiplication at the collector. These curves should be compared with those of Fig. 7.9c, which apply to a (*pnp*) transistor that operates with collector-to-base voltages that are too small for avalanche multiplication to be significant. Note that the effects of carrier multiplication in the space-charge layer can be seen at voltages well below V_a, which is about 98 volts for the transistor shown in Fig. 7.22. For example, at about 60 volts the collector current exceeds the emitter current in magnitude because of carrier multiplication in the collector junction.

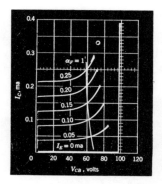

Figure 7.22   Common-base collector characteristics, showing the effects of avalanche multiplication and breakdown at the collector junction. The locus of points at which $I_C = I_E$ ($\alpha_F = 1$) has been added.

The consequences of avalanche multiplication are more complicated and subtle when the transistor is operated in the common-emitter configuration. Holes and electrons are produced *in pairs* by the avalanche multiplication process in the collector junction. Carriers of the collector-majority type are swept into the collector by the electric field and contribute directly to the collector current. Carriers of the opposite type are swept into the *base* region where they *reduce* the required base current. If the avalanche multiplication factor becomes large enough, the polarity of the base current actually reverses.

because the avalanche multiplication process in the collector junction is providing more majority carriers to the base than are necessary to support recombination in the base and emitter. Inasmuch as the common-emitter collector characteristics are normally shown with base current as a parameter, these curves are quite sensitive to *small amounts* of avalanche multiplication, which becomes apparent for collector voltages well below the avalanche breakdown value. The total collector current, including the secondary current produced by impact ionization, is

$$I_C = -M(\alpha_F I_E + I_{CO}) \tag{7.37}$$

Kirchhoff's current law requires that

$$I_B = -(I_E + I_C) \tag{7.38}$$

If I_E is eliminated between Eqs. 7.37 and 7.38, we obtain

$$I_C = \frac{M\alpha_F}{1 - M\alpha_F} I_B - \frac{M}{1 - M\alpha_F} I_{CO} \tag{7.39}$$

This result shows that the total-signal common-emitter current gain, which is the coefficient of I_B, has a singularity when

$$M\alpha_F = 1 \tag{7.40}$$

The value of V_{CB} ($\simeq V_{CE}$) at which Eq. 7.40 is satisfied is called the *sustaining voltage* V_s. Because α_F is only slightly less than unity, relatively small values of M satisfy Eq. 7.40. Consequently, the sustaining voltage is much smaller

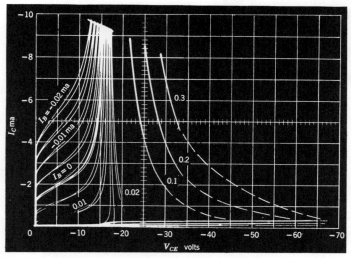

Figure 7.23   Common-emitter output characteristics, showing the effects of avalanche multiplication and the associated reversal of base current.

than the avalanche breakdown voltage at which the singularity in M occurs. For typical numerical values of α_F, the sustaining voltage is one-tenth to one-third of the avalanche breakdown voltage. Inasmuch as the current gain α_F depends on the quiescent current at which the transistor operates, the sustaining voltage is current-dependent. Consequently, the sustaining voltage generally appears as a contour and not as a constant-voltage line on the common-emitter collector characteristics, as shown in Fig. 7.23. The avalanche breakdown voltage V_a of the collector junction of this transistor is about 67 volts. The sustaining voltage V_s, at which no base current is required to produce unbounded collector current, is about 15 volts. These curves should be compared with those of Fig. 7.9d, which are limited to collector-to-base voltages that are too small to produce a significant amount of avalanche multiplication.

Note that it is possible to operate a bipolar transistor with collector voltages larger than the sustaining voltage. In this region of operation the base current has the opposite sign.

REFERENCES

7.1   P. E. Gray *et al.*, *Physical Electronics and Circuit Models of Transistors*, Wiley, New York, 1964.

7.2   R. D. Thornton *et al.*, *Characteristics and Limitations of Transistors*, Wiley, New York, 1966.

PROBLEMS

P7.1   This problem is concerned with the component of base current that feeds recombination in the base. Show that this current, which we denote by I_{BA}, can be written as

$$I_{BA} = \delta_B I_C$$

where

$$\delta_B = \frac{1}{2}\left(\frac{W}{L_b}\right)^2$$

Here L_b denotes the diffusion length of minority carriers in the base

$$L_b = \sqrt{D_b \tau_b}$$

and W denotes the base width. The dimensionless coefficient δ_B is called the *base defect*. It can be made small by making the base width small compared to the diffusion length.

P7.2   This problem is concerned with the component of base current that supports the injection of base-region majority carriers into the emitter. We assume that the emitter region can be characterized, with respect to the flow of minority carriers, as a thin-base diode. Thus, in accordance with Eq. 7.6b, the current associated with electrons injected across the emitter junction from base *to emitter* in a *pnp* transistor is

$$I_{BB} = -\frac{qAD_e n_{eo}}{W_e}(e^{qV_{EB}/kT} - 1)$$

In this equation, A denotes the area of the emitter-base junction, D_e the diffusion coefficient of minority carriers in the emitter, W_e the width of the low-recombination portion of the emitter, and n_{eo} the equilibrium minority-carrier concentration in the emitter. Show that the current I_{BB} that results from injection from base to emitter can be written as

$$I_{BB} = \delta_E I_C$$

where

$$\delta_E = \frac{D_e W n_{eo}}{D_b W_e p_{bo}}$$

Here D_b, W, and p_{bo} have their usual meanings. The dimensionless coefficient δ_E is called the *emitter defect*. Since n_{eo}/p_{bo} is approximately equal to N_D/N_A, where N_D is the donor concentration in the *n*-type base and N_A is the acceptor concentration in the *p*-type emitter, the emitter defect can be made small by doping the emitter much more heavily than the base ($N_A \gg N_D$).

P7.3   If we neglect the extraction into the base of collector-region minority carriers, the total base current is

$$I_B = I_{BA} + I_{BB}$$

where I_{BA} and I_{BB} are defined in Problems 7.1 and 7.2. Express β_F and α_F (Eqs. 7.10) in terms of the emitter and base defects δ_E and δ_B.

P7.4   As we have seen, the transistor functions as a control valve as a consequence of the flow of *minority* carriers across the base from the emitter to the collector. Furthermore, the distribution and flow of minority carriers in this region is analogous, in considerable detail, to the situation in an asymmetric thin-base diode of the type considered in Section 4.3. Consider an *npn* transistor (*not pnp*, as in the text) that has the following characteristics:

(1) The emitter is doped much more heavily than the base.

(2) There is negligible recombination in the base, and negligible injection into the emitter.

(3) All of the applied voltage at either junction appears as a change in the height of the potential barrier in the junction space-charge layer.

(4) The junctions are planar and parallel, and the width of the base between the space-charge-layer edges is W.

(5) The reference directions for the terminal variables are as shown in Fig. 7.5.

(6) The injection level everywhere is low.

(*a*) Assume that the collector junction is zero-biased ($V_{CB} = 0$) and that the emitter junction is forward-biased ($V_{EB} < 0$). Determine the excess-carrier concentrations, $n'_b(0)$ and $n'_b(W)$ at the edges of the base. The equilibrium minority-carrier concentration in the base is n_{bo}. Compare these boundary conditions with those of the diode studied in Section 4.3.

(*b*) The injected electron current is essentially constant across the base. Use this fact together with the boundary conditions of (*a*) to determine the excess concentration $n'_b(x)$. Sketch and dimension your result.

(*c*) Sketch and dimension $n_b(x)$, $p_b(x)$, the electron current density J_e, and the hole current density J_h (both defined normal to the junctions and with a reference direction from the emitter to the collector).

(*d*) Calculate the collector current I_C as a function of V_{EB} for $V_{CB} = 0$ by evaluating the slope of $n'_b(x)$. Be sure that the polarity is right, and assume a junction area of A.

(*e*) Now assume that there is recombination in the base, characterized by a lifetime τ_b. Calculate the base current by evaluating the total excess charge in the base and taking into account recombination. Express the base current as a function of V_{EB}. Be sure the polarity is right.

(*f*) Note that the emitter current can be expressed in terms of the base and collector currents. Use this fact to evaluate I_E.

(*g*) Show that the current-voltage relationships obtained in (*d*), (*e*), and (*f*) are expressed by the model of Fig. 7.13*b*. Evaluate β_F and I_1, which are positive constants. Note that $I_B \ll I_C$ implies $\beta_F \gg 1$. This, in turn, requires $W^2 \ll 2D_b\tau_b$.

Although we assumed zero collector-to-base voltage, the model is valid, as an approximation, for any value of *reverse* bias ($V_{CB} > 0$) at the collector junction, *if the emitter junction is forward-biased* ($V_{EB} < 0$).

P7.5 Write the *I-V* relationships implied by the models of Fig. 7.9 and show that they are equivalent to Eqs. 7.4a, 7.7, and 7.9.

P7.6 Show that the model of Fig. 7.11*b* is equivalent to that of Fig. 7.11*a* by writing the *I-V* relationships implied by each and showing that these algebraic relationships are equivalent.

P7.7 Verify Eq. 7.35, which expresses the output voltage of the circuit of Fig. 7.20 in terms of the input voltage and the circuit parameters.

P7.8 Verify Eq. 7.23, which expresses the output voltage of the circuit of Fig. 7.16*b* in terms of the input voltage and the supply voltage. Note that this result reduces to Eq. 7.16 when R_E and V_O are set equal to zero.

P7.9 A common-emitter amplifier that uses an *npn* transistor is shown in Fig. 7.24.

(*a*) Sketch a model for the transistor that is analogous to the *pnp* model shown in Fig. 7.10*b*.

(*b*) Sketch and label a circuit in which the transistor in Fig. 7.24 is replaced by the model derived in (*a*).

(*c*) Derive an expression for the output voltage E_O in terms of E_B, E_C, and the other parameters of the circuit. Compare this result with Eq. 7.23.

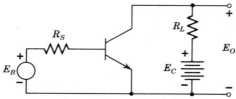

Figure 7.24   A common-emitter amplifier that uses an *npn* transistor.

P7.10 The static *V-I* characteristics of a transistor can be represented in graphical form. Many different graphical presentations of the static characteristics are possible, corresponding to the different choices of independent and dependent variables. The most common type of graphical characteristic describes the transistor in the common-emitter configuration in terms of the variables shown in Fig. 7.25*a*. Generally, I_B and V_{CE} are taken as the independent variables. Consequently, the functional relationships presented in the graphs are

$$I_C = I_C(I_B, V_{CE})$$
$$V_{BE} = V_{BE}(I_B, V_{CE})$$

The characteristics shown in Fig. 7.25*b* are reasonably typical of a lower-power *pnp* silicon transistor. Notice that these curves do not show the behavior of the device for $V_{CE} > 0$; they show only that region of operation for which V_{CE} is negative.

Explain briefly, in terms of the internal physical behavior of the transistor, the following features of the characteristics:

(*a*) The input characteristic is approximately independent of V_{CE} (for negative V_{CE}).

(*b*) The collector current is approximately proportional to the base current.

(*c*) The collector current is essentially independent of V_{CE}.

P7.11 The circuit of a common-base amplifier is shown in Fig. 7.26. The transistor operates in the active region.

(*a*) Sketch a circuit model of this amplifier in which the transistor is represented by the *npn* form of a model which differs from that shown in

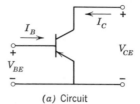

(a) Circuit

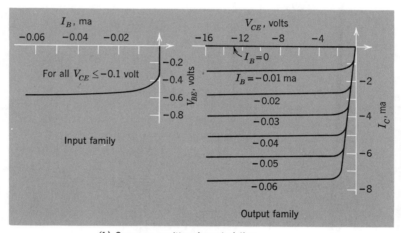

(b) Common–emitter characteristics

Figure 7.25 Common-emitter configuration and characteristics.

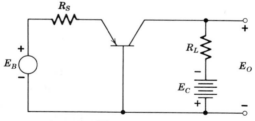

Figure 7.26 A common-base amplifier.

Fig. 7.9a only in that the exponential diode is replaced by a piecewise-linear diode characterized by a threshold voltage V_O and a forward resistance R_E.

(b) Derive an expression for the output voltage E_O in terms of the input voltage E_B, the supply voltage E_C, and the other parameters of the circuit.

(c) Determine the values of E_B at which the transistor is at the boundaries of the active region, that is, at the edge of saturation and at the edge of cutoff.

P7.12 Repeat Problem 7.11 for the *common-collector* amplifier shown in Fig. 7.27. Use as a model of the transistor the *npn* form of the piecewise-linear model shown in Fig. 7.10*b*.

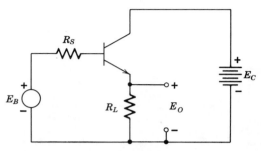

Figure 7.27 A common-collector amplifier.

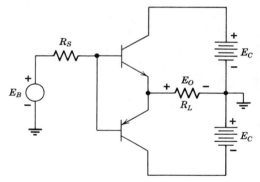

Figure 7.28 A push-pull amplifier.

P7.13 The *npn* and *pnp* transistors in the circuit of Fig. 7.28 are *matched*, that is, they have the same values of β_F, of emitter diode threshold voltage V_O, and of emitter diode forward resistance R_E.

(*a*) Sketch a circuit model of this amplifier in which the transistors are represented by piecewise-linear models of the form shown in Fig. 7.10*b*.

(*b*) Derive an expression for the output voltage E_O in terms of the input voltage E_B, the supply voltage E_C, and the other parameters of the model. Note that the two transistors are never *simultaneously* in the active region; when one transistor conducts, the other is cut off.

(*c*) Sketch and dimension the voltage transfer characteristic derived in (*b*) for the full range of input voltages for which neither transistor is saturated.

(*d*) This circuit is to be used as a linear amplifier, that is, the output voltage E_O is intended to be a replica in form of the input voltage E_B. In view of the transfer characteristic sketched in (*c*), what can you say about the usefulness of this circuit as a linear amplifier? Can you modify the circuit in a way that will eliminate the "dead zone" that exists near $E_B = 0$ in the transfer characteristic?

P7.14 The circuit of a simple common-emitter transistor amplifier is shown in Fig. 7.29. The transistor characteristics are shown in Fig. 7.25.

(a) The collector supply voltage V_{CC} and the load resistor R_L place a linear constraint on I_C and V_{CE} $(= v_O)$. Determine the constraint, and plot it on the output family (assume that no current is supplied at the output terminals).

(b) The input voltage v_I and the base resistor R_B place a linear constraint on I_B and v_{BE}. Determine the constraint and plot it on the input family for several values of v_I in the range $-6 < v_I < +1$ volt.

(c) Determine graphically v_O versus v_I for v_I in the range defined in (b). Plot your results on linear coordinates and dimension the curve. This relationship is referred to as the *forward transfer characteristic* of the amplifier.

P7.15 The amplifier discussed in Problem 7.14 is to be used to amplify a sine wave. The circuit that provides v_I can be modeled as shown in Fig. 7.30.

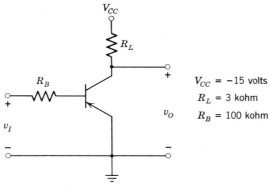

$V_{CC} = -15$ volts
$R_L = 3$ kohm
$R_B = 100$ kohm

Figure 7.29   A common-emitter amplifier.

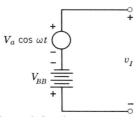

Figure 7.30   Bias and signal sources.

(a) Assume that $V_{BB} = 3$ volts. What is v_O when there is no sinusoidal component (i.e., when $V_a = 0$)? What is the maximum value of V_a for which the time-varying component of v_O is approximately sinusoidal? What is the corresponding amplitude of the sinusoidal component of v_O?

(b) What value of V_{BB} permits the amplifier to develop the largest possible sinusoidal time-varying component of v_O?

(c) Note that the amplifier can be regarded as a system or "black box" for which v_I is the input variable and v_O is the output variable. Is the amplifier a linear system? Can it be regarded as a linear system if the permissible range of values of v_I is limited?

CHAPTER EIGHT

Dynamic Models for Bipolar Transistors

8.1 Dynamic Operation and Charge Stores[*]

The models developed in Chapter 7 are applicable only under static or nearly static conditions. At the physical level, these models account for currents associated with the diffusion of carriers across the base region (I_E, I_C) and for currents associated with the recombination of carriers in the base and the injection of carriers into the emitter (I_B). These static models do not account for the components of current required to change internal charge stores. Consequently, they become inaccurate whenever the internal charge stores, in either the neutral base region or the space-charge layers, change rapidly. We now extend our hierarchy of transistor models to include the charging components of the terminal currents that appear whenever the internal charge stores change rapidly. First, we consider the currents associated with changes in the store of excess carriers in the neutral base region. Then we turn our attention to changes in the dipole layers of charge in the space-charge layers. Once again we consider a *pnp* transistor and assume active-region operation.

8.1.1 Charge Stores in the Neutral Regions

As we have seen in Section 7.3.1, there is a one-to-one correspondence between the static distribution of excess carriers in the base and the *static* terminal voltages and currents. Specifically, the collector and emitter currents are proportional to the *gradient* of the excess-carrier distribution, as shown by Eqs. 7.2 and 7.9. Furthermore, the component of the base current that supports recombination in the base is proportional to the *area* under the excess-carrier distribution (Eq. 7.6a), and the component that supports injection into the emitter can be similarly expressed (Eq. 7.6c). In devising a dynamic model for the transistor, it is helpful to express all three terminal currents, which are proportional to $p_b'(0)$, in terms of the *excess charge* stored in the base. The excess charge, denoted by q_F, is defined in Eq. 7.5, which is repeated here:

$$q_F = qA[\tfrac{1}{2}p_b'(0)W] \qquad (8.1)$$

If this relationship is used to express the collector current (Eq. 7.3) and the total base current (the *sum* of Eqs. 7.6a and 7.6c) in terms of q_F, we obtain *for static conditions*

$$I_C = \frac{-q_F}{\tau_F} \qquad (8.2a)$$

$$I_B = \frac{-q_F}{\tau_{BF}} \qquad (8.2b)$$

---

[*]This chapter can be delayed without loss of continuity until the *start* of Chapter 21.

The coefficients τ_F and τ_{BF}, which have dimensions of time, involve the parameters of the transistor structure. That is,

$$\tau_F = \frac{W^2}{2D_b} \tag{8.3a}$$

$$\tau_{BF} = \frac{1}{\dfrac{1}{\tau_b} + \dfrac{2D_e n_{eo}}{W W_e p_{bo}}} \tag{8.3b}$$

Division of Eq. 8.2a by Eq. 8.2b shows that *under static conditions* the ratio of these coefficients is equal to the common-emitter current gain. That is,

$$\frac{I_C}{I_B} = \frac{\tau_{BF}}{\tau_F} \tag{8.4}$$

$$= \beta_F$$

If injection into the emitter is neglected, implying that p_{bo} is much greater than n_{eo}, the expression for τ_{BF} reduces to τ_b. This limiting value checks with our intuition, since in such a case the static base current is entirely the consequence of recombination in the base, and the net rate of recombination is simply q_F/τ_b.

The static emitter-to-base voltage is related to q_F through Eqs. 7.1a and 7.5 which reduce, upon elimination of $p_b'(0)$, to

$$q_F = \frac{qAWp_{bo}}{2}(e^{qV_{EB}/kT} - 1) \tag{8.5}$$

Notice that forward bias on the emitter junction produces positive excess-carrier concentrations and positive values of q_F.[1] Once again we emphasize that the base region between the space-charge layers is electrically neutral and contains no net charge. Thus the charge q_F, which in a *pnp* transistor resides on the excess minority carriers, is neutralized by a charge $-q_F$, which resides on the excess majority carriers. It is necessary to distinguish carefully between the minority- and majority-carrier excess charges because, as we shall see, they have distinctly different ways of entering or leaving the base region.

We now extend the simple charge-current and charge-voltage relationships to encompass dynamic or time-varying situations. In doing so, *we assume that the time rates of change of the terminal-pair voltages and terminal currents are small enough for the internal base-region charge distribution to change as a*

---

[1] Although our development is phrased in terms of a *pnp* transistor, an analogous argument can be made for *npn* devices. In applying this point of view in *npn* transistors, we adopt the same convention for q_F, that is, *positive* excess-carrier concentrations in the base, produced by *forward* bias on the emitter junction, produce *positive* values of q_F. Consequently, the equations analogous, in an *npn* unit, to Eqs. 8.2 have plus signs on the right, while the equation analogous to Eq. 8.5 differs only in that the exponent contains $-V_{EB}$ rather than V_{EB}.

succession of static distributions. More precisely, we assume that the excess-carrier distribution changes so slowly that if a motion picture were made of the changing charge distribution, each frame in the sequence would be essentially indistinguishable from a picture of an appropriate static distribution. Furthermore, the particular static distribution to which a certain frame in the motion picture corresponds is that which would result if the emitter-to-base voltage were stationary at the instantaneous value that existed when the frame was exposed. This limitation on rate of change implies that the *instantaneous* base-region excess-carrier distribution is, even under dynamic conditions, *approximately triangular*, just as it is under static conditions.

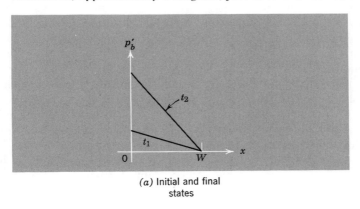

(*a*) Initial and final
states

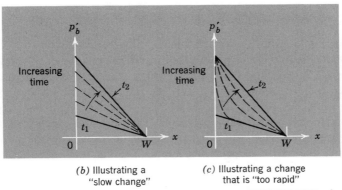

(*b*) Illustrating a   (*c*) Illustrating a change
"slow change"   that is "too rapid"

Figure 8.1   The instantaneous charge distribution in the base can be regarded as a static distribution if the rate of change is not too large.

   This limitation on rate of change, which is of major importance in our evolution of circuit models for transistors, is illustrated in Fig. 8.1. In Fig. 8.1*a* we show two static distributions, one corresponding to time t_1 and the other to some later time t_2. Clearly both the emitter-to-base voltage and the store of excess carriers have increased in the interval from t_1 to t_2. In Fig. 8.1*b* we show the instantaneous charge distribution at several instants of time in the range $t_1 < t < t_2$ for a rate of change small enough for our assumption of *quasi-static* intermediate states to be satisfied; at every instant of time between the initial and final states the charge distribution is approximately triangular. For contrast, we show in Fig. 8.1c a set of intermediate instantaneous charge distributions for a rate of change which is so large that it violates our quasi-static approximation. In particular, Fig. 8.1c is drawn for a situation in which v_{EB} increases to its new value instantaneously, in a steplike manner. Although $p_b'(0)$ immediately jumps to its new value, the charge distribution cannot follow instantaneously because it takes time for the extra minority carriers required by the final state to diffuse across the base and augment the excess-carrier distribution at every point in the base.

We shall find that our refusal to consider "too rapid" changes, such as that shown in Fig. 8.1c, does not seriously limit the utility of the dynamic model that we now develop. On the contrary, our limitation to rates of change that can be represented quasi-statically (Fig. 8.1b) yields a dynamic circuit model that is useful and reasonably accurate in all circuit situations for which the dynamic behavior of the transistor is of practical interest.

Since we are assuming that the instantaneous base-region excess-charge distribution changes as a succession of steady-state distributions which are *triangular*, the *instantaneous* collector current is proportional to the *instantaneous* excess charge, and the constant of proportionality is τ_F, which was introduced in Eq. 8.2a for a static situation. That is,

$$i_C = \frac{-q_F}{\tau_F} \tag{8.6a}$$

where i_C denotes the instantaneous collector current.[2]

The instantaneous base current can be related to the instantaneous excess charge in the base by recognizing that the base is electrically neutral and that the excess majority carriers that neutralize the injected excess minority carriers can be supplied *only* at the base terminal. Base-region majority carriers cannot be supplied across the junctions; they are in short supply in both the emitter and collector, where they constitute the minority carriers.[3] Since majority carriers can be supplied to the base only at the base terminal, *the base charge is governed solely by the base current.*

The majority carriers that flow into the base do two things. First, some of these carriers augment the store of excess majority carriers in the base; this component is given by dq_F/dt. Second, some of these carriers feed the recombination of excess carriers in the base and the injection of base-region

<hr />

[2] Instantaneous total values of the terminal voltages and currents are denoted by lowercase variables with uppercase subscripts.

[3] We assume that avalanche multiplication in the collector junction does not contribute significant numbers of majority carriers to the base. Thus this development is valid for collector voltages that are small compared with the sustaining voltage.

majority carriers into the emitter; this component is described by q_F/τ_{BF}. Thus we can write an equation that amounts to a statement of conservation of majority carriers in the base under dynamic conditions.

$$-i_B = \frac{dq_F}{dt} + \frac{q_F}{\tau_{BF}} \qquad (8.6b)$$

Notice that i_B is the instantaneous current (regarded as a flow of positive charge) *into* the base. Consequently, $-i_B$ can be regarded as a measure of the electron flow (base-region majority carriers in a *pnp* transistor) *into* the base.[4] Note that this equation holds true for arbitrary rates of change of the terminal variables and charge distribution and is quite general.

Under static conditions, the charge-changing component of the base current vanishes and Eq. 8.6b reduces to the corresponding static result, which is expressed by Eq. 8.2b.

Equations 8.6 express the base and collector currents in terms of the base-region excess charge; Kirchhoff's current law yields the corresponding component of the emitter current:

$$i_E = -(i_B + i_C) \qquad (8.7a)$$

or

$$i_E = \frac{dq_F}{dt} + \frac{q_F}{\tau_{BF}} + \frac{q_F}{\tau_F} \qquad (8.7b)$$

Finally, the instantaneous emitter-to-base voltage v_{EB} is related to q_F in the same manner as in Eq. 8.5, which is a direct consequence of the triangular nature of the distribution (for $p_b'(0) \gg p_{bo}$):

$$q_F = \frac{qAWp_{bo}}{2}(e^{qv_{EB}/kT} - 1) \qquad (8.8)$$

The model for the dynamic behavior of a transistor expressed by Eqs. 8.6, 8.7b, and 8.8 is called the *charge-control* model. This description reflects the fact that the instantaneous collector current is controlled by the base-region excess charge, for dynamic as well as static conditions.

The restriction that must be satisfied by the terminal currents in order for the quasi-static limitation to apply can be inferred from Eq. 8.7a. The base-region minority carriers move solely by diffusion for low injection. Consequently, the minority-carrier current crossing any transverse plane in the base is proportional to the *slope* of the excess-carrier distribution at that plane. For example, the emitter and collector currents for an instantaneous

---

[4] In developing the relationship between base charge and base current, we have neglected the component of base current which is required to change the excess charge stored in the emitter. Usually the excess charge stored in the emitter is small compared with that stored in the base, so that this approximation is legitimate.

distribution for which q_F is *increasing* must be proportional to the slopes shown in Fig. 8.2. If the distribution is to be reasonably approximated by a triangle, the slope at $x = 0$ cannot differ greatly from the slope at $x = W$. That is, the emitter current cannot differ greatly in value from the collector current. This condition can be *met only if the instantaneous base current is not comparable to the instantaneous emitter or collector current*, as shown by Eq. 8.7a. It is met in the majority of circuit applications simply because we are usually required to supply substantially more "output" (collector) current than is available as "input" (base) current. Consequently, we are generally interested in situations for which the base current is not comparable to the collector current, even under dynamic conditions.

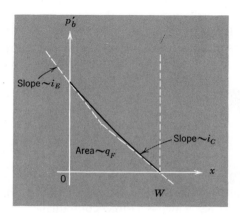

Figure 8.2   Illustration of the limitation imposed by the quasi-static assumption.

The active-region charge-control model, which is embodied in Eqs. 8.6, 8.7b, and 8.8, can, of course, be represented in network terms. In order to arrive at such a model, we introduce the nonlinear capacitance or charge store shown in Fig. 8.3a. Like the capacitance that is familiar from linear network theory, this element has the property that the current through it is the time derivative of the charge stored on it. That is,

$$i = \frac{dq}{dt} \tag{8.9a}$$

However, unlike a capacitance, the charge stored on the element is a *nonlinear* function of the voltage across it. In this case

$$q = Q_{FO}(e^{qv/kt} - 1) \tag{8.9b}$$

where

$$Q_{FO} = \frac{qAWp_{bo}}{2} \tag{8.9c}$$

The constant Q_{FO} thus defines the "value" of this new element.

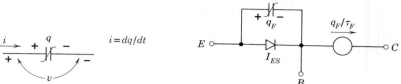

(a) Symbol for nonlinear capacitance (b) A dynamic transistor model

Figure 8.3 A network model that represents the dynamic active-region behavior of a *pnp* transistor.

By making use of the new element, the charge-control equations can be represented in network terms as shown in Fig. 8.3b. The dependent current generator in the collector lead is controlled by the charge q_F on the nonlinear charge store, in accordance with Eq. 8.6a. The components in the emitter leg can be found by substituting Eq. 8.9b into Eq. 8.7b, to obtain

$$I_E = I_{ES}(e^{qv_{EB}/kT} - 1) + \frac{dq_F}{dt} \tag{8.10a}$$

where

$$I_{ES} = Q_{FO}\left(\frac{1}{\tau_F} + \frac{1}{\tau_{BF}}\right) \tag{8.10b}$$

Thus the emitter leg of the model contains an exponential diode in parallel with a nonlinear capacitance, as shown in the figure.

Clearly, this model must reduce to the simpler static model of Fig. 7.9a when the voltage v_{EB} is constant (or changing very slowly). For this to occur, the constant I_{ES} in Eqs. 8.10 must equal $I_1(1 + \delta)$. Also, for the models to match, we require that in the charge-control representation, under static conditions

$$\left|\frac{i_C}{i_E}\right| = \alpha_F$$

Thus from Eqs. 8.6a and 8.7b

$$\alpha_F = \frac{q_F/\tau_F}{q_F(1/\tau_F + 1/\tau_{BF})}$$

Multiplying through by τ_{BF}, we obtain

$$\alpha_F = \frac{\tau_{BF}/\tau_F}{\tau_{BF}/\tau_F + 1}$$

Clearly, this relation is satisfied if, as before, we require

$$\frac{\tau_{BF}}{\tau_F} = \beta_F \tag{8.11}$$

The operating conditions under which the dynamic model reduces to the simpler static model are of interest because they define the speed range over which the static model applies. An examination of Eqs. 8.6 shows that they reduce to Eqs. 8.2, which together with Eq. 8.5 define the static model whenever

$$\frac{dq_F}{dt} \ll \frac{q_F}{\tau_{BF}}$$

or, equivalently,

$$\left(\frac{1}{q_F}\frac{dq_F}{dt}\right)\tau_{BF} \ll 1$$

The term in parentheses is the fractional rate of change of q_F. Thus *the static model applies if the fractional amount by which q_F changes in a time interval τ_{BF} is small.* Since τ_{BF} is usually less than 10^{-6} sec and may be as small as 10^{-8} sec, the static model is applicable for quite rapid changes.

8.1.2   Charge Stores in the Space-Charge Layers

We have thus far focused on the consequences of changes in the excess-carrier charge store in the neutral base region. There are also charge stores in the space-charge layers, and these charge stores require charging currents whenever the junction voltages change with time. We now extend our dynamic model to account for these charging currents.[5]

The charge stored in either half of the dipole layer at the emitter junction is a function of v_{EB}, which governs the width of the space-charge layer. We describe this charge by q_{VE}, which is the difference between the magnitude of the charge for any v_{EB} and the corresponding equilibrium value. Thus $q_{VE} = 0$ when $v_{EB} = 0$, and q_{VE} is positive for forward bias.

An *increase* in v_{EB} corresponds in a *pnp* transistor to an *increase* in q_{VE} and requires the flow of majority carriers into both sides of the space-charge layer. This current, which augments the charge in the space-charge layer, is

$$i = \frac{dq_{VE}}{dt} \tag{8.12}$$

This current must be added to i_E (Eq. 8.7) and subtracted from i_B (given by Eq. 8.6b), in order to represent the effects of changing charge in the emitter space-charge layer.

The situation at the collector junction is analogous. The charge component q_{VC} changes in response to changes v_{CB}; the associated charge-changing current affects both i_C and i_B. When these space-charge-layer charging currents are added to the currents associated with excess-carrier injection

[5] We have already encountered these charging currents in our analysis of the diode; see Section 4.4.1.

and storage in the bulk regions we obtain

$$i_C = -\frac{q_F}{\tau_F} + \frac{dq_{VC}}{dt} \tag{8.13a}$$

$$i_B = -\frac{dq_F}{dt} - \frac{q_F}{\tau_{BF}} - \frac{dq_{VE}}{dt} - \frac{dq_{VC}}{dt} \tag{8.13b}$$

$$i_E = \frac{dq_F}{dt} + \frac{q_F}{\tau_{BF}} + \frac{q_F}{\tau_F} + \frac{dq_{VE}}{dt} \tag{8.13c}$$

Since the currents associated with charge changes in the space-charge layers are proportional to the rate of change of the corresponding charge, they can be represented in circuit terms by means of appropriately defined non-linear capacitances. The charge-voltage relationships for both abrupt and linearly graded junctions are shown in Fig. 4.16, which is repeated here as Fig. 8.4. Most diffused-junction transistors have an impurity profile near the collector that is reasonably well described by the uniformly-graded junction model. On the other hand, the impurity profile near the emitter is often steep enough so that the abrupt-junction model provides a better fit there. The curves of Fig. 8.4 show that except for small junction voltages the

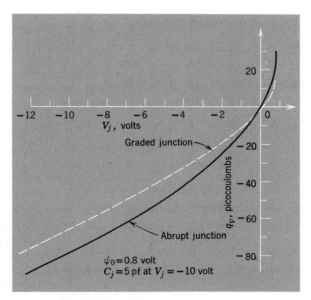

Figure 8.4 The voltage dependence of the charge q_v, which is the majority-carrier charge that must be supplied to each side of the dipole layer when the voltage changes from zero to V. The curves apply to abrupt and linearly graded junctions having the same incremental capacitance at -10 volt.

charge-voltage relationships are not strongly nonlinear. Consequently, these relationships can often be modeled by means of *linear* capacitances. The capacitance value corresponds to the *slope* of the charge-voltage relationship. That is,

$$i = C_j \frac{dv}{dt} \tag{8.14a}$$

where

$$C_j = \frac{dq_v}{dv} \tag{8.14b}$$

The circuit model that results when nonlinear capacitances arising from charge stores are added is shown in Fig. 8.5. This network model is precisely equivalent to the model of Eqs. 8.13.

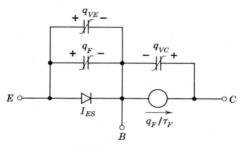

Figure 8.5   A dynamic network model that includes the space-charge-layer charging currents.

All of the models developed in Chapter 7 and in this chapter are referred to as *total-signal* models because they relate the total values of the terminal voltages and currents.[6] The static models of Chapter 7 apply to stationary or nearly stationary situations in which the terminal variables are changing slowly enough for the transistor to behave statically. On the other hand, the dynamic charge-control models of this chapter extend our hierarchy of total-signal models to include situations in which the variables are changing quite rapidly.

Although this development has been phrased entirely in terms of *pnp* transistors, the conclusions and the models we have developed are applicable to *npn* devices as well. Since the base-region excess charge q_F is, by definition, a positive quantity for active-region operation of both *pnp* and *npn* transistors, all components of the terminal currents that depend on q_F have the opposite sign in *npn* transistors. Furthermore, the terms arising from changes in q_{VE} and q_{VC} also change sign because the majority carriers that charge and

[6] These models are sometimes called *large-signal models* because they relate variables that can be large, at least in comparison with the incremental or small-signal variables that we shall discuss in Chapter 11 and to which incremental models apply.

discharge the space-charge layers have inverted signs in *npn* transistors as contrasted with *pnp* units. Thus the *npn* equations that are analogous to Eqs. 8.8 and 8.13 are

$$q_F = \frac{qAWn_{bo}}{2}(e^{-qv_{EB}/kT} - 1) \tag{8.15a}$$

$$i_C = \frac{q_F}{\tau_F} - \frac{dq_{VC}}{dt} \tag{8.15b}$$

$$i_B = \frac{dq_F}{dt} + \frac{q_F}{\tau_{BF}} + \frac{dq_{VE}}{dt} + \frac{dq_{VC}}{dt} \tag{8.15c}$$

$$i_E = -\frac{dq_F}{dt} - \frac{q_F}{\tau_{BF}} - \frac{q_F}{\tau_F} - \frac{dq_{VE}}{dt} \tag{8.15d}$$

The corresponding *npn* charge-control circuit model is shown in Fig. 8.6, which should be compared with the *pnp* form shown in Fig. 8.5. Note that the exponential diode and the dependent generator are reversed, and all three nonlinear capacitances have the opposite polarity.

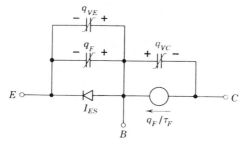

Figure 8.6   A dynamic model for *npn* transistors (active-region operation).

8.1.3   Comparison of Neutral-Region and Space-Charge-Layer Charge Stores

The discussion in the preceding two sections shows that to change the state of operation of a transistor it is necessary to supply or remove charge at the base terminal. Some of the charge that flows in or out at the base terminal changes the charge store in the neutral region (q_F), and some of it changes the charge stored in the space-charge layers at the emitter and collector junctions (q_{VE} and q_{VC}). Both q_F and q_{VE} depend explicitly on the instantaneous emitter-base voltage v_{EB}. Thus any change in v_{EB} produces changes in *both* q_F and q_{VE}, and the charging component of the base current must divide accordingly.

A comparison of these two charge changes is shown in Fig. 8.7, in which both q_F and q_{VE} are plotted versus v_{EB}. The numerical values chosen are

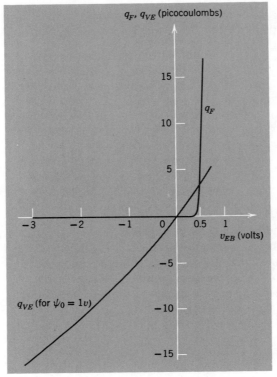

Figure 8.7 A comparison of the dependence of base-region charge q_F and emitter space-charge-layer charge q_{VE} on emitter base voltage V_{EB}.

typical of lower-power silicon transistors.[7] The curves show that for all emitter-to-base voltages less than about 0.45 volt, the space-charge-layer charge dominates, whereas for emitter-to-base voltages greater than about 0.5 volt (i.e., for collector currents in the range of milliamperes) the neutral-base-region charge dominates. These comparisons indicate that the charging component of the base current goes mostly to changing the space-charge layer charge if the emitter-to-base voltage is less than the threshold voltage, whereas the current goes mostly to changing neutral-base-region charge if the voltage is greater than the threshold voltage.

8.2 Applications of the Charge-Control Model
8.2.1 A Common-Emitter Current Amplifier

The *pnp* transistor in the circuit of Fig. 8.8*a* is arranged as an amplifier in the common-emitter configuration. The voltage source in the output loop is polarized to reverse-bias the collector junction. Consequently, the device

---

[7] The q_{VE} versus v_{EB} relationship used in this comparison is that of a linear-graded junction.

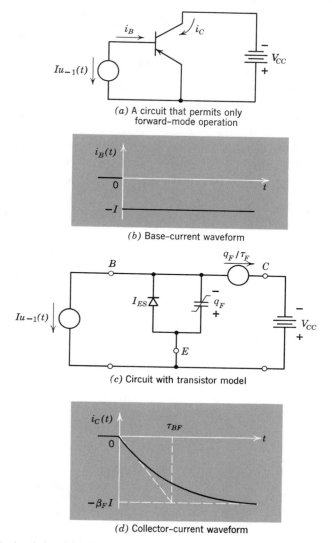

(a) A circuit that permits only
forward–mode operation

(b) Base–current waveform

(c) Circuit with transistor model

(d) Collector–current waveform

Figure 8.8   A circuit in which V_{CE} is constant even though i_C changes.

operates as a control valve that responds to the base current. We now
consider the consequences of an abrupt change of the base current at $t = 0$,
as shown in Fig. 8.8b. We use the dynamic model developed in Section 8.1
to determine the transient response of the collector current.

   The collector-to-emitter voltage is constrained to be constant by the fixed
voltage source V_{CC}. The change in emitter-to-base voltage that occurs is of
the order of a tenth of a volt (an increase of 25 mv increases the collector

current by a factor of $e \simeq 2.7$). Therefore, both v_{EB} and v_{CB} change by only a fraction of a volt. We assume that the junction voltage changes are small enough for the changes in the space-charge-layer charge stores to be negligible compared with the changes in the neutral-base-region charge store, and use the charge-control model shown in Fig. 8.3b as a circuit characterization of the transistor. This model appears in the circuit in Fig. 8.8c.

For $t < 0$, both the base current i_B and the base-region charge store q_F are zero. At $t = 0$, the base current changes abruptly to $-I$, and excess charge begins to accumulate in the base, in accordance with Eq. 8.6b. The first-order linear differential equation has a particular integral,

$$(q_F)_p = I\tau_{BF} \tag{8.16a}$$

and a homogeneous solution,

$$(q_F)_h = Ce^{-t/\tau_{BF}} \tag{8.16b}$$

The complete solution is

$$q_F(t) = (q_F)_p + (q_F)_h = I\tau_{BF}(1 - e^{-t/\tau_{BF}}) \tag{8.16c}$$

in which the constant of integration C has been chosen to satisfy the initial condition $q_F(0+) = 0$. The instantaneous collector current is, from Eq. 8.6a,

$$i_C(t) = -I\frac{\tau_{BF}}{\tau_F}(1 - e^{-t/\tau_{BF}}) \tag{8.16d}$$

However, the ratio τ_{BF}/τ_F is simply the static short-circuit common-emitter current gain β_F. Thus

$$i_C(t) = -\beta_F I(1 - e^{-t/\tau_{BF}}) \tag{8.16e}$$

The waveform of the collector current is shown in Fig. 8.8d. The collector-current waveform exhibits the time constant τ_{BF}, which is characteristic of the internal behavior of the device.

Although this particular example illustrates the effect of a drive that constrains the base current, the charge-control model can also be applied for a drive characterized by an arbitrary Thévenin equivalent network. In this regard, Eqs. 8.6b and 8.8 constitute a parametric description of the dynamic $i_B - v_{EB}$ relationship, in which q_F is the parameter.

Whether the source constrains the base current (as in this example) or the base-to-emitter voltage, or simply applies a prescribed current-voltage constraint at the base-emitter terminals, we must be sure that the rate of change of q_F established by the drive is not too large. A reasonable check on this can be provided by comparing, at every instant, the base current with the collector current. If the base current is not comparable to the collector current, we are assured that the internal charge distribution is approximately triangular.[8] This condition is met in most circuits of practical importance simply because the circuit usually must provide a reasonable current gain.

8.2.2   A Voltage-Driven Amplifier

We next consider the common-emitter amplifier shown in Fig. 8.9a. Note that an *npn* transistor is used. The circuit differs from that of Fig. 8.8a in that the base drive is provided not by a current source, but by a voltage source through a parallel RC network. The source voltage changes at $t = 0$ from the value V_- to the value V. We assume that V is much greater than V_- and that V_- is just below the threshold of conduction, that is, about 0.4 volt. Thus for $t < 0$, $i_B \simeq 0$ and $i_C \simeq 0$. A little thought will show that the change in v_{EB} that commences at $t = 0$ is only a few tenths of a volt. Therefore, since the collector-to-emitter voltage is fixed, we once again neglect the space-charge-layer charging currents and use the *npn* equivalent of the simple model of Fig. 8.3b. The circuit that results when the transistor is replaced by this model is shown in Fig. 8.9b.

We assume that V is large compared with the maximum value of the emitter-base voltage of the transistor. Thus the base current can be specified directly in terms of the source voltage. Specifically, the base current is[9]

$$i_B = \frac{v(t)}{R} + C\frac{dv(t)}{dt} \tag{8.17a}$$

Since the change in $v(t)$ is a step function, and since the base current is negligible for $t < 0$, the base current contains both a step (the first term) and an impulse (the second term), as shown in Fig. 8.9d. That is, since V is much greater than V_-,

$$i_B(t) \simeq \frac{V}{R}u_{-1}(t) + CVu_0(t) \tag{8.17b}$$

We next must evaluate the time dependence of the base charge by solving the *npn* analog of Eq. 8.6b, which is

$$i_B = \frac{dq_F}{dt} + \frac{q_F}{\tau_{BF}} \tag{8.17c}$$

Instead of proceeding formally to obtain a solution, we can make use of the linearity of this equation and apply superposition. We already know the

---

[8] For the present example this condition is met for all times except those in the range $0 < t < \tau_F$, where $|i_C|$ is less than $|i_B| = I$. Observation of the waveforms in a circuit like that of Fig. 8.8 shows that the predictions of the charge-control model are indeed inaccurate in this range; the waveform of $i_C(t)$ has a continuous slope, and is "rounded off" at $t = 0$. Nevertheless, most of the change in collector current occurs for $t > \tau_F$, and the predictions of the model are very accurate in that range of time. See Reference 7.1, Chapter 10.

[9] Actually the base current is a function of the voltage difference $v(t) - v_{BE}$. Since v_{BE} lies in the range from 0.4 to 0.7 volt, the base current can be approximated by Eq. 8.17a if V is much larger than 0.7 volt.

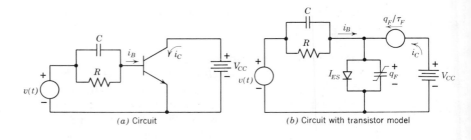

(a) Circuit   (b) Circuit with transistor model

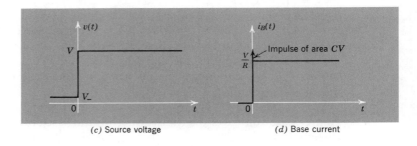

(c) Source voltage   (d) Base current

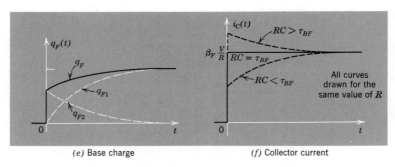

(e) Base charge   (f) Collector current

Figure 8.9   A common-emitter amplifier with a speedup capacitor.

solution of the differential equation for the first component of the base current, which is a step. This component of the base charge is, by analogy with Eq. 8.16c with $I = V/R$,

$$q_{F1}(t) = \frac{V\tau_{BF}}{R}(1 - e^{-t/\tau_{BF}}) \tag{8.18a}$$

The second component of the base current, the impulse, is equal to RC times the derivative of the first component. Consequently, the corresponding component of the base charge must be RC times the derivative of q_{F1}:

$$q_{F2} = CVe^{-t/\tau_{BF}} \tag{8.18b}$$

The total base charge is

$$q_F = q_{F1} + q_{F2}$$

$$= \frac{V}{R}\tau_{BF}\left(1 - e^{-t/\tau_{BF}} + \frac{RC}{\tau_{BF}}e^{-t/\tau_{BF}}\right) \tag{8.18c}$$

The base charge and its two components are shown in Fig. 8.9e. The relative size of the two components in Eq. 8.18c, hence the shape of q_F, obviously depend on the size of the time constant RC compared with τ_{BF}.

If RC is equal to τ_{BF}, the base charge increases immediately to its final value with no transient, and the collector current, which is simply

$$i_C = \frac{q_F}{\tau_F} \tag{8.19}$$

likewise has no transient, as shown in Fig. 8.9f. The physical interpretation of this situation is straightforward: the impulse associated with C inserts just enough charge into the base at $t = 0$ to bring the collector current to its final value instantly, and the step associated with R sustains the recombination of that charge.

If the capacitance is increased so that RC is greater than τ_{BF}, the collector current overshoots. In this case the steady component of i_B is insufficient to support the recombination of all of the charge inserted initially by C, and the initial excess disappears by recombination with time constant τ_{BF}.

If, on the other hand, C is decreased, so that RC is less than τ_{BF}, the steady component of i_B is more than adequate to support the initial charge inserted by C, and the total charge gradually builds up until the base current is just balanced by recombination. The sensitivity of the collector-current waveform to the relative sizes of RC and τ_{BF} can be employed, as we shall see in Chapter 22, in the measurement of τ_{BF}.

Clearly the capacitance has the effect of making the collector current change more rapidly; compare Fig. 8.9f with Fig. 8.8d. For this reason it is sometimes called a "speed-up capacitor" when it is used to increase the speed of transistor switching circuits.

Although the analysis of this circuit is simple, we should pause to consider the validity of the charge-control model under the circumstances in which we have used it. Clearly, the base current is *not* small compared with the collector current; at $t = 0$, the base current is impulsive while the collector current is approximately zero. Even in this extreme case, the predictions of the model are very accurate, however. This accuracy is illustrated in Fig. 8.10 where $i_C(t)$ is shown for $C = 0$ and for $RC = \tau_{BF}$. It is clear that the change at $t = 0$ for $RC = \tau_{BF}$ is rapid indeed, and can reasonably be approximated by a step. Of course, if one were to observe the collector current waveform with a much faster sweep, the rounding-off near $t = 0$ would be more evident. The important point is that the predictions of the model are reasonably

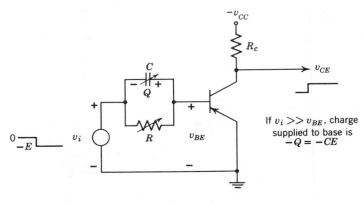

(a) Circuit arrangement.

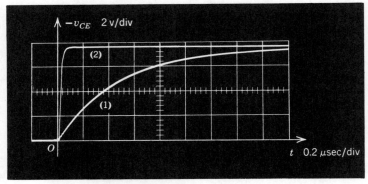

(b) Waveforms of collector voltage.
(1) Capacitor C absent, response as in Fig. 8.8 d.
(2) With adjustment so that $RC = \tau_{BF}$

Figure 8.10   The collector current waveforms for two values of C.

accurate *in the frame of reference established by the time* τ_{BF}. The predictions of the charge-control model are reasonably accurate, even though the conditions of operation violate grossly the key assumption of quasi-static behavior used in its development, because the base excess-charge adjusts itself very quickly to a triangular distribution.

8.2.3 A Resistively-Loaded Amplifier

Although the circuits just considered provide simple examples of the use of a dynamic circuit model for a transistor, the transistors in these circuits are not really useful as control valves because there is no provision for a load or output device at the collector. A more interesting circuit is shown in Fig. 8.11 ; the resistance R represents a load to which the transistor supplies current. The transistor operates in the active region as long as i_C is not too large.

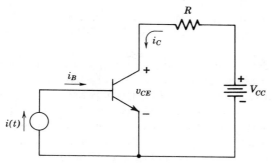

Figure 8.11   A common-emitter amplifier with a resistive load.

Since the collector-to-emitter voltage v_{CE} obviously changes as i_C changes, it is no longer possible to ignore the charging currents associated with the collector space-charge-layer charge store. However, we shall continue to neglect the charging currents required by q_{VE} because the changes in the forward emitter-base voltage are likely to be quite small. Thus Eqs. 8.15 apply, with the terms in dq_{VE}/dt neglected. In order to avoid complicating the problem with nonlinear mathematics, we assume that the collector junction is graded (see Fig. 8.4) and that over the range of v_{CB} of interest the terms in dq_{VC}/dt can be represented by a linear capacitance; that is,

$$i = \frac{dq_{VC}}{dt}$$

$$= \left(\frac{dq_{VC}}{dv_{CB}}\right)\frac{dv_{CB}}{dt}$$

is replaced by

$$i = -C_{jc}\frac{dv_{CB}}{dt} \tag{8.20}$$

The equations of interest thus are

$$i_C = \frac{q_F}{\tau_F} + C_{jc}\frac{dv_{CB}}{dt} \tag{8.21a}$$

$$i_B = \frac{dq_F}{dt} + \frac{q_F}{\tau_{BF}} - C_{jc}\frac{dv_{CB}}{dt} \tag{8.21b}$$

The constraint imposed by the resistive load and voltage source is

$$v_{CE} = V_{CC} - i_C R \tag{8.21c}$$

Finally, since we are assuming that v_{EB} is small, we have

$$v_{CB} = v_{CE} - v_{EB}$$

$$\simeq v_{CE} \tag{8.21d}$$

These four equations (Eqs. 8.21) can be solved for i_C once the base current is specified. The homogeneous portion of the solution contains two natural frequencies.

Rather than develop this solution in detail, we make a further approximation, which reduces the set of equations to one having only a single natural frequency and a very simple solution. The approximation hinges on the fact that although the junction capacitance term $(C_{jc}\, dv_{CB}/dt)$ appears as a component of *both* i_C and i_B, it generally has much more influence on the base current equation because the collector current is usually much larger than the base current. Thus we replace Eq. 8.21a by

$$i_C \simeq \frac{q_F}{\tau_F} \tag{8.22a}$$

As a result of this approximation, Eqs. 8.21b, 8.21c, and 8.21d reduce to

$$i_B = \frac{dq_F}{dt}\left[1 + \frac{RC_{jc}}{\tau_F}\right] + \frac{q_F}{\tau_{BF}} \tag{8.22b}$$

Finally, if we change the time scale to

$$t' = \frac{t}{1 + \dfrac{RC_{jc}}{\tau_F}} \tag{8.23}$$

we obtain

$$i_B = \frac{dq_F}{dt'} + \frac{q_F}{\tau_{BF}} \tag{8.24}$$

which is formally the same as the base current–base charge relationship employed in the preceding two examples where space-charge-layer charging currents were neglected. Thus this approximate treatment, which is valid when the current gain is not too small, reduces the problem to one that contains only a single time constant and that we have studied previously. The results are the same if we scale the time coordinate appropriately. The net effect of the charging current required by q_{VC} is to slow down the transient response of the circuit. In accordance with Eq. 8.23, times are *increased* by the factor $1 + RC_{jc}/\tau_F$.

Although these examples suffice to generate some feeling for the dynamic behavior of transistor circuits, it is clear that we are greatly hampered by the highly nonlinear nature of the dynamic model. If we wish to make "pencil and paper" calculations, we either must ensure such circuit constraints that the nonlinearities are of no consequence, as in the first two examples, or must make approximations liberally, as in the last example.

Fortunately, the charge-control model is very amenable to automatic computational methods, so that many important problems that are too complex for "pencil and paper" analysis can be solved easily with the aid of a digital computer, as we shall see in Chapter 22.

PROBLEMS

P8.1   Verify Eqs. 8.3 by expressing the collector current given by Eq. 7.3, and the base current given by the *sum* of Eqs. 7.6a and 7.6c, in terms of q_F.

P8.2   The *pnp* transistor whose charge-voltage characteristics are illustrated in Fig. 8.7 is operated in a circuit in which the emitter-to-base voltage is constrained to the range

$$-3 \text{ volt} < v_{EB} < 0.6 \text{ volt}$$

(*a*) It is desired to approximate the emitter-space-charge-layer charge store by a linearized capacitance. What value should C_{JE} have for a reasonable fit over the prescribed range of voltage?

(*b*) The emitter-to-base voltage is initially -3 volt; it changes rapidly to 0.6 volt, at which time the collector current is 10 ma. The collector charge-control time constant τ_F has a value of 5×10^{-9} sec. How much charge must be supplied at the base terminal during this transition? Assume that the transition occurs so rapidly that negligible charge is lost by recombination during the transition interval, and that the collector-to-base voltage does not change, so that $dq_{VC} = 0$.

(*c*) What fraction of the charge supplied at the base terminal during the transition is absorbed by the emitter space-charge-layer charge store? What fraction is absorbed by the neutral-base-region charge store q_F?

(*d*) Assume that the base current is *constant* during the transition described in (*b*) and has a value of -0.5 ma. What is the duration of the transition interval?

Answers. (*a*) $C_{JE} \simeq 5.5$ pf.; (*b*) Approximately 70 pc.; (*d*) 14 nsec.

P8.3   This problem is concerned with the circuit shown in Fig. 8.12*a*, in which the base is driven from a voltage source through a source resistance R_S. The voltage source undergoes a step transition at $t = 0$ as shown in Fig. 8.12*b*. Assume that the transistor can be described by the model of Fig. 8.6 with the following parameters:

$$\tau_F = 10^{-8} \text{ sec}$$

$$\beta_F = 50$$

$$I_{ES} = 10^{-9} \text{ amp}$$

$$q_{VE} = 10^{-10}[\psi_0{}^{\frac{2}{3}} - (\psi_0 - v_{BE})^{\frac{2}{3}}] \text{ coulomb}$$

$$q_{VC} = 2 \times 10^{-10}[\psi_0{}^{\frac{2}{3}} - (\psi_0 - v_{BC})^{\frac{2}{3}}] \text{ coulomb}$$

where $\psi_0 = 1$ volt and v_{BE} and v_{BC} are in volts. Assume that $V_{CC} = 10$ volts, $R_S = 1$ kohm.

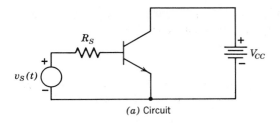

(a) Circuit

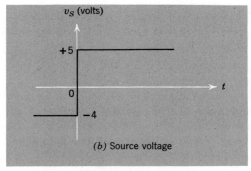

(b) Source voltage

Figure 8.12   A common-emitter amplifier.

(a) Determine v_{BE}, v_{BC}, i_B, and i_C for $t < 0$, at which time the transistor is cut off.

(b) Determine q_{VE}, q_{VC}, and q_F for $t < 0$.

(c) Determine v_{BE}, v_{BC}, i_B, and i_C for $t \gg 0$, after the transient has ended.

(d) Determine q_{VE}, q_{VC}, and q_F for $t \gg 0$.

(e) Assume that q_{VE} and q_{VC} are zero, and derive a nonlinear differential equation for $q_F(t)$. Do *not* neglect v_{BE} in comparison with v_S. Can this equation be solved without resorting to numerical methods?

(f) Can you derive a nonlinear differential equation for $q_F(t)$ for the case in which q_{VE} and q_{VC} are *not* negligible?

P8.4   This problem is concerned with an approximate method of evaluating the transient currents in the circuit of Fig. 8.12. Assume that the transistor model and parameter values described in Problem P8.3 apply here as well.

(a) Determine the value of base-to-emitter voltage at which q_{VE} is equal to q_F. Denote this voltage by V_T.

For v_{BE} less than V_T assume that q_F and the current in the exponential diode are negligibly small and approximate q_{VE} and q_{VC} by linear capacitances C_{JE} and C_{JC}.

(b) Sketch and label an approximate circuit model that applies for $v_{BE} < V_T$. Specify values for C_{JE} and C_{JC}.

(c) Evaluate $i_B(t)$, $i_C(t)$, and $v_{BE}(t)$ for $0 < t < t_T$, where t_T denotes the time at which v_{BE} is equal to V_T. Evaluate t_T. Assume that $v_S(t)$ has the form shown in Fig. 8.12b.

For v_{BE} greater than V_T (or, equivalently, for $t > t_T$) assume that q_{VE}, q_{VC} are negligibly small compared with q_F and neglect the *variation* in v_{BE} compared with v_S, that is, assume that v_{BE} is fixed at the value v_T for purposes of base-current evaluation.

(d) Sketch and label an approximate circuit model that applies for $t > t_T$.

(e) Evaluate $i_B(t)$, $i_C(t)$, and $v_{BE}(t)$ for $t > t_T$. Note that the base current is constant for $t > t_T$ and the charge q_F is *continuous* at $t = t_T$.

(f) Sketch and dimension the complete waveforms of $i_B(t)$, $i_C(t)$, and $v_{BE}(t)$.

P8.5 The problem is concerned with the circuit shown in Fig. 8.8a. The amplitude of the base current step is 0.5 ma. The observed final value of the collector current is -10 ma, and the initial slope of the collector-current waveform is 25 ma/μsec. Determine the values of the charge-control parameters τ_F and τ_{BF}.

Answers. $\tau_F = 20$ nsec., $\tau_{BF} = 0.4$ μsec.

P8.6 This problem is concerned with the circuit shown in Fig. 8.9. The parameters are:

$$V_- = 0.3 \text{ volt}$$
$$V = 15 \text{ volts}$$
$$R = 20 \text{ kohm}$$

The final value of the collector current is observed to be 30 ma. When $C = 60$ pf, the collector current increases to its final value essentially instantaneously.

(a) Determine the values of the charge-control parameters τ_F, τ_{BF}, and β_F.

(b) Assume that C is fixed at 60 pf but that R is decreased to 15 kohm. Compute, sketch, and dimension $i_C(t)$.

(c) Assume that C is increased to 100 pf but that R is fixed at 20 kohm. Compute, sketch, and dimension $i_C(t)$.

Answers. (a) $\tau_F = 30$ nsec., $\tau_{BF} = 1.2$ μsec., $\beta_F = 40$.

P8.7 Verify Eq. 8.22b.

P8.8 This problem is concerned with the differential equations that describe the circuit of Fig. 8.11.

(a) Reduce Eqs. 8.21 to a single second-order differential equation for $i_C(t)$. The base current $i_B(t)$ is the driving function in this equation.

(b) Assume that $\tau_{BF} = 10^{-7}$ sec, $\tau_F = 10^{-9}$ sec, and $C_{jc}R = 10^{-8}$ sec. Compute the two natural frequencies of the differential equation developed in (a) and compare these natural frequencies with the natural frequency of Eq. 8.24.

CHAPTER NINE

MOS Field-Effect Transistors

9.1   Introduction

We have already encountered an example of an active device in which control action depends on the modulation of a conductance by an electric field: the MOS field-effect transistor discussed in Chapter 1 and illustrated in Fig. 9.1. In this device the electric field produced in the insulating layer by the gate electrode controls the charge in the semiconductor channel, thereby governing the current in the source-to-drain path.

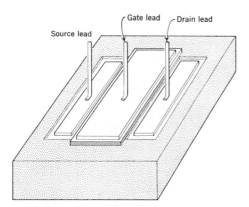

Figure 9.1   An MOS field-effect transistor structure.

Our study of the electrical properties of semiconductors provide the background that is necessary for a quantitative study of field-effect transistors. Therefore, we now explore these devices in detail with the twin objectives of developing an understanding of the physical electronics and of devising circuit models that describe the electrical behavior of these active components.

At the outset we focus attention on the *metal-oxide-semiconductor* or MOS field-effect transistor.[1] The physical structure of an *n*-channel MOSFET is shown in Fig. 9.2. This transistor is made by the silicon planar diffusion technology described in Chapter 5. It is produced on a semiconductor substrate that is either intrinsic or very lightly doped with acceptors to make it high-resistivity *p*-type. As a first step, two *n*-type regions are produced by selective diffusion of donor impurities. These regions, which are shown in Fig. 9.2*b*, constitute the source and drain regions of the transistor. Next, a layer of silicon dioxide is grown across the entire semiconductor surface, and

---

[1] These devices are also known as insulated-gate field-effect transistors or IGFETs. This name emphasizes that the gate electrode is *insulated* from the channel by the oxide layer.

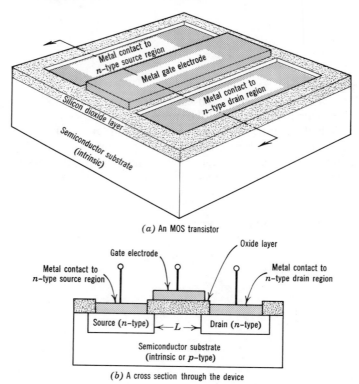

(*a*) An MOS transistor

(*b*) A cross section through the device

Figure 9.2 Physical structure of a metal-oxide-semiconductor field-effect transistor (MOSFET). Not to scale.

windows are opened in this oxide layer over the underlying *n*-type source and drain regions. Finally, metal films are deposited in the windows and on the oxide layer between the source and drain regions. Two of these metallized regions provide ohmic contacts to the source and drain regions. The third, middle, metal layer is insulated from the semiconductor by the oxide layer; it constitutes the gate electrode.

In order to clearly illustrate the structure, it is necessary to distort the relative dimensions grossly. In reality, the total substrate area occupied by an MOS transistor is of the order of $150 \, \mu.^2$ The diffused source and drain regions are from 5 to 10 μ deep and are separated by only 10 to 20 μ (dimension L in Fig. 9.2*b*). The oxide layer is commonly about 0.1 μ thick.

When the gate electrode is open-circuited, there is essentially no conducting path between the source and the drain. Whereas the substrate material between these regions has high, but finite, resistivity, the middle region is coupled to the source and drain regions through junctions. The junctions are "back-to-back," so that one or the other is reverse-biased for either polarity of source-to-drain voltage, thereby preventing conduction through the intervening intrinsic region.

When the gate electrode is made *positive* with respect to the source and drain regions, an electric field is produced in the oxide layer under the gate electrode. This field originates on positive charge in the metal gate electrode and terminates on negative charge in the underlying semiconductor. The negative charge consists of *electrons* that are drawn into the substrate semiconductor from the source and drain regions, as soon as the gate electrode is made positive. This situation is illustrated in Fig. 9.3a, which displays only the principal features of the structure. The electronic charge is mobile and thus provides a conducting path or *channel* between source and drain. The conductance of the channel that is induced by the gate depends on the gate-to-source or gate-to-drain voltage. This dependence can be shown either by plotting the source-to-drain channel conductance

$$G_C = \frac{I_D}{V_{DS}}$$

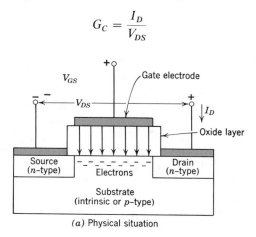

(a) Physical situation

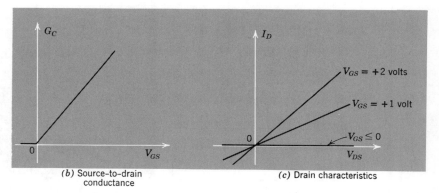

(b) Source-to-drain
conductance

(c) Drain characteristics

Figure 9.3   A conducting channel between source and drain can be induced by making the gate positive with respect to source and drain.

versus the gate-to-source voltage V_{GS}, as in Fig. 9.3b, or by plotting the drain current versus the drain-to-source voltage with V_{GS} as a parameter, as shown in Fig. 9.3c. The latter family of curves is called the *drain characteristics* of the transistor.

The potential of the MOS device as a control valve should be obvious from Fig. 9.3. Since no appreciable current is required in the gate circuit, because of the insulation provided by the oxide layer, very little power is needed to control the flow of power in a loop containing the source-to-drain path.

This discussion has tacitly assumed that the drain-to-source voltage is small compared with the gate-to-source voltage. In such cases the magnitude of the oxide-layer field is nearly the same at every point along the length of the induced channel, and the resulting channel conductivity is uniform. If, on the other hand, the drain-to-source voltage is *positive* and comparable to the gate-to-source voltage, the electric field varies along the channel, as shown in Fig. 9.4a. The field is greatest at the source end of the channel, where the voltage across the oxide layer is V_{GS}, and the smallest near the drain end of the channel, where the voltage across the oxide layer is less by V_{DS}. In this case, the induced charge density varies along the length of the channel, and it is no longer possible to describe the channel in terms of a linear conductance. Thus the drain characteristics become nonlinear, as shown in Fig. 9.4b. For a fixed positive value of V_{GS} the drain current saturates as V_{DS} increases. The drain current reaches its saturation value when the voltage across the drain end of the oxide layer reaches zero. At this point there is no accumulation of charge at the drain end of the channel. A further increase in V_{DS} does not affect the drain current because, as we shall see in Section 9.3, it does not influence the induced charge density along most of the channel length.

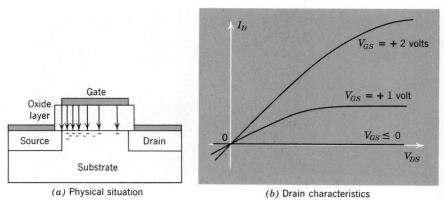

(a) Physical situation   (b) Drain characteristics

Figure 9.4 When the drain-to-source voltage is not negligible, the drain characteristics become nonlinear.

We now wish to study the physical electronics of the MOS transistor in quantitative detail, in order to evaluate the terminal I-V characteristics and to develop circuit models that characterize the electrical behavior of the device. First, however, we must explore some of the properties of semiconductor surfaces and develop the relationships between electric fields at the surface and the carrier concentrations and conductivity there.

9.2   Electrical Properties of Semiconductor Surfaces
9.2.1   Carrier Concentrations at the Surface

MOS transistors depend for their operation on a conducting *channel*, which is induced in the surface of the substrate semiconductor by the electric field that the gate electrode produces in the oxide layer. The carrier concentrations in the induced channel are related to the field in the oxide layer by Gauss's law, which was given in Eq. 2.5:

$$\oint_S \epsilon \mathscr{E}_n \, dS = Q \tag{9.1}$$

Here Q denotes the net charge within the volume included in the closed surface S, ϵ is the dielectric permittivity of the oxide layer, and $\mathscr{E}_n$ is the outward normal component of the electric field crossing the surface S. The charge Q in the substrate can have three components:

1. Immobile surface charge of either polarity may be present at the interface between the oxide layer and the semiconductor. This charge, which we denote by γ_s, arises from the disruption of the periodic crystalline structure at the semiconductor surface and from impurities that are trapped at the oxide-semiconductor interface.
2. Mobile electrons are drawn into the channel region from the n-type source and drain region as soon as the gate voltage is applied. These carriers support conduction in the induced channel and are responsible for the operation of the MOS transistor.
3. Immobile negative ions are left in the channel because holes are drawn into the source and drain from the channel region as soon as V_{GS} is applied. Clearly, these immobile ions cannot support conduction.

For simplicity, we assume in this introductory analysis that the surface charge γ_s is zero, and return in Section 9.3.4 to remove this restriction.

We apply Gauss's law to the surface of the semiconductor in the channel region, as shown in Fig. 9.5. We assume that V_{GS} is positive and V_{DS} is zero. The volume element that we consider is boxlike, having surfaces of area ΔA parallel to the oxide-semiconductor interface. We require that d be large enough so that the volume element includes all of the "skin" in which the channel is induced; in silicon devices this condition is met if d is a fraction of a micron. Because the oxide layer contains no volume charge density, the electric field there is uniform and is directed normal to the interface. We

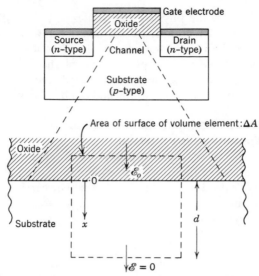

Figure 9.5   The electric field in the oxide layer is related to the charge in the semiconductor surface by Gauss's law.

denote this oxide field by $\mathcal{E}_o$, as shown in Fig. 9.5. The electric field is zero at the lower surface of the volume element because the distance d is large enough for the carrier concentrations there to be undisturbed. Consequently, Gauss's law requires that

$$-\epsilon \mathcal{E}_o \, \Delta A = Q = \int_0^d \rho(x) \, \Delta A \, dx \tag{9.2}$$

where ϵ denotes the permittivity of the oxide, and $\rho(x)$ denotes the volume charge density associated with the disturbed mobile-carrier concentrations. That is,

$$\rho = q(\Delta p - \Delta n) \tag{9.3}$$

where Δp and Δn are the deviations of the hole and electron concentrations in the channel from the corresponding bulk values.

9.2.2   Depletion, Inversion, and Accumulation Layers

The effect of the oxide-layer field $\mathcal{E}_o$ on the channel charge density and on the hole and electron concentrations near the surface is illustrated in Fig. 9.6. These sketches are drawn for a field directed toward the semiconductor, that is, for $\mathcal{E}_o$ positive. The channel charge density ρ is negative, in accordance with Eq. 9.2, as shown in Fig. 9.6a. The electric field in the oxide layer terminates on this charge, which is produced by an increase in the electron concentration and a decrease in the hole concentration, as shown in Fig. 9.6b.

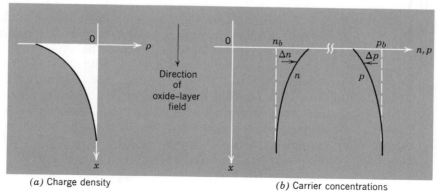

(a) Charge density   (b) Carrier concentrations

Figure 9.6   A depletion layer is produced when the majority-carrier concentration is moderately reduced by the field.

Specifically, the field terminates in part on extra electrons under the gate and in part on the exposed (ionized) acceptor atoms.

The charge distribution shown in Fig. 9.6a is, at every value of x, proportional to the difference between the perturbations Δn and Δp, in accordance with Eq. 9.3. The unperturbed carrier concentrations, which are characteristic of the bulk substrate semiconductor, are denoted by n_b and p_b, as shown in the sketch. For the case illustrated, the substrate is p-type; thus the channel along the surface is made less strongly p-type by the electric field in the oxide. The channel in this case is said to be a *depletion layer* because the majority-carrier concentration is *reduced* near the surface.

The spatial distribution of the channel charge within the semiconductor surface is governed by Gauss's law and by the Boltzmann relations (Eqs. 3.36) that couple the carrier concentrations to the electrostatic potential (see Problem P9.1).

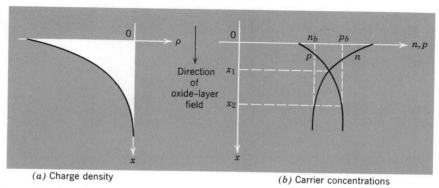

(a) Charge density   (b) Carrier concentrations

Figure 9.7   An inversion layer is produced when the field is strong enough to invert the carrier concentrations near the surface.

If the bulk material is less strongly p-type, or if the surface field is stronger, the carrier concentrations near the surface may be inverted, as shown in Fig. 9.7. Although the bulk material is p-type, the surface layer in this case is n-type, and the surface layer is separated from the bulk material by a space-charge layer associated with the pn junction, as shown in Fig. 9.8. The channel in this case is said to contain an *inversion layer*. The inversion layer extends from the surface to $x = x_1$, where the carrier concentrations are equal. The region between x_1 and x_2 is a depletion layer, as can be seen in Figs. 9.7 and 9.8.

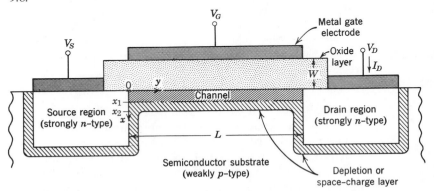

Figure 9.8 The inversion layer is isolated from the substrate on which it is formed by a depletion layer, that is, a pn junction is formed.

Clearly, it is possible to form a different type of channel either by reversing the field or by starting with an n-type substrate. For example, the sketches in Fig. 9.9 apply to a MOSFET in which the substrate is n-type and the oxide-

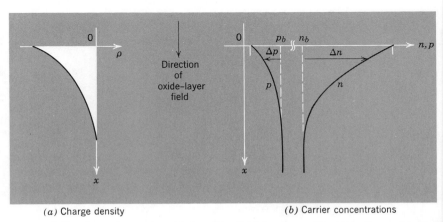

(a) Charge density   (b) Carrier concentrations

Figure 9.9 An accumulation layer is produced when the field increases the majority-carrier concentration.

layer field $\mathscr{E}_o$ is positive as before. Because we still require negative charge to terminate the field, the surface must in this case be made more strongly n-type by the electric field. The channel so formed is called an *accumulation layer*.

To calculate the relative magnitudes of Δn and Δp in any of the three types of layers discussed above, we assume that the dielectric is lossless and that V_{DS} is zero. Under these conditions there is no direct current anywhere in the system. Focusing attention on the x-directed flows of holes and electrons in the semiconductor, we write

$$J_{hx} = q\mu_h p\mathscr{E}_x - qD_h\frac{dp}{dx} \tag{9.4a}$$

$$J_{ex} = q\mu_e n\mathscr{E}_x + qD_e\frac{dn}{dx} \tag{9.4b}$$

where $\mathscr{E}_x$ is the field in the substrate and channel. Because there is no x-directed current,

$$J_{hx} + J_{ex} = 0$$

But to avoid a violation of the second law of thermodynamics involving a continuous generation of carriers at the bottom of the substrate and a continuous recombination of these carriers at the top, that is, to satisfy the condition of detailed balance (Section 2.2.1), we must also insist that J_{ex} and J_{hx} be *independently* zero. This is the same condition that was imposed in our discussion of semiconductor material in equilibrium; hence we reach the same conclusion. Specifically, in the channel

$$np = n_i^2 \tag{9.5}$$

or

$$(n_b + \Delta n)(p_b + \Delta p) = n_i^2 \tag{9.6}$$

Let us illustrate the relative sizes of Δn and Δp by substituting some typical numbers into Eq. 9.6. For silicon near room temperature $n_i \simeq 10^{10}$ cm^{-3}. Hence let us assume that in the p-type substrate $p_b = 10^{12}$ cm^{-3} and $n_b = 10^8$ cm^{-3}. If now Δn at some point in the channel is 10^{14}, then from Eq. 9.6 we have

$$p_b + \Delta p = \frac{10^{20}}{10^8 + 10^{14}} \simeq 10^6 \text{ cm}^{-3}$$

$$\Delta p = 10^6 - 10^{12} \simeq -10^{12} \text{ cm}^{-3}$$

Thus in the case Δn is two orders of magnitude larger than $|\Delta p|$. Clearly, regardless of how much larger we make Δn, Δp is limited to -10^{12} cm^{-3} corresponding to complete depletion of holes from the channel. Hence for any Δn larger than 10^{14} cm^{-3}, Δn will be much larger than Δp, and we can approximate Eq. 9.3 by

$$\rho = q(\Delta p - \Delta n) \simeq -q\,\Delta n \tag{9.7}$$

The gate voltage required to produce an inversion layer such that Δn is 10^{14} cm^{-3} is of the order of 3 mv for an oxide thickness of 0.1 μ (see Problem 9.1).

9.3   Static Volt-Ampere Characteristics of the MOS Transistor
9.3.1   Drain Characteristics for V_{DS} Much Less Than V_{GS}

The carrier-concentration variations that produce the channel charge described by $\rho(x)$ influence the conductivity of the semiconductor near the surface. It is this modulation of conductivity in the channel that is responsible for operation of the MOS transistor. We now relate the conductivity change to the carrier-concentration changes and thus to $\rho(x)$ and the oxide-layer field $\mathscr{E}_o$.

The current that flows in the source-to-drain path in an MOS transistor flows parallel to the oxide-semiconductor interface. In terms of the coordinates defined in Fig. 9.10, the channel current flows in the y direction. We consider an electric field in this direction, which we denote by $\mathscr{E}_y$, and calculate the current I_y that results from the drift of the mobile charge in the induced channel.

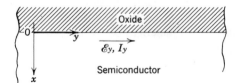

Figure 9.10   The channel conductance is defined for current flow parallel to the oxide-semiconductor interface.

We assume that the channel is comprised of a strong n-type inversion layer on a p-type substrate so that conduction in the channel is dominated by electrons. That is, we consider an n-channel device. Of course, the discussion that follows could just as well have been phrased in terms of a channel that was strongly p-type.

The current I_y, which results from electron flow in the channel, can be expressed in terms of Δn, the perturbation of the electron concentration in the channel. The y-directed drift current density associated with Δn is

$$J_y = q\mu_e\,\Delta n\mathscr{E}_y \tag{9.8}$$

where μ_e denotes the electron mobility. Of course, the conductivity varies in the x direction, reflecting the fact that Δn is largest just inside the interface and decreases as x increases.[2] The total y-directed current associated with Δn is

$$I_y = q\mu_e h \int_0^d \Delta n \, \mathscr{E}_y \, dx \tag{9.9a}$$

where h denotes the channel width, that is, the dimension of the channel in the direction normal to the plane in Fig. 9.10. The upper limit d of the integral is chosen to include the entire channel region, that is, the integral includes the entire region in which Δn is nonzero. We initially restrict discussion to the case where V_{DS} is much smaller than V_{GS}. Under these conditions, the oxide-layer field $\mathscr{E}_o$ will be nearly uniform along the channel length, as indicated in Fig. 9.3a. That is, $\mathscr{E}_x$ will be independent of y. It follows from Maxwell's equations that because

$$\oint_c \mathscr{E} \cdot d\mathbf{s} = 0$$

$\mathscr{E}_y$ must be independent of x. Thus Eq. 9.9a becomes:

$$I_y = q\mu_e h \mathscr{E}_y \int_0^d \Delta n \, dx \tag{9.9b}$$

We must now relate Δn to the field $\mathscr{E}_o$, hence to V_{GS}. Because there is still no static gate current even with V_{DS} not zero, Eq. 9.6 remains valid. Hence, assuming a strong inversion layer, we find from Eqs. 9.2 and 9.7

$$-\epsilon\mathscr{E}_o = \int_0^d -q \, \Delta n \, dx \tag{9.10}$$

By eliminating the integral between Eqs. 9.9b and 9.10, we obtain

$$I_y = \epsilon\mu_e h \mathscr{E}_y \mathscr{E}_o \tag{9.11}$$

This equation shows that the y-directed current is *linearly* related to both the x-directed field in the oxide and the y-directed field. This dependence of the source-to-drain current on the field in the oxide layer is called the *field effect*; it is the basic physical mechanism on which MOS transistors operate.

Equation 9.11 can be used to verify the drain characteristics postulated in Fig. 9.3c. We have assumed that $\mathscr{E}_x$ is independent of y; hence it follows from Eq. 9.10 that Δn is also independent of y. With the charge uniformly distributed in the y direction, $\mathscr{E}_y$ will be uniform:

$$\mathscr{E}_y = -\frac{V_{DS}}{L} \tag{9.12}$$

---

[2] We assume that the mobility is independent of x. This is not completely accurate because surface scattering reduces the mobilities significantly in the surface layer.

where L is the length of the channel. Also, ignoring contact potentials, we have

$$\mathcal{E}_o \simeq \frac{V_{GS}}{W} \tag{9.13}$$

where W is the thickness of the oxide layer. Substituting these values into Eq. 9.11, we obtain

$$I_D = -I_y = \frac{\epsilon\mu_e h}{LW} V_{DS} V_{GS} \tag{9.14a}$$

Thus the drain current is linearly related to both V_{DS} and V_{GS} in this region, as we postulated in Section 9.1 and Fig. 9.3c. The relationship can also be expressed in terms of a source-to-drain conductance G_C:

$$G_C = \frac{I_D}{V_{DS}} = \frac{\epsilon\mu_e h}{LW} V_{GS} \tag{9.14b}$$

This expression confirms the sketch of G_C presented in Fig. 9.3b. If we had considered the case in which the channel was strongly p-type, we would have obtained a proportionality similar to Eq. 9.11; only the constant multiplier would be different (see Problem P9.2).

If Δn and Δp are comparable, that is, if the channel is *not* strongly extrinsic, the channel current and the oxide-layer field are *not* linearly related; Eq. 9.11 does not apply (see Problem P9.3).

This discussion has focused on the current carried by the carrier-concentration perturbations that are produced in the channel by the field effect. Thus the concentration employed in Eq. 9.8 is Δn, *not* the total electron concentration $n_b + \Delta n$. The drift currents associated with n_b, the electron-concentration characteristic of the bulk semiconductor, and with p_b, the corresponding hole concentration, have been neglected because these currents do not contribute to conduction in the source-to-drain path through the channel. In n-channel MOS transistors such as those we have considered, the substrate is usually lightly-doped p-type material. Consequently, any path from the source contact to the drain contact through the substrate must pass through two "back-to-back" pn junctions. One or the other of these junctions is reverse-biased for either polarity of source-to-drain voltage, thereby preventing significant current through the substrate. The inversion layer produced by the oxide-layer field is n-type, however. Consequently, the channel is in good contact with the source and drain regions so that substantial electron drift currents can flow from the source to the drain through the channel. It is this current that is given by Eq. 9.11. Of course, the n-type channel is isolated from the p-type substrate by a pn junction, as shown in Fig. 9.8.

9.3.2   Static Drain Characteristics for V_{DS} Comparable to V_{GS}

For values of V_{DS} comparable to V_{GS}, we can no longer neglect the voltage drop along the channel in determining the oxide-layer field $\mathscr{E}_o$. In this case we denote the potential between the oxide-substrate interface and the source terminal by $V(y)$. This voltage is a function of the distance y along the channel because of y-directed electric field that produces drain current in the channel. The voltage across the oxide layer at any point y is thus

$$V_{GS} - V(y)$$

and the corresponding electric field in the oxide layer, which corresponds to $\mathscr{E}_o$ in Fig. 9.5, is

$$\mathscr{E}_o = \frac{V_{GS} - V(y)}{W} \tag{9.15}$$

We again assume that the inversion layer produced by the field is strongly n-type and extends along the entire channel. The total channel current is, from Eq. 9.9a,

$$I_y = qh\mu_e \int_0^d \mathscr{E}_y \, \Delta n \, dx \tag{9.16}$$

We know from Maxwell's equations that

$$\oint_c \mathscr{E} \cdot ds = 0 \tag{9.17a}$$

or, in differential form

$$\frac{\partial \mathscr{E}_x}{\partial y} = \frac{\partial \mathscr{E}_y}{\partial x} \tag{9.17b}$$

Thus because $\mathscr{E}_x$ is now a function of y, $\mathscr{E}_y$ must also be a function of x. At the top of the channel, $\mathscr{E}_x$ is approximately equal to $\mathscr{E}_o$, the oxide-layer field. Hence, from Eq. 9.15, we know that at the top of the channel

$$\frac{\partial \mathscr{E}_x}{\partial y} = -\frac{1}{W} \frac{\partial V(y)}{\partial y} \tag{9.18}$$

$$= \frac{1}{W} \mathscr{E}_y$$

Thus Eq. 9.17b becomes

$$\frac{\partial \mathscr{E}_y}{\partial x} = \frac{\mathscr{E}_y}{W} \tag{9.19}$$

Eq. 9.19 determines the slope of $\mathscr{E}_y$ right at the top edge of the channel. We know that $\mathscr{E}_x$ decreases as we penetrate into the channel; hence it is reasonable to assume that $\partial \mathscr{E}_x/\partial y$ also decreases. On this basis, Eq. 9.19 expresses the *maximum* value of $\partial \mathscr{E}_y/\partial x$, and for larger x, that is, deeper in the channel, the slope will be less. It follows that over the small distance d, the range of the integral in Eq. 9.16, the fractional change in $\mathscr{E}_y$ will be at most

$$\frac{\Delta \mathscr{E}_y}{\mathscr{E}_y} = \frac{\Delta x}{W} = \frac{d}{W} \tag{9.20}$$

Thus if d, the channel depth, is much smaller than W, the oxide-layer thickness, $\mathscr{E}_y$ does not change significantly over the range of the integral in Eq. 9.16, and we can write

$$I_y \simeq qh\mu_e \mathscr{E}_y \int_0^d \Delta n \, dx \tag{9.21}$$

Substituting for the integral from Eqs. 9.10 and 9.15, we obtain

$$I_y = h\mu_e \epsilon \mathscr{E}_y \left[\frac{V_{GS} - V(y)}{W} \right] \tag{9.22}$$

This relationship is obviously invalid when $V_{GS} - V(y)$ is small, that is, when the inversion layer has just been formed. As discussed in Section 9.2, the channel current is not linearly related to the surface field in such cases. Consequently, our analysis is inaccurate when the voltage across the oxide layer is less than a few millivolts (see Problem P9.1). Recognizing that on the basis of the previous assumptions, $\mathscr{E}_y$ in the channel is simply $-dV/dy$, we find that

$$I_y = -\frac{h\mu_e \epsilon}{W} \frac{dV}{dy} [V_{GS} - V(y)] \tag{9.23a}$$

The channel current must be independent of y and must, in fact, equal the drain current I_D (except for a change of sign). Thus Eq. 9.23a can be written as

$$I_D \, dy = \frac{h\mu_e \epsilon}{W} (V_{GS} - V) \, dV \tag{9.23b}$$

This differential equation can now be integrated to find I_D:

$$I_D \int_0^L dy = \frac{h\mu_e \epsilon}{W} \int_0^{V_{DS}} (V_{GS} - V) \, dV \tag{9.24}$$

Of course, this result is valid only when $V_{GS} - V$ is greater than zero, that is, when the inversion layer extends along the entire channel. Subject to this limitation, we determine the static drain characteristics to be

$$I_D = \frac{h\mu_e \epsilon}{WL} \left[V_{GS} V_{DS} - \frac{V_{DS}^2}{2} \right] \quad \text{for} \quad V_{DS} \leqslant V_{GS}, V_{GS} \geqslant 0 \tag{9.25}$$

The drain characteristics given by Eq. 9.25 are shown in Fig. 9.11, where I_D is plotted versus V_{DS}, with V_{GS} as a parameter. The curves extend only to the points at which $V_{DS} = V_{GS}$; larger values of V_{DS} violate our assumption that there is a strong inversion layer formed along the entire channel.

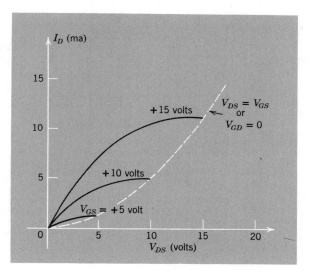

Figure 9.11   Drain characteristics of an MOS transistor. Only the region that corresponds to $V_{GD} > 0$ is shown.

9.3.3   Static Drain Characteristics for V_{DS} Greater Than V_{GS}

When the drain voltage exceeds the gate voltage, the electric field in the oxide layer at the drain end of the channel reverses direction, and the inversion layer no longer reaches all the way to the end of the channel. There is in fact a *small depleted region* at the drain end of the channel. The electric field in this depleted region originates on donor atoms in the heavily doped *n*-type drain region and terminates on electronic charge in the inversion layer toward the source and on the gate electrode. This situation is illustrated in Fig. 9.12, where we show field maps for three values of drain-to-source voltage. The density of the field lines is proportional to the field intensity, and their direction shows the direction of the electric field. Note that when the drain-to-gate voltage is positive, as in Fig. 9.12c, the inversion layer ends somewhat short of the drain region. There is a short depletion region between the end of the inversion layer and the drain region.

Current flows through this region because there is an intense electric field in the negative *y* direction, which causes electrons to flow from the end of the inversion layer to the drain. The resulting drain current is only slightly greater than the value that exists when $V_{DS} = V_{GS}$, because this current is

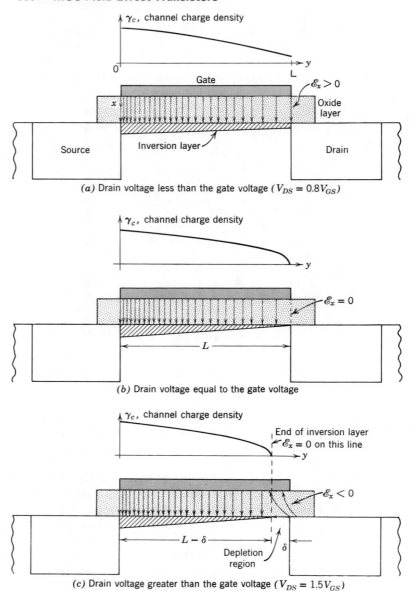

Figure 9.12   Maps showing the distribution of the electric field in the oxide and near the semiconductor surface.

governed by the potential distribution in the source portion of the channel where the inversion layer is formed, and that potential distribution is nearly the same for $V_{DG} > 0$ as it is for $V_{DG} = 0$. The inversion layer is now somewhat shorter, having a length of $L - \delta$, where δ is the length of the depleted region at the drain, but this shortening has only a small effect on the drain current.

Thus, for drain voltages in excess of the gate voltage, the drain current is nearly constant and is given by Eq. 9.25, with $V_{DS} = V_{GS}$. That is,

$$I_D = \frac{h\mu_e\epsilon}{WL}\left(\frac{V_{GS}^2}{2}\right) \qquad \text{for} \quad V_{DS} > V_{GS}, V_{GS} \geqslant 0 \qquad (9.26)$$

These characteristic curves are plotted in Fig. 9.13, along with the characteristics for V_{DS} less than V_{GS}, Eq. 9.25. For comparison, a set of measured characteristic curves are shown in Fig. 9.14. The major difference between

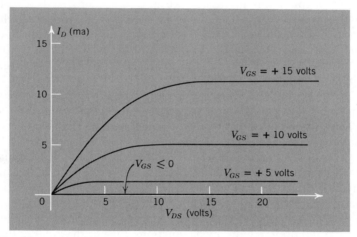

Figure 9.13   Complete drain characteristics. When V_{DS} exceeds V_{GS}, the current saturates.

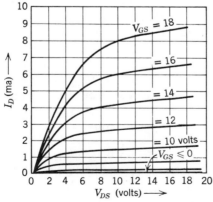

Figure 9.14   Measured drain characteristics. These curves differ from the theoretical curves of Fig. 9.13 in that the slope in the saturation region is nonzero. (Adapted from Fred P. Heiman, in J. T. Wallmark and H. Johnson, eds., *Field Effect Transistors: Physics Technology and Applications*, 1966, with permission of Prentice-Hall, Inc., Englewood Cliffs, N.J.)

the two sets of characteristics is that the measured curves have a nonzero slope in the saturation region where V_{DS} exceeds V_{GS}. This slope is a manifestation of the shortening of the inversion layer described in connection with Fig. 9.12c. As V_{DS} increases, the excess voltage $V_{DS} - V_{GS}$ appears across the depletion region at the drain end of the channel. Thus the depletion region must widen somewhat to accommodate larger values of $V_{DS} - V_{GS}$, and this widening reduces the length of the inversion layer slightly, producing a small increase in drain current; Eq. 9.26 shows that I_D increases as L decreases. The nonzero slope produced by this effect is usually small enough to ignore, and we shall not improve our model to account for it.

Throughout this discussion we have considered only *positive* values of gate-to-source voltage and have implied that a conducting channel is not formed when the gate voltage is negative. This assumption is supported by the measured characteristics of Fig. 9.14, in which the drain current is approximately zero for negative values of V_{GS}. The physical reason for this situation requires some discussion.

It should be clear from our examination of surface layers in Section 9.2 that with a p-type substrate, negative values of gate voltage V_{GS} will produce a *hole* accumulation layer in the channel region. The field in the oxide layer will originate on majority-carrier holes, and the hole population in the surface layer will be increased above the corresponding bulk value. Thus the surface conductance will be increased because of the presence of this accumulation layer. If this is the case, why is there no drain current when a voltage exists between the source and the drain? The reason is that the p-type accumulation layer that is formed by negative values of gate voltage is isolated from the source and drain regions by pn junctions. One or the other of these junctions is reverse-biased for each polarity of V_{DS}, and the "back-to-back" junctions cannot support drain current. Equivalently, the p-type accumulation layer cannot support drain current because neither the source nor the drain constitutes a "source" of holes. Thus there is negligible drain current for negative values of V_{GS}.

In developing the static model expressed by Eq. 9.25 we have assumed that V_{DS} is positive, that is, we have considered only the first quadrant of the drain characteristics. However, no fundamental change in operation occurs for V_{DS} negative. As long as V_{GS} is positive and V_{DS} is less than V_{GS}, we have a conducting channel between source and drain. This channel can conduct current in either direction with equal ease because there are no pn junctions in the source-channel-drain path. Thus Eq. 9.25a is also an adequate description of the third-quadrant V-I characteristics of the MOSFET.

Third-quadrant characteristics have been added to the familiar first-quadrant drain characteristics in Fig. 9.15. Note that the drain current increases in magnitude without limit in the third quadrant because more negative values of V_{DS} cause the gate-to-drain voltage to become more positive, thereby *increasing* the conductance of the inversion layer at the drain end of the channel. For the same reason, the transistor conducts when V_{DS} is negative even though V_{GS} is zero; an inversion layer is developed along the entire channel, becoming weakest at the source end. In fact, for V_{DS} negative, there is a set of characteristics for V_{GS} *negative*, provided that $V_{DS} < V_{GS}$ (see Problem P9.4).

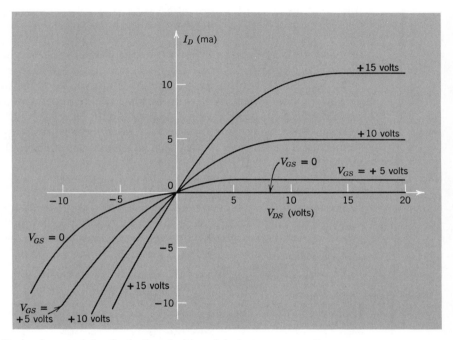

Figure 9.15   Drain characteristics for both polarities of drain-to-source voltage.

9.3.4   Effects of Surface Charge

The transistor whose physical electronics we have analyzed, and whose drain characteristics are shown in Fig. 9.15, is called an *n-channel enhancement-mode* MOS transistor. This name is applied because conduction occurs in a channel that is an *n*-type inversion layer (formed on a *p*-type substrate) and because drain current is zero when the gate is open-circuited and is *enhanced* by positive values of V_{GS}. Of course, *p-channel* enhancement-mode transistors can also be made, using the same fabrication techniques. Such devices have *p*-type source and drain regions and operate with *negative* values of gate-to-source voltage. Their drain characteristics are similar in shape to the curves of Fig. 9.15 except that the curves are rotated about the origin by 180°. Thus the normal region of operation, in which the drain current saturates, falls in the third quadrant.

MOS structures can also be operated in a mode that differs quantitatively from that described in Sections 9.3.2 and 9.3.3. To illustrate this mode of operation, we consider an n-channel device having the same physical structure as shown in Fig. 9.8. We assume, however, that owing to differences in surface treatment during fabrication, there is a layer of *positive surface charge* at the interface between the oxide and the semiconductor, and we characterize this charge layer by a surface charge density γ_s, which is uniform and independent of the gate voltage.[3] In such a case, part of the x-directed electric field in the channel originates on the gate electrode and part on the positive surface charge. Now the channel charge density is governed by a linear combination of the oxide-layer electric field and the surface charge density.

To find the relationship among the oxide-layer field $\mathscr{E}_o$, the surface charge γ_s, and the charge density $\rho(x)$ in the channel, we again apply Gauss's law to a volume element at the substrate-oxide interface, as shown in Fig. 9.16. As before, we choose the dimension d large enough to include all of the channel, so that the field at the bottom of the box is zero. Gauss's law now yields

$$- \epsilon \mathscr{E}_o \, \Delta A = \gamma_s \, \Delta A + \int_0^d \rho(x) \, \Delta A \, dx \qquad (9.27)$$

where $\rho(x)$ is, as before, the volume charge density within the substrate. Thus for a channel with a strong inversion layer, such that Δn is much larger

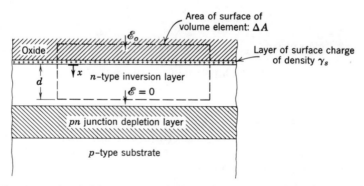

Figure 9.16 The charge density in the channel is governed by both the electric field in the oxide layer and the charge density at the oxide-semiconductor interface.

[3] The techniques presently used in producing such a layer of positive surface charge on a p-type or intrinsic substrate involve a great amount of "art" and are often proprietary in nature. However, two general types of techniques can be distinguished. An extremely shallow (less than 0.05 μ) diffusion of donor atoms can be diffused into the surface of the channel. A surface layer of positively charged donor ions results. Alternatively, the oxide layer can be grown in an atmosphere of dry hydrogen. Such treatment forms a layer of positive charges at the oxide-semiconductor interface.

in magnitude than Δp, Eq. 9.27 can be rewritten as

$$q \int_0^d \Delta n \, dx = -\int_0^d \rho(x) \, dx = \epsilon \mathscr{E}_o + \gamma_s \tag{9.28}$$

It is clear from Eq. 9.28 that with fixed positive charge γ_s on the oxide-substrate interface, an inversion layer is formed even when the gate is open-circuited and that a conducting channel between source and drain exists under these conditions. Positive values of gate voltage enlarge the field just inside the oxide-semiconductor interface, strengthen the inversion layer, and increase the source-to-drain conductance, and thus the drain current. On the other hand, negative values of gate voltage *reduce* the field just inside the semiconductor, weaken the inversion layer, and decrease the drain current. The drain characteristics that result are shown in Fig. 9.17, which should be compared with Fig. 9.14. A field-effect transistor having these characteristics is conventionally called an *n-channel depletion-mode MOS transistor*. This name is used because the channel conductance that exists for $V_{GS} = 0$ can be reduced or *depleted* by making V_{GS} negative. In reality this name is somewhat misleading, since the device can be operated with gate-to-source voltages of both polarities.

The static drain characteristics developed in Sections 9.3.2 and 9.3.3 can easily be adapted to the depletion-mode device. We simply recognize that the surface charge characterized by γ_s can be accounted for in the analysis by offsetting the gate voltage appropriately. That is, on substituting Eqs. 9.28 and 9.15 into Eq. 9.22, we obtain

$$I_y = h\mu_e \epsilon \mathscr{E}_y \left(\frac{V_{GS} - V_P - V(y)}{W} \right) \tag{9.29}$$

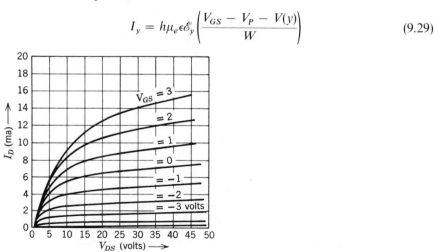

Figure 9.17   Measured drain characteristics of an *n*-channel depletion-mode MOS transistor. (Adapted from Fred P. Heiman, in J. T. Wallmark and H. Johnson, eds., *Field Effect Transistors: Physics, Technology, and Applications*, with permission of Prentice-Hall, Inc., Englewood Cliffs, N.J.)

where the constant V_P is given by

$$V_P = -\frac{\gamma_s W}{\epsilon} \tag{9.30}$$

The voltage V_P, which is called the *pinch-off voltage*, has a simple interpretation—it is the value of gate-to-channel voltage at which the inversion layer disappears. That is, I_y is zero when $V_{GS} - V(y) = V_P$. The transistor whose curves are shown in Fig. 9.17 has $V_P \simeq -5$ volt.

The analysis of Sections 9.3.2 and 9.3.3 can be thus adapted to the depletion-mode transistor simply by replacing V_{GS}, wherever it occurs, by $V_{GS} - V_P$. Consequently, the static drain characteristics that supplant Eqs. 9.25 and 9.26 are

$$I_D = \frac{h\mu_e\epsilon}{WL}\left[(V_{GS} - V_P)V_{DS} - \frac{V_{DS}^2}{2}\right]$$

$$\text{for} \quad V_{DS} \leqslant V_{GS} - V_P, \quad V_{GS} - V_P \geqslant 0 \tag{9.31a}$$

$$I_D = \frac{h\mu_e\epsilon}{WL}\left[\frac{(V_{GS} - V_P)^2}{2}\right] \quad \text{for} \quad V_{DS} > V_{GS} - V_P, V_{GS} - V_P \geqslant 0 \tag{9.31b}$$

9.4 Dynamic Models for MOS Transistors

The models just discussed, of which Eq. 9.25 is an example, are *static*. That is, the voltages applied to the transistor are assumed to change very slowly with time, if at all. A moment's reflection about the physical structure and operating principles of the MOS transistor suggests two ways in which this static analysis must be modified to account for voltages that may change rapidly.

1. From the point of view of the gate and source terminals, the transistor is a parallel-plate capacitor in which the gate electrode and the channel are the plates and the oxide layer is the dielectric. Thus we expect there to be capacitive gate current when the gate-to-source voltage changes.

2. Some time is required for the majority carriers to traverse the channel as they go from source to drain. If the gate voltage changes significantly during this *transit time*, the *static* expressions that we have obtained for drain current may no longer apply.

We now evaluate both the gate current under dynamic conditions and the transit time for majority-carrier flow in the channel. We shall see that gate current constitutes the principal new dynamic feature of the device and that transit-time considerations do not impose a serious limitation.

In this discussion of dynamic effects we consider only operation in the *saturated* portion of the drain characteristics; that is, we restrict the drain-to-source voltage V_{DS} to values greater than or equal to $V_{GS} - V_P$. Since most applications of MOS transistors involve operation with saturated drain current, the dynamic analysis of the device is simplified appreciably by this restriction.

9.4.1 Capacitive Effects

To evaluate the dynamic gate current, we compute the total charge on the gate electrode. Once again we focus on the *n*-channel enhancement-mode transistor shown in Fig. 9.8. For simplicity, we assume that the pinch-off voltage V_P is zero. Recall that the electric field in the oxide layer is then given by Eq. 9.15. Thus the density of surface charge on the gate electrode is

$$\gamma_G = \epsilon \mathscr{E}_o$$

$$= \epsilon \left(\frac{V_{GS} - V(y)}{W} \right) \tag{9.32}$$

This charge density is greatest at the source end of the channel and decreases to zero at the end of the inversion layer. Because we are concerned with behavior when the drain current is saturated, we assume that V_{DS} is equal to V_{GS} so that the inversion layer just disappears at the drain end of the channel. The *total* charge on the gate electrode is

$$Q_G = h \int_0^L \gamma_G \, dy \tag{9.33a}$$

where h is the width of the channel and L is the channel length. Substituting from Eq. 9.32, we obtain

$$Q_G = \frac{h\epsilon}{W} \int_0^L [V_{GS} - V(y)] \, dy \tag{9.33b}$$

One way of evaluating this integral is to find $V(y)$. This can be done by integrating Eq. 9.23:

$$I_D \int_0^y dy = \frac{h\mu_e \epsilon}{W} \int_0^V (V_{GS} - V) \, dV \tag{9.34}$$

For $V_{GS} = V_{DS}$, we obtain

$$I_D y = \frac{h\mu_e \epsilon}{W} \left[V_{DS} V(y) - \frac{V^2(y)}{2} \right] \tag{9.35}$$

On substituting for I_D and the constants from Eq. 9.26 and solving the quadratic (see Problem P9.5), we find that

$$V(y) = V_{DS}(1 - \sqrt{1 - y/L})$$ (9.36)

A plot of V versus y is shown in Fig. 9.18. The shape of this curve agrees with our physical intuition because Δn is much larger at the source end of the channel; hence we expect less voltage drop along the channel at that end than at the drain end.

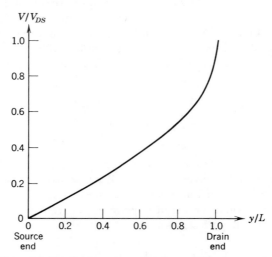

Figure 9.18   Potential distribution along the channel for the case in which $V_{DS} = V_{GS}$.

On substituting for $V(y)$ in Eq. 9.33b and integrating, we obtain

$$Q_G = \frac{h\epsilon}{W}V_{DS}\int_0^L \sqrt{1 - y/L}\, dy$$

$$= \tfrac{2}{3}\frac{hL\epsilon}{W}V_{DS}$$ (9.37)

This equation can be simplified once we recognize that the capacitance between gate and channel for $V_{DS} = 0$, that is, a uniform channel, is just

$$C_o = \frac{\epsilon hL}{W}$$ (9.38)

Recalling that the preceding derivation assumes $V_{DS} = V_{GS}$, we have

$$Q_G = \tfrac{2}{3}C_o V_{GS}$$ (9.39)

Thus the gate charge is *linearly* related to the gate-to-source voltage. Consequently, the gate current can be modeled in terms of an effective gate-to-source capacitance C_{gs}, that is,[4]

$$i_G = \frac{dQ_G}{dt} = C_{gs}\frac{dv_{GS}}{dt} \tag{9.40a}$$

where

$$C_{gs} = \tfrac{2}{3}C_o \tag{9.40b}$$

That is, the gate-to-source capacitance at the edge of saturation is two-thirds of the value of the capacitance of the gate-oxide-channel sandwich when the channel is uniform (as would be the case with no drain current).

When V_{DS} increases above V_{GS} and the drain current becomes saturated, the gate-to-source capacitance given by Eq. 9.40b still applies. In this region the potential distribution in the channel is only weakly influenced by V_{DS}; the gate charge is essentially independent of V_{DS} and is still given by Eq. 9.39. Thus we can approximate the dynamic behavior of the MOS transistor when the drain current is saturated by the model shown in Fig. 9.19a in which the static model developed earlier (Eq. 9.26) is augmented by the gate-to-source capacitance given by Eq. 9.40b. We use a *nonlinear* voltage-dependent current source to model the saturated drain current.

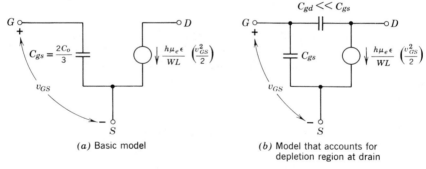

(a) Basic model (b) Model that accounts for depletion region at drain

Figure 9.19 Dynamic MOS transistor models for use when the drain current is saturated.

There is, of course, a depletion layer formed between the end of the channel and the drain region when V_{DS} exceeds V_{GS}, as shown in Fig. 9.12c. The excess voltage $V_{DS} - V_{GS}$ is taken up across this depletion layer. Since some of the field that originates on the drain region terminates on the gate, there is an electrostatic coupling between gate and drain. The dynamic consequences of this coupling can be crudely modeled as shown in Fig. 9.19b by adding a capacitance between gate and drain. Although we cannot evaluate this *overlap capacitance* easily, the nature of the structure insures that C_{gd} is small compared with C_{gs}.

[4] Once again, we denote instantaneous time-dependent variables by lowercase symbols with uppercase subscripts.

9.4.2   Transit Time

We now compute the transit time of carriers through the channel in order to determine the rates of change at which transit-time effects may become important. Since we have determined the potential distribution along the channel (Eq. 9.36), we could evaluate the transit time by determining $\mathscr{E}_y$ and thus the electron velocity $\mu_e \mathscr{E}_y$ at every point along the channel (see Problem P9.7). Instead of proceeding in this manner, we make use of the results already obtained to evaluate the transit time *under saturation conditions*.

The *total* majority-carrier charge in the channel is simply the negative of the charge on the gate. Thus the total channel charge at the edge of saturation is

$$Q_C = -Q_G$$
$$= -\tfrac{2}{3} C_o V_{GS} \tag{9.41}$$

This charge is in motion along the channel from source to drain. The quantity of charge that flows out the drain end of the channel in a time interval equal to the transit time is simply Q_C. Such is the definition of the transit time τ_t. Consequently the static drain current I_D must be

$$I_D = \frac{-Q_C}{\tau_t} \tag{9.42}$$

The minus sign is required because Q_C flows in opposition to the assumed reference direction for I_D. The transit time can thus be expressed in terms of the *static* drain current and the *static* channel charge:

$$\tau_t = -\frac{Q_C}{I_D} \tag{9.43a}$$

Using Eqs. 9.26 and 9.37, we obtain

$$\tau_t = \frac{4}{3}\left(\frac{L^2}{\mu_e}\right) V_{GS}^{-1} \tag{9.43b}$$

To illustrate typical values for the transit time with saturated drain current, we consider an *n*-channel MOS transistor having $L = 10\,\mu$ and $\mu_e = 10^3$ cm^2/volt-sec. When $V_{GS} = 1$ volt, the transit time is about 1.3 nsec. As long as the fractional change in V_{GS} is small during this time interval, we can be certain that any transit-time effects can be disregarded, and the static model for the dependence of I_D on V_{GS} can be used without significant error.

The lower bound on transit-time effects can be put in perspective by considering the relative sizes of the gate and drain currents under dynamic conditions. Equations 9.40a and 9.42 yield

$$\frac{i_G}{i_D} = \left(\frac{1}{Q_C}\frac{dQ_C}{dt}\right)\tau_t \tag{9.44}$$

We are normally concerned with applications in which there is *current gain*, that is, in which the gate current is small compared with the drain current. Equation 9.44 shows that in such cases the fractional amount by which Q_C changes in one transit time is small (note that the factor in parentheses is the fractional rate of change of Q_C). Thus if the gate current is small compared with the drain current—if there is substantial current gain—an analysis in which we ignore transit-time effects produces negligible error in the evaluation of the channel charge distribution and the drain current.

The discussion just completed suggests a *charge-control model* for the field-effect transistor operating with saturated drain current. We can regard V_{GS} as establishing a certain channel charge Q_C in accordance with Eq. 9.41 (V_{GS} also establishes the transit time in accordance with Eq. 9.43b). The channel charge in turn controls the saturated drain current in accordance with Eq. 9.42. A model that embodies these relationships is shown in Fig. 9.20. The accuracy of this model can be improved by adding a gate-to-drain capacitance, as shown by the dashed lines.

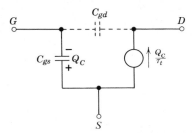

Figure 9.20   A charge control model for an MOS transistor.

Although we have based our discussion on an *n*-channel enhancement-mode transistor, the conclusions can be adapted to *p*-channel devices and to transistors that operate in the depletion mode as well. In all these cases the gate-source capacitance under saturated drain current conditions is given by Eq. 9.40b.

9.5   Circuit Applications of MOS Transistors
9.5.1   Common-Source Amplifiers

MOS field-effect transistors require negligible current at the gate terminal. To exploit this feature of their behavior, the active devices are often used in the *common-source* configuration, in which the source terminal is included in both the input and output loops. The circuit of an elementary common-source amplifier is shown in Fig. 9.21a. The symbol used is standard for an *n*-channel device. The symbol for a *p*-channel device differs only in that the *n* is replaced by *p*. The operation of this circuit can be studied graphically as shown in Fig. 9.21b. The drain characteristics illustrated are for an enhancement-mode device. For any value of $v_{GS} = v_I$, the state of the circuit is determined by finding the point of intersection of the corresponding curve of i_D versus v_{DS} and the load line that characterizes the constraint imposed by V_{DD} and R_L. Thus for $v_I = +3V$, the point of operation is denoted by P. The corresponding value of the output voltage v_O is determined by projecting the point P on the v_{DS} axis as shown (see problem P9.8).

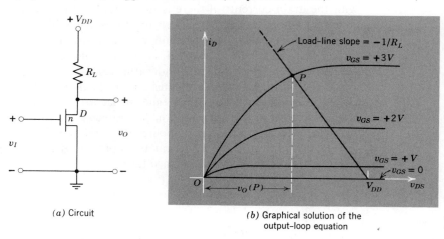

(a) Circuit

(b) Graphical solution of the output–loop equation

Figure 9.21 A common-source amplifier.

MOS transistors are unique among semiconductor active devices in that they have extraordinarily small input or gate currents and in that the drain current versus gate-to-source voltage characteristic is square-law in the saturation region. Gate current in an MOS transistor results solely from leakage in the insulating oxide layer and from leakage paths in the encapsulation of the device. These currents can easily be reduced to the range of 10^{-15} to 10^{-16} amp, even when the gate-to-source voltage is in the 5 to 10 volt range.

Because the gate current is extremely small, MOS transistors are used in electrometer applications in which minute currents or voltages are sensed and amplified. For example, the current developed by certain atomic particle counters such as ionization chambers may be in the range of 10^{-12} to 10^{-14} amp: an MOS transistor can be used to sense the current by responding to the voltage developed by this current in a high-value precision resistor and can do so without appreciably loading the sensor. These transistors can also be used as sensitive detectors of charge. To illustrate, we consider an MOS transistor having a gate current of 10^{-15} amp and a gate-to-source capacitance of 10^{-11} farad (10 pf). A charge of 10^{-10} coulomb on the gate will develop a gate-to-source voltage of 10 volts and will be reduced by only 1% as a consequence of leakage currents after a time interval of 10^3 sec, or about 17 min.

The *square-law* nature of the relationship between the saturated drain current and the gate-to-source voltage can be employed when multiplication of signals is required. For example, if v_{GS} is proportional to a given signal (and if the transistor is operated in the saturation region), the drain current i_D will be proportional to v_{GS}^2. Thus i_D provides a measure of the instantaneous power associated with v_{GS}. If v_{GS} is controlled by the *sum* of two signals $f(t)$ and $g(t)$, the drain current will be proportional to

$$[f(t) + g(t)]^2 = f^2(t) + g^2(t) + 2f(t)g(t) \qquad \text{for} \quad f(t) + g(t) > 0$$

In many cases the drain current components proportional to $f^2(t)$ and $g^2(t)$ can be removed by filtering or balancing,[5] thus leaving a component proportional to the instantaneous product of the input signals.

9.5.2   Voltage-Controlled Linear Resistances

MOS transistors can also be used as linear resistances in which the value of the resistance between source and drain is controlled by the gate-to-source voltage. The drain characteristics of Eq. 9.25 reduce, for V_{DS} small compared with V_{GS}, to

$$I_D = \left[\frac{h\mu_e \epsilon}{WL} V_{GS} \right] V_{DS} \tag{9.45}$$

Thus, for $V_{DS} \ll V_{GS}$, the source-to-drain path can be characterized by a resistance of value

$$R_D = \frac{V_{DS}}{I_D}$$

$$= \frac{WL}{h\mu_e \epsilon} V_{GS}^{-1} \tag{9.46}$$

One use of voltage-controlled resistances is in adjustable linear attenuators. Such a circuit is shown in Fig. 9.22a. As the control voltage V_C increases, the source-to-drain resistance decreases, thereby reducing the voltage division

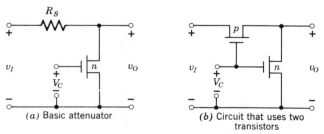

(a) Basic attenuator   (b) Circuit that uses two
                                  transistors

Figure 9.22   Variable linear attenuators using MOS transistors.

[5] See Reference 9.4.

ratio v_O/v_I (see Problem P9.11). An attenuator circuit that uses two MOS transistors as variable resistors is shown in Fig. 9.22b. The p-channel unit in the series arm is an enhancement-mode device, whereas the n-channel unit in the parallel arm is a depletion-mode device. Thus when the control voltage V_C is zero, the series transistor has a very high resistance, the parallel transistor has a low resistance, and the voltage division ratio v_O/v_I is small. If V_C is made *negative*, the resistance of the series unit decreases, the resistance of the parallel unit increases, and the voltage-division ratio increases (see Problem P9.12).

REFERENCES

9.1   L. J. Sevin, Jr., *Field-Effect Transistors*, McGraw-Hill, New York, 1965.

9.2   W. Gosling, *Field-Effect Transistor Applications*, Wiley, New York, 1965.

9.3   J. T. Wallmark and H. Johnson, *Field-Effect Transistors*, Prentice-Hall, Englewood Cliffs, N.J., 1966.

9.4   C. D. Todd, *Junction Field-Effect Transistors*, Wiley, New York, 1968. (This text has an extensive bibliography.)

PROBLEMS

P9.1   This problem is concerned with the relationship between the gate voltage and the carrier concentrations in the channel of an MOS transistor. Consider an n-channel device with a p-type substrate; the channel consists of an inversion layer that is isolated from the substrate by a depletion layer, as shown in Fig. 9.8.

(a) Equation 9.1 expresses Gauss's law in integral form. Consider a rectangular volume element of thickness dx and show that the differential form of Gauss's law is

$$\frac{d\mathscr{E}}{dx} = \frac{\rho}{\epsilon}$$

where ρ denotes the volume charge density.

(b) Assume that the charge in the inversion layer is dominated by the electrons. Use the Boltzmann relation (Eq. 3.36b) to show that Gauss's law can in this case be approximated by

$$\frac{d\mathscr{E}}{dx} = -\frac{qn_i}{\epsilon}e^{q\psi/kT}$$

where ψ is the electrostatic potential ($\psi = 0$ when $n = n_i$).

(c) Note that because $\mathscr{E} = -d\psi/dx$, $d\mathscr{E}/dx = -\mathscr{E}(d\mathscr{E}/d\psi)$, and integrate the equation developed in (b) to obtain

$$\mathscr{E}(0)^2 - \mathscr{E}(x_1)^2 = \frac{2kT}{\epsilon}[n(0) - n(x_1)]$$

where x_1 is the depth of the inversion layer (see Fig. 9.8).

(d) Since we assume a strong inversion layer, we have $\mathscr{E}(0) \gg \mathscr{E}(x_1)$ and $n(0) \gg n(x_1)$. Show that in this case the field at the surface of the inversion layer can be written as

$$\mathscr{E}(0) = \frac{kT/q}{L_D}$$

where

$$L_D = \sqrt{\frac{\epsilon kT}{2q^2 n(0)}}$$

is the *Debye length* at the surface. The depth of the inversion layer x_1 is several Debye lengths.

(e) Consider a silicon device in which $\epsilon = 10^{-12}$ farad/cm. Near room temperature $kT/q = 25$ mv. Evaluate the Debye length for a surface concentration of $n(0) = 10^{14}$ cm^{-3}. Evaluate the electric field $\mathscr{E}(0)$ at the surface of the semiconductor. If the oxide layer has a thickness of 0.1 μ, what value of gate-to-channel voltage is required to produce these values of $\mathscr{E}(0)$ and $n(0)$?

P9.2 Consider a p-channel MOS transistor in which channel conduction is dominated by *holes*.

(a) Obtain an expression for the y-directed hole drift current in the channel. This relationship is analogous to Eq. 9.8, which applies for an n-channel device.

(b) Note that in a p-channel device $\rho \simeq q\Delta p$ and derive an expression for I_y that is analogous to Eq. 9.11. Use the reference direction for $\mathscr{E}_o$ specified in Fig. 9.5.

P9.3 This problem is concerned with the relationship between oxide-layer field and channel current when the hole and electron perturbations are comparable.

(a) Obtain an expression for the total y-directed drift current in the channel.

(b) Derive an expression for $\mathscr{E}_o$ in terms of the integrals of Δn and Δp. Since Δn and Δp are *not* independent (See Eq. 9.6), it is possible, in principle, to express I_y as a function of $\mathscr{E}_o$. This functional relationship is nonlinear whenever Δn and Δp are comparable.

P9.4 The drain-current expressions of Eqs. 9.25 and 9.26 apply for V_{GS} greater than or equal to zero. If V_{DS} is positive, the drain current is positive and the inversion layer is strongest at the *source* end: if V_{DS} is negative, the drain current is negative and the inversion layer is strongest at the *drain* end. The n-channel MOSFET can be operated with negative *values* of V_{GS} if V_{DS} is *more negative* than V_{GS}. In such cases V_{GD} is *positive* and an inversion layer is formed in the channel. This inversion layer is strongest at the *drain* end of the channel and weakens toward the source end. Show that the drain characteristics in this region of operation are described by

$$
I_D = \begin{cases}
0 & V_{DS} > V_{GS}, V_{GS} < 0 \\
-\dfrac{h\mu_e \epsilon}{WL} \dfrac{(V_{DS} - V_{GS})^2}{2} & V_{DS} < V_{GS}, V_{GS} < 0
\end{cases}
$$

P9.5 This problem is concerned with the voltage distribution along the channel of an *n*-channel MOSFET which is operating at the edge of saturation.

(*a*) Verify Eq. 9.35.

(*b*) Substitute for I_D in Eq. 9.35 the expression for saturation-region drain current given by Eq. 9.26, and solve the resulting equation for $V(y)$. Sketch and dimension $V(y)$.

(*c*) Compute, sketch, and dimension $\mathscr{E}_y(y)$. Why does the *y*-directed field have a singularity at the drain end of the channel?

(*d*) Verify Eq. 9.37.

P9.6 A *p*-channel enhancement-mode MOSFET is normally operated with both V_{DS} and V_{GS} negative. The drain current, which results from the flow of *holes* from source to drain, is also negative.

(*a*) Consider a *p*-channel enhancement-mode device that has the physical structure shown in Fig. 9.8 and develop expressions for I_D that are analogous to Eqs. 9.25 and 9.26. Specify the ranges of V_{GS} and V_{DS} for which these expressions apply.

The pinch-off voltage in a *p*-channel depletion-mode device is *positive*, corresponding to negative surface charge at the oxide layer-semiconductor interface.

(*b*) Develop expressions for I_D that apply to a *p*-channel depletion-mode device having a pinch-off voltage of V_P, that is, develop relationships that are analogous to Eqs. 9.31. Specify the ranges of V_{GS} and V_{DS} for which these expressions apply.

P9.7 This problem is concerned with the direct evaluation of the channel transit time at the edge of saturation.

(*a*) Use the expression for $V(y)$ given by Eq. 9.36 to determine $\mathscr{E}_y(y)$ and the electron drift velocity $u_y(y)$.

(*b*) Evaluate the time required for an electron to move from source to drain. *Suggestion.* The time required to move through the distance dy at y is $dy/u_y(y)$. Show that your expression for the transit time is equivalent to the expression of Eq. 9.43b.

P9.8 The *n*-channel enhancement-mode transistor whose drain characteristics are shown in Fig. 9.14 is operated in the common source configuration shown in Fig. 9.21a. The drain supply voltage is $V_{DD} = +16$ volts and the load resistance is $R_L = 2$ kohm. Making use of graphical techniques, determine, sketch, and dimension the voltage transfer characteristic v_O versus v_I for v_I in the range from -2 to $+18$ volts.

P9.9 This problem is concerned with an n-channel MOSFET in which the pinch-off voltage is nonzero. The physical structure is shown in Fig. 9.8.

(a) When the drain-to-source voltage is very small, the channel can be described by means of a linear conductance G_C (see Fig. 9.3b). Derive an expression for G_C in terms of V_{GS} and the pinch-off voltage V_P.

(b) The channel conductance that occurs when V_{GS} is zero is denoted by G_0. Determine an expression for G_0, and use it to express the saturated drain current, given by Eq. 9.31b, in terms of G_0, V_P, and $(V_{GS} - V_P)$.

(c) The saturated drain current that occurs when V_{GS} is zero is denoted by I_{DO}. Express I_{DO} in terms of G_0 and V_P.

A certain n-channel MOSFET has $V_P = -3$ volt, $G_0 = 5 \times 10^{-4}$ mho, and $C_o = 10$ pf.

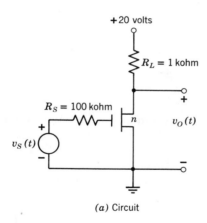

(a) Circuit

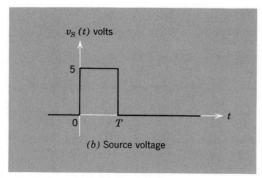

(b) Source voltage

Figure 9.23 An MOSFET pulse amplifier.

(d) What is the drain current when $V_{GS} = 2$ volts, $V_{DS} = 6$ volts? What is the corresponding value of gate-to-source capacitance C_{gs}? What is the channel transit time τ_t?

Answers. (d) $I_D \simeq 2.1$ ma, $C_{gs} \simeq 6.7$ pf, $\tau_t \simeq 16$ nsec.

P9.10 The transistor in the circuit of Fig. 9.23a has $V_P = 0$. When $V_{GS} = V_{DS} = +5$ volts, the drain current is 4 ma. The gate-to-source capacitance when there is no drain current is 5 pf.

(a) Assume that T is large enough so that the output voltage $v_O(t)$ reaches a steady value before the input pulse ends. What is this value of $v_O(t)$? Is the transistor operating in the saturated portion of the drain characteristics?

(b) Assume $T = 1\,\mu$sec. Compute, sketch, and dimension $v_O(t)$ for $0 < t < 3\,\mu$sec.

Answers. (a) $v_O = 16$ v.

P9.11 The transistor in the circuit of Fig. 9.22a is an enhancement-mode device with a pinch-off voltage of zero. When $V_C = +1$ volt, the source-to-drain resistance is 10 kohm. The series resistance R_S has a value of 5 kohm. Derive an expression for the voltage-division ratio v_O/v_I for values of V_C in the range from -2 to 10 volts. Sketch and dimension this relationship.

P9.12 When the control voltage V_C in the circuit of Fig. 9.22b is $+1$ volt, the n-channel MOSFET has a source-to-drain resistance of 10 kohm and the p-channel MOSFET has a source-to-drain resistance of 1 kohm. The p-channel MOSFET is a depletion-mode device having a pinch-off voltage of $+8$ volts and the n-channel MOSFET is an enhancement-mode device with a pinch-off voltage of zero. Derive an expression for the voltage-division ratio v_O/v_I for values of V_C in the range from -2 to 10 volts. Sketch and dimension this relationship on the same coordinates used in Problem P9.11.

CHAPTER TEN

Junction Field-Effect Transistors

We now turn our attention to field-effect transistors in which the electric field that modulates the conductance is developed in the space-charge layer of a *pn* junction, and develop circuit models that characterize the behavior of these *unipolar* junction transistors.[1]

10.1 Physical Structure

Most junction field-effect transistors employ a structure in which the channel is sandwiched between two junction-space-charge layers, as shown in Fig. 10.1, in which an *n*-channel device is illustrated. The two *p*-type regions are

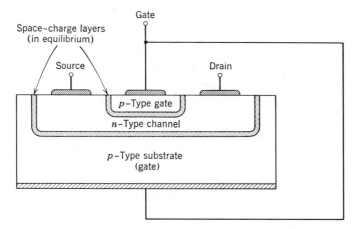

Figure 10.1 Cross section of an *n*-channel junction field-effect transistor. Not to scale.

connected together to form the gate electrode. Since control action occurs in the channel region between the junction-space-charge layers, we study the conduction mechanism in this region, using the somewhat idealized rectangular model shown in Fig. 10.2. The relative dimensions are grossly distorted in this sketch; typically the channel is at least 10 times as long as it is wide, and it may be several hundred times as long. Although we base our analysis on an *n*-channel device, the behavior of *p*-channel devices is completely analogous.

The channel is assumed to be uniformly doped and to have a length L, as indicated in Fig. 10.2. The separation of the *p*-type gate regions, which are

---

[1] These devices are called unipolar because their operation involves only one type of carrier. That is, current flow in the channel is dominated by the majority carriers in the channel, and minority carriers play no significant role in the operation of the device.

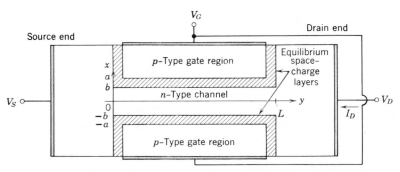

Figure 10.2   A physical model for the channel region of an *n*-channel junction field-effect transistor. Not to scale.

assumed to be much more heavily doped than the channel, is $2a$. Because the space-charge layers associated with the two junctions penetrate into the channel region, the channel width is less than $2a$. We denote the channel width by $2b$. Figure 10.2 shows the device in equilibrium, when the space-charge-layer penetration is uniform. We shall find that the penetration is not uniform when drain current flows. Thus the channel half width b will, in general, be a function of y, the coordinate along the channel. The dimension of the channel normal to the plane of Fig. 10.2 is h.

The junction field-effect transistor is normally operated with the junctions reverse-biased. Thus in the *n*-channel structure that we are considering V_G must be negative with respect to V_S and V_D. Since channel-region majority carriers normally flow from source to drain, we must have V_D greater than V_S to produce a channel field in the $-y$ direction. This field causes electron flow toward the drain, and the drain current I_D is positive for the reference direction indicated.

Control action in this structure occurs because increased reverse bias on the junctions causes the space-charge layers to penetrate the channel more deeply, thus reducing the half width b, lowering the conductance between source and drain, and decreasing the drain current.

For simplicity in the analysis that follows, we neglect voltage drops in the *n*-type regions outside the narrow channel. That is, we assume that the channel potential at $y = 0$ is the source voltage V_S and that the potential at $y = L$ is the drain voltage V_D.

10.2   Static Drain Characteristics
10.2.1   Operation with Small Values of Source-to-Drain Voltage
We now wish to evaluate the drain current and to determine its dependence on the gate and drain voltages. We first consider the situation when the voltage difference between the drain and the source is small compared with that between gate and channel. In this case the variation of the space-charge-

layer width along the channel will be negligible, and the channel profile will be uniform, as in Fig. 10.2.

We denote the channel potential by V. Since we have assumed that V_{DS} is small, V is approximately equal to V_S, the source voltage. Thus the voltage across either junction is simply $V_G - V_S = V_{GS}$, which is a *negative* quantity.

To determine the channel width, we use the *depletion approximation* (Section 4.2.1) to evaluate the space-charge-layer width. Thus the space charge, the electric field, and the potential in the *upper* space-charge layer have the form shown in Fig. 10.3. The situation in the lower space-charge

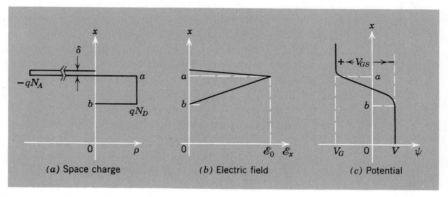

| (a) Space charge | (b) Electric field | (c) Potential |

Figure 10.3 Electrical conditions in the space charge layer.

layer is a mirror image of these curves and can be obtained by reflecting the sketches across the plane at $x = 0$. We have assumed that the p-type gate regions are doped much more heavily than the n-type channel, that is, $N_A \gg N_D$. Consequently, most of the potential drop occurs in the n-type portion of the space-charge layer, and we have

$$V_{GS} = -\tfrac{1}{2}(a - b)\mathscr{E}_0 \tag{10.1a}$$

where $\mathscr{E}_0$ denotes the maximum value of the x-directed field, as shown in Fig. 10.3b.[2] This field is determined by applying Gauss's law to the charge distribution of Fig. 10.3a. Thus

$$\mathscr{E}_0 = \frac{qN_D}{\epsilon}(a - b) \tag{10.1b}$$

where ϵ denotes the dielectric permittivity of the semiconductor. Elimination of $\mathscr{E}_0$ between Eqs. 10.1a and 10.1b yields the following expression for the channel half width:

$$b = a - \left(-\frac{2\epsilon}{qN_D}V_{GS}\right)^{1/2} \tag{10.2}$$

---

[2] In writing Eq. 10.1a, we neglect the contact potential of the junction in comparison with V_{GS}. Had we accounted for the contact potential, the left side of this equation would be $V_{GS} - \psi_0$.

This relationship confirms our qualitative reasoning concerning the dependence of the channel width on the junction reverse voltage. As V_{GS} becomes more negative, the channel half width b decreases, thereby reducing the conductance between source and drain. The width of the conducting channel drops to zero when V_{GS} has the value V_P, where

$$V_P = -\frac{a^2 q N_D}{2\epsilon} \tag{10.3}$$

This parameter is called the *pinch-off voltage*. It ranges in value from a few volts in transistors intended for low-voltage operation to about 100 volts in high-voltage units. When V_{GS} decreases to the pinch-off voltage, there is no longer a conducting path between source and drain, because the space-charge layers have merged and the channel region is completely depleted of mobile carriers. In this sense the junction FET resembles a depletion-mode MOS field-effect transistor. In both cases there is a conducting path from source to drain for $V_{GS} = 0$, and this conducting path disappears when $V_{GS} = V_P$.

The channel half-width, given by Eq. 10.2, can be expressed in terms of V_P. Thus

$$b = a\left[1 - \left(\frac{V_{GS}}{V_P}\right)^{1/2}\right] \tag{10.4}$$

The conductance of the source-to-drain path is that of a rectangular bar of semiconductor of length L, height h, half width b, and conductivity $q\mu_e n_o$, where μ_e is the electron mobility and $n_o = N_D$ is the equilibrium electron concentration. Thus the source-to-drain conductance is

$$G = q\mu_e n_o \frac{2hb}{L} \tag{10.5a}$$

or, using the expression for b given by Eq. 10.4,

$$G = G_0\left[1 - \left(\frac{V_{GS}}{V_P}\right)^{1/2}\right] \tag{10.5b}$$

where

$$G_0 = \frac{2q\mu_e n_o ha}{L} \tag{10.5c}$$

denotes the channel conductance when V_{GS} is zero. Consequently, the drain characteristics when V_{DS} is small are described by

$$I_D = GV_{DS}$$

or

$$I_D = G_0\left[1 - \left(\frac{V_{GS}}{V_P}\right)^{1/2}\right]V_{DS} \quad \text{for} \quad V_{DS} \text{ small} \tag{10.6}$$

These output characteristics have the form shown in Fig. 10.4, in which I_D is plotted versus V_{DS}, with V_{GS} as a parameter. Although the field-effect transistor is normally operated with both V_{DS} and I_D positive, so that current flows in the channel from source to drain, the curves are carried into the third quadrant to emphasize that the device behaves as a linear conductance that is controlled by V_{GS} for *both* polarities of V_{DS}, so long as V_{DS} is small enough for the potential variation along the channel to be negligible. No curves are shown for positive value of V_{GS}, since the device is always operated with the gate junctions reverse-biased. Inasmuch as these reverse-biased junctions support very little gate current, it is unnecessary to describe the input characteristics graphically; we simply note that the gate current is approximately zero.

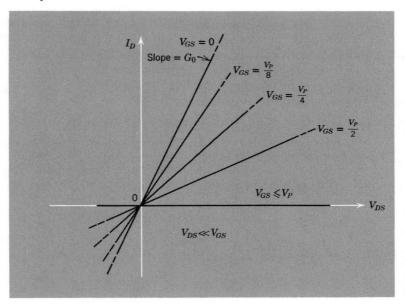

Figure 10.4 Output characteristics for small values of V_{DS}.

There are some applications for field-effect transistors operating in the linear region illustrated in Fig. 10.4. For example, the device can be used in voltage-controllable attenuators as shown in Fig. 9.22 or as a component in a variable-phase-shift network.

10.2.2 Operation below Pinch-Off

If the drain-to-source voltage is not negligibly small, the penetration of the space-charge layer into the channel is not uniform along the channel, but increases toward the drain end, as shown in Fig. 10.5. Of course, the channel current density also increases toward the drain end because the drain current

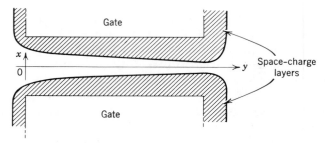

Figure 10.5 Channel profile when drain current flows.

is crowded into the thinner channel. We assume that the rate of change of
the channel half height with position along the channel is small enough so
that at every point along the channel the one-dimensional analysis of the
space-charge layer (Fig. 10.3) applies.[3] The electrostatic potential V in the
conducting portion of the channel is now dependent on y. We assume, for
the moment, that $V_G - V(y)$ is greater than V_P throughout the channel; that
is, we assume that the channel is *not* pinched off.

The y-directed current density at y is

$$J_y(y) = q\mu_e n_o \left[-\frac{dV(y)}{dy} \right] \tag{10.7}$$

since $-dV(y)/dy$ is the longitudinal (y-directed) field at y. The total channel
current crossing the plane at y thus is

$$I_y = 2hb(y)J_y(y) \tag{10.8}$$

For our assumption of gradually changing channel height, the one-dimensional evaluation of b applies. We use the approximation for b given by
Eq. 10.4 to express $b(y)$ in terms of the reverse voltage $[V_G - V(y)]$ at y. Thus

$$b(y) = a \left[1 - \left(\frac{V_G - V(y)}{V_P} \right)^{\frac{1}{2}} \right] \tag{10.9}$$

Consequently, the current at y can be written as

$$I_y = -2ahq\mu_e n_o \left[1 - \left(\frac{V_G - V(y)}{V_P} \right)^{\frac{1}{2}} \right] \frac{dV(y)}{dy} \tag{10.10}$$

Since I_y must be independent of y and is, in fact, equal to $-I_D$, Eq. 10.10
constitutes a first-order differential equation in $V(y)$. If we integrate this
equation from the source at $y = 0$, where $V(y) = V_S$, to the drain at $y = L$,

---

[3] If the channel height changes rapidly, this gradual approximation does not apply, and
Gauss's law must be solved for a two-dimensional charge distribution.

where $V(y) = V_D$, and solve for $I_D = -I_y$, we obtain

$$I_D = G_0 \left\{ V_{GS} \left[1 - \frac{2}{3} \left(\frac{V_{GS}}{V_P} \right)^{1/2} \right] - V_{GD} \left[1 - \frac{2}{3} \left(\frac{V_{GD}}{V_P} \right)^{1/2} \right] \right\} \qquad (10.11a)$$

This result, which is valid only for $V_{GD} \geqslant V_P$ (and, of course, for $V_{GS} \geqslant V_P$), can be put in a form that expresses the drain current in terms of the gate-to-source voltage V_{GS} and the drain-to-source voltage V_{DS}, since $V_{GD} = V_{GS} - V_{DS}$. The resulting expression is

$$I_D = G_0 \left\{ \frac{2V_{GS}}{3} \left[\left(\frac{V_{GS} - V_{DS}}{V_P} \right)^{1/2} - \left(\frac{V_{GS}}{V_P} \right)^{1/2} \right] + V_{DS} \left[1 - \frac{2}{3} \left(\frac{V_{GS} - V_{DS}}{V_P} \right)^{1/2} \right] \right\}$$

$$\text{for} \quad V_{GS} - V_{DS} \geqslant V_P, \; V_{GS} \geqslant V_P \qquad (10.11b)$$

This equation constitutes the drain characteristic of the field-effect transistor for gate-to-drain voltages greater than the pinch-off voltage; it has the form shown in Fig. 10.6, in which I_D is plotted versus V_{DS}, with V_{GS} as a parameter. The curves are continued only to the point where $V_{GS} - V_{DS} = V_P$, beyond which the analysis does not apply.

10.2.3   Operation beyond Pinch-Off

For values of gate-to-drain voltage that are more negative than the pinch-off voltage the situation is complex. The space-charge layer penetrates com-

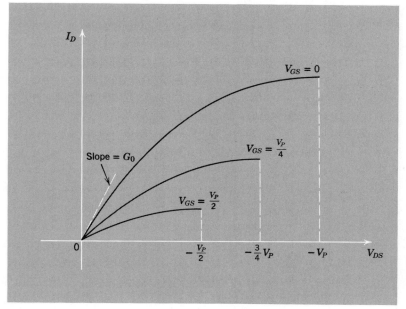

Figure 10.6   Common-source output characteristics for operation below pinch-off.

pletely through the channel at the drain end, as shown in Fig. 10.7a. The drain current density increases greatly at the drain end of the channel, and the drain current flows through the space-charge region δ that lies between the end of the channel at L and the neutral n-type drain region. The potential at the tip of the channel is approximately $V_{GS} - V_P$, that is, the *total* potential drop along the channel is V_P. The potential in the drain region is V_{DS}, which is assumed to exceed $V_{GS} - V_P$ by ΔV. Thus the excess drain voltage ΔV appears across the space-charge layer between the tip of the channel and the drain region. There is an intense $-y$-directed field in this region which originates on donor ions in the space-charge layer and terminates on electrons in the channel. It is this field that causes the electrons that constitute drain current to flow out the tip of the channel into the drain region.

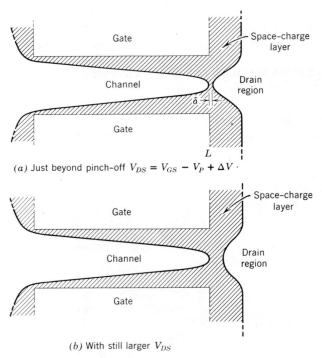

(a) Just beyond pinch-off $V_{DS} = V_{GS} - V_P + \Delta V$ ·

(b) With still larger V_{DS}

Figure 10.7 Channel profiles for operation above pinch-off.

The potential distribution in the space-charge layer near the tip of the channel cannot be obtained by a one-dimensional solution of Gauss's law, and the gradual approximation does not apply there. Although detailed analysis of the electrical conditions near the tip of the channel is complex, and will not be undertaken here, the results are simple and intuitively reasonable.

As V_{DS} increases above $V_{GS} - V_P$, most of the increase appears as a voltage drop across the space-charge layer at the channel tip, in which the electric field is high. The length of the space-charge region increases as V_{DS} increases, as illustrated in Fig. 10.7b. However, relatively large increases of V_{DS} can be accommodated with small increases in δ. Therefore, the length of the region in which the gradual approximation holds true decreases relatively little, electrical conditions in this region change very little, and the drain current remains approximately constant at the value that it had when V_{DS} reached $V_{GS} - V_P$. Thus we can extend the common-source output characteristics into the *pinch-off region* of operation by extending the curves along lines of constant current, as shown in Fig. 10.8.

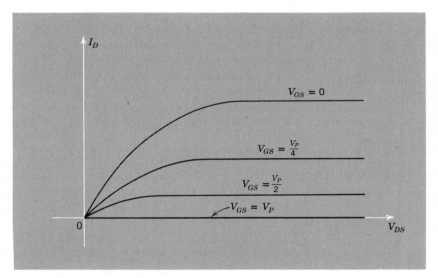

Figure 10.8   Complete drain characteristics.

Consequently, the current-voltage relationship of our idealized field-effect transistor is, according to Eq. 10.11b,

$$
I_D = \begin{cases} G_0 \left\{ \dfrac{2V_{GS}}{3}\left[\left(\dfrac{V_{GS} - V_{DS}}{V_P} \right)^{1/2} - \left(\dfrac{V_{GS}}{V_P} \right)^{1/2} \right] + V_{DS}\left[1 - \dfrac{2}{3}\left(\dfrac{V_{GS} - V_{DS}}{V_P} \right)^{1/2} \right] \right\} \\ \qquad \text{for} \quad V_{GS} \geqslant V_P,\ V_{GS} - V_{DS} \geqslant V_P \qquad\qquad (10.12) \\[4pt] G_0 \left\{ -\dfrac{V_P}{3} + V_{GS}\left[1 - \dfrac{2}{3}\left(\dfrac{V_{GS}}{V_P} \right)^{1/2} \right] \right\} \qquad \text{for} \quad V_{GS} > V_P, \\ V_{DS} > V_{GS} - V_P \end{cases}
$$

When the field-effect transistor operates above pinch-off, the drain current is determined principally by the potential distribution in that portion of the channel to the left of the pinch-off point. This portion of the channel supports a longitudinal voltage drop of V_P and has a length only slightly less than the full channel length L. Consequently, the current that it establishes is, for constant V_{GS}, essentially independent of V_{DS}. The drain current that is established in the gradual region is simply fed into the space-charge region to the right of the pinch-off point, through which it flows to the drain.

10.3   Dynamic Considerations

The dynamic features of a junction FET are, like the MOS structure studied in Section 9.4, dominated by the gate charge. Thus the static model given by Eq. 10.12 can be extended to include rapid variations in the junction voltages simply by adding a charge store that reflects the need for current at the gate terminal whenever the charge stored in the junction space-charge layer is changed. Because the field in the space-charge layer is nonlinearly dependent on the gate voltage, the charge store cannot, in general, be modeled by a linear capacitance. If, however, the range of gate voltage variation is restricted appropriately, the gate current can be modeled by an incremental space-charge-layer capacitance, just as in Section 4.4.1 (see Problem P10.5).

10.4   Comparison of MOS and Junction Field-Effect Transistors

Junction FETs and MOSFETs are remarkably similar in their operating principles and in their electrical characteristics. There are, however, two important differences that must not be overlooked.

First, junction FETs can only be operated in the depletion mode. If the gate junctions are forward-biased, excess-carrier injection occurs, and the gate current is substantial. Although the channel conductance is to some degree enhanced by the excess carriers, the device is never operated in this way because the gate current is undesirable.[4]

Second, even when a junction FET is operated with a reverse bias on the junction, the gate current is larger than it would be in a comparable MOSFET. The current produced by minority-carrier extraction across a reverse-biased junction is greater, per unit area, than the leakage current that is supported by the oxide layer in an MOS transistor. Thus insulated-gate devices are more useful in electrometer applications than are junction FETs.

For these reasons, and also because they are somewhat easier to manufacture, MOS field-effect transistors are more widely used than junction FETs.

---

[4] A structurally similar device, the *unijunction transistor*, does operate with a forward-biased junction. For a description of this two-terminal active device see Reference 10.2 or 10.3.

REFERENCES

10.1   L. J. Sevin, Jr., *Field-Effect Transistors*, McGraw-Hill, New York, 1965.

10.2   R. H. Mattson, *Electronics*, Wiley, New York, 1966, Section 3.4C.

10.3   J. G. Linvill and J. F. Gibbons, *Transistors and Active Circuits*, McGraw-Hill, New York, 1961, Section 8.2.

PROBLEMS

P10.1   This problem is concerned with the dependence of channel half width on gate-to-source voltage in a junction field-effect transistor for which the contact potential is *not* negligible.

(*a*) Derive an equation analogous to Eq. 10.2 that applies in this case.

(*b*) Derive an expression for the pinch-off voltage, and express the channel half width in terms of it, that is, derive an expression analogous to Eq. 10.4.

(*c*) Show that your results reduce to Eqs. 10.2, 10.3, and 10.4 when ψ_0 goes to zero.

P10.2   Consider an *n*-channel junction FET that has the structure shown in Fig. 10.2 and the following parameters:

$$N_A = 10^{18} \text{ cm}^{-3}$$

$$N_D = 10^{15} \text{ cm}^{-3}$$

$$n_i = 10^{10} \text{ cm}^{-3}$$

$$a = 2\mu$$

$$\epsilon = 10^{-12} \text{ farad/cm}$$

$$L = 20 \ \mu$$

$$h = 100 \ \mu$$

$$\mu_e = 10^3 \text{ cm}^2/\text{volt-sec}$$

(*a*) What is the contact potential ψ_0?

(*b*) What is the pinch-off voltage V_P?

(*c*) What is the channel conductance G_0 with zero gate-to-source voltage?

Answers. (*a*) $\psi_0 \simeq 0.75$ v; (*b*) $V_P \simeq -3.2$ v; (*c*) $G_0 \simeq 3.2 \times 10^{-4}$ mho.

P10.3   This problem is concerned with the potential distribution along the channel of an *n*-channel junction FET.

(*a*) Verify Eq. 10.10.

(*b*) Note that I_y is constant and equal to $-I_D$, and derive an expression for the channel potential (measured with respect to the source voltage) as a function of y. Plot your result with $V_{GS} = 0$ for three values of V_{DS}: $V_{DS} = -V_P/10$, $V_{DS} = -V_P/2$, and $V_{DS} = -V_P$.

(*c*) Use the result for $V(y)$ derived in (*b*) to verify Eqs. 10.11a and 10.11b.

P10.4 The maximum drain current of an n-channel junction FET occurs when $V_{GS} = 0$ and when V_{DS} is greater than $-V_P$. This current is denoted by I_{DO}.

(a) Derive an expression for I_{DO} in terms of G_0 and V_P.

(b) Evaluate I_{DO} for the transistor described in Problem P10.2.

P10.5 This problem is concerned with the dynamic behavior of an n-channel junction FET having the structure illustrated in Fig. 10.2. *Assume* that

(1) The gate regions are doped much more heavily than the channel region, which has a donor density of N_D.

(2) The junctions are abrupt.

(a) Making use of the depletion approximation, derive an expression for the total charge Q_G in the gate portions of the dipole layers at the junctions. Assume that v_{DS} is much less than $|V_P|$, and express your result in terms of the contact potential ψ_0 and the gate-to-source voltage v_{GS}.

(b) Derive an expression for the incremental gate-to-source capacitance C_{gs} for the case in which v_{DS} is much less than $|V_P|$. Express your result in terms of ψ_0 and the dc component of the gate-to-source voltage V_{GS}.

(c) Repeat parts (a) and (b) for the case in which the transistor is at the edge of saturation, that is, for $V_{DS} = V_{GS} - V_P$. *Suggestion*. The total gate charge Q_G can be obtained by making use of the potential distribution in the channel to evaluate the charge *density* in the gate half of the dipole layer as a function of y, and then integrating over y.

CHAPTER ELEVEN

Incremental Models for Transistors

11.1 Linear Operation of Active Circuits

There are many requirements in signal-processing systems for *linear amplification* of signals. The amplifiers used in music reproduction systems are a familiar example of this requirement. The signal produced by a phonograph cartridge, which may provide microwatts of power at millivolt levels, must be amplified to the level of the several watts of power required by a loudspeaker. Furthermore, the system that supplies this amplification must be *linear*.

We use the simple transistor amplifier shown in Fig. 11.1 to illustrate how a junction transistor—a representative active device—can be employed to obtain linear amplification. In this circuit, which is similar to the common-emitter amplifiers introduced in Chapter 7, the transistor is used as a control valve that modulates the flow of energy from a source of dc power, denoted by $-V_{CC}$, to a load characterized by R_L. The "handle" on this valve is v_I; when v_I is negative, the emitter junction is forward-biased and there is current in the load. On the basis of the models developed in Section 7.3.2 we expect the *static* transfer characteristic that relates v_O to v_I to have the general form shown in Fig. 11.1b.

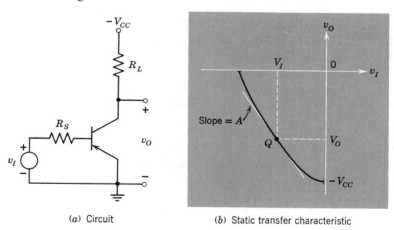

(a) Circuit   (b) Static transfer characteristic

Figure 11.1 A transistor amplifier with a resistive load. All voltages are specified with respect to ground.

We now assume that the input voltage v_I is comprised of two additive components: a quiescent or dc component V_I and a time-varying component v_i. The output voltage can be resolved into a similarly defined pair of additive components. The quiescent or dc component V_O of the output voltage is related to V_I through the transfer characteristic as shown in Fig. 11.1*b*; the point Q denotes the *operating point* of the amplifier. The signal component v_i of the input voltage causes the instantaneous ‚voltages and currents in the amplifier to deviate from Q. If v_i is small enough, the signal component v_o of the output voltage will be a *linear* homogeneous function of v_i. That is, v_o will be linearly dependent on v_i, which is the desired property for a linear signal-processing system. If v_i changes slowly enough so that the static transfer characteristic is an adequate description of the relationship between v_O and v_I, the signal component of the output will be approximated by

$$v_o = Av_i$$

where A is the *slope* of the transfer characteristic at the operating point Q. If v_i changes more rapidly, the relationship between v_o and v_i will involve time derivatives of these variables as well, and will not be obtainable from the static transfer characteristic. However, the relationship between v_o and v_i will still be a linear homogeneous one *if v_i is small enough.*

If v_i is small enough for v_o to be linearly dependent on it, the circuit is said to be *incrementally linear* and v_o and v_i are called *incremental variables*. We now seek a characterization of the active device and circuit that embodies the linear relationships between v_o, v_i, and the other incremental variables. We first develop models that represent the relationships among the incremental components of the electrical variables at the terminals of the active device, that is, the terminal currents and terminal-pair voltages.

11.2   Incremental Models for Active Devices
11.2.1   Modeling Techniques

There are essentially two alternative approaches to the development of incremental models for active devices. Both routes, though quite different in detail, lead, of course, to the same conclusions concerning the incremental behavior of a device.

The first route starts with the physical laws that govern the internal physical behavior of a device—laws such as the flow relations for holes and electrons, conservation laws, the Boltzmann relations, and Gauss's law—and with a description of the structure of the device. The physical relationships that describe internal behavior are expressed in terms of quiescent and incremental components of the relevant *internal* variables, such as carrier concentrations and current densities, and are linearized for an incremental disturbance at some operating point. The resulting *linear* relationships among the *incremental* components of the *internal* variables are analyzed to determine the desired relationships among the incremental components of the *terminal* variables—the voltages and currents.

The second route starts with a description of the electrical behavior of the device in terms of relationships among the instantaneous total *terminal* variables, that is, the terminal currents and terminal-pair voltages. Of course, these relationships must previously be obtained by analysis of the internal physical behavior. These total-variable terminal descriptions are linearized at some operating point to determine directly the *linear* relationships among the incremental components of the terminal variables. Since we desire incremental descriptions that embody dynamic effects—that is, are applicable when the incremental variables change rapidly—it is necessary to start with total-variable models that are *dynamic* (e.g., the charge control model for a bipolar junction transistor); a total-variable *static* model will not suffice.

These alternative approaches to the incremental modeling of active devices are contrasted in Fig. 11.2. We illustrate both approaches in this chapter. Specifically, we linearize the total-variable *V-I* relationships developed in Chapter 9 to obtain an incremental model for field-effect transistors, while we base the incremental characterization of bipolar

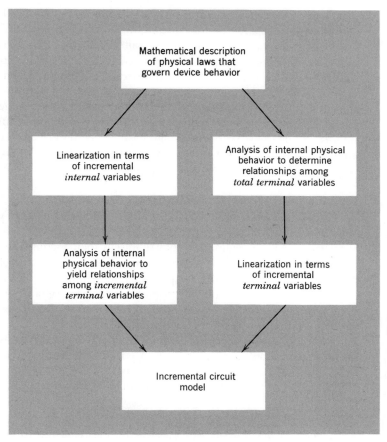

Figure 11.2 Comparison of alternative methods of developing linear incremental circuit models.

transistors on a linearized analysis of the internal physical behavior of that device. In both cases, the linear relationships among the incremental components of the terminal variables can be interpreted in terms of *network models*—models that are interconnections of familiar linear circuit elements such as resistances, capacitances, and controlled or dependent sources.

11.2.2   Choice of Variables and Notation

Transistors are three-terminal devices and can be characterized at the terminals by three currents and three terminal-pair voltages. As we have seen, Kirchhoff's current law can be used to express any one current in terms of the other two currents, and Kirchhoff's voltage law can be used to express any one terminal-pair voltage in terms of the other two voltages. Consequently, we need deal with only two terminal currents and two terminal-pair voltages in our development of incremental models.

In accordance with the notation first introduced in Chapter 1, and applied again in Chapter 6, we denote instantaneous total voltages and currents by lowercase variables with uppercase subscripts (i_A, v_B, etc.). We denote quiescent or dc components by uppercase variables with uppercase subscripts (I_A, V_B, etc.), while instantaneous incremental components are denoted by lowercase variables with lowercase subscripts (i_a, v_a, etc.). Inasmuch as we are dealing with linear relationships among the incremental variables, the important special case of exponential time functions is of interest. Since these exponential signals are often described in terms of their complex amplitudes, we reserve uppercase variables with lowercase subscripts (I_a, V_b, etc.) for complex amplitudes.

11.3   Incremental Models for Field-Effect Transistors

As we have seen in Chapters 9 and 10, MOS and junction field-effect transistors have similar electrical behavior. Thus these devices can be treated together in developing models that represent their incremental behavior. In the following development we treat in detail the specific case of a MOSFET and then extend the results to apply as well to junction FETs.

We base this discussion on an *n-channel* device operating in either the enhancement or the depletion mode. However, we shall later see that the models we develop are equally applicable to p-channel devices. Because most amplifier applications of FETs involve operating these transistors in the region of *saturated* drain current, that is, with the drain end of the channel pinched off, we limit our incremental analysis to that region of behavior.[1] For an *n*-channel device, the corresponding condition on the voltages is:

$$v_{GS} - V_P < v_{DS} \tag{11.1a}$$

[1] Problem 11.1 deals with incremental analysis below pinch-off when the drain current is not saturated.

or, equivalently,

$$v_{GD} < V_P \tag{11.1b}$$

where V_P denotes the pinch-off voltage. Finally, we assume that the terminal-pair voltages are not changing so rapidly that transit-time effects must be considered.

11.3.1   Linearization of the Total-Variable Models

Under the conditions described by Eqs. 11.1, that is, when the drain current is saturated and independent of v_{DS}, the gate and drain currents are, in accordance with Eqs. 9.31b and 9.40a,

$$i_G = \frac{2}{3} C_o \frac{dv_{GS}}{dt} \tag{11.2a}$$

$$i_D = \frac{h\mu_e \epsilon}{WL} \frac{(v_{GS} - V_P)^2}{2} \tag{11.2b}$$

In these equations C_o denotes the capacitance of the gate-oxide-layer-channel sandwich when there is no drain current, μ_e is the electron mobility in the channel, ϵ is the dielectric permittivity in the oxide layer, W is the thickness of the oxide layer, and L is the channel length. These equations for the gate and drain currents ignore the overlap capacitance between gate and drain illustrated in Fig. 9.19b; our analysis is simplified if we later add that capacitance to the incremental model that results from the linearization of Eqs. 11.2.

The gate-to-source voltage can be expressed in terms of its dc and incremental components as follows:

$$v_{GS} = V_{GS} + v_{gs} \tag{11.3}$$

The gate and drain currents can be similarly expressed. When Eq. 11.3 is substituted into the gate current expression of Eq. 11.2a, we obtain

$$I_G = 0 \tag{11.4a}$$

$$i_g = \frac{2}{3} C_o \frac{dv_{gs}}{dt} \tag{11.4b}$$

The drain current, given by Eq. 11.2b, is nonlinearly dependent on v_{GS}. A Taylor's series expansion about the operating point Q, where $v_{GS} = V_{GS}$, is of the form:

$$i_D = i_D \Big|_Q + \frac{di_D}{dv_{GS}}\Big|_Q v_{gs} + \frac{1}{2!} \frac{d^2 i_D}{dv_{GS}^2}\Big|_Q v_{gs}^2$$

$$+ \text{ higher-order terms} \tag{11.5a}$$

If we use Eq. 11.2b to evaluate the first two terms in this expansion, and assume that v_{gs} is small enough for the second- and higher-order terms to be *negligibly small*, we obtain

$$i_D = \frac{h\mu_e\epsilon}{WL}\frac{(V_{GS} - V_P)^2}{2} + \frac{h\mu_e\epsilon}{WL}(V_{GS} - V_P)v_{gs} \qquad (11.5b)$$

Thus we have, since $i_D = I_D + i_d$,

$$I_D = \frac{h\mu_e\epsilon}{WL}\frac{(V_{GS} - V_P)^2}{2} \qquad (11.6a)$$

$$i_d = \frac{h\mu_e\epsilon}{WL}(V_{GS} - V_P)v_{gs} \qquad (11.6b)$$

The relationships among the operating point or dc variables given by Eqs. 11.4a and 11.6a are, of course, the static relationships developed in Chapter 9. The *linear* relationships among the *incremental* variables, given by Eqs. 11.4b and 11.6b, constitute a partial incremental model for the FET. It is convenient to write these linear relationships in the following form:

$$i_g = C_{gs}\frac{dv_{gs}}{dt} \qquad (11.7a)$$

$$i_d = g_m v_{gs} \qquad (11.7b)$$

where

$$C_{gs} = \tfrac{2}{3}C_o \qquad (11.8a)$$

$$g_m = \frac{h\mu_e\epsilon}{WL}(V_{GS} - V_P) \qquad (11.8b)$$

The coefficient C_{gs} is called the *incremental gate-to-source capacitance*; it ranges in value in typical MOS transistors from 2 to 20 pf. The coefficient g_m is called the *transconductance*; it expresses the basic control action of the FET in incremental terms. That is, an incremental increase in gate-to-source voltage increases the electric field in the oxide layer and draws more charge into the channel region. Consequently, there is a proportional increase in the drain current; the transconductance is the constant of proportionality. In typical MOS devices g_m may range from 0.1 to 10 mmho. Note that the transconductance and the dc drain current are *not* independent; g_m can be expressed in terms of I_D and $V_{GS} - V_P$ (see Problem P11.2).

The overlap capacitance, which exists between the gate and the drain end of the channel and which we designate here by C_{gd}, supports an incremental current

$$i = C_{gd}\frac{dv_{gd}}{dt} \qquad (11.9)$$

The current must be added to i_g and subtracted from i_d. Thus when the overlap capacitance is accounted for, the incremental description of the

MOS transistor becomes

$$i_g = C_{gs}\frac{dv_{gs}}{dt} + C_{gd}\frac{dv_{gd}}{dt} \qquad (11.10a)$$

$$i_d = g_m v_{gs} - C_{gd}\frac{dv_{gd}}{dt} \qquad (11.10b)$$

The incremental gate-to-drain capacitance C_{gd} usually lies in the range from 0.1 to 1 pf. Clearly, it is much smaller than C_{gs}.

11.3.2   An Incremental Circuit Model

The linear relationships given by Eqs. 11.10 constitute an incremental model for the field-effect transistor. These equations can be interpreted in terms of a network comprised of linear circuit elements as shown in Fig. 11.3. The constraints implied by this network are precisely equivalent to the relationships given by Eqs. 11.10. This equivalence can be seen by recognizing that Eq. 11.10a is obtained by writing Kirchhoff's current law at the node marked g while Eq. 11.10b is obtained by summing the currents at the node marked d. Thus the network of Fig. 11.3 is a description of the incremental behavior of the transistor; it can be employed *in place of the transistor* in circuit calculations involving only incremental variables, as we shall see in Section 11.5.

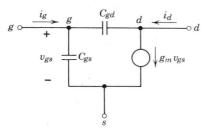

Figure 11.3   An incremental model for a field-effect transistor.

11.3.3   Extrinsic Elements

The model of Fig. 11.3 accounts for the incremental consequences of the basic mechanism of operation of the MOS field-effect transistor. That mechanism involves the modulation of channel conductance and drain current by an electric field produced by charge on the gate. In an actual MOS transistor there are several subsidiary mechanisms that are second-order in nature but influence the incremental behavior of the device. The two most important of these subsidiary effects are:

1. Some portion of the actual drain-to-source voltage appears across resistances associated with the source and drain regions and with the ohmic contacts to these regions.

2. There is capacitive coupling between the leads to the transistor and the case or header on which the device is mounted. There is also capacitance between the source and drain regions and the *p*-type substrate on which the transistor is made. In integrated-circuit assemblies this substrate capacitance is dominant and the interlead capacitances are quite small.

These effects are often referred to as *extrinsic* in the sense that they are not basic to the operation of the device but rather arise from unavoidable external considerations. An incremental model that accounts for these extrinsic or parasitic effects is shown in Fig. 11.4. This model is constructed by adding five extrinsic elements—three interlead capacitances and two lead resistances—to the basic model of Fig. 11.3. The series source and drain resistances r_s and r_d may range in value from about 10 ohms to several hundred ohms, while the interlead capacitances have values in the range from 0.2 to 1 pf (C'_{ds} is often somewhat larger because of capacitive coupling through the *pn* junctions that isolate the source and drain regions from the substrate). Although there are very few circuit situations in which *all* of the extrinsic elements in the model of Fig. 11.4 matter, it is important to be aware of their existence since these elements tend to make the actual "internal" or "intrinsic" transistor less accessible at the terminals.

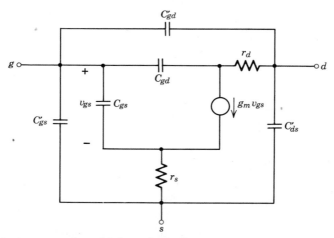

Figure 11.4 An incremental model for a field-effect transistor that includes the extrinsic elements associated with electrostatic coupling between leads and with source and drain series resistance.

11.3.4 Incremental Models for *p*-Channel and Junction Field-Effect Transistors

Although the analysis of Section 11.3.1 is based on an *n*-channel field-effect transistor, the results, expressed in terms of the models of Figs. 11.3 or 11.4, are applicable to p-channel devices as well. A p-channel device differs in terminal description from an n-channel device only in that *all* terminal pair voltages and *all* terminal currents have the opposite polarity (for the same standard reference directions). Consequently, the incremental relationships have exactly the same form as Eqs. 11.10, and the models we have devised apply without change. Of course, the expression for g_m analogous to Eq. 11.8b must contain a minus sign to reflect the fact that $V_{GS} - V_P$ is negative for a p-channel device.

A junction FET is very similar to a MOSFET: the terminal currents are related to the terminal-pair voltages by equations that are similar in form to Eqs. 11.2 (e.g., compare Eqs. 10.12 with Eqs. 9.31). Thus the incremental models of Figs. 11.3 and 11.4 apply as well to junction FETs, although the incremental parameters depend differently on the operating point.

The operating-point dependence of the transconductance of an n-channel junction FET can be determined by differentiation of the conduction component of the drain current, given by Eqs. 10.12, in accordance with the definitions of Eq. 11.5a. The result is, for operation with *saturated* drain current (see Problem P11.3),

$$g_m = G_0\left[1 - \left(\frac{V_{GS}}{V_P}\right)^{1/2}\right] \tag{11.11a}$$

Since the gate-to-source voltage cannot be positive in an n-channel junction FET, the transconductance is a maximum for $V_{GS} = 0$. The maximum static drain current, which occurs in saturation, with $V_{GS} = 0$, is, from Eq. 10.12b, $-G_0 V_P/3$ (V_P is a negative quantity in an n-channel junction FET). Consequently, the maximum transconductance may be written as

$$G_0 = g_{mo} = -\frac{3I_{D0}}{V_P} \tag{11.11b}$$

where I_{D0} denotes the maximum static drain current (see Problem P10.4).

11.4   Incremental Models for Bipolar Transistors

As we have seen in Chapter 7, bipolar junction transistors are useful as active devices when they are operated with the emitter forward-biased and the collector junction reverse-biased, that is, when they are operated in the *active region*. We now consider in detail the incremental analysis of the distribution and flow of carriers in bipolar transistors, and develop models for the incremental behavior of these devices when they operate in the active region. Once again we consider first a *pnp* structure and later extend our analysis to include *npn* structures.

11.4.1   Incremental Physical Behavior

We focus first on the components of the incremental terminal currents associated with the distribution and flow of excess carriers in the neutral regions of the transistor. Then we evaluate the components of the incremental currents that result from changes in the dipole layers of space charge at the two junctions. In this analysis we follow the left-hand path in Fig. 11.2 and linearize the relationships among the *internal* variables.

The minority-carrier distribution in the base is approximately triangular for an operating point in the active region, as shown in Fig. 7.2. The minority-carrier concentration at the emitter edge of the base is governed by the emitter-base voltage, in accordance with Eq. 4.11a:

$$p_b(0) = p_{bo}e^{qv_{EB}/kT} \tag{11.12}$$

The concentration at the collector edge is approximately zero [in comparison with $p_b(0)$] as long as the collector junction is reverse-biased by at least several kT/q.

We now consider the consequences of incremental changes in the junction voltages. That is, we assume that v_{EB} changes from V_{EB} to $V_{EB} + \Delta v_{EB}$ and that v_{CB} changes from V_{CB} to $V_{CB} + \Delta v_{CB}$, and we determine the effects of these changes on the base-region minority-carrier distribution and on the terminal currents.[2]

An incremental component Δv_{EB} causes the base-region carrier distribution to change, as shown in Fig. 11.5. This sketch is drawn for positive Δv_{EB}. There are three consequences of the carrier distribution change shown in Fig. 11.5. First, the slope of the distribution increases. This implies an increase in collector current, which results from the increased diffusion of minority carriers across the base. Second, the excess-minority-carrier charge store in the base increases by an amount proportional to the white area in Fig. 11.5. Since the base region is quasi-neutral, more excess-majority carriers must be

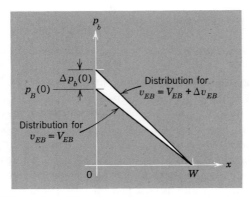

Figure 11.5 Illustration of the effect of a change in the emitter-to-base voltage on the minority-carrier distribution in the base; Δv_{EB} is positive for this sketch.

[2] We write Δv_{EB} and Δv_{CB} rather than simply v_{eb} and v_{cb} to identify unambiguously the incremental components of the variables for this initial development. We later drop the Δ notation and use only the lowercase variables with lowercase subscripts.

fed in at the base to neutralize the extra minority carriers. Third, the increased emitter-base voltage means that the injection of base-region majority carriers into the *emitter* has increased, while the increased excess-carrier population in the base means that recombination there proceeds at a greater net rate. For both these reasons there must be an increase in the steady base current that feeds recombination in emitter and base. We now evaluate the incremental current components that result from these changes in the excess-carrier distribution.

First, we evaluate the incremental component of the minority-carrier concentration at the emitter edge of the base. For $v_{EB} = V_{EB} + \Delta v_{EB}$, Eq. 11.12 becomes

$$p_b(0) = p_{bo}e^{qV_{EB}/kT}e^{q\Delta v_{EB}/kT} \tag{11.13}$$

For small enough values of Δv_{EB}, the second exponential can be approximated by a linear dependence on Δv_{EB}. Specifically,

$$e^{q\Delta v_{EB}/kT} \simeq 1 + \frac{q\Delta v_{EB}}{kT} \qquad \text{for} \quad \Delta v_{EB} \ll \frac{kT}{q} \tag{11.14}$$

Thus for small values of Δv_{EB}, Eq. 11.13 becomes

$$p_b(0) = p_{bo}e^{qV_{EB}/kT} + (p_{bo}e^{qV_{EB}/kT})\frac{q\,\Delta v_{EB}}{kT} \tag{11.15}$$

The first term on the right side of Eq. 11.15 does not depend on Δv_{EB}. It corresponds to the quiescent or dc component of $p_b(0)$; to be explicit, we denote this dc component by $p_B(0)$. The second term is linearly dependent on the incremental component of the junction voltage. It corresponds to the incremental component of $p_b(0)$, and we denote it by $\Delta p_b(0)$. Thus

$$\Delta p_b(0) = p_B(0)\frac{q}{kT}\Delta v_{EB} \tag{11.16}$$

In evaluating the incremental base and collector currents associated with $\Delta p_b(0)$, *we assume that $\Delta p_b(0)$ changes slowly enough so that the instantaneous excess-carrier distribution is approximately triangular.* In other words, we assume that Δv_{EB} changes slowly enough so that the instantaneous distribution changes as a succession of static distributions. This quasi-static approximation, which was used in Section 8.1.1 as the basis for the charge-control model, makes evaluation of the incremental currents simple because the form of the distribution is known at the outset.

The incremental collector current Δi_C can be expressed in terms of the change in the slope of the minority-carrier distribution. That is,

$$\Delta i_C = -\left(-qAD_b\frac{d\,\Delta p_b}{dx}\right) \tag{11.17a}$$

The factor in parentheses is the incremental longitudinal diffusion current. The outer minus sign is required because in a *pnp* transistor the holes flow *out* at the collector terminal while the reference direction for Δi_C is such that positive Δi_C corresponds to the flow of positive charge *in* at the collector. An inspection of Fig. 11.5 shows that $d\,\Delta p_b/dx$ is approximately $-\Delta p_b(0)/W$. Thus the incremental collector current is

$$\Delta i_C = -qAD_b\frac{\Delta p_b(0)}{W} \tag{11.17b}$$

or, using Eq. 11.16,

$$\Delta i_C = -\left[qAD_b\frac{p_B(0)}{W}\right]\frac{q}{kT}\Delta v_{EB} \tag{11.17c}$$

Now the factor in brackets is just the magnitude of the quiescent or dc collector current $|I_C|$ at the operating point for which the minority-carrier concentration at the emitter edge of the base is $p_B(0)$. This identification can be seen from Fig. 11.5 or from Eq. 7.3 [since $p'_b(0) \simeq p_b(0)$]. Thus Eq. 11.17c can be written as

$$\Delta i_C = -g_m\,\Delta v_{EB} \tag{11.18}$$

where

$$g_m = \frac{q}{kT}|I_C| \tag{11.19}$$

The constant of proportionality, g_m, is called the *incremental transconductance*. It is linearly dependent on the dc collector current and has a value at $|I_C| = 1$ ma, $T = 300°$K, of about 1 ma/25 mv or 0.04 mho.

The incremental component Δq_B of the base-region excess-carrier charge store is proportional to the white area shown in Fig. 11.5. Consequently, Δq_B is

$$\Delta q_B = qA[\tfrac{1}{2}\Delta p_b(0)W] \tag{11.20a}$$

or, using Eq. 11.16,

$$\Delta q_B = \frac{W^2}{2D_b}\left[qAD_b\frac{p_B(0)}{W}\right]\frac{q}{kT}\Delta v_{EB} \tag{11.20b}$$

Once again the factor in brackets is the magnitude of the dc collector current. Thus Δq_B can be written as

$$\Delta q_B = C_b\,\Delta v_{EB} \tag{11.20c}$$

where

$$C_b = \frac{W^2}{2D_b}g_m \tag{11.20d}$$

These relationships show that C_b, which is called the *base-charging capacitance*, provides a measure of the charge that must be supplied at the base to accommodate a change in emitter-to-base voltage. The corresponding component of the base current is

$$\Delta i_{BQ} = -\frac{d\Delta q_B}{dt} \tag{11.21a}$$

or

$$\Delta i_{BQ} = -C_b\frac{d\,\Delta v_{EB}}{dt} \tag{11.21b}$$

The minus sign is required because the carriers fed in at the base to neutralize Δq_B are electrons. The base-charging capacitance has the same dependence on quiescent collector current as does g_m. For $|I_C| = 1$ ma, C_b commonly ranges from 5 to 200 pf.

The component of base current that feeds the increased recombination in the base region is

$$\Delta i_{BR}|_{\text{base}} = -\frac{\Delta q_B}{\tau_b} \tag{11.22a}$$

where τ_b denotes the base-region lifetime. The component that supports the increased reverse injection of base-region majority carriers into the emitter (where these carriers recombine) is also proportional to $\Delta p_b(0)$, and thus to Δq_B. This component, which is obtained by linearization of Eq. 7.6c (see Problem P11.4) is

$$\Delta i_{BR}|_{\text{emitter}} = -\frac{2D_e}{W_e W}\frac{n_{eo}}{p_{bo}}\Delta q_B \tag{11.22b}$$

where D_e and W_e denote the minority-carrier diffusion coefficient and the width of the emitter region, and n_{eo} is the equilibrium minority-carrier concentration in the emitter.

The full incremental component of the base current that feeds the increased recombination in base and emitter is, from Eqs. 11.22a and b,

$$\Delta i_{BR} = -\left(\frac{1}{\tau_b} + \frac{2D_e}{W_e W}\frac{n_{eo}}{p_{bo}}\right)\Delta q_B \tag{11.22c}$$

Or, using Eq. 11.20c to express Δq_B in terms of Δv_{EB},

$$\Delta i_{BR} = -g_\pi\,\Delta v_{EB} \tag{11.23a}$$

where

$$g_\pi = \left(\frac{W^2}{2D_b\tau_b} + \frac{D_e}{D_b}\frac{W}{W_e}\frac{n_{eo}}{p_{bo}}\right)g_m \tag{11.23b}$$

The parameter g_π is known as the *incremental input conductance*. Note that g_π has the same dependence on $|I_C|$ as does g_m. For $|I_C| = 1$ ma, g_π generally lies between 4×10^{-3} and 10^{-4} mho; it is smaller than g_m by a factor that ranges from 10 to 500 in typical transistors.[3]

The total incremental base current is the sum of the base-charging and recombination components given by Eqs. 11.21b and 11.23a. Thus we have

$$\Delta i_B = -g_\pi \Delta v_{EB} - C_b \frac{d \Delta v_{EB}}{dt} \tag{11.24}$$

The dependence of Δi_C and Δi_B on the incremental component of the emitter-base voltage Δv_{EB} is expressed by Eqs. 11.18 and 11.24. These incremental current components are manifestations of the changed distribution and flow of minority carriers in the base. In deriving these relationships we have assumed that the collector junction is reverse-biased; the results are independent of the exact value of the reverse voltage at the collector because the minority-carrier concentration at the collector edge of the base is negligibly small for *all* reverse voltages greater than a few kT/q. Therefore, the incremental component of the minority-carrier distribution in the base is independent of Δv_{CB}, and Eqs. 11.18 and 11.24 hold true for all values of Δv_{CB}.[4]

The linear relationships given by Eqs. 11.18 and 11.24 can be interpreted in terms of a network model comprised of linear circuit elements, as shown in Fig. 11.6. Thus Eq. 11.24 is a statement of Kirchhoff's current law at the base node, while Eq. 11.18 is the corresponding statement at the collector node.

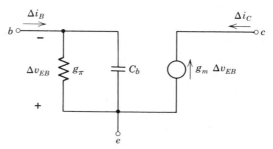

Figure 11.6 An incremental model for a bipolar transistor that accounts only for the consequences of excess carriers in the base.

---

[3] Note in this regard that the factor in parentheses in Eq. 11.23b is simply δ, the base defect defined by Eq. 7.7.

[4] There is a second-order dependence of the distribution on Δv_{CB}, which results from the fact that the width of the neutral-base region must change as v_{CB} changes, because the width of the space-charge layer depends on v_{CB}. See Section 7.5.1. For the present, we neglect this base-width modulation effect.

The incremental description given by Eqs. 11.18 and 11.24 and by Fig. 11.6 depends on our assumption that Δv_{EB} changes slowly enough so that the instantaneous incremental excess-carrier distribution is always approximately triangular. If the distribution is approximately triangular, the emitter current, which is proportional to the slope of the distribution at the emitter edge of the base, will be approximately equal in magnitude to the collector current, which is proportional to the slope of the distribution at the collector edge of the base. In such cases, the base current, which is proportional to the *difference* between emitter and collector currents, will be small compared with either the emitter or the collector current. Consequently, the incremental model we have developed is valid under dynamic conditions whenever the rate of change of Δv_{EB} is small enough so that $|\Delta i_B|$ is small compared with $|\Delta i_C|$. Inspection of Eqs. 11.18 and 11.24 shows that, since $g_\pi \ll g_m$, this condition is met whenever

$$C_b \frac{d\,\Delta v_{EB}}{dt} \ll g_m\,\Delta v_{EB} \qquad (11.25a)$$

or, using Eq. 11.20d, whenever

$$\frac{W^2}{2D_b}\left(\frac{1}{\Delta v_{EB}}\frac{d\,\Delta v_{EB}}{dt}\right) \ll 1 \qquad (11.25b)$$

The factor in parentheses is the fractional rate of change of Δv_{EB}. The coefficient $W^2/2D_b$ has dimensions of time; we denote it by τ_B.

$$\tau_B = \frac{W^2}{2D_b} \qquad (11.25c)$$

This parameter[5] has values in typical transistors that range from 100 to about 0.2 nsec. Equation 11.25b is satisfied, and the incremental model we have developed is valid, if the fractional amount by which Δv_{EB} changes in the time interval τ_B is small. In such cases the instantaneous incremental base current will be small compared with the instantaneous incremental collector current. For situations in which the incremental variables have sinusoidal time dependence, Eq. 11.25b amounts to a restriction on the maximum frequency at which the model is applicable. Specifically, the model of Eqs. 11.18 and 11.24 is *valid only for frequencies much less than* τ_B^{-1}.

The incremental model of Eqs. 11.18 and 11.24 and Fig. 11.6 describes the first-order consequences of minority-carrier transport across the base. We now extend this model to account for the changes in the charge stored in the space-charge layers that straddle the metallurgical junctions. Since the space-charge-layer width depends on the instantaneous junction voltage, displacement currents of majority carriers must be supplied to both sides of

---

[5] The parameter is identical to the time constant τ_F defined in our development of a total-variable charge-control model that is valid in the active region; see Eqs. 8.3.

the space-charge layer whenever a junction voltage changes with time. As we have seen for the junction diode (Section 4.4.1), the physical effects of these displacement currents can be characterized, for *incremental* changes in junction voltage, by means of incremental junction or space-charge-layer capacitances. Thus the incremental collector current must be increased by the amount

$$C_{jc} \frac{d\,\Delta v_{CB}}{dt}$$

and the base current must be reduced by a like amount. The coefficient C_{jc} denotes the incremental collector space-charge-layer capacitance. Similarly, the emitter current must be increased, and the base current must be decreased, by

$$C_{je} \frac{d\Delta v_{EB}}{dt}$$

where C_{je} denotes the emitter space-charge-layer capacitance. When these terms are added to the incremental currents, Eqs. 11.18 and 11.24 become

$$\Delta i_C = -g_m\,\Delta v_{EB} + C_{jc}\frac{d\,\Delta v_{CB}}{dt} \tag{11.26a}$$

$$\Delta i_B = -g_\pi\,\Delta v_{EB} - C_b\frac{d\,\Delta v_{EB}}{dt} - C_{je}\frac{d\,\Delta v_{EB}}{dt} - C_{jc}\frac{d\,\Delta v_{CB}}{dt} \tag{11.26b}$$

These equations constitute our basic incremental model for a bipolar transistor.

11.4.2 An Incremental Circuit Model

The linear relationships given by Eqs. 11.26 can be interpreted in terms of a network model comprised of linear circuit elements, as shown in Fig. 11.7. The circuit constraints embodied in this network are precisely equivalent to the relationships of Eqs. 11.26. Thus Eq. 11.26a is a statement of Kirchhoff's

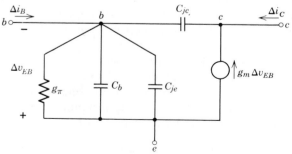

Figure 11.7   An incremental model for bipolar transistors.

current law at node c, and Eq. 11.26b is the corresponding statement at node b. This circuit model can also be obtained simply by adding the space-charge-layer capacitances C_{je} and C_{je} to the incomplete model shown in Fig. 11.6. An equivalent form of the model is shown in Fig. 11.8. The emitter junction capacitance C_{je} has been combined with the base-charging capacitance C_b, and the notation has been changed slightly to reflect standard usage. In particular, the polarities of both the dependent generator and the voltage that actuates it have been inverted, the Δ notation has been dropped, and the symbol appropriate to a complex amplitude rather than a time function has been used. *The model of Fig. 11.7 is the simplest incremental model capable of representing, over wide ranges of operating conditions, the incremental behavior of a bipolar transistor biased in the active region.*

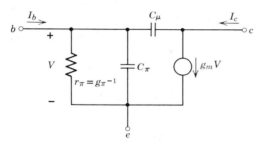

Figure 11.8   An incremental model that illustrates the notation employed in this book.

The incremental model for bipolar transistors shown in Fig. 11.8 is very similar to the basic incremental model for unipolar or field-effect transistors shown in Fig. 11.3. Both contain input capacitance, a capacitance between input and output, and a current generator at the output that is dependent on the input voltage. They differ only in that the model for the bipolar transistor contains an input conductance that is not present in the model for an FET. Because these models are so similar, we shall find that many aspects of the incremental analysis of active electronic circuits are equally applicable to both classes of active devices.

The numerical values of the parameters that are used in the models discussed in this section must, of course, be inferred from measurements made at the terminals. This is a complex topic, in itself, and we shall return to it in Chapter 12. Here it is sufficient to say that measurements at the terminals can be used as the basis for parameter determination. This does not mean that the physically-oriented model is not more useful than the measured properties alone. The physically-oriented model is quite explicit about frequency dependence; it provides a framework for understanding the consequences of operating-point and environmental changes, and it contains only linear passive elements and sources. These are advantages of enormous practical importance.

11.4.3 Extrinsic Elements

The incremental model of Fig. 11.8 for bipolar transistors embodies the results of an analysis of a somewhat idealized structural and physical model in which second-order phenomena were omitted. We now consider the incremental consequences of several second-order effects that we previously ignored.

We have seen that majority carriers must enter the base region from the base terminal when the transistor operates in the active region. These carriers, which are electrons in the case of a *pnp* transistor, feed recombination in the base and the emitter and neutralize the injected minority carriers in the base. The direction of flow of these majority carriers is *transverse* or normal to the flow of minority carriers, as shown in the cross section of Fig. 11.9.

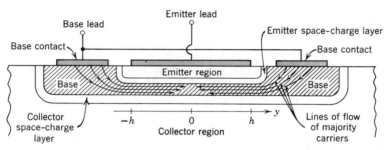

Figure 11.9 Base-region majority carriers flow into the base parallel to the junction planes.

The base-region majority carriers flow into the active region between emitter and collector largely by *drift*. Consequently, there are transverse voltage drops in the base region. For this reason, the voltage in the active base region is always smaller in magnitude than the voltage at the base terminal. Consequently, the collector current is not controlled directly by the external emitter-to-base voltage.[6]

There is no simple satisfactory physical model that can be used to account for this effect quantitatively. The problem is two-dimensional and is complicated by the fact that the injection level in the base is usually high under operating conditions for which these transverse voltage drops are important. Nevertheless, the circuit consequences of this transverse voltage drop must not be ignored. We arbitrarily model the incremental consequences of this

---

[6] Note also that because of the transverse voltage drops, the forward bias on the emitter junction is less at the midplane of the device than at the outer regions of the emitter base junction. Consequently, the longitudinal hole current that flows from emitter to collector is *not* uniformly distributed along the transverse coordinate but is crowded toward the outer portions of the base where the forward bias on the emitter junction is largest. This crowding is called *pinch-out*. It is particularly important for operation at high currents or high powers, and may seriously limit the current-handling capability of a transistor.

effect by adding a series resistance to our basic incremental model as shown in Fig. 11.10. This resistance, called *base resistance* and denoted by r_x, has values that may range from a few ohms to about 100 ohms. It is an important parameter in high-frequency incremental applications because the capacitances C_μ and C_π must be charged through it. Even though we are unable to assign a value to r_x on theoretical grounds (and may even have difficulty in measuring its value precisely, as we shall see in Chapter 12), it is included in our model to emphasize that the "internal" base voltage is not directly accessible at the base terminal.

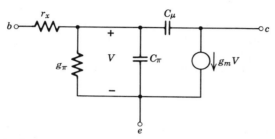

Figure 11.10 An incremental model that includes base resistance.

The incremental model shown in Fig. 11.10 is known as the *hybrid-pi* model; it consists of a pi-type configuration of elements to which r_x is added. This model is adequate in accuracy or precision of description for many bipolar transistor applications.

When a transistor is mounted on a header and provided with leads, inter-lead capacitances are introduced. These electrostatic couplings can be modeled by adding a pi of capacitances to the terminals of our incremental model as shown in Fig. 11.11. The capacitance C_{bc} includes, in addition to interlead capacitance, the incremental space-charge capacitance associated

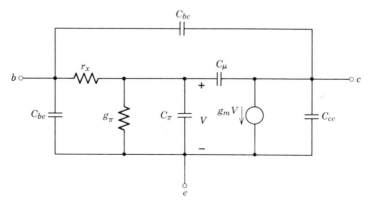

Figure 11.11 An incremental model that includes base resistance and interlead capacitances.

with those portions of the collector junction that lie outside the active base region, that is, outside $y = \pm h$ in the structure of Fig. 11.9. This portion of the collector junction is sometimes called the *overlap diode*, and the corresponding component of C_{bc} is called the *overlap capacitance*.

When a transistor is included as a component of an integrated circuit, the interlead capacitances are smaller than if the same device were isolated and mounted on a header. However, the junction that isolates the transistor from the substrate contributes a collector-to-substrate capacitance that must often be accounted for in the incremental model.

Throughout our analysis of transistor physical electronics we have assumed that with reverse bias on the collector junction the excess-carrier distribution in the base is independent of the collector-to-base voltage. In reality this is not quite correct, and, as discussed in Section 7.5.1, there is a second-order dependence of the excess-carrier distribution on v_{CB}. This dependence occurs because the width W of the neutral base region changes as v_{CB} changes, since the width of the collector space-charge layer depends on the voltage across that junction. This coupling is called *base-width modulation*. Its incremental consequences can be modeled by adding conductances in parallel with C_μ and the $g_m V$ generator. However, the currents carried by these additional elements are important only when the voltage gain from base to collector is in excess of 100 or 200; such voltage gains are larger than are achieved in most circuit configurations. Consequently, these elements can in most cases be omitted from the model.[7]

The incremental model shown in Fig. 11.11 suffices for all of the bipolar transistor applications we shall consider. Even with this relatively simple model there are very few circumstances in which *all* eight parameters that appear in the model would be used simultaneously in an analysis of the incremental behavior of a circuit. Were this not the case, the resulting description would be too complex and unwieldy to be useful. Thus one of the problems that often faces the circuit designer is: Under what conditions, and for what ranges of signal frequency or speed, are some (perhaps most) of the elements in the incremental model unimportant? These questions will be faced in Chapter 14.

11.4.4 Models for *npn* Transistors

All of the conclusions of this section, including the incremental models of Figs. 11.8, 11.10, and 11.11, are directly applicable to *npn* bipolar transistors. These devices differ from *pnp* devices only in that the emitter, base, and collector regions are of opposite conductivity type, and the roles of holes and electrons are interchanged. Consequently, *all* terminal currents and *all* terminal-pair voltages have the opposite polarity (for the same reference directions). These polarity reversals cancel out in the linear incremental

---

[7] For further discussion of base-width modulation effects see Reference 7.1.

relationships analogous to Eqs. 11.26. Thus Eqs. 11.26 and Figs. 11.8, 11.10, and 11.11 apply to *both npn* and *pnp* transistors. Since we have expressed the transconductance g_m in terms of the *magnitude* of the dc collector current (Eq. 11.19), it too is insensitive to the polarity of the terminal variables.

11.5 Applications of Incremental Models

We now consider several elementary transistor circuits in order to illustrate the application of incremental models in circuit analysis. For the present we consider only low-speed or low-frequency situations in which *all* of the capacitances in our transistor models carry negligible current. Thus these capacitances can all be removed from the transistor models and replaced by open circuits. We shall see in Chapter 14 that this condition is not as severe as it may at first seem; many modern transistors can be characterized by resistive models for sinusoidal signals having frequencies as high as a few megahertz.

11.5.1 A Common-Emitter Amplifier

As a first example of the use of incremental models in the analysis of amplifier circuits we return to the common-emitter configuration shown in Fig. 11.1a. We assume that the input voltage v_I is comprised of a quiescent component V_I and an incremental component v_i, which has a complex amplitude V_i. Similarly, we regard the output voltage v_O as comprised of a quiescent component V_O and an incremental component v_o having a complex amplitude V_o. The quiescent component V_O of the output voltage is related to the corresponding component V_I of the input voltage through the static transfer characteristic, as shown in Fig. 11.1b. The quiescent component V_I of the input is chosen to bias the transistor in the active region. If v_i is small enough, we expect the incremental component of the output to be linearly dependent on v_i; it is this linear relationship that we wish to explore.

We can employ the model shown in Fig. 11.12a as a characterization of the incremental behavior of the bipolar transistor. This model differs from the more complete models of Fig. 11.10 and 11.11 only in that the capacitances have been removed and the input conductance has been converted to a resistance $r_\pi = g_\pi^{-1}$.

The incremental circuit that results when the model of Fig. 11.12a is inserted in the circuit of Fig. 11.1a is shown in Fig. 11.12b. It is important to notice that quiescent or dc sources do *not* appear in the incremental circuit. When an incremental model is inserted in a circuit, all dc sources must be set to zero because these sources have no incremental components. More specifically, all dc voltage sources must be replaced by short circuits, and all dc current sources must be replaced by open circuits. Thus the left end of the resistance R_S is returned to ground through V_i, the incremental component of the input voltage source, and V_I, the quiescent component, is suppressed. Similarly, the top end of the resistance R_L is returned directly to ground

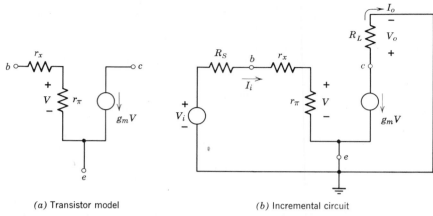

(a) Transistor model   (b) Incremental circuit

Figure 11.12   Incremental model and circuit for the amplifier shown in Fig. 11.1a.

because the power source denoted by $-V_{CC}$ has no incremental component.

The incremental circuit has two independent loops. Consequently, the *voltage transfer ratio* V_o/V_i can be written by inspection of the circuit. For input loop we have

$$\frac{V}{V_i} = \frac{r_\pi}{r_x + r_\pi + R_S} \tag{11.27a}$$

while for the output loop we have

$$\frac{V_o}{V} = -g_m R_L \tag{11.27b}$$

Thus the voltage transfer ratio or *common-emitter voltage gain* is

$$\frac{V_o}{V_i} = \left(\frac{V_o}{V}\right)\left(\frac{V}{V_i}\right) = -\frac{g_m r_\pi R_L}{r_x + r_\pi + R_S} \tag{11.28}$$

The input current I_i is given by

$$I_i = \frac{V}{r_\pi} \tag{11.29a}$$

while the output current is simply

$$I_o = -g_m V \tag{11.29b}$$

Hence the *current transfer ratio* or *common-emitter current gain* I_o/I_i is

$$\frac{I_o}{I_i} = -g_m r_\pi \tag{11.30}$$

The dimensionless product $g_m r_\pi$ occurs frequently in the incremental analysis of bipolar transistor circuits. Since it is a property of the transistor model, it is distinguished by a separate symbol

$$g_m r_\pi = \beta_o \tag{11.31}$$

The physical interpretation of β_o is straightforward; *it is the low-frequency short-circuit base-to-collector (or common-emitter) current gain.* The parameter β_o is not strongly dependent on the quiescent collector current: Eq. 11.23b shows that r_π, which is g_π^{-1}, is proportional to g_m^{-1}. Consequently, the strong dependence of g_m on $|I_C|$ is *not* reflected in β_o, which usually lies in the range from 10 to 500.

The voltage transfer ratio given by Eq. 11.28 can also be expressed in terms of β_o. Note that this ratio can be quite large, as long as R_L is not much less than $r_x + r_\pi + R_S$.

The fact that the amplifier circuit of Fig. 11.1 may have a voltage gain greater than unity is not, in itself, particularly interesting or important. A simple transformer may be arranged to have a "voltage gain" greater than unity by making the ratio of output turns to input turns greater than unity. The important point about a linear amplifier which uses a control valve such as a transistor is that the circuit may *deliver more signal power to a load than the power required to control the valve.*

In terms of the circuit of Fig. 11.1, the instantaneous voltage across the load resistance R_L is

$$v_O = V_O + v_o \tag{11.32}$$

Thus the instantaneous power delivered to R_L is

$$p_R = \frac{v_O{}^2}{R_L} = \frac{V_O{}^2}{R_L} + \frac{v_o{}^2}{R_L} + \frac{2V_O v_o}{R_L} \tag{11.33}$$

If we restrict the class of incremental signals we are dealing with to those that have zero average value (sinusoids are in this class), the *average* power delivered to the load is, from Eq. 11.33,

$$\langle p_R \rangle = \frac{V_O{}^2}{R_L} + \frac{\langle v_o{}^2 \rangle}{R_L} \tag{11.34}$$

where $\langle p_R \rangle$ denotes the time-average power delivered to the load. The first term on the right side of Eq. 11.34 represents the power delivered to R_L in the absence of signal, that is, under quiescent conditions. The second term is the additional power delivered to R_L because of the presence of the incremental signal. The cross term vanishes in the average because $\langle v_o \rangle$ is assumed to be zero.[8] The second term on the right side of Eq. 11.34 has a simple interpretation in terms of the incremental circuit of Fig. 11.11b; the average *signal* power delivered to the load is simply equal to the power developed in the

---

[8] The signal, which has zero average value, and the dc component are considered to be *orthogonal*; that is, $\langle V_o v_o \rangle \equiv 0$

load in the *incremental circuit*. Similarly, the *signal* power supplied to the circuit at the input terminal is equal to the power delivered to the incremental circuit by the incremental input voltage source. If we assume that the circuit of Fig. 11.11*b* is excited by a sinusoidal signal, the average power delivered to the load is

$$P_o = \frac{|V_o|^2}{2R_L} \tag{11.35a}$$

and the average power supplied by the input signal source V_i is

$$P_i = \frac{|V_i|^2}{2(R_S + r_x + r_\pi)} \tag{11.35b}$$

The factors of 2 appear in these expressions because V_o and V_i denote the complex amplitudes of the sinusoidal signals and because the average value of $(Ve^{j\omega t})^2$ is $|V|^2/2$.

We may define the incremental power gain of this circuit as $A_p = P_o/P_i$, whence

$$A_p = \left|\frac{V_o}{V_i}\right|^2 \left(\frac{R_S + r_x + r_\pi}{R_L}\right) \tag{11.36}$$

Clearly A_p may be much greater than unity. That is, the incremental output voltage may develop far more power in the load than is provided by the incremental signal source at the input. In terms of the incremental circuit, this extra power is supplied by the dependent generator. Thus the dependent generator represents the function of the control valve as a power modulator.

The incremental circuit shown in Fig. 11.11*b* is an example of the class of networks called *active circuits*. The name originates from the fact that the incremental circuit contains a source of energy (the dependent generator) and has the capability of incremental power gain. It is active in contrast to passive circuits, which cannot supply energy.

The incremental circuit that we have examined in this example is considered to be *unilateral* because there is no coupling of the output back to the input of the model. The coupling represented by the dependent $g_m V$ generator is, of course, one-way coupling. It is the unilateral nature of the incremental model for this circuit that permits us to split the circuit into two parts and to solve the input and output networks separately.

11.5.2   A Common-Collector Amplifier

As a second example of incremental circuit analysis, we consider the circuit shown in Fig. 11.13*a*. The *npn* transistor in this circuit is connected in the common-collector configuration; that is, the collector is incrementally grounded. We use the resistive incremental model of Fig. 11.12*a* (with $r_x = 0$) to represent the transistor and thus obtain the incremental circuit shown in

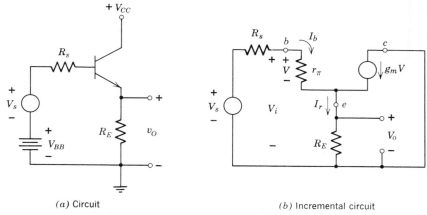

(a) Circuit   (b) Incremental circuit

Figure 11.13 A common-collector amplifier.

Fig. 11.13b. Note that the two dc voltage sources V_{BB} and V_{CC} are replaced in the incremental circuit by short circuits.

We now wish to evaluate the incremental voltage transfer ratios V_o/V_i and V_o/V_s. These are *not* the same because there is a drop across the Thevenin equivalent source resistance R_s. In making this calculation, we assume that no current flows at the output terminal; that is, there is no load at the emitter other than that represented by R_E.

The incremental circuit of Fig. 11.13b contains four nodes. Thus we could determine the distribution of voltages and currents, and evaluate the required transfer functions, by writing Kirchhoff's current law at three nodes and solving the resulting equations. Instead of proceeding in such a formal manner, which produces little insight into the workings of the circuit, we proceed in a step-by-step fashion, noting important general features of the circuit as we progress.

The base-to-ground voltage V_i can be written as

$$V_i = V + V_o \tag{11.37}$$

However,

$$V = r_\pi I_b \tag{11.38a}$$

and

$$V_o = I_r R_E \tag{11.38b}$$

The current I_r in R_E is simply $I_b + g_m V$. Thus, using Eq. 11.38a, V_o can be written as

$$V_o = (1 + g_m r_\pi) R_E I_b$$

or

$$V_o = (\beta_o + 1) R_E I_b \tag{11.39}$$

since $g_m r_\pi$ is, by definition, equal to β_o. Finally, Eq. 11.37 reduces to

$$V_i = [r_\pi + (\beta_o + 1)R_E]I_b \qquad (11.40)$$

Thus the voltage transfer ratio V_o/V_i is

$$\frac{V_o}{V_i} = \frac{(\beta_o + 1)R_E}{r_\pi + (\beta_o + 1)R_E} \qquad (11.41)$$

This ratio clearly has a value that is always less than unity; usually the parameter values are such that V_o is only slightly less than V_i. In many cases the common-collector circuit may be characterized by an incremental voltage transfer ratio of approximately unity. In this sense the incremental emitter-to-ground voltage "follows" the incremental base-to-ground voltage. Therefore, the circuit is often referred to as an *emitter follower*.

The incremental resistance that is presented to the signal source by the amplifier can be found directly from Eq. 11.40. This incremental base-to-ground resistance presented by the transistor and R_E is

$$R_i = \frac{V_i}{I_b}$$

$$= r_\pi + R_E(\beta_o + 1) \qquad (11.42)$$

The contribution of the emitter resistance R_E to this equivalent input resistance is augmented by the factor $(\beta_o + 1)$ because every unit of base current produces β_o units of collector current, and *both* currents flow in R_E. Thus although the emitter follower has a voltage transfer ratio that cannot exceed unity, it can have a current transfer ratio (I_r/I_b in the present example) that is quite large.

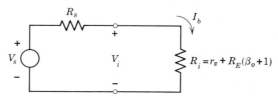

Figure 11.14   Incremental circuit that can be used to determine the loading of the emitter-follower on the signal source.

From the point of view of the signal source, the incremental circuit of the emitter follower can be replaced by the circuit shown in Fig. 11.14. The ratio of V_i to V_s is given by a voltage divider relationship.

$$\frac{V_i}{V_s} = \frac{R_i}{R_i + R_s} \qquad (11.43a)$$

The voltage transfer ratio that relates V_o to V_s can be obtained by multiplying together the ratios given in Eqs. 11.41 and 11.43a. This multiplication gives the correct overall transfer ratio, since we have accounted for the loading of the amplifier in formulating V_i/V_s. The result is

$$\frac{V_o}{V_s} = \frac{(\beta_o + 1)R_E}{R_s + r_\pi + (\beta_o + 1)R_E} \qquad (11.43b)$$

We conclude this example of incremental analysis by illustrating the evaluation of the equivalent Thévenin source resistance seen looking back into the emitter follower at its output terminals. More precisely, we represent the emitter follower at its output terminals by the Thévenin equivalent network shown in Fig. 11.15, and evaluate the equivalent source resistance R_o.

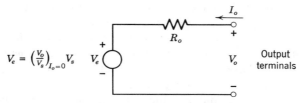

$$V_e = \left(\frac{V_o}{V_s}\right)_{I_o=0} V_s$$

Figure 11.15   A Thévenin equivalent for an amplifier.

Although there are several ways of evaluating this equivalent resistance, we shall make the calculation here by setting the input source V_s to zero (thereby forcing the source in Fig. 11.15 to be zero), applying a test voltage V_t to the amplifier at the output terminals, and computing the resulting response current I_t. The equivalent source resistance is simply V_t/I_t.

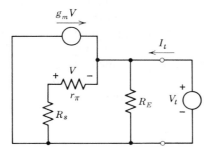

Figure 11.16   Incremental circuit of the emitter-follower with $V_s = 0$.

The incremental circuit of the emitter follower is redrawn in Fig. 11.16 for $V_s = 0$. We apply the test voltage V_t and compute I_t. Clearly, V is given by

$$V = -V_t\left(\frac{r_\pi}{r_\pi + R_s}\right) \qquad (11.44a)$$

The response current is, therefore,

$$I_t = \frac{V_t}{R_E} + \frac{V_t}{r_\pi + R_s} + \frac{g_m r_\pi V_t}{r_\pi + R_s} \tag{11.44b}$$

Finally, the output resistance R_o is obtained by solving Eq. 11.44b for V_t/I_t.

$$R_o = R_E \left\| \left(\frac{r_\pi + R_s}{\beta_o + 1} \right) \right. \tag{11.45}$$

The result has a simple interpretation. The output resistance consists of R_E in parallel with an equivalent resistance presented by the transistor. This equivalent resistance is $(r_\pi + R_s)/(\beta_o + 1)$. The factor $(\beta_o + 1)$ appears in the denominator of the expression because every unit of current that flows in the base produces β_o units of current in the collector; thus $(\beta_o + 1)$ units of current must be supplied at the emitter.

In summary, the common-collector amplifier or emitter follower behaves incrementally as an amplifier with nearly unity voltage gain, but with a current gain from base to emitter of $(\beta_o + 1)$. Consequently, an impedance connected between emitter and ground looks $(\beta_o + 1)$ times as big when viewed from base to ground. For the same reason, an impedance connected between base and ground looks $(\beta_o + 1)^{-1}$ times as big when viewed from emitter to ground.

11.5.3 An FET Phase Splitter

The FET amplifier circuit shown in Fig. 11.17a cannot be classified either as common-source or common-drain, even though the input signal is connected to the gate electrode of the n-channel FET. In fact, there are two equal load resistors, and outputs are taken from *both* source and drain terminals.

The incremental circuit that results when the dc bias sources (V_{DD} and V_{GG}) are supressed and when the FET is represented by the model of Fig. 11.3 (with the capacitances removed) is shown in Fig. 11.17b. Note that the variables in this circuit are represented by their complex amplitudes.

We wish to evaluate the incremental voltage transfer ratios V_s/V_i and V_d/V_i. Inspection of the source-drain loop yields

$$V_s = g_m R V \tag{11.46a}$$

and

$$V_d = -g_m R V \tag{11.46b}$$

Thus the two incremental output voltages have equal magnitudes but opposite signs. This should come as no surprise, since it is clear from the circuit of Fig. 11.17a that the same current flows in *both* resistances denoted by R (recall that the gate current is negligible).

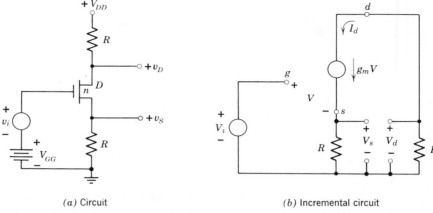

(a) Circuit	(b) Incremental circuit

Figure 11.17 An FET amplifier with two outputs.

The incremental gate-to-source voltage is

$$V = V_i - V_s$$

or, using Eq. 11.46a,

$$V = V_i - g_m R V$$

Thus we have, solving for V,

$$V = \frac{V_i}{1 + g_m R} \tag{11.47}$$

Consequently, the two voltage transfer ratios are

$$\frac{V_s}{V_i} = \frac{g_m R}{1 + g_m R} \tag{11.48a}$$

$$\frac{V_d}{V_i} = -\frac{g_m R}{1 + g_m R} \tag{11.48b}$$

These voltage transfer ratios have a magnitude that is slightly less than unity. In this sense the circuit resembles the emitter follower discussed in the preceding section. However, since this circuit produces two output signals, which are identical except for polarity, it is often called a *phase splitter*.

As a further example of incremental analysis we pause to compute the incremental output resistance seen looking back into the circuit at each of the two output terminals. Instead of proceeding as we did in the preceding section, we determine output resistances by forming the ratios of the open-circuit voltages to the short-circuit current that can be developed at each output terminal.

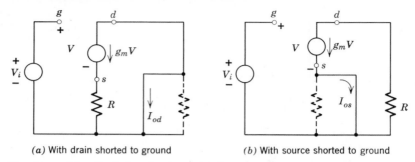

(a) With drain shorted to ground   (b) With source shorted to ground

Figure 11.18 Circuits used in calculating the short-circuit output currents.

Consider first the situation when the drain terminal is incrementally shorted to ground *while the source terminal is left open.* The corresponding circuit is shown in Fig. 11.18a. Clearly Eq. 11.47 applies, and the short-circuit output current I_{od} is

$$I_{od} = -\frac{g_m V_i}{1 + g_m R} \tag{11.49a}$$

The corresponding open-circuit output voltage is, from Eq. 11.48b,

$$V_d = -\frac{g_m R V_i}{1 + g_m R} \tag{11.49b}$$

Thus the incremental Thévenin equivalent output resistance is

$$R_{od} = \frac{V_d}{I_{od}} = R \tag{11.49c}$$

When the source terminal is incrementally shorted to ground *while the drain terminal is left open,* the circuit of Fig. 11.18b applies. In this case $V = V_i$, and we have

$$I_{os} = g_m V_i \tag{11.50a}$$

The corresponding open-circuit output voltage is, from Eq. 11.48a,

$$V_s = \frac{g_m R V_i}{1 + g_m R} \tag{11.50b}$$

Thus in this case the incremental Thévenin equivalent output resistance is

$$R_{os} = \frac{V_s}{I_{os}} = \frac{R}{1 + g_m R}$$

or

$$R_{os} \simeq R \| g_m^{-1} \tag{11.50c}$$

These calculations show that the incremental output resistance looking back in at the source terminal (with the drain terminal open) is *not* simply R, as in the other case; rather, it is the parallel combination of R and a resistance $1/g_m$. This result can be interpreted by saying that the Thévenin equivalent resistance seen looking back *into the FET* at its source terminal is g_m^{-1}.

The preceding calculations emphasize that the Thévenin equivalent resistances seen looking back into the output terminals *one at a time* differ; compare Eqs. 11.49c and 11.50c. Nevertheless, the incremental output voltages, which are equal when the output terminals are not loaded, remain equal *if the output terminals are simultaneously and equally loaded*. This can be seen from the circuit of Fig. 11.17a; if the external loads are equal, the voltages developed must be the same because the same current flows in both parallel combinations of external load and resistance R. The output resistance calculations, in which we looked *one at a time* at each output, do not apply if the output terminals are equally loaded (see Problem P11.15).

11.5.4 A Voltage Regulator*

Now that the concept of incremental analysis has been introduced, it is possible to study in more detail the performance of the voltage regulator circuit discussed in Section 7.4.3. Once the basic dc design of the regulator has been worked out, that is, breakdown voltage, half-wave rectifier output voltage, transistor dissipation, and so on, have been determined, it is appropriate to focus attention on the incremental properties of the circuit. To illustrate, we shall calculate the change of the output voltage resulting from a small change in rectifier voltage or a small change in output load.

In the regulator circuit diagram, Fig. 11.19a, the rectifier has been modeled by a circuit appropriate for calculating the change in output voltage arising from, say, a small change in the ac line voltage feeding the rectifier. The effect of a line-voltage change on the rectifier output is represented by an incremental voltage source e_i in series with E_I. The incremental model for the regulator circuit is shown in Fig. 11.19b. As indicated in Section 11.5.1, to generate this circuit, all independent dc voltage sources (in this case, source E_I and the source E_Z representing the breakdown diode) are shorted out, and all independent dc current sources (there are none here) are open-circuited. The transistor is represented by a simple g_m, r_π resistive incremental model. The voltage symbols in the figure are lowercase with lowercase subscripts to indicate *time-varying incremental* quantities.

To find the relation between e_o and e_i we could write loop equations and solve, as in Section 7.4.3. An easier method is to form the Thévenin equivalent of the entire regulator circuit except for R_L, that is, the circuit to the left of points xx in Fig. 11.19b. The open-circuit voltage of this Thévenin circuit can be obtained by inspection because R_L removed in Fig. 11.19b, there

---

* This Section, which depends upon Sections 6.4.3 and 7.4.3, can be omitted in an introductory study without loss of continuity.

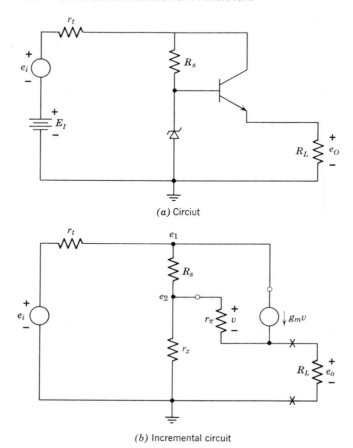

(*a*) Circiut

(*b*) Incremental circuit

Figure 11.19   Incremental analysis of a regulator circuit.

can be no incremental emitter current, hence no incremental base current. Thus the Thévenin open-circuit voltage e_t is

$$e_t = e_i \frac{r_z}{r_z + R_s + r_t} \qquad (11.51)$$

One way of finding the Thévenin resistance is to apply a test excitation (voltage-source or current-source) to the *output* terminals of the incremental circuit, and compute the response (current or voltage) at the output with the *independent* source e_i set to zero. In Fig. 11.20 we have chosen to drive the output terminals with a test voltage v_t. (A voltage-source drive was chosen here somewhat arbitrarily: in this particular example the calculations for a voltage-source drive and a current-source drive involve about the same amount of work. See Problem 11.16.) To find the output resistance, we calculate the response current i_t and then form the ratio v_t/i_t.

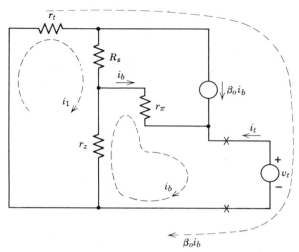

Figure 11.20   Calculation of the Thévenin resistance of the voltage regulator.

To find i_t, we write the two loop equations:

$$i_1(r_t + R_s + r_z) - i_b r_z + \beta_o i_b r_t = 0 \tag{11.52}$$

$$-i_1 r_z + i_b(r_z + r_\pi) = -v_t \tag{11.53}$$

Solving for i_b by applying Cramer's rule, we obtain

$$i_b = \frac{-v_t(r_t + R_s + r_z)}{(r_t + R_s + r_z)(r_z + r_\pi) + \beta_o r_t r_z - r_z^2} \tag{11.54}$$

Summing currents at the output node, we have

$$i_t = -i_b - \beta_o i_b \tag{11.55}$$

Substituting for i_b from Eq. 11.54, and solving for v_t/i_t, we obtain the Thévenin output resistance R_t of the voltage regulator

$$\frac{v_t}{i_t} \equiv R_t = \frac{r_\pi}{\beta_o + 1} + \frac{[R_s + (\beta_0 + 1)r_t]r_z}{(r_t + R_s + r_z)(\beta_o + 1)} \tag{11.56}$$

This resistance is a direct indication of how much the regulator output voltage will change as a result of changing load current. A small value for R_t compared to R_L means that e_o will stay nearly constant with changing load current, here simulated by changing R_L.

The first term in Eq. 11.56 is easy to interpret. It is the resistance r_π as seen from the emitter lead, hence divided by $(\beta_o + 1)$, as in an emitter follower circuit (see Section 11.5.2). The second term is more complicated. However, examination of Eq. 11.56 shows that this term is never bigger than the diode resistance r_z, and for large R_s is more like $r_z/(\beta_o + 1)$, that is, the diode resistance transformed down in resistance by the emitter-follower action. Thus it is clear that the output resistance of this regulator could well be a small fraction of an ohm.

To find the relation between e_o and e_i, we form the Thévenin circuit, as shown in Fig. 11.21, and find

$$e_o = \frac{R_L}{R_L + R_t} e_t \tag{11.57}$$

Hence from Eq. 11.51

$$e_o = \frac{r_z}{r_z + R_s + r_t} \cdot \frac{R_L}{R_L + R_t} e_i \tag{11.58}$$

It is now clear that to minimize the effect on the output voltage of line voltage changes, here represented by the source e_i, we should make resistance R_s as large as possible. We note from Eq. 11.56 that such action has the further desirable effect of lowering the Thévenin output resistance.

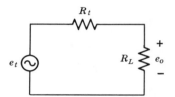

Figure 11.21   Incremental model that applies at the regulator output terminals.

PROBLEMS

P11.1   For operation below pinch-off in an enhancement-mode MOSFET with $V_p = 0$ and with *unsaturated* drain current, the drain current has, in accordance with Eq. 9.25, the following dependence on v_{GS} and v_{DS}:

$$i_D = \frac{h\mu_e\epsilon}{WL}\left(v_{GS}v_{DS} - \frac{v_{DS}^2}{2}\right)$$

In this case the incremental drain current can be written as

$$i_d = g_m v_{gs} + g_o v_{ds}$$

where g_o is the *incremental drain conductance*. Following the procedure described in Section 11.3.1, derive expressions for g_m and g_o in this case.

P11.2   The incremental transconductance for operation with saturated drain current is given by Eq. 11.8b. Express g_m in terms of the static drain current I_D, the static gate-to-source voltage V_{GS}, and V_P.

P11.3 Use the n-channel junction FET saturated drain-current expression of Eq. 10.12b to verify the expression for the incremental transconductance given by Eq. 11.11a.

P11.4 The component of the static base current that feeds the reverse injection of base-region majority carriers into the emitter is given by Eq. 7.6c Linearize this relationship and make use of the definition of Δq_B given by Eq. 11.20a to verify Eq. 11.22b.

P11.5 This problem is concerned with the upper frequency limitation of the incremental model developed for bipolar transistors in Section 11.4.1. *Assume* that Δv_{EB} has a *sinusoidal* time dependence with frequency ω and show that the model of Eqs. 11.18 and 11.24 yields a base current that is small compared with the collector current whenever $\omega \ll \tau_B^{-1}$, where τ_B is defined by Eq. 11.25c. The triangular approximation for the incremental excess carrier concentration in the base is valid whenever the base current is small compared with the collector current.

P11.6 This problem is concerned with an alternative derivation of an incremental model for a bipolar transistor. It is based on a linearization of the dynamic current-voltage relationships associated with the charge-control model developed in Chapter 8. We begin by ignoring the charging currents associated with the dipole layers at the junction space-charge layers, and focus on the currents associated with the excess-carrier charge store in the quasi-neutral base region.

(a) Use Eqs. 8.6 and 8.8 to show that the base and collector currents in a *pnp* transistor can be written as

$$i_C = -\frac{Q_{FO}}{\tau_F}(e^{qv_{EB}/kT} - 1)$$

$$i_B = -Q_{FO}\frac{q}{kT}e^{qv_{EB}/kT}\dot{v}_{EB} - \frac{Q_{FO}}{\tau_{BF}}(e^{qv_{EB}/kT} - 1)$$

where Q_{FO} is the constant defined by Eq. 8.9c and $\dot{v}_{EB}$ denotes dv_{EB}/dt.

(b) Note that the collector current i_C is a function of one variable: v_{EB}. Expand this nonlinear function in a Taylor's series about $v_{EB} = V_{EB}$, and obtain a linear relationship between i_c, the incremental component of the collector current, and v_{eb}, the incremental component of the emitter-base voltage. Show that your result is equivalent to Eqs. 11.18 and 11.19.

(c) Note that the base current i_B is a function of *two* variables: v_{EB} and $\dot{v}_{EB}$. Expand this nonlinear function in a two-dimensional Taylor's series about the point $v_{EB} = V_{EB}$, $\dot{v}_{EB} = 0$, and obtain a linear relationship between i_b, the incremental component of the base current, and v_{eb}. Show that your result is equivalent to Eq. 11.24 and the parameter definitions of Eqs. 11.20d and 11.23b. In this regard, recall that $\delta = \beta_F^{-1} = \tau_F/\tau_{BF}$.

(d) Show that the linear relationships developed in (b) and (c) are equivalent to the model of Fig. 11.6. Note that this model can be extended to include space-charge-layer charging currents by adding C_{je} and C_{jc}, as in Fig. 11.7.

P11.7 The incremental behavior of a *pnp* transistor may be represented by the circuit model shown in Fig. 11.22.

For a temperature of 300°K, the sketches in Fig. 11.22 show the dependence in the active region of:

(a) DC collector current I_C on dc base current I_B.

(b) Stored minority-carrier charge in the base, q_F, on I_C.

(c) Charge q_{VC} in either half of the collector-junction space-charge layer on collector-to-base voltage V_{CB}.

Estimate numerical values for g_m, g_π, C_π, and C_μ at an operating point of $I_C = -2$ ma, $V_{CE} = V_{CB} \simeq -10$ volt. Assume that the *emitter* space-charge-layer capacitance is a negligible component of C_π, and neglect charge storage in the emitter.

Answers. $g_m = 0.08$ mho, $r_\pi = 1.25$ kohm, $C_\pi = 160$ pf, $C_\mu = 30$ pf.

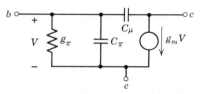

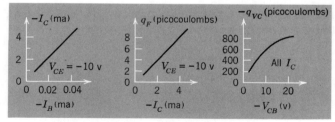

Figure 11.22   Incremental model and parameters.

P11.8 The circuit shown in Fig. 11.23 is basically a common-emitter amplifier; its properties are modified by the emitter resistor R_E.

(a) For what *approximate* range of input voltage v_I is the transistor in the active gain region? Express your result in terms of V, R_L, R_E, R_B, and β_F, and neglect V_{EB} compared with v_I.

(b) For v_I in the range determined in (a), find the incremental voltage gain of the circuit

$$A_v = \frac{v_o}{v_i}$$

Assume $\beta_o = \beta_F$ and $r_x = r_\pi = 0$.

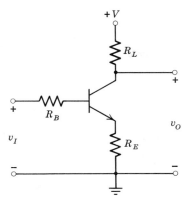

Figure 11.23 A common-emitter amplifier with an emitter resistor.

The common-emitter current gain β_o of transistors varies enormously, even for units that are nominally the same. For example, 5:1 variations in β_o for a particular type number are not uncommon. Clearly, these variations in β_o influence the incremental voltage gain of the simple transistor amplifier considered above; it is often important to reduce the dependence of gain on β_o in order that the electrical behavior of the circuit be known more precisely.

(c) For the circuit whose incremental gain was determined in (b), compute the fractional change of A_v per unit fractional change in β_o. That is, determine

$$\gamma = \frac{(dA_v/A_v)}{(d\beta_o/\beta_o)}$$

This ratio is a measure of the sensitivity of A_v to changes in β_o.

(d) Evaluate A_v and γ for $R_E = 0$. Assume that $R_L = 10\,\text{kohm}$, $R_B = 0.5\,\text{kohm}$, and $\beta_o = 100$. How much does A_v change if β_o decreases by 20% when $R_E = 0$?

(e) What value should R_E have if γ is to be 0.1? Assume that $R_L = 10\,\text{kohm}$, $R_B = 0.5\,\text{kohm}$, and $\beta_o = 100$. How much does A_v change if β_o decreases by 20% when R_E has the value found here?

P11.9 This problem is concerned with the linear incremental behavior of a *pnp* transistor biased in the forward active region (forward-biased emitter, reverse-biased collector). To first order, the incremental currents depend only on the incremental emitter-base voltage v_{eb} and are independent of the incremental collector-base voltage. This dependence can be represented by

$$i_b = -\left(C_b \frac{dv_{eb}}{dt} + \frac{v_{eb}}{r_\pi} \right) \Bigg\} \quad \text{for all } v_{cb}$$

$$i_c = -g_m v_{eb}$$

For exponential excitations, these equations become

$$I_b = -\left(sC_b + \frac{1}{r_\pi}\right)V_{eb}$$

$$\left.\begin{array}{l}\\ I_c = -g_m V_{eb}\end{array}\right\} \quad \text{for all } V_{cb}$$

to which I_b, I_c, V_{eb}, and V_{cb} denote complex amplitudes and s is the complex frequency.

The incremental behavior characterized by these equations can be represented by several circuit models (interconnections of linear passive elements and dependent sources), which differ principally in the choice of the variable that actuates the dependent current generator in the collector lead. Develop the following three incremental circuit models for the transistor.

A model in which the incremental collector current is produced by a dependent current generator that is controlled by:

(a) The incremental emitter-base voltage V_{eb}.

(b) The incremental base current I_b. The coefficient of the dependent generator is frequency dependent.

(c) The incremental emitter current I_e. The coefficient of the dependent generator is frequency dependent.

P11.10 The circuit of an elementary common-emitter amplifier is shown in Fig. 11.24.

(a) Estimate the quiescent operating point of the transistor, that is, find I_C and V_{CE} when $v_i \equiv 0$. Assume that $\beta_F = 50$. *Make reasonable approximations. (Suggestion.* Note that C can be replaced by an open circuit under quiescent conditions, and compare V_C with an order-of-magnitude estimate of V_{EB}.)

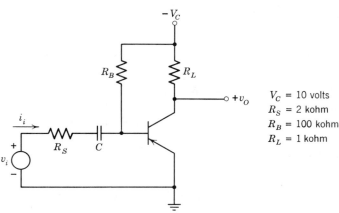

$V_C = 10$ volts
$R_S = 2$ kohm
$R_B = 100$ kohm
$R_L = 1$ kohm

Figure 11.24 Common-emitter amplifier.

(b) Using the hybrid-pi incremental model for the transistor, sketch a circuit that characterizes the incremental behavior of the circuit.

(c) Assume that the incremental parameters of the transistor are

$$r_\pi = 250 \text{ ohms} \qquad C_\pi = 200 \text{ pf}$$

$$g_m = 0.2 \text{ mho} \qquad C_\mu = 4 \text{ pf}$$

There is a range of frequencies for which the coupling capacitor C can be regarded as a short circuit for increments, while both C_π and C_μ can be regarded as open circuits for increments. In this frequency range, evaluate the incremental voltage gain V_o/V_i and the incremental input resistance V_i/I_i. Obtain literal expressions for these ratios before substituting numbers for the parameters.

P11.11   A more practical form of common-emitter amplifier is shown in Fig. 11.25.

(a) Estimate the quiescent operating point of the transistor, that is, find I_C and V_{CE} when $v_i \equiv 0$. Assume that $\beta_F = 50$. *Make reasonable approximations. (Suggestion.* Neglect the base current I_B in determining the base-to-ground voltage established by the divider comprised of R_{B1} and R_{B2}. Neglect V_{EB} in determining the emitter-to-ground voltage.)

(b) Using the hybrid-pi model, sketch a circuit that characterizes the incremental behavior of the circuit.

(c) Assume that

$$r_\pi = 250 \text{ ohms}$$

$$g_m = 0.2 \text{ mho}$$

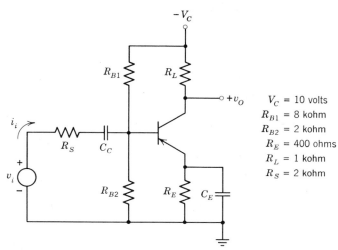

$$V_C = 10 \text{ volts}$$
$$R_{B1} = 8 \text{ kohm}$$
$$R_{B2} = 2 \text{ kohm}$$
$$R_E = 400 \text{ ohms}$$
$$R_L = 1 \text{ kohm}$$
$$R_S = 2 \text{ kohm}$$

Figure 11.25   An amplifier with bias network.

Consider frequencies low enough so that C_μ and C_π can be regarded as open circuits for increments. Compute both the incremental voltage gain V_o/V_i and the incremental input resistance V_i/I_i for (1) and (2) below. Obtain literal expressions before substituting numerical values for the parameters.

(1) Assume that both C_C and C_E are incremental short circuits. This is the usual situation.

(2) Assume that C_C is an incremental short circuit, but remove C_E (replace it with an open circuit).

Compare the two sets of values and explain why C_E is usually included in circuits such as this one.

P11.12   The circuit of a two-transistor linear amplifier is shown in Fig. 11.26. The dc current source is for bias purposes; if it were not present the first transistor would be constrained to operate with a collector current approximately equal to the base current of the second transistor.

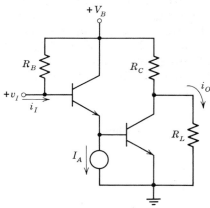

Figure 11.26   A two-stage amplifier.

(*a*) Sketch and label an incremental model that characterizes the *low frequency* incremental behavior of this circuit. Omit C_π and C_μ from both transistor models.

(*b*) Calculate literal expressions for the following incremental ratios.

(1) The incremental transconductance $G = I_o/V_i$, where I_o is the complex amplitude of the incremental component of the output current and V_i is the complex amplitude of the incremental component of the input voltage.

(2) The incremental input resistance $R_i = V_i/I_i$, where I_i is the complex amplitude of the incremental component of the input current.

P11.13   The circuit of a *common-base* amplifier is shown in Fig. 11.27. In this circuit, V_s and R_s comprise the Thévenin equivalent of an incremental signal source; V_s denotes the complex amplitude of the signal source, while

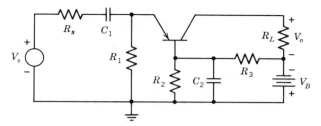

Figure 11.27   A common-base amplifier.

V_o denotes the complex amplitude of the incremental output voltage. The resistances R_1, R_2, and R_3 establish an appropriate quiescent operating point. The capacitance C_1 couples the signal source to the amplifier, while C_2 bypasses the base to ground for signals.

(a) Sketch and label a complete incremental model for this circuit. Include both C_1 and C_2 in your model, and use a hybrid-pi model to represent the transistor.

There is a range of frequencies for which the capacitances C_1 and C_2 have negligibly small reactances, while the capacitances C_π and C_μ have negligibly small admittances. In this *midband range* the incremental voltage gain V_o/V_i is *independent of frequency*.

(b) Sketch and label a simplified incremental model that is adequate for analysis of behavior in the midband range.

(c) Using the model obtained in (b), determine a literal (i.e., algebraic) expression for the midband value of the voltage gain V_o/V_i.

P11.14   Although field-effect transistors have very small dc gate currents, the gate capacitance introduces a capacitive input reactance that may be very important at high frequencies. One technique of reducing or eliminating the input-loading effects of the gate capacitance is called neutralization; it is

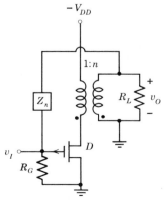

Figure 11.28   A neutralized common-source amplifier.

illustrated in Fig. 11.28. The current fed back through the neutralizing impedance Z_n is intended to cancel the current fed back through the gate-to-drain capacitance, thereby reducing the effective input capacitance of the amplifier. Use the incremental model of Fig. 11.3 to characterize the transistor and determine an expression for the value of Z_n that will exactly neutralize the effect of C_{gd} at the gate. Assume that the transformer is ideal, and express your result in terms of C_{gd} and n, the turns ratio.

P11.15   This problem is concerned with the FET phase-splitter circuit shown in Fig. 11.17. Assume that both output terminals are loaded with a resistance R_L, that is, a resistance R_L is connected from source to ground and an equal resistance R_L is connected from drain to ground. Evaluate the incremental output resistance seen at either the source or the drain terminals under this condition of simultaneous and equal loading.

P11.16   Consider the elementary voltage regulator circuit shown in Fig. 11.19. Assume that an incremental current source of value i_t is connected at the output terminals (marked xx in Fig. 11.19b) and evaluate the Thévenin equivalent output resistance by calculating the corresponding incremental output voltage v_t. Show that your result is equivalent to Eq. 11.56.

CHAPTER TWELVE

Determination of Incremental Parameters

From the point of view of numerical calculations, any transistor model is only as accurate as the parameter values used in it. Therefore, we now turn to the important problem of determining the small-signal model parameters for a given transistor at a given operating point. We discuss this problem in two stages:

1. We outline the steps necessary to determine the model parameters at one particular dc operating point.
2. We determine how the parameters vary with dc voltage, dc current, and transistor temperature so that the parameter values that have been determined can be converted to values appropriate for some other operating point.

The incremental models discussed in this book have been derived either directly or indirectly from consideration of the basic semiconductor physics of the devices. However, numerical values for the parameters in these models cannot in general be derived from physical considerations. Rather, they must be inferred from measurements at the terminals of the device. Thus before proceeding with the detailed discussion of parameter determination, we first consider some general aspects of two-port network measurements.[1]

12.1 Two-Port Network Descriptions

The various driving-point and transfer impedances and admittances that can be measured directly on a three-terminal network (or the three two-port networks that can be made out of it) require some careful description. We must not only say *what* is being measured, but also at *which* of the terminals it is being done and what the *load* is on the other terminals. All of this terminal measurement description has been condensed into standard symbols which often appear on the transistor data sheets and in the literature. The language involved is that of two-port (or two-terminal-pair) linear network theory.

The transistor is a *three-terminal* network. For incremental signals, it can be characterized as a linear *two-port* or as a *two-terminal-pair element* (Fig.

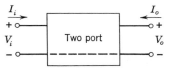

Figure 12.1 Assignment of terminal-pair voltages and currents to a two-port.

[1] Readers familiar with two-port parameters can turn directly to Section 12.1.5 without loss of continuity.

12.1). The notation used in the illustration indicates that the terminal-pair voltages and currents assigned to each of the ports are complex amplitudes of incremental components. These variables are related by two linear equations, but before writing these equations, it is necessary to decide which two variables will be regarded as independent. There are six possible choices of independent variables, each of which leads to a different set of two-port parameters, as listed in Table 12.1.

Table 12.1

Independent Variables	Designation
V_i and V_o	y parameter
I_i and I_o	z parameter
I_i and V_o	h parameter or hybrid parameter
V_i and I_o	g parameter
V_o and I_o	$ABCD$ or general circuit parameter
V_i and I_i	$A'B'C'D'$

In the subsections that follow, the first four of these descriptions are briefly reviewed.

12.1.1   *y* **Parameters**

If the voltages are regarded as the independent variables, the currents are dependent, and the appropriate linear constraints for the two-port network are

$$I_i = y_i V_i + y_r V_o \tag{12.1a}$$

$$I_o = y_f V_i + y_o V_o \tag{12.1b}$$

The coefficients y_i, y_f, and so forth, are called the incremental *y parameters* or *admittance parameters* of the device (they have the dimensions of admittances). Since the currents and voltages are complex amplitudes, the *y* parameters are ratios of complex amplitudes, hence functions of complex frequency *s*.

The notation employed in Eqs. 12.1 is intended to facilitate identification of the nature of the parameters. Thus y_i denotes the incremental *input* admittance when the incremental output voltage is zero, as can be seen in Eq. 12.1a. That is,

$$y_i \equiv \left. \frac{I_i}{V_i} \right|_{V_o = 0} \tag{12.2a}$$

Similarly, y_o is the incremental *output* admittance, measured with the input voltage zero (see Eq. 12.1b).

$$y_o \equiv \left. \frac{I_o}{V_o} \right|_{V_i = 0} \tag{12.2b}$$

Thus both y_i and y_o are driving-point admittances, defined under short-circuit conditions at the other terminal pair. The other two y parameters are transfer admittances; they relate the current at one short-circuited terminal pair to the voltage applied at the other terminal pair. Specifically, the *forward* transfer admittance y_f is

$$y_f \equiv \frac{I_o}{V_i}\bigg|_{V_o = 0} \tag{12.2c}$$

while the *reverse* admittance y_r is

$$y_r \equiv \frac{I_i}{V_o}\bigg|_{V_i = 0} \tag{12.2d}$$

Any set of two-port parameters can be interpreted in terms of a circuit model. The model appropriate to the admittance parameters is shown in Fig. 12.2. The rectangular boxes denote two-terminal networks having the indicated admittances. The model is seen to be equivalent to Eqs. 12.1 by writing Kirchhoff's current law at the nodes designated i and o.

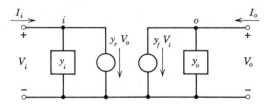

Figure 12.2   A y-parameter model.

12.1.2   z Parameters

If the currents are chosen as the independent variables, the appropriate two-port parameters are the *impedance parameters or z parameters*:

$$V_i = z_i I_i + z_r I_o \tag{12.3a}$$

$$V_o = z_f I_i + z_o I_o \tag{12.3b}$$

These parameters are also ratios of complex amplitudes. The input-parameter z_i and the output parameter z_o are driving-point impedances, defined with the other terminal-pair *open-circuited*. Similarly, the forward and reverse parameters are open-circuit transfer impedances. It should be evident that the impedance parameters are *not* the reciprocals of the corresponding admittance parameters (see Problem P12.1).

12.1.3   h Parameters

If the input current I_i and the output voltage V_o are chosen as the independent variables, the associated two-port incremental parameters are the *h*-parameters or *hybrid parameters*:

$$V_i = h_i I_i + h_r V_o \tag{12.4a}$$

$$I_o = h_f I_i + h_o V_o \tag{12.4b}$$

Since the independent variables are mixed, the *h* parameters are mixed dimensionally.

$$h_i \equiv \left.\frac{V_i}{I_i}\right|_{V_o = 0} = \text{input impedance with the output shorted} \tag{12.5a}$$

$$h_o \equiv \left.\frac{I_o}{V_o}\right|_{I_i = 0} = \text{output admittance with the input open} \tag{12.5b}$$

$$h_f \equiv \left.\frac{I_o}{I_i}\right|_{V_o = 0} = \text{short-circuit forward current transfer ratio} \tag{12.5c}$$

$$h_r \equiv \left.\frac{V_i}{V_o}\right|_{I_i = 0} = \text{open-circuit reverse voltage transfer ratio} \tag{12.5d}$$

A circuit model appropriate to the hybrid parameters is shown in Fig. 12.3. In this model, the box containing h_i denotes a two-terminal network that has an *impedance* h_i, and the box containing h_o denotes a two-terminal network that has an *admittance* h_o.

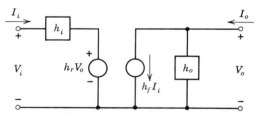

Figure 12.3 An *h*-parameter model.

12.1.4 *g* Parameters

A fourth set of two-port parameters, the *g* parameters, results when the input voltage and output current are taken as independent variables. These parameters are of value in formulating one of the four possible feedback amplifier configurations (see Chapter 18). The *g*-parameter description is analogous to the *h* description above, hence will not be covered formally here (see Problems P12.2 and P12.3).

It should be clear that *any* set of two-port parameters can be expressed in terms of any other set of parameters. These transformations are entirely straightforward, although uninspiring.[2]

---

[2] These transformations are developed in some detail and the complete results are tabulated in Reference 12.1, for example.

12.1.5 Transistor Configuration Notation

The transistor can be represented as a two-port in several ways. For a bipolar transistor, there are three useful configurations: common-base, common-emitter, and common-collector, as shown in Fig. 12.4. For the FET, there are three: common-source, -drain, and -gate. Each of the two-port descriptions (h, y, etc.) that we have discussed is applicable to any of these configurations. The parameters are, of course, different—often grossly different. Therefore, it is important to specify the configuration unambiguously. As a matter of standard practice, this configuration identification is accomplished by *adding a second subscript to the two-port parameters*. Thus h_{ib} is understood to denote the input hybrid parameter of a transistor in the common-base configuration, y_{re} denotes the reverse transfer admittance of a bipolar transistor in the common-emitter configuration, and y_{fs} is the forward transfer admittance of an FET in the common-source connection.[3]

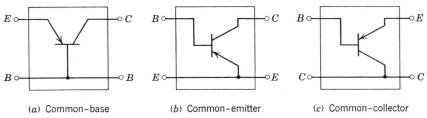

(a) Common–base (b) Common–emitter (c) Common–collector

Figure 12.4 The three possible ways of representing a transistor as a two-port.

12.1.6 General Comments on Two-Port Parameters

The two-port parameters provide a general and rather formal characterization that can be applied to *any incrementally linear, three-terminal device*. The two-port parameters for transistors are ratios of polynomials in complex frequency s, and each parameter depends in general on the quiescent operating point as well as on the device temperature. In the next section, we shall see that these parameters can be evaluated from measurements in a straightforward manner; the technique is suggested by the parameter definitions themselves, as given in Eqs. 12.2 and 12.5.

It is possible to use circuit models such as those shown in Figs. 12.2 and 12.3, together with measured values of the parameters, as a complete incremental characterization of a transistor. In particular, it is often convenient in calculations involving narrow-band amplifiers to model the transistors in this way. However, for general use these models have distinct drawbacks. Each of the parameters is a complex number varying in a more or less complicated way with frequency, ambient temperature, and operating point

---

[3] For a given device, any set of parameters can be transformed to the same (or a different) set of parameters for a different configuration. The transformations for bipolar transistors (all 316 of them) are tabulated in Reference 12.1.

and bearing no simple relation to the physics of the device. This complexity robs the circuit designer of any intuitive grasp of a problem and forces him to employ a multitude of graphs or tables describing how each parameter varies with frequency, temperature, voltage, and current.

12.2   Measurement of Hybrid-Pi Parameters

We turn now to one of the central issues of this chapter—the determination of numerical values for the elements of the hybrid-pi model (Fig. 12.5). This determination can be made either by direct measurement on the transistor at the desired operating point or by calculation from measured data normally supplied by a transistor manufacturer. In the latter case, the measurements are made at some standard current, often $I_C = 10$ ma, so that the parameter values must subsequently be converted to values appropriate for the desired operating point. This conversion will be discussed in Section 12.3.

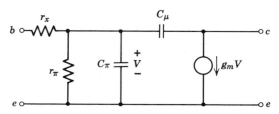

Figure 12.5   Hybrid-pi model.

Four of the five hybrid-pi parameters can be obtained by making the following measurements at the device terminals:

1. The incremental low-frequency common-emitter short-circuit current gain β_o.[4]

2. The common-emitter unity-gain frequency ω_T (sometimes called the gain-bandwidth product).

3. The dc collector current I_C at which β_o and ω_T were measured.

4. The common-base output capacitance C_{ob}.

Fortunately, most transistor specification sheets give these parameters, or data from which they can be deduced.

12.2.1   Determining g_m from I_C

The dependent-source parameter g_m is the one parameter that we do not measure either directly or indirectly. Instead, we rely on the validity of the

---

[4] The incremental short-circuit current gain is called h_{fe} in h-parameter notation, but, for historical reasons, it is also called β. The low-frequency value of β or (h_{fe}) is designated as β_o. The quantity β_F, although closely related to β_o, is the parameter used in large-signal models, where, by definition, it is not a function of voltage or current.

physical relation between g_m and I_C, discussed in Section 11.4.1:

$$g_m = \frac{q}{kT}|I_C| \tag{12.6}$$

This method of determination is accurate if $|I_C|$ is much larger than I_{CO}, but small enough so that the condition of low-level injection applies.

12.2.2   Determining r_π from g_m and β_o

The value of r_π can be determined by operating the transistor in the common-emitter configuration and measuring the low-frequency short-circuit current gain. That is, we measure h_{fe} or β at a frequency low enough that the capacitive effects in the transistor model can be ignored. A circuit model that is appropriate under these conditions is shown in Fig. 12.6. For this circuit,

$$\frac{I_c}{I_b} = h_{fe} \equiv \beta_o = g_m r_\pi \tag{12.7}$$

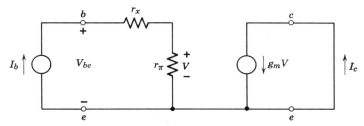

Figure 12.6   Circuit model for h_{fe} and h_{ie} measurement to determine r_π and r_x, respectively.

Thus if we measure the short-circuit current gain β_o at some low frequency and calculate g_m from Eq. 12.6, we can find r_π:

$$r_\pi = \frac{\beta_o}{g_m} \tag{12.8}$$

Manufacturers frequently specify on data sheets a value for h_{FE}, called the dc current gain, or pulsed dc current gain (because of the pulse technique used in the measurement). This parameter is by definition the ratio of the *total* collector current to *total* base current:

$$h_{FE} = \frac{I_C}{I_B} \tag{12.9}$$

For silicon transistors, where the effects of I_{CO} can be neglected, h_{FE} is approximately equal to h_{fe}; hence this dc current gain can be used in Eq. 12.7 to determine r_π.

12.2.3 **Determining** C_μ **from** C_{ob}

The value of the capacitor C_μ can be determined by measuring the capacitance between base and collector leads of the transistor with the emitter incrementally open-circuited, as indicated in Fig. 12.7. Here we are in effect measuring the output capacitance of the transistor in the common-base connection, a quantity usually denoted as C_{ob}. The g_m generator, r_π, and C_π do not enter into this measurement, because with the emitter open-circuited, V must be zero. To show this, we sum the currents at the emitter node:

$$(g_\pi + sC_\pi)V + g_mV = 0$$

The only solution to this equation [other than $s = -(g_m + g_\pi)/C_\pi$] is $V = 0$.

With g_m, g_π, and C_π in effect removed for this measurement, the network reduces to the series combination of r_x and C_μ. If we perform the measurement at a frequency such that

$$\frac{1}{\omega C_\mu} \gg r_x \tag{12.10}$$

then

$$C_\mu \simeq C_{ob} \tag{12.11}$$

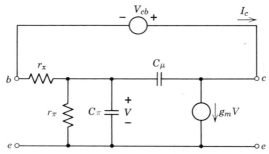

Figure 12.7 Circuit for C_{ob} measurement to determine C_μ.

12.2.4 **Determining** C_π **from** C_μ, g_m, **and** ω_T

An appropriate value for C_π can be determined from a measurement of the short-circuit current gain h_{fe} at high frequencies. We can find the required relationship from Fig. 12.8. Because of the short-circuit output constraint, the voltage V can be found by inspection:

$$V = \frac{I_b}{g_\pi + s(C_\pi + C_\mu)} \tag{12.12}$$

Thus if we neglect the current fed forward through C_μ (see Section 14.5), the short-circuit current gain β is

$$\beta = \frac{I_c}{I_b} = h_{fe} = \frac{g_m}{g_\pi + s(C_\pi + C_\mu)} \tag{12.13}$$

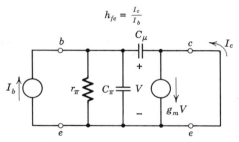

Figure 12.8 Incremental circuit from which C_π can be inferred.

If we have already determined g_m, g_π, and C_μ, a measurement of β at any frequency where the capacitors have a significant effect will yield the required value for C_π.

The calculation of C_π is simplified if we make the measurement of β at a frequency high enough so that g_π no longer has an appreciable effect on β. To show this graphically, and also to tie in other parameters commonly given on data sheets that can be used to determine C_π, we plot in Fig. 12.9 the magnitude and phase of β as a function of frequency. As can be seen from Eq. 12.13, the low-frequency asymptote of the magnitude curve will be $g_m r_\pi$,

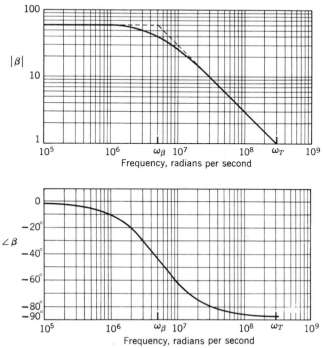

Figure 12.9 Magnitude and phase of β for the circuit in Fig. 12.8.

and there will be a single break downward, occurring at a frequency

$$\omega_\beta = \frac{g_\pi}{(C_\pi + C_\mu)} \tag{12.14}$$

That is, ω_β is *the frequency where the magnitude of the common-emitter short-circuit current gain is down to 0.707 of its low-frequency value.* At frequencies much above ω_β, g_π is no longer important, and the magnitude curve becomes asymptotic to a line with a slope of -1 on log-log coordinates. That is, in this frequency range,

$$|h_{fe}| = |\beta| \simeq \frac{g_m}{\omega(C_\pi + C_\mu)} \tag{12.15}$$

If the high-frequency asymptote is extrapolated, then at a frequency designated as ω_T, the asymptotic value falls to one. It is important to note that we *extrapolate* $|\beta|$, because the value of $|\beta|$ measured on an actual transistor will *not* be unity at ω_T. Other effects neglected here, such as header and overlap-diode capacitance, emitter lead inductance, and fundamental frequency limitations in the hybrid-pi model, make the model predictions inaccurate in this frequency range. Thus ω_T is defined as the frequency where $|\beta|$ *extrapolated* from the slope $= -1$ region falls to unity. From Eq. 12.15, we have

$$\omega_T = \frac{g_m}{(C_\mu + C_\pi)} \tag{12.16}$$

This expression can be used to determine C_π:

$$C_\pi = \frac{g_m}{\omega_T} - C_\mu \tag{12.17}$$

Often manufacturers do not give the value of ω_T directly. Because of the measurement inaccuracies already discussed, they prefer to specify $|h_{fe}|$ at some frequency between ω_β and ω_T. It should be clear from Eqs. 12.15 and 12.16, or from Fig. 12.9, that if we measure h_{fe} at some frequency ω in the asymptotic region

$$\omega_T = \omega|h_{fe}(\omega)| \tag{12.18}$$

and

$$\omega_T = \beta_o \omega_\beta \tag{12.19}$$

12.2.5   Determination of r_x

As discussed in Chapter 11, the base resistance r_x arises from several second-order physical mechanisms. For this reason, it is the one element in our model that changes value somewhat with frequency. It is difficult to measure, and rarely can we obtain a value for it either directly or indirectly from the information given in manufacturers' data sheets. Fortunately, in transistors manufactured by modern diffused technology, the base resistance is small enough that it does not play a dominant role in circuit calculations.

The low-frequency value of the base resistance r_x can sometimes be determined by using the circuit shown in Fig. 12.6 to measure at low frequencies the short-circuit input impedance h_{ie}. By inspection,

$$\frac{V_{be}}{I_b} = h_{ie} = r_x + r_\pi \tag{12.20}$$

Thus if we measure h_{ie} and if we know r_π from Eq. 12.8, we have

$$r_x = h_{ie} - r_\pi \tag{12.21}$$

Because r_x is usually much smaller than r_π, this determination may be quite inaccurate, since it depends on the difference between two large numbers. This problem will be acute if the determination is based on manufacturers' published data: Eq. 12.21 will in this case often yield meaningless negative values for r_x.

The high-frequency value of r_x can be found from a measurement of y_{ie} at high frequencies. From Fig. 12.5 we see that at frequencies much above ω_β

$$y_{ie} = \frac{g_x s(C_\pi + C_\mu)}{g_x + s(C_\pi + C_\mu)} \tag{12.22}$$

(See Problem P12.4.) As the frequency increases, the real part of y_{ie} will approach a constant. Specifically, for frequencies well above $\omega_b = g_x/(C_\pi + C_\mu)$,

$$\mathrm{Re}[y_{ie}] = g_x \tag{12.23}$$

The high-frequency r_x can also be found from h_{ie} (see Problem P12.5), but the determination in terms of y_{ie} is less sensitive to the parasitic effects of header capacitance (see Problem P12.6).

At high frequencies, the base resistance in most transistors tends to approach a small constant value, often called the extrinsic base resistance, which for many transistors can be as small as 25 ohms.

12.2.6 Summary of Measurements

All the measurements for determining the hybrid-pi element values have been summarized in Table 12.2 for ready reference. Examples that illustrate the use of these relations are given in Section 12.3.6.

12.3 Variation of the Hybrid-Pi Parameters with Voltage, Current, and Temperature

We now turn to the second step in parameter determination: finding how the parameter values of the hybrid-pi model vary with voltage, current, and temperature. Once these relations are known, it is possible to convert a set of parameters measured at some standard operating point to values appropriate to the specific operating point of interest.

Table 12.2

Hybrid-Pi Element	Quantity to Measure	Relationship
g_m	I_C	$g_m = \dfrac{q}{kT}|I_C|$
r_π	β_o	$r_\pi = \dfrac{\beta_o}{g_m}$
$r_x \begin{cases} \text{low-frequency} \\ \text{high-frequency} \end{cases}$	$h_{ie}|_{1000\text{Hz}}$ $y_{ie}|_{\omega \gg \omega_b}$	$r_x = h_{ie}|_{1000\text{Hz}} - r_\pi$ $g_x = \text{Re}[y_{ie}]_{\omega \gg \omega_b}$
C_μ	C_{ob}	$C_\mu \simeq C_{ob}$
C_π	ω_T	$C_\pi = \dfrac{g_m}{\omega_T} - C_\mu$

Our discussion will be based on the physical relations for the hybrid-pi parameters which we developed in Chapter 11. However, a few words of caution are needed before we proceed. Recall that the idealized theory in Chapter 11 assumes a uniform base region in the transistor, abrupt junctions, and low-level injection. These conditions are seldom met in practice. It turns out, however, that failure to precisely meet these assumptions does *not* cause first-order changes in the physical relations. Thus over reasonable ranges of voltage, current, or temperature, we can expect the idealized physical relations to hold. For example, if a parameter is measured at $I_C = 10$ ma, we should be able to use the idealized physical relations to find the value of the parameter at, say, 1 ma or 20 ma, but not 0.001 ma or 100 ma.

Because the topology of the hybrid-pi model was derived directly from the underlying physical principles of the device, it is not surprising that the

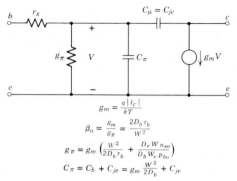

$$g_m = \frac{q|I_C|}{kT}$$
$$\beta_o = \frac{g_m}{g_\pi} = \frac{2D_b \tau_b}{W^2}$$
$$g_\pi = g_m \left(\frac{W^2}{2D_b \tau_b} + \frac{D_e W n_{eo}}{D_b W_e P_{bo}} \right)$$
$$C_\pi = C_b + C_{je} = g_m \frac{W^2}{2D_b} + C_{je}$$

Figure 12.10 Idealized physical relations for hybrid-pi parameters.

entire discussion of variations of the hybrid-pi parameters with voltage, current, and temperature hinges on the variation of only a few physical parameters with these quantities. Figure 12.10 summarizes the physical relations among the hybrid-pi parameters. The key physical parameters are clearly g_m, D_b, W, and C_j. Assuming low-level injection, the pertinent equations are the following:

$$\text{Transconductance: } g_m = \frac{q|I_C|}{kT} \tag{12.24}$$

$$\text{Diffusion coefficient: } D = \mu\frac{kT}{q} \tag{12.25}$$

Mobility μ: independent of voltage and current
Lifetime τ_b: independent of voltage and current
Incremental junction capacitance: $C_j = K(\psi_0 - V)^{-n}$ $\qquad$ (12.26)
where $n = \frac{1}{2}$ for abrupt junction devices and $\frac{1}{3}$ for graded junctions
Base width W: narrows as V_{CB} is increased (see Section 7.5.1)

12.3.1   Dependence on Collector Current

It is clear that none of the preceding relations except g_m involves collector current. Hence, from Fig. 12.10, the hybrid-pi parameters vary with current as shown in Table 12.3.

Table 12.3   Variation of Hybrid-Pi Parameters with I_C

Parameter	Effect of Increasing $|I_C|$
g_m, g_π, C_b	increase linearly
C_{je}, C_μ, β_o	independent of $|I_C|$

Because C_π is equal to $C_b + C_{je}$, C_π is almost linear with $|I_C|$, except at current levels low enough that C_{je} dominates the expression.

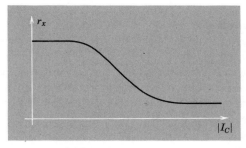

Figure 12.11   Variation of low-frequency base resistance with $|I_C|$.

Because of pinch-out, and conductivity modulation of the neutral base region, the low-frequency value of r_x decreases with increasing $|I_C|$, as sketched in Fig. 12.11. At high frequencies, r_x consists only of the extrinsic base resistance, hence should be nearly independent of $|I_C|$.

12.3.2   Dependence on Collector Voltage

Because g_m, D_b, and τ_b are independent of collector voltage, the change with voltage of the model parameters C_π, C_μ, and g_π arises through W. As already noted, W decreases for increasing $|V_{CB}|$. In the active region, $|V_{BE}|$ will be constant at about 0.6 volt for silicon. Thus for $|V_{CB}|$ greater than a few volts, $|V_{CB}|$ will be nearly equal to $|V_{CE}|$. We find, therefore, from Fig. 12.10 and Eq. 12.26, that the transistor parameters vary with V_{CE} as shown in Table 12.4.

Table 12.4   Variation of Hybrid-Pi Parameters with V_{CE}

Parameter	Effect of Increasing $|V_{CE}|$
g_m, C_{je}	independent of $|V_{CE}|$
g_π, C_b	decrease
β_o	increases (g_m/g_π)
C_μ	decreases (varies as $|V_{CE}|^{-n}$)

$n = \frac{1}{2}$ for abrupt junctions and $\frac{1}{3}$ for linearly graded junctions.

Because the base width narrows with increasing $|V_{CE}|$, we would expect the base resistance, a phenomenon associated with transverse majority-carrier flow, to increase with increasing $|V_{CE}|$. However, at constant $|I_C|$, narrowing the base width will increase the pinch-out, which reduces the base resistance. The competition between these mechanisms makes a general statement about base resistance variation with $|V_{CE}|$ difficult, since the relative magnitude of each effect in a given transistor will depend on operating point. If the collector current is sufficiently low that no appreciable pinch-out occurs, the base resistance will *increase* with increasing $|V_{CE}|$.

12.3.3   Temperature Dependence

We study in this section the variation of the hybrid-pi parameters with temperature, *assuming that I_C and V_{CE} are held fixed*. It should be remembered, however, that in an actual transistor circuit, variations of the operating point $(V_{CE}$ and $I_C)$ with temperature may cause more change in the parameters than do the direct temperature-induced changes described here.

Because W is independent of temperature, the dependence of the parameters on temperature arises through variations in τ_b and D_b. The minority-carrier lifetime τ_b increases with increasing temperature, particularly in silicon where rapid thermal motion of carriers at high temperatures is thought to make "capture" of minority carriers by imperfections less likely. Table 12.5, which is based on Table 1.2 and Eq. 3.69 in Reference 12.2, gives the temperature dependence of mobility and diffusion coefficient.

Table 12.5

Material	Temperature Dependence of Mobility	Temperature Dependence of Diffusion Coefficient
Holes in germanium Holes and electrons in silicon $\Big\}$	$T^{-2.3}$ to $T^{-2.7}$	$T^{-1.3}$ to $T^{-1.7}$
Electrons in germanium	$T^{-1.7}$	$T^{-0.7}$

The mobility values were derived for majority carriers, but for the impurity concentrations of interest in transistors, the minority-carrier mobilities have the same temperature dependence.

Clearly, the temperature dependence of β_o is complicated, arising as it does from competing effects of D_b and τ_b. Thus we resort to measured data. A normalized plot of β_o versus temperature for low-power transistors (Fig. 12.12) shows a steady increase, the sharpest increase being for silicon (primarily because of the increase in τ_b).

On the basis of Table 12.5 and Fig. 12.12, we find the data shown in Table 12.6. The parameter r_x increases with increasing temperature, primarily

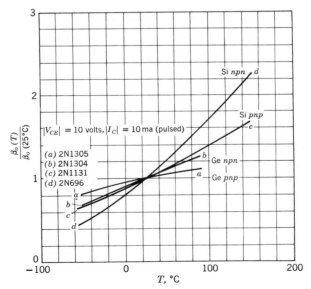

Figure 12.12 β_o versus T for typical transistors.

because a reduction in majority-carrier mobility (see Table 12.5) reduces conductivity.

Table 12.6 Variation of Hybrid-Pi Parameters with Temperature

Parameter	Variation with Increasing T
g_m	$\dfrac{1}{T}$
β_o	increase (Fig. 12.12)
r_π	T^{1+} (product of T and appropriate function in Fig. 12.12)
C_b	$\begin{cases} T^{0.3} \text{ to } T^{0.7} \text{ for silicon and for germanium } pnp \\ T^{-0.3} \text{ for germanium } npn \end{cases}$
C_μ, C_{je}	independent of T

12.3.4 Summary

The results of Sections 12.3.1, 12.3.2, and 12.3.3 are summarized in Table 12.7.

Table 12.7 Variation of Hybrid-Pi Parameters with Voltage, Current, and Temperature

Parameter	Idealized Physical Relation	Variation with Increasing		
		$|I_c|$	$|V_{CE}|$	T
g_m	$\dfrac{q|I_c|}{kT}$	linear	independent	$\dfrac{1}{T}$
g_π	$g_m\dfrac{W^2}{2D_b\tau_b}$	linear	decreases	$\dfrac{1}{T^{1+}}$
$C_\pi \begin{cases} C_b \\ C_{je} \end{cases}$	$g_m\dfrac{W^2}{2D_b}$; $K(\psi_0 - V)^{-n}$	linear ; independent	decreases ; independent	$T^{-0.3}$ to $T^{+0.7}$; independent
r_x	?	decreases at high current (Fig. 12.11)	?	increases
C_μ	$K(\psi_0 - V)^{-n}$	independent	decreases $|V_{CE}|^{-n}$	independent
β_o	$g_m r_\pi$	independent	increases steadily	increases (Fig. 12.12)

$n = \frac{1}{2}$ for abrupt junctions and $\frac{1}{3}$ for linearly-graded junctions.

12.3.5 Comparison with Some Published Data

It is helpful at this point to compare qualitatively some of the data presented in Table 12.7, derived largely on physical grounds by consideration of an idealized model, with published data obtained experimentally. To this end we first show in Fig. 12.13 experimental data indicating the variation of β_o with collector current. Although β_o is not constant, as we had predicted, it is often close to it. In Fig. 12.13c for example, β_o varies by about $\pm 10\%$ over three decades of collector current, from 0.5 to 500 ma. The transistor in Fig. 12.13a is not as good as this, whereas the transistor in b is obviously much better ($\pm 5\%$ over five decades).[5]

Next we examine experimental data on the variation of f_T with V_{CE} and I_C, and compare these results with the corresponding variation of f_T derived from

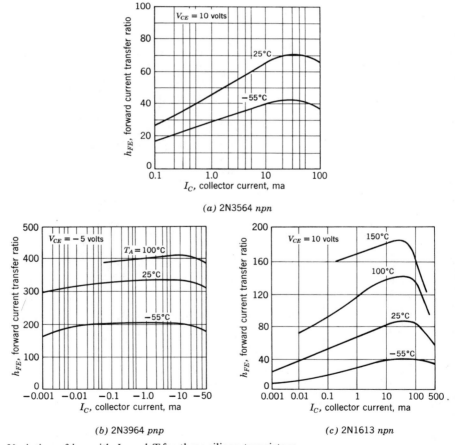

(a) 2N3564 *npn*

(b) 2N3964 *pnp*   (c) 2N1613 *npn*

Figure 12.13 Variation of h_{FE} with I_C and T for three silicon transistors.

[5] The variation of β_o with current is discussed in Reference 12.3.

Table 12.7. Experimental data on the variation of $f_T = \omega_T/2\pi$ with voltage and current are often plotted as a series of contours in the $I_C - V_{CE}$ plane, as shown in Fig. 12.14a and b. The intersection of these contours with a given horizontal line gives the variation of f_T with I_C alone. For example, for $V_{CE} = 2$ volts, the plot in Fig. 12.14a indicates that f_T increases steadily from 100 MHz at low currents to 700 MHz for I_C in the range of 20 to 30 ma. Our first-order analysis agrees with these data because, on the basis of Table 12.7, $\omega_T = g_m/(C_\pi + C_\mu)$ ought to increase with increasing current, since g_m and C_π increase linearly with currents, whereas C_μ is constant.

Because our entire analysis is predicated on low-level injection, it is not surprising that it does not correctly predict the high-current behavior of f_T. Specifically Table 12.7 indicates that ω_T should be constant at currents high enough to make C_π much larger than C_μ, but the data in Fig. 12.14a show

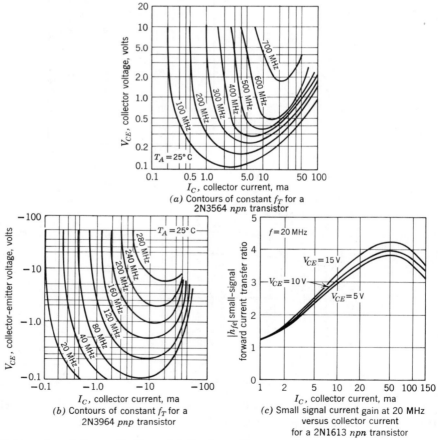

(a) Contours of constant f_T for a
2N3564 *npn* transistor

(b) Contours of constant f_T for a
2N3964 *pnp* transistor

(c) Small signal current gain at 20 MHz
versus collector current
for a 2N1613 *npn* transistor

Figure 12.14 Data on f_T variations with V_{CE} and I_C for three silicon transistors.

clearly that ω_T in fact falls rapidly above 50 ma. This matter is discussed in more detail in Reference 12.3.

The intersection of the f_T contours with a given *vertical* line in Fig. 12.14a and b gives the variation of f_T with V_{CE} alone. The plots show that f_T increases monotonically with increasing collector voltage. This result substantiates our first-order analysis, because according to Table 12.7, g_m is constant and both C_π and C_μ decrease with increasing $|V_{CE}|$ (see Problem P12.8).

Figure 12.14c shows another form of presenting f_T data.[6] Here the value of f_T must be deduced from the plot by using Eq. 12.18. This amounts to nothing more than a change in vertical scale: we change the units to f_T (MHz) and multiply the numbers by 20. Thus this plot shows the same general variation of f_T with voltage and current as already discussed.

12.3.6 Examples of Hybrid-Pi Parameter Determination from Data Sheets

Suppose that we wish to obtain the hybrid-pi parameters for a 2N3564 *npn* silicon transistor at an operating point of $I_C = 5$ ma and $V_{CE} = 5$ volts. Pertinent excerpts from the 2N3564 data sheet are shown in Table 12.8.

Table 12.8 Some Electrical Characteristics of a 2N3564 *npn* Silicon Transistor at $T = 25°C$

Symbol	Characteristics	Minimum	Typical	Maximum	Unit	Test Conditions
h_{fe}	Low-frequency Current gain ($f = 1$ kHz)	20	80			$I_C = 15$ ma, $V_{CE} = 10$ volts
$|h_{fe}|$	High-frequency current gain* ($f = 100$ MHz)	4	7.5			$I_C = 15$ ma, $V_{CE} = 10$ volts
r_b'	Real part of h_{ie} ($f = 350$ MHz)		30		ohm	$I_C = 15$ ma, $V_{CE} = 10$ volts
C_{obo}	Open-circuit output capacitance		2.5	3.5	pico-farad	$V_{CB} = 10$ volts, $I_E = 0$

* On many data sheets the magnitude signs are omitted

At the desired operating point of 5 ma, we find from Eq. 12.6 that

$$g_m = \frac{q|I_C|}{kT} = \frac{|I_C| \text{ ma}}{25}$$

$$= \frac{5}{25} = 0.2 \text{ mho}$$

From the low-frequency h_{fe} data in Table 12.8 we know that $\beta_o = 80$ at $I_C = 15$ ma, and we can reasonably assume that this applies at the desired operating point of 5 ma as well. If a more accurate determination is required,

[6] On many data sheets the magnitude signs on h_{fe} are omitted.

the data sheet also gives h_{FE} versus current (Fig. 12.13a). This plot shows only a few percent decrease in β_o from 15 to 5 ma. Hence, from Eq. 12.8, we have

$$r_\pi = \frac{\beta_o}{0.2} = 400 \text{ ohms}$$

Table 12.8 gives $C_{ob} = 2.5$ pf at $V_{CB} = 10$ volts. Thus C_μ at this operating point is approximately 2.5 pf. The C_μ value can now be scaled to that appropriate to the desired operating point on the basis that

$$C_\mu \sim V_{CB}^{-\frac{1}{3}}$$

for this *npn* graded-junction device. Thus $C_\mu = 2.5(10/5)^{\frac{1}{3}} = 3.16$ pf at $V_{CB} = 5$ volts $\simeq V_{CE}$ (see Problem P12.9). For this transistor the manufacturer also supplies on the data sheet a plot of C_{ob} versus bias voltage (Fig. 12.15); hence the required information can also be obtained directly from this graph. (See Problem P12.10).

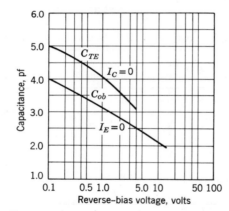

Figure 12.15 Input and output capacitance versus reverse-bias voltage for a 2N3564 *npn* silicon transistor. C_{TE} is the emitter junction space-charge-layer capacitance, C_{je}.

To find C_π, we note first that at $I_C = 15$ ma and $V_{CE} = 10$ volts, from Table 12.8 and Eq. 12.18,

$$f_T = 7.5 \times 100 = 750 \text{ MHz}$$

Thus from Eq. 12.17, again at $I_C = 15$ ma and $V_{CE} = 10$ volts and using units of kilohms, picofarads, and nanoseconds, we have

$$C_\pi = \frac{600}{0.75 \times 2\pi} - 2.5 = 126 \text{ pf}$$

Now we must convert this value to one appropriate for the desired operating point of $I_C = 5$ ma and $V_{CE} = 5$ volts. If we assume that C_π is dominated by the base charging capacitance C_b,

$$C_\pi \simeq C_b$$

then C_π scales linearly with I_C. Thus at $I_C = 5$ ma and $V_{CE} = 10$ volts

$$C_\pi = 126 \times \frac{5}{15} = 42 \text{ pf}$$

To convert to $V_{CE} = 5$ volts, instead of 10 volts, we need to know the relation between W and V_{CE}. Lacking this information, we assume that the change in V_{CE} from 10 to 5 volts is not going to significantly increase C_π. Hence $C_\pi \simeq 42$ pf.

If more detailed information on the variation of f_T with voltage and current is supplied, a more accurate determination of C_π can be made. For this

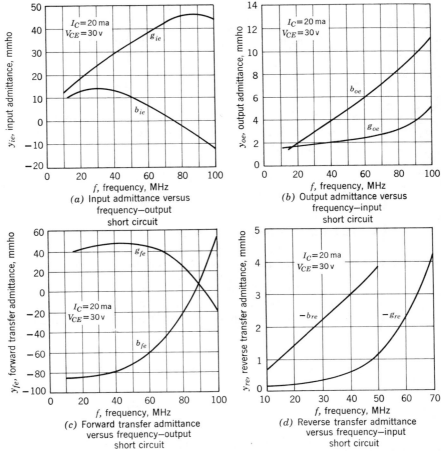

Figure 12.16 Typical common-emitter y parameters, 2N1613. g = real part, b = imaginary part.

transistor, the manufacturer included in the data sheet the f_T contours shown in Fig. 12.14a. From this plot, we find that at $I_C = 5$ ma and $V_{CE} = 5$ volts

$$f_T = 600 \text{ MHz}$$

Hence, at the desired operating point,

$$C_\pi = \frac{200}{2\pi \times 600} - 3.2 = 50 \text{ pf}$$

For this particular transistor, data on the real part of h_{ie} at high frequencies is given. If header capacitance can be ignored, then from Fig. 12.5, at frequencies well above ω_β,

$$\text{Re}[h_{ie}] = r_x \tag{12.27}$$

(see Problem P12.5). Hence, from Table 12.8 at $I_C = 15$ ma and $V_{CE} = 10$ volts,

$$r_x = 30 \text{ ohms}$$

It is difficult to accurately convert r_x to a value appropriate for the desired operating point; thus to a first approximation we may as well take 30 ohms as the appropriate value.

In some data sheets (the 2N1613, for example) typical y parameters versus frequency are given, as shown in Fig. 12.16. In this case, r_x can be obtained from y_{ie} by using Eq. 12.23 (see Problem P12.11).

12.4   FET Small-Signal Parameters

The parameters for the FET small-signal model shown in Fig. 12.17 can be obtained from three measurements at the device terminals:

(1) y_{fs}, the common-source forward short-circuit transadmittance
(2) C_{iss}, the common-source input capacitance
(3) C_{rss}, the common-source reverse transfer capacitance

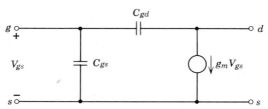

Figure 12.17   FET small-signal model.

12.4.1 Measurement of g_m

It is clear from an inspection of the model (Fig. 12.17) that the forward short-circuit transadmittance is

$$y_{fs} = \frac{I_d}{V_{gs}}\bigg|_{V_{ds}=0} = g_m - sC_{gd} \tag{12.28}$$

Hence a measurement of y_{fs} at any convenient low frequency will give g_m.

The parameter g_m can also be obtained from the vertical spacing of the FET dc output characteristics at the operating point:

$$g_m = \frac{\Delta I_D}{\Delta V_{GS}}\bigg|_{\Delta V_{DS}=0} \tag{12.29}$$

The variation of g_m with operating point and temperature in a MOSFET can be inferred from Eq. 11.8b. In the active region

$$g_m = \frac{h\mu_e\epsilon}{WL}(V_{GS} - V_P) \tag{12.30}$$

Because the constants are independent of voltage and current, we see from Eq. 12.30 that g_m is linearly dependent on the gate-to-source voltage and independent of V_{DS}. The temperature-dependence of g_m arises from the majority-carrier mobility. Hence for an n-channel device, we expect from Table 12.5 that g_m will vary as $T^{-2.5}$.

For the junction field-effect transistor (JFET), we find from Eqs. 11.11a and 10.5c that above pinch-off

$$g_m = G_0\left[1 - \left(\frac{V_{GS}}{V_P}\right)^{\frac{1}{2}}\right] \tag{20.31a}$$

where

$$G_0 = \frac{2q\mu_e n_o ha}{L} \tag{20.31b}$$

The constant G_0 is independent of voltage and current, so that the JFET g_m is independent of V_{DS}, but decreases for increasing V_{GS}, dropping to zero for $V_{GS} = V_P$.

12.4.2 Measurement of C_{gd} and C_{gs}

An examination of Fig. 12.17 shows that the short-circuit reverse transfer admittance will be purely capacitive and equal to $-j\omega C_{gd}$. Hence

$$C_{gd} = C_{rss} \tag{12.32}$$

Also from Fig. 12.17 we see that the input admittance with the output short-circuited, that is, y_{ie}, will be purely capacitive, equal to $j\omega(C_{gd} + C_{gs})$.

Hence

$$C_{iss} = C_{gd} + C_{gs} \tag{12.33}$$

Thus

$$C_{gs} = C_{iss} - C_{gd} \tag{12.34}$$

REFERENCES

12.1 W. W. Gärtner, *Transistors*, Van Nostrand, Princeton, N.J., 1960.

12.2 R. B. Adler et al., *Introduction to Semiconductor Physics*, Wiley, New York, 1964.

12.3 R. D. Thornton et al., *Characteristics and Limitations of Transistors*, Wiley, New York, 1966.

12.4 B. D. Wedlock, "Direct Determination of the Pinch-off Voltage of a Depletion-Mode Field-Effect Transistor," *Proc. IEEE*, January 1969, p. 75.

12.5 F. F. Kuo, *Network Analysis and Synthesis*, Wiley, New York, 1962.

12.6 F. Weinert, "Scattering Parameters Speed Design of High-Frequency Transistor Circuits," *Electronics*, September 5, 1966.

PROBLEMS

P12.1 (See page 411.) Prove that z_i is related to y_i by the equation

$$z_i = \left(y_i - \frac{y_f y_r}{y_o} \right)^{-1} \tag{12.35}$$

P12.2 Write the two linear equations describing the two-port network in Fig. 12.1 in which the input voltage and output current are the independent variables. Use these equations to derive definitions for the g parameters similar in form to Eqs. 12.5. (See page 412.)

P12.3 In certain cases, particularly at high frequencies, it is easier to measure the parameters of a two-port when the network is terminated in a 50-ohm resistive load rather than a short or open as required in Section 12.1. The resulting parameters are called *scattering parameters* or s parameters.[7] Relate these parameters to the y parameters defined in Section 12.1.1.

P12.4 Calculate y_{ie} for the hybrid-pi model in Fig. 12.5, hence verify Eq. 12.22 for frequencies above ω_β. (See page 419.)

P12.5 Calculate h_{ie} for the hybrid-pi model in Fig. 12.5. Find an expression for calculating r_x from h_{ie} at frequencies above ω_b. (See page 419.)

P12.6 Calculate y_{ie} and h_{ie} for the hybrid-pi model including header capacitance, Fig. 12.18. Find in each case an expression for calculating r_x for frequencies above ω_b. (See page 419.)

P12.7 Devise a set of relations for finding the hybrid-pi parameters directly from the scattering parameters derived in Problem P12.3.

[7] See References 12.5 and 12.6.

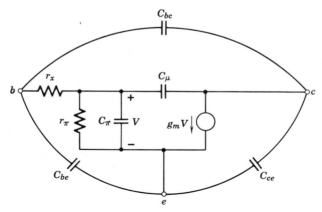

Figure 12.18   Hybrid-pi model, including header and overlap capacitance.

P12.8   Using Fig. 12.14b, plot curves of f_T versus I_C for $V_{CE} = -5$ volt and f_T versus V_{CE} for $I_C = -10$ ma. Superimpose on these plots a sketch of the corresponding functional relationship based on Eq. 12.16 and Table 12.7. Comment on similarities and differences. (See page 427.)

P12.9   For the example given in Section 12.3.6, page 427, make a more accurate calculation of C_μ by taking into account the difference between V_{CB} and V_{CE}. Compare with the value of 3.2 pf obtained in the text.

P12.10   As an alternative to the procedure outlined in the text (Section 12.3.6), find C_μ at $V_{CE} = 5$ volts from the graph in Fig. 12.15. Compare with the value of 3.2 pf obtained in the text. These answers differ because of two distinct discrepancies, one in the original data, the other in our first-order analysis. Identify and explain each discrepancy. (See page 428.)

P12.11   Find r_x for the 2N1613 at $I_C = 20$ ma, $V_{CE} = 30$ volts, using the y-parameter data in Fig. 12.16. (See page 430.)

P12.12   Find where possible appropriate values for the hybrid-pi parameters at $I_C = 5$ ma., $V_{CE} = 4$ volts for a 2N1613 transistor, using only the data listed in Table 12.9. Use "typical" values.

Table 12.9   Some Electrical Characteristics for a 2N1613 transistor at $T = 25°C$

Symbol	Characteristics	Mini-mum	Typical	Maxi-mum	Units	Test Conditions
h_{FE}	DC pulse current gain	35	80			$I_C = 10$ ma, $V_{CE} = 10$ volts
$|h_{fe}|$	high frequency current gain ($f = 20$ mc)	3	4			$I_C = 50$ ma, $V_{CE} = 10$ volts
C_{ob}	output capacitance		18	25	pico-farads	$I_E = 0$, $V_{CB} = 10$ volts

P12.13 Figures 12.13, 12.14, 12.16, and 12.19 contain considerably more data on the 2N1613 than given in Table 12.9. Repeat Problem P12.12 using these figures. Compare with the answers obtained in Problem P12.12, and explain any significant discrepancies.

P12.14 The input admittance in Fig. 12.16 has an *inductive* component above about 70 MHz. Explain this. What does the simple hybrid-pi model predict? Is this prediction valid at these frequencies for this transistor? Explain.

P12.15 Using the appropriate data from Figs. 12.13, 12.14, and 12.19, estimate the hybrid-pi parameter values for a 2N3964 (*pnp*) at $I_C = -10$ ma, $V_{CE} = -10$ volt.

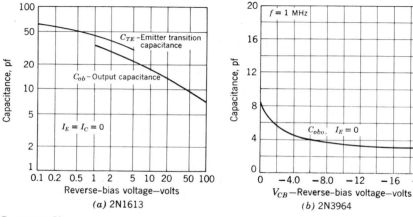

Figure 12.19 C_{ob} versus V_{CB}.

P12.16 For a certain MOSFET with $V_P = 0$ we have at $V_{DS} = -15$ volts, $V_{GS} = -10$ volts

$$y_{fs} = 4000 \text{ mmho}$$

$$C_{iss} = 11 \text{ pf}$$

$$C_{rss} = 1.6 \text{ pf}$$

(a) Find the FET incremental model parameters.
(b) Find new values of g_m and C_{gs} appropriate for an operating point of $V_{DS} = -30$ volt, $V_{GS} = -20$ volt.

CHAPTER THIRTEEN

Biasing of Field-Effect and Bipolar Transistors

So far in our discussion of amplifiers we have concentrated on calculations of signal voltages and currents, since these signals are the *raison d'être* of amplifiers. However, to achieve signal amplification, it is necessary to *bias* the transistor into the active region. In this chapter we discuss in detail several important aspects of bias networks in amplifiers: how to establish a given operating point and how to design a network that will maintain a given operating point in spite of changes in transistor parameters.

Amplifier bias networks must be carefully designed to overcome two deficiencies in transistors. First, as we saw in Chapter 12, transistor incremental parameters vary significantly with temperature. Second, substantial variations in parameters occur among supposedly identical transistors bearing the same type number. For example, in bipolar transistors β_F and I_{CO} may each have a spread of five to one in a batch of supposedly identical units. In this chapter we develop methods of biasing that prevent these transistor deficiencies from causing circuit malfunction or failure.

13.1 Factors Involved in the Selection of an Operating Point

13.1.1 The Allowed Operating Region

For a linear amplifier, there is a definite area on the transistor output characteristics within which the transistor operating point must be located. This area, which we call the *allowed operating region*, is determined by the voltage, current, and power limitations of the transistor and by the gross nonlinearities in the transistor characteristics. The allowed operating region on the output characteristics of a MOSFET curve has been indicated by shading in Fig. 13.1. A large part of the boundary of this region is formed by the *maximum dissipation curve*, the dividing line between safe and unsafe operation in terms of the average power dissipation of the device. The equation for the curve is $V_{DS}I_D = P_C$, which is a hyperbola when plotted on the output characteristics. The dissipation rating is based on the need to keep the MOSFET below the temperature at which transistor reliability and performance are impaired because of permanent changes in semiconductor properties or failure of soldered joints. This temperature is 85 to 105°C for germanium and usually about 200°C for silicon. Note that the dissipation rating is an *average* power rating. It is sometimes possible by careful design for the peak power to exceed this average rating for short periods of time, as long as internal peak temperatures are not excessive, but then a special investigation of the appropriate power ratings must be carried out (unless the manufacturer happens to supply the needed information).

The allowed operating region is also bounded in part by the voltage limitation, which appears on Fig. 13.1 as a vertical line. A maximum value of

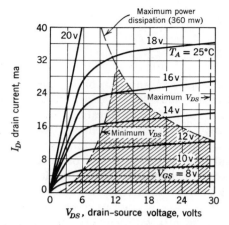

Figure 13.1   FET common-source ouput characteristics, showing allowed operating region.

V_{DS} is usually specified to assure operation of the FET below the breakdown voltage, in this case the breakdown between source and drain. The limitation imposed by other breakdown voltages, for example, between gate and drain, can also be shown as a contour on output characteristics.

The remainder of the boundary of the allowed operating region is coincident with the boundary of the saturation region, that is, the region over which the output characteristics are straight and parallel. For this n-channel MOSFET, the minimum voltage boundary is thus determined by the requirement that

$$V_{DS} > V_{GS} - V_P$$

The minimum drain current is $I_D = 0$.

A similar allowed operating region can be found on the output characteristics of a bipolar transistor. A typical set of common-emitter curves for a *pnp* germanium transistor are shown in Fig. 13.2. Again part of the boundary of the allowed operating region is formed by the maximum power dissipation hyperbola $V_{CE}I_C = P_C$. For the bipolar devices, most of the power is dissipated in the collector junction; hence this rating is designed to keep the collector junction below the critical temperature of about 85°C for germanium and about 200°C for silicon.

The boundaries imposed on the allowed operating region by maximum voltage and current ratings appear in Fig. 13.2 as vertical and horizontal lines respectively. A maximum value of V_{CE} is usually specified to assure operation of the bipolar transistor below the *sustaining voltage*, the voltage at which the collector current becomes large regardless of value of applied base current (see Section 7.5.2). The maximum I_C specification, on the other hand, is often not an absolute limit in the sense that the transistor will be destroyed,

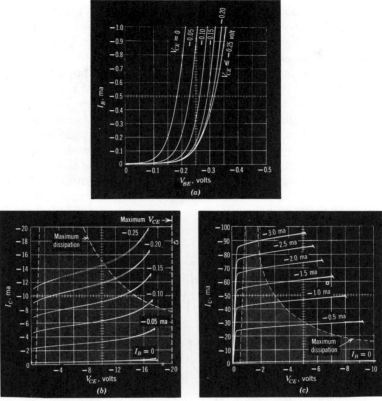

Figure 13.2   Common-emitter characteristics. (*a*) Input characteristics; (*b*) and (*c*) output characteristics plotted on two different scales. Allowed operating region indicated by shading.

but is a convenient way for the manufacturer to limit the region over which he must meet other transistor specifications.

The remainder of the boundary of the allowed operating region is coincident with the boundary of the forward active region. That is, for the transistor characteristics shown in the figure, the collector voltage must always be more negative than about -0.5 volt if the transistor is to stay out of saturation. Also, the collector current must be sufficiently negative to keep the transistor out of the cutoff region or, in other words, to ensure that the emitter diode remains forward-biased.

For the particular transistor shown in Fig. 13.2, the maximum rating for the input voltage is $V_{EB} = -25$ volt (i.e., reverse voltage on the emitter diode). It is clear that the maximum rating for the input voltage does not further restrict the choice of operating point for a linear amplifier operating with the emitter junction forward-biased. However, for other circuit applications, particularly pulse circuits, input ratings may be of considerable importance.

13.1.2   Location and Control of Operating Point

We have defined by Figs. 13.1 and 13.2 the allowed operating region for a transistor linear amplifier. The operating point must be located somewhere within the shaded area. The next questions are: precisely where within the shaded region do we locate the operating point and how accurately must we maintain it? To answer these questions, we consider the three important reasons for maintaining a stable operating point: maintenance of linear operation, control of dissipation, and control of the small-signal parameters.

Maintenance of Linear Operation. In a transistor amplifier required to have large signal amplitudes at the output (e.g., an output voltage swing of several

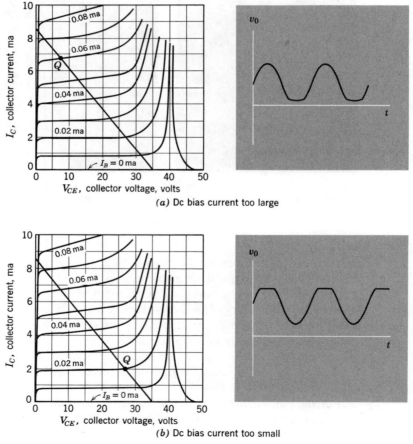

(a) Dc bias current too large

(b) Dc bias current too small

Figure 13.3   Distortion of the output voltage because of incorrect biasing.

volts), an important design consideration is the selection and control of the operating point to maintain linear operation. In bipolar circuits we must prevent the amplifier from distorting at any temperature as a result of saturation of the collector diode or reverse-biasing of the emitter diode at the extremes of the voltage swings. These problems are illustrated in Fig. 13.3.

In Fig. 13.3a, the dc bias current is too large, so the transistor is driven into saturation for part of each cycle of the input waveform. In Fig. 13.3b, the bias current is too small, so the transistor is periodically driven into cutoff. (A lecture demonstration which illustrates these effects is given in Section 13.8.1).

To find the bias requirement for maintaining linear operation, we look at the variation of the dc transistor characteristics as a function of temperature. In the germanium bipolar transistor (Fig. 13.4a) the dominant temperature effect on the output characteristic is a shift upward caused by the large increase in I_{CO}. However, as can be seen in the figure, the boundaries between the normal region and the saturation and cutoff regions do not change significantly with temperature. Thus in spite of the large change in the characteristics, the correct way to maintain linear operation is to maintain the operating point at approximately the same values of I_C and V_{CE}. Note that if we do this, I_B will have to change markedly with temperature and, in fact, may have to reverse polarity.

For silicon bipolar transistors, in which the dominant temperature effect on the output characteristics is an increase of β_F with increasing temperature, the normal-region boundaries again change by only a very small amount (see Fig. 13.4b). Therefore, it is again best to maintain approximately constant values of I_C and V_{CE}.

To prevent gross nonlinearity in an FET amplifier with substantial output voltage swing, we must maintain the bias point in such a way that regardless of temperature, the output voltage swing can be provided without forcing i_D to be zero or v_{DS} to be less than $V_{GS} - V_P$. That is, the instantaneous operating point must not touch or cross the two lower boundaries shown in Fig. 13.1.

The variation of the static characteristics of an MOS transistor with temperature is shown in Fig. 13.5. The dominant temperature effect is a *decrease* in I_D with increasing temperature for a given value of V_{GS}. This measured behavior is in general agreement with the theory developed in Chapter 9, specifically Eq. 9.31b:

$$I_D = \frac{h\mu_e\epsilon}{WL}\frac{(V_{GS} - V_P)^2}{2} \text{ for } V_{DS} > V_{GS} - V_P \tag{13.1}$$

The dominant temperature-dependent parameter in this equation is the mobility μ_e, and from Table 12.5, μ_e in silicon varies as $T^{-2.5}$. Thus Eq. 13.1 predicts a decrease in I_D with increasing temperature, which is in agreement with the experimental data in Fig. 13.5.

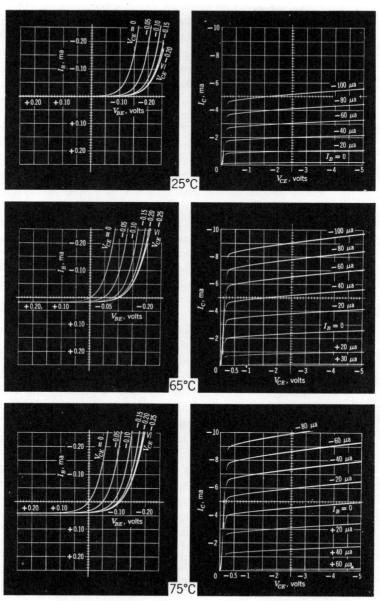

Figure 13.4a Common-emitter characteristics of *pnp* germanium-alloy transistor, measured at 25°, 65°, and 75°C.

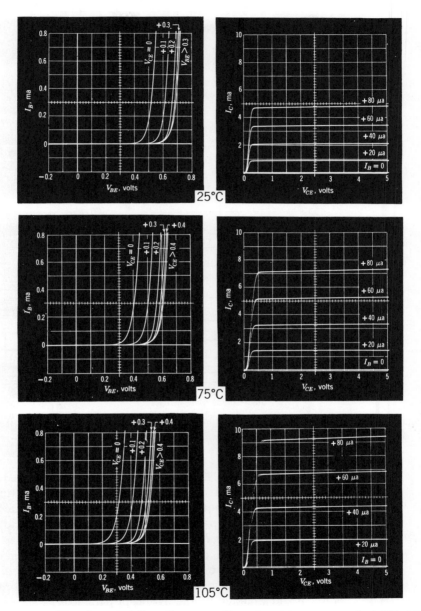

Figure 13.4*b*   Common-emitter characteristics of an *npn* silicon transistor, measured at 25°, 75°, and 105°C.

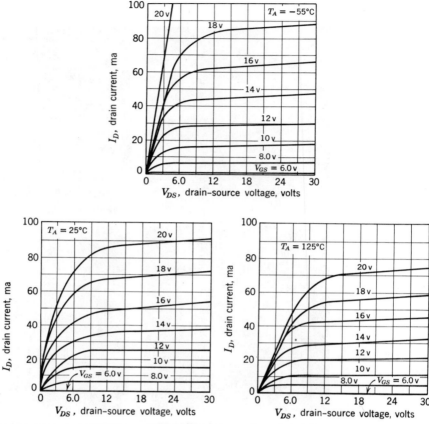

Figure 13.5   Output characteristics of an *n*-channel MOSFET at three temperatures.

Examination of Fig. 13.5 will indicate that if the required output voltage swing can be obtained satisfactorily at the highest operating temperature, then a satisfactory output swing at low temperatures is assured if we maintain the operating point approximately fixed in the I_D-V_{DS} plane.

Control of Small-signal Parameters. In transistor amplifiers where linearity is not a problem (i.e., output swings of millivolts rather than volts), an important consideration in bias network design is the control of small-signal parameters. For bipolar transistors, this is a complicated problem, because, as we saw in Chapter 12, the hybrid-pi parameters depend in a variety of ways on collector voltage, collector current, and junction temperature. Although it is possible to keep a single parameter fairly constant as a function of temperature (see Problem P13.1), a fairly wide variation in some of the other parameters will occur at the same time. Thus, except in some special design problems, we may as well try here again to keep I_C and V_{CE} approximately constant as the temperature changes. In this way we at least avoid problems of variation of the small-signal parameters with current and voltage, if not with temperature. A similar conclusion can be reached for MOS devices.

Control of Transistor Dissipation. It is clear from Section 13.1.1 that regardless of output swing, we must control the biasing of the transistor in such a way as to keep the average dissipation of the device below its maximum value, or, in terms of the static output characteristics, to keep the operating point below the maximum-power-dissipation contour. In many amplifier designs, the dc load line will intersect the maximum-power-dissipation contour, and it is entirely possible with improper bias design for the operating point to shift with temperature in such a way as to burn out the transistor.

In bipolar devices, the bias problem is further aggravated by an effect called *thermal run-away*, which can be explained as follows. The collector-to-base junction of the transistor, where essentially all of the dissipation occurs, is obviously not in perfect thermal contact with the transistor case, let alone with the surroundings. That is, there is some "thermal resistance" between the junction and the case, and between the case and ambient. Thus the power dissipated in the transistor will heat the junction to a temperature considerably above ambient. The internal increase in temperature will cause a change in the transistor characteristics, as shown in Fig. 13.4. Under unfavorable bias conditions, this change in transistor characteristics causes a large increase in the bias current, hence a further increase in power dissipation and internal temperature. This cyclic chain of events, which causes a rapid rise in transistor temperature and usually results in destruction of the transistor, is called thermal run-away. It is clear that the power dissipation can be controlled, hence thermal run-away prevented, if the biasing circuit is designed to keep the operating point approximately fixed in the I_C-V_{CE} plane.

The design of the bias network is further complicated by the fact that the allowable device dissipation is itself a function of ambient temperature. Recall that the device dissipation rating is based on the maximum temperature of the semiconductor material—85°C for germanium and about 200°C for silicon. Because of the thermal resistance between the semiconductor and the transistor case, the allowable dissipation must decrease linearly to zero as the ambient temperature approaches the maximum semiconductor temperature, as shown in Fig. 13.6. In bias designs where internal dissipation is a limiting factor, we are thus forced to design for the "worst case" by operating below the dissipation corresponding to the *maximum* anticipated temperature.

We conclude that for all three reasons—maintenance of linear operation, control of power dissipation, and control of small-signal parameters—often the best we can do is try to hold the operating point in the output plane approximately constant. It should be clear that this conclusion, although

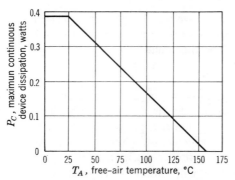

Figure 13.6   Free-air temperature-dissipation derating curve.

reached by considering the problem of variation of parameters with temperature, also applies to variation of parameters for any other reason. For
example, when any one of several bipolar transistors of the same type
number but with different values of β_F must be used in a circuit, we can
again ensure satisfactory operation by trying to hold I_C and V_{CE} approximately constant.

13.2   Biasing Networks for Field-Effect Transistors

Biasing of a single-stage field-effect transistor is a relatively simple matter
for two reasons. First, the dc characteristics of the device are not so temperature-dependent as are bipolar devices (compare Fig. 13.5 with Fig. 13.4b)
and, second, the input circuit of the device draws virtually zero direct current.

13.2.1   Simple Bias Network for an Enhancement-Mode MOSFET

It is clear from MOSFET output characteristics (Fig. 13.5) that for linear
operation of an n-channel device in the enhancement mode, we want both
V_{DS} and V_{GS} to be positive. Thus both the dc drain voltage and the dc gate
voltage can be derived from a single power supply, as shown in Fig. 13.7a.
Because the gate draws almost no dc current (I_G is of the order of 10^{-12} amps),
the design of the bias network is trivial. We select R_1 and R_2 to achieve the
desired V_{GS}, using the relation

$$V_{GS} = \frac{R_2}{R_1 + R_2} V \tag{13.2}$$

To avoid upsetting the bias point, the input signal is applied through a
coupling capacitor C_C, as shown in Fig. 13.7a. Calculations involving C_C
will be taken up in Chapter 14.

The simple bias circuit shown in Fig. 13.17a has one drawback. Because
V_{GS} is fixed, the operating point will change with temperature. To illustrate,
let us assume that R_L in Fig. 13.7a is 500 ohms and V_{CC} is 30 volts. A reasonable value for V_{GS} might be 14 volts, because the resultant operating point

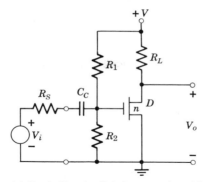

(a) Simple bias circuit (enhancement mode)

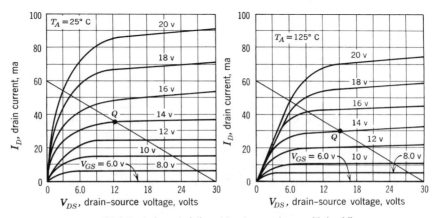

(b) Output characteristics at two temperatures, with load lines

Figure 13.7   Biasing of n-channel MOSFET.

will allow a reasonable output voltage swing at both 125 and 25°C, as can be seen from the output characteristics in Fig. 13.7b. It is clear from these characteristics that the operating point is not independent of temperature. Specifically, the load-line construction yields a quiescent I_D of 36 ma at 25°C and 30 ma at 125°C.

13.2.2   A More Stable Biasing Circuit

If the 20% change in quiescent drain current noted above cannot be tolerated in some particular circuit application, a simple modification can be made in the bias network to improve the bias stability: a resistor R can be added in series with the source lead, as shown in Fig. 13.8. Now V_{GS} is partially dependent on the drain current:

$$V_{GS} = V\left(\frac{R_2}{R_1 + R_2}\right) - I_D R \tag{13.3}$$

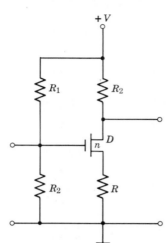

Figure 13.8   MOSFET bias circuit with improved stability.

Because of the square-law relation between V_{GS} and I_D (Eq. 13.1), an analytical treatment comparing the relative bias stability in Figs. 13.7*a* and 13.8 is tedious. Thus we rely on a plausibility argument, backed up by a numerical example.

Suppose that the drain current in Fig. 13.8 tends to decrease (e.g., because of an increase in ambient temperature). We see from Eq. 13.3 that because of the presence of the resistor R in the circuit, V_{GS} will tend to increase. We see from the MOSFET output characteristics (Fig. 13.7*b*) that this increase in V_{GS} will tend to *increase* I_D, thereby partially offsetting the change in the characteristic curves.[1] Let us illustrate this process by a numerical example.

Suppose that we use the same transistor as in Section 13.2.1, except that here we choose $R_L = R = 250$ ohms and $V = 30$ volts. The load line in this case has a slope of $-1/(R_L + R)$, because R_L and R appear in series in the output loop. We again bias at $I_D = 36$ ma at 25°C by setting V_{GS} equal to 14 volts. Thus from Eq. 13.3 (the units are volts, milliamperes and kilohms)

$$\frac{R_2}{R_1 + R_2} = \frac{V_{GS} + I_D R}{V}$$

$$= \frac{14 + 36 \times 0.25}{30} = 0.77 \tag{13.4}$$

At 125°C, V_{GS} will no longer be 14 volts, because of the change in I_D. A trial-and-error solution involving the output characteristics for 125°C

---

[1] This is an illustration of the general principle of stabilization by *negative feedback*, a topic to be discussed at length in Chapter 18.

(Fig. 13.7b) and the equation for V_{GS},

$$V_{GS} = 30 \times 0.77 - 0.25\, I_D$$

will indicate that at 125°C, the drain current is about 34 ma. Thus the quiescent I_D changes by only 6% in this circuit—more stable, by a factor of 3, than the circuit with no resistor in the source lead. It should be clear from Eq. 13.3 that increasing R will result in a further improvement in bias stability. However, this improvement is obtained at a price: there is substantial power wasted in resistors R_1, R_2, and R, and the maximum output voltage swing has been substantially reduced (for a given power supply voltage).

Because we still wish to operate the FET as a common-source amplifier, resistor R must be bypassed by a large capacitor C, as shown in Fig. 13.9. This capacitor is selected to provide a low impedance at all signal frequencies of interest, so that for incremental calculations the FET source terminal is grounded. The design of the coupling and bypass networks will be treated in Chapter 14.

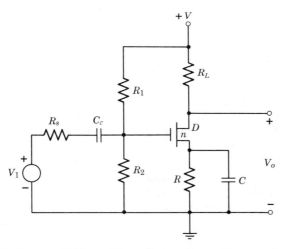

Figure 13.9 Single-stage FET amplifier with coupling and bypass capacitors.

13.2.3 Bias Circuits for a Depletion-Mode FET

For a depletion-mode FET, we require opposite polarities for V_{GS} and V_{DS}. Thus the simple biasing scheme that we used for the enhancement-mode MOSFET would require two separate power supplies. For this reason we turn directly to the bias network with a resistor in series with the source lead (Fig. 13.10), because this circuit requires only one dc supply.

For the n-channel JFET shown in the figure, V_{GS} must be negative. We achieve this by making V_S positive with respect to ground by an amount of

$$V_S = I_D R \tag{13.5}$$

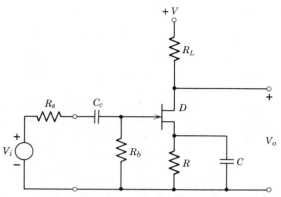

Figure 13.10 Bias network for an n-channel JFET (junction FET) or depletion-mode MOSFET. The transistor symbol shown is the standard symbol for a JFET.

Because the gate draws negligible current, V_G is approximately zero regardless of the value of R_b; hence

$$V_{GS} = -I_D R \tag{13.6}$$

This equation can be used to find R, knowing the desired operating point.

13.3 A Simple Common-Emitter Biasing Circuit
13.3.1 Analysis

The most obvious method of biasing a silicon common-emitter amplifier is to use a bias resistor R_b (Fig. 13.11a) to supply the required dc current to the base of the transistor. The signal can then be applied at the input terminals through a suitable coupling capacitor, as we shall see in Chapter 14. To find the appropriate design relationships, we substitute for the transistor the active-region, total-variable model of Fig. 7.10b. The temperature dependence in silicon appears in two parameters: β_F (see, for example, Fig. 13.4b or Fig. 12.12) and V_D. The design equation can be found by writing the equation for the input loop, recalling that both I_B and $\beta_F I_B$ flow through resistor r_d:

$$E_C - V_D = I_B[R_b + (\beta_F + 1)r_d] \tag{13.7}$$

Using the relation

$$I_C = \beta_F I_B \tag{13.8}$$

we can write Eq. 13.7 in two useful forms. For *analysis* of bias circuits, we wish to know I_C in terms of β_F:

$$I_C = \frac{\beta_F[E_C - V_D]}{R_b + (\beta_F + 1)r_d} \tag{13.9}$$

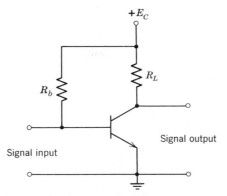

(a) Single-stage amplifier using a silicon transistor

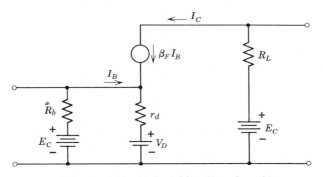

(b) Total-variable circuit model (active region only)

Figure 13.11   Simple bias circuit for a bipolar transistor.

For *design* of bias networks we wish to find the value of R_b required to yield a certain collector current:

$$R_b = \frac{\beta_F[E_C - V_D]}{I_C} - (\beta_F + 1)r_d \qquad (13.10)$$

Equation 13.10 shows clearly one serious drawback of this biasing circuit: there is very little room for design trade-off to improve performance. The values of E_C, I_C, and R_L are usually determined on the basis of the desired small-signal properties of the amplifier: gain, output swing, bandwidth, and so on. If these are in fact fixed, then the value of R_b is determined, and there is no possibility of adjusting bias network parameters to improve bias stability. In a word, you take what you get.

13.3.2   Example

To illustrate, suppose that we wish to operate the silicon transistor whose characteristics are shown in Fig. 13.4b at an operating point for $T = 25°C$ of

$$V_{CE} = 5 \text{ volts}$$

$$I_C = 4 \text{ ma}$$

Assume that the supply voltage E_C is 10 volts.
From Fig. 13.4b, at 25°C

$$\beta_F \simeq \frac{4.8}{0.08} = 60$$

The value of V_D at room temperature for silicon is about 0.6 volt, and at these current levels r_d is about 5 ohms. Thus from Eq. 13.10, using units of volts, milliamperes, and kilohms, we have

$$R_b = \frac{60(10 - 0.6)}{4} - (61)0.005$$

$$= 140 \text{ kohm}$$

But it is clear from Fig. 13.4b and Eq. 13.9 that the operating point in this design does *not* stay constant with changing temperature. Specifically,

$$\beta_F(105°) \simeq \frac{9.4}{0.08} = 118$$

Recall from Chapter 7 that V_D changes by about $-2\text{mv}/°C$. Thus

$$V_D(105°) = 0.6 - (105 - 25)(0.002) = 0.44 \text{ volt}$$

Therefore, from Eq. 13.9, the operating point at 105°C is

$$I_C = \frac{118(10 - 0.44)}{140 + 119(0.005)} \simeq 8 \text{ ma}$$

The dc bias current has doubled, principally because β_F has nearly doubled, and R_b and E_C form a virtual current source for base drive. Moral : keeping a constant dc base current does *nót* yield good bias stability. It should be pointed out, however, that for restricted applications where transistor dissipation is small and the ambient temperature is fairly constant, this simple bias design may prove to be entirely satisfactory.[2]

13.4   A Practical Common-Emitter Biasing Circuit
13.4.1   Analysis

Two simple changes in the bias network of Fig. 13.11 greatly increase the operating-point stability of the circuit. These changes (Fig. 13.12a) include the addition of an external emitter resistor R_e and the use of a resistive

[2] For an appropriate lecture demonstration, see Section 13.8.

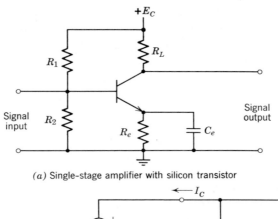

(a) Single-stage amplifier with silicon transistor

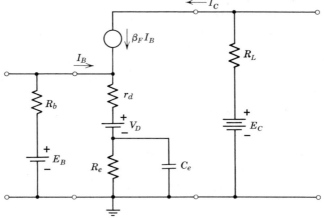

$$R_b = R_1 \| R_2, \quad E_B = E_C R_2/(R_1 + R_2)$$

(b) Total-variable circuit model for forward active region only

Figure 13.12 Improved biasing circuit for a bipolar transistor.

voltage divider R_1 and R_2 to supply the dc base bias current. In the circuit model of Fig. 13.12b this voltage divider has been replaced by its Thévenin equivalent: an open-circuit voltage

$$E_B = E_C \frac{R_2}{R_1 + R_2} \tag{13.11}$$

and a Thévenin resistance

$$R_b = R_1 \| R_2 \tag{13.12}$$

As we shall see in Chapter 14, the *emitter bypass capacitor* C_e is needed to provide a low impedance at signal frequencies from emitter to ground. However, C_e appears as an open circuit to the dc bias currents and thus does not enter into the present discussion.

Comparison of Fig. 13.12b with Fig. 13.11b shows clearly the essential differences between the two circuits, but it also indicates that the circuits are *topologically identical*. Thus the bias equations can be written by direct analogy from Eqs. 13.9 and 13.10:

$$I_C = \frac{\beta_F[E_B - V_D]}{R_b + (\beta_F + 1)(r_d + R_e)} \tag{13.13}$$

$$R_b = \frac{\beta_F[E_B - V_D]}{I_C} - (\beta_F + 1)(r_d + R_e) \tag{13.14}$$

The increased design freedom is obvious. We now have three independent parameters E_B, R_b, and R_e to adjust in order to set the operating current I_C. However, this freedom also makes Eq. 13.14 virtually useless as a design equation: we have too much choice. Nonetheless, the general design guidelines are clear from Eq. 13.13. If we make R_e large enough so that the term $(\beta_F + 1)R_e$ dominates the denominator, then the unpredictable β_F term virtually cancels out of the equation. Also, if we make E_B large (it has a limiting value of E_C, of course), the effects of variations in V_D with temperature are minimized. Unfortunately, the values of R_b and R_e also influence the signal specifications of the circuit. Resistor R_b appears in parallel with the transistor input and thus acts as an undesired shunt to incoming signal currents. Resistor R_e reduces the maximum output signal amplitude by reducing the effective dc power supply voltage: the dc voltage available to drive the collector circuit of the amplifier is only $E_C - I_E R_e$. Clearly, the last two conditions on signal performance conflict with the previous conditions based on bias stability alone.

13.4.2 Handbook Design

A "handbook" compromise design that is effective in many noncritical applications involving relatively constant ambient temperatures is the following. Given the desired operating point, select a value of R_e to make the voltage drop $|I_E R_e|$ about 3 or 4 volts. This will ensure a large enough value for E_B (see Eq. 13.15) so that changes in the V_D term in Eq. 13.13 will be suitably suppressed, yet allow a reasonable output signal amplitude for reasonable values of supply voltage E_C. Now make R_b about ten times R_e. For transistors with $\beta_F \simeq 100$, this choice suppresses β_F variations in Eq. 13.13 by a factor of about 10 compared to a design with R_e equal to zero, but still allows R_b to be large enough to prevent excessive shunting of the input signal to ground. Next, calculate E_B by summing the voltage drops around the input loop in Fig. 13.12b:

$$E_B = I_B[R_b + (\beta_F + 1)(R_e + r_d)] + V_D \tag{13.15}$$

Equation 13.15 can be solved to find the value of E_B by substituting the appropriate values for I_B and V_D at the operating point for $T = 25°C$. These values can be read directly off the transistor characteristics, if a complete set is available. Otherwise, they can be approximated by noting that $V_D \simeq 0.6$ volt (silicon) and $I_B \simeq I_C/\beta_F$.

The last step is to convert R_b and E_B into the equivalent input network of Fig. 13.12a. To find R_1 and R_2, we solve Eqs. 13.11 and 13.12:

$$R_1 = \frac{E_C}{E_B} R_b \tag{13.16}$$

$$R_2 = \frac{R_1 R_b}{R_1 - R_b} \tag{13.17}$$

13.4.3   Example

To illustrate the "handbook" design procedure, let us choose element values for the circuit of Fig. 13.12a to meet the same specifications as in the example in Section 13.3.2:

Operating point at 25°C: $V_{CE} = 5$ volts, $I_C = 4$ ma
Power supply voltage: $E_C = 10$ volts
Transistor characteristics (Fig. 13.4b):

	$T = 25°C$	$T = 105°C$
β_F	60	118
V_D	0.6 volt	0.44 volt

We first calculate values for R_e, R_b, and E_B, to achieve the desired operating point at 25°C. Assuming that $|I_E R_e| \simeq I_C R_e = 3$ volts, we obtain

$$R_e = \frac{3}{4} = 0.75 \text{ kohm}$$

Using the "handbook" criterion, we find

$$R_b \simeq 10 R_e = 7.5 \text{ kohm}$$

To check on input loading, we compare this value with the transistor input resistance. Because C_e provides a low impedance path from emitter to ground at signal frequencies, the input impedance for signals is $r_x + r_\pi$. At $I_C = 4$ ma

$$r_\pi = \frac{\beta_o}{g_m} \simeq \frac{\beta_F}{g_m} = 60 \times \frac{25}{4} = 375 \text{ ohms}$$

If r_x is assumed to be about 25 ohms, the input resistance of the transistor at signal frequencies is 400 ohms. Clearly, R_b does not significantly shunt the input signal.

From Eq. 13.15,

$$E_B = \frac{4}{60} [7.5 + 61(0.75)] + 0.6 = 4.16 \text{ volts}$$

Application of Eqs. 13.16 and 13.17 yields the desired values of R_1 and R_2 to complete the design:

$$R_1 = \frac{10}{4.16}(7.5) = 18 \text{ kohm}$$

$$R_2 = \frac{18(7.5)}{18 - 7.5} = 12.8 \text{ kohm}$$

Now let us check the bias stability of the circuit by using Eq. 13.13 to calculate the new operating current at 105°C for the element values above:

$$I_C = \frac{118(4.16 - 0.44)}{7.5 + 119(0.75)}$$

$$= 4.54 \text{ ma}$$

As predicted, the 100% increase in bias current that occurred in the simple bias circuit in Section 13.3.2 has been reduced in the more practical bias design of Fig. 13.12a to a modest 13%.[3]

For many bias design problems (e.g., those involving a large range of operating temperature, large variations in β_F, or large output signals) the simple design procedure given above will not yield satisfactory results. Under these conditions, we must carry out in detail the design problem of finding the resistor values required to achieve a certain specified stability of the operating point. This is the subject of the next section.

13.5 Detailed Bias Network Design*
13.5.1 Derivation of Design Equation

In the design of the bias network in Fig. 13.12, we have three unknowns: R_b, R_e, and E_B (or, alternatively, R_1, R_2, and R_e). In Section 13.4.1 we derived the relation between these parameters and the dc collector current:

$$I_C = \frac{\beta_F(E_B - V_D)}{R_b + (\beta_F + 1)(r_d + R_e)} \tag{13.18}$$

If I_C is specified, this equation, together with two additional independent equations, can be used to find the bias network parameters R_b, R_e, and E_B.

A little thought will show that if we specify both a *maximum* and a *minimum* I_C, then Eq. 13.18 provides *two* independent relations for determining the network parameters, one at the minimum temperature T_1 and one at the maximum temperature T_2. For the single-stage biasing circuit in question, I_C will always increase with temperature (see Eq. 13.18). Thus in writing the two equations, the maximum I_C must be associated with the high-temperature

---

[3] For an appropriate lecture demonstration, see Section 13.8.

* In an introductory course, this section and Section 13.6.3 may be omitted without loss of continuity.

β_F and V_D, and the minimum I_C with the corresponding low-temperature values. The two equations can be used to eliminate E_B, leaving us with one equation relating R_b to R_e. We still do not obtain a unique solution, but appropriate values for these resistors can now be found by using some of the other design constraints as guidelines.

Before plunging ahead, let us make two obvious simplifications in Eq. 13.18. For most transistors, β_F is large enough that we can replace $\beta_F + 1$ by β_F. Also, for most bias designs, we will want to use a value of external emitter resistor R_e much bigger than r_d, in order to obtain the desired bias stability. Hence we can neglect r_d. On this basis, if we divide the numerator and denominator of Eq. 13.18 by β_F and then cross-multiply to clear the fraction, we obtain for the low temperature, T_1,

$$I_C(\text{min})\left[\frac{R_b}{\beta_F(T_1)} + R_e\right] = E_B - V_D(T_1) \tag{13.19}$$

At the high temperature, T_2,

$$I_C(\text{max})\left[\frac{R_b}{\beta_F(T_2)} + R_e\right] = E_B - V_D(T_2) \tag{13.20}$$

Subtracting Eq. 13.20 from Eq. 13.19, collecting terms, and solving for R_b, we obtain the desired design equation:

$$R_b = \frac{V_D(T_2) - V_D(T_1) + [I_C(\text{max}) - I_C(\text{min})]R_e}{I_C(\text{min})/\beta_F(T_1) - I_C(\text{max})/\beta_F(T_2)} \tag{13.21}$$

Note that in spite of the seeming complexity, everything on the right-hand side of Eq. 13.21 except R_e is a known constant, so that the equation is no more complicated than

$$R_b = AR_e - B$$

The design is not frozen, however, for we still have two unknowns and only one equation. The trade-offs involved in selecting values of R_e and R_b can best be illustrated by a numerical example.

13.5.2   Example

As in earlier examples, we specify the desired operating point as $V_{CE} = 5$ volts, $I_C = 4$ ma, the temperature range at 25 to 105°C, and the transistor parameters as

	$T_1 = 25°C$	$T_2 = 105°C$
β_F	60	118
V_D	0.6 volt	0.44

In addition, we specify a 10% limit on collector current change with temperature. Thus $I_C(\text{min}) = 4$ ma, $I_C(\text{max}) = 4.4$ ma. Using volts, milliamperes, and kilohms in Eq. 13.21, we obtain

$$R_b = \frac{0.44 - 0.6 + (4.4 - 4.0)R_e}{4.0/60 - 4.4/118}$$

$$= -5.5 + 13.8 R_e$$

Any value of R_e greater than 0.4 kohm will yield positive values of R_b; however, R_b should if possible be greater than 4 kohm to avoid excessive loss of gain (see the gain calculation in Section 13.4.3). Thus a suitable design might be

$$R_b = 4 \text{ kohm}$$

$$R_e = \frac{9.5}{13.8} = 0.69 \text{ kohm}$$

(see Problem P13.2.) The size of R_e is limited by the collector supply voltage and the desired output voltage amplitude, factors that will not be examined further in this example.

13.5.3 Design with Specified Output Signal Amplitude

Some additional calculations are needed if the design is specified in terms of the maximum output signal amplitude rather than the maximum and minimum dc collector current. Specifying the swing is tantamount to specifying the currents, but it takes a modest amount of analysis to establish the interrelation. Recall that in Section 13.1 limits were placed on collector current and collector voltage to ensure operation in the forward active region. Specifically, the total instantaneous collector current i_C must always be greater than zero, to keep the emitter diode always in forward bias. Also, the total instantaneous collector voltage v_{CE} must always be greater than about 0.5 volt to keep the transistor out of saturation. From these limits and the specified output amplitude we can calculate the maximum and minimum I_C.

We first calculate the consequences of the limit on i_C. For sinusoidal signals, the collector current in Fig. 13.12 is made up of two orthogonal components:

$$i_C = I_C + I_c \sin \omega t \qquad (13.22)$$

Rewriting this expression in terms of the peak signal voltage V_o, and including the current constraint stated above, we obtain

$$i_C = \left(I_C + \frac{V_o}{R_L} \sin \omega t \right) > 0 \qquad (13.23)$$

Thus we obtain an expression for the minimum dc bias current in terms of output signal amplitude:

$$I_C > \frac{V_o}{R_L} \qquad (13.24)$$

This same concept is shown graphically in Fig. 13.13, in which dc load lines (white) and ac load lines (black) have been superimposed on a set of common-emitter output characteristics. The length of the ac load line has been chosen here to represent the peak-to-peak excursions of the sinusoidal output voltage and current. Also, the operating point has been chosen so that i_C just goes to zero once in each cycle. Clearly, the operating point cannot be moved farther down on the load line without forcing the transistor into cutoff for a portion of the cycle, and thus causing distortion of the output waveform.

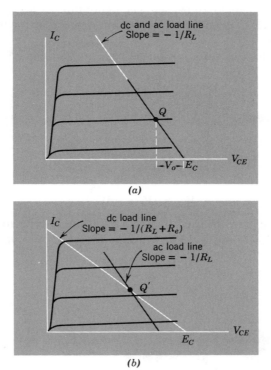

(a)

(b)

Figure 13.13   Load lines for calculating the minimum collector current. Transistor characteristics measured at 25°C.

Figure 13.13a illustrates a simple case in which R_e is zero, hence the ac and dc load lines are identical. From the geometry of the figure it is clear that for the operating point Q adjusted as shown, the bias current must be such that

$$I_C = \frac{V_o}{R_L} \tag{13.25}$$

Even with R_e present in the circuit, the load-line construction in Fig. 13.13b is basically similar to that discussed above. The equation relating the dc network parameters in the collector-emitter loop is, from Fig. 13.12,

$$V_{CE} = E_C - I_C R_L + I_E R_e \qquad (13.26)$$

Because I_E is very nearly equal to $-I_C$, this equation can be rewritten as

$$V_{CE} \simeq E_C - I_C(R_L + R_e) \qquad (13.27)$$

indicating that the dc load line in Fig. 13.13b should have a slope equal to $-1/(R_L + R_e)$ and a horizontal axis intercept of E_C. The ac load line, on the other hand, still has a slope of $-1/R_L$, since C_e is assumed to have almost zero impedance at signal frequencies. The figure thus shows that even with R_e present, Eq. 13.25 is still the appropriate expression for minimum dc collector current.

We turn next to the limitation on dc collector current imposed by the constraint

$$v_{CE} > 0.5 \text{ volt} \qquad (13.28)$$

For sinusoidal signals, the collector voltage is made up of two orthogonal components:

$$v_{CE} = V_{CE} - V_o \sin \omega t \qquad (13.29)$$

Combining Eqs. 13.28 and 13.29, we obtain the constraint

$$V_{CE} > (V_o + 0.5) \qquad (13.30)$$

This condition can be converted to a constraint on dc collector current by substituting for V_{CE} from Eq. 13.27. On solving for I_C, we obtain

$$I_C < \frac{E_C - (V_o + 0.5)}{R_L + R_e} \qquad (13.31)$$

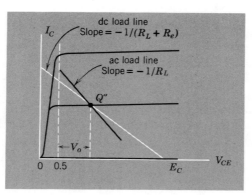

Figure 13.14   Load lines for calculating the maximum I_C. Transistor characteristics measured at 105°C.

It is helpful to visualize in terms of a graphical load-line construction the constraint imposed by Eqs. 13.30 and 13.31. The ac load line in Fig. 13.14 has been located on the output characteristics so that the instantaneous collector voltage v_{CE} just drops down to about 0.5 volt once in each cycle, thereby just maintaining linear operation. Clearly, the operating point cannot be moved farther up the load line without causing the transistor to saturate for one part of the cycle and thus distorting the output waveform. The condition imposed on V_{CE} by Eq. 13.30 is now obvious from the figure. If desired, Eq. 13.31 can be derived from the geometry of the figure.

To summarize, for bias design problems in which the maximum output signal voltage V_o is one of the specified parameters, the corresponding constraints on maximum and minimum dc collector current are

$$I_C(\text{min}) = \frac{V_o}{R_L} \tag{13.32}$$

$$I_C(\text{max}) = \frac{E_C - (V_o + 0.5)}{R_L + R_e} \tag{13.33}$$

13.5.4 Example

Suppose that we wish to design an amplifier circuit that must be capable of developing an 8-volt peak-to-peak sinusoidal voltage across a 500-ohm load resistor, using a power supply voltage of 11 volts. For simplicity, we use the same transistor specifications as in Section 13.5.2. From Eq. 13.32,

$$I_C(\text{min}) = \frac{4}{0.5} = 8 \text{ ma}$$

and from Eq. 13.33,

$$I_C(\text{max}) = \frac{11 - (4.5)}{0.5 + R_e} \text{ ma}$$

Unfortunately, R_e is one of the parameters we are trying to find. We could substitute Eqs. 13.32 and 13.33 into Eq. 13.21 and solve the resulting expression, which is quadratic in R_e in the numerator and linear in R_e in the denominator. However, a trial-and-error solution seems more appropriate. Note first that the two equations provide an upper bound on R_e, because $I_C(\text{max})$ must be greater than $I_C(\text{min})$. Hence the limiting case is

$$\frac{11 - 4.5}{0.5 + R_e} = 8$$

$$R_e(\text{max}) = 0.31 \text{ kohm}$$

For this value of R_e, $I_C(\text{max})$ equals $I_C(\text{min})$, so that perfect bias stabilization is required—an impossible condition for this circuit. On the other hand, we have already seen in Section 13.3 that the design conditions may be difficult to meet for $R_e = 0$. Hence a reasonable first try is $R_e = 0.15$ kohm, for which we have

$$I_C(\text{max}) = \frac{6.5}{0.5 + 0.15} = 10 \text{ ma}$$

Now substituting these values and the transistor parameters from Section 13.5.2 into Eq. 13.21, we obtain

$$R_b = \frac{0.44 - 0.6 + (10 - 8)0.15}{8/60 - 10/118}$$

$$= 2.9 \, \text{kohm}$$

This design meets the stability requirements, and R_b will cause less than 10% decrease in the current gain of the stage. The values of the actual bias resistors R_1 and R_2 (Fig. 13.12a) can now be found from Eqs. 13.16, 13.17, and 13.15 (neglecting r_d).

For those who wish to squeeze the last drop of performance out of the circuit, it is possible by repeated solution of the design example to plot a curve of R_b versus R_e, as shown in Fig. 13.15. For the particular specifications and parameters, a broad maximum in the curve is observed, indicating that the circuit can be adequately stabilized without excessive loss in current gain for any value of R_e lying between 70 and 200 ohms.

In the light of Fig. 13.15, it is now clear that a good initial guess for R_e is a value about one half of the upper bound on R_e (see Prob. P13.3). Note, however, that the curve is not always of this shape. If the specifications are

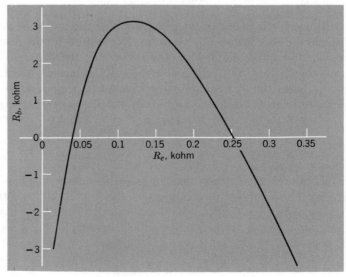

Figure 13.15 Plot of R_b versus R_e.

less stringent, the R_b curve may go to infinity for some value of R_e, or it may monotonically increase for decreasing R_e. (See Section 13.6.3, Fig. 13.18, and Problem P13.4.) In these cases an initial guess of one half of the maximum R_e is still appropriate, but larger values of R_b, with correspondingly less reduction in current gain, may result for $R_e = 0$.

The values of R_b calculated from Eq. 13.21 and plotted in Fig. 13.15 are limiting values, because in the solution we used limiting values of I_C, rather than the set of allowed values implied by Eqs. 13.24 and 13.31. By keeping these inequalities in the derivation, it can be shown that the curve in Fig. 13.15 is in fact an *upper bound* on R_b. That is, any value of R_b *less than that plotted* meets the stability specification of the circuit. Such values of R_b correspond to designs in which I_C does not rise as high as the limiting value $I_C(\max)$ at the high-temperature limit.

13.5.5   Parameter Variation because of Manufacturing Tolerance

The preceding discussion on transistor biasing was phrased in terms of variations of β_F and V_D with temperature. However, all of the design methods apply equally well to the problem of obtaining satisfactory circuit performance in spite of the spread in β_F and V_D in a given transistor type resulting from manufacturing tolerances. The problem is obviously of considerable importance in the design of any circuit that must be produced in quantity.

The important difference between this problem and the temperature problem is that now the changes in β_F and V_D are no longer correlated. However, examination of Eq. 13.13, the general relation for I_C in terms of the circuit parameters, indicates that the *worst case*, that is, the maximum increase in I_C, occurs when β_F goes up and V_D goes down. This is precisely the case that we studied in connection with temperature variations. Thus we conclude that design expressions such as Eq. 13.21 can be directly applied to the problem of parameter tolerance, provided that we reinterpret $\beta_F(T_2)$ and $\beta_F(T_1)$ to be the maximum and minimum values of β_F as specified in the data sheet. Also, we must similarly redefine $V_D(T_1)$ and $V_D(T_2)$, although variations of this parameter among transistors of a given type should be minimal. The other design methods of Sections 13.3 and 13.4 are also directly applicable to this problem, as are the germanium bias designs to be discussed in the next section.

13.6   Bias Design for Germanium Transistors*
13.6.1   Derivation of Bias Equations

In Sections 13.2, 13.3, and 13.4, three methods for designing silicon transistor biasing networks were developed. The bias design problem for germanium transistors, though in principle the same as that for silicon, is in fact somewhat

---

* The use of germanium transistors has decreased markedly in the past few years because of the advent of inexpensive silicon devices. Therefore, this section has been written in such a way that it can be omitted without loss of continuity. To obtain the bias equations for a *pnp* silicon device, set I_{co} to zero in Eqs. 13.36 and 13.37.

more complicated, because I_{CO} becomes an important temperature-dependent element in the transistor model. The temperature dependence of I_{CO} is *exponential*, in contrast to the approximately linear dependence for β_F and $V_D(T)$, so that the variation of I_{CO} is often the dominant problem in germanium transistors.

The I_{CO} problem can be quickly brought into focus by noting that the collector current in the total-variable model for a germanium *pnp* transistor[4] (Fig. 13.16) is

$$I_C = \beta_F I_B - (\beta_F + 1)I_{CO} \tag{13.34}$$

If we use a bias network of the type shown in Fig. 13.11, in which the base current is held almost constant, Eq. 13.34 indicates that the exponential increase in I_{CO} with temperature will result in a corresponding change in I_C, compounded by the increase in β_F. For a typical germanium transistor, I_{CO} will be of the order of 1 μa at 25°C and 60 μa at 85°C, so that the term $(\beta_F + 1)I_{CO}$ in Eq. 13.34 will surely become a significant, even dominant, part of the collector current within this temperature range. Thus we conclude that any bias circuit for germanium transistors that keeps the base current constant will have intolerably bad bias stability.

We therefore turn directly to the bias circuit in Fig. 13.17, which, because of the presence of R_e, does *not* keep base current constant. To find I_C in terms of the circuit parameters, we first write the equation for the input loop:

$$E_B = -I_B[R_b + (\beta_F + 1)R_e] + R_e(\beta_F + 1)I_{CO} + V_D \tag{13.35}$$

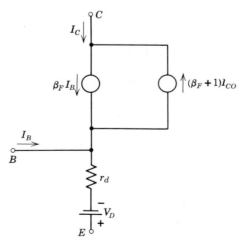

Figure 13.16   Active-region total-variable model for a germanium *pnp* transistor.

---

[4] The change to a *pnp* transistor at this point is *independent* of the change to germanium. Rather, the switch was made to document the changes of sign in the bias equations that result when the analysis is done in terms of *pnp* transistors.

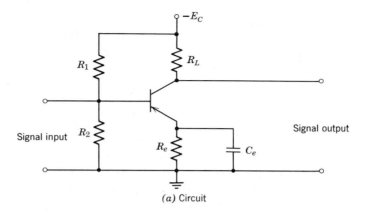

(a) Circuit

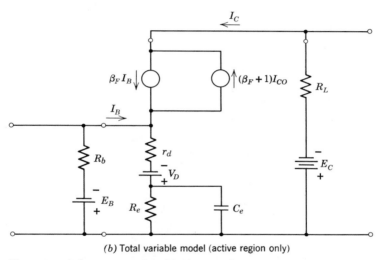

(b) Total variable model (active region only)

Figure 13.17.   Bias network for a germanium bipolar transistor.

(We have assumed at the outset that R_e is much larger than r_d). Eliminating I_B between Eqs. 13.34 and 13.35, we obtain (see Problem P13.5)

$$-I_C = \frac{\beta_F[E_B - V_D] + (\beta_F + 1)I_{CO}(R_b + R_e)}{R_b + (\beta_F + 1)R_e} \qquad (13.36)$$

13.6.2   Handbook Design Example

Surprisingly enough, the "handbook design" method discussed in Section 13.4.2 also works reasonably well for germanium transistors, as can be seen from the following numerical example.

We wish to design the circuit in Fig. 13.17 to have a room-temperature operating point of $V_{CE} = -5$ volt, $I_C = -4$ ma. The temperature range is specified as 25 to 75°C. The characteristics of the germanium transistor over the range are as follows:

$$\beta_F(25°) = 100, \qquad \beta_F(75°) = 120$$

$$I_{CO}(25°) = 1 \; \mu a$$

$$V_D(25°) = 0.2 \text{ volt}$$

(The β_F is not as temperature-dependent in germanium as it is in silicon, as can be seen from the plots of β_o versus temperature, Fig. 12.12.) We first design for the desired operating point at 25°C. Assuming a 4-volt drop across R_e, we have

$$R_e \simeq \frac{4}{|I_c|} = 1 \text{ kohm}$$

Thus

$$R_b \simeq 10 \, R_e = 10 \text{ kohm}$$

For this value of R_b, input loading will not be important (see Problem P13.6).
To find E_B from Eq. 13.35, we need I_B. It is clear from Eq. 13.34 and the given value of I_{CO} that at 25°C

$$I_B \simeq \frac{I_C}{\beta_F} = \frac{-4}{100} = -0.04 \text{ ma}$$

Hence from Eq. 13.35

$$E_B = 0.04(10 + 101) + 101(0.001) + 0.2$$

$$= 4.74 \text{ volts}$$

The values of R_1 and R_2 in Fig. 13.17a can be found from Eqs. 13.16 and 13.17.
To find the bias stability of the "handbook" design, we calculate the new operating current at 75°C. Assuming that I_{CO} doubles every 10°C and V_D changes by about -2 mv/°C, we find

$$I_{CO}(75°) = 32 \; \mu a$$

$$V_D(75°) = 0.1 \text{ volt}$$

Substituting these values into Eq. 13.36, we have

$$-I_C = \frac{120(4.74 - 0.1) + 11(121)0.032}{10 + (121)(1)}$$

$$I_C = -4.57 \text{ ma}$$

which represents a 14% increase in bias current.

13.6.3 Detailed Bias Network Design Example for Germanium *(pnp)*[*]

If the "handbook design" does not provide satisfactory bias stability, we can use the more sophisticated design method outlined in Section 13.5. By specifying the maximum and minimum allowable collector current, we can obtain from Eqs. 13.36 a bias design relation for germanium *pnp* transistors (see Problem P13.7):

$$R_b = \frac{V_D(T_1) - V_D(T_2) + [I_C(\text{max}) - I_C(\text{min}) + \Delta I_{CO}]R_e}{I_C(\text{min})/\beta_F(T_1) - I_C(\text{max})/\beta_F(T_2) - \Delta I_{CO}} \tag{13.37}$$

where

$$\Delta I_{CO} = I_{CO}(T_2) - I_{CO}(T_1) \tag{13.38}$$

These equations, together with Eqs. 13.35, 13.16, and 13.17, are sufficient to design the resistive bias network of Fig. 13.17. (The corresponding equations for an *npn* germanium transistor are given in Problem P13.8.)

To illustrate, suppose that we wish to calculate the values of resistors R_1, R_2, and R_e in Fig. 13.17, assuming that $R_L = 500$ ohms and $E_C = 10$ volts. Also, assume that the circuit must be capable of developing a 3-volt peak sinusoidal output voltage over a temperature range of 25 to 65°C. The transistor specifications are:

$$\beta_F(25°) = 45, \qquad \beta_F(65°) = 65$$

$$I_{CO}(25°) = 1 \ \mu a$$

$$V_D(25°) = 0.2 \ \text{volt}$$

On the basis that I_{CO} in germanium doubles every 10°C and V_D decreases by 2 mv/°C, we find at $T = 65°C$ that

$$I_{CO}(65°) = 16 \ \mu a$$

$$V_D(65°) = 0.12 \ \text{volt}$$

Using Eqs. 13.32 and 13.33 (with a change in sign because of the *pnp* transistor in this example), we find

$$I_C(\text{min}) = -\frac{V_o}{R_L} = -\frac{3}{0.5} = -6 \ \text{ma}$$

$$I_C(\text{max}) = -\frac{E_C - (V_o + 0.5)}{R_L + R_e} = -\frac{6.5}{0.5 + R_e} \ \text{ma}$$

The maximum value of R_e in this equation is that for which $I_C(\text{max})$ equals $I_C(\text{min})$. Thus

$$R_e(\text{max}) = \frac{6.5}{6} - 0.5 = 0.58 \ \text{kohm}$$

[*] This subsection should be omitted if Section 13.5 was omitted.

A reasonable first guess for R_e is half of this value, that is, $R_e = 0.3$ kohm, from which we have

$$I_C(\text{max}) = -8.1 \text{ ma}$$

$$R_b = \frac{0.2 - 0.12 + (-8.1 + 6 + 0.015)0.3}{-6/45 + 8.1/65 - 0.015}$$

$$= 23.7 \text{ kohm}$$

To complete the design, we use Eqs. 13.35, 13.16, and 13.17 to find that

$$R_1 = 46 \text{ kohm}$$

$$R_2 = 49 \text{ kohm}$$

Many other designs are possible, depending on the initial assumption of the value of R_e. These designs are summarized in Fig. 13.18, in which the values of R_b calculated from Eq. 13.37 are plotted against the assumed values of R_e. The rather surprising shape of this curve requires some explanation. First, recall that we used the *limiting* values of I_C in evaluating Eq. 13.37, hence the curve gives the limiting value of R_b that will meet the design specifications. It can be shown that in region A, the curve is a *lower* bound. That is, any (positive) value for R_b greater than the graphed value in this

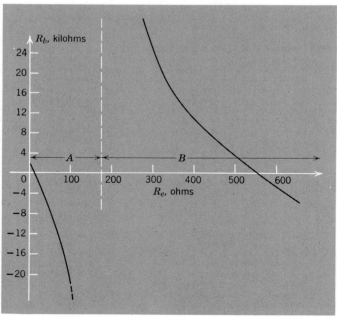

Figure 13.18   Plot of R_b versus R_e.

region is acceptable (subject to any specification on the minimum current gain of the circuit). In region B, the curve is an *upper bound*.

Note that the specifications are sufficiently easy to meet in this example, so that the circuit can be stabilized for $R_e = 0$. In fact, for R_e about 100 ohms, the circuit has to be *destabilized* by making R_b negative in order to get to the upper limit of I_C.

13.7 Biasing Other Transistor Circuit Configurations
13.7.1 Common-Base

If the base of a common-base stage is grounded, both a positive and a negative power supply are required for biasing, as shown in Fig. 13.19a. To avoid the expense of two supplies, we can use a voltage divider to set the base at a few volts from ground, (positive for this *npn* transistor), as shown in Fig. 13.19b. To maintain common-base operation at signal frequencies, the base is by-passed to ground by capacitor C_b. Comparison of Fig. 13.19b with the

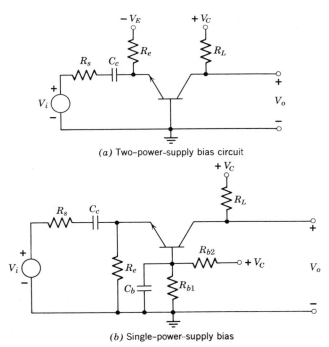

(a) Two–power–supply bias circuit

(b) Single–power–supply bias

Figure 13.19   Bias network for bipolar common-base amplifiers.

common-emitter circuit in Fig. 13.12 indicates that the two bias networks are topologically identical. Hence all of the analysis and design methods discussed in this chapter apply virtually unchanged to the common-base bias network in Fig. 13.19b (see Problem P13.9).

13.7.2   Common-Drain and Common-Collector

Typical biasing arrangements for the two "follower" circuits are shown in Fig. 13.20. In each case it is necessary to set the input terminal at some fixed potential above ground to achieve the desired operating point. Note that the topology of these bias networks is identical to the common-emitter networks already discussed, so that the same design techniques can be applied here (see Problem P13.10).

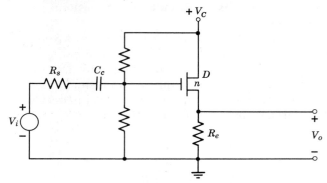

(a) FET source follower (common–drain)

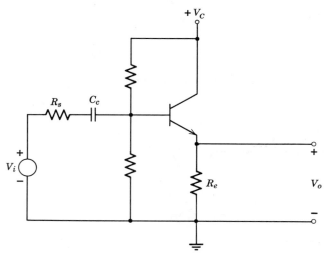

(b) Bipolar emitter follower (common–collector)

Figure 13.20   Bias networks for "follower" circuits.

13.8   Lecture Demonstrations

13.8.1   Selection of Operating Point

By using dual-trace amplifiers in both the x and y axes of a plug-in oscilloscope, it is possible to display simultaneously transistor characteristics and a load line. In this way the effects on amplifier performance of changes in ambient temperature can be demonstrated. The circuit is shown in Fig. 13.21. The staircase and ramp waveforms needed for generating the common-emitter output characteristics of T_1 on the screen of the Tektronix Type 561 oscilloscope are obtained from the transistor curve tracer.

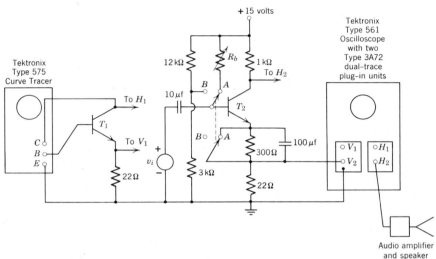

Figure 13.21   Lecture demonstration on biasing.

Transistors T_1 and T_2 (the transistor being biased) should have closely matched characteristics and should be thermally bonded together. Clearly, a dual transistor is ideal.

With the switch in position A, the bias circuit is as described in Section 13.31, hence is quite unstable, whereas when the switch is in position B the circuit is well stabilized.

Observe first only the output characteristics by operating only H_1 and V_1. Then with the switch at A, observe the "load line" (v_i large), the operating point ($v_i = 0$), and the locus of signal swing (v_i moderate). The line plotted is not quite a true load line, because the 22-ohm resistor is measuring emitter current rather than collector current. This is particularly noticeable in saturation.

Now turn on the audio amplifier, and adjust the bias resistor to demonstrate the effects of too little, optimum, and too much dc collector current.

13.8.2   Effect of Temperature on Transistor Biasing

Using the same circuit as above, Fig. 13.21, set the switch to position A, turn on the audio amplifier, and heat the pair of transistors gently. The characteristics will move because of increasing β_F, and for germanium transistors, because of increasing I_{CO}. With constant-base-current biasing, the operating point and signal locus will move in step with the characteristics. Eventually, saturation-region operation will result. Cool off the transistors (aerosol spray freezing solutions are helpful here) to show that the trip has been nondestructive. If desired, the cycle can be repeated, this time observing the output signal, that is, the collector voltage of T_2, as a function of time.

Now switch to position B to make the circuit well stabilized, and heat. This time the characteristics behave as before, but the operating point moves only a small amount. For germanium transistors the base current may well reverse, so that the base step polarity on the curve tracer should be switched from positive to negative several times during the run.

PROBLEMS

P13.1   Prove that r_π in a silicon transistor can be kept fairly constant as the temperature is varied by biasing so that I_B stays constant. (See page 444.)

P13.2   Design a bias circuit for a silicon transistor that will keep the operating point within 5% of 10 ma over a temperature range of 25 to 150°C. Assume that β_F varies from 100 to 200 over this range. (See page 458.)

P13.3   Design a bias circuit using the same transistor and temperature range as in Problem P13.2 to accommodate a 6-volt peak-to-peak output signal amplitude across a 1-kohm load resistor, using a 10.5-volt power supply. (See page 462.)

P13.4   Solve Problem P13.3 for several different values of R_e (on a computer, if possible), hence plot a curve of R_b versus R_e for this design. Identify clearly the allowed values of R_b and R_e. (See page 463.)

P13.5   Starting with Eqs. 13.34 and 13.35, derive Eq. 13.36.

P13.6   For the germanium transistor bias design discussed in Section 13.6.2, estimate the incremental input resistance of the transistor at the specified operating point. Use this value to estimate the reduction in current gain of the circuit caused by the presence of resistor R_b. (See page 466.)

P13.7   Following the method outlined in Section 13.5, verify Eq. 13.37.

P13.8   Redraw Fig. 13.17 so that it represents the bias network for a germanium *npn* transistor. Analyze this circuit to prove that the appropriate bias design equations analagous to Eqs. 13.37 and 13.35 in this case are

$$R_b = \frac{V_D(T_2) - V_D(T_1) + [I_C(\max) - I_C(\min) - \Delta I_{CO}]R_e}{I_C(\min)/\beta_F(T_1) - I_C(\max)/\beta_F(T_2) + \Delta I_{CO}} \qquad (13.37)$$

$$E_B = I_B[R_b + (\beta_F + 1)R_e] + R_e(\beta_F + 1)I_{CO} + V_D \qquad (13.38)$$

P13.9   Design the common-base bias network shown in Fig. 13.19 so that it is possible to obtain a 3-volt peak-to-peak swing across the load resistor R_L from 25 to 125°C. Assume that $R_L = 300$ ohms, $V_C = 5$ volts. The silicon transistor has a β_F of 75 at 25°C, and 130 at 125°C.

P13.10   Design bias networks for the two follower circuits in Fig. 13.20 so that each can produce an output signal V_o of 4 volts, peak-to-peak, from 25 to 125°C. Assume that $R_e = 100$ ohms, $V_C = 6$ volts, and the transistor parameters are as in Problem P13.9, and Fig. 13.5.

CHAPTER FOURTEEN

Low-Frequency and High-Frequency Response Calculations

14.1 Coupling Capacitors

To achieve satisfactory performance from the single-stage amplifiers discussed in Chapter 13, it is often necessary to add a coupling capacitor to the network, as shown in the simple bias circuits in Figs. 14.1a and b. The

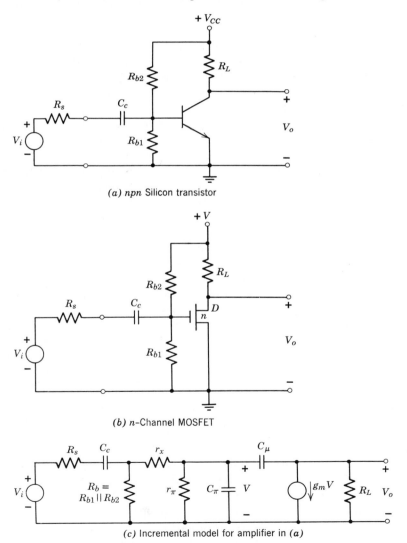

(a) npn Silicon transistor

(b) n-Channel MOSFET

(c) Incremental model for amplifier in (a)

Figure 14.1 Typical single-stage amplifiers.

coupling capacitor C_c couples the signal into the amplifier input but prevents the signal source (or previous transistor circuit) from upsetting the dc voltage established by the bias network. Because of the obvious similarity between these two circuits, we shall phrase the initial discussion in terms of the bipolar transistor only, realizing that the same conclusions also apply to the FET circuit.

14.1.1 Bipolar Transistor Circuit Models with Restricted Frequency Range
The incremental circuit model for the *npn* transistor amplifier of Fig. 14.1*a* is shown in Fig. 14.1*c*. This network is sufficiently complicated that a calculation of the transfer function in full generality would be tedious and relatively unrewarding. A given numerical problem could, of course, be solved on a computer, using the methods to be discussed in the next chapter, but this would give little insight into network design, our principal concern.

Fortunately, in active circuits the design problem is often easier than the analysis problem, because the design specification gives *a priori* knowledge about certain aspects of the circuit. In the present case, we are trying to design a common-emitter amplifier, and such an amplifier will have a specified range of frequencies over which the transfer function V_o/V_i must be nearly constant. For example, in an audio amplifier, the specification might call for constant gain from 20 Hz to 20 kHz; a video amplifier might be "flat" from 100 kHz to 6 MHz. As long as this so called *midfrequency range* is at least a few decades wide, all the capacitors in Fig. 14.1*c* must have no effect on the distribution of network currents and voltages over most of the range. It follows that we must be able to abstract from the figure a circuit model applicable only over this midfrequency range in which each capacitor is replaced by either a short circuit or open circuit.[1] We know from Chapter 11 that C_π and C_μ are relatively small capacitors (1 to 1000 pf). Thus over the midfrequency range, the impedances of C_π and C_μ will be small enough compared to adjacent circuit impedances to appear like open circuits. Also, the coupling capacitor C_c must in the midrange be large enough to appear like a short circuit, because if it were an open circuit, the gain would be zero. Thus we abstract from Fig. 14.1*c* the *midfrequency incremental circuit model* of Fig. 14.2*a* by short-circuiting C_c and open-circuiting C_π and C_μ.

As the frequency is increased above the midrange, C_c is still a short circuit, but the gain begins to fall off because of the effects of C_π and C_μ. An appropriate circuit model is shown in Fig. 14.2*b*.

As the frequency is decreased below the midrange, the amplifier output voltage is going to fall, because the impedance of C_c becomes increasingly large compared to adjacent circuit impedances as we go down in frequency. Capacitors C_π and C_μ appeared as open circuits in the midrange, hence

---

[1] An all-pass network can have reactive elements and still have a constant response magnitude, but the present circuit does not have this configuration.

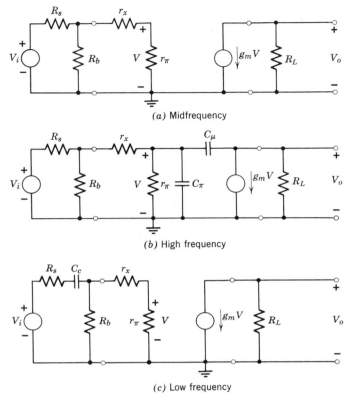

(a) Midfrequency

(b) High frequency

(c) Low frequency

Figure 14.2 Incremental circuit models for a single-stage bipolar transistor amplifier in Fig. 14.1a, applicable over restricted frequency ranges. In each case $R_b = R_{b1} \| R_{b2}$.

continue to appear as open circuits in the low-frequency range. The low-frequency circuit model of Fig. 14.2c reflects these facts.

14.1.2 FET Circuit Models with Restricted Frequency Range

The preceding analysis, although phrased in terms of a bipolar transistor amplifier, is applicable almost verbatim to FET amplifiers. Specifically, it is possible to use the same reasoning as above to obtain the midfrequency, high-frequency, and low-frequency circuit models for a single-stage FET amplifier, as shown in Fig. 14.3.

In the first part of this chapter we concentrate on various aspects of the low-frequency design problem: how to select coupling capacitors (and, later, emitter and source bypass capacitors) to obtain some specified low-frequency response. In the second half of the chapter we discuss methods of analysis and design associated with the high-frequency performance of transistor circuits. Because the FET has virtually infinite input impedance at

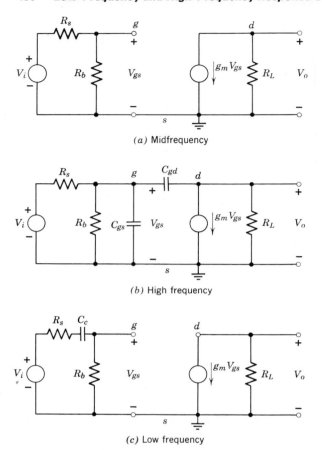

(a) Midfrequency

(b) High frequency

(c) Low frequency

Figure 14.3   Circuit models for the FET amplifier in Fig. 14.1b, applicable over restricted frequency ranges. In each case $R_b = R_{b1} \| R_{b2}$.

low frequencies, the FET circuit (Fig. 14.3c) is somewhat simpler than the corresponding bipolar transistor circuit (Fig. 14.2c). Thus we start the design discussion in terms of the FET circuit.

14.1.3   Selection of C_c for Common-Source FET Amplifier
To find the design relations for C_c in Fig. 14.1b, we first find the low-frequency transfer function V_o/V_i. By inspection of Fig. 14.3c, we have

$$V_{gs} = \frac{R_b}{R_b + R_s + 1/sC_c} V_i \tag{14.1}$$

and

$$V_o = -g_m V_{gs} R_L \tag{14.2}$$

Combining Eqs. 14.1 and 14.2, we obtain

$$\frac{V_o}{V_i} = -\left(\frac{R_b}{R_b + R_s}\right)g_m R_L \left(\frac{s}{s + 1/(R_b + R_s)C_c}\right) \tag{14.3}$$

The selection of C_c to obtain a specified low-frequency 0.707 point[2] ω_l is now obvious. Equation 14.3 has a single pole at

$$s_a = \frac{-1}{(R_b + R_s)C_c} \tag{14.4}$$

and for single-pole functions

$$\omega_l = |s_a| \tag{14.5}$$

Thus to achieve a given low-frequency response,

$$C_c = \frac{1}{\omega_l(R_b + R_s)} \tag{14.6}$$

14.1.4   Example: Common-Source Amplifier

We wish to determine the value of C_c in Fig. 14.1b such that the magnitude of the voltage gain V_o/V_i of the amplifier is down to 0.707 of the midfrequency value at 50 Hz. We assume that from previous gain and bias calculations we have the following transistor and bias network parameters:

$$R_s = 50\text{ kohm} \qquad g_m = 1\text{ mmho}$$
$$R_b = 500\text{ kohm} \qquad R_L = 100\text{ kohm}$$

The required value of C_c is, from Eq. 14.6 (in kilohms, microfarads, and milliseconds),

$$C_c = \frac{1}{2\pi \times 0.050(500 + 50)}$$

$$= 0.0058\ \mu\text{f}$$

If we wish to plot the frequency response, we need to calculate the mid-frequency gain, that is, the constant in Eq. 14.3:

$$A_o = \frac{V_o}{V_i}(\text{midfrequency}) = -\left(\frac{R_b}{R_b + R_s}\right)g_m R_L \tag{14.7}$$

$$= -\frac{500}{550} \times 100 \times 1$$

$$= -91$$

[2] The frequency where the magnitude of an output voltage or current has dropped to 0.707 of its midfrequency value is called the *0.707 frequency* or the *0.707 point*, or the *break frequency*, or the *band edge*. With a resistive load, the output power of such a circuit has dropped to $(0.707)^2 = 0.5$ of its midfrequency value at this frequency, thus the 0.707 frequency is also called the *half-power frequency*, or the *3 db frequency*. For review material on these matters, and on the matter of calculating transfer functions and natural frequencies both formally and by inspection, see References 14.1, 14.2, or 14.3.

The pole-zero plot and the plots of magnitude and phase of V_o/V_i are shown in Figs. 14.4a and b. To illustrate the performance of the network in the time domain, we show in Fig. 14.4c the response of the circuit to a 1-mv step of voltage. This response could be found by solving the differential equation

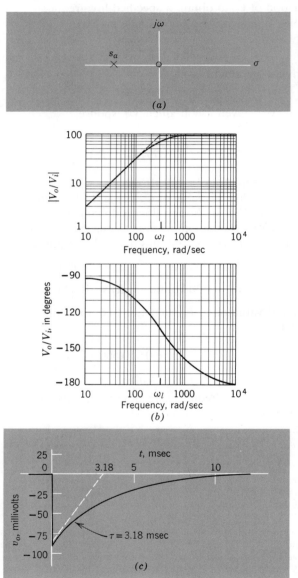

Figure 14.4   (a) Pole-zero pattern, (b) frequency response, and (c) step response for circuit in Fig. 14.3c.

for the network with a unit step applied at the input or by applying Laplace transform methods to Eq. 14.3. However, for this simple single-pole problem, the response can be found by inspection. The capacitor will appear as a short circuit to the sudden step, so that the initial step in the output will be A_o times the input step. Thus a 1-mv input step will cause an initial output step of -91 mv. The final value of the output response will be zero, and the time constant will be

$$\tau = \frac{1}{|s_a|}$$

Hence, from Eq. 14.5,

$$\tau = \frac{1}{\omega_l} = \frac{1}{0.314} = 3.18 \text{ msec}$$

It is often convenient to measure the low-frequency performance of an amplifier by measuring its step response. This is usually done by applying a low-frequency square wave, as illustrated in Fig. 14.5. The exponential decay in the square-wave response has a time constant τ; hence this decay or "droop" can be used to find τ, s_a, and ω_l. Figure 14.5 can also be used to calculate the size of coupling capacitor required to amplify a square wave without introducing excessive droop (see Problem P14.1).

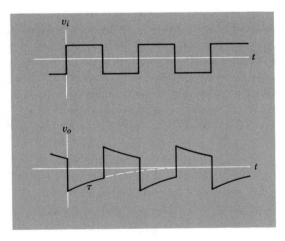

Figure 14.5 Square-wave response.

14.1.5 Selection of C_c in the Bipolar Transistor Amplifier

We could find the appropriate design equation for C_c in the bipolar transistor amplifier of Fig. 14.1a by calculating directly the low-frequency transfer function, as in Section 14.1.4. However, to illustrate another useful analysis technique, we use a slightly different approach. We first find the general form of the low-frequency transfer function by inspection[2] and then calculate the pole directly. To find the general form of the transfer function, we note first that the low-frequency circuit model (Fig. 14.6) has only one capacitor, hence this network has only one natural frequency. At zero frequency the gain goes to zero because C_c will become an open circuit (that is why it is in the circuit: to isolate the dc bias voltage from the voltage source V_i). At "high" frequencies (i.e., the midfrequency range of the complete circuit) the gain of the network is constant. To produce this asymptotic behavior, we need a function of the form

$$\frac{V_o}{V_i} = \frac{A_o s}{s - s_b} \tag{14.8}$$

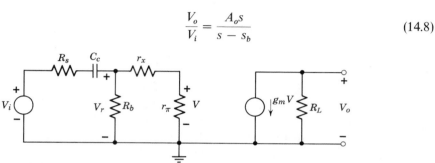

Figure 14.6 Low-frequency incremental circuit model for the transistor circuit shown in Fig. 14.1*a*.

We can find the natural frequency s_b by exploiting the following definition: A natural frequency is that complex frequency which will give rise to a zero of admittance measured across the terminals of any connected part of the network.[3] Thus if we write the expression for the admittance appearing between the terminals of capacitor C_c and set this admittance equal to zero, we obtain

$$s_b C_c + \frac{1}{R_s + R_b \| (r_x + r_\pi)} = 0$$

Solving for the natural frequency, we find that

$$s_b = - \frac{1}{C_c [R_s + R_b \| (r_x + r_\pi)]} \tag{14.9}$$

Because we again have a single-pole transfer function, ω_l is equal to $|s_b|$; hence from Eq. 14.9 the design equation for C_c to produce a given low-frequency 0.707 point ω_l is

$$C_c = \frac{1}{\omega_l [R_s + R_b \| (r_x + r_\pi)]} \tag{14.10}$$

---

[3] The qualifier "connected" is required here because of the problem of *separate parts* of a network. In Fig. 14.6, for example, the generator $g_m V$ and R_L form a separate part, because in this model they are not coupled back to the input circuit. Thus the natural frequency arising from C_c cannot be calculated by looking for a zero of admittance across R_L.

If the complete low-frequency transfer function is desired, we must calculate the constant A_o in Eq. 14.8. From this equation it is clear that A_o is the voltage gain of the network at a frequency high enough so that s is much larger than $|s_b|$, or, in other words, at a frequency where C_c appears as a short circuit. Thus the constant A_o is just the midfrequency voltage gain of the original circuit. By taking the Thévenin equivalent of V_i, R_s, and R_b with C_c shorted, we find that

$$A_o = \frac{V_o}{V_i}(\text{midfrequency}) = -\left(\frac{R_b}{R_b + R_s}\right)\left(\frac{r_\pi}{r_\pi + r_x + R_b\|R_s}\right)g_m R_L \quad (14.11)$$

Substitution of Eqs. 14.9 and 14.11 into Eq. 14.8 will yield the complete voltage gain expression for the network in Fig. 14.6 (see Problem P14.2).

Because this circuit is so similar to the FET circuit in Sections 14.1.3 and 14.1.4, numerical calculations have been relegated to the problems (see Problem P14.3).

14.2   Emitter or Source-to-Ground Bypass Capacitor

As we saw in Chapter 13, it is often necessary to add a resistor in series with the emitter lead of a transistor (or source lead of an FET) to achieve satisfactory bias stabilization. If both positive and negative power supply voltages are available, then the circuit configuration shown in Fig. 14.7a is often used. Such an arrangement is particularly convenient for amplifiers with tuned LC circuits at input and output (see, for example, Figs. 17.7 and 17.15). An *emitter bypass capacitor* C_e is needed in such circuits to provide a low-impedance path from emitter to ground. If C_e were not present, signal currents would flow through R_e, and an appreciable reduction in voltage gain would result, as we saw in Section 11.5.3 (see Problem P14.4).

14.2.1   Bypass Capacitor Calculations for Bipolar Amplifier

To find the design equation that specifies C_e in terms of the desired low-frequency 0.707 point ω_1, we calculate the voltage gain V_o/V_i for the low-frequency incremental circuit model (Fig. 14.7b). The general form of this transfer function can be found by noting that the network has only one natural frequency and constant finite gain at both very low and "high" frequencies. These conditions dictate a transfer function of the form

$$\frac{V_o}{V_i} = A_o\frac{s - s_c}{s - s_d} \quad (14.12)$$

Following the procedure suggested in the preceding section, we find the natural frequency of the network by finding the total admittance between the two terminals of C_e. We first calculate the net resistance R_T appearing in parallel with C_e. The circuit for such a calculation is shown in Fig. 14.8. Comparison of this figure with Fig. 11.13, Section 11.5.2, shows that the

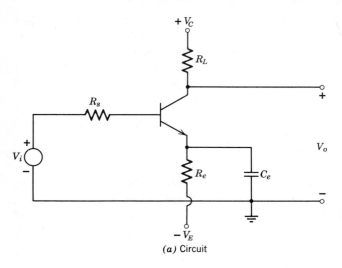

(a) Circuit

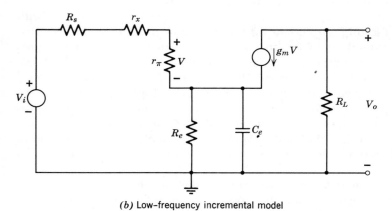

(b) Low-frequency incremental model

Figure 14.7   Single-stage bipolar transistor amplifier biased with two power supplies.

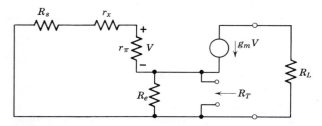

Figure 14.8   Circuit for calculating Thévenin equivalent resistance R_T appearing in parallel with C_e.

resistance R_T is just the Thévenin equivalent output resistance of the common-collector circuit (the presence of R_L does not affect these calculations). Thus R_T is

$$R_T = R_e \left\| \left(\frac{r_x + r_\pi + R_s}{\beta_o + 1} \right) \right.$$

(14.13)

The admittance expression is

$$sC_e + \frac{1}{R_T} = 0$$

Hence the natural frequency is

$$s_d = -\frac{1}{C_e R_T}$$

(14.14)

The zero in Eq. 14.12 will occur at a frequency where the admittance between emitter and ground in Fig. 14.7b goes to zero, because with zero emitter admittance it will not be possible to drive any signal current into the base. On this basis we write the admittance equation as

$$\frac{1}{R_e} + sC_e = 0$$

(14.15)

Thus the zero occurs at a frequency

$$s_c = -\frac{1}{R_e C_e}$$

(14.16)

(see Problem P14.5). The complete voltage gain expression is, from Eqs. 14.14 and 14.16,

$$\frac{V_o}{V_i} = A_o \frac{s + 1/R_e C_e}{s + 1/R_T C_e}$$

(14.17)

where the midfrequency gain A_o is, by inspection of Fig. 14.7b with C_e shorted,

$$A_o = -\frac{r_\pi}{R_s + r_x + r_\pi} g_m R_L$$

(14.18)

(see Problem P14.6).

Because this transfer function has both a pole and a zero, the general formula for finding the value of C_e required to achieve a given value of ω_l is somewhat more complicated than the coupling capacitor expression calculated in Section 14.1.5. Note, however, that the pole in Eq. 14.17 will always be at a higher frequency than the zero by a factor R_e/R_T. If this factor is greater than 7 or 8, the 0.707 frequency will be determined primarily by the pole, that is,

$$\omega_l \simeq |s_d|$$

(14.19)

Hence, from Eq. 14.14,

$$C_e \simeq \frac{1}{\omega_l R_T}$$

(14.20)

14.2.2   Example: Common-Emitter Amplifier

Let us calculate the size of the emitter bypass capacitor required to achieve a 50-Hz lower 0.707 frequency for the circuit in Fig. 14.7. We assume that from gain and bias calculations we have the following values for the transistor and bias parameters:

$$R_L = 910 \text{ ohms} \qquad r_x = 100 \text{ ohms}$$

$$R_s = 1 \text{ kohm} \qquad r_\pi = 400 \text{ ohms}$$

$$R_b = 10 \text{ kohm} \qquad g_m = 0.1 \text{ mho}$$

$$R_e = 0.3 \text{k}$$

Because in this example

$$R_T = 0.3 \left\| \frac{0.1 + 0.4 + 1}{40 + 1} \right. = 0.033 \text{ kohm}$$

the pole in Eq. 14.17 will be further out than the zero by a factor of

$$\frac{s_d}{s_c} = \frac{R_e}{R_T} = \frac{0.3}{0.033}$$

$$= 9.2$$

Thus the 0.707 frequency will be influenced very little by the zero, and we can use Eq. 14.20 to find C_e:

$$C_e = \frac{1}{2\pi \times 0.050 \times 0.033}$$

$$= 96 \ \mu\text{f}$$

From Eq. 14.16, the zero is

$$s_c = -\frac{1}{0.3 \times 96} = -0.035 \text{ msec}^{-1}$$

To plot the frequency response and step response, we need the midfrequency gain and dc gain. The midfrequency gain A_o is, from Eq. 14.18,

$$A_o = -\frac{0.4}{0.1 + 0.4 + 1}(100 \times 0.91)$$

$$= -24.3$$

The gain at zero frequency can be calculated directly from the network (Fig. 14.7*b*) with C_e set to zero (see Problem P14.4). Alternatively, it can be

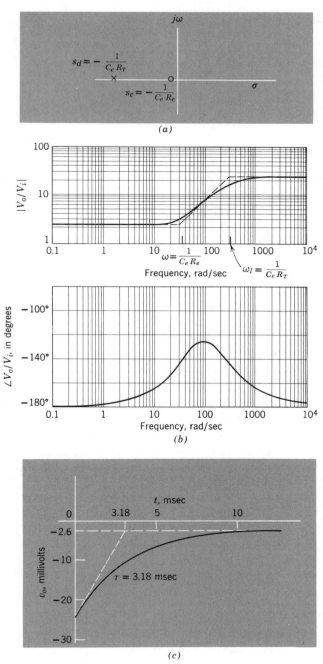

Figure 14.9 (a) Pole-zero pattern, (b) frequency response, and (c) step response of V_o/V_i for Fig. 14.7*b*.

calculated from Eq. 14.17 by setting s equal to zero. In either case the result is

$$\frac{V_o}{V_i}\bigg|_{dc} = A_o \frac{R_T}{R_e} = -\frac{g_m r_\pi R_L}{r_x + r_\pi + R_e(1 + \beta_o) + R_s} \qquad (14.21)$$

$$= -\frac{40 \times 0.91}{1.5 + 0.3 \times 41}$$

$$= -2.64$$

(Comparison of this value with the midfrequency gain of -24.3 shows clearly the loss in gain that would result if the emitter resistor were left unbypassed.) The pole-zero pattern and frequency response for the network are shown in Figs. 14.9a and b.

The response of the network to a unit step can be calculated by the method discussed in Section 14.1.4. Assuming a 1-mv input step, the output will initially be -24.3 mv. Because the network has gain of -2.64 at zero frequency, the final value of the response will be -2.64 mv. The time constant of the decay is

$$\tau = \frac{1}{|s_d|} = 3.18 \text{ msec.}$$

This step response is plotted in Fig. 14.9c (see Problem P14.7).

14.2.3 Source-to-Ground Bypass Capacitor

A typical two-power-supply biasing configuration for an FET circuit is shown in Fig. 14.10a. The bypass capacitor provides a low-impedance path from the source lead to ground, to maximize the midfrequency gain. The low-frequency incremental circuit model is shown in Fig. 14.10b. The similarity to Fig. 14.7b is obvious: the only difference is that r_π and r_x are missing in the FET circuit. The derivation of the transfer function V_o/V_i is left to the reader (see Problem P14.8); we shall obtain the results here by letting r_π approach infinity and r_x approach zero in the equations of Section 14.2.1. On this basis the low-frequency transfer function is

$$\frac{V_o}{V_i} = A_o \frac{s + 1/R_e C_e}{s + 1/R_T C_e} \qquad (14.22)$$

where

$$R_T = \frac{1}{G_e + g_m} = R_e \| g_m^{-1} \qquad (14.23)$$

$(G_e = 1/R_e)$, and

$$A_o = -g_m R_L \qquad (14.24)$$

Except for the changes in R_T and A_o, the design problem is similar to that discussed in Section 14.2.2, hence will not be repeated here (see Problem P14.9).

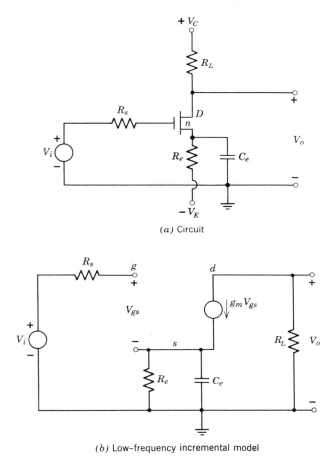

(a) Circuit

(b) Low–frequency incremental model

Figure 14.10   A single-stage FET amplifier with two-power-supply bias.

14.3   Bias Circuits with Coupling and Bypass Capacitors

Most single-stage amplifiers are operated from a single power supply rather than the two-power-supply configuration discussed in Section 14.2. Thus well-stabilized bias designs that include an emitter (or a source-to-ground) resistor R_e require both a coupling capacitor and (for high gain) a bypass capacitor, as shown in Fig. 14.11. Even after we suppress the effects of the transistor dynamics by assuming a two-decade midfrequency region, we still have a somewhat more complicated design problem than before, because in general the 0.707 frequency for V_o/V_i will be a function of both C_e and C_c. However, it is a relatively simple matter to force the design so that either C_e or C_c alone controls the value of ω_l. Although the resulting circuit is not always optimal from an economic point of view, it is satisfactory and simple.

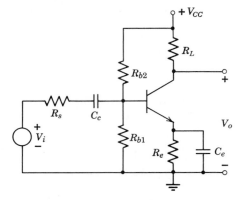

(a) *npn*-Bipolar transistor

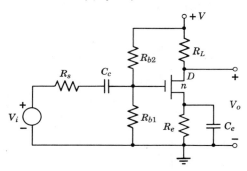

(b) *n*-Channel MOSFET

Figure 14.11 Typical single-stage transistor amplifiers with coupling capacitors C_c and bypass capacitors C_e.

(If price is a dominant consideration, other completely different approaches to the bias problem, such as that discussed in Section 16.1.4, will probably prove more economical.)

14.3.1 Selection of C_c and C_e for an FET Amplifier

The low-frequency incremental model for the common-source FET amplifier in Fig. 14.11*b* is shown in Fig. 14.12. As in the simpler single-capacitor examples discussed above, we start the design discussion by calculating the transfer function V_o/V_i. This function has two poles because of the two independent energy-storage elements, and capacitor C_c introduces a zero at zero frequency. At "high" frequencies, the voltage gain is constant. To match these conditions, the transfer function must have two zeros in addition to the two poles:

$$\frac{V_o}{V_i} = A_o \frac{s(s - s_e)}{(s - s_f)(s - s_g)} \tag{14.25}$$

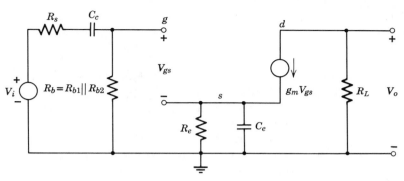

Figure 14.12   Low-frequency incremental circuit model for the FET amplifier in Fig. 14.11*b*.

Because the FET at low frequencies has infinite input resistance, the circuit in Fig. 14.12 divides into two subcircuits that *do not interact*. That is, when we calculate natural frequencies by looking for a zero of admittance across C_c, *we do not see the other subcircuit containing* C_e, and vice versa. Hence the natural frequency calculations in this case are identical to those associated with Figs. 14.3*c* and 14.10*b*. Specifically

$$s_f = -\frac{1}{(R_b + R_s)C_c} \tag{14.26}$$

$$s_g = -\frac{G_e + g_m}{C_e} \tag{14.27}$$

Also, the zero must be the same as before:

$$s_e = -\frac{1}{R_e C_e} \tag{14.28}$$

There are many ways of selecting capacitor sizes in this circuit to meet a specified lower 0.707 frequency, but perhaps the simplest (although probably not the most economical) is to choose C_c and C_e such that the pole involving C_c is the *dominant low-frequency pole*. We are free to do this because specifying just ω_l does not completely specify the two unknown elements C_c and C_e. Thus we can add another constraint to force s_f to be dominant. First we select C_c such that $|s_f| = \omega_l$. That is, from Eq. 14.26 we have

$$C_c = \frac{1}{\omega_l(R_s + R_b)} \tag{14.29}$$

Then we select C_e such that s_g is at least a factor of 10 lower in frequency than s_f. That is,

$$|s_g| = \frac{|s_f|}{10} = \frac{\omega_l}{10}$$

Now, from Eq. 14.27,

$$C_e = \frac{10}{\omega_1}(G_e + g_m) \tag{14.30}$$

Comparison of Eqs. 14.27 and 14.28 indicates that the zero is always lower in frequency than s_g by a factor $G_e/(G_e + g_m)$, so that this design ensures that we have a simple single-pole cutoff at ω_1, unaffected by either the zero or pole arising from C_e.

If the complete transfer function V_o/V_i is desired, then we see from Eq. 14.25 that the only constant not yet evaluated is A_o. This is just the mid-frequency voltage gain:

$$A_o = -\frac{R_b}{R_b + R_s}g_m R_L \tag{14.31}$$

Thus the complete low-frequency gain expression can be found by substituting Eqs. 14.26, 14.27, 14.28, and 14.31 into Eq. 14.25. (See Problem P14.10.)

14.3.2   Selection of C_c and C_e for a Common-Emitter (Bipolar) Amplifier

The low-frequency incremental model for a typical single-stage common-emitter amplifier (Fig. 14.11a) is shown in Fig. 14.13. As with the corresponding FET circuit, this network has two natural frequencies, but in contrast to the previous circuit, here the capacitors are *interacting*. If we try to find the natural frequencies by looking for a zero of admittance across some element, we obtain a quadratic involving both C_e and C_c. Thus the two roots of this quadratic (the two natural frequencies) are each dependent on *both* C_e and C_c. Analysis and design of this general case is best postponed until the next chapter, where appropriate techniques are developed for handling networks with interacting capacitors (see Problem P15.20).

It is possible, however, to introduce a plausible "handbook design" at this point, which is usable although not optimum. The handbook design is based on the fact that specifying just the low-frequency cutoff ω_1 does not completely specify the two unknown elements C_e and C_c. Thus we are at

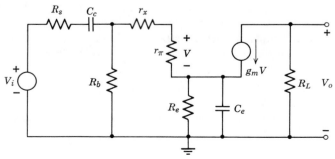

Figure 14.13   Low-frequency incremental circuit model for the bipolar amplifier in Fig. 14.11a.

liberty to add another constraint. Clearly the design will be simplified if we choose a constraint that ensures that ω_l *will depend primarily on one of the capacitor values.*

An appropriate simplifying constraint is suggested by the calculations in Sections 14.1.5 and 14.2.1. If, for example, we make C_e very large, we can approximate it in the vicinity of ω_l by a short circuit. Under these circumstances the cutoff is dominated by C_c alone, and the design in Section 14.1.5 applies. On the other hand, if we make C_c very large, the cutoff will be dominated by C_e alone, and the design method outlined in Section 14.2.1 applies. The question is, how large must a capacitor be to be "very large"? For this handbook design we can calculate the value of both C_e or C_c on the basis that the other capacitor is large, then arbitrarily *make one capacitor ten times as large* as the calculated value, to satisfy the "other capacitor very large" requirement. If this procedure is followed, the low-frequency transfer function will have one dominant natural frequency,

$$|s| \simeq \omega_l$$

This method of design is illustrated in the following numerical example.

14.3.3 Example

Let us select appropriate values for C_c and C_e in Fig. 14.13 to yield a voltage transfer function V_o/V_i with a lower 0.707 point at 50 Hz. Assume that $R_s = 1\,\text{kohm}$, $R_e = 0.3\,\text{kohm}$, and $R_b = 10\,\text{kohm}$. The power supply voltage will be adjusted to yield an operating point of $I_C = 2.5\,\text{ma}$, $V_{CE} = 5\,\text{volts}$. At this operating point $\beta_o = 40$ and $r_x = 100$ ohms.

Based on the transistor data given above,

$$g_m = \frac{2.5}{25} = 0.1\,\text{mho}$$

$$r_\pi = \frac{\beta_o}{g_m} = 400\,\text{ohms}$$

$$r_x = 100\,\text{ohms}$$

By happy coincidence, these are the same numerical values used in Section 14.2.2. Thus we know that if capacitor C_c were "very large," C_e would have to be 96 μf to yield a 50-Hz low-frequency 0.707 point. If C_e were "very large," then from Section 14.1.5, Eq. 14.10,

$$C_c = \frac{1}{2\pi \times 0.050[1 + 10\|(0.1 + 0.4)]}$$

$$= 2.16\,\mu\text{f}$$

Following the handbook design outlined above, we now make one of these capacitors a factor of 10 larger to satisfy the "other capacitor very large" requirement. Clearly, from the point of view of both size and economy we should increase the smaller capacitor (unless the voltage rating of C_c is much larger than that of C_e). Hence the final capacitor values are

$$C_c = 22 \ \mu f \approx 20 \ \mu f$$

$$C_e = 96 \ \mu f \approx 100 \ \mu f$$

The dominant low-frequency pole in this design will be determined primarily by capacitor C_e and will have a value

$$s_c \simeq -\omega_l = -50 \times 2\pi$$

$$= -314 \ \text{sec}^{-1}$$

14.4   Selection of C_c and C_e in Other Circuit Configurations
14.4.1   Common-Base Circuit

As we have seen in Section 13.7.1, the single-power-supply biasing circuit for the common-base transistor (Fig. 14.14) is identical in topology to the common-emitter biasing network with emitter resistor. In spite of the fact that the coupling and bypass capacitors are in different locations than before (compare Fig. 14.14 to Fig. 14.11a), the design method discussed in Section 14.3.2 can be readily adapted to the common-base circuit. Specifically, we calculate the value of C_c necessary to achieve the desired low-frequency response on the basis that C_b is large enough not to influence the calculation. Then C_b is calculated by assuming that C_c is large. As can be readily verified (see Problem P14.11), the appropriate relations are

$$C_c = \cfrac{1}{\omega_l \left(R_s + R_e \left\| \cfrac{r_x + r_\pi}{\beta_o + 1} \right\| \right)} \tag{14.32}$$

$$C_b = \cfrac{1}{\omega_l \{ R_b \| [r_x + r_\pi + (R_s \| R_e)(\beta_o + 1)] \}} \tag{14.33}$$

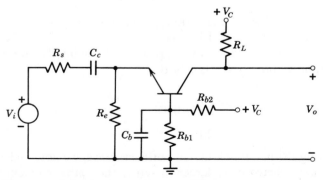

Figure 14.14   Bias network for a common-base amplifier.

Finally, either C_c or C_b is increased by a factor of 10 above the value calculated in Eq. 14.32 or Eq. 14.33, to satisfy the "other capacitor large enough" condition in the original calculation.

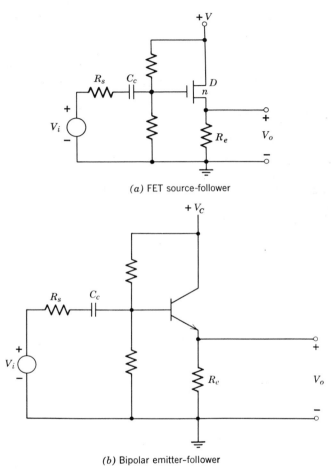

(a) FET source-follower

(b) Bipolar emitter-follower

Figure 14.15 Bias networks for "follower" circuits.

14.4.2 The "Follower" Circuits

Single-stage source-follower and emitter-follower circuits require a coupling capacitor but no bypass capacitor, as can be seen from Fig. 14.15. The method of selection of C_c for these circuits is identical in principle to that discussed in Sections 14.1.3 and 14.1.5 (see Problems P14.12 and P14.13).

14.5 High-Frequency Performance of Common-Emitter Amplifiers

We turn now to the second major topic of this chapter—the study of the high-frequency behavior of single-stage amplifiers. We noted in the preceding sections that the limit on low-frequency response of such an amplifier is set by the size of the coupling and bypass capacitors, and not by the transistor. In fact, we saw in Section 7.4.2 that the response can be extended down to zero frequency by proper balancing technique to separate the signal voltages from the power-supply voltages. At high frequencies, the response is limited not by external circuit elements, but by transistor dynamics, represented in our small-signal models by capacitors C_π and C_μ, or C_{gs} and C_{gd}. With present-day transistors, single-stage amplifiers can be built that will amplify signals over a wide range of frequencies: zero to above 50 MHz.

14.5.1   Transfer Function

To study the high-frequency behavior of transistor circuits, we first calculate the transfer function E_o/E_i at high frequencies for the single-stage common-emitter amplifier shown in Fig. 14.16a. Then we introduce an approximation that greatly simplifies single-stage analysis and design.

We have already shown in Section 14.1.1 that an appropriate incremental model for high-frequency analysis can be obtained by assuming that the coupling capacitors are short circuits. Such a model is shown in Fig. 14.16b.

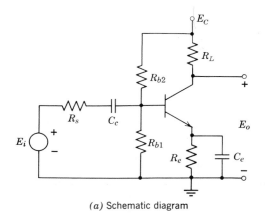

(a) Schematic diagram

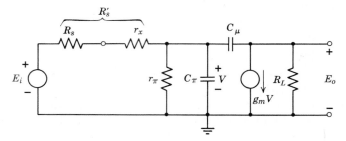

(b) High-frequency incremental circuit model

Figure 14.16   Single-stage bipolar amplifier.

(We assume for simplicity that $R_b = R_{b1} \| R_{b2}$ is much larger than $r_x + r_\pi$ or R_s, and thus can be neglected.) A quick inspection reveals significantly fewer nodes than loops in this circuit model; hence nodal analysis, together with admittance notation ($g_\pi = 1/r_\pi$, etc.), is employed. To further simplify the analysis, the resistors R_s and r_x are combined into a single resistor:

$$R_s' = \frac{1}{G_s'} = R_s + r_x \tag{14.34}$$

The Kirchhoff current law relation for node V is

$$E_i G_s' = [G_s' + g_\pi + s(C_\pi + C_\mu)]V - sC_\mu E_o \tag{14.35a}$$

For node E_o,

$$0 = (g_m - sC_\mu)V + (G_L + sC_\mu)E_o \tag{14.35b}$$

Solving Eqs. 14.35 for E_o by Cramer's rule, we find the transfer function E_o/E_i of the incremental circuit:

$$\frac{E_o}{E_i} = -\frac{G_s'(g_m - sC_\mu)}{[G_s' + g_\pi + s(C_\pi + C_\mu)](G_L + sC_\mu) + sC_\mu(g_m - sC_\mu)} \tag{14.36}$$

Next we multiply numerator and denominator by R_L, expand the denominator, and order by increasing powers of s.

$$\frac{E_o}{E_i} = -\frac{G_s' R_L(g_m - sC_\mu)}{G_s' + g_\pi + s[C_\pi + C_\mu + C_\mu R_L(g_m + g_\pi + G_s')] + s^2 C_\pi C_\mu R_L} \tag{14.37}$$

This transfer function has a right half-plane zero at

$$s_z = \frac{g_m}{C_\mu} \tag{14.38}$$

corresponding to the frequency at which the current flowing through C_μ exactly cancels the current from the g_m generator at the output node. We can also see from Eq. 14.37 that, as expected, the transfer function has two poles. These poles are in the left half-plane (as required) because the denominator coefficients are all of the same sign.

14.5.2   The One-Pole Approximation

Recall from Section 11.4.1 that a fundamental limitation on the range of validity of the hybrid-pi model is

$$\omega \ll \frac{2D_b}{W^2} = \frac{g_m}{C_b}$$

Comparing this equation with that for ω_T,

$$\omega_T = \frac{g_m}{C_\pi + C_\mu} \tag{14.39}$$

we conclude that the model is valid only for frequencies substantially less than ω_T. If we impose this restriction, then from Eq. 14.39,

$$|sC_\pi| \ll g_m \tag{14.40}$$

$$|sC_\mu| \ll g_m \tag{14.41}$$

On the basis of Eq. 14.40, we have

$$|s^2 C_\pi C_\mu R_L| \ll |sC_\mu g_m R_L| \tag{14.42}$$

Hence the s^2 term in the denominator of Eq. 14.37 can be neglected. Furthermore, on the basis of Eq. 14.41 we can also neglect the sC_μ term in the numerator. Thus Eq. 14.37 reduces to a *one-pole expression*:

$$\frac{E_o}{E_i} = -\frac{G'_s g_m R_L}{G'_s + g_\pi + s[C_\pi + C_\mu + C_\mu R_L(g_m + g_\pi + G'_s)]} \tag{14.43}$$

It can be shown that the pole we have neglected is always larger in magnitude than ω_T (see Problem P14.14).

A further simplification results when we note that because

$$\beta_o = g_m/g_\pi \tag{14.44}$$

g_π can always be neglected compared to g_m, assuming reasonable values for β_o. On this basis, Eq. 14.43 reduces to

$$\frac{E_o}{E_i} = -\frac{G'_s R_L g_m}{G'_s + g_\pi + s\{C_\pi + C_\mu[1 + (g_m + G'_s)R_L]\}} \tag{14.45}$$

These calculations would be of no lasting consequence were it not possible to interpret Eq. 14.45 in terms of a simple circuit. To this end, note that the denominator term $sC_\mu[1 + (g_m + G'_s)R_L]$ appears directly added to C_π. Thus we say that in circuit terms, the capacitor C_π appears to be paralleled by a capacitance $C_\mu[1 + (g_m + G'_s)R_L]$.

A circuit model based on this concept is shown in Fig. 14.17, and a rapid calculation will show that the circuit possesses the voltage transfer function given in Eq. 14.45 (see Problem P14.15). Forward transfer and input impedance calculations using this circuit are particularly simple because the circuit is *unilateral*; hence solution of simultaneous equations is not required.

Several important conclusions can now be drawn concerning the analysis of any simple common-emitter amplifier with resistive source and load.

1. Subject to the frequency limits used in deriving Eq. 14.45, the *transistor plus resistive load* in the amplifier circuit can be replaced by a unilateral circuit having only one capacitor C_t, where

$$C_t = C_\pi + C_\mu[1 + (g_m + G'_s)R_L] \tag{14.45}$$

as shown in Fig. 14.17. It is important to note that this is *not* a transistor model but rather an *equivalent circuit for the transistor plus resistive load*.

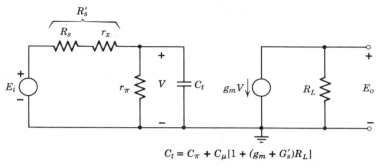

$$C_t = C_\pi + C_\mu[1 + (g_m + G'_s)R_L]$$

Figure 14.17   A circuit interpretation of the one-pole approximation.

2. Clearly, the circuit is valid for calculation of forward transfer function and input impedance only. The circuit *cannot be used for reverse transfer and output impedance calculations.*

3. At frequencies low enough so that capacitors C_π and C_μ do not influence performance, E_o/E_i is equal to A_o, the midband gain, given by Eq. 14.11. This fact is obvious from Fig. 14.17. It is also obvious from Eq. 14.45 once the two identical forms of the voltage divider expression are recognized:

$$\frac{r_\pi}{r_x + R_s + r_\pi} = \frac{G'_s}{G'_s + g_\pi} \tag{14.47}$$

(see Problem P14.16).

4. The frequency ω_h at which the magnitude of the voltage gain E_o/E_i falls to 0.707 of its midfrequency value is identical to the pole frequency for this single-pole function. That is,

$$\omega_h = |s_p| = \frac{G'_s + g_\pi}{C_\pi + C_\mu[1 + (g_m + G'_s)R_L]} \tag{14.48a}$$

$$= \frac{G'_s + g_\pi}{C_t} \tag{14.48b}$$

The result is quite obvious from Eq. 14.45, but note that Eqs. 14.48 can be obtained directly by inspection from Fig. 14.17, because $G'_s + g_\pi$ is the net conductance appearing across the terminals of C_t. Thus equations such as Eq. 14.45 need not be memorized.

5. The range of frequencies over which the approximate gain relation (Eq. 14.45) is valid can be calculated quite readily from Eqs. 14.40 and 14.42. At frequencies substantially above ω_h, only the s term in the denominator of Eq. 14.45 will be important. Hence at a frequency such that

$$|s| = \frac{g_m}{10C_\pi} \simeq \frac{\omega_T}{10}$$

the term in s^2 in Eq. 14.37 that we previously ignored has the magnitude

$$|s^2 C_\pi C_\mu R_L| = \frac{s C_\mu g_m R_L}{10} \tag{14.49}$$

Thus under worst-case conditions in which the $s C_\mu g_m R_L$ term in the denominator of Eq. 14.45 is dominant, we find from Eq. 14.49 that we have neglected a quadrature term in Eq. 14.37 that is one tenth of the dominant term. We conclude that for $|s| = \omega_T/10$, the neglect of the s^2 term in Eq. 14.37 introduces a 6° phase error and negligible amplitude error. For frequencies below $\omega_T/10$, even this small error vanishes.

6. Examination of Eqs. 14.48 or Fig. 14.17 indicates that the bandwidth of the common-emitter amplifier increases as the load resistance R_L decreases, because $C_\mu(g_m + G_s')R_L$ decreases. (We assume here that the transistor dc voltages and currents are somehow held constant as R_L is varied.) However, inspection of Eq. 14.45 shows that when R_L is decreased to yield more bandwidth, the midfrequency gain of the circuit is reduced. Note, however, that the bandwidth does not increase in direct proportion to the gain reduction. In fact, we see from Eq. 14.45 that for R_L small, the gain approaches zero, whereas the bandwidth approaches a limiting value of

$$\omega_h|_{R_L \to 0} = \frac{G_s' + g_\pi}{C_\pi + C_\mu} \tag{14.50}$$

The effect on gain and bandwidth of changing R_L is shown graphically in Fig. 14.18.

7. Equation 14.48 or Fig. 14.17 also shows that the bandwidth of the amplifier can be increased by decreasing R_s. However, it is clear from Eq.

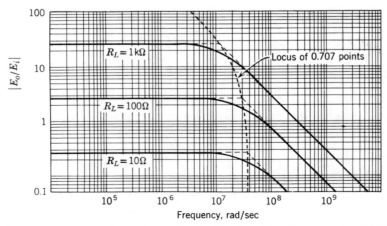

Figure 14.18   Frequency response for various values of load resistor R_L: assuming that the bias is adjusted in each case to maintain a fixed operating point for the transistor.

14.48 that no amount of juggling of resistors R_s and R_L in the simple common-emitter circuit of Fig. 14.16 can ever increase the bandwidth beyond the frequency

$$\omega_b = \frac{g_x + g_\pi}{C_\pi + C_\mu} \simeq \frac{g_x}{C_\pi + C_\mu} \tag{14.51}$$

This frequency, a function of the fundamental parameters associated with the base of the transistor, is often called the *transverse cutoff frequency* of the base.[4]

14.5.3   Example: Analysis

To illustrate some of the techniques developed above, let us calculate the voltage gain and bandwidth of the common-emitter amplifier shown in Fig. 14.19a. Assume that the pertinent transistor parameters are:

$$\text{Large signal}: \beta_F \simeq 80$$

$$\text{Small signal at } V_{CE} = 10 \text{ volts, } I_C = 15 \text{ ma}:$$

$$C_\mu = 2.5 \text{ pf}$$

$$\beta_o = 80$$

$$f_T = 750 \text{ MHz}$$

$$r_x = 30 \text{ ohms}$$

The first step in the analysis is to find the dc operating voltage and current. We note that the designer was obviously trying to operate the transistor in the linear-active region; hence we initially assume that the analysis of Section 13.4.1 applies. On this basis we can find I_C by applying Eq. 13.13:

$$I_C = \frac{(E_B - V_D)\beta_F}{R_b + (\beta_F + 1)R_e}$$

Here

$$E_B = \frac{2.7}{2.7 + 7.5} \times 15 = 4 \text{ volts}$$

and

$$R_b = 2.7 \| 7.5 = 2 \text{ kohm}$$

Hence, assuming that V_D is 0.6 volts, the collector current is, in units of volts, milliamperes, and kilohms,

$$I_C = \frac{(4 - 0.6)80}{2 + (80 + 1)0.2} = 15 \text{ ma}$$

---

[4] It is possible to achieve larger bandwidths than ω_b by addition of other circuit elements, such as a series emitter resistor. See References 14.4 and 14.5.

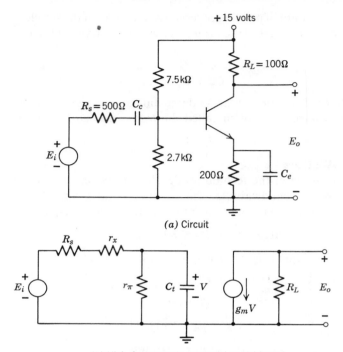

(a) Circuit

(b) High-frequency incremental model based on the one-pole approximation

Figure 14.19 Common-emitter amplifier.

Also,

$$V_{CE} \simeq 15 - I_C(R_L + R_e)$$

$$= 15 - 15(0.1 + 0.2) = 10.5 \text{ volts}$$

These numbers indicate that the transistor is indeed in the active region, thereby justifying the use of Eq. 13.13.

The operating point is very close to that at which the small-signal parameters are specified, so that no parameter scaling is required. Thus the hybrid-pi parameter values for the incremental model (Fig. 14.19b) are, in units of kilohms and picofarads (yielding time in nanoseconds),

$$g_m = \frac{q|I_C|}{kT} = \frac{15}{25} = 0.6 \text{ mho} = 600 \text{ mmho}$$

$$g_\pi = g_m/\beta_o = 600/80 = 7.5 \text{ mmho}$$

$$r_\pi = \frac{1}{7.5} = 0.133 \text{ kohm}$$

$$C_\pi = \frac{g_m}{\omega_T} - C_\mu = \frac{600}{2\pi \times 0.750} - 2.5 = 125 \text{ pf}$$

and thus

$$C_t = C_\pi + C_\mu[1 + (g_m + G_s')R_L] = 125 + 2.5(1 + [600 + 1/0.53] \times 0.1) = 278 \text{ pf}$$

Now, by inspection of Fig. 14.19b, we see that the midfrequency voltage gain is

$$\frac{E_o}{E_i}(\text{midfrequency}) = \frac{r_\pi}{r_\pi + R_s + r_x}(-g_m R_L)$$

$$= -\frac{(0.133)(600)(0.1)}{0.133 + 0.5 + 0.03} = -12$$

The circuit has a single pole at

$$s_1 = -\frac{g_\pi + G_s'}{C_t} = -\frac{7.5 + 1/0.53}{278} = -0.034 \text{ nsec}^{-1}$$

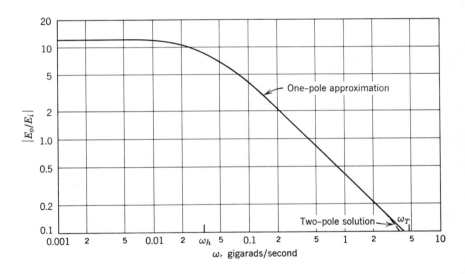

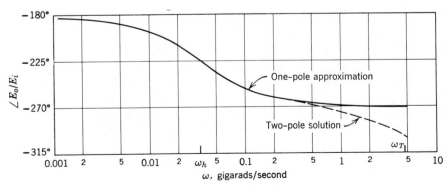

Figure 14.20   Frequency response of single-stage amplifier in Fig. 14.19.

so that the upper 0.707 frequency will be

$$\omega_h = 0.034 \text{ Grad/sec}$$

(1 Grad = 1 gigaradian = 10^9 radians), or

$$f_h = 5.4 \text{ MHz}$$

To check this answer, which is based on the one-pole approximation, we calculate the two poles and the zero in E_o/E_i from Eq. 14.37. The zero is

$$s_z = \frac{g_m}{C_\mu} = \frac{600}{2.5} = 240 \text{ nsec}^{-1}$$

and the two poles, calculated by finding the roots of the denominator quadratic, are

$$s_1 = -0.0335 \text{ nsec}^{-1}$$

$$s_2 = -8.95 \text{ nsec}^{-1}$$

As predicted, $|s_2|$ is greater than ω_T. Clearly, the poles are widely separated in this case; hence it should be no surprise that the two calculations for the dominant pole agree so closely. To further justify the neglect of the non-dominant pole and the zero, we plot in Fig. 14.20 the magnitude and phase of the transfer function E_o/E_i for both solutions. For frequencies less than $\omega_T/10$, the difference between the two solutions is obviously very small.

14.5.4 Example: Design

Suppose that we wish, if possible, to redesign the amplifier in Fig. 14.19 so that it has a bandwidth of 10 MHz, while maintaining the same dc operating point for the transistor. According to Eq. 14.51, the largest possible band-width for this configuration and operating point is the transverse cutoff frequency

$$\omega_b = \frac{g_x + g_\pi}{C_\pi + C_\mu} = \frac{33 + 7.5}{125 + 2.5} = 0.318 \text{ Grad/sec}$$

or

$$f_b = 50.7 \text{ MHz}$$

Thus the design is possible. But clearly there is no unique solution: many different combinations of R_s and R_L will yield the desired bandwidth. To constrain the design more tightly, we assume that the minimum allowed value for R_s is 50 ohms, corresponding to the output resistance of most RF signal generators. Because we obviously want maximum gain from the circuit, R_s should be at this minimum value. From Eq. 14.48

$$C_t = \frac{g_\pi + G'_s}{\omega_h} = \frac{7.5 + 10^3/(50 + 30)}{2\pi \times 0.01} = 318 \text{ pf}$$

Now, Eq. 14.46 can be used to find R_L.

$$C_t = C_\pi + C_\mu[1 + (g_m + G_s')R_L] \simeq 125 + 2.5(1 + 0.6R_L) = 318 \text{ pf}$$

Therefore

$$R_L = 127 \text{ ohms}$$

To maintain the same operating point, some small changes in the bias network are required (see Problem P14.17).

14.6   High-Frequency Performance of Common-Source Amplifiers

The circuit and high-frequency incremental models for a single-stage FET amplifier, developed earlier in this chapter, are repeated for convenience in Fig. 14.21. Because the incremental model for the FET is so similar to the hybrid-pi model for the bipolar transistor, almost all of the conclusions reached in Section 14.5.2 can be applied to FET amplifiers. In particular, the one-pole approximation can also be applied to circuits such as Fig. 14.21.

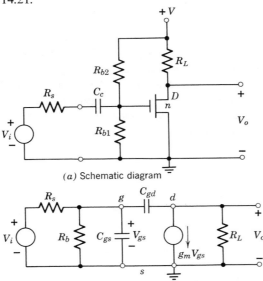

(a) Schematic diagram

(b) High-frequency incremental circuit model

Figure 14.21   FET common-source amplifier.

14.6.1   Transfer Function

The high-frequency transfer function V_o/V_i for Fig. 14.21b can be found by direct analysis, or by setting $g_\pi = 0$ and $r_x = 0$ in Eq. 14.37. Because r_x is zero, G_s' reduces to G_s, hence

$$\frac{V_o}{V_i} = -\frac{G_s R_L(g_m - sC_{gd})}{G_s + s[C_{gs} + C_{gd} + C_{gd}R_L(g_m + G_s)] + s^2 C_{gs}C_{gd}R_L} \quad (14.52)$$

(We have again assumed that R_b is much larger than R_s.) For frequencies such that

$$|sC_{gs}| \ll g_m \qquad (14.53)$$

then

$$|s^2 C_{gs} C_{gd} R_L| \ll |sC_{gd} R_L(g_m + G_s)| \qquad (14.54)$$

and Eq. 14.52 becomes a *one-pole function*. Also, because C_{gd} is usually smaller than C_{gs}, Eq. 14.53 also implies $|sC_{gd}| \ll g_m$. It follows that for frequencies well below

$$s = \frac{g_m}{C_{gs}} \qquad (14.55)$$

Eq. 14.52 reduces to

$$\frac{V_o}{V_i} = -\frac{G_s g_m R_L}{G_s + s[C_{gs} + C_{gd} + C_{gd} R_L(g_m + G_s)]} \qquad (14.56)$$

As was the case with the bipolar amplifier, it is possible to make a very simple circuit interpretation of Eq. 14.56. The equation contains a term related to the basic gain of the circuit, that is, $-g_m R_L$, and a voltage divider term, here in admittance form. The simple circuit of Fig. 14.22 reflects these two features. Because the augmented capacitance C_t appears directly at the input terminals of the FET, it is often referred to as *Miller effect capacitance*, conforming to terminology used with vacuum tubes.

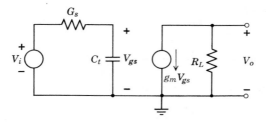

$$C_t = C_{gs} + C_{gd} [1 + (g_m + G_s)R_L]$$

Figure 14.22   The one-pole approximation in circuit form.

Many of the comments in Section 14.5.2 about the one-pole model for a bipolar amplifier apply to Eq. 14.56 and Fig. 14.22 as well. Briefly:

1. The unilateral circuit with one capacitor of value

$$C_t = C_{gs} + C_{gd}[1 + (g_m + G_s)R_L] \qquad (14.57)$$

is not a transistor model, but an incremental equivalent circuit for the FET *plus the resistive load.*

2. The circuit is not valid for output impedance or reverse transfer calculations.

3. The 0.707 frequency ω_h is

$$\omega_h = \frac{G_s}{C_t}$$

$$= \frac{G_s}{C_{gs} + C_{gd}[1 + (g_m + G_s)R_L]} \qquad (14.58)$$

4. The bandwidth is increased by decreasing R_L and R_s. For small R_L, the bandwidth limit is

$$\omega_h = \frac{G_s}{C_{gs} + C_{gd}} \qquad (14.59)$$

For small R_s, the bandwidth limit is

$$\omega_h = \frac{1}{C_{gd}R_L} \qquad (14.60)$$

14.6.2 Example

We wish to design a single-stage FET amplifier to have the same bandwidth as the bipolar amplifier in Section 14.5.3, that is, 5.4 MHz or 0.034 Grad/sec. The source resistance is specified as 500 ohms. The small-signal parameters of the FET at the specified operating point of $V_{DS} = 15$ volts, $V_{GS} = 14$ volts are

$$y_{fs} = 5\,\text{mmho}$$

$$C_{iss} = 11 \text{ pf}$$

$$C_{rss} = 2 \text{ pf}$$

Thus the parameters in the FET model are

$$g_m = 5\,\text{mmho}$$

$$C_{gs} = C_{iss} - C_{rss} = 9 \text{ pf}$$

$$C_{gd} = C_{rss} = 2 \text{ pf}$$

To find the value of R_L required to achieve the desired bandwidth, we can solve for R_L in Eq. 14.58:

$$R_L = \frac{G_s/\omega_h - C_{gs} - C_{gd}}{C_{gd}(g_m + G_s)}$$

$$= \frac{2/0.034 - 9 - 2}{2(5 + 2)}$$

$$= 3.4 \,\text{kohm}$$

The mid-frequency gain of the stage will be

$$\frac{V_o}{V_i} = -g_m R_L$$

$$= -5 \times 3.4$$

$$= -17$$

14.7   Overall Frequency and Step Response of a Single-Stage Amplifier
14.7.1   Approximate Transfer Function (Dominant Poles Only)

We have now examined both the low-frequency response and the high-frequency response of single-stage transistor amplifiers. The design method evolved in Section 14.3 assures us that at low frequencies the response of an amplifier with both coupling and bypass capacitors is dominated by one pole. Thus for low frequencies the transfer function can be approximated by the function

$$\frac{V_o}{V_i} \simeq \frac{A_o s}{s - s_1} \tag{14.61}$$

down to about $\omega_l/3$, at which point the other pole begins to have a significant effect on the transfer function. We showed in Section 14.5.2 that at high frequencies the transfer function is also dominated by one pole; hence for high frequencies, but below $\omega_T/10$, the transfer function is approximately

$$\frac{V_o}{V_i} = \frac{A_o}{1 - s/s_2} \tag{14.62}$$

(See, for example, Eq. 14.45.)

Clearly, these two equations can be combined to yield a single approximate transfer function valid from $\omega_l/3$ to $\omega_T/10$. To be consistent with these results, this function must be of the form

$$\frac{V_o}{V_i} \simeq \frac{A_o s}{(s - s_1)(1 - s/s_2)} \tag{14.63}$$

This expression, based on the dominant poles only, can now be used to find the approximate overall frequency response and step response of a transistor amplifier.

14.7.2   Example: Calculation of R_L for a Bipolar Transistor Amplifier

We now complete the design of the bipolar transistor amplifier discussed in Section 14.3.3 by calculating the maximum value for the load resistor R_L which will yield a constant voltage transfer function V_o/V_i from 50 Hz to 1 MHz (0.707 points). At the designated operating point of $I_C = 2.5$ ma,

$V_{CE} = 5$ volts, the high-frequency parameters of the transistor are $f_T = 200$ MHz, $r_x = 0.1$ kohm, and $C_{ob} = 5$ pf. The circuit is shown in Fig. 14.23a.

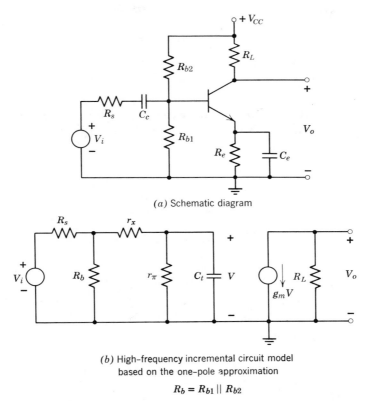

(a) Schematic diagram

(b) High–frequency incremental circuit model
based on the one–pole approximation

$$R_b = R_{b1} \| R_{b2}$$

Figure 14.23   Common-emitter   amplifier.

Although stated in somewhat different language, the specification for ω_l is the same in this example as in Section 14.3.3. Hence all of the low-frequency parameter values calculated there are appropriate here.

The value of the load resistor R_L will be determined in this design by the requirement for an upper 0.707 frequency of 1 MHz. Capacitors C_c and C_e do not enter into this calculation, because at this frequency they are virtual short circuits. For example, the impedance of C_c at 1 MHz is

$$Z = \frac{1}{2\pi \times 10^6 \times 20 \times 10^{-6}}$$

$$= 0.008 \text{ ohm}$$

The hybrid-pi parameters for this transistor are (in picofarads, kilohms, and nanoseconds) $g_m = 100$ mmho, $r_\pi = 0.4$ kohm, $r_x = 0.1$ kohm, and

$$C_\mu \simeq C_{ob} = 5 \text{ pf}$$

$$C_\pi = \frac{g_m}{\omega_T} - C_\mu$$

$$= \frac{100}{2\pi(0.2)} - 5 = 75 \text{ pf}$$

If we use the one-pole approximation, the high-frequency circuit model (this time including R_b) is shown in Fig. 14.23b. By inspection, the 0.707 frequency will be

$$\omega_h = \frac{G_t}{C_t} \tag{14.64}$$

where G_t is the net conductance facing C_t:

$$G_t = g_\pi + \frac{1}{r_x + R_s \| R_b}$$

$$= 2.5 + \frac{1}{0.1 + 0.91}$$

$$= 3.5 \text{ mmho}$$

Hence, from Eq. 14.64,

$$C_t = \frac{3.5}{2\pi \times 10^{-3}} = 558 \text{ pf}$$

To find R_L, recall that

$$C_t \simeq C_\pi + C_\mu(1 + g_m R_L)$$

Solving for R_L, we obtain

$$R_L = \frac{558 - 75 - 5}{5 \times 100} = 0.96 \text{ kohm}$$

14.7.3 Frequency Response
Let us now find the approximate overall frequency response for this amplifier. First we find the parameters in Eq. 14.63. Because in this approximate design we have used only the two dominant poles, and these two are many orders of magnitude apart,

$$s_1 \simeq -\omega_l = -314 \text{ sec}^{-1}$$

$$s_2 \simeq -\omega_h = -0.00628 \text{ nsec}^{-1}$$

The midband gain A_o in Eq. 14.63 can be found by applying Eq. 14.11 (page 485):

$$A_o = \left(\frac{-10}{10 + 1}\right)\left[\frac{40(0.96)}{10\|1 + 0.1 + 0.4}\right]$$

$$= -24.8$$

The magnitude and phase of V_o/V_i plotted from Eq. 14.63 using these numbers are shown in Fig. 14.24. Because we have included only dominant poles, this function has been graphed only over the range $(\omega_l/3) < \omega < (\omega_T/10)$.

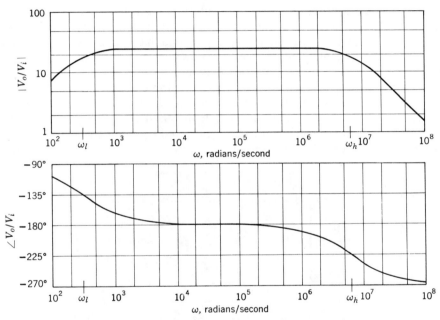

Figure 14.24 Complete frequency response of amplifier in Fig. 14.23 (dominant poles only).

14.7.4 Step Response

An approximation to the response of the amplifier to a step of voltage can be calculated on the basis of the approximate transfer function given by Eq. 14.63. We are assuming that the response is dominated by the two poles s_1 and s_2. Thus the step response will consist of two exponentials:

$$v_o(t) = K_1 e^{-s_1 t} + K_2 e^{-s_2 t} \qquad (14.65)$$

where, from Section 14.7.3,

$$s_1 = -314 \text{ sec}^{-1}$$

$$s_2 = -6.3 \times 10^6 \text{ sec}^{-1}$$

The constants K_1 and K_2 in Eq. 14.65 can be evaluated from the known initial conditions in the network. Because $v_o(t)$ is zero immediately following the step, K_1 must be the negative of K_2. Also, because the poles are so widely separated, the K_2 term will go to zero very rapidly, leaving v_o essentially equal to K_1. Thus

$$|K_1| \simeq A_o$$

Hence for a 1-mv input step, the output voltage in millivolts is

$$v_o(t) = 24.8[e^{-(6.3 \times 10^6)t} - e^{-314t}]$$

It is obviously very difficult to plot this function on a single linear time scale. The first exponential goes to completion in about a microsecond, during which time the second exponential has changed value by less than 1%. Hence we plot the response as shown in Fig. 14.25, with a greatly expanded time scale for the first microsecond.

The range of validity of the dominant-pole solution in terms of the time response is not as clean-cut as for the frequency response. We know, however, that the *complete* incremental model for the circuit contains four energy storage elements, C_π, C_μ, C_c, and C_e. Thus the step response is actually the sum of *four* rather than two exponentials. One of these additional

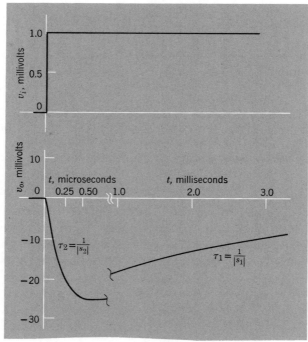

Figure 14.25   Step response of amplifier in Fig. 14.23.

exponentials, corresponding to a pole above ω_T, will be extremely rapid and thus will change the plot in Fig. 14.25 only for the first few nanoseconds. The other additional exponential, corresponding to a very low pole below ω_l, will be essentially constant for the time interval plotted. We conclude that the step response based on the dominant poles only is not correct for the first several nanoseconds, and is not correct for times greater than about 10 msec.

14.7.5   Square-Wave Testing

Because the step response of the amplifier is in fact primarily determined by the location of the two dominant poles, this response is a very convenient method for evaluating amplifier performance. The rise time of the amplifier output voltage can be used to determine ω_h because, for a simple exponential, the time required to get from 10 to 90% of the final value is

$$t(90\%) - t(10\%) = t_{\text{rise}} = 2.2\tau$$

$$= \frac{2.2}{\omega_h} \tag{14.66}$$

Equation 12.66 is often written as

$$t_{\text{rise}} \times f_h = \frac{2.2}{2\pi} = 0.35 \tag{14.67}$$

that is, the *product of rise time and bandwidth is equal to 0.35*.

In addition, the droop can be used to measure τ_1 (Fig. 14.25), hence s_1 and ω_l. For small droop, the exponential is nearly linear:

$$e^{-t/\tau_1} \simeq 1 - \frac{t}{\tau_1} \tag{14.68}$$

Thus a 10% droop in t sec implies that

$$\tau_1 = 10t$$

For laboratory measurement purposes, it is obviously desirable to use a periodic input waveform rather than a "one-shot" transient like a step function. This can be achieved with no essential change in the results by using a square wave as the driving signal, as shown in Fig. 14.26. The only requirement on the square wave is that its period be long enough to permit a satisfactory measurement of τ_1. Thus the square-wave period should be longer than, say, $0.2 \tau_1$. It should be clear that for an amplifier in which s_1 and s_2 differ by more than a few orders of magnitude, it will not be possible to observe both the rise and droop on the same oscilloscope time scale. (See Problem P14.18.)

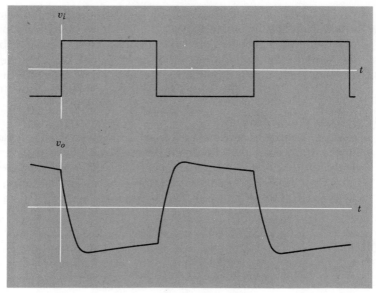

Figure 14.26 Square-wave response. For a broad-band amplifier, the rise and fall will not be visible on the same time scale.

REFERENCES

14.1 E. A. Guillemin, *Introductory Circuit Theory*, Wiley, New York, 1958.

14.2 A. G. Bose and K. N. Stevens, *Introductory Network Theory*, Harper and Row, New York, 1965.

14.3 M. E. Van Valkenburg, *Network Analysis*, Prentice-Hall, Englewood Cliffs, N.J., 1964.

14.4 R. D. Thornton et al., *Multistage Transistor Circuits*, Wiley, New York, 1965.

14.5 D. O. Pederson, *Electronic Circuits*, prelim. ed., McGraw-Hill, New York, 1965.

14.6 G. E. Valley and H. Wallman, *Vacuum Tube Amplifiers*, McGraw-Hill, New York, 1948.

14.7 *The General Radio Experimenter*, Vol. 42, Nos. 11–12 (December, 1968).

14.8 J. F. Gibbons, *Semiconductor Electronics*, McGraw-Hill, New York, 1966.

PROBLEMS

P14.1 Derive an expression for calculating the size of the coupling capacitor C_c in Fig. 14.3 required to produce a droop of less than 10% of the peak amplitude of a square wave of period T (see Fig. 14.5). Using the element values introduced in Section 14.1.4, calculate the required value of C_c for a 50-Hz square wave. Compare the result with that calculated in Section 14.1.4 and explain any difference. (See page 483.)

P14.2 By direct calculation on the circuit in Fig. 14.6, derive the complete voltage gain expression for the circuit and verify that the midfrequency gain A_o and low-frequency pole s_b are given by Eqs. 14.11 and 14.9. (See page 484.)

P14.3 Determine the value of C_c in Fig. 14.1*a* such that the low-frequency 0.707 point or band edge is at 50 Hz. Assume $R_s = 1$ kohm, $R_{b1} = 12$ kohm, $R_{b2} = 50$ kohm, $r_x = 20$ ohms, $r_\pi = 300$ ohms, $g_m = 300$ mmho.

P14.4 Calculate the incremental voltage gain of the circuit in Fig. 14.7*a* at zero frequency and compare the result with the midfrequency gain given by Eq. 14.18. Express the ratio A_o/A(low) both in terms of R_e and R_T (Eq. 14.13) and s_c and s_d (Eqs. 14.14 and 14.16). (See pages 485 and 488.)

P14.5 Verify, by direct calculation of V_o/V_i in Fig. 14.7*b*, the location of the network zero, as given by Eq. 14.16. (See page 487.)

P14.6 Verify by direct calculation that Eq. 14.17 is the correct voltage transfer function for the circuit in Fig. 14.7*b*. (See page 487.)

P14.7 Find a literal expression for the response $v_o(t)$ of the circuit in Fig. 14.7*b* for $v_i(t)$ a unit step of voltage. (See page 490.)

P14.8 Find by direct calculation from Fig. 14.10 the voltage gain V_o/V_i for the circuit, and verify Eq. 14.22. Find the gain at zero frequency, and compare with Eq. 14.24. Express the gain ratio in terms of g_m and R_e, and also in terms of the pole and zero frequencies. (See page 490.)

P14.9 Design the FET amplifier in Fig. 14.10 to meet the same design specifications given in Section 14.1.4, that is, a lower 0.707 frequency of 50 Hz, with

$$R_s = 50 \text{ kohm} \qquad g_m = 1 \text{ mmho}$$

$$R_L = 100 \text{ kohm} \qquad R_e = 10 \text{ kohm}$$

(See page 490.)

P14.10 Select the bias capacitors for the FET amplifier in Fig. 14.11*b* to yield a low-frequency cutoff of 10 Hz. Assume $R_s = 10$ kohm, $R_L = 50$ kohm, $R_e = 8$ kohm, R_{b1} and R_{b2} large, $g_m = 3$ mmho. To verify the design, calculate the midfrequency voltage gain and the low-frequency poles and zeros. Use these values to plot on log paper the magnitude and phase of V_o/V_i. (See page 494.)

P14.11 Verify Eqs. 14.32 and 14.33 by examining Fig. 14.14. (See page 496.)

P14.12 (*a*) Derive the design formula for calculating the coupling capacitor size to produce a given low-frequency band edge ω_l for the FET source-follower circuit in Fig. 14.15*a*.

(*b*) Find C_c to yield a 10 Hz low-frequency band edge, assuming $R_s = 10$ kohm, $R_e = 10$ kohm, $R_{b1} \| R_{b2} = 1$ megohm, and $g_m = 2$ mmho. Calculate the midband voltage gain. (See page 497.)

P14.13 (a) Derive the design formula for calculating the coupling capacitor size to produce a given low-frequency band edge ω_l for the emitter-follower circuit in Fig. 14.15b.

(b) Find C_c to yield a 10-Hz low-frequency band edge, assuming $R_s = 1\ kohm$, $R_e = 1500\ ohms$, R_{b1}, R_{b2} large, and $g_m = 100\ mmho$. Calculate the midband voltage gain. (See page 497.)

P14.14 An approximate expression for factoring a quadratic, accurate within 10% for real roots separated by a factor of 10 or more, is

$$Q(s) = i_2 s^2 + i_1 s + i_o \simeq i_2 \left(s + \frac{i_o}{i_1} \right) \left(s + \frac{i_1}{i_2} \right)$$

That is, the roots of a polynomial are approximately equal to minus the *ratio of adjacent coefficients of the polynomial*. Apply this approximation to the denominator quadratic in Eq. 14.37, and prove that the higher root is always greater in magnitude than ω_T. (See page 500.)

P14.15 Calculate the voltage gain E_o/E_i of the circuit in Fig. 14.17, hence verify that it has the transfer function specified by Eq. 14.45. (See page 500.)

P14.16 Show that the two forms of the voltage-divider expression in Eq. 14.47 are identical.

P14.17 Complete the redesign of the circuit in Section 14.5.4 and Fig. 14.19 by choosing new values of bias resistors to maintain the original dc operating point of $I_C = 15\ ma$, $V_{CE} = 10\ volts$. (See page 507.)

P14.18 Calculate the amount of droop (expressed as a fraction of the peak amplitude) which would result if a 100-Hz square wave were applied to the amplifier designed in Sections 14.3.3, 14.7.2, and 14.7.3. Also, calculate the rise time. (See page 515.)

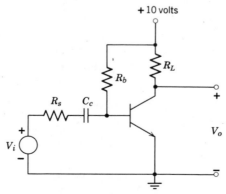

Figure 14.27 A simple common-emitter amplifier.

P14.19 Reasoning from the asymptotic behavior of the circuit in Fig. 14.10, show that Eq. 14.12 is also the general form of the transfer function V_o/V_i for the FET circuit with an emitter bypass capacitor.

P14.20 The circuit in Fig. 14.27 is to be designed to give a flat midfrequency region many decades wide. Specifically, the lower half-power frequency, or lower 0.707 frequency, must be at $\omega_l = 100$ rad/sec and the upper 0.707 frequency ω_h must be at 10 Mrad/sec.

(a) Draw the complete incremental model.

(b) Draw the mid-, high-, and low-frequency models.

(c) For $R_s = 1$ kohm, $R_L = 400$ ohms, R_b large, $\beta_o = 100$, $I_C = 5$ ma, $r_x = 50$ ohms, $C_\mu = 5$ pf, and $f_T = 500$ MHz, find C_e to meet the requirement on ω_l. Prove that the transistor is not good enough to meet the design requirement on ω_h.

(d) What is the midfrequency gain V_o/V_i?

(e) Redesign the circuit, using the same transistor, to meet the original specifications. What is the midfrequency gain of your new circuit?

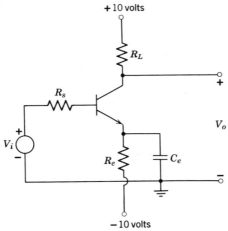

Figure 14.28 A common-emitter amplifier with two bias supplies.

P14.21 Ignoring all high-frequency problems in the circuit of Fig. 14.28, calculate the low-frequency poles and zeros. Assume $\beta_o = 50$, $r_\pi = 250$ ohms, $r_x \simeq 0$, $C_\pi = C_\mu \simeq 0$, $R_L = R_s = R_e = 1$ kohm, and $C_e = 100$ μf. Sketch and dimension the low- and midfrequency steady-state response, and the output voltage versus time in response to a 1-mv input step at $t = 0$. Make sure your answers are consistent. There are very close ties between the step response and the frequency response.

P14.22 Design a single-stage amplifier to have a midband gain magnitude of 100, and a response (to the 0.707 points) from 200 Hz to 10 MHz. The source resistance is specified as 50 ohms, and the collector resistor R_L is 200 ohms.

P14.23 Design a single-stage transistor amplifier similar to that in Fig. 14.16 to have a midband gain of -50. The amplifier must pass the pulse waveform shown in Fig. 14.29 (except for the dc component) with less than 10% droop on *either side*, measured with respect to the appropriate peak amplitude. Also, the pulse rise time must be 0.5 μsec.

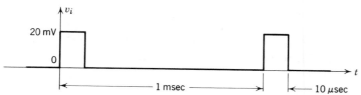

Figure 14.29   Pulse waveform.

P14.24 The circuit shown in Fig. 14.30 uses an *npn* silicon diffused transistor. It has a midband voltage gain of -32, an upper 0.707 frequency of 15.9 MHz, and a value of C_μ of 3 pf. To obtain more gain, the designer increased the value of R_L to 300 ohms. Find the new gain, and the new upper 0.707 frequency. *Neglect r_x in all calculations.* Justify your model parameters. Make reasonable approximations, and state them.

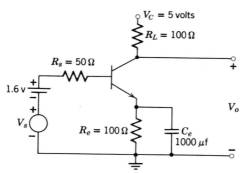

Figure 14.30   Common-emitter amplifier.

CHAPTER FIFTEEN

Multistage Amplifiers

15.1 Cascode Amplifier Analysis: Gain and Bandwidth

Significant new design possibilities appear when we progress from the single-stage circuits discussed in previous chapters to multistage designs. For example, we can achieve very large gains when common-emitter stages are cascaded (i.e., the output of one stage is connected to the input of the second stage), because the system gain will usually be of the order of the product of the gains of the individual stages. However, accompanying these new design possibilities are new design problems. For example, multistage amplifiers have many natural frequencies, which are usually complicated functions of many of the capacitances in the incremental model. For this reason we shall be forced to use a digital computer in multistage amplifier design.

Our general approach to the design of multistage amplifiers will be to use admittedly crude approximations to obtain first-cut parameter values for the amplifier. Then we calculate for this amplifier the poles and zeros, gain, and 0.707 frequency. Finally, these results are compared with the original specifications, and appropriate modifications are made in the amplifier to overcome any discrepancies.

15.1.1 Gain

Because we wish to rely rather heavily on computer-aided analysis, it is somewhat simpler to introduce the multistage amplifier discussion in terms of a specific example. We have chosen for this example the so-called *cascode* two-stage amplifier shown in Fig. 15.1a. Transistor T_1 is a standard common-emitter circuit except that the collector load is a second transistor rather than the usual resistor. Transistor T_2 is a common-base stage: the signal enters at the emitter and leaves at the collector, the base being held at a constant potential by a battery. In the course of the discussion the advantages and disadvantages of this common-emitter common-base cascode will become apparent.

With respect to dc power flow from the power supply, the two transistors are in series, and the collector currents I_{C1} and I_{C2} are very nearly equal. If the bias network is properly chosen, both transistors operate in the forward active region; hence we can make first-cut gain calculations using crude α_F and β_F models (see Section 7.3) for the transistors, as shown in Fig. 15.1b. The diagram makes clear that the collector voltage V_{CE} of T_1 is determined almost entirely by the base battery voltage of T_2:

$$V_{CE1} \simeq V_{B2} \tag{15.1}$$

and thus

$$V_{CE2} \simeq V_C - V_{B2} - I_C R_L \tag{15.2}$$

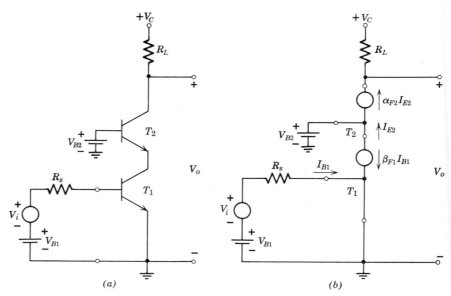

Figure 15.1 Cascode amplifier.

For this simple model, the gains can be calculated by inspection:

$$\frac{\Delta I_{C2}}{\Delta I_{B1}} = \beta_{F1}\alpha_{F2} \tag{15.3}$$

$$\frac{V_o}{V_i} = -\frac{\Delta I_{C2}R_L}{\Delta I_B \Delta I_{B1} R_s} = -\beta_{F1}\alpha_{F2}\frac{R_L}{R_s} \tag{15.4}$$

It is clear from Eqs. 15.3 and 15.4 that because α_F is always less than one (except in the now-obsolete point-contact transistor), the second transistor does not increase either the current gain or voltage gain in this circuit.

One important reason for adding a second transistor as in Fig. 15.1 is that this transistor, because it is operating as a common-base rather than common-emitter amplifier, can operate with a much larger collector voltage. Specifically, the collector voltage of a common-base stage is limited by the avalanche voltage of the collector junction, rather than the sustaining voltage. Other reasons for connecting the second transistor in this way become apparent only after a detailed examination of the high-frequency performance of the circuit.

15.1.2 Node Equations

To examine the high-frequency behavior of the cascode amplifier, we first form in Fig. 15.2 a complete small-signal model based on the hybrid-pi model. We can now find by inspection the general form of the transfer

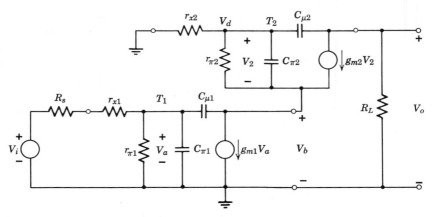

Figure 15.2   Incremental model of cascode amplifier.

function V_o/V_i. There are four independent energy-storage elements (independent in the sense that there are no nodes fed solely by inductors, and no loops formed only of capacitors), so the circuit has four natural frequencies. To find the form of the numerator, we note first that at $s = 0$, the network has finite gain, hence there cannot be any s factors in the numerator. Next, we observe that for s large, all capacitors become short circuits, but only one of these short circuits, namely $C_{\pi 1}$, reduces V_o/V_i to zero (see Problem P15.1). Thus at high frequencies we expect V_o/V_i to vary as $1/s$. The only form of the transfer function consistent with these requirements is

$$\frac{V_o}{V_i} = \frac{K(s - s_a)(s - s_b)(s - s_c)}{(s - s_d)(s - s_e)(s - s_f)(s - s_g)} \tag{15.5}$$

To find the parameters in Eq. 15.5, we must write and solve a complete set of equations for the network in Fig. 15.2. There are four independent nodes (assuming that R_s and r_{x1} are summed to form one new resistor R_s'), so we select as independent variables the four node-to-ground voltages.

In this and subsequent diagrams, a voltage V next to a node (in this case V_d) is assumed to be a node-to-ground voltage. The polarity is defined such that if V is positive, the node voltage is positive with respect to ground. A straightforward application of Kirchhoff's current law to each node yields

$$G_s'V_i = [G_s' + g_{\pi 1} + s(C_{\pi 1} + C_{\mu 1})]V_a - sC_{\mu 1}V_b$$

$$0 = (g_{m1} - sC_{\mu 1})V_a + [g_{\pi 2} + g_{m2} + s(C_{\pi 2} + C_{\mu 1})]V_b - (g_{\pi 2} + g_{m2} + sC_{\pi 2})V_d$$

$$0 = -(g_{\pi 2} + sC_{\pi 2})V_b + [g_{x2} + g_{\pi 2} + s(C_{\pi 2} + C_{\mu 2})]V_d - sC_{\mu 2}V_o$$

$$0 = -g_{m2}V_b + (g_{m2} - sC_{\mu 2})V_d + (G_L + sC_{\mu 2})V_o$$

$$\text{(15.6a through d)}$$

It is obvious at this point that any attempt to find the actual transfer function V_o/V_i in literal form is going to be a tedious and unrewarding task. Hence we are forced to carry forward the discussion from here on using specific numerical values. For simplicity, but certainly subject to change pending further insight, we choose identical operating points of $I_C = 10$ ma, $V_{CE} = 10$ volts for the transistors. Assume the following transistor specifications at this operating point:

$$g_m = 0.4 \,\text{mho} \qquad \beta_o = 100$$

$$r_\pi = 250 \,\text{ohms} \qquad r_x = 20 \,\text{ohms}$$

$$C_\pi = 100 \,\text{pf} \qquad C_\mu = 5 \,\text{pf}$$

Also, assume that $R_s = R_L = 200$ ohms.

Converting all conductances to units of millimhos, we obtain

$$g_m = 400 \qquad g_x = 50 \qquad g_\pi = 4$$

$$G_L = 5 \qquad G_s' = \frac{1}{0.2 + 0.02} = 4.5$$

Substituting these values (in units of millimhos, picofarads, and nanoseconds) into Eqs. 15.6, we obtain

$$4.5V_i = (8.5 + s105)V_a - s5V_b \tag{15.7a}$$

$$0 = (400 - s5)V_a \cdot + (404 + s105)V_b - (404 + s100)V_d \tag{15.7b}$$

$$0 = \qquad\qquad - (4 + s100)V_b \quad + (54 + s105)V_d - s5V_o \tag{15.7c}$$

$$0 = \qquad\qquad - 400V_b \qquad\qquad + (400 - s5)V_d + (5 + s5)V_o \tag{15.7d}$$

It still requires a formidable amount of effort to solve these numerical equations for the transfer function V_o/V_i; hence we quite naturally turn to the digital computer for help. We first make a fairly accurate determination of the amplifier bandwidth by means of the computer. Then in subsequent sections we discuss an approximate technique that allows us to estimate amplifier performance for first-cut design purposes.

15.1.3   Bandwidth Calculations via the Digital Computer[1]

Recall that we can find the expression for V_o/V_i from Eqs. 15.7 by applying Cramer's rule:

$$\frac{V_o}{V_i} = \frac{4.5 \,\Delta_{14}}{\Delta}$$

[1] Readers who do not have access to a digital computer can omit Section 15.1.3 without loss of continuity. However, it may prove helpful to return to the last paragraph of this section after finishing Section 15.2.3.

where Δ denotes the determinant of the set of equations, and Δ_{14} denotes the minor formed by striking the first row and fourth column of the complete determinant.

The natural frequencies of the network are those frequencies at which voltages can exist at the terminals when V_i is zero. This condition can exist only if the determinant Δ is zero. Hence the poles of V_o/V_i can be found by finding the roots of the characteristic equation

$$\Delta = 0$$

A similar argument can be used to show that the zeros of V_o/V_i are the roots of the equation

$$\Delta_{14} = 0$$

Thus to find the poles and zeros of V_o/V_i, we need a program to solve equations of the form $\Delta = 0$.

Most computation facilities have programs for solving the *eigenvalue problem*, that is, the question of what values of s satisfy the expression

$$\begin{vmatrix} a_1 + s & b_1 & c_1 \dots \\ a_2 & b_2 + s & c_2 \dots \\ a_3 & b_3 & c_3 + s \dots \\ \cdot & \cdot & \cdot \\ \cdot & \cdot & \cdot \\ \cdot & \cdot & \cdot \end{vmatrix} = 0 \qquad (15.8)$$

where the coefficients a_1, b_1, and so forth are real. The determinant of Eqs. 15.7 can be reduced to the form shown in Eq. 15.8 by standard determinant-manipulation techniques: essentially we have to diagonalize and normalize to unity the s coefficients of the determinant. This too can be done by the computer. If this reduction is performed on Eq. 15.7, the eigenvalues of the resulting determinant are in fact the roots of the original characteristic equation. Two computer programs that find roots by this method are listed in the appendices. The program in Appendix C is written in Fortran IV. NATFREQS, written in APL, is in Appendix D.

When the determinant Δ and the minor Δ_{14} of Eq. 15.7 are processed by one of these programs, the poles and zeros of V_o/V_i are found to be as follows:

Zeros	Poles
$s_a = 8.0 \text{ nsec}^{-1}$	$s_d = -0.0806 \text{ nsec}^{-1}$
$s_b = -2.02 + j5.99$	$s_e = -0.644$
$s_c = -2.02 - j5.99$	$s_f = -4.05$
	$s_g = -16.45$

There are many ways to find the 0.707 frequency ω_h from these computer results. For example, the magnitude of each factor in Eq. 15.5 can be plotted versus ω (preferably on log-log paper) and the results combined graphically to yield the overall response magnitude $|V_o/V_i|$. The 0.707 frequency can then be read off the graph.

If one pole is at a much lower frequency than the zeros and the other poles, that is, if we have *one dominant pole* s_1, then a first approximation for ω_h is

$$\omega_h \simeq |s_l| \tag{15.9}$$

In our example, this approximation yields

$$\omega_h \simeq 0.0806 \text{ Grad/sec}$$

$$f_h \simeq 12.9 \text{ MHz}$$

A more accurate formula for finding ω_h, applicable when the zeros are at a much higher frequency than the dominant poles (as they clearly are here), can be readily derived from Eq. 15.5. First we simplify the expression by assuming that s_a, s_b, and s_c are large enough in magnitude so that in the vicinity of ω_h we can consider the numerator as a constant, K', where

$$K' = -Ks_a s_b s_c \tag{15.10}$$

Then we divide through Eq. 15.5 by $s_d s_e s_f s_g$, obtaining

$$\frac{V_o}{V_i} = \frac{K''}{(1 - s/s_d)(1 - s/s_e)(1 - s/s_f)(1 - s/s_g)} \tag{15.11}$$

The magnitude of the transfer function for $s = j\omega$ is

$$\left.\left|\frac{V_o}{V_i}\right|\right|_{s=j\omega} \simeq \left|\frac{K''}{(1 - j\omega/s_d)(1 - j\omega/s_e)(1 - j\omega/s_f)(1 - j\omega/s_g)}\right| \tag{15.12}$$

It is convenient in finding the magnitude of the right-hand side to square both sides of the equation. *If all poles are real,*

$$\left|\frac{V_o}{V_i}\right|^2 = \frac{(K'')^2}{(1 + \omega^2/s_d^2)(1 + \omega^2/s_e^2)(1 + \omega^2/s_f^2)(1 + \omega^2/s_g^2)} \tag{15.13}$$

Expanding, we obtain

$$\left|\frac{V_o}{V_i}\right|^2 = \frac{(K'')^2}{1 + \omega^2(1/s_d^2 + 1/s_e^2 + 1/s_f^2 + 1/s_g^2) + \omega^4(1/s_d^2 s_e^2 + \cdots) + \cdots} \tag{15.14}$$

Because we have assumed that s_d, s_e, s_f, and s_g are real, the coefficients in this equation must be positive, so that $|V_o/V_i|$ must be a monotonic function of ω^2. We wish to find the 0.707 frequency ω_h, at which point $|V_o/V_i|^2 = (K'')^2/2$. Clearly

$$\omega_h < |s_d|, |s_e|, |s_f|, |s_g| \tag{15.15}$$

Thus we can find an approximate value for ω_h from Eq. 15.14 by using only the first two terms in the denominator:

$$\left.\left|\frac{V_o}{V_i}\right|^2\right|_{\omega=\omega_h} = \frac{(K'')^2}{2} \simeq \frac{(K'')^2}{1 + \omega_h{}^2(1/s_d{}^2 + 1/s_e{}^2 + 1/s_f{}^2 + 1/s_g{}^2)} \tag{15.16}$$

Solving for ω_h, we obtain

$$\frac{1}{\omega_h{}^2} = \frac{1}{s_d{}^2} + \frac{1}{s_e{}^2} + \frac{1}{s_f{}^2} + \frac{1}{s_g{}^2} \tag{15.17}$$

(Clearly, this method can be extended to a network with any number of natural frequencies.) Substitution of the computer-generated values into Eq. 15.17 yields

$$\omega_h = 0.0799 \text{ Grad/sec}$$

$$f_h = 12.7 \text{ MHz}$$

Because the natural frequencies are so widely separated in this case, and Eq. 15.17 indicates that the natural frequencies enter into the ω_h expression as the sum of squares, the simple and the more accurate expressions for ω_h in this example yield almost identical results.

To emphasize one of the advantages of this cascode connection (Fig. 15.1), we digress at this point to calculate for comparison purposes the bandwidth of a corresponding single-stage amplifier. To have approximately the same gain, the single-stage amplifier must have a load resistor of 200 ohms (compare Eq. 15.4 with Eq. 11.28). Hence, from Eq. 14.48, the bandwidth will be

$$\omega_h \simeq \frac{G_s' + g_\pi}{C_\pi + C_\mu(1 + [g_m + G_s']R_L)}$$

$$\simeq \frac{8.55}{100 + 5[1 + 400(0.2)]}$$

$$= 0.0169 \text{ Grad/sec}$$

or

$$f_h \simeq 2.7 \text{ MHz}$$

Comparing this result to the bandwidth estimate for the cascode, we note that the inclusion of the second transistor leads to an increase of about a factor of 5 in bandwidth for the same midfrequency gain. The reason for this substantial difference can be found in numerical calculation for ω_h above. There we see that the capacitive term resulting from C_μ is very large for the single-stage amplifier because $g_m R_L$ is large. In the cascode connection, the common-emitter stage operates into a very low impedance, that is, the emitter of the second stage. Hence in the cascode the effect of $C_{\mu1}$ on the bandwidth is quite small.

15.1.4 Bandwidth Calculations with Complex Poles

Frequently the computer calculations on the cascode amplifier will indicate a complex pole pair in the transfer function. If this pole pair is closer to the origin than the other poles, Eq. 15.17 will be increasingly in error as the poles get farther from the real axis. If the complex pole pair approaches the configuration of a *two-pole Butterworth filter,*

$$s_1 = -\alpha + j\alpha$$

$$s_2 = -\alpha - j\alpha$$

then the bandwidth should be calculated on the basis of the Butterworth filter formula rather than from Eq. 15.17. For the two-pole Butterworth filter,

$$\omega_h = 1.41|\alpha| \tag{15.18}$$

The frequency response of a Butterworth filter is said to be "maximally flat," because if the poles are any farther off the real axis than specified above, the magnitude of the response begins to have a hump in it.[2]

15.1.5 Step Response

Once the pole and zero locations have been found, the rise time of the multi-stage amplifier can be calculated fairly readily. As we saw in Chapter 14, for real poles the step response is the sum of a number of exponentials, one for each pole in the transfer function. If one pole s_{dom} is dominant, then one exponential will dominate the response, and

$$t_{rise} \simeq \frac{2.2}{s_{dom}} \tag{15.19a}$$

If there is no dominant pole, but the poles are all real, then because rise times add approximately quadratically,

$$(t_{rise})^2 = t_{r1}{}^2 + t_{r2}{}^2 + t_{r3}{}^2 \cdots$$

$$= (2.2)^2\left(\frac{1}{s_1{}^2} + \frac{1}{s_2{}^2} + \frac{1}{s_3{}^2}\cdots\right)$$

Thus, from Eq. 15.17, for circuits with real poles

$$t_{rise} \simeq \frac{2.2}{\omega_h} = \frac{0.35}{f_h} \tag{15.19b}$$

If the amplifier has complex poles, as discussed in Section 15.1.4, there will be ringing in the step response. For the two-pole Butterworth filter configuration, for example, there will be a 4.3% overshoot in the response.[2]

---

[2] Butterworth filters are discussed in more detail in Chapter 19, and References 15.1 and 15.2.

15.2 Open-Circuit Time Constants as a Design Aid

Although the computer solution discussed above provides a simple method for analyzing multistage circuits, it unfortunately provides almost no insight into *design*. For example, the computer solution gives no guidance about how best to redesign the cascode circuit to increase its bandwidth, because the analysis does not identify the circuit elements primarily responsible for the bandwidth limitation. Thus we must develop additional analysis methods that give such insight. However, because we have computer methods to provide accurate answers, the additional methods can be quite approximate, hence simple and rapid.

One such method involves calculating ω_h from a group of easily computed network time constants. Unfortunately, it takes a good deal longer to derive on a rational basis the relation between ω_h and these time constants than it does to make the actual calculation. The proof is in two parts. The first part establishes the relation between ω_h and the first two terms of the transfer function denominator polynomial, and the second relates the same denominator terms to the time constants.*

15.2.1 Relationship between ω_h and the First Two Denominator Terms of the Transfer Function

If we multiply out the denominator of Eq. 15.5, and again assume (as in Section 15.1.3) that the zeros in that equation will not influence the bandwidth calculation, we obtain an expression of the form

$$\frac{V_o}{V_i} = \frac{K'}{a_0 + a_1 s + a_2 s^2 + a_3 s^3 + s^4} \tag{15.20}$$

The magnitude of this expression at $s = j\omega_h$ is

$$\left|\frac{V_o}{V_i}\right|_{s=j\omega} = \left|\frac{K'}{a_0 + ja_1\omega_h - a_2\omega_h{}^2 - ja_3\omega_h{}^3 + \omega_h{}^4}\right|$$

Again assuming that the network natural frequencies s_d, s_e, s_f, and s_g are real, we can apply the same argument as that following Eq. 15.12 to find an approximate value for ω_h. That is, we square both sides of the equation, and solve for ω_h by noting from Eq. 15.20 that at the 0.707 frequency ω_h,

$$\left|\frac{V_o}{V_i}\right|_{s=j\omega_h}^2 = \frac{(K')^2}{2a_0{}^2}$$

If we discard all terms above $\omega_h{}^2$, we obtain

$$\omega_h \simeq \frac{a_0}{\sqrt{a_1{}^2 - 2a_0 a_2}} \tag{15.21}$$

---

* In an introductory course, the proofs in the next two subsections can be omitted without loss in continuity, because the important results of the proofs have been restated at the beginning of Section 15.2.3.

(see Problem P15.2). A simpler but less accurate approximation results if we neglect the a_0a_2 term in Eq. 15.21:

$$\omega_h \simeq \frac{a_0}{a_1} \qquad (15.22)$$

This approximation is particularly useful because it gives ω_h in terms of the ratio of the first two coefficients in Eq. 15.20, and this ratio can usually be found by inspection of the network, as we shall now show.

15.2.2   Finding a_1/a_0 and a_{n-1}/a_n by Inspection of the Network

To find the general relationship between a_1/a_0 and the network elements, we consider a linear active network that contains n capacitors and no other energy storage. For simplicity, we develop the relation for a_1/a_0 for the three-capacitor network of Fig. 15.3a, recognizing that the proof can be readily generalized. Disregarding any terminal pairs originally associated with the network, we assign a voltage and current to each of the terminal pairs associated with the capacitors, as shown in the figure.

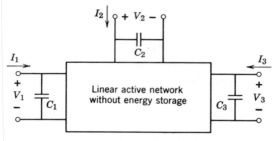

(a) Capacitors identified by terminal pair

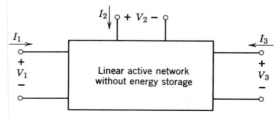

(b) Network with capacitors removed

Figure 15.3   Representation of a linear active network containing three capacitors.

We subsequently have need for two sets of low-frequency parameters:

1. The short-circuit conductances, that is, the conductance measured at each port with all other ports short-circuited.
2. The open-circuit resistances, that is, the resistance measured at each port with all other ports open-circuited.

To find these, we remove the capacitors, as shown in Fig. 15.3b, and represent the linear active network that remains by the node equations given in Eqs. 15.23. Any *independent* sources within the box are assumed to be set to zero; the effects of any *dependent* sources within the box must be included in the equations:

$$I_1 = g_{11}V_1 + g_{12}V_2 + g_{13}V_3 \tag{15.23a}$$

$$I_2 = g_{21}V_1 + g_{22}V_2 + g_{23}V_3 \tag{15.23b}$$

$$I_3 = g_{31}V_1 + g_{32}V_2 + g_{33}V_3 \tag{15.23c}$$

We can find the short-circuit conductances G_{js} by noting that Eqs. 15.23 are in y-parameter form (see Section 12.1.1). Thus from the definition of y_i or y_o (Eqs. 12.2a and b), *the short-circuit conductance at terminal-pair j is just g_{jj}*:

$$G_{js} = g_{jj} \tag{15.24}$$

To find the open-circuit resistances, designated by R_{jo}, we solve Eqs. 15.23 for V_j in terms of I_j, with all other currents equal to zero. For convenience we use the shorthand notation of determinants. We designate the g determinant as

$$\Delta_g = \begin{vmatrix} g_{11} & g_{12} & g_{13} \\ g_{21} & g_{22} & g_{23} \\ g_{31} & g_{32} & g_{33} \end{vmatrix} \tag{15.25}$$

and the cofactors by $(\Delta_g)_{jk}$. For example,

$$(\Delta_g)_{11} = \begin{vmatrix} g_{22} & g_{23} \\ g_{32} & g_{33} \end{vmatrix} \tag{15.26}$$

With this notation Cramer's rule yields

$$V_j = I_j \frac{(\Delta_g)_{jj}}{\Delta_g}$$

Thus the open-circuit resistance at terminal-pair j is

$$R_{jo} = \frac{(\Delta_g)_{jj}}{\Delta_g} \tag{15.27}$$

When the capacitors are present at the terminal pairs, as shown in Fig. 15.3a, the complete network can be represented by a set of node equations with the following admittance determinant, which is obtained by adding the appropriate capacitive susceptances to the conductances on the principal diagonal of Δ_g:

$$\Delta_y = \begin{vmatrix} g_{11} + sC_1 & g_{12} & g_{13} \\ g_{21} & g_{22} + sC_2 & g_{23} \\ g_{31} & g_{32} & g_{33} + sC_3 \end{vmatrix} \tag{15.28}$$

The natural frequencies of the complete network are those frequencies at which voltages can exist at the terminals when $I_1 = I_2 = I_3 = 0$. This condition can be met only if $\Delta_y = 0$. Inspection of Eq. 15.28 shows that Δ_y will contain, in general, all powers of s from s^0 up to s^3. If there are n capacitors and no capacitor loops, the highest power of s in the characteristic equation is n:

$$\Delta_y = 0 = a_0 + a_1 s + a_2 s^2 + a_3 s^3 \tag{15.29}$$

If all natural frequencies have negative real parts, the network is stable, and there then will be no missing coefficients in the middle of the equation. That is, in our example with three capacitors, a_3 can be zero if there is a capacitor loop, but if a_3 and a_0 are nonzero, then a_1 and a_2 must also be nonzero.

Some of the coefficients in Eq. 15.29 can be identified relatively easily by inspection of Δ_y, Eq. 15.28. The coefficient a_0, the constant term, is simply Δ_y when $s = 0$, or equivalently, a_0 is equal to Δ for the network with all the capacitors removed. That is,

$$a_0 = \Delta_g \tag{15.30}$$

The coefficient a_1 (that of the first power of s) must be the sum of three terms, each of which contains one capacitance multiplied by the cofactor of the corresponding element in the conductance determinant. On this basis, a_1 is

$$a_1 = C_1(\Delta_g)_{11} + C_2(\Delta_g)_{22} + C_3(\Delta_g)_{33} \tag{15.31}$$

Thus the desired ratio a_1/a_0 is

$$\frac{a_1}{a_0} = C_1 \frac{(\Delta_g)_{11}}{\Delta_g} + C_2 \frac{(\Delta_g)_{22}}{\Delta_g} + C_3 \frac{(\Delta_g)_{33}}{\Delta_g} \tag{15.32}$$

However, $(\Delta_g)_{jj}/\Delta_g$ is the open-circuit resistance seen by C_j, as shown in Eq. 15.27. Consequently,

$$\frac{a_1}{a_0} = R_{1o}C_1 + R_{2o}C_2 + R_{3o}C_3 = \sum_j \tau_{jo} \tag{15.33}$$

where τ_{jo} denotes the time constant of the jth capacitor calculated with all other capacitors *open-circuited*. Open-circuiting all capacitors but one usually breaks a complicated network into several simpler subnetworks. Hence the open-circuit resistances R_{jo} can often be found by inspection (*no energy-storage elements are involved in this calculation*).

We also derive at this point a second relation among the coefficients of the denominator polynomial, which is useful for finding the low-frequency 0.707 point of an amplifier. In Eq. 15.29, the coefficient a_3 (or in general the coefficient of the s^n term) results from multiplying the susceptive parts of the elements on the principal diagonal:

$$a_3 = C_1 C_2 C_3 \tag{15.34}$$

The coefficient a_2 (in general the coefficient of the s^{n-1} term), which also results from multiplying terms on the principal diagonal, contains three terms, each of which involves all capacitors except one:

$$a_2 = C_2 C_3 g_{11} + C_1 C_3 g_{22} + C_1 C_2 g_{33} \tag{15.35}$$

Hence

$$\frac{a_2}{a_3} = \frac{g_{11}}{C_1} + \frac{g_{22}}{C_2} + \frac{g_{33}}{C_3} \tag{15.36}$$

$$\equiv \sum_j \frac{1}{\tau_{js}} \tag{15.37}$$

where τ_{js} denotes the time constant of the jth capacitor calculated with all other capacitors *shorted* (see Eq. 15.24). Shorting all capacitors but one usually collapses a complicated network sufficiently so that again the time constants can be determined by inspection.

15.2.3   Relation between ω_h and the Open-Circuit Time Constants

In the preceding section we proved that for an RC network with no capacitor loops, the ratio of the coefficient of the s term to the constant term in the denominator of the gain expression is (in general)

$$\frac{a_1}{a_0} = R_{1o}C_1 + R_{2o}C_2 + \cdots + R_{no}C_n = \sum \tau_{jo} \tag{15.38}$$

where R_{jo} denotes the resistance seen by the jth capacitor and τ_{jo} denotes the time constant of the jth capacitor, both calculated with all other capacitors open-circuited. In Section 15.2.1 we showed that a rough approximation to the 0.707 frequency ω_h could be found from the same two coefficients:

$$\omega_h \simeq \frac{a_0}{a_1} \tag{15.39}$$

Combining the two results, we obtain a very simple relationship between ω_h and the open-circuit time constants which provides valuable design insight:

$$\omega_h \simeq \frac{1}{\sum \tau_{jo}} \tag{15.40}$$

This relation will allow us to localize to some extent the circuit elements limiting the amplifier bandwidth, by indicating which open-circuit time constant is dominant in the bandwidth calculation. Let us illustrate this by calculating these time constants for the cascode circuit introduced in Sections 15.1.1 and 15.1.2.

15.2.4   Example

For convenience the incremental circuit for the cascode amplifier has been repeated in Fig. 15.4a. When all capacitors but $C_{\pi 1}$ are open-circuited, as

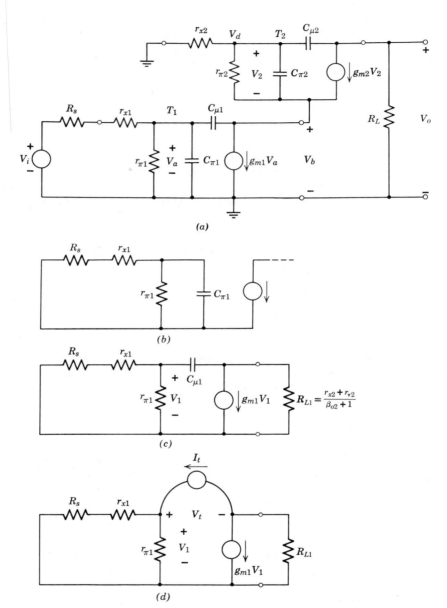

(a)

(b)

(c)

(d)

Figure 15.4 Calculation of open-circuit time constants associated with transistor T_1 in the cascode circuit.

shown in Fig. 15.4*b*, the input network becomes decoupled from the remainder of the circuit, thereby making it possible to calculate τ_{1o} by inspection. In units of kilohms, picofarads, and nanoseconds,

$$R_{1o} = r_{\pi 1} \| (r_{x1} + R_s)$$

$$= 0.25 \| 0.22 = 0.117 \, \text{kohm}$$

Thus

$$\tau_{1o} = C_{\pi 1} R_{1o}$$

$$= 100(0.117) = 11.7 \, \text{nsec}$$

Figure 15.4*c* shows the network that results when only capacitor $C_{\mu 1}$ remains in the circuit. The input impedance of transistor T_2 reduces to

$$R_{L1} = \frac{r_{x2} + r_{\pi 2}}{\beta_{o2} + 1}$$

$$\simeq \frac{0.270}{100} = 0.0027 \, \text{kohm}$$

under these conditions. Even with this simplification, the calculation of R_{2o}, the resistance facing $C_{\mu 1}$, cannot be done by inspection. A fairly straightforward way of finding R_{2o} is to apply a test current I_t to the terminals in question, as shown in Fig. 15.4*d*, and calculate the resultant voltage. We choose a current source for the test source because this will allow us to calculate V_1 most readily. By inspection

$$V_1 = I_t[r_{\pi 1} \| (r_{x1} + R_s)]$$

$$= I_t R_{1o}$$

Thus

$$\frac{V_t}{I_t} = R_{2o} = R_{1o} + g_m R_{1o} R_{L1} + R_{L1}$$

$$= 0.117 + 400(0.117)0.0027 + 0.0027$$

$$= 0.243 \, \text{kohm}$$

Hence

$$\tau_{2o} = C_{\mu 1} R_{2o} = 5(0.243)$$

$$= 1.22 \, \text{nsec}$$

The circuit in Fig. 15.5*a* results when all capacitors in Fig. 15.4*a* except $C_{\pi 2}$ are set to zero. The simplest way to find R_{3o} facing $C_{\pi 2}$ is to set $C_{\pi 2}$ to zero, apply a voltage source V_t across the capacitor terminals, and calculate the resulting current I_t (see Problem P15.3). The current generator $g_{m1} V_1$ is

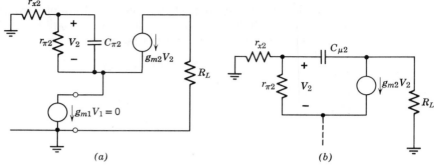

Figure 15.5 Calculation of R_{3o} and R_{4o} associated with transistor T_2 in the cascode circuit.

not excited under these conditions, hence appears as an open circuit. However, generator $g_{m2}V_2$ is excited and is in fact the dominant factor in G_{3o}:

$$\frac{I_t}{V_t} = G_{3o} = g_{\pi2} + g_{m2} = 4 + 400$$

$$= 404 \text{ mmhos}$$

That is,

$$R_{3o} = 2.47 \text{ ohms}$$

Hence

$$\tau_{3o} = \frac{C_{\pi2}}{G_{3o}} = \frac{100}{404}$$

$$= 0.247 \text{ nsec}$$

Figure 15.5b can be used to calculate the fourth open-circuit time constant. Applying an excitation across capacitor $C_{\mu2}$ cannot cause any current to flow through the $r_{\pi2}, g_{m2}$ branch because with generator $g_{m1}V_1$ an open circuit, we must have

$$V_2 = -g_{m2}V_2 r_{\pi2}$$

and for positive coefficients the only solution to this equation is $V_2 = 0$. Hence

$$R_{4o} = r_{x2} + R_L = 0.02 + 0.2$$

$$= 0.22 \text{ kohm}$$

and

$$\tau_{4o} = R_{4o}C_{\mu2} = 0.22(5)$$

$$= 1.1 \text{ nsec}$$

Thus the sum of the open-circuit time constants is

$$\Sigma \tau_{jo} = 11.7 + 1.22 + 0.25 + 1.1$$

$$= 14.27 \text{ nsec}$$

Now, from Eq. 15.40,

$$\omega_h \simeq \frac{1}{14.27} = 0.07 \text{ Grad/sec}$$

(a result that is about 13% lower than the more accurate calculation in Section 15.1.3).

The important insight that we gain from this calculation is that the dominant factor limiting the bandwidth of this amplifier is the time constant τ_{1o}. Hence reducing $C_{\pi 1}, r_{x1}, r_{\pi 1}$, or R_s will pay big dividends in increased bandwidth, whereas reducing any other resistor or capacitor values will bring about only minimal changes.

To verify this conclusion, two additional computer calculations were made on the amplifier of Fig. 15.4a. In the first, $C_{\pi 1}$ was reduced from 100 to 50 pf, and in the second, $C_{\pi 2}$ was reduced from 100 to 50 pf. The results are summarized in Table 15.1, along with the results of the original computer calculation.

Table 15.1

	$C_{\pi 1} = 100 \text{ pf}$ $C_{\pi 2} = 100 \text{ pf}$	$C_{\pi 1} = 50 \text{ pf}$ $C_{\pi 2} = 100 \text{ pf}$	$C_{\pi 1} = 100 \text{ pf}$ $C_{\pi 2} = 50 \text{ pf}$
s_d	$-0.0806 \text{ nsec}^{-1}$	-0.17 nsec^{-1}	-0.0803
s_e	-0.64	-0.44	-0.67
s_f	-4.05	-4.45	-7.20
s_g	-16.5	-20.8	-17.9
ω_h	79.9 Mrad/sec	159 Mrad/sec	79.7 Mrad/sec

Thus when $C_{\pi 1}$ is halved, the bandwidth nearly doubles, as predicted. Also as predicted, when $C_{\pi 2}$ is halved, no significant bandwidth improvement results (although the very slight bandwidth decrease comes as a bit of a surprise).

To further reinforce the concept of open-circuit time constants, the reader is urged to calculate τ_{1o} and τ_{2o} for the single-stage common-emitter amplifier discussed at the end of Section 15.1.3 and to compare the results with those obtained for the cascode (see Problem P15.4).

15.2.5 A Useful Computational Check

It is a simple matter to check for consistency between the open-circuit time constants and the natural frequencies. By equating the ratio a_1/a_0 in Eq.

15.20 to the ratio of the first two terms in the multiplied-out denominator of Eq. 15.11, we find

$$\frac{a_1}{a_0} = -\left[\frac{1}{s_d} + \frac{1}{s_e} + \frac{1}{s_f} + \frac{1}{s_g}\right] \tag{15.41}$$

Hence, from Eq. 15.38, we find

$$-\left[\frac{1}{s_d} + \frac{1}{s_e} + \frac{1}{s_f} + \frac{1}{s_g}\right] = \sum_j \tau_{jo} \tag{15.42}$$

or, in general,

$$-\sum_j \frac{1}{s_j} = \sum_j \tau_{jo} \tag{15.43}$$

Note that this is an *exact* expression, hence can be used as a check on the calculations to as many significant figures as one wishes to use in carrying out the calculations (see Problems P15.5, P15.6, and P15.7). In the present example, for $C_{\pi 1} = C_{\pi 2} = 100$ pf, $-\Sigma 1/s_j = 14.3$, which agrees within slide-rule accuracy with $\Sigma \tau_{jo} = 14.27$ as calculated on page 539.

15.2.6   Multistage Design Procedure

We are now in a position to outline a relatively simple method for designing multistage amplifiers to meet some given gain and bandwidth specification. It should be emphasized that the method suggested below is *not* unique. Many different design procedures are possible, and the reader is urged to explore other methods, or, better yet, devise his own.

In the design procedure we shall follow in this and the next chapter, we first find the resistive parameters R_L, g_m, r_π, and so on, that are required to make the network meet the midfrequency gain specification. Then we calculate the open-circuit resistances. From the specification on the high-frequency 0.707 point, ω_h, we calculate $\Sigma \tau_{jo}$ using Eq. 15.40. Now, using the relation

$$\sum \tau_{jo} = \sum R_{jo} C_j \tag{15.44}$$

we can select a transistor with appropriate values of C_π and C_μ, keeping in mind such factors as the relative cost and availability of transistors to meet the requirements. This completes the first-cut design of the amplifier (other than biasing and the coupling and bypass capacitors).

Next we write the node equations for the mid- and high-frequency circuit model just derived, and calculate the poles, and ω_h for the specified transfer function (voltage gain, for example). If the computed value of ω_h is unacceptably far from the specified value, certain specific C_π and C_μ values (hence transistors) can be changed. As we saw above, the open-circuit time constants provide an excellent guide as to which element should be changed. This design procedure is shown in flow-chart form in Fig. 15.6.

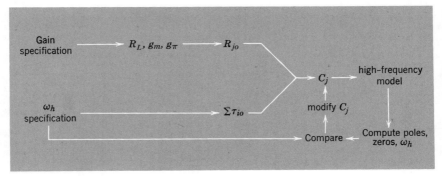

Figure 15.6   Flow chart for multistage design.

The design procedure to meet a specified low-frequency 0.707 point ω_l is similar to that outlined above except that it is based on the *short-circuit time constants*. We illustrate the general procedure in the next section in terms of the design of a bias network for the cascode amplifier. Examples of high-frequency design to meet a specified upper band edge ω_h are given in Chapter 16.

15.3   Cascode Amplifier Low-Frequency Design[3]
15.3.1   Calculation of Resistor Values

For simplicity, the cascode circuit introduced in Section 15.1.1 employed a very rudimentary and impractical biasing scheme. In this section, we discuss the design of a more practical arrangement. As can be seen from the circuit in Fig. 15.7, the bias network is a simple extension of the networks discussed in Chapter 13. The voltage divider now has three resistors R_{b1}, R_{b2}, and R_{b3} in order to establish the base voltage of transistor T_2 as well as of T_1. Also, a third capacitor C_b has been added to provide an ac short circuit from the base of T_2 to ground.

From the point of view of dc bias stability, this circuit is inherently somewhat more stable than a comparable single-stage design. The base current of transistor T_2 flows through resistor R_{b1}, producing an added voltage drop that tends to oppose any temperature-induced changes in the operating point. However, because the base currents of the two transistors are comparable, and usually much smaller than the current through R_{b1}, R_{b2}, and R_{b3}, the improvement in stability is minor. Hence the bias resistors can be chosen using the methods of Chapter 13 if we ignore the effects of the second transistor and assume that the Thévenin resistance facing the base of T_1 is

$$R_b \simeq R_{b3} \| (R_{b2} + R_{b1}) \tag{15.45}$$

[3] This section can be covered after Chapter 16 without loss of continuity.

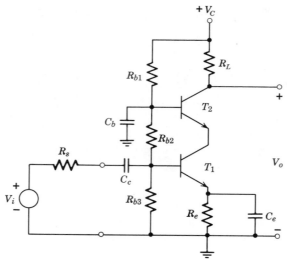

Figure 15.7 Biasing circuit for a cascode amplifier.

For brevity, we follow the "handbook" design method of Section 13.4.2 to select R_{b1}, R_{b2}, and R_{b3} to give the desired collector current of 10 ma. First we choose a 300-ohm emitter resistor to provide a 3-volt drop from emitter to ground. Then we choose R_b about ten times R_e, say 5 kohm. If for simplicity we neglect the base current flowing in the voltage divider, then choosing $V_C = 22$ volts, $R_{b1} = 24$ kohm, $R_{b2} = 6$ kohm, $R_{b3} = 6$ kohm will set the base-to-ground voltages of T_1 and T_2 to 3.7 and 7.4 volts respectively (for more exact calculations, see Problems P15.8, P15.9, and P15.10). Now let us turn to the more interesting aspect of the design: how to select values of C_c, C_e, and C_b to yield a given low-frequency 0.707 point.

15.3.2 Calculation of Coupling and Bypass Capacitor Values
The complete incremental model for the cascode circuit in Fig. 15.7 would have seven capacitors in it. However, if the high- and low-frequency 0.707 points are specified as

$$\omega_h = 80 \text{ Mrad/sec}$$

$$\omega_l = 1000 \text{ rad/sec}$$

then we obviously have a wide midfrequency region of constant gain. It follows from the discussion in Section 14.1.1 that we must be able to split up this seven-capacitor incremental model into two simpler models. Specifically, we are justified in drawing a *low-frequency incremental model* as shown in Fig. 15.8, in which C_π and C_μ are open-circuited. Also, we can draw a *high-frequency incremental model* in which C_c, C_e, and C_b are short-circuited. This is exactly the incremental model we worked with in Section 15.1.

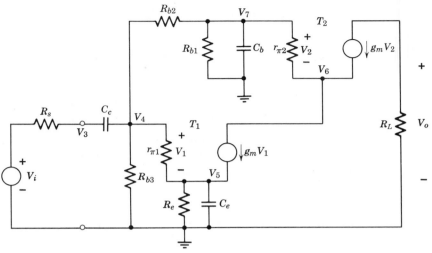

Figure 15.8 Low-frequency incremental model for the cascode amplifier in Fig. 15.7.

The general form of the low-frequency gain expression can be found by inspection of Fig. 15.8. Note that for simplicity we have represented the transistors by r_π, g_m models, since the omission of r_x does not change the essential character of the calculation. Because there are three independent capacitors in the network, the gain expression V_o/V_i has three poles. Also, V_o/V_i is zero at zero frequency because of C_c, and finite at "high frequencies" (actually the midfrequency for the whole circuit). The only expression that meets all of these conditions is

$$\frac{V_o}{V_i} = \frac{Ks(s - s_i)(s - s_k)}{(s - s_m)(s - s_n)(s - s_o)} \tag{15.46}$$

It is the *highest* pole in this expression that will primarily determine the low-frequency cutoff of the amplifier.

The capacitors in the low-frequency circuit model (Fig. 15.8) clearly interact (see Section 14.3.2); hence we expect each of the three poles in Eq. 15.46 to be a function of all three capacitors. The problem is thus quite analogous to the high-frequency design problem discussed in Section 15.1, so that it is not surprising that techniques closely related to those discussed in Sections 15.1 and 15.2 will be employed in the solution. Specifically, we use the *short-circuit* time constants discussed in Section 15.2.2 to find the capacitor values.

Although it may not be obvious at this point, the zeros in Eq. 15.46 will always be at frequencies lower than the highest pole, and to simplify the discussion we somewhat arbitrarily assume that all three zeros are at zero frequency. (We shall return later to test this assumption and correct it if necessary.) On this basis, the voltage gain becomes

$$\frac{V_o}{V_i} = \frac{Ks^3}{(s - s_m)(s - s_n)(s - s_o)} \tag{15.47}$$

On multiplying out the denominator, we obtain

$$\frac{V_o}{V_i} = \frac{K's^3}{a_3 s^3 + a_2 s^2 + a_1 s + 1} \tag{15.48}$$

Following a line of reasoning exactly analogous to that in Section 15.2.1, we can derive an approximate expression for ω_l in terms of the coefficients of the denominator polynomial:

$$\omega_l \simeq \frac{a_2}{a_3} \tag{15.49}$$

(see Problem P15.11). By combining this result with Eq. 15.37, we obtain

$$\omega_l \simeq \sum_j \frac{1}{\tau_{js}} \tag{15.50}$$

where τ_{js} denotes the time constant of the jth capacitor calculated with all other capacitors in the network *shorted*.

For this design we require $\omega_l = 1000$ rad/sec; thus

$$\omega_l = 1000 = \frac{1}{\tau_{1s}} + \frac{1}{\tau_{2s}} + \frac{1}{\tau_{3s}}$$

The design problem is underconstrained, in the sense that this equation does not specify the three capacitors uniquely; hence as a first cut we arbitrarily set the three time constants equal. Thus

$$\tau_{1s} = \tau_{2s} = \tau_{3s} = 3 \times 10^{-3} \text{ sec}$$

Now the specific capacitor values can be calculated.

To find C_c, we must first find the resistance facing C_c when C_e and C_b are shorted. The network appropriate for this calculation is shown in Fig. 15.9a. By inspection

$$R_{1s} = R_s + R_{b3} \| R_{b2} \| r_{\pi 1}$$

Using numbers from Section 15.1.2,

$$R_{1s} = 0.2 + 6 \| 6 \| 0.25$$

$$= 0.43 \text{ kohm}$$

Hence

$$C_c = \frac{\tau_{1s}}{R_{1s}} = \frac{3}{0.43} = 7 \ \mu\text{f}$$

To find C_e, we first find R_{2s} by shorting C_c and C_b in Fig. 15.8, thereby obtaining the simpler circuit shown in Fig. 15.9b. We can find the resistance

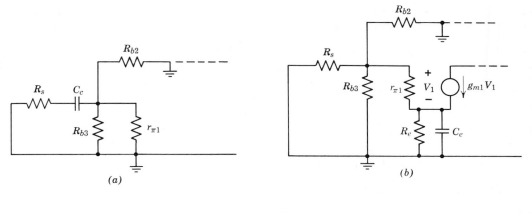

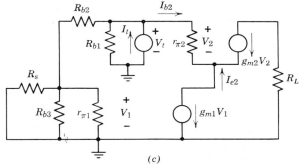

Figure 15.9 Circuits for calculating the short-circuit resistances for Fig. 15.8.

by inspection, by using the common-collector impedance-transforming relation:

$$R_{2s} = \frac{(R_s \| R_{b3} \| R_{b2}) + r_{\pi 1}}{\beta_o + 1} \Bigg\| R_e$$

$$= \frac{0.2 \| 6 \| 6 + 0.25}{101} \Bigg\| 0.3$$

$$= 4.3 \text{ ohms}$$

Thus

$$C_e = \frac{\tau_{2s}}{R_{2s}} = \frac{3}{4.3 \times 10^{-3}} = 700 \ \mu\text{f}$$

In Fig. 15.9c we have shorted C_c and C_e, and replaced C_b by a voltage source V_t. Now R_{3s}, the resistance facing C_b, can be calculated as the ratio V_t/I_t. We resort to the voltage-source method because the involvement of both dependent sources makes calculation by inspection somewhat hazard-ous. From the figure

$$V_1 = \frac{r_{\pi 1} \| R_{b3} \| R_s}{(r_{\pi 1} \| R_{b3} \| R_s) + R_{b2}} V_t$$

and

$$I_{b2} = -(1 - \alpha_2)I_{e2} = (1 - \alpha_2)g_{m1}V_1$$

Hence

$$I_t = \frac{V_t}{R_{b1}} + \frac{V_t}{R_{b2} + r_{\pi 1} \| R_{b3} \| R_s} + \frac{V_t(1 - \alpha_2)g_{m1}(r_{\pi 1} \| R_{b3} \| R_s)}{r_{\pi 1} \| R_{b3} \| R_s + R_{b2}}$$

The parallel resistance is

$$r_{\pi 1} \| R_{b3} \| R_s = 0.25 \| 6 \| 0.2 = 0.109 \text{ kohm}$$

Then

$$G_{3s} = \frac{I_t}{V_t} = \frac{1}{24} + \frac{1}{6 + 0.109} + \frac{(400/101)0.109}{6 + 0.109}$$

$$= 0.276 \text{ mmho}$$

and

$$C_b = \tau_{3s}G_{3s} = 3 \times 0.276$$

$$= 0.83 \ \mu\text{f}$$

The capacitor values in the design are spread by three orders of magnitude. This probably indicates that the design is not optimum from the point of view of either cost or physical size. Fortunately, there are an infinite number of capacitor sets that satisfy the design equation,

$$\omega_l = 1000 \simeq \frac{1}{\tau_{1s}} + \frac{1}{\tau_{2s}} + \frac{1}{\tau_{3s}}$$

because the design problem is underconstrained. It is now clear from the short-circuit resistor values calculated above that we can reduce to some extent the spread in capacitor values by choosing τ_{2s} smaller than τ_{1s} and τ_{3s}. Thus a reasonable second cut at the design might be

$$\tau_{2s} = 1.25 \text{ msec}$$

$$\tau_{1s} = \tau_{3s} = 10 \text{ msec}$$

Combining these time constants with the corresponding short-circuit resistances, we obtain

$$C_c = \frac{10}{0.43} = 23.2 \ \mu\text{f}$$

$$C_e = \frac{1.25}{4.3} = 290 \ \mu\text{f}$$

$$C_b = 10 \times 0.276 = 2.76 \ \mu\text{f}$$

The cost of this design will be somewhat lower than that of the previous one (see Problem P15.12).

15.3.3 Verification of Design Using a Digital Computer[4]

Having selected element values, we resort to a computer calculation to verify the design. To find the natural frequencies of the low-frequency model (Fig. 15.8), we first write the node equations:

$$V_i G_s = V_3(G_s + sC_c) - V_4 sC_c \tag{15.51a}$$

$$0 = -V_3 sC_c + V_4(G_{b3} + G_{b2} + g_{\pi 1} + sC_c) - V_5 g_{\pi 1} - V_7 G_{b2} \tag{15.51b}$$

$$0 = -V_4(g_{\pi 1} + g_{m1}) + V_5(G_e + g_{m1} + g_{\pi 1} + sC_e) \tag{15.51c}$$

$$0 = V_4 g_{m1} - V_5 g_{m1} + V_6(g_{m2} + g_{\pi 2}) - V_7(g_{m2} + g_{\pi 2}) \tag{15.51d}$$

$$0 = -V_4 G_{b2} - V_6 g_{\pi 2} + V_7(G_{b1} + G_{b2} + g_{\pi 2} + sC_b) \tag{15.51e}$$

$$0 = V_6 g_{m2} - V_7 g_{m2} + V_o G_L \tag{15.51f}$$

It is clear from the circuit that node V_o has no energy-storage elements connected to it and voltage V_o does not couple back into the rest of the network. Hence we can eliminate Eq. 15.51f from the node equations and still obtain the correct natural frequencies. (In terms of the determinant, column 6 contains only one term, G_L; hence G_L is a constant factor multiplying the five-by-five cofactor Δ_{66}.) Substituting the numerical values calculated above into these equations (units of millimhos, microfarads, and milliseconds), we obtain

$$5V_i = (5 + s23.2)V_3 - s23.2V_4$$

$$0 = -s23.3V_3 + (4.34 + s23.2)V_4 \qquad - 4V_5 \qquad\qquad - 0.17V_7$$

$$0 = \qquad\qquad - 404V_4 + (407.33 + s290)V_5$$

$$0 = \qquad\qquad 400V_4 \qquad - 400V_5 + 404V_6 \qquad\qquad - 404V_7$$

$$0 = \qquad\qquad - 0.17V_4 \qquad\qquad\qquad - 4V_6 + (4.21 + s2.76)V_7$$

$$\text{(15.52a through e)}$$

Although these equations are a complete and correct description of the network, a minor difficulty arises when one tries to solve the resulting determinant by converting to the eigenvalue form, Eq. 15.8. The problem is that there are only three natural frequencies (see Eq. 15.46) but we have five node equations. Stated in another way, the determinant of Eqs. 15.52 will not be fifth-order in s but only third-order, because Eq. 15.52d contains no s terms, and the s terms can be eliminated from Eq. 15.52a by substituting from Eq. 15.52b. The computer programs in Appendices C and D automatically

---

[4] Readers who do not have access to a digital computer can omit this subsection without loss of continuity.

perform this reduction. Using either of these programs, we obtain for the low-frequency roots

$$s_m = -0.916 \text{ msec}^{-1}$$

$$s_n = -0.084$$

$$s_o = -0.0084$$

(see Problem P15.13).

A rapid check on all calculations to this point can be made using a relation similar to Eq. 15.43. We can show from Eqs. 15.11 and 15.20 that

$$\frac{a_{n-1}}{a_n} = -(s_d + s_e + s_f + s_g) \tag{15.53}$$

Hence from Eq. 15.37

$$s_d + s_e + s_f + s_g = -\sum \frac{1}{\tau_{js}} \tag{15.54}$$

or, in general,

$$-\sum_j s_j = \sum \frac{1}{\tau_{js}} \tag{15.55}$$

In this example, we have

$$-\sum s_j = 0.916 + 0.084 + 0.0084$$

$$= 1.008 \text{ msec}^{-1}$$

which provides a close check, because $\Sigma 1/\tau_{js} = 1000$ rad/sec.

The zeros of the transfer function can be found by evaluating the roots of the appropriate minor, Δ_{16}, of Eqs. 15.51:

$$s_i = -0.0115 \text{ msec}^{-1}$$

$$s_k = -0.076 \text{ msec}^{-1}$$

The low-frequency transfer function thus is

$$\frac{V_o}{V_i} = \frac{K's(s + 0.076)(s + 0.0115)}{(s + 0.916)(s + 0.084)(s + 0.0084)}$$

Direct calculation of the 0.707 frequency ω_l by finding $|V_o/V_i|^2$ and setting it equal to $(K')^2/2$, yields

$$\omega_l = 0.92 \text{ krad/sec}$$

This is a simple computation if we ignore the lowest pole and zero as being clearly unimportant in this calculation. The value of ω_l is within 8% of the desired value, thus validating the low-frequency design (see Problem P15.14).

Furthermore, the actual design will use commercially available capacitor sizes, and not the odd sizes calculated. These deviations from the design values, together with the relatively large tolerances on electrolytic capacitors, will render the 8% design error insignificant.

To find ω_l in more complicated examples, an approximate relation can be obtained from Eq. 15.46 in much the same way as was done for ω_h in Section 15.1.3. The result is

$$\omega_l{}^2 = s_m{}^2 + s_n{}^2 + s_o{}^2 + \cdots \tag{15.56}$$

(see Problem P15.15). If zeros are mixed in with the nondominant poles, the derivation can be extended to yield

$$\omega_l{}^2 = s_m{}^2 + s_n{}^2 + s_o{}^2 - 2s_i{}^2 - 2s_k{}^2 \cdots \tag{15.57}$$

(see Problem P15.16). If a nondominant pole and a zero are close together, say within 20%, it is best to cancel the pair and calculate ω_l on the basis of the remaining poles and zeroes.

REFERENCES

15.1   G. E. Valley and H. Wallman, *Vacuum Tube Amplifiers*, McGraw-Hill, New York, 1948.

15.2   F. F. Kuo, *Network Analysis and Synthesis*, Wiley, New York, 1962.

15.3   L. E. Dickson, *New First Course in the Theory of Equations*, Wiley, New York, 1962.

15.4   *APL\360 User's Manual*, Thomas J. Watson Research Center, IBM, 1968.

PROBLEMS

P15.1   At very high frequencies, that is, for s large, each capacitor in a circuit begins to look like a short circuit. Short-out the capacitors in Fig. 15.2 and show that regardless of what order the short circuits are applied, there is only *one* short-circuited path to ground, hence at very high frequencies the transfer function V_o/V_i must behave as $1/s$. (See page 525.)

P15.2   Calculate $|V_o/V_i|^2$ from Eq. 15.20, and from this derive the approximate expression for ω_h given by Eq. 15.21.

P15.3   In Fig. 15.5a, set $C_{\pi 2}$ equal to zero, apply a test current source I_t to the terminals, and calculate the resulting voltage V_t. Compare with the results for R_{3o} given on page 538. Comment on the ease of calculation by this method and the voltage-source method used in the text.

P15.4   Calculate the open-circuit time constants for the single-stage common-emitter amplifier discussed at the end of Section 15.1.3. Compare the values with the corresponding values in the cascode amplifier. Explain any large differences. (See page 539.)

P15.5 Apply Eq. 15.43 to the cascode amplifier calculations in Sections 15.1.3 and 15.2.4, to verify the result given on page 539.

P15.6 Apply Eq. 15.43 to the modified cascode amplifier outlined in Table 15.1 ($C_{\pi 1} = 50$ pf, $C_{\pi 2} = 100$ pf), thereby checking the time constant and natural frequency calculations. (See page 539.)

P15.7 (a) Find the two high-frequency poles of the single-stage amplifier discussed at the end of Section 15.1.3.

(b) Check these calculations and those made in Problem P15.4 using Eq. 15.43.

P15.8 Calculate the dc base-to-ground voltages in Fig. 15.7, assuming $R_{b1} = 24$ kohm, $R_{b2} = 6$ kohm, $R_{b3} = 6$ kohm, $R_e = 300$ ohm, $V_C = 22$ volts, $R_L = 200$ ohms. Include the effects of base current. The transistor parameters are given on page 526. (See page 542.)

P15.9 Calculate the stability of the operating points established in the "handbook design" of the cascode bias network given in Section 15.3.1. The circuit parameters are given in Problem P15.8. Assume that both transistors are silicon, with β_F equal to 100 at 25°C, and 160 at 125°C. (See page 542.)

P15.10 Design the bias network for the cascode amplifier in Fig. 15.7, using the more sophisticated design method outlined in Section 13.5. (See page 542.)

P15.11 Derive Eq. 15.49 from Eq. 15.48. (See page 544.)

P15.12 Using any electronics supply catalog as a reference, calculate the cost and total volume of the capacitors in the two low-frequency designs discussed in Section 15.3.2. Use the nearest standard values to those tabulated below.

	Design 1	Design 2
C_c	7 μf / 10 volts	23 μf / 10 volts
C_e	700 μf / 4 volts	290 μf / 4 volts
C_b	0.83 μf / 10 volts	2.7 μf / 10 volts

Will a further reduction in τ_{2s} decrease the cost? Explain.

P15.13 Eliminate V_3 and V_6 from Eqs. 15.52 and then find the three natural frequencies of the network from the remaining 3×3 determinant. Compare the results with the values of s_m, s_n, s_o given in the text.

P15.14 Complete the design of the bias capacitor network in Section 15.3.3 by calculating the low-frequency 0.707 point from the computed poles and zeros given on page 548. Compare with the results given by Eqs. 15.56 and 15.57.

P15.15 Derive Eq. 15.56.

P15.16 Derive Eq. 15.57.

P15.17 Estimate the rise time of the cascode amplifier whose parameters are given in Section 15.1.2.

P15.18 Calculate the exact 0.707 frequency ω_h for the two amplifier gain expressions

$$\frac{V_o}{V_i} = \frac{K}{(s + 1)^3}$$

$$\frac{V_o}{V_i} = \frac{K}{(s + 1)(s + 100)(s + 100)}$$

Now calculate approximate values for ω_h in each case, using Eqs. 15.17 and 15.9. Tabulate your results for ready comparison, and comment on the accuracy of the two approximate methods.

P15.19 Multiply out the denominators of the expression in Problem P15.18, hence find ω_h from Eq. 15.22. Compare with the corresponding answers in Problem P15.18, and comment.

P15.20 Choose coupling and bypass capacitors for the single-stage amplifier discussed in Section 14.3.3, except in this case use the low-frequency design method developed in Section 15.3. Design for a low-frequency 0.707 point of 50 Hz. Compare with the values derived in Chapter 14, and estimate the relative cost of the two designs.

P15.21 Write the node equations for the circuit in Fig. 15.10. Enter the coefficients on the computer and find the natural frequencies of the circuit. Now *explain* in physical terms the solution you obtain.

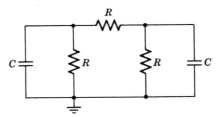

Figure 15.10 Simple circuit; $C = 1\mu f$, $R = 1$ ohm.

P15.22 For the single-stage common-emitter amplifier shown in Fig. 14.16, calculate on the computer the natural frequencies of the high-frequency incremental circuit model, assuming the following element values: $g_m = 400$ mmho, $g_\pi = 4$ mmho. $C_\pi = 150$ pf, $C_\mu = 5$ pf, $r_x = 25$ ohms. R_{b1} and R_{b2} very large, $R_e = 300$ ohms, $C_c = C_e = 1000$ μf, $R_s = 200$ ohms. Sketch the frequency response (magnitude and phase) of $V_o/V_i(j\omega)$ based on this calculation. Use log-log coordinates for simplicity. Compare these results with those obtained using the one-pole approximation in Section 14.5.2.

P15.23   Design a multistage amplifier to meet the following minimum specifications:

$$\text{midband voltage gain (magnitude)} = 3000$$
$$\text{Upper 0.707 frequency } f_h = 2\,\text{MHz}$$
$$\text{resistance } R_s \text{ of signal generator} = 100\,\text{ohms}$$

Ignore biasing considerations, except for specifying the operating point (V_{CE}, I_C, or V_{DS}, I_D) for each active device. Keep economic factors in mind: transistors with f_T greater than 1000 MHz became quite expensive, as do devices with C_μ less than 1 pf. Tabulate your results. Verify your design on the computer.

CHAPTER SIXTEEN

Further Examples of Multistage Amplifiers

16.1 Design of a Common-Emitter Cascade

In the preceding chapter, we have interleaved theory and example in the development of a design procedure for multistage amplifiers. To illustrate this design procedure, we work out in this chapter two further examples, virtually uninterrupted by new theory. In the present section we discuss two- and three-stage common-emitter cascades, and in the following section we cover the so-called emitter-coupled pair.

Let us now try to design a cascade of common-emitter stages to meet the following specifications:

> Voltage gain (magnitude): at least 7000
> High-frequency band edge or 0.707 point f_h : at least 3 MHz
> Source resistance R_s : 50 ohms

Such a specification is clearly impossible to meet with a single-stage amplifier (see, for example, the calculation at the end of Section 15.1.3). However, both a two-stage design with a gain per stage of about 85 and a three-stage design with a per-stage gain of about 19 appear possible. Thus let us first rough out a two-stage and a three-stage design which meet the gain and bandwidth specifications, setting aside for the moment all dc bias considerations.

16.1.1 Gain Calculations

A two-stage common-emitter cascade is shown in Fig. 16.1a. The rudimentary biasing circuit is adjusted so that both transistors operate in the active region; hence the incremental model of Fig. 16.1b is appropriate for midband gain calculations. By inspection, the midband voltage gain is

$$\frac{V_o}{V_i} = \underbrace{\left(\frac{r_{\pi 1}}{r_{\pi 1} + r_{x1} + R_s}\right)}_{\text{voltage divider}} g_{m1} \underbrace{\left(\frac{R_{L1}}{R_{L1} + r_{\pi 2} + r_{x2}}\right)}_{\text{current divider}} r_{\pi 2} g_{m2} R_{L2} \qquad (16.1)$$

Since many transistors have maximum f_T for collector currents in the range of 10 to 20 ma, let us initially assume that $I_C = 10$ ma. Also, since many transistors have β_o values of about 100, let us base the design on this value. Hence

$$g_m = 0.4 \text{ mho}$$
$$r_\pi = 250 \text{ ohms}$$
$$r_x = 25 \text{ ohms (typical for this collector current)}$$

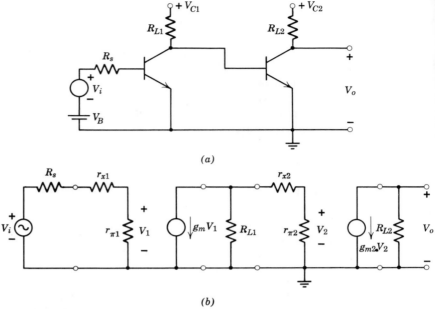

Figure 16.1 Two-stage common-emitter cascade.

Equation 16.1 can now be used together with the specified voltage gain of 7000 to find values for R_{L1} and R_{L2}:

$$\frac{100}{325}\left(\frac{R_{L1}}{275 + R_{L1}}\right)(100R_{L2}) > 7000$$

Many choices of R_{L1} and R_{L2} are possible, but to maintain the validity of our simplified hybrid-pi model it is necessary that $g_m R_L$ be less than about 100. Hence

$$R_{L2} \leqslant 250 \text{ ohms}$$

To meet the gain specification with $R_{L2} = 250$ ohms,

$$R_{L1} \geqslant 2760 \text{ ohms}$$

The final choice of values will be dictated by the bandwidth requirement, as we shall see shortly.

For the three-stage design the voltage gain expression is similar in form to Eq. 16.1:

$$\frac{V_o}{V_i} = -\left(\underbrace{\frac{r_{\pi 1}}{r_{\pi 1} + r_{x1} + R_s}}_{\substack{\text{voltage} \\ \text{divider}}}\right)g_{m1}\left(\underbrace{\frac{R_{L1}}{R_{L1} + r_{\pi 2} + r_{x2}}}_{\substack{\text{current} \\ \text{divider}}}\right)r_{\pi 2}g_{m2}$$

$$\times \left(\underbrace{\frac{R_{L2}}{R_{L2} + r_{\pi 3} + r_{x3}}}_{\substack{\text{current} \\ \text{divider}}}\right)r_{\pi 3}g_{m3}R_{L3} \qquad (16.2)$$

In this equation R_{L1}, R_{L2}, and R_{L3} must satisfy the inequality

$$\frac{100}{325}\left(\frac{R_{L1}}{275 + R_{L1}}\right)100\left(\frac{R_{L2}}{275 + R_{L2}}\right)(100R_{L3}) > 7000$$

Again many sets of resistor values meet this requirement, and the final choice will be dictated by many other considerations, including bandwidth. To obtain some feeling for the orders of magnitude of the load resistors, we note that if we arbitrarily assume $R_{L1} = R_{L2} = R_{L3}$, any value of R_L greater than 60 ohms will meet the gain specification. This value is so low that we would be wise to reduce the collector current on the first stage, thereby reducing transistor noise at the expense of gain. This possibility will be examined later.

16.1.2   Bandwidth Calculations

To select transistors that meet the bandwidth specification, we draw the complete incremental model for the circuit (Fig. 16.2) and calculate the

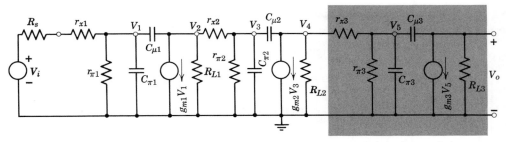

Omit for 2-stage design

Figure 16.2   Complete incremental model for the two- and three-stage common-emitter cascade.

open-circuit resistances. The calculations are almost identical to those for the common-emitter stage in Fig. 15.4a, hence they will not be worked out in detail. The small portion of the circuit pertinent to the calculation of R_{1o}, the resistance facing $C_{\pi 1}$ when all other capacitors are open-circuited, is shown in Fig. 16.3a. Clearly,

$$R_{1o} = r_{\pi 1}\|(r_{x1} + R_s) \tag{16.3}$$

Similarly, R_{3o}, the resistance facing $C_{\pi 2}$, is

$$R_{3o} = r_{\pi 2}\|(r_{x2} + R_{L1}) \tag{16.4}$$

and in the three-stage design, R_{5o}, the resistance facing $C_{\pi 3}$, is

$$R_{5o} = r_{\pi 3}\|(r_{x3} + R_{L2}) \tag{16.5}$$

That portion of the circuit in Fig. 16.2 appropriate for the calculation of R_{2o}, the open-circuit resistance facing $C_{\mu 1}$, is shown in Fig. 16.3b. A calculation of this type was discussed in Section 15.2.4, so that we can modify the

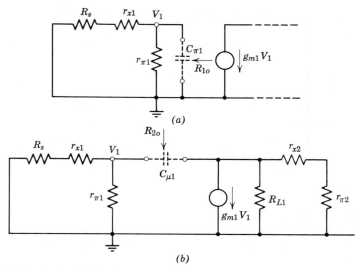

Figure 16.3   Subcircuits for calculating R_{jo} in a common-emitter cascade.

result to fit this configuration:

$$R_{2o} = R_{1o} + (1 + R_{1o}g_{m1})[R_{L1}\|(r_{x2} + r_{\pi2})] \qquad (16.6)$$

Similarly, for R_{4o}, the resistance facing $C_{\mu2}$ in the two-stage design

$$R_{4o} = R_{3o} + (1 + R_{3o}g_{m2})R_{L2} \qquad (16.7)$$

For the three-stage design,

$$R_{4o} = R_{3o} + (1 + R_{3o}g_{m2})[R_{L1}\|(r_{x3} + r_{\pi3})] \qquad (16.8)$$

and

$$R_{6o} = R_{5o} + (1 + R_{5o}g_{m3})R_{L3} \qquad (16.9)$$

To find the transistor f_T that is required in the two-stage design to produce the specified bandwidth, we substitute the appropriate numerical values into Eqs. 16.3, 16.4, 16.6, and 16.7. Assuming $R_{L1} = 2.75$ kohm, $R_{L2} = 0.25$ kohm, as calculated above,

$$R_{1o} = 0.057 \text{ kohm}$$

$$R_{2o} = 6.06 \text{ kohm}$$

$$R_{3o} = 0.23 \text{ kohm}$$

$$R_{4o} = 23.4 \text{ kohm}$$

A good high-frequency transistor operating with V_{CE} greater than a few volts will have C_μ as small as 2 pf. For this value,

$$\tau_{2o} = R_{2o}C_{\mu 1} = 6.06 \times 2 = 12.1 \text{ nsec}$$

$$\tau_{4o} = R_{4o}C_{\mu 2} = 23.4 \times 2 = 46.8 \text{ nsec}$$

To meet the specification that $f_h = 3$ MHz, we know from Eq. 15.40 that

$$\sum \tau_{jo} \simeq \frac{1}{\omega_h} = \frac{1}{2\pi \times 0.003} = 53 \text{ nsec}$$

Unfortunately, even for the smallest values of R_{L1} and R_{L2} that meet the gain specification

$$\tau_{2o} + \tau_{4o} = 58.9 \text{ nsec}$$

Because there is no "time" left for τ_{1o} and τ_{3o}, we conclude that it is not possible to meet the specified gain and bandwidth with a two-stage design.

The preceding calculations, although unsuccessful in terms of the two-stage amplifier, nevertheless offer important insight for the three-stage design. Clearly, the large size of R_{2o} and R_{4o} was the dominant cause of the failure. Inspection of Eqs. 16.6 and 16.7 shows that each of these resistances is dominated by a term of the form $R_i g_m R_o$, where R_i is the parallel combination of some resistors at the *input* of the transistor and R_o the parallel combination of resistors at the *output*. The problem in the two-stage design is that R_i, g_m, and R_o cannot be reduced without sacrificing gain, and we have no gain to spare.

In the three-stage design, on the other hand, we have ample gain, as shown by the fact that R_{L1}, R_{L2}, and R_{L3} could be reduced to 60 ohms and still meet the gain specification. Thus we now have the freedom to sacrifice gain in order to increase bandwidth. It should therefore be possible to achieve a successful design that meets both the gain and bandwidth specifications.

For collector currents in the milliampere range, transistor noise will in general decrease as the collector current is decreased.[1] Thus a substantial reduction in transistor noise will result, without excessive reduction in gain, if the first stage is operated at 1-ma collector current rather than 10 ma. There will almost certainly be enough gain in the first stage so that the second stage will not introduce any significant amount of noise to the amplifier. However, it is still wise to reduce the second-stage collector current somewhat in order to provide a gradual change in impedance levels from the first stage to the last. For this reason we somewhat arbitrarily choose $I_{C2} = 5$ ma. Assuming that β_o does not fall below its 10-ma value at these lower currents, we obtain the transistor parameters listed in Table 16.1.

[1] See References 16.1 and 16.2.

Table 16.1 Transistor Parameters

	T_1	T_2	T_3
I_C (ma)	1	5	10
g_m (mmho)	40	200	400
r_π (kohm)	2.5	0.5	0.25
r_x (kohm)	0.2	0.05	0.025

Now we must select R_{L1}, R_{L2}, and R_{L3}. Recall from the preceding discussion that, at least for the two-stage design, the critical resistance values in the bandwidth calculation were the $R_i g_m R_o$ terms. For the output stage, $R_o = R_{L3}$, where for the other stages R_o is of the form $R_L \| (r_x + r_\pi)$. Hence, to keep the three $R_i g_m R_o$ terms comparable, R_{L3} must be smaller than R_{L1} and R_{L2}. In fact, because of the decrease in impedance levels from T_1 to T_2 to T_3, as indicated in Table 16.1, it makes sense to have a corresponding decrease in R_L, that is,

$$R_{L1} > R_{L2} > R_{L3}$$

Using the original R_L estimate (page 557) as a starting point, we try $R_{L3} = 60$ ohms, $R_{L2} = 120$ ohms, $R_{L1} = 300$ ohms. The resulting gain is

$$\frac{V_o}{V_i} = -\frac{100}{2.75}\left(\frac{0.3}{0.3 + 0.55}\right)100\left(\frac{0.12}{0.12 + 0.275}\right)100(0.06)$$

$$= -2340$$

which does not meet the specification of $|V_o/V_i| = 7000$. Hence we try

$$R_{L1} = 500 \text{ ohms}$$

$$R_{L2} = 200 \text{ ohms}$$

$$R_{L3} = 100 \text{ ohms}$$

which yields a voltage gain of -7250.

Because of the rather complicated interdependence of the gain and time-constant equations, it is not intuitively obvious whether this choice of load resistors will yield an acceptable design. There are two possible ways of proceeding. We can choose a transistor that we know is good enough, then check the time constants to validate this assumption. Alternatively, we can calculate the six open-circuit resistances, then select values of C_π, hence the transistor f_T to meet the bandwidth specification. If these values are unsatisfactory for any reason, we can modify the values of R_L and iterate.

Let us follow the latter course. Using Eqs. 16.3, 16.4, 16.5, 16.6, 16.8, and 16.9 we find

$$R_{1o} = 0.228 \text{ kohm} \qquad R_{2o} = 2.88 \text{ kohm}$$
$$R_{3o} = 0.262 \text{ kohm} \qquad R_{4o} = 6.43 \text{ kohm}$$
$$R_{5o} = 0.118 \text{ kohm} \qquad R_{6o} = 4.92 \text{ kohm}$$

(Note that R_{2o}, R_{4o}, and R_{6o} differ by only a factor of 2 because of the tapering of the R_L values.) Again assuming $C_\mu = 2$ pf,

$$\tau_{2o} + \tau_{4o} + \tau_{6o} = 2(14.23) = 28.46 \text{ nsec}$$

Hence

$$\tau_{1o} + \tau_{3o} + \tau_{5o} = \Sigma\tau_{jo} - 28.5 = 53 - 28.5 = 24.5 \text{ nsec}$$

For equal values of C_π for the three transistors,

$$C_\pi = \frac{24.5}{0.228 + 0.262 + 0.118} = 40.3 \text{ pf}$$

Recall, however, from Chapter 12 that C_π is roughly proportional to collector current. Thus a design with equal values of C_π in the three stages requires three different transistor types. To design for a *single* transistor type,

$$\frac{C_{\pi 1}}{I_{C1}} \simeq \frac{C_{\pi 2}}{I_{C2}} \simeq \frac{C_{\pi 3}}{I_{C3}}$$

or, in this example,

$$C_{\pi 3} = 10C_{\pi 1}$$
$$C_{\pi 2} = 5C_{\pi 1}$$

Thus

$$0.228C_{\pi 1} + 0.262(5C_{\pi 1}) + 0.118(10C_{\pi 1}) = 2.72C_{\pi 1} = 24.5 \quad (16.10)$$
$$C_{\pi 1} = 9.0 \text{ pf}$$
$$C_{\pi 2} = 45 \text{ pf}$$
$$C_{\pi 3} = 90 \text{ pf}$$

On this basis the required value of f_T for the three transistors is about

$$f_T \text{ at } 10 \text{ ma} = \frac{400}{(90 + 2)2\pi} \simeq 0.7 \text{ GHz} = 700 \text{ MHz}$$

This value is readily obtainable with present-day transistors, hence the values of R_L selected are acceptable.

16.1.3 Design Check

The rough design is now complete. To obtain a more accurate bandwidth figure, we use the computer to find the natural frequencies. If the results are unacceptably far from the design value, it may be necessary to make a simple proportional adjustment in the C_π values.

The network can be described by six node equations if we combine r_{x1} and R_s into a single resistance R_s':

$$R_s' = r_{x1} + R_s \tag{16.11}$$

An appropriate set of node-to-datum voltages are indicated in Fig. 16.2. For node 1 we have

$$G_s' V_i = V_1[G_s' + g_{\pi1} + s(C_{\pi1} + C_{\mu1})] - sC_{\pi1}V_2 \tag{16.12a}$$

The remaining five equations are equally simple to derive:

$$0 = (g_{m1} - sC_{\mu1})V_1 + (g_{x2} + G_{L1} + sC_{\mu1})V_2 - g_{x2}V_3 \tag{16.12b}$$

$$0 = -g_{x2}V_2 + [g_{x2} + g_{\pi2} + s(C_{\pi2} + C_{\mu2})]V_3 - sC_{\mu2}V_4 \tag{16.12c}$$

$$0 = (g_{m2} - sC_{\mu2})V_3 + (g_{x3} + G_{L2} + sC_{\mu2})V_4 - g_{x3}V_5 \tag{16.12d}$$

$$0 = -g_{x3}V_4 + [g_{x3} + g_{\pi3} + s(C_{\pi3} + C_{\mu3})]V_5 - sC_{\mu3}V_o \tag{16.12e}$$

$$0 = (g_{m3} - sC_{\mu3})V_5 + (G_{L3} + sC_{\mu3})V_o \tag{16.12f}$$

The numerical values that we calculated above can now be substituted into these equations, and the poles calculated on the computer. The results are

$$s_1 = -0.0251 \text{ nsec}^{-1}$$

$$s_2 = -0.0943$$

$$s_3 = -0.409$$

$$s_4 = -9.55$$

$$s_5 = -18.22$$

$$s_6 = -28.56$$

(As a check for mathematical errors both in the time-constant calculations and in the node equations,

$$-\sum \frac{1}{s_j} = 53.05 \text{ nsec}$$

$$\sum \tau_{jo} = 53.0 \text{ nsec}$$

which is well within slide-rule accuracy.)

Because of the simple structure of the network, the zeros can be found by inspection from Fig. 16.2. Note first that at very high frequencies, the capacitors $C_{\pi1}$, $C_{\pi2}$, $C_{\pi3}$ form three shunt paths to ground for the signal, so that we expect the transfer function V_o/V_i to fall off as $1/s^3$. To achieve this asymptotic behavior with six poles, we must have three zeros in the transfer function. As in the single-stage common-emitter amplifier, these zeros arise from cancellation between the signal fed forward by g_m and that fed forward by C_μ. Thus the zeros are all in the right half plane:

$$s_7 = \frac{40}{2} = 20 \text{ nsec}^{-1}$$

$$s_8 = \frac{200}{2} = 100 \text{ nsec}^{-1}$$

$$s_9 = \frac{400}{2} = 200 \text{ nsec}^{-1}$$

The zeros can equally readily be found by inspection from the network equations (see Problem P16. 1).

It is clear from these results that ω_h will be determined predominantly by s_1 and s_2. Hence, from Eq. 15.17,

$$\omega_h \simeq \left(\frac{1}{0.025^2} + \frac{1}{0.094^2}\right)^{-\frac{1}{2}} = 0.0242 \text{ Grad/sec}$$

$$f_h = 3.85 \text{ MHz}$$

Thus our first approximation to the design has produced an amplifier with an upper 0.707 frequency about 28 % larger than the minimum value specified. For many applications this will be entirely satisfactory, because often the transistor parameters may not be known to any greater accuracy than this.

Note, however, that it would be possible to meet the specified f_h with transistors having about 30 % lower f_T than those chosen above. To iterate the design, we first increase $\Sigma\tau_{jo}$ by 28 %:

$$\Sigma\tau_{jo} = 53 \times \frac{3.85}{3.0} = 68 \text{ nsec}$$

If we select transistors with the same C_μ as before, the sum of the C_μ time constants will still be 28.5 nsec. Hence

$$\tau_{1o} + \tau_{3o} + \tau_{5o} = 68 - 28.5 = 39.5 \text{ nsec}$$

and, from Eq. 16.10,

$$C_{\pi 1} = \frac{39.5}{2.72} = 14.5 \text{ pf}$$

$$C_{\pi 2} = 73 \text{ pf}$$

$$C_{\pi 3} = 145 \text{ pf}$$

Therefore,

$$f_T \text{ at } 10 \text{ ma} = \frac{400}{(145 + 2)2\pi} = 0.43 \text{ GHz} = 430 \text{ MHz}$$

a reduction of almost 40% over the original design value. Checking this new design on the computer, we find that

$$s_1 = -0.0205 \text{ nsec}^{-1}$$

$$s_2 = -0.0654$$

$$s_3 = -0.270$$

$$s_4 = -7.82$$

$$s_5 = -15.50$$

$$s_6 = -26.21$$

$$\omega_h \simeq \left(\frac{1}{0.0205} + \frac{1}{0.065}\right)^{-\frac{1}{2}} = 0.0196 \text{ Grad/sec}$$

$$f_h = 3.12 \text{ MHz}$$

For this example the iterated design has no appreciable economic advantage over the original design, because 450-MHz transistors are priced about the same as 750-MHz units. However, if f_T values were a factor of 2 higher, a substantial price differential might result.

16.1.4   Bias Considerations[2]

The three-stage common-emitter amplifier can be biased a stage at a time by simply cascading three stages of the type shown in Fig. 14.11a. However, a much simpler yet elegant way of biasing the cascade is shown in Fig. 16.4. Note first that the transistors are *direct-coupled*, that is, the collector of one transistor is connected directly to the base of the succeeding transistor. Such a connection is possible with bipolar transistors because in the forward active region V_{BE} is always larger than the minimum value of V_{CE} corresponding to saturation. For example, for an *npn* silicon transistor, $V_{BE} \simeq 0.6$ volt, whereas $V_{CE}(\text{sat}) \simeq 0.2$ volt. This relationship is true for any bipolar transistor, for the base-to-emitter voltage corresponds to the voltage drop across one forward-biased diode, whereas the collector saturation voltage is the *difference* between two forward-biased diode drops.

Because we are using silicon transistors in this design, $V_{BE} \simeq 0.6$ volt; thus

$$V_{CE1} = V_{CE2} \simeq 0.6 \text{ volt}$$

One disadvantage of such a low collector voltage is that C_μ will be large in these transistors, because, as we saw in Chapter 12,

$$C_\mu = K(\psi_0 + |V_{CB}|)^{-1/3}$$

---

[2] If desired, this section can be read after Chapter 18, which discusses feedback.

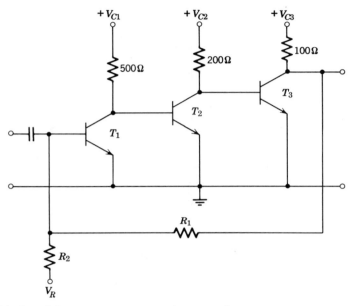

Figure 16.4   Biasing of three-stage common-emitter cascade.

for the diffused transistor (see, for example, Fig. 12.15). If this is a serious problem, forward-biased diodes can be added in series with the emitter leads to T_2 and T_3 to increase V_{CE1} and V_{CE2}.

It should be clear from the discussion in Chapter 13 that direct-coupling three transistors without other provisions for bias stabilization will result in completely unsatisfactory operation. For example, a change as small as 1 μa in I_{C1} will cause I_{C3} to change by about $\beta_F{}^2$ μa or 10 ma, a 100% change in collector current. To overcome this problem, we add a large resistor R_1 between output and input of the amplifier. This resistor senses the dc collector voltage of T_3 and uses this information to control the base current of T_1. In this way the amplifier can automatically correct for changes in its own operating point.

If we assume silicon transistors, the two principal temperature-dependent elements in the dc model will be β_F and the base-to-emitter voltage. An appropriate *total-variable* circuit is shown in Fig. 16.5. To simplify the analysis, the $V_B(T)$ generators associated with T_2 and T_3 have been omitted, on the basis that V_B changes in the input stage will be amplified by all three stages, hence will dominate in the bias calculations. Also, we postulate that

$$R_1 \gg R_{L3} \tag{16.13}$$

and then check this assumption in the final design.

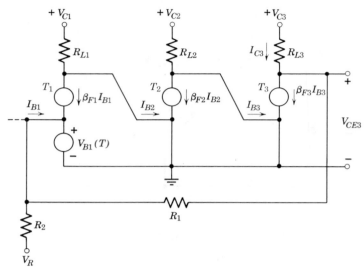

Figure 16.5   Total-variable circuit model of the circuit in Fig. 16.4.

As already pointed out, resistor R_1 feeds information about the operating point of T_3 back to the amplifier input. Specifically

$$I_{B1} \simeq \frac{-V_{B1}(T)}{R_1 \| R_2} + \frac{V_R}{R_2} + \frac{V_{CE3}}{R_1} \qquad (16.14)$$

The collector current $\beta_{F1} I_{B1}$ can then control the operating point of transistor T_3 :

$$I_{C3} = (\beta_{F1} I_{B1}) \beta_{F2} \beta_{F3} + \frac{V_{C2} \beta_{F3}}{R_{L2}} - \frac{V_{C1} \beta_{F2} \beta_{F3}}{R_{L1}} \qquad (16.15)$$

$$V_{CE3} = V_{C3} - R_{L3} I_{C3} \qquad (16.16)$$

Substituting Eq. 16.15 into Eq. 16.16, we obtain

$$V_{CE3} = V_{C3} - \beta_F{}^3 R_{L3} I_{B1} - V_{C2} \beta_F \frac{R_{L3}}{R_{L2}} + V_{C1} \beta_F{}^2 \frac{R_{L3}}{R_{L1}} \qquad (16.17)$$

if we assume identical values of β_F for the three transistors. To prove that the circuit will indeed stabilize the operating points, we eliminate I_{B1} between Eqs. 16.14 and 16.17 :

$$V_{CE3} \simeq \frac{V_{C3} + \beta_F{}^3 R_{L3} \left[\dfrac{V_{B1}(T)}{R_1 \| R_2} - \dfrac{V_R}{R_2} \right] - V_{C2} \beta_F \dfrac{R_{L3}}{R_{L2}} + V_{C1} \beta_F{}^2 \dfrac{R_{L3}}{R_{L1}}}{1 + \dfrac{R_{L3}}{R_1} \beta_F{}^3} \qquad (16.18)$$

Because β_F is of the order of 100, the term containing $\beta_F{}^3$ will dominate the numerator. Now if we can design the circuit so that in the denominator

$$\frac{R_{L3}}{R_1} \beta_F{}^3 \gg 1 \tag{16.19}$$

Eq. 16.18 reduces to

$$V_{CE3} \simeq V_{B1}(T) \left[\frac{R_1 + R_2}{R_2} \right] - V_R \frac{R_1}{R_2} \tag{16.20}$$

Equation 16.20 can also be derived on the basis of an intuitive argument. If the transistors in Fig. 16.4 have reasonable values of β_F, the base current I_{B1} must be *extremely* small, that is, only a few microamperes, even when resistor R_1 is connected from the amplifier output back to the input. Thus to a first approximation we assume

$$I_{B1} = 0$$

To achieve this, the voltage V_{CE3} in Fig. 16.5 must be such that the open-circuit voltage of the voltage divider R_1, R_2 is exactly equal to $V_{B1}(T)$:

$$V_{CE3} \frac{R_2}{R_1 + R_2} + V_R \frac{R_1}{R_1 + R_2} = V_{B1}(T) \tag{16.21}$$

By solving this equation for V_{CE3}, we again obtain Eq. 16.20.

It is clear from Eq. 16.20 that to make V_{CE3} as insensitive as possible to changes in $V_{B1}(T)$, the voltage V_R should be large and negative. Suppose, for example, that we want V_{CE3} to be about 5 or 6 volts. If we choose

$$V_R = -10 \text{ volt}$$

$$R_1 = 10 \text{ kohm}$$

$$R_2 = 20 \text{ kohm}$$

(which satisfy the conditions specified by Eqs. 16.13 and 16.19), then substitution into Eq. 16.20 yields

$$V_{CE3} = 0.6 \left(\frac{30}{20} \right) + 10 \left(\frac{10}{20} \right)$$

$$= 5.9 \text{ volts}$$

(see Problem P16.2). For this choice of values, a 10-mv change in $V_{B1}(T)$ will cause only a 15-mv change in V_{CE3}, which is less than a 1% change in the operating point (see Problem P16.3).

Unfortunately, the circuit as it stands in Fig. 16.4 will suppress changes in the input *signal* just as effectively as it suppresses changes in $V_{B1}(T)$. To maintain the desired ac gain of 7000, it is necessary to add a capacitor C_1 as shown in Fig. 16.6, to prevent the ac signal from flowing back from output to input via resistor R_1. The value of C_1 required to achieve a given low-frequency response can be found by calculating the resistance facing C_1, with the other bypass capacitors and the coupling capacitor *shorted*, as discussed in Section 15.3.2. The value of this short-circuit resistance will turn out to be surprisingly low, orders of magnitude smaller than R_1, because of the influence of the high-gain amplifier. Thus the required value of C_1 will often be quite large.

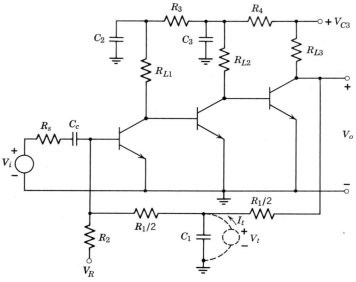

Figure 16.6   Complete bias network for three-stage common-emitter cascade.

A simple way to calculate the short-circuit resistance facing C_1 is to apply a test voltage source V_t across the terminals of C_1, as shown by the dashed lines in Fig. 16.6, and calculate the resulting increment of current I_t. Using a g_m, r_π model, and assuming R_s much smaller than R_2, we obtain

$$I_{b1} \simeq \frac{V_t}{R_1/2}\left[\frac{R_s}{R_s + r_{\pi1}}\right] \tag{16.22}$$

Hence

$$V_o \simeq \frac{\beta_o^{\,3}V_t}{R_1/2}R_{L3}\frac{R_s}{R_s + r_{\pi1}}$$

Now we can find the current I_t by superposition, assuming that R_1 is much larger than R_{L3} and $r_{\pi1}$:

$$I_t \simeq \frac{V_t}{R_1/2} + \frac{V_t}{R_1/2} + V_t\left(\frac{2\beta_o^{\,3}R_{L3}}{R_1}\right)\left(\frac{1}{R_1/2}\right)\frac{R_s}{R_s + r_{\pi1}} \tag{16.23}$$

Therefore,

$$G_{1s} = \frac{I_t}{V_t} = 4G_1 \left[1 + \frac{\beta_o{}^3 R_{L3} R_s}{R_1(R_s + r_{\pi 1})} \right] \tag{16.24}$$

For the present numerical example, $R_{L3} = 100$ ohms, $R_1 = 10$ kohm, $R_s = 50$ ohms, and $r_{\pi 1} = 2.5$ kohm so that

$$G_{1s} = 4 \times 0.1 \left[1 + \frac{10^6 \times 0.1 \times 50}{10(50 + 2500)} \right] = 80 \text{ mmho}$$

That is, the short-circuit resistance appearing across C_1 is only 12.5 ohms. Clearly, C_1 will have to be quite large to achieve good low-frequency response.

For a high-gain amplifier of this type it is usually necessary to add the *decoupling network* R_3, R_4, C_2, and C_3 shown in Fig. 16.6. This network serves a dual purpose. First, the proper dc operating voltages and currents for transistors T_1, T_2, and T_3 can be derived from a single power-supply voltage V_{C3} by appropriate choice of R_3 and R_4 (see Problem P16.4). Second, undesired coupling from T_3 back to T_2 and T_1 via R_3 and R_4 can be eliminated by making capacitors C_2 and C_3 short circuits at all signal frequencies of interest. If coupling were to occur between T_3 and T_1 because voltage V_{C3} did not come from an ideal zero-impedance power supply, and C_2 and C_3 were too small, undesired and unpredictable amplifier performance (such as low-frequency oscillations) would result. For this reason, C_2 and C_3 should be large enough to appear as short circuits compared to adjacent circuit resistances at the low-frequency cutoff ω_l.

Note also that great care must be taken in the layout of any high-gain amplifier to minimize stray capacitive coupling from output to input. Even a fraction of a picofarad of stray capacitance in this location can cause important changes in the amplifier high-frequency response.

16.2 Emitter-Coupled Amplifier

As another example of the high-frequency design procedure outlined in Section 15.2, let us select suitable transistors for the so-called *emitter-coupled* amplifier shown in Fig. 16.7a. This amplifier is made up of a common-collector stage driving a common-base stage, so that we can expect high current-gain and less-than-unity voltage gain in the first stage and high voltage-gain with less-than-unity current gain in the second stage. Thus the effect of the space-charge capacitance C_μ should be small in both stages, for the same reasons as in the cascode design of Section 15.1.

16.2.1 Preliminary Analysis

Before carrying out the design, it is necessary to do a modest amount of analysis to gain understanding of circuit operation. Because the emitters of both transistors go to a negative supply voltage and the collectors go to a positive supply voltage, whereas the bases are approximately at ground

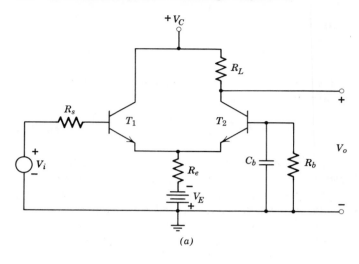

(a)

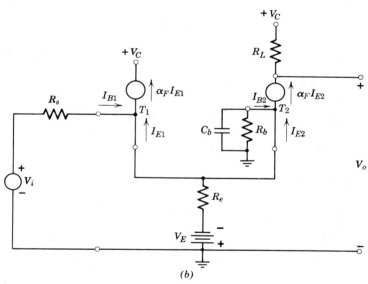

(b)

Figure 16.7   Emitter-coupled pair.

potential, we expect operation in the active-gain region for both transistors. Hence a crude calculation of circuit performance can be obtained using the simple α_F model for the transistors, as shown in Fig. 16.7b. For biasing purposes the two transistors are connected in parallel; hence for well-matched transistors the emitter currents I_{E1} and I_{E2} will be approximately equal for $R_b = R_s$.[3] In this case

$$I_{E1} \simeq I_{E2} \simeq -\frac{V_E}{2R_e + R_s/(\beta_F + 1)} \qquad (16.25)$$

(see Problem P16.5).

At signal frequencies, bypass capacitor C_b is a short circuit, so that from the point of view of the flow of signals, the amplifier is a common-collector, common-base cascade. Because we have used such a simple model, the incremental signal currents can be calculated by superposition:

$$I_{b1} = \frac{V_i}{R_s} \qquad (16.26)$$

Hence

$$I_{e1} = -(\beta_{F1} + 1)\frac{V_i}{R_s} \qquad (16.27)$$

Almost all of this current will flow into the emitter of T_2, causing a collector current

$$I_{c2} = -\alpha_{F2}I_{e2} = -\frac{\alpha_{F2}(\beta_{F1} + 1)V_i}{R_s} \qquad (16.28)$$

Thus the voltage gain of the cascade is

$$\frac{V_o}{V_i} = -\frac{I_{c2}R_L}{V_i} = \alpha_{F2}(\beta_{F1} + 1)\frac{R_L}{R_s} \qquad (16.29)$$

A somewhat more accurate calculation of the voltage gain can be made from the midfrequency incremental model of the circuit, shown in Fig. 16.8. The voltage gain V_4/V_i of the common-collector stage can be found from

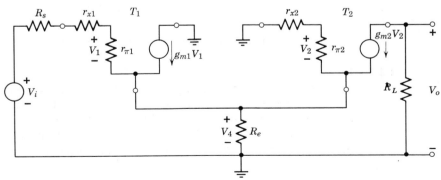

Figure 16.8 Midfrequency incremental model for the emitter-coupled pair, Fig. 16.7.

[3] If R_s is not too much larger than the transistor base resistance (not shown in this over-simplified model), then R_b and C_b can be omitted, and the base of T_2 grounded directly, without unduly unbalancing the collector currents.

Eq. 11.43b once the "load" on this stage has been determined. The load is the parallel combination of R_e and the input resistance of the common-base stage:

$$R_1 = R_e \left\| \left(\frac{r_{x2} + r_{\pi 2}}{\beta_{o2} + 1} \right) \right. \tag{16.30}$$

Hence, from Eq. 11.43b,

$$\frac{V_4}{V_i} = \frac{(\beta_{o1} + 1)R_1}{(\beta_{o1} + 1)R_1 + r_{x1} + r_{\pi 1} + R_s} \tag{16.31}$$

The voltage gain of the common-base stage is

$$\frac{V_o}{V_4} = g_{m2} R_L \frac{r_{\pi 2}}{r_{\pi 2} + r_{x2}} \tag{16.32}$$

Thus the overall voltage gain of the cascade is

$$\frac{V_o}{V_i} = \left[\frac{(\beta_{o1} + 1)R_1}{(\beta_{o1} + 1)R_1 + r_{x1} + r_{\pi 1} + R_s} \right] \left[\frac{\beta_{o2} R_L}{r_{\pi 2} + r_{x2}} \right] \tag{16.33}$$

where R_1 is specified by Eq. 16.30. In many designs R_e will be much larger than $(r_{x2} + r_{\pi 2})/(\beta_{o2} + 1)$, in which case the interstage load reduces to

$$R_1 \simeq \frac{r_{x2} + r_{\pi 2}}{\beta_{o2} + 1} \tag{16.34}$$

If now we assume that $\beta_{o1} = \beta_{o2}$, Eq. 16.33 reduces to

$$\frac{V_o}{V_i} \simeq \frac{\beta_{o2} R_L}{r_{x1} + r_{\pi 1} + r_{x2} + r_{\pi 2} + R_s} \tag{16.35}$$

an expression quite consistent with our original crude estimate in Eq. 16.29.

16.2.2 Design

Suppose that we wish to design an emitter-coupled amplifier with a gain of 15 and a bandwidth of 8 MHz. Assume further that the source resistance R_s is 500 ohms and that "other considerations" dictate a collector current in each transistor of 2 ma. Many transistors have a β_o of 100 in this current range, so let us use this value for the first-cut design. For $I_C = 2$ ma,

$$g_m = \frac{qI_C}{kT} = \frac{2}{25} = 0.08 \text{ mho} = 80 \text{ mmho}$$

$$r_\pi = \frac{\beta_o}{g_m} = \frac{100}{80} = 1.25 \text{ kohm}$$

At these current levels, r_x might be about 150 ohms. We can now use the gain specification and Eq. 16.35 to calculate the value of R_L:

$$\frac{V_o}{V_i} = 15 = \frac{100\,R_L}{2(1.25 + 0.15) + 0.5}$$

$$R_L = \frac{3.3 \times 15}{100} = 0.495\,\text{kohm} \simeq 500\,\text{ohms}$$

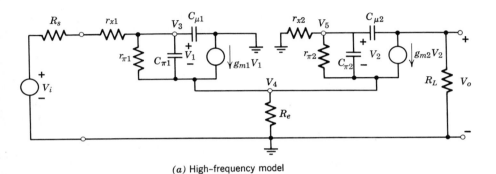

(a) High-frequency model

(b) Subcircuit for calculating R_{1o}

Figure 16.9   Incremental models for the emitter-coupled pair, Fig. 16.7.

The complete incremental model for the circuit is shown in Fig. 16.9a. To calculate the values of $C_{\pi1}$, $C_{\mu1}$, and $C_{\pi2}$, $C_{\mu2}$ required to meet the bandwidth specification, we must first calculate the open-circuit resistances faced by each of these capacitors. To find the resistance R_{1o} facing $C_{\pi1}$ when the other capacitors are open-circuited, we abstract from Fig. 16.9a the pertinent portion of the circuit, shown in Fig. 16.9b. The input resistance of the second transistor appears as a load on the first transistor in this calculation; this effect has been represented in the figure by the single resistance of value

$(r_{x2} + r_{\pi 2})/(\beta_{o2} + 1)$. Following the same technique as before, we apply a voltage V_t across the terminals where $C_{\pi 1}$ is normally connected, and find the resulting current I_t. The ratio V_t/I_t is the desired resistance.

$$I_t = \frac{V_t}{r_{\pi 1}} + \frac{V_t}{R_s + r_{x1} + R_1} + g_{m1}V_t \frac{R_1}{R_s + r_{x1} + R_1} \qquad (16.36)$$

where R_1, the net load from emitter to ground on the first transistor, is given by Eq. 16.30. The third term in Eq. 16.36 was derived by noting that the current $g_{m1}V_t$ divides between two paths, one containing R_1 and the other, the generator V_t, r_{x1}, and R_s. It follows directly from Eq. 16.36 that

$$R_{1o} = \frac{V_t}{I_t} = r_{\pi 1} \left\| \frac{R_s + r_{x1} + R_1}{1 + g_{m1}R_1} \right. \qquad (16.37)$$

$$\simeq r_{\pi 1} \left\| \frac{R_s}{2} \right. \qquad (16.38)$$

assuming that R_1 is approximately equal to $r_{\pi 2}/\beta_{o2}$.

Figure 16.10a is appropriate for calculating R_{2o}, the open-circuit resistance facing $C_{\mu 1}$. The value of R_{2o} can be found by inspection if the resistance R_1 is transformed out of the emitter lead by the method discussed in Section

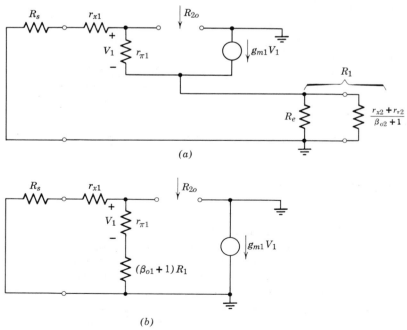

(a)

(b)

Figure 16.10 Subcircuits for calculating R_{2o}.

11.5.2, Eq. 11.42. The result is shown in Fig. 16.10b. Now by inspection

$$R_{2o} = (R_s + r_{x1}) \| [r_{\pi 1} + (\beta_{o1} + 1)R_1] \tag{16.39}$$

where R_1 is given by Eq. 16.30 (see Problem P16.6).

The subcircuit appropriate for the calculation of R_{3o}, the open-circuit resistance facing $C_{\pi 2}$, is shown in Fig. 16.11. For these calculations the only

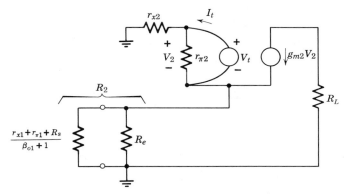

Figure 16.11 Subcircuit for calculating R_{3o}.

pertinent parameter of the first transistor is its output resistance, hence this is all that we include in the circuit. The calculation is identical in principle to the calculation of R_{1o}, hence will not be repeated in detail (see Problem P16.7). The result is

$$R_{3o} = r_{\pi 2} \left\| \frac{r_{x2} + R_2}{1 + g_{m2}R_2} \right. \tag{16.40}$$

where R_2 is the net resistance from emitter to ground for transistor T_2 :

$$R_2 = R_e \left\| \frac{r_{x1} + r_{\pi 1} + R_s}{\beta_{o1} + 1} \right. \tag{16.41}$$

Although it is possible to calculate R_{4o}, the open-circuit resistance facing $C_{\mu 2}$, from the subcircuit shown in Fig. 16.12a, it is easier to first transform the resistance R_2 out of the emitter lead, as shown in Fig. 16.12b. Now R_{4o} can be found in a manner exactly analogous to the calculation in an ordinary common-emitter stage. That is, if we let

$$R_A = r_{x2} \| [r_{\pi 2} + R_2(\beta_{o2} + 1)] \tag{16.42}$$

then from our previous common-emitter calculations,

$$R_{4o} = R_A + R_L + kg_{m2}R_A R_L \tag{16.43}$$

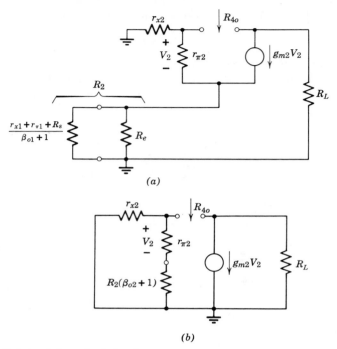

(a)

(b)

Figure 16.12   Subcircuit for calculating R_{4o}.

The constant k reflects the fact that the g_m generator is excited only by the voltage across $r_{\pi 2}$:

$$k = \frac{r_{\pi 2}}{r_{\pi 2} + R_2(\beta_{o2} + 1)} \tag{16.44}$$

Substituting the numerical values from pages 572 and 573 into Eqs. 16.37, 16.39, 16.40, and 16.43, we obtain (assuming that $R_e = 1$ kohm)

$$R_{1o} = 0.252 \text{ kohm} \qquad R_{2o} = 0.54 \text{ kohm}$$

$$R_{3o} = 0.064 \text{ kohm} \qquad R_{4o} = 2.97 \text{ kohm}$$

Let us try to design with $C_{\mu 1} = C_{\mu 2} = 3$ pf:

$$\tau_{2o} = 3 \times 0.54 = 1.62 \text{ nsec}$$

$$\tau_{4o} = 3 \times 2.97 = 8.91 \text{ nsec}$$

$$\overline{\tau_{2o} + \tau_{4o} = 10.53 \text{ nsec}}$$

To meet the specification of an 8-MHz bandwidth

$$\sum \tau_{jo} \simeq \frac{1}{\omega_h} = \frac{1}{2\pi(0.008)} = 19.9 \text{ nsec}$$

Hence

$$\tau_{1o} + \tau_{3o} = 19.9 - 10.5 = 9.4 \text{ nsec}$$

One possible choice for $C_{\pi 1}$ and $C_{\pi 2}$, useful for integrated circuit designs in which fabrication is simplified if all transistors are identical, requires $C_{\pi 1} = C_{\pi 2}$. Then

$$\tau_{1o} + \tau_{3o} = 9.4 = 0.252 C_{\pi 1} + 0.064 C_{\pi 1}$$

Therefore,

$$C_{\pi 1} = C_{\pi 2} = \frac{9.4}{0.316} \simeq 30 \text{ pf}$$

Thus the transistors should have an f_T at 2 ma of

$$f_T = \frac{g_m}{2\pi(C_\pi + C_\mu)} = \frac{80}{2\pi(33)} = 0.39 \text{ GHz} = 390 \text{ MHz}$$

Note that for this emitter-coupled amplifier, the dominant time constants are τ_{1o} associated with $C_{\pi 1}$ and τ_{4o} associated with $C_{\mu 2}$. As predicted, $C_{\mu 1}$ is not important because there is no signal fed back through it (compare with a common-emitter amplifier). If r_{x2} were zero, $C_{\mu 2}$ would also be unimportant, because again there would be no signal fed back from the output to the input of the transistor. But for finite r_x, and large R_L to give substantial voltage gain, the time constant associated with $C_{\mu 2}$ takes on a dominant role.

16.2.3 Design Check via Computer Analysis

To check this design, we use the computer to find the poles and zeros of V_o/V_i, and then calculate the actual 0.707 frequency. Referring to Fig. 16.9a, if R_s and r_{x1} are treated as a single resistor R'_s of value

$$R'_s = R_s + r_{x1}$$

then the circuit has four independent nodes. One possible set of node voltage variables are the node-to-ground set V_3, V_4, V_5, and V_o. The corresponding node equations are

$$V_i G'_s = V_3[G'_s + g_{\pi 1} + s(C_{\pi 1} + C_{\mu 1})] - V_4(g_{\pi 1} + sC_{\pi 1})$$

$$0 = -V_3(g_{\pi 1} + g_{m1} + sC_{\pi 1}) + V_4[G_e + g_{\pi 1} + g_{m1} + g_{\pi 2} + g_{m2}$$

$$+ s(C_{\pi 1} + C_{\pi 2})] - V_5(g_{\pi 2} + g_{m2} + sC_{\pi 2})$$

$$0 = -V_4(g_{\pi 2} + sC_{\pi 2}) + V_5[g_{x2} + g_{\pi 2} + s(C_{\pi 2} + C_{\mu 2})] - sC_{\mu 2}V_o$$

$$0 = -V_4(g_{m2}) + V_5(g_{m2} - sC_{\mu 2}) + V_o(G_L + sC_{\mu 2})$$

$$(16.45a \text{ through } d)$$

On substituting the numerical values calculated in Section 16.2.2, we obtain the following determinant from Eqs. 16.45 (in units of millimhos, picofarads, and nanoseconds):

$$\Delta = \begin{vmatrix} 2.34 + s33 & -0.8 - s30 & 0 & 0 \\ -80.8 - s30 & 162.6 + s60 & -80.8 - s30 & 0 \\ 0 & -0.8 - s30 & 7.5 + s33 & -s3 \\ 0 & -80 & 80 - s3 & 2 + s3 \end{vmatrix}$$

Computer solution of this determinant yields the following network natural frequencies:

$$s_1 = -7.09 \text{ nsec}^{-1}$$

$$s_2 = -2.78$$

$$s_3 = -0.48$$

$$s_4 = -0.0579$$

(As a check on the numerical calculations to this point,

$$-\sum \frac{1}{s_j} = 19.89 \text{ nsec}$$

$$\sum \tau_{jo} = 19.9 \text{ nsec}$$

which is well within slide-rule accuracy.)

To find the zeros of V_o/V_i, we note from Eqs. 16.45 that we must find the roots of the expression $G_s' \Delta_{14} = 0$. Clearly, G_s' is just a scale factor in this calculation, so we use the computer to find the roots of the equation $\Delta_{14} = 0$. The resulting roots, the zeros of V_o/V_i, are

$$s_5 = -2.69 \text{ nsec}^{-1}$$

$$s_6, s_7 = -1.35 \pm j2.04 \text{ nsec}^{-1}$$

Clearly ω_h will be dominated by s_4 and s_3. Hence

$$\omega_h \simeq \left(\frac{1}{0.058^2} + \frac{1}{0.48^2} \right)^{-\frac{1}{2}}$$

$$= 0.0577 \text{ Grad/sec}$$

$$f_h = 9.2 \text{ MHz}$$

a close match to the design bandwidth of 8 MHz.

16.3 Multistage Amplifiers Using Both FET and Bipolar Transistors

Often amplifiers are designed with both FET and bipolar transistors in order to take advantage of the unique properties of each of these devices.

Two examples will be discussed briefly in this section, a common-source, common-base (cascode) circuit and a common-drain, common-base circuit.

16.3.1   Common-Source, Common-Base Pair

A typical common-source, common-base amplifier is shown in Fig. 16.13a. This combination has all of the advantages of the corresponding bipolar cascode circuit discussed in Section 15.1, and in addition has a very high input impedance. These facts are readily apparent when one compares the two mid- and high-frequency incremental models in Fig. 16.13b and Fig. 15.2. The two diagrams are topologically identical, except for r_x and r_π in the first stage.

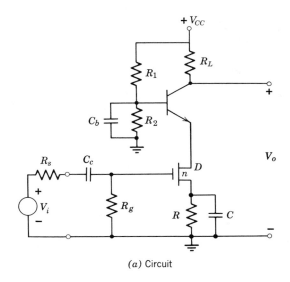

(a) Circuit

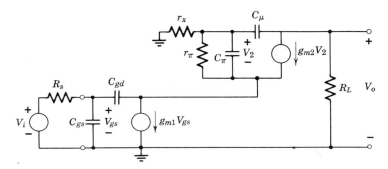

(b) Mid–and high–frequency incremental model,
assuming that R_g is much larger than R_s

Figure 16.13   Common-source, common-base cascode.

The midfrequency voltage gain can be obtained quite readily by inspection. Recall that the current gain of the common-base stage is slightly less than one. Thus the current through R_L is almost $g_{m1}V_{gs}$. Hence

$$A_v = \frac{V_o}{V_i} = -g_{m1}R_L \tag{16.46}$$

Because g_m in an FET is lower than in a bipolar transistor, unless the latter is operated at currents below 0.1 ma, the voltage gain of the FET-bipolar cascode will be lower, for a given value of R_L, than the corresponding circuit using two bipolar devices.

The bandwidth calculations for the circuit in Fig. 16.13 are almost identical to the calculations in Sections 15.1 and 15.2, but a little simpler because $r_{\pi 1}$ and r_{x1} are not present. Therefore, these matters will not be pursued further here (see Problems P16.8 and P16.9).

16.3.2   Common-Drain, Common-Base Pair

The FET-bipolar equivalent of the emitter-coupled pair is shown in Fig. 16.14a. The dc voltage V_B can be obtained by using a voltage divider from the

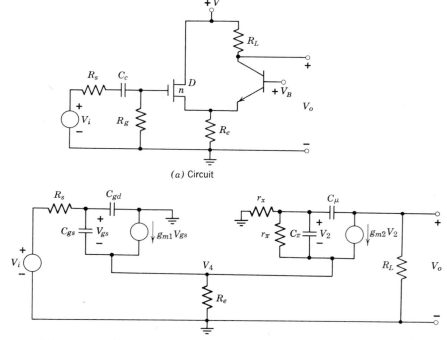

(*a*) Circuit

(*b*) Incremental mid–and high–frequency model, assuming that R_g is much larger than R_s

Figure 16.14   Common-drain, common-base pair.

voltage V, provided that a suitable bypass capacitor is connected from base to ground.

If we assume that R_e is much larger than the input resistance of the common-base stage, that is,

$$R_e \gg \frac{r_x + r_\pi}{\beta_o + 1} \tag{16.47}$$

then the midfrequency voltage gain is relatively easy to calculate by inspection from the incremental model (Fig. 16.14b). From Section 11.5.3, Eq. 11.48a, the voltage gain of the common-drain stage is

$$\frac{V_4}{V_i} = \frac{g_{m1} R_1}{1 + g_{m1} R_1} \tag{16.48}$$

where

$$R_1 = \frac{r_x + r_\pi}{\beta_o + 1} \tag{16.49}$$

The voltage gain of the common-base stage is

$$\frac{V_o}{V_4} = \frac{r_\pi}{r_x + r_\pi} g_{m2} R_L \tag{16.50}$$

Hence

$$\frac{V_o}{V_i} = \left(\frac{g_{m1} R_1}{1 + g_{m1} R_1} \right) \left(\frac{r_\pi}{r_x + r_\pi} \right) g_{m2} R_L \tag{16.51}$$

where R_1 is given by Eq. 16.49. Because R_1 is liable to be of the order of 10 ohms and g_{m1} is usually a few millimhos, the gain of the common-drain stage will be substantially less than unity, less than 0.1, in fact. Hence Eq. 16.51 reduces to

$$\frac{V_o}{V_i} \simeq g_{m1} R_L \tag{16.52}$$

the same magnitude we obtained for the FET-bipolar cascode.

Comparison of the incremental circuit model for the common-drain, common-base pair (Fig. 16.14b) with the corresponding model for the emitter-coupled pair (Fig. 16.9a) indicates that the circuits are topologically identical except for the omission of r_{x1} and $r_{\pi1}$ in the former. Hence analysis and design involving the upper 0.707 frequency ω_h are identical for the two circuits and will not be repeated here (see Problems P16.10 and P16.11).

16.4   More Complicated Multistage Structures

Multistage amplifiers are frequently more complicated than the two- and three-stage examples discussed in this chapter. This is especially true of integrated circuit amplifiers, because the cost of the final unit is (within limits) almost independent of the number of transistors in the unit. Fortunately, it is frequently possible to visualize these more complicated circuits as simple combinations of the basic multistage circuits that we have already discussed. Two examples are shown here: a broad-band video amplifier and direct-coupled operational amplifier.

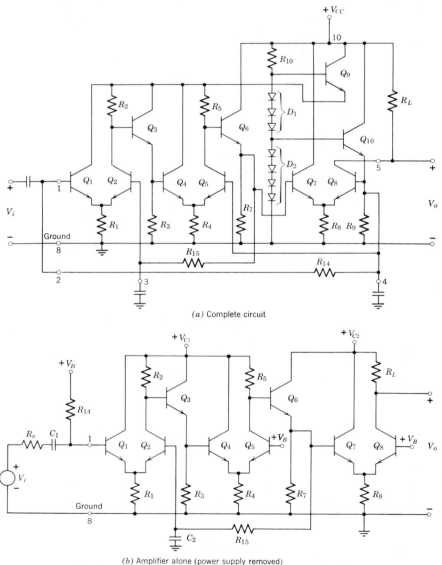

(a) Complete circuit

(b) Amplifier alone (power supply removed)

Figure 16.15   An integrated-circuit video amplifier.

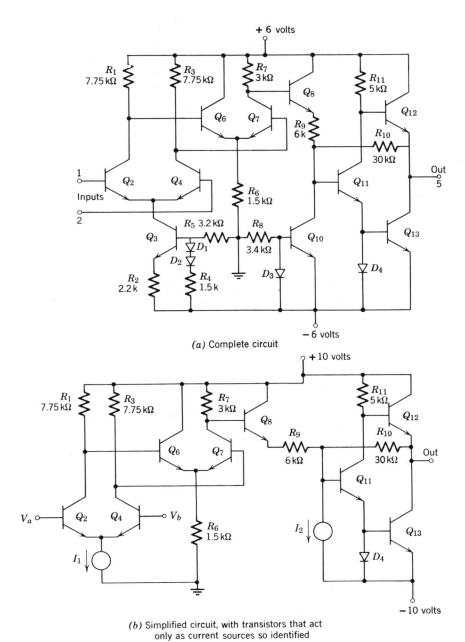

(a) Complete circuit

(b) Simplified circuit, with transistors that act
only as current sources so identified

Figure 16.16   An integrated-circuit operational amplifier.

The video amplifier[4] (Fig. 16.15) consists of a cascade of three emitter-coupled pairs, coupled together in each case by a common-collector stage. In this design the emitter-coupled pairs are sufficiently isolated that it is safe to calculate the natural frequencies of each pair independently and to assume that the dominant poles of the entire circuit are just the dominant poles of each pair (see Problem P.16.13). Note that the amplifier is biased by a method closely analogous to that discussed in Section 16.1.4, except that the corrective signal comes back via resistor R_{15} to the common-base stage rather than to the amplifier input stage.

The schematic diagram for an integrated-circuit operational amplifier[5] is shown in Fig. 16.16. Because the circuit is designed to amplify dc signals as well as ac signals, the input stages have a balanced configuration similar to that discussed in Section 7.4.2. Analysis and design of such balanced circuits are covered in detail in References 16.5 and 16.6. Suffice it to say that for balanced drives at the amplifier input, we need consider only *one half* of each balanced pair. Under these conditions the first part of the circuit reduces to a two-stage common-emitter cascade, consisting of transistors Q_4 and Q_7, followed by a common-collector isolating stage, Q_8.

The operation of the output stage is dominated by the feedback circuit R_9 and R_{10}, so that further discussion of the circuit at this point is inappropriate.

REFERENCES

16.1   R. D. Thornton et al., *Characteristic and Limitations of Transistors*, Wiley, New York, 1966.

16.2   J. F. Gibbons, *Semiconductor Electronics*, McGraw-Hill, New York, 1966.

16.3   *RCA Linear Integrated Circuits Fundamentals*, Technical Series IC-40, Radio Corporation of America, 1966.

16.4   *MC 1430 Operational Amplifier Integrated Circuits*, DS 9057, Motorola Semiconductors, Pheonix, 1966.

16.5   R. D. Thornton et al., *Multistage Transistor Circuits*, Wiley, New York, 1965.

16.6   A. H. Hoffait and R. D. Thornton, *Limitations of Transistor Amplifiers. Proc. IEEE*, February, 1964.

16.7   H. Camenzind, *Circuit Design for Integrated Circuits*, Addison Wesley, Reading, Mass., 1968.

PROBLEMS

P16.1   Show that the zeros of V_o/V_i in Fig. 16.2 can be found by inspection from Eqs. 16.12, once the equations are written in determinant form (See page 563.)

---

[4] See Reference 16.3.
[5] See Reference 16.4.

P16.2   Substitute the numerical values given on page 567 and in Section 16.1.2 into Eq. 16.18, hence for this example justify the approximations made in deriving Eq. 16.20.

P16.3   For the bias network of Fig. 16.4, calculate $\partial V_{CE3}/\partial \beta_{F1}(T)$ and $\partial V_{CE3}/\partial V_{B1}$, both before and after resistor R_1 is added from output to input. Use the results to calculate the improvement in bias stability arising from the addition of R_1. (See page 567.)

P16.4   Complete the design of the bias network for the amplifier in Fig. 16.6. Specifically, calculate appropriate values for C_c, C_1, C_2, C_3, R_3, and R_4 to bias the transistor as required in Sections 16.1.2 and 16.1.4, and achieve a lower band-edge frequency or 0.707 point of 50 Hz. Assume $V_{CE3} = 5.9$ volts.

P16.5   Using Fig. 16.7b, verify Eq. 16.25. (See page 571.)

P16.6   Apply the transformation suggested in Section 11.5.1, Eq. 11.42, to Fig. 16.10a, hence calculate the open-circuit resistance facing $C_{\mu 1}$, in Fig. 16.9a. Check your answer with Eq. 16.39.

P16.7   Use Fig. 16.11 to calculate R_{3o}, the open-circuit resistance faced by $C_{\pi 2}$ in Fig. 16.9a. Hence verify Eq. 16.40.

P16.8   Select transistors for the circuit in Fig. 16.13a to achieve a gain of 100 and an upper 0.707 frequency f_h of 5 MHz. Assume $R_s = 100$ ohms. (See page 580.)

P16.9   Using the results of P16.8, design the bias network for the circuit in Fig. 16.13a to achieve a low-frequency 0.707 point of 10 Hz.

P16.10   Repeat P16.8 for the circuit of Fig. 16.14a.

P16.11   Using the results of P16.10, design the bias network for the circuit in Fig. 16.14a to achieve a low-frequency 0.707 point of 10 Hz.

P16.12   It is clear from inspection of Fig. 16.17 that capacitor C_1 will have very little effect on the transfer function V_2/V_1. But there is an open-circuit time constant associated with C_1, and from Chapter 15, the upper band edge of the circuit should be

$$\omega_h \simeq \frac{1}{\Sigma \tau_{jo}}$$

Which of these contradictory statements is correct? Explain.

P16.13   Estimate the upper break frequency of the integrated amplifier in Fig. 16.15b, assuming that the transistors are similar to the 2N3564 described in Chapter 12. Assume $I_C = 2$ ma, $V_{CE} = 2$ volts, $r_x = 50$ ohms. Let $R_2 = R_5 = R_L = 500$ ohms, $R_1 = R_4 = R_8 = 250$ ohms, $R_s = 50$ ohms. Neglect the effects of R_3, R_7, R_{14}, R_{15}.

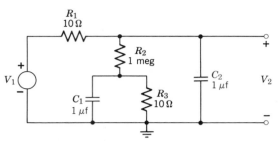

Figure 16.17 Simple circuit.

P16.14 Write the node equations for the feedback amplifier shown in Fig. 19.19b. Calculate the poles of V_o/V_s, assuming identical transistors with $\beta_o = 50$, $r_\pi = 250$ ohms, $r_x = 25$ ohms, $C_\pi = 50$ pf, $C_\mu = 5$ pf. Also assume $R_e = 0.1$ ohm, $R_s = 1000$ ohms, and $R_L = 50$ ohms. Assume that R_{L1}, R_{L2}, and R_{L3} are large enough to be neglected.

P16.15 Find the midband voltage gain V'_o/V_i and the natural frequencies of the circuit shown in Fig. 19.24a. Use the element values given in Section 19.3.2, and assume that R_f is very large.

P16.16 Find the open-circuit resistance R_T facing C_1 in Fig. 20.5a. Assume $\beta_o = 50$, $r_\pi = 250$ ohms, $r_x = 25$ ohms, and R_{L1}, R_{L2} large enough to have negligible effect on the calculation. Also, assume $R_e = 0$, $R_L = 50$ ohms.

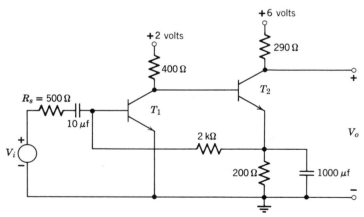

Figure 16.18 Two-stage amplifier.

P16.17 For the silicon transistor amplifier shown in Fig. 16.18
(a) Estimate the dc collector currents of the transistors. An answer within 20 % is adequate, so *make reasonable approximations*. Assume $\beta_F = 200$.
(b) Draw the mid- and high-frequency incremental model.
(c) Explain with the aid of appropriate equations how to find within 30 % the upper 0.707 frequency ω_h of the voltage gain V_o/V_i. The equations should

be in terms of the circuit parameters in the model of (*b*), that is r_x, r_π, and so on.

(*d*) A computer solution for this amplifier yields for the high-frequency poles

$$s_1 = -0.0035 \text{ nsec}^{-1}$$

$$s_2 = -0.018$$

$$s_3 = -1.66$$

$$s_4 = -6.85$$

Estimate ω_h.

(*e*) Calculate the lower 0.707 frequency ω_l.

P16.18 For the emitter-coupled circuit in Fig. 16.15, prove that the quiescent dc voltage at the base of Q_4 is equal to the quiescent dc input voltage at the base of Q_1, hence that this three-transistor unit can be cascaded as a block. Assume $R_1 = R_4$, $R_2 = 2R_1$, and V_{C1} is twice the voltage established on the bases of Q_1 and Q_2.

P16.19 Calculate the size of capacitor C_b in the emitter-coupled amplifier, Fig. 16.7*a*, required to give the amplifier a lower 0.707 frequency of 100 Hz. Use the element values specified Section 16.2.2. and assume $R_e = 2 \text{ kohm}$, $R_b = 500 \text{ ohms}$.

P16.20 Design a broadband transistor amplifier with midfrequency voltage gain magnitude of 3000 and a bandwidth of 10 MHz. More specifically, design the amplifier to have an upper 0.707 frequency f_h between 10 MHz and 15 MHz. The source resistance is specified as 50 ohms, and the source voltage is 200 microvolts rms. Verify f_h on the computer. The components used must be within the present state of the art. Furthermore, for reasons of economy, assume that transistors must have an f_T less than 1 GHz (lower, if possible) and C_μ at least 2 pf. Assume that r_x is about one-tenth of r_π. Elementary biasing schemes, which provide only minimal bias stability, are acceptable. Do not calculate the coupling and bypass capacitor sizes. Summarize the major features of your design:

(1) Tabulation of all values stage by stage.

(2) Sum of open-circuit time constants (state units).

(3) Sum of reciprocal poles (state units).

(4) Attach a complete circuit diagram.

(5) Attach a computer print-out of the high-frequency determinant in numerical form, and a print-out of the high-frequency poles and zeros (state units).

(6) Midfrequency gain.

(7) Upper 0.707 frequency.

(8) In the body of the report, support your design with an explanation of each step in your solution.

CHAPTER SEVENTEEN

Tuned Transistor Amplifiers

17.1 Analysis of a Single-Stage Tuned Amplifier

In previous chapters we have discussed the analysis and design of wide-band transistor amplifiers. In this chapter we examine briefly a quite different type of amplifier—one that is designed to amplify only a narrow band of frequencies adjacent to some *center frequency* ω_o. Such a *narrow-band amplifier* can be used to selectively amplify one signal, a television signal, for example, at a frequency ω_o while rejecting other signals (or noise) at frequencies removed from ω_o.

17.1.1 Parallel Resonance in a Passive *RLC* Circuit

Since the design of most narrow-band amplifiers is based on the properties of the *RLC* tuned circuit, let us briefly review some of these properties. A simple parallel tuned circuit with current-source drive is shown in Fig. 17.1.

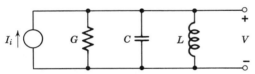

Figure 17.1 A parallel-resonant *RLC* circuit.

By inspection, the output voltage is

$$V = \frac{I_i}{G + sC + 1/sL} \tag{17.1}$$

At low frequencies the impedance V/I_i is dominated by the inductive term, whereas at high frequencies the capacitive term dominates. At some intermediate frequency $s = j\omega_o$, these terms cancel out, and the impedance reaches a maximum and is resistive. That is, the *resonant frequency* ω_o is the frequency where the imaginary part of the impedance V/I_i goes to zero:

$$\omega_o C - \frac{1}{\omega_o L} = 0 \tag{17.2}$$

$$\omega_o = \frac{1}{\sqrt{LC}} \tag{17.3}$$

Clearly, at resonance

$$V = \frac{I_i}{G} = I_i R \tag{17.4}$$

One particularly convenient way of calculating the shape of the resonant curve is to introduce a change of variable in Eq. 17.1. Specifically, we let

$$s' = s - j\omega_o \tag{17.5}$$

That is, we examine the impedance in terms of the *deviation* from the resonant frequency ω_o. On this basis, writing Eq. 17.1 in admittance form for convenience, we obtain

$$Y = \frac{I_i}{V} = G + j\omega_o C + s'C + \frac{1}{j\omega_o L + s'L} \tag{17.6}$$

If ω' is much smaller than ω_o, we can approximate the last term in Eq. 17.6 by using the first two terms of its binomial expansion. Hence

$$Y \simeq G + j\omega_o C + s'C + \frac{1}{j\omega_o L} + \frac{s'}{\omega_o^2 L} \tag{17.7}$$

On substituting for $\omega_o L$ from Eq. 17.2 and for ω_o^2 from Eq. 17.3, we obtain

$$Y \simeq G + 2s'C \tag{17.8}$$

Thus Eq. 17.1 becomes

$$V = \frac{I_i}{G + 2s'C} \tag{17.9}$$

This is exactly the functional form we would obtain for the simple parallel *RC* circuit shown in Fig. 17.2a. Thus we immediately know the general shape of the frequency response $V(j\omega)$ for our *RLC* circuit (Fig. 17.1). The output voltage magnitude will fall to 0.707 of its midfrequency value when

$$\omega' = \frac{G}{2C} \tag{17.10}$$

and for ω' much larger than this, the voltage will fall off as $1/\omega'$ (Fig. 17.2c). Recall, however that ω' is the frequency *deviation* from ω_o ; thus both positive and negative values of ω' are allowed. Therefore, there is another 0.707 point below ω_o, at a frequency

$$\omega' = -\frac{G}{2C} \tag{17.11}$$

For frequencies much lower than this, the voltage again falls off as $|1/\omega'|$. We conclude from Fig. 17.2c that the bandwidth measured between 0.707 points on the resonant curve is

$$\text{bandwidth} = \Delta\omega = \frac{G}{C} \tag{17.12}$$

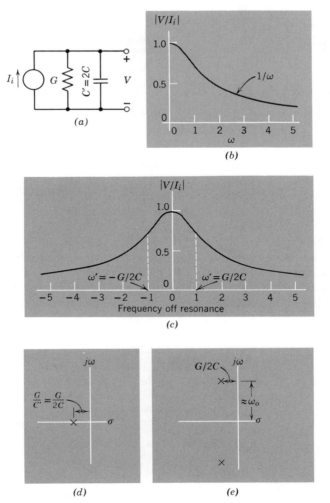

Figure 17.2   Response of a parallel *RLC* circuit. (*a*) *RC* circuit. (*b*) Normalized response of *RC* circuit. (*c*) Normalized response of corresponding *RLC* circuit. (*d*) Pole-zero plot for circuit in (*a*). (*e*) Pole-zero plot for corresponding *RLC* circuit.

The *s*-plane plots of the natural frequencies for the low-pass circuit in Fig. 17.2*a* and the band-pass circuit in Fig. 17.1 are shown in Figs. 17.2*d* and *e* respectively to facilitate their comparison. The close relationship between the low-pass and the band-pass circuits is often stated in terms of the "low-pass to band-pass transformation,"[1] which we shall refer to in subsequent discussions.

[1] See Reference 17.1, p. 274.

The bandwidth of an RLC circuit is also frequently stated in terms of a parameter Q, defined as

$$Q = \frac{\text{center frequency}}{\text{bandwidth}} = \frac{\omega_o}{\Delta\omega} \qquad (17.13)$$

Thus for this circuit, from Eqs. 17.3, 17.12, and 17.13, we have

$$Q = \frac{\omega_o C}{G} = \frac{R}{\omega_o L} \qquad (17.14)$$

17.1.2 Transistor Amplifier with an RLC Load

Suppose that the parallel RLC circuit in Fig. 17.1 is used as a load on a single-stage transistor amplifier, as shown in Fig. 17.3a. It should be clear from the incremental model (Fig. 17.3b) that if the resonant frequency of the tuned circuit is low enough that C_π and C_μ carry negligible current at resonance, then the amplifier response V_o/V_i will have the general form shown in Fig. 17.2c (see Problem P17.1). Thus at low frequencies the circuit in Fig. 17.3a will operate entirely satisfactorily as a narrow-band tuned amplifier.

However, many tuned amplifiers are operated at relatively high frequencies (10 to 100 MHz in television receivers, for example) in which case we cannot

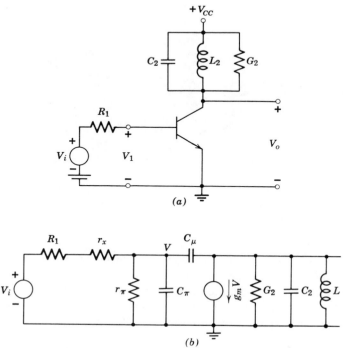

Figure 17.3 Single-tuned transistor amplifier.

ignore C_π and C_μ in the analysis. These capacitors give rise to two important problems in narrow-band amplifier design. First, the resonant frequency of the tuned circuit is now not solely dependent on the passive components L_2 and C_2, but is also a function of the (somewhat unreliable) transistor parameters. Specifically at frequencies below ω_β, the total capacitance appearing in parallel with L is

$$C_{\text{total}} = C_2 + C_\mu \left[1 + \frac{g_m}{g_\pi + 1/(R_1 + r_x)} \right] \qquad (17.15)$$

(see Problem P17.2). The effect of the transistor parameters on ω_o can be minimized if it is possible to choose C_2 two or three orders of magnitude larger than C_μ.

The second and much more serious effect of C_π and C_μ on circuit behavior is that when a second tuned circuit is added at the transistor *input*, C_μ provides a bilateral coupling between the input and output tuned circuits. Because of this coupling, it may be difficult to *align* the amplifier, that is, to adjust the two tuned circuits to give a smooth symmetric resonant response centered at ω_o. In some cases the circuit will become unstable and *oscillate* : we obtain a roughly sinusoidal output voltage even when the input signal is set to zero.

17.1.3 Instability

The discussion of instability in common-emitter tuned amplifiers could be carried out directly in terms of the circuit in Fig. 17.3b. However, because we eventually want to compare the stability and alignability of several different amplifier configurations, we start with a general analysis in terms of y parameters and later relate the y's to the hybrid-pi parameters of the particular circuit in question. To this end we show in Fig. 17.4 a y-parameter two-port representation of an active network with tuned circuits at both input and output. Problems of alignability and instability in such a circuit arise because of the coupling between the two tuned circuits via the forward and reverse generators y_{fe} and y_{re}. The consequences of this coupling can be investigated in a number of ways. One fairly direct method is to examine the input admittance I_1/V_1 of the two-port and tuned load and observe the effect of this admittance on the input tuned circuit.

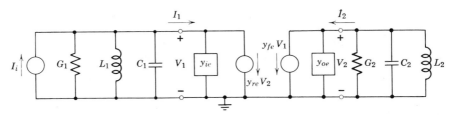

Figure 17.4 Incremental circuit model in y-parameter form of an amplifier with tuning at both input and output.

To simplify the analysis, let us designate the admittances of the isolated input and output tuned circuits by Y_1 and Y_2. That is,

$$Y_1 = G_1 + sC_1 + \frac{1}{sL_1} \tag{17.16}$$

$$Y_2 = G_2 + sC_2 + \frac{1}{sL_2} \tag{17.17}$$

The corresponding resonant frequencies are ω_{o1} and ω_{o2}. We can find the input admittance of the two-port with tuned circuit load by writing the node equations for this part of the circuit:

$$I_1 = y_{ie}V_1 + y_{re}V_2 \tag{17.18}$$

$$0 = y_{fe}V_1 + (y_{oe} + Y_2)V_2 \tag{17.19}$$

From Cramer's rule

$$\frac{V_1}{I_1} = \frac{y_{oe} + Y_2}{y_{ie}(y_{oe} + Y_2) - y_{fe}y_{re}} \tag{17.20}$$

Thus the input admittance of this part of the circuit is

$$Y_{in} = \frac{I_1}{V_1} = y_{ie} - \frac{y_{fe}y_{re}}{y_{oe} + Y_2} \tag{17.21}$$

(see Problem P17.3). Because Y_2 varies so drastically in the vicinity of the resonant frequency ω_{o2} (see Fig. 17.2c), there is a possibility that G_{in}, the real part of Y_{in}, will be negative for some values of ω. If the *net* conductance $G_{in} + G_1$ across the input tuned circuit is *zero* at the resonant frequency ω_{o1} of the input LC circuit, the system will oscillate. In terms of the s plane, the circuit under these conditions has a pair of conjugate natural frequencies on the j axis at $\pm j\omega_{o1}$, hence is unstable. For $G_{in} + G_1$ negative at some value of ω, the linear circuit model has right-half-plane poles, and the response is dominated by exponentially growing signals.

To illustrate this concept of zero or negative input conductance, let us examine the input admittance of the specific tuned amplifier in Fig. 17.3. We first find y_{fe} and y_{re} for the amplifier alone, in terms of the hybrid-pi parameters. (See Problem P17.4.) The forward parameter y_{fe} can be calculated using the circuit shown in Fig. 17.5a. By inspection, the voltage V is

$$V = V_1 \frac{g_x}{g_x + g_\pi + s(C_\pi + C_\mu)} \tag{17.22}$$

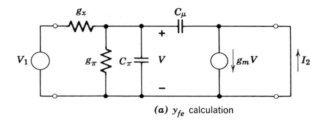

(a) y_{fe} calculation

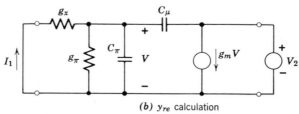

(b) y_{re} calculation

Figure 17.5 Circuits for calculating y parameters.

Hence y_{fe} is

$$y_{fe} = \frac{I_2}{V_1} = \frac{g_x}{g_x + g_\pi + s(C_\pi + C_\mu)}[g_m - sC_\mu] \qquad (17.23)$$

A similar calculation, using Fig. 17.5b, yields y_{re} (see Problem P17.5).

$$y_{re} = \frac{-g_x}{g_x + g_\pi + s(C_\pi + C_\mu)}[sC_\mu] \qquad (17.24)$$

Both expressions (in fact, all four y parameters) have a pole at the transverse cutoff frequency:

$$\omega_b = \frac{g_x + g_\pi}{C_\pi + C_\mu} \qquad (17.25)$$

If we assume for simplicity that we are operating the tuned amplifier at frequencies well below ω_b, then Eqs. 17.23 and 17.24 can be simplified to

$$y_{fe} \simeq \frac{g_x}{g_x + g_\pi}(g_m) \simeq g_m. \qquad (17.26)$$

$$y_{re} = \frac{-g_x}{g_x + g_\pi}(sC_\mu) \simeq -sC_\mu \qquad (17.27)$$

Substituting those values into Eq. 17.21, we obtain

$$Y_{\text{in}} = y_{ie} + \frac{j\omega C_\mu g_m}{y_{oe} + Y_2} \tag{17.28}$$

Below the resonant frequency of the output circuit, $y_{oe} + Y_2$ will be inductive, that is, $y_{oe} + Y_2$ will be of the form $g - jb$ (see Eqs. 17.8 and 17.5). In this case the *real part* of the second term in Eq. 17.28 will be *negative*. Thus Y_{in} can have a negative real part, and the net conductance $G_{\text{in}} + G_1$ can be zero.

17.1.4   Alignability

Although it is possible to establish in more detail the conditions for instability in tuned amplifiers,[2] in many practical cases the problem of *alignability* poses more stringent constraints on the circuit design than the problem of instability. The nature of the alignment problem is readily apparent from Eq. 17.21 and Fig. 17.4. The admittance Y_{in} appears directly in parallel with the input tuned circuit, and it is clear that Y_{in} can be a strong function of the parameters of the output tuned circuit (through Y_2). Hence as the output circuit is tuned by varying L_2 or C_2, the input circuit will be detuned because of changes in Y_{in}. Clearly, when the input circuit is adjusted, a corresponding detuning of the output circuit occurs. This interaction between input and output tuning makes alignment difficult and also leads to asymmetric response curves, an undesirable characteristic if the amplifier is to handle modulated signals without distortion.

Problems of alignment and asymmetry are greatly reduced by making the troublesome second term in Eq. 17.21 much smaller than the admittance of the input circuit. That is, we design the circuit so that

$$\left| \frac{y_{fe} y_{re}}{y_{oe} + Y_2} \right| \ll |y_{ie} + Y_1| \tag{17.29a}$$

or

$$|y_{fe} y_{re}| \ll |(y_{ie} + Y_1)(y_{oe} + Y_2)| \tag{17.29b}$$

This condition is somewhat simplified if we look for the *worst case* of the inequality, that is, the conditions on Y_1 and Y_2 that make the right-hand side of Eq. 17.29b *smallest*. Clearly, we minimize the right-hand side if we assume that the tuned circuits are at resonance, such that $Y_1 = G_1$ and $Y_2 = G_2$. Furthermore, we assume that y_{ie} and y_{oe} are negligible compared to G_1 and G_2 respectively. On this basis, Eq. 17.29b reduces to the simple condition that for ease of alignment and symmetrical resonant response curves, we require that at the resonant frequency

$$|y_{fe} y_{re}| \ll G_1 G_2 \tag{17.30}$$

[2] See, for example, References 17.2 and 17.3.

Obviously, this condition ensures circuit stability as well, by ensuring that the net conductance $G_{in} + G_1$ appearing in parallel with L_1 and C_1 will always be positive (see Eq. 17.21). From an engineering point of view, reducing $|y_{fe}y_{re}|$ to about 10 or 20% of $G_1 G_2$ will assure stability and, in most cases, reasonable alignability as well.

17.2 Example: Single-Stage Common-Emitter Tuned Amplifier
17.2.1 A 455-kHz Single-Tuned Amplifier

Suppose that we wish to design a tuned amplifier for the intermediate-frequency amplifier in an AM radio. Such an amplifier should have a center frequency of 455 kHz and a bandwidth of 10 kHz. Let us first use as a basic circuit layout the single-tuned amplifier shown in Fig. 17.3. Furthermore, let us use a 2N3564 transistor operating at $I_C = 5$ ma, $V_{CE} = 5$ volts. Hence from Section 12.3.6

$$g_m = 0.2 \text{ mho}$$

$$r_\pi = 400 \text{ ohms}$$

$$r_x = 30 \text{ ohms}$$

$$C_\pi = 50 \text{ pf}$$

$$C_\mu = 2.5 \text{ pf}$$

Also

$$f_\beta = \frac{f_T}{\beta_o} = \frac{600}{80} = 7.5 \text{ MHz}$$

Thus the desired resonant frequency of 0.455 MHz is well below f_β, and C_π can be neglected.

At resonance, this amplifier has a purely resistive load G_2 and thus has a voltage gain at ω_o of

$$\frac{V_o}{V_i} = -\frac{r_\pi}{R_1 + r_x + r_\pi} \left(\frac{g_m}{G_2} \right) \tag{17.31}$$

If the source resistance R_1 is specified as 250 ohms, then a 500-ohm load resistance ($G_2 = 2$ mmho) will give a voltage gain of

$$\frac{V_o}{V_i} = -\left(\frac{400}{250 + 30 + 400} \right)(0.2 \times 500) = -59$$

Now that the load conductance is known, we can calculate C_2 and L_2. From Eq. 17.12 (in units of millimhos, picofarads, and nanoseconds) we have

$$C_2 = \frac{G_2}{\text{bandwidth}} = \frac{2}{10 \times 2\pi \times 10^{-6}}$$

$$= 3.18 \times 10^4 \text{ pf}$$

Because C_μ is orders of magnitude smaller than C_2, the transistor output capacitance will not affect the tuning in this design. The value of L_2 required to bring the circuit to resonance at 455 kHz is, from Eq. 17.3 (in units of millimhos, picofarads, microhenrys, and nanoseconds),

$$L_2 = \frac{1}{\omega_o^2 C} = \frac{1}{(2\pi \times 0.455 \times 10^{-3})^2 (3.18 \times 10^4)}$$

$$= 3.96 \; \mu h$$

The value of inductance obtained above is rather small for 455-kHz operation, in the sense that it is difficult to get high Q coils of this size at this frequency. To obtain a design with more suitable element values, we can insert a small transformer between G_2 and the output LC circuit to transform impedance levels. Another way is to utilize the impedance-transforming properties of a tapped inductor (sometimes called an *autotransformer*) as shown in Fig. 17.6. If the coefficient of coupling between the two sections

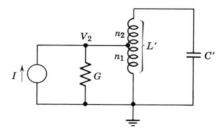

Figure 17.6 Tapped inductor for changing impedance levels.

of the inductor is close to unity, the resonant circuit in Fig. 17.6 will be identical (in terms of I and V_2) to Fig. 17.1, provided that

$$\frac{L'}{L} = \left(\frac{n_1 + n_2}{n_1}\right)^2 \qquad (17.32)$$

and

$$\frac{C'}{C} = \left(\frac{n_1}{n_1 + n_2}\right)^2 \qquad (17.33)$$

(see Problem P17.6). In the present example a 9 to 1 ratio of n_2 to n_1 increases L to about 0.4 mh and reduces C to about 320 pf, both of which are more acceptable values than those originally calculated.

Because in this example we have only one tuned circuit, the issues of alignment and circuit stability do not come up. Let us now face these issues by trying next to extend the present design to obtain a 455-kHz amplifier with both input and output tuning, as shown in Fig. 17.7.

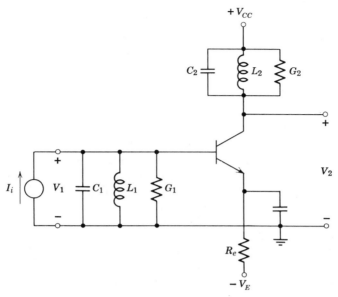

Figure 17.7   Single-stage transistor amplifier with input and output tuning.

17.2.2   A 455-kHz Amplifier with Input and Output Tuning

To apply the general alignment criterion (Eq. 17.30) to the single-stage amplifier of Fig. 17.7, we must first evaluate y_{fe} and y_{re} for frequencies near ω_o. This evaluation must in the present example be done in terms of the hybrid-pi parameters, because that is the form of the transistor data. If y-parameter transistor data are available (see, e.g., Fig. 12.16), we can omit this step and proceed directly to the design (see Problem P17.7).

For this transistor, the transverse cutoff frequency is, in units of millimhos, picofarads, and nanoseconds,

$$\omega_b = \frac{g_x + g_\pi}{C_\pi + C_\mu} = \frac{33 + 2.5}{50 + 2.5} = 0.67 \text{ Grad/sec}$$

$$= 108 \text{ MHz}$$

Clearly, we are operating well below ω_b, so that the approximate expressions for y_{fe} and y_{re} given by Eqs. 17.26 and 17.27 are applicable here:

$$y_{fe} \simeq g_m$$

$$y_{re} \simeq -sC_\mu$$

Hence from Eq. 17.30, for ease of alignment of a single-stage amplifier operating below ω_b, we must select G_1 and G_2 such that

$$g_m\omega_oC_\mu \ll G_1G_2 \tag{17.34}$$

For this particular amplifier,

$$g_m \omega_o C_\mu = 200 \times 2\pi \times 0.455 \times 10^{-3} \times 2.5$$
$$= 1.43 \text{ mmho}^2$$

If we assume $G_1 = 4$ mmho and $G_2 = 2$ mmho as in Section 17.2.1,

$$G_1 G_2 = 4 \times 2 = 8 \text{ mmho}^2$$

Thus the condition of Eq. 17.34 is satisfied, although not by as large a factor as one might expect, considering that the transistor is being operated at a frequency more than an order of magnitude below f_β.

Note that if the alignment condition had not been adequately satisfied, we would have been forced to raise G_2, hence to reduce the voltage gain (see Eq. 17.31). Stated in general terms, in tuned amplifiers there is a design trade-off between alignability and voltage gain.

Because we have two resonant circuits, the bandwidth of each must be greater than 10 kHz in order to achieve an overall 10-kHz passband. This bandwidth shrinkage as a result of multiple poles was observed in Chapter 15. For a cascade of n synchronously-tuned stages it can be shown that

$$\text{overall bandwidth} \simeq \frac{\text{one-stage bandwidth}}{1.2\sqrt{n}} \tag{17.35}$$

(The same relation for bandwidth shrinkage also applies to a cascade of noninteracting low-pass RC stages. In fact, Eq. 17.35 can be derived most readily by working with the low-pass case. See Problem P17.8.) Thus when $n = 2$, each resonant circuit must be designed with a bandwidth of

$$\Delta\omega \simeq 10 \times 1.2\sqrt{2} = 17 \text{ kHz}$$

to achieve the desired 10-kHz overall bandwidth.

Knowing G_1, G_2, ω_o, and $\Delta\omega$, we can now find C_1, C_2, L_1, and L_2, as discussed in Section 17.2.1 (see Problem P17.9).

17.2.3 Stagger Tuning

In many tuned amplifiers it is desirable to have a flatter passband with steeper skirts than is obtainable with synchronously tuned circuits. Such a passband can be obtained by *stagger tuning*,[3] that is, tuning the input and output circuits to slightly different frequencies. The flattest possible passband (called *maximally flat*) is obtained by using the band-pass equivalent to the Butterworth low-pass filter mentioned in Chapter 15. Plots of the frequency response of two cascaded synchronously tuned stages and two flat-staggered stages (Fig. 17.8) show quite clearly the improvement in the response curve that can be obtained by stagger tuning.

[3] See Reference 17.1, p. 176.

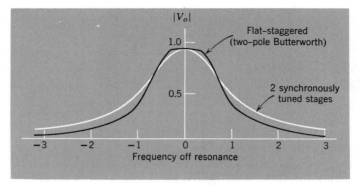

Figure 17.8   Plots of frequency response for a cascade of two noninteracting tuned circuits, normalized with respect to amplitude and bandwidth.

Recall from Chapter 15 that the pole configuration for the low-pass two-pole Butterworth filter is

$$s_1 = -\alpha + j\alpha$$

$$s_2 = -\alpha - j\alpha$$

That is, the poles lie on the arc of a circle, as shown in Fig. 17.9*a*. The corresponding pole locations for the band-pass Butterworth filter are shown in Fig. 17.9*b*. (Clearly the pole constellations in Figs. 17.9*a* and *b* are related by the low-pass to band-pass transformation mentioned in Section 17.1.1. See Reference 17.1, p. 276.) The bandwidth $\Delta\omega'$ of this band-pass filter is equal to the *diameter* of the pole circle.

To achieve the pole constellation shown in Fig. 17.9*b* with the double-tuned amplifier of Fig. 17.7, we merely tune the two resonant circuits to slightly different frequencies. By inspection of Fig. 17.9*b*,

$$\omega_{o1} = \omega_o + 0.35\,\Delta\omega' \tag{17.36}$$

$$\omega_{o2} = \omega_o - 0.35\,\Delta\omega' \tag{17.37}$$

To find the bandwidths required, we compare the pole configuration of Fig. 17.9*b* with that of Fig. 17.2 and conclude that

$$\frac{G_1}{2C_1} = 0.707\,\frac{\Delta\omega'}{2}$$

Thus

$$\Delta\omega_1 = \frac{G_1}{C_1} = 0.707\,\Delta\omega' \tag{17.38}$$

A similar expression applies to the bandwidth $\Delta\omega_2$ of the second tuned circuit. Further detailed calculations are left to the problems (see Problem P17.10).

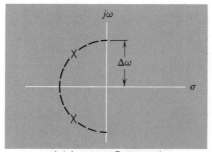

(a) Low–pass Butterworth

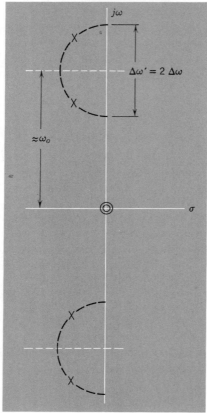

(b) Band–pass Butterworth

Figure 17.9   Pole-zero patterns for second-order Butterworth filters.

Because the "step response" is preserved by the low-pass to band-pass transformation,[4] we know that if a sinusoid at frequency ω_o is suddenly applied to the stagger-tuned amplifier, the envelope of the response will have

[4] See Reference 17.1, p. 274.

a small peak in it, as shown in Fig. 17.10. If such a peak cannot be tolerated the amplifier should be synchronously tuned.

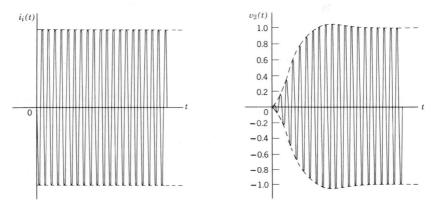

Figure 17.10 Normalized response of a stagger-tuned amplifier to a suddenly applied sinusoid.

17.2.4 Tuned Amplifier at 10.7 MHz

Suppose that we wish to use the transistor specified in Section 17.2.1 in an FM intermediate-frequency amplifier. Such a circuit might have a center frequency of 10.7 MHz and a bandwidth of 0.2 MHz.

First let us estimate the size of G_1 and G_2 required to ensure alignability at these frequencies. For this transistor

$$\omega_b = \frac{g_x + g_\pi}{C_\pi + C_\mu} = \frac{33.3 + 2.5}{50 + 2.5}$$

$$= 0.68 \text{ Grad/sec}$$

Because $\omega_o = 2\pi \times 0.0107 = 0.067$ Grad/sec, we are operating well below ω_b ; thus Eq. 17.34 is still valid for this computation. Hence

$$|y_{fe}y_{re}| \simeq g_m\omega_oC_\mu = 200 \times 0.067 \times 2.5$$

$$= 33.5 \text{ mmho}^2$$

Therefore, for alignability

$$G_1G_2 \gg 33.5 \text{ mmho}^2$$

Choosing $G_1 = G_2 = 20$ mmho will yield a stable amplifier with acceptable alignability. The voltage gain at resonance will be

$$\frac{V_2}{V_1} = \frac{-y_{fe}}{G_2} \simeq \frac{-200}{20}$$

$$= -10$$

If we try to increase the gain at resonance, the amplifier will become more and more difficult to align and will have an unsymmetric resonant response.[5]

Again the calculations of capacitor and inductor values are similar to those done in Sections 17.2.1 and 17.2.3, so will not be carried out here (see Problem P17.11).

17.3 Example: Tuned Emitter-Coupled Pair

It should be clear from the examples in Section 17.2, especially the 10.7-MHz amplifier in Section 17.2.4, that the alignability criterion (Eq. 17.34) can set a severe limit on the gain of a double-tuned transistor amplifier of the type shown in Fig. 17.7. In particular, if the center frequency of that amplifier were increased from 10.7 to 100 MHz, the stage gain would have to be reduced to an unacceptably low value to preserve the same ratio of $G_1 G_2$ to $y_{re} y_{fe}$. Thus it is desirable to design high-frequency tuned amplifiers using two-transistor building blocks for the basic active circuit, in order to reduce the product $|y_{fe} y_{re}|$. One such circuit is the emitter-coupled pair discussed

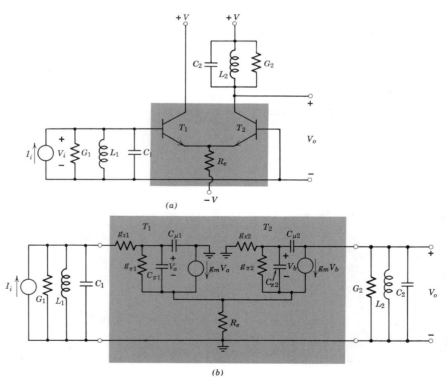

Figure 17.11 Tuned amplifier using an emitter-coupled pair.

[5] These properties can be illustrated rather vividly by means of the lecture demonstration circuit discussed in Section 17.4.

in Chapter 16. Recall from Section 16.2 that the effect of C_μ in this circuit is greatly reduced because the collector of the first transistor is incrementally grounded.

A tuned amplifier using an emitter-coupled transistor pair is illustrated in Fig. 17.11a. To show quantitatively the improvement in alignability of this circuit over a single transistor stage, we must calculate y_{fe} and y_{re} for the amplifier section in Fig. 17.11b. The exact expressions for these parameters can be found by solving the node equations for the circuit (Eqs. 16.45). However, the circuit is complicated enough to make this a rather tedious and unrewarding exercise. Thus we perform an approximate calculation valid for frequencies below ω_b. (As before, if published data on y_{fe} and y_{re} for the pair are available, this step is not required in an actual design calculation.)

To calculate y_{fe}, we short the output of the transistor pair, then calculate the ratio I_2/V_1, as shown in Fig. 17.12a. Note that both $C_{\mu1}$ and $C_{\mu2}$ are connected to ground in this circuit. Thus neither will play an important role in this calculation, and can be neglected. Recall from Section 16.2 that R_e will almost always be negligibly large compared with the associated transistor impedances. On the basis of these two assumptions we can transform g_{x2},

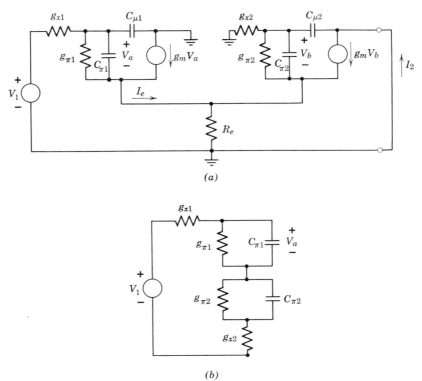

(a)

(b)

Figure 17.12   Calculation of y_{fe}.

$g_{\pi 2}$, and $C_{\pi 2}$ into the emitter lead, by multiplying by $\beta + 1$ and then transform them again by dividing by $\beta + 1$, so that they appear in series with $C_{\pi 1}$ and $g_{\pi 1}$. (See Problem P17.18.) The result of this double transformation is shown in Fig. 17.12b. Now for r_x much smaller than z_π, (i.e., for ω less than ω_b; see Eq. 17.25) and assuming identical transistors, we have

$$V_a \simeq \frac{V_1}{2} \tag{17.39}$$

The output current I_2 can now be obtained by inspection of Fig. 17.12a as follows:

$$I_e \simeq g_m V_a \tag{17.40}$$

Because transistor T_2 is a common-base stage,

$$I_2 = -\alpha I_e \simeq -I_e \tag{17.41}$$

Hence by combining Eqs. 17.39, 17.40, and 17.41, we find that

$$y_{fe} = \frac{I_2}{V_1} = -\frac{g_m}{2} \tag{17.42}$$

The reverse parameter y_{re} can be found from the circuit in Fig. 17.13. This time $C_{\mu 2}$ is not connected to ground, so that it plays a dominant role in the calculation, but we can continue to neglect the effect of $C_{\mu 1}$. To simplify the calculation of y_{re}, we use the same double transformation as before to bring g_{x1}, $g_{\pi 1}$, and $C_{\pi 1}$ in series with $g_{\pi 2}$ and $C_{\pi 2}$, as shown in Fig. 17.13b. If we now assume that $1/sC_{\mu 2}$ is much smaller than the total base-circuit impedance, then

$$I_\mu \simeq sC_{\mu 2} V_2 \tag{17.43}$$

The current through $z_{\pi 2}$ is thus

$$I_z = sC_{\mu 2} V_2 \left(\frac{r_{x2}}{r_{x2} + r_{x1} + z_{\pi 2} + z_{\pi 2}} \right) \tag{17.44}$$

Also

$$I_1 = -\frac{I_z(\beta_2 + 1)}{\beta_1 + 1} \simeq -I_z \tag{17.45}$$

By combining Eqs. 17.44 and 17.45 we find, assuming identical transistors and neglecting r_x in the denominator of Eq. 17.44 (i.e., ω less than ω_b),

$$y_{re} = \frac{I_1}{V_2} = -sC_{\mu 2} \left(\frac{g_\pi + sC_\pi}{2g_x} \right) \tag{17.46}$$

These calculations of y_{fe} and y_{re} are, in general, consistent with published data for an integrated-circuit emitter-coupled pair (Figs. 17.14a and b).

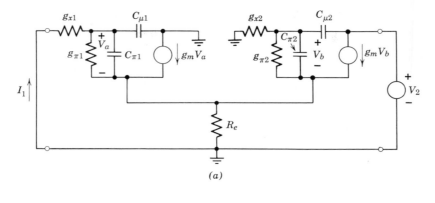

(a)

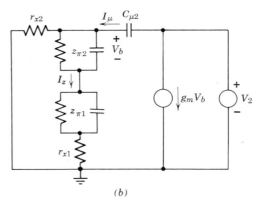

(b)

Figure 17.13   Calculation of y_{re}.

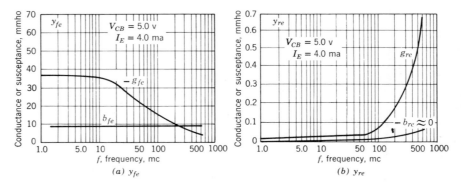

Figure 17.14   Transfer-admittances for an integrated-circuit emitter-coupled pair. g = real part, b = imaginary part.

We conclude from Eqs. 17.42 and 17.46 that for the emitter-coupled pair

$$y_{fe}y_{re} = g_m s C_\mu \left(\frac{g_\pi + sC_\pi}{4g_x} \right) \tag{17.47}$$

so that the alignability criterion for this circuit in terms of the hybrid-pi parameters is

$$\left| g_m s C_\mu \left(\frac{g_\pi + sC_\pi}{4g_x} \right) \right| \ll |G_1 G_2| \tag{17.48}$$

We are now in a position to compare the alignability of the emitter-coupled pair with that of the single-stage common-emitter amplifier. Recall from Section 17.2.2 that for the latter

$$y_{fe}y_{re} = -g_m s C_\mu \tag{17.49}$$

Comparing this result with Eq. 17.47, we note that the emitter-coupled pair is easier to align by a factor

$$K = \left| \frac{4g_x}{g_\pi + sC_\pi} \right| \tag{17.50}$$

At frequencies below ω_β, this factor is approximately $4r_\pi/r_x$, and on this basis it could well be of the order of 50 or 100. Clearly, the factor reduces with increasing frequency, but even at ω_b, the upper limit of our analysis, the emitter-coupled circuit is still better by about a factor of 4 (see Problem P17.12).

Now that the alignability criterion for the emitter-coupled amplifier has been established, all remaining calculations for synchronous tuning and stagger tuning are identical to those presented in Section 17.2, hence will not be repeated here (see Problems P17.13, P17.14, and P17.15).

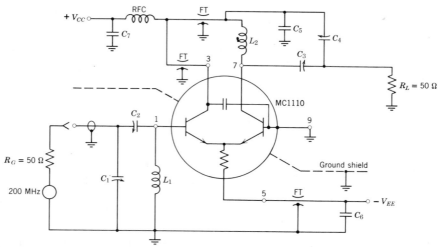

Figure 17.15 A 200-MHz tuned amplifier using an integrated emitter-coupled circuit. See Reference 17.4.

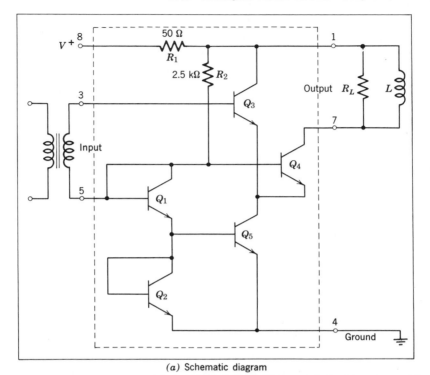

(*a*) Schematic diagram

(*b*) Photomicrograph of the corresponding integrated circuit chip. 0.020″ across. (See plate I.)

Figure 17.16   A more complicated integrated-circuit emitter-coupled amplifier.

A complete 200-MHz emitter-coupled tuned amplifier is shown in Fig. 17.15. Note that it employs a single integrated circuit for the active component and that the integrated circuit contains the two transistors, the emitter resistor, and a bypass capacitor to ensure that at signal frequencies the collector of T_1 will be grounded through the base of T_2.

To obtain the proper impedance levels for the tuned circuits, the designer has chosen to tap the capacitors (C_1, C_2 and C_3, C_4) rather than tap the inductors, as was discussed in Section 17.2.1 (see Problem P17.16).

A somewhat more complicated integrated circuit emitter-coupled amplifier is shown in Fig. 17.16. Transistors Q_3 and Q_4 form the active pair. Transistors Q_1 and Q_2 are diode-connected to provide the dc bias for Q_5, which acts as a constant-current source for the emitters of Q_3 and Q_4.

A photomicrograph of this amplifier is shown in Fig. 17.16b. The overall size of the integrated circuit shown in the figure is 20 mils by 20 mils.

17.4   Lecture Demonstrations

The circuit shown in Fig. 17.17 can be used to demonstrate instability and alignment problems in tuned amplifiers.

1. With the switch in position A, the circuit is a single-stage amplifier. Set resistors R_1 and R_2 to low values and tune the resonant circuits to the same frequency (approximately 10 MHz). Now increase R_1 and R_2. The gain will increase, but the circuit will become more difficult to align, and the response curve will become asymmetric. For large values of R_1 and R_2, the circuit will become unstable.

2. With the switch in position B, we have an emitter-coupled amplifier. Now the amplifier will be stable and the response symmetric for much larger values of R_1 and R_2, hence much larger gain.

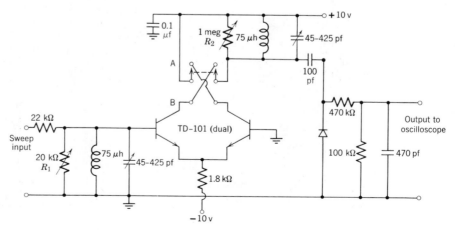

Figure 17.17   Tuned-amplifier demonstration.

REFERENCES

17.1 G. E. Valley and H. Wallman, *Vacuum Tube Amplifiers*, McGraw-Hill, New York, 1948.

17.2 C. L. Searle et al., *Elementary Circuit Properties of Transistors*, Wiley, New York, 1964.

17.3 J. G. Linvill and J. F. Gibbons, *Transistors and Active Circuits*, McGraw-Hill, New York, 1961.

17.4 *Semiconductor Data Manual*, Motorola Semiconductors, Phoenix, 1965.

PROBLEMS

P17.1 Select element values for the tuned circuit in Fig. 17.3 such that the amplifier can selectively amplify the 19-kHz pilot tone in an FM stereo receiver. The circuit should have a Q of 50.

P17.2 Prove that at frequencies below ω_β, the net capacitance appearing in parallel with L_2 and G_2 in Fig. 17.3b is given by Eq. 17.15.

P17.3 Calculate the admittance $Y_{in} = I_1/V_1$ in Fig. 17.4 by applying a voltage V_1 to the input terminals of the y model (after removing I_i, G_1, L_1, and C_1) and calculating the resultant current. Hence verify Eq. 17.21.

P17.4 Calculate the y parameters y_{fe} and y_{re} of the hybrid-pi model by writing the node equations for the model with voltage-source drives at both input and output, then solving for the appropriate transfer functions. Compare your answers with Eqs. 17.23 and 17.24. (See page 596.)

P17.5 Calculate $y_{re} = I_1/V_2$ from Fig. 17.5b, by assuming that the voltage V is sufficiently smaller than V_2 that the current through C_μ is approximately $sC_\mu V_2$. Hence verify Eq. 17.24.

P17.6 Calculate the input admittance $y = I/V_2$ for the tuned circuit with tapped inductor, Fig. 17.6. Compare this with the input admittance of the simple tuned circuit in Fig. 17.1, hence verify Eqs. 17.32 and 17.33.

P17.7 Check the alignability of a single-stage amplifier of the type shown in Fig. 17.7, using a 2N1613 transistor operating at $I_C = 20$ ma, $V_{CE} = 30$ volts. Use the y-parameter data given in Fig. 12.16. Assume $G_1 = 4$ mmho, $G_2 = 2$ mmho. (See page 601.)

P17.8 Prove Eq. 17.35 by assuming a cascade of n noninteracting low-pass RC stages, with an overall transfer function of

$$\frac{V_o}{V_i} = K\left(\frac{1}{1 + j\omega}\right)^n \tag{17.51}$$

Show from this expression that the overall bandwidth of the cascade is

$$\text{overall bandwidth} = (\text{one-stage bandwidth}) \times \sqrt{2^{1/n} - 1} \tag{17.52}$$

Then simplify to Eq. 17.35.

P17.9 Complete the design of the synchronously tuned amplifier in Section 17.2.2 by finding values for C_1, C_2, L_1, and L_2 to meet the specified 455-kHz center frequency and 10-kHz bandwidth. Use tapped inductors if necessary. (See page 602.)

P17.10 Complete the design of the stagger-tuned amplifier in Section 17.2.3 by finding values for C_1, C_2, L_1, and L_2 to achieve a center frequency of 455 kHz and a bandwidth of 10 kHz. (See page 603.)

P17.11 Complete the design of the synchronously tuned 10.7 MHz amplifier in Section 17.2.4 by choosing C_1, C_2, L_1, and L_2 to give the desired center frequency and a 0.2-MHz bandwidth. (See page 606.)

P17.12 Design an emitter-coupled synchronously tuned amplifier of the type shown in Fig. 17.11 to have a 10.7-MHz center frequency and a 0.2-MHz bandwidth. Use the transistor parameters specified in Section 17.2.1. Compare the alignability of this design with that in Section 17.2.4. (See page 610.)

P17.13 Repeat Problem P17.12, except use flat-stagger tuning. (See page 610.)

P17.14 Compare the alignability of a 50-MHz single-stage tuned amplifier of the type shown in Fig. 17.7 to an emitter-coupled amplifier, Fig. 17.11. Use the transistor parameters given in Section 17.2.1, and assume $R_1 = R_2 = 50$ ohms.

P17.15 Design an emitter-coupled tuned amplifier of the type shown in Fig. 17.11 to have a center frequency of 50 MHz and a bandwidth of 2 MHz. Assume $R_1 = R_2 = 50$ ohms. Base the design on the integrated circuit data given in Fig. 17.14. Neglect the effects of y_{ie} and y_{oe}.

P17.16 Calculate the impedance-transforming equation for a tuned circuit with tapped capacitors, as shown in Fig. 17.18. (See page 612.)

P17.17 For the emitter-coupled tuned amplifier shown in Fig. 17.19, assume that for both transistors $\beta_o = 50$, $\omega_T = 10^9$ rad/sec, $r_x = 50$ ohms, $C_\mu = 2$ pf, at the operating point (for both transistors) of $I_C = 2.5$ ma, $V_{CE} = 5$ volts. It is desired to operate the amplifier at a center frequency

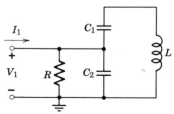

Figure 17.18   Impedance-transforming circuit using two capacitors.

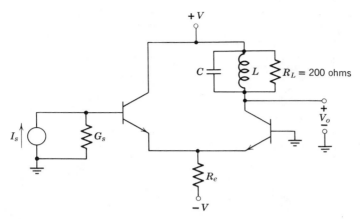

Figure 17.19 Tuned amplifier.

of $\omega_o = 10^8$ rad/sec, with a bandwidth between 0.707 points of 5×10^6 rad/sec ($Q = 20$).

(a) Choose L and C to give the desired response

(b) If another tuned circuit is added at the input; will the circuit yield a reasonably symmetrical resonant response? This is an approximate calculation, so *feel free to use reasonable approximations*, including neglecting R_e.

P17.18 Show that the low-frequency impedance-transforming properties of the common-collector amplifier, developed in Section 11.5.2, can be generalized. Specifically, prove that an emitter impedance Z_e can be moved above the emitter node in the hybrid-pi model to appear in series with $z_\pi = (g_\pi + sC_\pi)^{-1}$ if we transform the impedance to $Z_e(\beta + 1)$. Similarly, prove that the impedance z_π can be moved to below the emitter node to appear in series with Z_e if we transform its impedance to $z_\pi/(\beta + 1)$.

CHAPTER EIGHTEEN

Feedback

18.1 Basic Properties of Feedback Amplifiers

No amplifier is ideal. For example, no amplifier is perfectly linear, that is to say, the output voltage waveform is not an exact scaled replica of the input voltage waveform. Even if the amplifier is reasonably linear for some range of input voltage, the voltage gain of the amplifier will vary with changes in power-supply voltages or temperature because of variations in transistor characteristics with dc operating point and temperature. These and many other amplifier limitations can be minimized by applying *negative feedback* to the amplifier.

18.1.1 Gain

The concept of negative feedback as applied to amplifiers can be illustrated by means of the signal-flow block diagram shown in Fig. 18.1*a* or the electrical block diagram in Fig. 18.1*b*. To apply feedback to an amplifier, we must add two components, a precision attenuator, and a comparator. For simplicity we assume that the transfer functions of the three blocks are independent of frequency. Also, for the moment we suppress the issue of

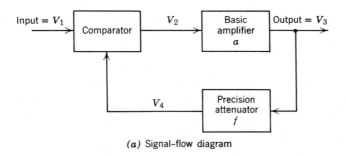

(*a*) Signal–flow diagram

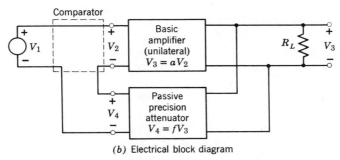

(*b*) Electrical block diagram

Figure 18.1 Block diagrams of a feedback amplifier.

loading of the basic amplifier by the feedback network, by assuming that the basic amplifier in Fig. 18.1 has infinite input resistance and zero output resistance. Under these conditions the output voltage V_4 of the precision attenuator is a precisely scaled-down version of the amplifier output voltage V_3. The voltage V_4 is compared with the input voltage V_1, and the *difference* between the two voltages is fed to the amplifier. That is,

$$V_2 = V_1 - V_4 \tag{18.1}$$

Combining this equation with the input-output relations of the basic amplifier and the precision attenuator

$$V_3 = aV_2 \tag{18.2}$$

$$V_4 = fV_3 \tag{18.3}$$

and eliminating V_2 and V_4, we find that the voltage gain A of the complete feedback amplifier, often called the *closed-loop gain*, is

$$\frac{V_3}{V_1} = A = \frac{a}{1 + af} \tag{18.4}$$

The effect of the negative feedback is now evident. If the product af is much larger than unity, Eq. 18.4 reduces to

$$A = \frac{V_3}{V_1} \simeq \frac{1}{f} \tag{18.5}$$

That is, the relationship between V_3 and V_1 depends only on f and is nearly independent of a. This is an important result because the gain a of the basic amplifier is a function of temperature, power-supply voltages, and so on, as pointed out above. On the other hand, the "gain" f can be precisely controlled, for the attenuator can be constructed from reliable R, L, and C components, the values of which are much less sensitive to operating conditions. The overall voltage gain A is approximately independent of a when a is large because the amplifier input voltage V_2 required to produce V_3 is then the difference between two much larger voltages V_1 and fV_3. Consequently, if a for some reason drops by a factor of 2, only a trivial change in V_3 is needed to double V_2, thereby compensating for the loss of gain.

It should be emphasized at the outset that although the present discussion is phrased in terms of voltage gain, we do not build amplifiers just to obtain voltage gain. That we can obtain with a transformer. What we are really interested in is power gain or power-handling capability—the ability to amplify a very low-power (and low-voltage) signal, so that substantial signal power can be delivered to a load, for example, a loudspeaker or a meter coil. This fact should be kept in mind in the subsequent discussion.

18.1.2   Desensitivity

Let us now calculate with more precision the sensitivity of the feedback amplifier gain A to changes in the gain a of the basic amplifier. Taking the differential of Eq. 18.4 (assuming small changes in a and constant f), we obtain

$$dA = \frac{1}{(1 + af)^2}\, da \tag{18.6}$$

We can now find the fractional change in A from this result and Eq. 18.4:

$$\frac{dA}{A} = \frac{1}{1 + af}\frac{da}{a} \tag{18.7}$$

(see Problem P18.1). Thus a given percentage change in a is *suppressed* in the overall gain A by a factor $1 + af$. For example, if the product af equals 99, then a 10% change in a gives rise to only a 0.1% change in A.

Clearly we pay a price for this improvement in amplifier performance. Comparison of Eqs. 18.2 and 18.4 indicates that the application of negative feedback has resulted in a *reduction* in gain. Specifically, the ratio of the gain of the overall feedback amplifier to the gain of the basic amplifier is

$$\frac{A}{a} = \frac{1}{1 + af} \tag{18.8}$$

Thus the overall gain is reduced by exactly the same factor by which gain changes are suppressed. In the numerical example cited above, the feedback has suppressed changes in gain by a factor of 100, but this improvement in performance is obtained at the expense of a reduction in gain by a factor of 100. Fortunately, unstabilized gain is readily obtainable (e.g., by adding more transistor stages). Thus the trade-off of unstabilized gain for stability is not a serious limitation on the use of feedback.

For the polarities and interconnections specified as in Fig. 18.1, the feedback is by definition *negative* or *inverse* if a and f have the same algebraic sign. However, in more complicated configurations it is not always easy to apply this criterion. A surer method of checking for negative feedback can be seen from inspection of Eq. 18.8. Specifically, if a small increase in the magnitude of f from zero *reduces* $|A|$ below $|a|$, the feedback is by definition *negative*.

18.1.3   The Effect of Feedback on Extraneous Signals

The performance of amplifiers is often limited by the presence of extraneous signals, such as power-supply hum, thermal noise, and cross-talk from adjacent amplifiers. Under certain specific circumstances, negative feedback can be used to reduce the effect of these extraneous signals, but in many other circumstances, feedback produces no improvement whatsoever. We shall differentiate between these extremes by means of a few simple examples.

Let us examine first the effects of extraneous signals at the input of an amplifier. A block diagram appropriate for this calculation is shown in Fig. 18.2a. It is almost obvious that because the desired signal V_1 and the extraneous signal V_n enter the feedback amplifier at essentially the same point, it is going to be difficult for the amplifier to preferentially amplify V_1 but not V_n. To show this formally, we write the output voltage V_3 by superposition, using Eq. 18.4:

$$V_3 = \frac{a}{1 + af}V_1 + \frac{a}{1 + af}V_n \tag{18.9}$$

A useful measure of amplifier performance in this case is the signal-to-noise ratio—the ratio of signal amplitude to amplitude of the extraneous signal at some point in the network. It is clear from Eq. 18.9 that the signal-to-noise ratio at the output of the feedback amplifier in Fig. 18.2a is

$$\frac{S}{N} = \frac{V_1}{V_n} \tag{18.10}$$

which is the same result that would be obtained from the amplifier a alone (Fig. 18.2b). Hence we conclude that in general *feedback cannot improve the signal-to-noise ratio of an amplifier if the unwanted signal enters at the amplifier input.*

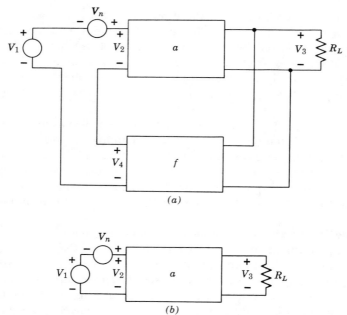

Figure 18.2   Effect of feedback on extraneous signals at the amplifier input.

We have already discussed (in Chapter 16) an apparent contradiction to this statement. In Section 16.1.4, feedback was introduced around a three-stage amplifier to make the operating point of the output transistor stable in spite of changes in V_{B1}. A careful examination of Fig. 16.5 reveals that the "extraneous signal" source V_{B1} and the source of desired signals V_i are in effect both connected to the amplifier input, because both give rise to a base current V/R_s. The improvement in signal-to-noise ratio, or more accurately the signal-to-*drift* ratio, in this amplifier occurs because the signal is *ac* whereas the drift is essentially *dc*. Thus it is possible by adding capacitor C_b to the feedback network to apply the feedback *selectively*, that is, we have large amounts of feedback at dc and no feedback at signal frequencies.

Next let us examine the effect of feedback if the extraneous signal is being introduced at some point other than the amplifier input. A general representation of this case is shown in Fig. 18.3a. Here we assume that we have two amplifiers a_1 and a_2. Amplifier a_2 is assumed to have associated with it an extraneous signal V_n, whereas amplifier a_1 is assumed to be noise-free. Again using superposition, we find the output voltage V_3 to be

$$V_3 = \frac{a_1 a_2}{1 + a_1 a_2 f} V_1 + \frac{a_2}{1 + a_1 a_2 f} V_n \tag{18.11}$$

Thus the signal-to-noise ratio at the amplifier output is

$$\frac{S}{N} = \frac{a_1 V_1}{V_n} \tag{18.12}$$

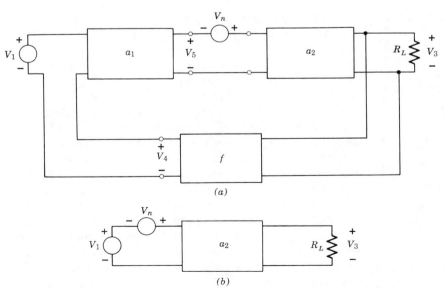

(a)

(b)

Figure 18.3   Effect of feedback on extraneous signals introduced at some point other than at the input.

which is a factor of a_1 better than would be achieved with amplifier a_2 alone (Fig. 18.3b). Thus if it is possible to build an amplifier a_1 *that does not have the same inherent problem of extraneous signals as amplifier a_2*, then it is possible to improve the output signal-to-noise ratio of a_2 by means of feedback. This condition implies that the extraneous signal V_n in Fig. 18.3 *cannot* be thermal noise associated with the amplifier input, because amplifier a_1 would then suffer from the same problem as a_2.

A practical example that can be adequately represented by Fig. 18.3 is the problem of power-supply hum associated with the output stage of an audio amplifier. Because such an output stage often operates with collector currents in the ampere range, it is expensive to provide adequate filtering for the dc power supplying this stage. On the other hand, because the preceding stages in the amplifier operate at much lower signal levels, power-supply filtering here is relatively inexpensive. Hence it is reasonable to represent the output power amplifier by the block a_2 in Fig. 18.3 and assume that V_n represents power-supply hum. Amplifier a_1 is then a second amplifier which operates at much lower signal levels from a well-filtered power supply. To be specific, assume that the power amplifier a_2 has a voltage gain of unity but a large power gain (which is why it is needed) and that V_n is a 120-cycle hum signal of 1-volt amplitude. The exact point at which the extraneous signal is introduced in a_2 is not important in this discussion, hence for simplicity we assume that it enters at the input of a_2. If the desired signal V_1 is also of 1-volt amplitude, then when a_2 is operated alone (Fig. 18.3b), the output signal-to-hum ratio is unity. If now a hum-free amplifier a_1 of gain 100 and a feedback network with f equal to one are added, then from Eq. 18.11, the output voltage will still contain about 1 volt of signal when the feedback network is used and the 1-volt input signal is applied to the *comparator*, but the hum signal will be reduced by a factor of 101. This reduction occurs because the voltage V_5 in Fig. 18.3a now contains a hum component exactly *inverted* with respect to the hum from V_n, and this component almost cancels the hum.

The results discussed above can be readily verified by observing the waveforms in the simple audio amplifier shown in Fig. 18.4a. When the power amplifier stage is operated with no feedback by placing the switch in position 1, the voltage V_5 is sinusoidal, whereas the output voltage V_3 contains a large unwanted hum component, as can be seen from Fig. 18.4b. When feedback is applied around the output stage and the low-level amplifier, (in this case a 709 operational amplifier) by moving the switch to position 2, we see from Fig. 18.4c that the hum disappears in the power-amplifier output voltage V_3, but the input V_5 to the power amplifier now contains an *inverted* hum signal required to cancel the hum.[1] The amplitude of the desired signal at the input to the power amplifier is almost the same with or without feedback. (See Problem P 18.25.)

[1] This discussion can be used as the basis of a simple yet very effective lecture demonstration. See Section 18.8.

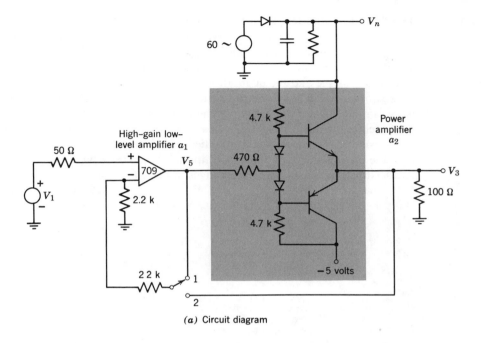

(a) Circuit diagram

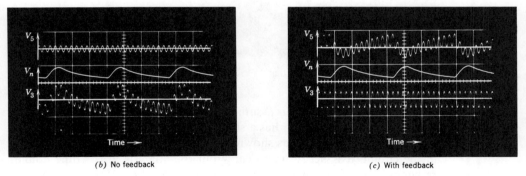

(b) No feedback   (c) With feedback

Figure 18.4   Oscilloscope photographs showing the effect of feedback on output-stage hum.

In summary, feedback can be used to reduce extraneous signals in an amplifier only if for some reason it is possible to build a *second* amplifier having substantial gain, and substantially better output signal-to-noise ratio than the original amplifier. In practice it is generally easier to minimize extraneous signals in amplifier stages for which power gain and high levels of output power are not important considerations. Thus the requirement for large voltage gain can be met in one amplifier, while the power capability, with the attendant problems of power-supply hum and others can be provided in a separate amplifier stage.

18.1.4 The Effect of Feedback on Distortion

In the preceding discussion we have assumed that all circuits in the block diagrams had linear transfer functions. We now examine the case where the amplifier is nonlinear. Specifically let us assume that the relation between the dc output voltage and the dc input voltage of the basic amplifier in Fig. 18.1 is as shown in Fig. 18.5. Because the assumed transfer characteristics are *incrementally* linear, we can apply the analysis in Section 18.1.1 separately over each of the linear ranges. On this basis we would expect that the overall transfer curve of the feedback amplifier would be substantially more linear than the transfer curve of the basic amplifier, because we have already shown that feedback tends to suppress changes in basic amplifier gain.

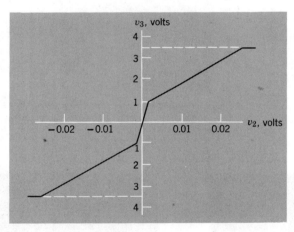

Figure 18.5 Transfer function of basic amplifier.

To be more specific, let us assume that for $|v_3|$ less than 1 volt, the transfer curve of the basic amplifier has a slope of 1000, while for $|v_3|$ between 1 and 3.5 volts, the slope is 100, as shown in Fig. 18.5. Because of the nonlinearity in the circuit, it is necessary to carry out the analysis in the time domain rather than the frequency domain. Thus we write Eqs. 18.1, 18.2, and 18.3 explicitly in terms of *incremental variables in the time domain*:

$$v_3(t) = av_2(t) \tag{18.13}$$

$$v_4(t) = fv_3(t) \tag{18.14}$$

$$v_2(t) = v_1(t) - v_4(t) \tag{18.15}$$

Hence

$$v_3(t) = \frac{a}{1 + af}v_1(t) \tag{18.16}$$

If we now assume that $f = 0.1$, then from Eq. 18.16, for $|v_3|$ less than 1 volt, the incremental output voltage is

$$v_3(t) = \frac{1000v_1(t)}{1 + (1000)(0.1)} = 9.9v_1(t)$$

and for $|v_3|$ between 1 and 3.5 volts, the slope of the transfer curve, that is, the incremental gain, is

$$\text{slope} = \frac{100}{1 + (100)(0.1)} = 9.1$$

Thus the application of negative feedback has reduced a 10 to 1 change in the basic amplifier incremental gain to a 9.9 to 9.1 change *over the same range of output voltage swing* (see Fig. 18.6). Clearly the price for this improved linearity is gain reduction. But in many instances this is not a serious problem. The lost gain can be recovered by adding a new amplifier at the input of the feedback amplifier, and this new amplifier, because it does not have to handle large signal amplitudes, can presumably be designed to introduce almost no distortion. So we reduce the amplification function of the large-signal portion of the system in order to improve its large-signal fidelity and then transfer the job of providing gain to the small-signal portions of the system, where the distortion is much less. In this type of problem, then, inverse feedback does lead to improvement in overall system linearity, without sacrifice of *system* gain.

It is very important to note, however, that the feedback becomes increasingly less effective as the incremental gain of the basic amplifier becomes

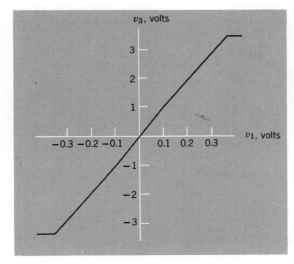

Figure 18.6   Transfer function of the complete feedback amplifier.

smaller. As an extreme example, when the basic amplifier discussed above *saturates* for $|v_3|$ greater than 3.5 volts, the incremental gain a goes to zero; hence incrementally both af and A also go to zero, as can be seen in Fig. 18.6. Thus there is a limit to the amount of nonlinearity that the feedback can correct. Every amplifier has fundamental "hard" limits on the output signal levels that it can produce. These hard limits, which arise because transistors in the amplifier cut off, saturate, or otherwise become grossly nonlinear, cannot be relieved by feedback.

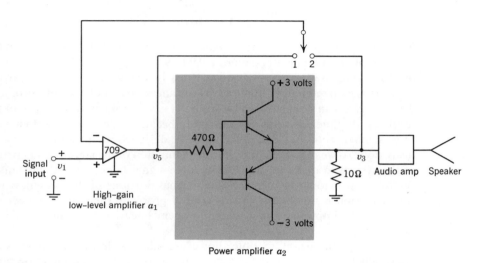

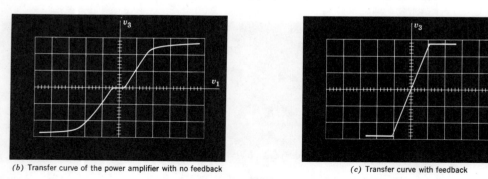

(b) Transfer curve of the power amplifier with no feedback   (c) Transfer curve with feedback

Figure 18.7   Demonstration of the effects of feedback on output-stage distortion.

A simple circuit that illustrates the effect of feedback on distortion is shown in Fig. 18.7a. Because the amount of distortion is related to the *output* signal level, to obtain a fair intercomparison it is important that the output signal with feedback be made equal to the output signal with no feedback. This is accomplished by switching the feedback as shown in Fig.

18.7*a.* With the switch in position 1, the power amplifier a_2 has no feedback, and the 709 operational amplifier with feedback has unity gain. When the switch is moved to position 2, overall feedback is applied around the low-level amplifier (the 709 operational amplifier) and the power amplifier, so that the overall gain is now unity.

An oscilloscope photograph of the transfer curve without output-stage feedback, v_3 versus v_1 (or v_5), is shown in Fig. 18.7*b.* The nonlinearity around the origin arises because neither output transistor conducts if v_5 is less than 0.4 volts peak. For large v_3, the transfer curve flattens because β_F falls at high currents, and finally because the transistor saturates. The transfer curve with overall feedback (switch in position 2) is shown in Fig. 18.7*c.* The improvement in linearity is obvious.

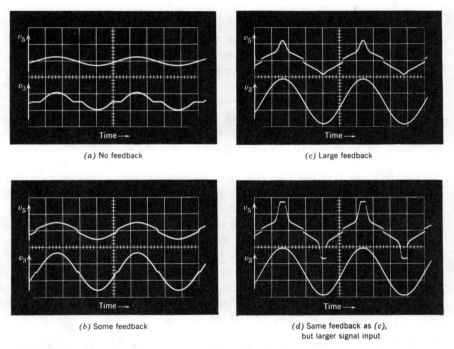

(*a*) No feedback

(*c*) Large feedback

(*b*) Some feedback

(*d*) Same feedback as (*c*), but larger signal input

Figure 18.8   Oscilloscope photographs showing the effect of feedback on output-stage distortion.

Shown in Fig. 18.8 are oscilloscope photographs of the input and output waveforms to the power amplifier, with and without the feedback, assuming in all cases a sinusoidal drive. The distortion in the output signal, so clearly visible in Fig. 18.8*a*, has virtually disappeared in Fig. 18.8*c.* To produce this nearly sinusoidal output signal, a dramatic change in the input voltage v_5 has been required, as can be seen from the figure. Because the *nonlinearity is still present* in the power amplifier a_2, it has been necessary to *predistort* the waveform at the input to a_2, in order to achieve an almost sinusoidal output signal. This has important consequences in terms of the design of the low-level amplifier which drives the power amplifier: the output stage of the low-level amplifier must be designed to handle signal amplitudes much larger than normal to allow for this predistortion.

Note that in Fig. 18.8d the power amplifier has been driven into saturation. The low-level amplifier tries valiantly to compensate for this, but it too eventually saturates. (For further details on the use of this circuit for a lecture demonstration, see Section 18.8.2.)

18.1.5 Summary

We have seen that when negative feedback is applied to an amplifier, the amplifier is *desensitized*, in that its gain is more constant than before, extraneous signals are suppressed under certain conditions, and distortion is reduced. We shall subsequently see that the bandwidth of the amplifier is also increased by feedback, and the input and output impedances are altered. These advantages are all obtained at a price: the voltage gain is reduced in direct proportion to the amount of desensitivity. However, voltage gain is usually easy to obtain, so that trading voltage gain for desensitivity is often a good bargain.

Several practical points deserve emphasis at this juncture. First, feedback stabilizes gain and reduces distortion only because it makes the gain depend on the properties of certain passive components in the network rather than the active components. These passive components are much more "ideal" than active devices such as transistors; they are much more linear and much more constant in value in spite of changing temperature, humidity, operating current, and similar factors.

Second, voltage gain is easy to obtain, power-handling capability is not. Stages in which power-handling capability is not a major issue can be made linear and free from certain extraneous signals such as power-supply hum to a much greater extent than stages in which power is an important issue. Thus we are willing to increase the voltage gain of a circuit by adding a low-level transistor stage if such a modification will improve the properties of the power-handling part of the circuit.

18.2 The Four Basic Feedback Circuit Topologies

In the preceding section the basic properties of feedback amplifiers were studied in terms of simple block diagrams. We now relate these block diagrams to actual transistor circuits, and develop ways of identifying the transfer functions *a* and *f* by inspection. Because we wish eventually to include capacitive effects in order to discuss the frequency response of feedback amplifiers, all remaining calculations in this chapter will be in terms of complex amplitudes of voltage and currents, that is, in the *frequency domain*. Thus we must assume from here on that all amplifiers are operated in the linear mode.

In addition to amplification (or attenuation), two signal processes are represented in the general feedback block diagram (Fig. 18.1a). These are *sampling* of an output voltage or current to feed a signal to the precision attenuator, and *comparison* of either voltages or currents at the input to derive a signal to feed to the basic amplifier. It follows that the general block diagram can be realized with transistor circuits in four distinct and topologically identifiable forms. These are shown in Figs. 18.9a, b, c, and d. It turns out to be much easier when dealing with actual circuits to differentiate among these types first by means of the *circuit topology* rather than what variable is sampled or compared. Thus we focus attention on the nature of the interconnections of the source, amplifier, and feedback network at the input and of the load, amplifier, and feedback at the output.

In Fig. 18.9a and b, the circuit topology at the input is clearly *loop* in character, that is, the source, the basic amplifier, and the feedback network are connected in a *loop* by the comparator. On the other hand, in Figs. 18.9c and d, we have *node* topology at the input, because the source, the basic amplifier, and the feedback network share a common *node* pair. Thévenin equivalent sources are shown when loop comparison is employed, and Norton equivalent sources are given for node comparison, because this choice, although not essential, will greatly simplify the analysis later on.

In a similar vein, there are two topologically distinct methods of sampling the signal at the output of the amplifier. In Figs. 18.9a and d the topology is *loop* in character, in that the basic amplifier output, the load, and the feedback network are connected in a loop. In these cases the feedback network samples the output or load *current*. In Figs. 18.9b and c we have *node* topology, because load, amplifier output, and feedback network share a common node pair. Thus the feedback network samples output or load *voltage*. It is vitally important that these identifications be made at the outset of any analysis or design, because the basic characteristics of the feedback amplifier, such as input impedance and output impedance, depend critically on the type of comparison and/or the type of sampling employed.

Transistor amplifier examples that correspond closely to each of the four two-port diagrams in Fig. 18.9 are shown in Fig. 18.10. The identification of node or loop comparison can be made once the source terminals, the basic amplifier input terminals, and the feedback network input terminals[2] have been identified. Similarly we can determine whether node or loop sampling has been employed at the output once we identify the load, the basic amplifier output, and the feedback network output terminals. Although the identification of the general topology of the feedback is reasonably clear in each amplifier in Fig. 18.10, in fact only Fig. 18.10c is unambiguously related to its counterpart in Fig. 18.9. However, we shall see later that if certain key

---

[2] For convenience in the two-port analysis, we designate the source end of the feedback network as the input and the load end as the output, in spite of the fact that the important flow of signals in the feedback network is from right to left.

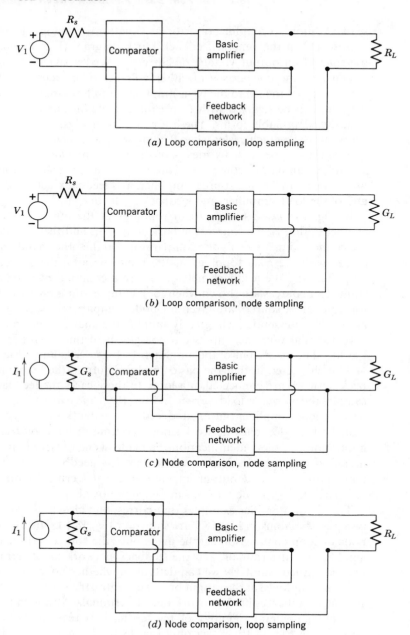

(a) Loop comparison, loop sampling

(b) Loop comparison, node sampling

(c) Node comparison, node sampling

(d) Node comparison, loop sampling

Figure 18.9 The four basic configurations of two two-ports for a feedback amplifier. The polarities show the normal reference directions for terminal voltages at the ports. These configurations are sometimes referred to in the literature as series-series, series-shunt, shunt-shunt, and shunt-series feedback.

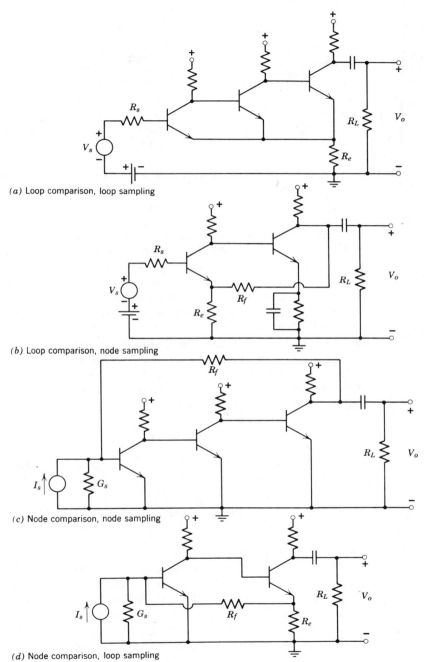

(a) Loop comparison, loop sampling

(b) Loop comparison, node sampling

(c) Node comparison, node sampling

(d) Node comparison, loop sampling

Figure 18.10   Transistor feedback amplifier examples that correspond closely to the two-port diagrams in Fig. 18.9.

assumptions are made, the remaining circuits in Fig. 18.10 also reduce to their counterparts in Fig. 18.9.

Although the discussion in this chapter will be confined to the four basic types of feedback connections, it is important to point out that combinations of two or more of these methods may also be used. In addition, it is often desirable to use a "nested" feedback configuration, in which the "basic amplifier" is itself composed of a more basic amplifier and a feedback network. Fortunately, in both cases the analysis methods discussed in this chapter can be applied with only minor modification.

18.3   Analysis and Design of Circuits Employing Node Comparison and Node Sampling

As long as we suppress the issue of loading the basic amplifier by the feedback network (precision attenuator), it is possible to make a clean distinction between the basic amplifier and the feedback network, as we did in Figs. 18.1*a* and *b*. In many feedback amplifier circuits, however, the passive elements in the feedback network represent significant impedances connected in series or in parallel with the basic amplifier. Thus it is no longer possible to have a basic amplifier "box" whose gain is completely independent of the passive elements in the feedback network. We can of course analyze any specific feedback circuit by direct application of Kirchhoff's voltage and current laws, ignoring the feedback aspects altogether. Feedback, after all, is an extremely helpful, but not absolutely essential, point of view. We resort to such direct analysis methods to verify approximate solutions in certain difficult cases. It is obviously better, however, to identify if possible an *a circuit* and an *f circuit* whose transfer functions are appropriate for use in the basic feedback relation

$$A = \frac{a}{1 + af} \tag{18.17}$$

Fortunately such an identification can be made on the basis of three key assumptions about the network parameters. Even more important, it is possible to identify *by inspection* that portion of the complete feedback amplifier circuit that forms the *a* circuit. Clearly this identification is central to the issue of rapid analysis and design of feedback circuits.

18.3.1   Analysis in Terms of Two-Ports

Let us now identify the *a* and *f* transfer functions for the simplest of the four circuits shown in Fig. 18.9 or Fig. 18.10—the circuit employing node comparison and node sampling (Fig. 18.9*c* or Fig. 18.10*c*). It is clearly preferable to make this identification in terms of the general two-port representation in Fig. 18.9*c* rather than some specific amplifier such as the one in Fig. 18.10*c*. Therefore we adopt the following procedure:

1. We evaluate the overall gain of the general network in Fig. 18.9*c*, casting the result in the "feedback form" (Eq. 18.17).

2. We identify from this result the a and f transfer functions.

3. We make appropriate approximations so that a and f have simple interpretations in terms of the circuit, thereby enabling us to find a and f by inspection directly from a circuit without carrying out the complete analysis in each case.

To carry out the general analysis, we must first decide which of the six possible two-port linear network descriptions (y, z, h, etc.) is the most appropriate representation for the two-ports in Fig. 18.9c. Clearly, with node comparison we should select the description in which the source and the input elements of the two-port are connected at one common node pair. Similarly, with node sampling, we want a two-port description with one common output node pair. The y-parameter description, involving short-circuit admittance parameters y_i, y_o, y_f, and y_r, meets these conditions. On this basis the complete "node-node" feedback amplifier (Fig. 18.9c or Fig. 18.10c) can be represented as the parallel interconnection of two y-parameter two-ports, as shown in Fig. 18.11. To distinguish between these two-ports, a second subscript has been added to the y parameters—an a for basic amplifier parameters and an f for parameters associated with the feedback network.

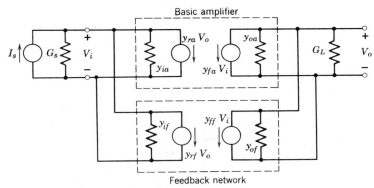

Figure 18.11   Representation in terms of y parameters of a feedback amplifier with node sampling and node comparison.

The analysis of the circuit in Fig. 18.11 is straightforward. The node equations are

$$I_s = (G_s + y_{ia} + y_{if})V_i + (y_{ra} + y_{rf})V_o \tag{18.18a}$$

$$0 = (y_{fa} + y_{ff})V_i + (G_L + y_{oa} + y_{of})V_o \tag{18.18b}$$

To simplify the algebra, we define two admittances:

$$Y_i = G_s + y_{ia} + y_{if} \tag{18.19}$$

and

$$Y_o = G_L + y_{oa} + y_{of} \tag{18.20}$$

Solving for V_o after substituting Eqs. 18.19 and 18.20 into Eqs. 18.18, we obtain

$$\frac{V_o}{I_s} = \frac{-(y_{fa} + y_{ff})}{Y_i Y_o - (y_{fa} + y_{ff})(y_{ra} + y_{rf})} \tag{18.21}$$

This equation can be manipulated into the "feedback form" (Eq. 18.17) in a number of different ways, but the most useful result for our purposes is obtained by dividing numerator and denominator of Eq. 18.21 by the product $Y_i Y_o$:

$$\frac{V_o}{I_s} = \frac{\dfrac{-(y_{fa} + y_{ff})}{Y_i Y_o}}{1 + \dfrac{-(y_{fa} + y_{ff})}{Y_i Y_o}(y_{ra} + y_{rf})} \tag{18.22}$$

This equation is in the form of Eq. 18.17 if we make the following identifications:

$$a = -\frac{y_{fa} + y_{ff}}{Y_i Y_o} \tag{18.23}$$

and

$$f = y_{ra} + y_{rf} \tag{18.24}$$

Meaningful circuit interpretations for a and f result only when we make three fundamental but eminently reasonable approximations. First, we must assume that the basic amplifier, and not the feedback network, supplies the gain in the system. Since the basic amplifier is designed to have substantial gain, whereas the feedback network is some sort of passive attenuator, this assumption is easy to justify. In terms of the y parameters, this approximation constrains the relative size of the two forward-transfer parameters y_{fa} and y_{ff}:

$$|y_{fa}| \gg |y_{ff}| \tag{18.25}$$

Second, we must assume that most of the signal fed back from output to input flows via the feedback network rather than backward through the basic amplifier. In y-parameter terms, this implies a constraint on the reverse-transfer parameters y_{ra} and y_{rf}:

$$|y_{ra}| \ll |y_{rf}| \tag{18.26}$$

A third condition, which we shall need in the next section, is that the basic amplifier be unilateral enough so that changes in its load admittance do not appreciably affect its input admittance, the same condition required in the tuned amplifier discussion, Section 17.1.4. Thus in y-parameter terms,

$$|y_{fa}y_{ra}| \ll |Y_i Y_o| \qquad (18.27)$$

When the constraints of Eqs. 18.25 and 18.26 are applied to Eqs. 18.22, 18.23, and 18.24, we obtain

$$\frac{V_o}{I_s} = A \simeq \frac{\dfrac{-y_{fa}}{Y_i Y_o}}{1 + \left(\dfrac{-y_{fa}}{Y_i Y_o}\right) y_{rf}} \qquad (18.28)$$

Consequently, by comparison with Eq. 18.17,

$$a \simeq \frac{-y_{fa}}{Y_i Y_o} = \frac{-y_{fa}}{(G_s + y_{ia} + y_{if})(G_L + y_{oa} + y_{of})} \qquad (18.29)$$

$$f \simeq y_{rf} \qquad (18.30)$$

Note that whereas certain parameters of the feedback network, specifically y_{if} and y_{of}, are contained in the a transfer function, the f transfer function now depends solely on the parameters of the passive attenuator. It should be clear from Section 18.1 that for successful operation of a feedback amplifier, *the f circuit must have this property.*

18.3.2   Circuit Representations for *a* and *f*

To avoid the unpleasant task of having to calculate the y parameters for each circuit under consideration, it is necessary to find simple circuit interpretations for the a and f transfer functions specified by Eqs. 18.29 and 18.30. To this end we note first that the circuit shown in Fig. 18.12*b* has a transfer function equal to

$$\frac{V_o'}{I_s} = \frac{-y_{fa}}{Y_i Y_o - y_{fa}y_{ra}} \qquad (18.31)$$

(This can be derived by direct calculation or by setting y_{ff} and y_{rf} to zero in Eqs. 18.18 and 18.21.) Thus this circuit will have the a transfer function prescribed in Eq. 18.29, *provided* that the amplifier is unilateral enough so that the $y_{fa}y_{ra}$ term in the denominator can be neglected, that is, provided Eq. 18.27 is satisfied. Recall from the tuned amplifier discussion that the product $|y_{fa}y_{ra}|$ is usually smaller for a cascade of stages than it is for any one stage alone. Thus the condition above will be valid for a multistage amplifier, even if it is doubtful for each individual stage.

By comparing the circuit in Fig. 18.12*b* to the complete feedback amplifier circuit, repeated for convenience in Fig. 18.12*a*, it is possible to deduce simple rules for forming the a circuit for any feedback amplifier that employs node comparison and node sampling.

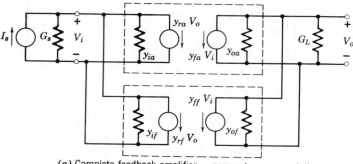

(a) Complete feedback amplifier, y–parameter representation

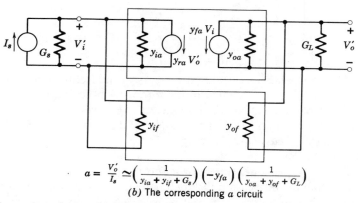

$$a = \frac{V_o'}{I_s} \simeq \left(\frac{1}{y_{ia} + y_{if} + G_s} \right) \left(-y_{fa} \right) \left(\frac{1}{y_{oa} + y_{of} + G_L} \right)$$

(b) The corresponding a circuit

Figure 18.12   Formation of the *a* circuit in *y*-parameter terms.

1. Identify the various components of the feedback amplifier: the source, the load, the basic amplifier, and the feedback network, as discussed in Section 18.2.

2. Form the *a* circuit by augmenting the basic amplifier by the elements y_{if} and G_s on the input and y_{of} and G_L on the output. That is, *all loading effects of the source, the feedback network, and the load are associated with the a circuit.*

The required augmentation of the basic amplifier can be found without calculating any *y* parameters and, in fact, without any calculation whatsoever. Specifically, the proper loading on the *a*-circuit *input* node produced by the source, the basic amplifier, and the feedback network is that which remains after *shorting the output node* of the complete feedback amplifier to destroy the feedback. Similarly the proper loading on the *a*-circuit *output* node produced by the load, the basic amplifier, and the feedback network is that which remains after *shorting the input node* of the complete feedback amplifier to destroy the feedback. An important feature of this feedback formulation is that the *a* circuit contains the complete basic amplifier *without modification*. Thus the formation of the *a* circuit amounts to nothing more than adding to the existing basic amplifier certain admittances normally associated with the feedback network. This feature is emphasized in Fig. 18.13a.

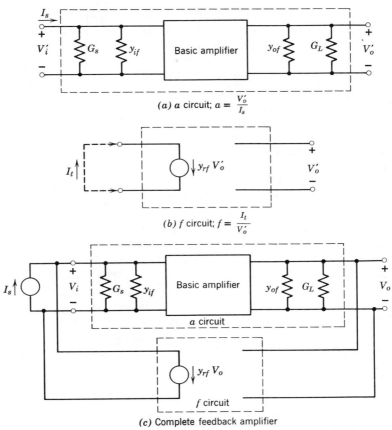

(a) *a* circuit; $a = \dfrac{V'_o}{I_s}$

(b) *f* circuit; $f = \dfrac{I_t}{V'_o}$

(c) Complete feedback amplifier

Figure 18.13   Formation of *a* and *f* circuits.

It turns out to be impossible to obtain for the *f* transfer function a simple circuit interpretation similar to the *a* circuit deduced above. The problem is that on the basis of the simplifying assumptions on page 636, the *f* transfer function (Eq. 18.30) is *by definition* y_{rf}, the short-circuit reverse transfer admittance of the feedback network. Because we have already accounted for the effects of y_{if} and y_{of} by including them in the *a* circuit, the *f* circuit turns out to be a pure transadmittance, with zero input and output admittances. Clearly no physical network element associated with the feedback network has these properties. Thus we must be content to calculate y_{rf} for the feedback network, and represent the f circuit as an ideal dependent current source $y_{rf}V'_o$ as shown in Fig. 18.13b. The parameter y_{rf} is calculated in accordance with the standard y-parameter rules: short the input of the feedback network, apply a voltage source V'_o at the output terminals, and calculate the current I_t flowing in the input short, as shown in Fig. 18.13b.

The a and f circuit of Figs. 18.13a and b have been reconnected in Fig. 18.13c to reestablish the complete feedback amplifier. Note that because of the way the f circuit has been defined, it does not load the a circuit in any way, nor is the f circuit transfer function changed by loading effects of the a circuit. Thus by forming the a and f circuits in the particular manner described above, we have in effect manipulated the general node-node feedback amplifier circuit into a form that *can again be described by the original block diagrams of Fig. 18.1.*

18.3.3 Design Example

Let us now apply these results to the specific node-comparison node-sampling feedback circuit shown in Fig. 18.14a (essentially a repeat of Fig. 18.10). The complete midfrequency incremental model is shown in Fig. 18.14b. Note that to conform with the node topology at the input, the input source has been transformed to a Norton equivalent.

Following the procedure outlined in Section 18.3.2 for finding the a circuit, we include the source resistance, the load G_L, and the transistor amplifier in the a circuit, as shown in Fig. 18.14c. The loading effect of the feedback network at the input of the a circuit is found by shorting the output node in Fig. 18.14b to ground; hence we see a conductance G_f to ground. In a similar manner we find the output loading by shorting the input node in Fig. 18.14b to ground; hence we see an additional conductance G_f to ground at the output of the a circuit. The incremental gain of the a circuit

$$a = \frac{V'_o}{I}$$

can now be calculated by inspection.

The f transfer function is calculated by shorting the input node in Fig. 18.14b, and applying a source V'_o at the output node, as shown in Fig. 18.14d. Thus for this circuit

$$f = \frac{I_t}{V'_o} = -G_f \tag{18.32}$$

The resulting f circuit is shown in Fig. 18.14e. These results can be verified readily by direct calculation from Fig. 18.14b (see Problem 18.2).

Suppose that we wish to design a feedback amplifier of the type shown in Fig. 18.14a to have a *closed-loop* voltage gain V_o/V_s of -100 and a desensitivity to basic amplifier parameter changes of about 70. Assume that $R_s = 50$ ohms. First we must translate these specifications into requirements on

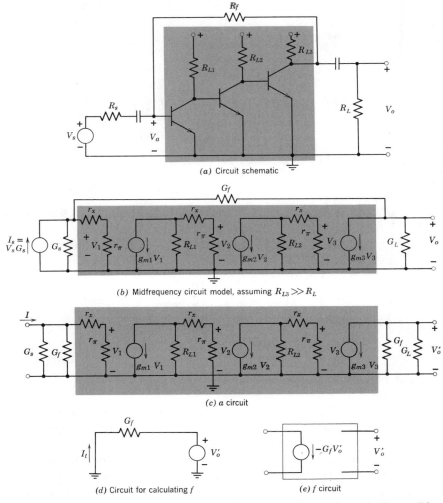

(a) Circuit schematic

(b) Midfrequency circuit model, assuming $R_{L3} \gg R_L$

(c) a circuit

(d) Circuit for calculating f

(e) f circuit

Figure 18.14   Node comparison, node sampling feedback amplifier. Shading indicates basic amplifier

A, f, and a. For this type of feedback A is not a voltage gain, but rather a transimpedance:

$$A = \frac{V_o}{I_s} = \frac{a}{1 + af} \qquad (18.33)$$

Thus

$$A = \frac{V_o}{V_s G_s} = -100 \times 50 = -5000 \text{ ohms}$$

From Eq. 18.7 the desensitivity is $1 + af$, and the specifications call for this to be "about 70." Hence from Eq. 18.33, the basic amplifier "gain," that is, transimpedance, must be

$$a = \frac{V'_o}{I_s} = A(1 + af) \simeq (-5000)(70) = -350 \,\text{kohm}$$

This corresponds to a voltage gain of the a amplifier of

$$\frac{V'_o}{V_s} = \frac{V'_o}{I_s R_s} = \frac{-350 \,\text{kohm}}{0.05 \,\text{kohm}} = -7000$$

An alternative calculation is

$$\frac{V'_o}{V_s} = \frac{V_o}{V_s}(1 + af) = (-100)(70) = -7000$$

Also, from Eq. 18.33, because a is large, the feedback transfer function must be

$$f \simeq \frac{1}{A} = \frac{1}{-5000 \,\text{ohm}} = -0.2 \,\text{mmho}$$

or, more accurately,

$$f = \frac{70 - 1}{-350 \,\text{kohm}} = -0.197 \,\text{mmho}$$

With all of the basic feedback parameters defined, we can now proceed with the detailed design.

In this example, the value of G_f is uniquely determined by f (see Eq. 18.32):

$$G_f = -f = 0.2 \,\text{mmho}$$

The parameters of the basic amplifier can be chosen on the basis of the a circuit incremental model shown in Fig. 18.14c. The gain of such a circuit has already been calculated in Section 16.1.1 (see Eq. 16.2), except for the minor modification that in the present problem the feedback conductance G_f appears in parallel with G_s on the input and G_L on the output. The design of this amplifier for prescribed gain has already been discussed in Section 16.1.2 and will not be repeated here. In fact, the three-stage design outlined in that section comes close to meeting our present specifications. Using Eq. 16.2 (modified to include the effect of G_f), the parameter values listed in Table 16.1 (page 560), and resistor values $R_{L1} = 500$ ohms, $R_{L2} = 200$ ohms, $R_L = 100$ ohms, $R_{L3} \gg R_L$, $G_f = 0.2$ mmho, we obtain

$$a = \frac{V'_o}{I} = -354 \,\text{kohm}$$

(see Problem 18.3). This completes the midfrequency design.[3]

[3] Although the above calculations are correct as far as they go, we shall find in Chapter 19 that if three identical transistors are used, the feedback amplifier as designed here is *hopelessly unstable*. That is, the amplifier has natural frequencies in the right half plane, hence exponentially growing natural modes.

To verify this design, we calculate the desensitivity and overall gain that will be achieved when the 5-kohm resistor is connected from output to input around the basic amplifier, as shown in Fig. 18.14a. The desensitivity is

$$1 + af = 1 + (-354)(-0.2) = 71.8$$

and an overall gain with feedback is

$$A = \frac{-354}{71.8} = -4.94\,\text{kohm}$$

Note that because we have employed node comparison and node sampling, what has actually been stabilized in this amplifier is the *transimpedance* V_o/I_s, and *not* the voltage gain V_o/V_s. If R_s is a reliable parameter, this is no problem, because

$$\frac{V_o}{V_s} = \frac{V_o}{I_s R_s} = \frac{A}{R_s} \tag{18.34}$$

In this example, the voltage gain is

$$\frac{V_o}{V_s} = AG_s = (-4.94)(20) = -99$$

Equation 18.34, when combined with the relationship

$$A \simeq \frac{1}{f} = -R_f \tag{18.35}$$

gives rise to an alternative point of view that is often useful for rapid circuit calculations. Specifically, from Eqs. 18.34 and 18.35, the overall voltage gain is just the ratio of two resistor values:

$$\frac{V_o}{V_s} \simeq -\frac{R_f}{R_s} \tag{18.36}$$

The validity of this simple relationship can be seen from Fig. 18.14a. Because the three-stage amplifier has a very large voltage gain, the voltage V_a at the base of the first transistor must be very small: fractions of a millivolt if V_o is a few volts. If the amplifier has substantial feedback, V_a will also be much smaller than V_s. Thus to a first approximation assume that

$$V_a \simeq 0 \tag{18.37}$$

Hence

$$I_{b1} \simeq 0 \tag{18.38}$$

The voltage V_o must adjust itself to satisfy these conditions. From Eq. 18.37, the voltage drop across R_s must be V_s, and the drop across R_f must be V_o. Also, because $I_{b1} \simeq 0$, these two resistor currents must be equal and opposite:

$$\frac{V_s}{R_s} = -\frac{V_o}{R_f} \qquad (18.39)$$

Hence Eq. 18.36. This simplified approach is particularly useful in dealing with operational amplifiers (see Fig. 16.16), because such amplifiers often have voltage gains as high as 10^5 or 10^6. In addition, they usually have a sufficiently low output impedance that the loading effects of the feedback network can be neglected. See Problems P.18.22 and P.18.25.

18.3.4   Loop Transmission

It is clear from the preceding section that one important parameter in feedback amplifier calculations is the desensitivity $1 + af$, which can often be approximated for large desensitivity as just af. Algebraically, the latter quantity in y-parameter terms is the product of Eqs. 18.29 and 18.30:

$$af = \frac{V'_o}{I_s}\frac{I_t}{V'_o} = \frac{I_t}{I_s} = \frac{-y_{fa}}{(y_{ia} + y_{if} + G_s)(y_{oa} + y_{of} + G_L)} y_{rf} \qquad (18.40)$$

But for the same reasons as before, it is helpful to have a simple circuit interpretation of this product, in addition to the circuits we already have for a and f alone. Because the f circuit does not load the a circuit, as pointed out above, it is possible to cascade the a and f circuits to obtain a new network whose transfer function is the product of the individual transfer functions, as given in Eq. 18.40. Such a cascade connection is shown in Fig. 18.15a. Thus the transfer function af, often called the *loop transmission*, is the current gain I_t/I_s measured with the feedback destroyed by disconnecting the f circuit at the amplifier input and *shorting* the now free input terminals of the f circuit. To emphasize that almost no circuit modifications are needed to make this calculation, we have in Fig. 18.15b redrawn the circuit of Fig. 18.15a with the feedback y-parameter box restored to its original condition. The important conclusion is that the transfer function I_t/I_s is the same for both circuits. Thus to calculate the loop transmission of a node-node circuit, use the following procedure:

1. Disconnect the feedback circuit at the amplifier input node.
2. Add an admittance y_{if} to the amplifier input.
3. Short the input terminals of the feedback network, and calculate the current that flows in this short in response to a current I_s at the amplifier input. As has already been pointed out, when the loop transmission is positive, that is, when the phase of af is zero, the feedback is by definition negative.

To illustrate this method of finding the loop transmission, we calculate af for the feedback amplifier designed in Section 18.3.3. Starting from the

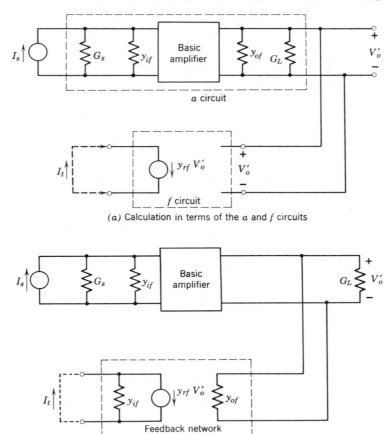

(a) Calculation in terms of the a and f circuits

(b) Calculation in terms of the original circuit of Fig. 18.12a

Figure 18.15   Circuits for calculating the loop transmission af.

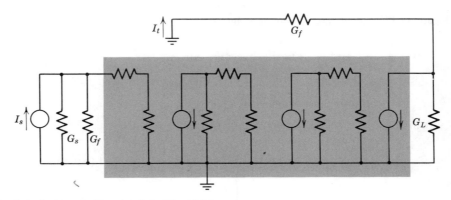

Figure 18.16   Calculation of af for circuit in Fig. 18.14.

incremental model for the complete feedback amplifier, Fig. 18.14*b*, we construct the circuit to calculate *af* (Fig. 18.16) by the following steps:

1. Disconnecting the feedback resistor G_f at the amplifier input and shorting the feedback resistor to ground.
2. Adding a conductance G_f across the amplifier input.

A calculation of I_t/I_s will agree with the product of the *a* and *f* factors obtained separately in Section 18.3.3 (see Problem 18.4).

18.3.5   Input and Output Admittances

In addition to the desensitivity issues discussed in Section 18.1, feedback is often employed to change the existing input or output impedance of the basic amplifier. It turns out that the effect of feedback on the input impedance is uniquely related to the type of input comparison employed, whereas the effect on the output impedance is uniquely related to the type of output sampling.

Clearly the easiest way of calculating the input admittance with node comparison is to apply a test voltage V_t to the amplifier input, and calculate the resultant current I_t. An appropriate *y*-parameter circuit is shown in Fig. 18.17. Note that in accordance with previous assumptions, we have neglected

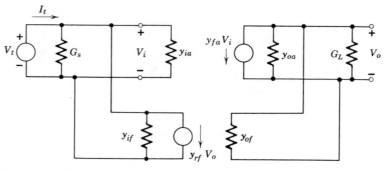

Figure 18.17   Calculation of input admittance.

y_{ra} and y_{ff}. On this basis the current I_t is

$$I_t = V_t(G_s + y_{ia} + y_{if}) + y_{rf}V_o \tag{18.41}$$

But because we neglect y_{ff},

$$V_o = \frac{-y_{fa}V_i}{G_L + y_{oa} + y_{of}} \tag{18.42}$$

Accordingly, from Eqs. 18.41 and 18.42, we find that the total input current I_t is

$$I_t = V_t\left(G_s + y_{ia} + y_{if} - \frac{y_{rf}y_{fa}}{G_L + y_{oa} + y_{of}}\right) \tag{18.43}$$

Therefore, the input admittance of the complete feedback amplifier is, from Eqs. 18.43 and 18.40.

$$\frac{I_t}{V_t} = Y_{in} = (G_s + y_{if} + y_{ia})(1 + af) \tag{18.44}$$

Hence the input admittance is increased from the value it would have with "no feedback" (in the sense $y_{rf} = 0$) by the same factor $1 + af$ that reduces the gain.

Of course, normally the input admittance of the amplifier system would be defined as what the source sees, and G_s is part of the source. So we should set $G_s = 0$ in Fig. 18.17 and Eq. 18.44 to get the proper value of Y_{in} for the amplifier system alone. But note that G_s appears *twice* in Eq. 18.44, directly in the first factor and buried in *af* in the second factor. Thus to obtain the correct answer by this method, the loop transmission *af* must be recalculated for $G_s = 0$. An easier way to find the input admittance of the feedback amplifier alone is simply to subtract G_s from the result given by Eq. 18.44. Either method gives the same result, of course.

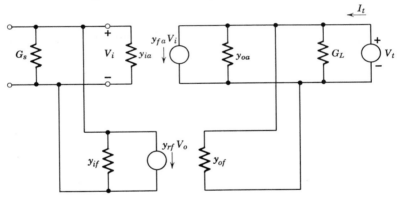

Figure 18.18   Calculation of output admittance.

To calculate the output admittance, apply a test voltage V_t to the output terminals as in Fig. 18.18 and find the resultant terminal current I_t. (See Problem P18.5). The result is

$$I_t = V_t\left(y_{of} + y_{oa} + G_L - \frac{y_{rf}y_{fa}}{G_s + y_{ia} + y_{if}}\right) \tag{18.45}$$

and thus, from Eqs. 18.45, 18.29, and 18.30, the output admittance of the complete feedback amplifier is

$$\frac{I_t}{V_t} = Y_{out} = (G_L + y_{oa} + y_{of})(1 + af) \tag{18.46}$$

Hence the output admittance is also increased from its value "without feedback" (*in the sense* $y_{rf} = 0$) *by the same factor* $1 + af$ *that reduces the gain.* The output admittance is normally defined without including G_L. So G_L should be either placed equal to zero in Eq. 18.46 (and again this must be done in *af* as well as in the first factor) or simply subtracted from Y_{out} given by Eq. 18.46.

To illustrate these concepts, we calculate the input and output admittance of the amplifier designed in Section 18.3.3. The input admittance of the *a* circuit alone is, from Fig. 18.14c,

$$Y_{in\,a} = G_s + G_f + \frac{1}{r_x + r_\pi}$$

which in this design is, from Section 18.3.3 and Table 16.1,

$$Y_{in\,a} = 20 + 0.2 + \frac{1}{2.5 + 0.2}$$

$$= 20.58 \text{ mmho}$$

So with feedback the input admittance according to Eq. 18.44 is increased to

$$Y_{in} = Y_{in\,a}(1 + af)$$

$$= (20.58)(71.8)$$

$$= 1480 \text{ mmho}$$

or

$$R_{in} = 0.675 \text{ ohm}$$

This value of input admittance includes the effect of G_s. However, the shunting effect of G_s is very small in this example. Specifically, the input admittance of the feedback amplifier alone is

$$Y = Y_{in} - G_s = 1460 \text{ mmho}$$

or

$$R = 0.685 \text{ ohm}$$

(see Problem P18.6).

The output admittance of the *a* circuit alone is, from Fig. 18.14c,

$$Y_{out\,a} = G_f + G_L$$

$$= 0.2 + 10$$

$$= 10.2 \text{ mmho}$$

So with feedback the output admittance in accordance with Eq. 18.46 increases to

$$Y_{out} = Y_{out\,a}(1 + af)$$

$$= (10.2)(71.8)$$

$$= 733 \text{ mmho}$$

or

$$R_{out} = 1.36 \text{ ohms}$$

The output admittance of the amplifier alone, exclusive of G_L, is

$$Y = Y_{out} - G_L$$

$$= 733 - 10$$

$$= 723 \text{ mmho}$$

or

$$R = 1.38 \text{ ohms}$$

18.3.6 Summary

Before discussing the other three basic feedback forms, let us summarize the important points developed so far concerning the application of feedback to transistor amplifiers. First, it is not possible in general to break up a transistor feedback amplifier into two *mutually independent* "boxes" with mutually independent transfer functions, as we did in the idealized examples in Section 18.1 (see, for example, Fig. 18.1). However, we have shown that we can derive by inspection an *a* circuit and an *f* circuit which possess many of the desirable properties of the boxes in Fig. 18.1. The *a* and *f* circuits are by definition those circuits whose transfer functions appear in the basic feedback expression:

$$A = \frac{a}{1 + af}$$

The *a* circuit contains the basic gain-producing portion of the complete amplifier, that is, the "basic amplifier" part of our original black box realization (Fig. 18.1). But the *a* circuit departs from the ideal basic amplifier concept in that it also includes the loading effects of source, output load, and feedback network. Thus the *a*-circuit transfer function is dependent to a greater or lesser extent on the elements in the feedback network.

The *f* circuit in this realization turns out to be a pure dependent source, with no resistances associated with it. The "gain" parameter in the dependent source is a function solely of the passive elements in the feedback network and is *independent* of the unreliable active elements in the circuit. Furthermore, because the *f* circuit is lossless, it does not load the *a* circuit. Thus the *f* circuit possesses the two most important properties of the precision attenuator in our black box idealization (Fig. 18.1).

Given a set of design parameters—for example, the closed-loop gain *A* and the densensitivity $1 + af$—it is relatively simple to find the values of *a* and *f* required to meet the specification. First,

$$a = A(1 + af)$$

If a is large, then

$$f \simeq \frac{\text{desensitivity}}{a}$$

18.4 Analysis and Design of Circuits Employing Loop Comparison and Sampling

We turn now to a second feedback amplifier example, that which uses loop comparison and loop sampling, as shown in Figs. 18.9a and 18.10a. Fortunately, we can make extensive use of the general y-parameter results in Sections 18.3.1 and 18.3.2, because from a network point of view, the present case of loop-loop feedback is clearly the *dual*[4] of the node-node case considered in Section 18.3. Thus we can minimize the mathematics and concentrate on the only new issue, that of manipulating an actual circuit of this type, such as Fig. 18.10a, into the feedback form. In fact, the reader who is facile enough with the theory of linear two-ports and the principle of duality to be willing to accept a simple interchange of letters ($y \rightarrow z$) as a proof can turn directly to Section 18.4.2.

18.4.1 Analysis in Terms of Two-Ports

The proper two-port configuration to use in analyzing the loop-loop feedback circuit of Fig. 18.9a is clearly the one that has current as the independent variable at both input and output. This is the z-parameter formulation, involving four open-circuit impedance parameters z_i, z_o, z_f, and z_r. To this end, two series-connected z-parameter two-ports are shown in Fig. 18.19.

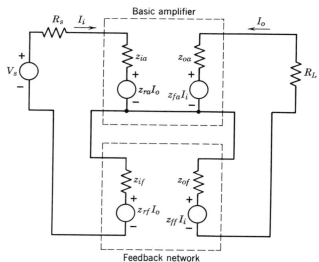

Figure 18.19 A z-parameter representation of a feedback amplifier employing loop comparison and loop sampling.

[4] See Reference 18.1, p. 42.

As before, we add second subscripts a and f to distinguish between basic amplifier parameters and feedback network parameters. Following a procedure exactly analogous to that in Section 18.3.1, we assume that the basic amplifier has all the gain, that is,

$$|z_{fa}| \gg |z_{ff}| \tag{18.47}$$

and the feedback network has all the feedback:

$$|z_{ra}| \ll |z_{rf}| \tag{18.48}$$

Finally, we assume that the basic amplifier is nearly unilateral:

$$|z_{fa}z_{ra}| \ll |Z_i Z_o| \tag{18.49}$$

where

$$Z_i = z_{ia} + z_{if} + R_s \tag{18.50}$$

$$Z_o = z_{oa} + z_{of} + R_L \tag{18.51}$$

Clearly, to preserve the loop topology at the input we must use a Thévenin equivalent source, a *voltage source* in series with R_s. Also, with loop sampling we should calculate the output *current*. On this basis, we find that

$$A = \frac{I_o}{V_s} \simeq \frac{\dfrac{-z_{fa}}{Z_i Z_o}}{1 + \left(\dfrac{-z_{fa}}{Z_i Z_o}\right) z_{rf}} \tag{18.52}$$

Hence

$$a \simeq \frac{-z_{fa}}{(z_{ia} + z_{if} + R_s)(z_{oa} + z_{of} + R_L)} \tag{18.53}$$

$$f \simeq z_{rf} \tag{18.54}$$

(see Problem P18.7).

18.4.2   Circuit Representations for a and f

If the basic amplifier is unilateral enough to satisfy the inequality in Eq. 18.49, the a circuit shown in Fig. 18.20a has the a transfer function specified by Eq. 18.53 (see Problem P18.8). Thus the rules for forming the a circuit for a given feedback amplifier of this type are as follows:

1. Identify the source, the load, the basic amplifier, and the feedback network by the methods discussed in Section 18.2.

2. Augment the basic amplifier with all loading effects of the source, the load, and the feedback network. To find the proper loading to be added to the input loop, *open the output loop* of the complete feedback amplifier to destroy the feedback. To find the loading to be added to the output loop, *open the input loop* of the complete feedback amplifier to destroy the feedback.

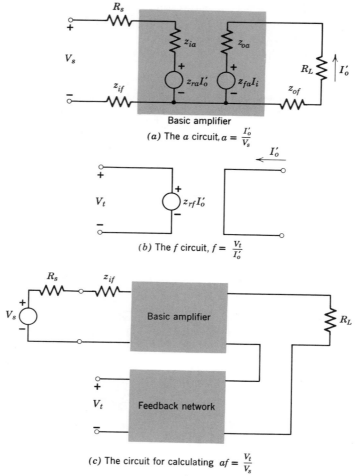

Basic amplifier

(a) The a circuit, $a = \dfrac{I'_o}{V_s}$

(b) The f circuit, $f = \dfrac{V_t}{I'_o}$

Basic amplifier

Feedback network

(c) The circuit for calculating $af = \dfrac{V_t}{V_s}$

Figure 18.20 Formulation of a and f circuits for loop-loop feedback.

Again the f circuit has no direct interpretation in terms of the circuit elements of the feedback network. The f transfer function, in accordance with Eq. 18.54, is an ideal transimpedance; thus the f circuit is an ideal current-controlled voltage source, with zero input and output impedances, as shown in Fig. 18.20b.

On the basis of Figs. 18.20a and b and Eqs. 18.53 and 18.54, the loop transmission af for loop-loop feedback is the voltage gain V_t/V_s calculated when (1) the feedback circuit is disconnected at the input and (2) an impedance z_{if} is added in series at the amplifier input. An appropriate circuit is shown in Fig. 18.20c.

The calculation of the effect of feedback on the input and output impedances is left as a problem (Problem P18.9). The result is that both the input impedance and the output impedance of the circuit in Fig. 18.20a are *increased* by a factor $1 + af$ when the feedback is applied:

$$Z_{\text{in}} = (z_{ia} + z_{if} + R_s)(1 + af) \tag{18.55}$$

$$Z_{\text{out}} = (z_{oa} + z_{of} + R_L)(1 + af) \tag{18.56}$$

Thus high input and output impedances can be obtained with this feedback connection.

18.4.3   Example

We turn now to the more difficult aspect of loop-loop feedback, that of manipulating a given circuit into the form of two two-ports connected in series, as in Fig. 18.19. The problem is that while it is quite straightforward to connect transistor circuits in parallel, a series connection has the significant disadvantage that the two circuits now *do not share a common ground*. This fact is clearly illustrated in Fig. 18.19. Note that it is not possible to specify a common ground for the source, the basic amplifier, and the feedback network or for the load, the amplifier, and the feedback network.

To illustrate by a specific example, let us examine the feedback circuit shown in Fig. 18.21a (essentially a repetition of Fig. 18.10a). Assume that we wish to design this circuit to have an overall gain with feedback of 2 mhos and a desensitivity of 50. The source and load resistors are specified as $R_s = 1000$ ohms, $R_L = 50$ ohms.

To carry out the design, we must first find the a and f circuits. Note, however, that this is not a pure loop-loop connection, because the amplifier load resistors are presumably connected to a grounded power supply. Hopefully, however, R_{L1}, R_{L2}, and R_{L3} can be made large enough so that the signal currents through them can be neglected. If such is the case, the basic amplifier is "floating," without any connection to ground, and so the loop-loop topology can be realized. This fact is evident from the incremental model shown in Fig. 18.21b, in which R_{L1}, R_{L2}, and R_{L3} have been omitted. Note that we have chosen a Thévenin source representation to conform with the loop comparison and that we choose the current I_o as the output variable because of the loop sampling.

It is now a relatively easy matter to find the a circuit and the f circuit. Applying the rules given in Section 18.4.2, we obtain the a circuit by first augmenting the basic amplifier on the input by R_s and R_e, as shown in Fig. 18.22a. This loading is found by open-circuiting the *output* loop in Fig. 18.21b. Then the output of the basic amplifier is augmented by adding R_L and R_e, as can be seen by open-circuiting the *input* loop in Fig. 18.21b. (The reader can verify that this is the correct a circuit by replacing the feedback resistor R_e in Fig. 18.21 by its two-port equivalent. See Problem

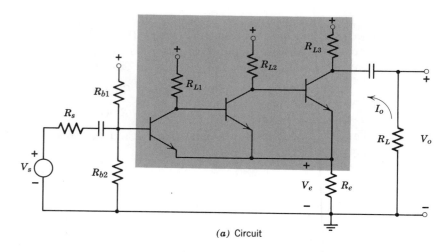

(a) Circuit

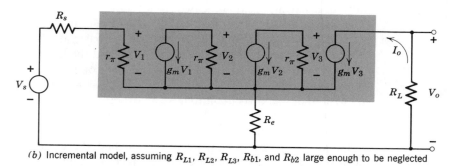

(b) Incremental model, assuming R_{L1}, R_{L2}, R_{L3}, R_{b1}, and R_{b2} large enough to be neglected

Figure 18.21   Three-stage amplifier with loop-loop feedback. Shading indicates basic amplifier.

P18.10.) By inspection, the *a* transfer function is

$$a = \frac{I'_o}{V_s} = \frac{\beta_o{}^3}{R_s + r_\pi + R_e} \tag{18.57}$$

It is quite easy to calculate the loop transmission from the *a* circuit. On the basis of Fig. 18.20c, the loop transmission for loop-loop feedback is V_t/V_s. Thus in this example we calculate in Fig. 18.22a the open-circuit voltage V_t across R_e in response to an applied voltage V_s.

$$af = \frac{V_t}{V_s} = \frac{\beta_o{}^3 R_e}{R_s + r_\pi + R_e} \tag{18.58}$$

The *f* circuit is a pure transimpedance z_{rf}. The value of z_{rf} can be calculated by applying a current source I'_o at the output of the feedback network and measuring the open-circuit voltage V_t at the input, as shown in Fig. 18.22b.

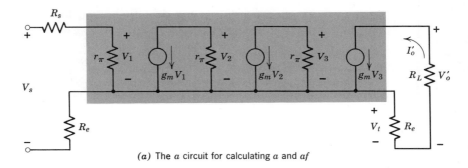

(a) The a circuit for calculating a and af

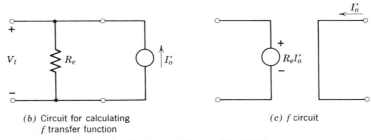

(b) Circuit for calculating
f transfer function

(c) f circuit

Figure 18.22   The a and f circuits for the feedback amplifier in Fig. 18.21.

Hence

$$f = z_{rf} = R_e \tag{18.59}$$

The resulting f circuit is shown in Fig. 18.22c.

Now we can proceed with the design. To obtain an overall gain with feedback of 2 mhos and a desensitivity of about 50, we require

$$a = A(1 + af)$$

$$= 2 \times 50$$

$$\simeq 100 \text{ mhos}$$

That is, the voltage gain of the a circuit should be

$$\frac{V'_o}{V_s} = \frac{-I'_o}{V_s} R_L = -100 \times 50$$

$$= -5000$$

To meet the desensitivity specification, af must be about 50. Thus

$$f = R_e = \frac{50}{100} = 0.5 \text{ ohm}$$

We can now select transistors and operating points for the basic amplifier. From Eq. 18.57, knowing that $R_s = 1000$ ohms,

$$a = 100 \simeq \frac{\beta_o{}^3}{1000 + r_\pi + 0.5}$$

If we select transistors with $\beta_o = 50$, then

$$r_\pi \simeq \frac{50^3}{100} - 1000 = 250 \text{ ohms}$$

Hence $g_m = 0.2$ mho, $I_C = 5$ ma.

To check the design, we note that the closed-loop gain of the complete feedback amplifier is

$$A = \frac{100}{1 + 100 \times 0.5} = 1.96 \text{ mhos}$$

which corresponds to a voltage gain of

$$\frac{V_o}{V_i} = \frac{-I_o R_L}{V_i} = -1.96 \times 50 = -98$$

An alternative calculation of the voltage gain can be found by inspection of Fig. 18.21*b*. If the three-stage amplifier has a large voltage gain, the emitter-base voltage of the first transistor will be very small. Thus the drop across R_s will be small, and hence the voltage V_e across R_e will be nearly equal to the source voltage V_s. But to a first approximation the current through R_L and the current through R_e are equal; thus from Fig. 18.21*a*

$$\frac{V_o}{V_e} \simeq -\frac{R_L}{R_e} \tag{18.60}$$

Hence the closed-loop voltage gain is approximately

$$\frac{V_o}{V_s} \simeq \frac{V_o}{V_e} = -\frac{R_L}{R_e} = -\frac{50}{0.5} = -100$$

The input resistance of the feedback amplifier will be, in accordance with Eq. 18.55,

$$R_{\text{in}} \simeq (250 + 0.5 + 1000)(50)$$

$$= 62 \text{ kohm}$$

(including R_s). An alternative calculation based on Eqs. 18.55 and 18.57, assuming $af \gg 1$, is

$$R_{\text{in}} \simeq \beta_o{}^3 R_e = 50^3 \times 0.5$$

$$= 62.5 \text{ kohm}$$

18.5   Feedback Circuits Employing Node Comparison and Loop Sampling

Formal analysis of a feedback circuit employing node comparison and loop sampling, such as that shown in Fig. 18.9d or Fig. 18.10d, should be carried out in terms of g parameters, because this two-port description uses voltage as the independent input variable and current as the independent output variable. However, it is not absolutely essential for us to carry out the analysis, because we have already discussed circuits with node comparison (Section 18.3) and circuits with loop sampling (Section 18.4). From these analyses, we know that the present problem should be formulated in terms of a Norton-equivalent *current-source* drive to be compatible with the node input topology. Furthermore, because of the loop sampling, we should calculate output *current*. (See Problem P18.11.) The discussions in Sections 18.3.2 and 18.4.2 concerning formation of the *a* and *f* circuits will serve as a guide for the corresponding calculations here.

To illustrate, let us find the *a* and *f* circuits for the feedback amplifier shown in Fig. 18.23a. The midfrequency incremental model based on r_π, g_m transistor models is shown in Fig. 18.23b. Note that to avoid a grounding problem, the designer did not employ pure loop sampling at the output. Specifically, the feedback network (R_e and R_f) is sampling the *emitter* current I_{e2} rather than the load current I_o. However, because the emitter and collector currents of a transistor are nearly equal in magnitude (and assuming that R_{L2} is large),

$$I_o \simeq I_c = -\alpha I_e \simeq -I_e \tag{18.61}$$

On this basis we see from Fig. 18.23b that the closest we can come to the topology of Fig. 18.9d is to associate the resistors R_f and R_e with the feedback network, because by so doing we form a loop at the output containing the amplifier, the load R_L, and the feedback network. The remaining elements (other than R_s) are associated with the basic amplifier. Resistor R_s can be associated with either the source, the amplifier, or the feedback network without appreciably changing the analysis.

We can now find by inspection the *a* and *f* circuits. To find the appropriate loading on the input of the *a* circuit, we destroy the feedback in Fig. 18.23b by open-circuiting the output loop, as discussed in Section 18.4.2. Any of the connections between basic amplifier output, feedback network, and load can be broken, but in this case it is simplest to break the loop at the emitter junction, as indicated by the x in Fig. 18.23b. To find the *a* circuit output loading, we *short* the input node of Fig. 18.23b, as discussed in Section 18.3.2. The *a* circuit developed on the basis of these rules is shown in Fig. 18.23c. The *a* transfer function

$$a = \frac{I_o'}{I_s}$$

can now be found relatively easily by inspection (see Problem P18.12) because we have manipulated the circuit into the form of a simple cascade

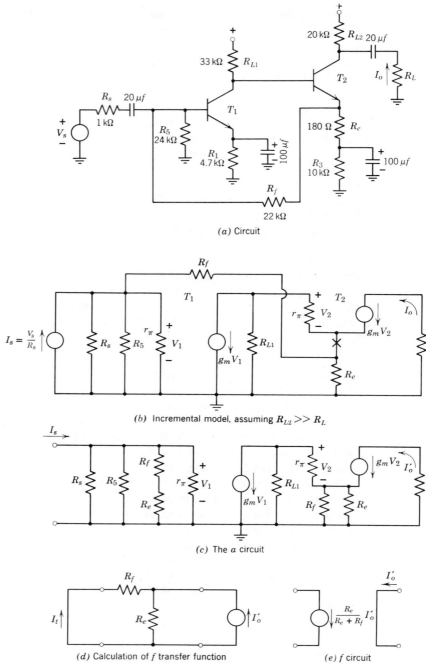

(a) Circuit

(b) Incremental model, assuming $R_{L2} \gg R_L$

(c) The a circuit

(d) Calculation of f transfer function

(e) f circuit

Figure 18.23 A two-stage feedback amplifier employing node comparison and loop sampling

of two common emitter stages—a simple approach that was not possible in
the circuit of Fig. 18.23b. This important difference illustrates the analytical
simplification that is often produced by employing the feedback point of view.

The f circuit must be a current source (because of the node comparison)
controlled by the output current (because of the loop sampling). Thus the
f transfer function is found by shorting the input of the feedback network in
Fig. 18.23b, and calculating the current ratio I_t/I_o', as shown in Fig. 18.23d.
The resulting f circuit is shown in Fig. 18.23e.

Analysis and design using the a and f circuits of Fig. 18.23 are now straightforward and will not be discussed here (see Problem P18.13).

18.6   Feedback Employing Loop Comparison and Node Sampling

The last of the four types of transistor feedback circuits is the type shown in
Fig. 18.9b or Fig. 18.10b (repeated in Fig. 18.24a) in which loop comparison
and node sampling is used. Formal analysis of circuits of this type should be
set up in terms of h-parameter two-ports, but again we draw on the results of
Sections 18.3 and 18.4 rather than carry out the complete analysis (see
Problem P18.14).

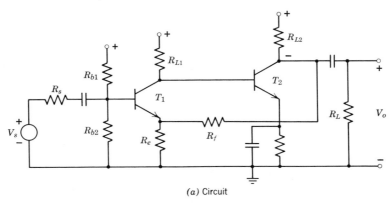

(a) Circuit

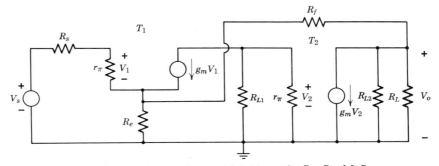

(b) Midfrequency incremental model assuming $R_{b1}, R_{b2}, \gg R_s$

Figure 18.24   Feedback amplifier employing loop comparison and node sampling.

As in the two previous examples, grounding problems inherent in the loop topology complicate the analysis. To maintain a common ground between the source and the amplifier, and also between the amplifier and the feedback network (required in this case because of the node output topology), we are forced to connect the feedback network in *series with the emitter of* T_1. Because of the common grounds, this is not pure loop comparison. However, by manipulating the incremental model (Fig. 18.24b) we can prove that it is still possible to form the *a* and *f* circuits in the usual manner. First we note from Fig. 18.24b that the closest we can come to Fig. 18.9b is to associate

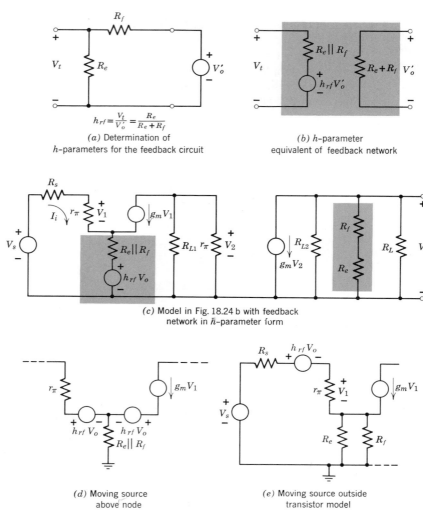

$$h_{rf} = \frac{V_t}{V_o'} = \frac{R_e}{R_e + R_f}$$

(a) Determination of
h-parameters for the feedback circuit

(b) h-parameter
equivalent of feedback network

(c) Model in Fig. 18.24 b with feedback
network in ħ-parameter form

(d) Moving source
above node

(e) Moving source outside
transistor model

Figure 18.25   Transformations at the amplifier input to obtain loop comparison.

resistors R_e and R_f with the feedback network, because only in this way can we form a loop at the input containing the basic amplifier, feedback network, and source. Next we find the h-parameter equivalent of the feedback circuit, neglecting as always the forward transfer parameter h_{ff}. This calculation is shown in Figs. 18.25a and b (see Problem P18.15). Next, the feedback circuit in Fig. 18.24b is replaced by this h-parameter equivalent, as shown in Fig. 18.25c.

We do not have a pure loop connection at the input in Fig. 18.25c because the current through the feedback elements $R_e \| R_f$ and $h_{rf}V_o$ is not the same as the input current I_i. To get around this problem, we move the feedback dependent source $h_{rf}V_o$ above the emitter node of transistor T_1. The steps necessary for this transformation are shown in Figs. 18.25d and e. First the voltage source is moved past the node by placing equal sources in both branches above the node as shown in Fig. 18.25d. This is an exact transformation. The voltage source in the right-hand branch will have no effect, because it is in series with the current source $g_m V_1$. Thus the complete amplifier input can be represented as in Fig. 18.25e. Now at last we have achieved true loop topology for the source V_s, the feedback signal $h_{rf}V_o$, and the a circuit input. Note that we did not move the resistance $h_{if} = R_e \| R_f$ when we moved the voltage source, because we want to associate this resistance with the a circuit anyway.

We can now form the a circuit and the f circuit corresponding to the complete feedback amplifier in Fig. 18.25c, modified as in Fig. 18.25e. These circuits are shown in Figs. 18.26a and b. It should be quite clear that after all this manipulation, these are *exactly* the circuits we would have obtained had

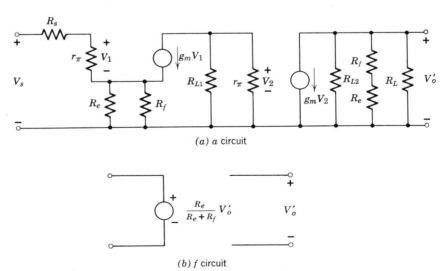

(a) a circuit

(b) f circuit

Figure 18.26 The a and f circuits for the feedback amplifier in Fig. 18.24.

we applied the rules for *a* circuit formation (Section 18.3.2 for input loading, Section 18.4.2 for output loading) *directly to the original incremental model*, as in Fig. 18.24*b* (see Problem P18.16). One important word of caution is in order before the reader assumes a general conclusion from this specific example. The key step from Fig. 18.25*d* to Fig. 18.25*e* begins to break down if the current source $g_m V_1$ is directly shunted by a significant impedance. Also, when capacitor C_μ is included in the model, the voltage source $h_{rf} V_o$ cannot be moved past the junction of C_μ and r_π; thus the pure loop topology again begins to evade us. The consequences of this problem will be discussed in more detail in the next chapter.

Analysis and design using the *a* and *f* circuits of Fig. 18.26 are now quite straightforward, hence will not be discussed further here (see Problem P18.17).

18.7 Summary

It should by now be clear that in transistor feedback amplifiers, the *topology* of interconnection of source, basic amplifier, passive feedback network, and load is the key factor in determining the method of analysis and all important parameters of the circuit. To emphasize this fact, we summarize in Table 18.1 the important results of the preceding sections, all of which are directly related to the topology of the input or output connections. Fortunately, there is a certain fundamental logic to the table-which obviates memorization. Clearly, a Thévenin source, with R_s and V_s in *series*, should be associated with loop topology. Also, it is obvious that we must open-circuit loops and short-circuit nodes, because shorting a loop (or open-circuiting a node) is not a clearly defined process. Thus while the table provides a handy summary and reference, it probably should not be memorized.

It is helpful at this point to return briefly to the question of the effect of feedback on input and output impedances. The appropriate equations have been presented in Sections 18.3.5 and 18.4.2, but often a more heuristic approach leads to better insight. To this end, note that the variable which is sampled at the output of a feedback amplifier tends to resist being changed. This follows from our general discussion in Section 18.1.1, or the more specific calculations in Sections 18.3.1 and 18.4.1. For example, we see from Eqs. 18.28, 18.29, and 18.30 that for large loop transmission *af*, the overall "gain" V_o/I_s of the node-node feedback amplifier in Fig. 18.12*a* is nearly independent of the basic amplifier gain *a*. Thus with *node* sampling, that is, sampling output *voltage*, the output voltage V_o tends to remain constant in spite of changes in *a*. Clearly, changing the load resistor R_L is one way of changing the gain of the *a* circuit, as we can see from Fig. 18.13*a*. It follows that feedback has stabilized the output voltage against changes in the load resistor R_L. This implies that the feedback has *reduced* the output impedance of the amplifier.

In a similar manner, with loop sampling we are sampling output *current*, so that the feedback tends to keep this current constant, in spite of changes in R_L. Hence the output impedance has been *increased* by the feedback.

Table 18.1

Input Considerations		
	Topology of Comparison	
	Node	Loop
Source representation	Norton	Thévenin
To find correct *output* loading for *a* circuit	*Short* input node of complete incremental model	*Open-circuit* input loop of complete incremental model
Loop transmission *af*	*Short-circuit* current gain I_t/I_s	*Open-circuit* voltage gain V_t/V_s
Input impedance compared to *a* circuit input impedance	Smaller by a factor $1 + af$	Larger by a factor $1 + af$

Output Considerations		
	Topology of Sampling	
	Node	Loop
Choose as output variable	Voltage	Current
Feedback tends to stabilize	Voltage	Current
Output impedance, compared to *a* circuit output impedance	Smaller by a factor $1 + af$	Larger by a factor $1 + af$
To find correct input loading for *a* circuit	*Short* output node of complete incremental model	*Open-circuit* output loop of complete incremental model

To establish the effect of feedback on the input resistance, a slightly different argument must be employed. It should be clear from the discussion in Section 18.1.1 that when the comparator forms the difference between the input voltage and the feedback voltage, the feedback action tends to reduce this difference voltage to a small value. In terms of the amplifier in Fig. 18.9*a*, the feedback tends to reduce the input voltage to the basic amplifier toward zero. This will tend in general to reduce the basic amplifier input current to zero as well. But because of the *loop* topology, this basic amplifier current is the same as the input current of the entire feedback amplifier. Thus for a fixed voltage V_1, and *loop* comparison, the feedback is going to tend to decrease the amplifier input current, or, in other words, to *increase* the apparent input impedance.

A similar argument applies to the feedback amplifiers employing *node* comparison (Fig. 18.9*c* or *d*). Again feedback tends to drive the basic amplifier input voltage and current to zero, but this time the feedback amplifier and the basic amplifier share a common input voltage because of the *node* topology. Thus for fixed input current I_1, the feedback tends to decrease the amplifier input voltage, or, in other words, to *decrease* the apparent input resistance.

18.8   Lecture Demonstrations
18.8.1   Hum Reduction

The circuit in Fig. 18.4a can be used to demonstrate both audibly and visually the effects of feedback on hum introduced in the output stage of an audio amplifier. The hum is introduced on the *npn* collector from a poorly-filtered power supply. To make the demonstration audible to a large class, the output signal from the power amplifier is fed to a high-quality audio amplifier and speaker.

With the switch in position 1, we have a simple power amplifier (with hum), preceded by a gain-of-ten amplifier. Thus the circuit is equivalent to the block diagram shown in Fig. 18.3*b*. The levels should be adjusted for an output signal-to-hum ratio of about unity. Changing the switch to position 2 introduces feedback around the power amplifier while keeping the overall gain the same as before. The appropriate block diagram for the circuit is now Fig. 18.3*a*. If desired, the switch may be replaced by a 10-kohm potentiometer, with the feedback brought to the center arm.

First, observe and listen to the output V_3 in the two cases. Then look (preferably with a dual-trace oscilloscope) at the input V_5 of the power amplifier, to see the *precontamination* of V_5 with hum of *reverse* polarity, which eventually cancels the amplifier hum. Typical oscilloscope traces are shown in Fig. 18.4.

18.8.2   Distortion Reduction

The circuit in Fig. 18.7 can be used to demonstrate audibly and visually the effects of feedback on distortion. With the switch in position 1, the circuit consists of the power amplifier preceded by a unity-gain amplifier. With the switch in position 2, feedback is applied around the power amplifier and the 709 operational amplifier. For a fair test, it is important that the output signal level stay nearly constant for the two cases, because clearly the distortion is level-sensitive. This condition is assured by setting f equal to the reciprocal of the power-amplifier gain.

Observe first the transfer curve (output voltage V_3 versus signal-source voltage) with and without feedback (see Figs. 18.7*b* and *c*). Then, using a sinusoidal input signal, listen to and observe the output signal V_3 with and without feedback. Then include in the visual presentation the *input* signal V_5 to the power amplifier, to indicate clearly the *predistortion* of this signal required to overcome the distortion in the amplifier. Typical oscilloscope traces are shown in Fig. 18.8.

Now introduce more varied program material as the signal source. Choose both classical and popular music. You will find some popular music surprisingly indestructable. Classical music with relatively simple tonal structure shows the distortion most obviously. Use hi-fi audio equipment for maximum effect, as distortion in the audio system will mask the desired effect.

REFERENCES

18.1   E. A. Guillemin, *Introductory Circuit Theory*, Wiley, New York, 1953.
18.2   S. Schwartz, *Selected Semiconductor Circuits Handbook*, Wiley, New York, 1960.
18.3   *GE Transistor Manual*, 7th ed., General Electric Company, 1964.

PROBLEMS

P18.1   In many cases the changes in basic amplifier gain a will not be small, as we assumed in deriving Eq. 18.7. Prove that for large changes in a the fractional change in closed-loop gain is

$$\frac{\Delta A}{A_1} = \left(\frac{1}{1 + a_2 f} \right) \frac{\Delta a}{a_1} \tag{18.62}$$

where A_1 and a_1 are the initial gain values and A_2 and a_2 the final values. (See page 621.)

P18.2   Verify Eq. 18.32 by calculating the transfer function V_o/I_s directly from Fig. 18.14b, and then manipulating the resulting expression into the form of Eq. 18.17. To simplify the calculations, make the same simplifying assumptions as in Section 18.3.1. This will yield expressions for a and f. Check f from Eq. 18.32 and a by calculating V_o'/I from Fig. 18.14c. (See page 640.)

P18.3   Calculate in literal form the transfer function V_o'/I for the a circuit in Fig. 18.14c. Using the numerical values given in the design example, Section 18.3.3 and also Section 16.1.2, verify the value for a given on page 642.

P18.4   Calculate the loop transmission $af = I_t/I_s$ for the circuit in Fig. 18.14a by the method suggested in Fig. 18.16. Check the results by forming the product af from Eq. 18.32 and the result from Problem P18.3. (See page 646.)

P18.5   Calculate the ratio I_t/V_t in Fig. 18.18 and verify that for node-node feedback, the output admittance is given by Eq. 18.46.

P18.6   Calculate the input admittance for the node-node feedback numerical example (see page 640), except make the calculation by assuming initially that $G_s = 0$. Compare with the value of 1460 mmho obtained in the text.

P18.7   By starting from Fig. 18.19 and following a method analogous to that in Section 18.3.1, derive Eqs. 18.52, 18.53, and 18.54.

P18.8 Calculate the transfer function I_o'/V_s for the *a* circuit in Fig. 18.20*a*, and compare with Eq. 18.53.

P18.9 By working from Fig. 18.19 in a manner analogous to that followed in Section 18.3.5, calculate the input and output impedances of a loop-loop feedback circuit, hence verify Eqs. 18.55 and 18.56.

P18.10 Replace the resistor R_e in Fig. 18.21*b* by its two-port equivalent, then divide the resultant circuit into *a* and *f* circuits. Hence verify the corresponding circuits in Fig. 18.22. (See page 653.)

P18.11 Draw the complete g-parameter representation of a feedback amplifier with node comparison and loop sampling. The basic topology is shown in Fig. 18.9*d*. Following a method analogous to that in Section 18.3.1, derive equations for *A*, *a*, and *f* for this type of feedback. (See page 657.)

P18.12 Find the *a*-circuit transfer function for the feedback amplifier shown in Fig. 18.23*a*. Assume $g_m = 40$ mmho, $r_\pi = 2$ kohm, $R_L = 1$ kohm. (See page 657.)

P18.13 Using the values given in Problem P18.12, calculate the closed-loop transfer function $A = I_o/I_s$, the loop transmission, the desensitivity, and the input and output impedances for the two-stage feedback amplifier in Fig. 18.23*a*. (See page 659.)

P18.14 Draw the complete *h*-parameter representation of a feedback amplifier with loop comparison and node sampling. The basic topology is shown in Fig. 18.9*b*. Following a method analogous to that in Section 18.3.1, derive equations for *A*, *a*, and *f* for this type of feedback. (See page 659.)

P18.15 Calculate the *h* parameters for the feedback network (R_f and R_e) in Fig. 18.24*b*, hence verify Fig. 18.25*b*. (See page 661.)

P18.16 Apply the appropriate rules for *a* circuit formation directly to the loop-comparison, node-sampling feedback amplifier in Fig. 18.24. Compare the result with Fig. 18.26*a*.

P18.17 Design a feedback amplifier (low- and midfrequency only) employing loop comparison and node sampling (Fig. 18.24*a*) to have a closed-loop voltage gain of 100 and a densitivity of 10. Assume $R_s = 100$ ohms and $R_L = 0.25$ kohm. Note that these specifications fix the value of *f*, hence the value of $R_e/(R_e + R_f)$. However, the impedance level of the divider is not determined. Discuss the effects of choosing large or small values for R_e and R_f. Choose values to yield maximum *a*. (See page 662.)

P18.18 For the feedback amplifier shown in Fig. 18.27[5]
  (*a*) What type of input comparison has been employed?
  (*b*) What type of output sampling?
  [5] See Reference 18.2.

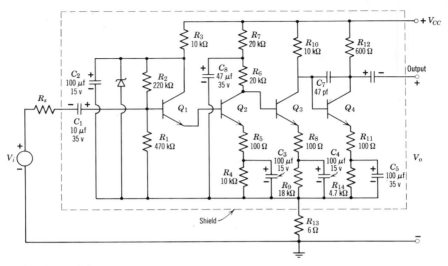

Figure 18.27 Feedback amplifier.

(c) Draw the midfrequency incremental model of the *a* circuit, using g_m, r_π models for the transistors. Neglect signal currents through R_{10}.

(d) Draw the *f* circuit.

(e) For $\beta_o = 30$, $R_s = 1000$ ohms, estimate within a factor of 2 the midfrequency values of *a* and *f*. Assume that Q_2 and Q_3 operate with about $\frac{1}{2}$ ma of collector current, and Q_4 has $I_C = 2$ ma.

(f) How much desensitivity does the amplifier have to changes in the basic amplifier gain?

(g) What is the function of C_8?

(h) What is the function of C_7?

(i) Calculate the input and output resistances (midband).

P18.19 (a) For the circuit in Fig. 18.28[6] state whether the designer has used node or loop comparison at the input, and node or loop sampling at the output.

(b) Draw the midfrequency *a* circuit using g_m, r_π transistor models and draw the circuit to calculate the *f* transfer function.

P18.20 The circuit in Fig. 18.29[7] has two feedback loops, one of which operates only at very low frequencies for bias stabilization (see Section 16.1.4).

(a) Identify the types of comparison and sampling for each feedback loop.

(b) Draw the midfrequency *a* circuit and *f* circuit.

[6] See Reference 18.3.
[7] See Reference 18.3.

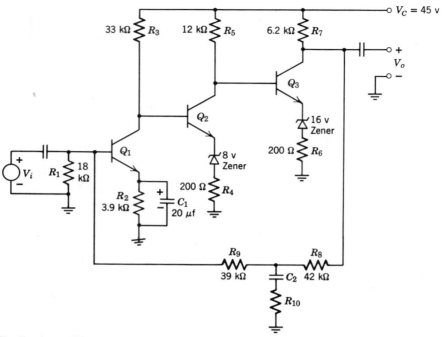

Figure 18.28   Feedback amplifier.

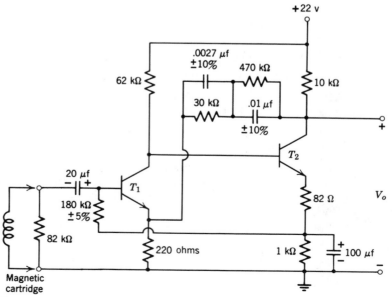

Figure 18.29   Phonograph preamplifier.

P18.21   Reexamine the bias stabilization circuit in Fig. 16.4 in the light of the feedback discussion in this chapter. By identifying the a and f circuits, find the transfer function from "input", $V_{B1}(T)$ in Fig. 16.5, to output V_{CE3}. Compare with the results in Section 16.1.4.

P18.22   Examine the output stage of the integrated-circuit operational amplifier in Fig. 16.16 from the feedback point of view. Specifically, calculate the voltage gain from the emitter of Q_8 to the output. What is the output resistance of the circuit?

P18.23   Design a circuit (low- and midfrequency only) to have a stable voltage gain (magnitude) of 10 and a desensitivity of 100. Assume $R_s = 0.1$ kohm, $R_L = 1$ kohm.

P18.24   For driving deflection coils in a magnetic-deflection oscilloscope made from a discarded television set, it is desirable to build an amplifier whose output current is proportional to its input voltage. Design a feedback amplifier (low- and midfrequency only) to provide a stable transfer function $I_o/V_i = 1$ mho and a desensitivity of 20.

P18.25   The triangular symbol used in Fig. 18.30 is the standard symbol for an operational amplifier. A positive voltage at the terminal marked $+$ gives rise to a positive output voltage; a positive voltage on the $-$ terminal gives a negative output voltage. One circuit realization of such an amplifier was given in Fig. 16.16. These amplifiers typically have very high voltage gain and current gain, high input impedance, and low output impedance. Hence approximate methods for calculating closed-loop gain, such as that discussed at the end of Section 18.3.3, yield excellent results.

(a) Calculate the voltage gain V_2/V_1 for the two circuits shown in Fig. 18.30.

(b) Often the circuit in Fig. 18.30b is operated with $R_1 = \infty$, $R_2 = 0$. What is the voltage gain V_2/V_1?

(c) Often the circuit in Fig. 18.30a is operated with resistor R_2 replaced by a capacitor C_2. What is the voltage gain V_2/V_1 in this case? What mathematical function does this circuit perform?

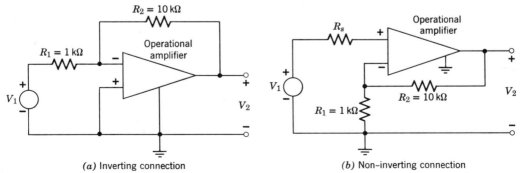

(a) Inverting connection   (b) Non-inverting connection

Figure 18.30   Feedback amplifiers using an operational amplifier as the basic amplifier.

CHAPTER NINETEEN

Feedback Amplifier Steady-State and Transient Response: Root Locus

19.1 The Stability Problem

The advantages of applying feedback to a transistor amplifier have been discussed in detail in Chapter 18. However, we have alluded only briefly to the problem of *instability*, a fundamental limitation on the amount of feedback that can be applied to a given circuit. In this chapter we examine at length this problem, and two other closely related design problems: (1) how to obtain a relatively constant frequency response without resonant peaks and (2) how to obtain fast rise times without overshoot. The problem of feedback amplifier stability arises when energy storage elements are present in the network. Thus network complexity will again force us to make considerable use of computer-aided pole-zero calculations of the type discussed in Chapter 15 to check feedback amplifier designs. However, it is as true here as in Chapter 15 that the computer often fails to provide design insight; therefore it is necessary to explore in some detail two feedback amplifier synthesis procedures, *root locus* and *Bode plot* calculations, in order to gain this insight.

To introduce the stability problem, let us study the locus of the natural frequencies of several feedback amplifier gain functions as we vary the amount of midband feedback. Throughout this chapter, we assume that in the midfrequency region of the amplifier, the *feedback is negative*. Also, to simplify the discussion, we assume in this introductory section that we have a basic amplifier and a precision attenuator with *mutually independent transfer functions*. That is, we revert for the moment to the simple block-diagram description of feedback amplifiers introduced in Section 18.1.

Suppose, first, that the basic amplifier in Fig. 19.1 has a single pole at $s = s_a$, on the negative real axis (i.e., s_a is negative):

$$a(s) = \frac{a_o}{1 - s/s_a} \qquad (19.1)$$

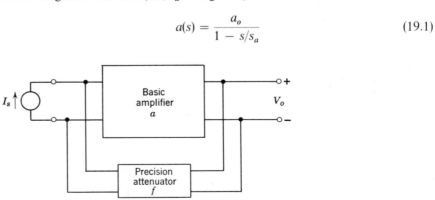

Figure 19.1 Block diagram of amplifier with node-node feedback.

where a_o is the midfrequency value of $a(s)$. If we assume that the precision attenuator is resistive, then the f transfer function is independent of frequency:

$$f(s) = f_o \tag{19.2}$$

On this basis the overall (closed loop) transfer function of the feedback amplifier is

$$A(s) = \frac{a}{1 + af} \tag{19.3}$$

$$= \frac{a_o}{1 + a_o f_o - s/s_a} \tag{19.4}$$

The feedback amplifier gain function $A(s)$ thus has one pole at

$$s_1 = s_a[1 + a_o f_o] \tag{19.5}$$

Because we are assuming that the feedback is negative at midband, $a_o f_o$ must be positive. Thus it is not possible to move the pole of $A(s)$ into the right half plane for any allowed value of the midband loop transmission $a_o f_o$. In fact, the pole of $A(s)$ stays on the negative real axis, and moves *away* from the origin as the amount of negative feedback is increased. Recall from linear circuit theory that a circuit with poles in the left half plane is *stable*, in the sense that its impulse response consists only of exponentially decaying waveforms.

Two other observations can be made at this point. First, note from Eq. 19.4 that the feedback has *increased* the upper 0.707 frequency by a factor of $1 + a_o f_o$ and *decreased* the midfrequency gain by the same factor. These effects are illustrated in Fig. 19.2, in which the magnitude of the closed-loop

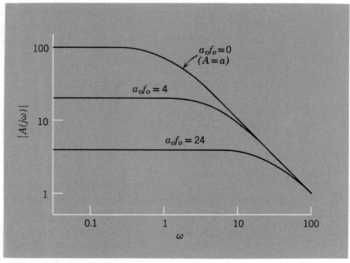

Figure 19.2   Normalized closed-loop gain magnitude versus ω for a one-pole system.

gain, $|A(j\omega)|$, has been plotted for various amounts of midband loop transmission $a_o f_o$. We conclude that for this simple case the product of midband gain and bandwidth, often called the gain-bandwidth product, remains constant as the amount of feedback is changed. Because of this simple relationship between gain and bandwidth, and because of the inherent stability of the single-pole feedback circuit, operational amplifiers are often stabilized by this method. Specifically they are stabilized by adding one large capacitor to the basic amplifier to produce *one dominant pole*. This method of stabilization will be discussed in more detail in Section 19.2.5.

Second, recall that feedback is fully effective in desensitizing an amplifier to parameter variations *only when the loop transmission is high*. Hence in the present example, as frequency is increased above $\omega = |s_a|$, the basic amplifier gain decreases (see Eq. 19.1 or Fig. 19.2) so that the desensitivity must also decrease.

Consider next a basic amplifier with two poles, at $s = s_a$ and $s = s_b$, and assume again that the poles are on the negative real axis (i.e., s_a and s_b are negative real numbers):

$$a(s) = \frac{a_o}{(1 - s/s_a)(1 - s/s_b)} = \frac{a_o}{1 + a_1 s + a_2 s^2} \tag{19.6}$$

We now find for the closed-loop gain, again assuming resistive feedback,

$$A(s) = \frac{a_o}{(1 + a_o f_o) + a_1 s + a_2 s^2} \tag{19.7}$$

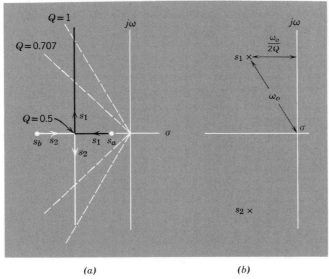

(a)   (b)

Figure 19.3   (a) Loci of natural frequencies s_1 and s_2 of $A(s)$ as $a_o f_o$ is increased from zero in Eqs. 19.7 and 19.8. (b) Geometric interpretation of Q.

From the denominator of Eq. 19.7, we find that the poles of $A(s)$ lie on the negative real axis for $a_o f_o$ less than $(a_1{}^2/4a_2) - 1$. For $a_o f_o$ greater than this value, $A(s)$ has a complex pole pair. A convenient way of presenting this information graphically is to plot the *root locus*, the loci in the *s* plane *of the poles of $A(s)$*, for increasing amounts of midband feedback, that is, increasing values of $a_o f_o$. To differentiate clearly in such plots between the poles of the basic amplifier and/or feedback network and the poles of the complete feedback amplifier, we designate the poles of $a(s)$ or $a(s)f(s)$ by letter subscripts, s_a, s_b, s_c, whereas poles of $A(s)$ are designated by numbers, s_1, s_2, s_3. Figure 19.3a shows the root-locus plot for s_1 and s_2, the poles of $A(s)$ in Eq. 19.7.

For convenience the pole locations have been expressed in terms of the Q of the circuit by rewriting Eq. 19.7 as

$$A(s) = \frac{A_o}{1 + (1/Q)(s/\omega_o) + (s/\omega_o)^2} \tag{19.8}$$

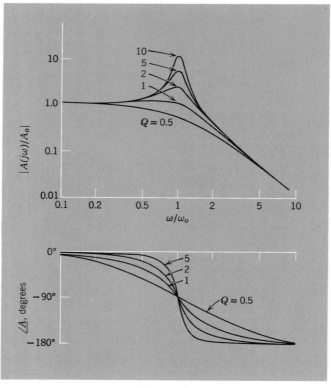

(*a*) Frequency response

Figure 19.4   Normalized response of an ideal two-pole feedback amplifier.

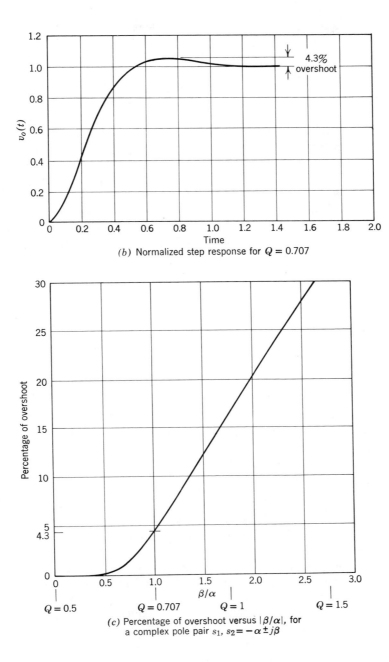

(b) Normalized step response for $Q = 0.707$

(c) Percentage of overshoot versus $|\beta/\alpha|$, for
a complex pole pair s_1, $s_2 = -\alpha \pm j\beta$

Figure 19.4, continued

where

$$\omega_o^2 = \frac{1 + a_o f_o}{a_2} \tag{19.9}$$

$$Q^2 = \frac{a_2[1 + a_o f_o]}{a_1^2} \tag{19.10}$$

The geometric interpretation of Q and ω_o is given in Fig. 19.3b. Note that for this two-pole example, the poles of $A(s)$ always lie in the left half plane; hence again the amplifier cannot be made unstable for any positive value of midband loop transmission. However, if the loop transmission is large enough so that the Q is much greater than unity, the amplifier will have a markedly peaked amplitude response and a damped oscillation in the step response. This is shown in Fig. 19.4 in which we have plotted the *normalized* frequency response and step response of the amplifier for various values of Q.

As a third example of a simple feedback amplifier, consider the case where the basic amplifier has three poles on the negative real axis:

$$a(s) = \frac{a_o}{(1 - s/s_a)(1 - s/s_b)(1 - s/s_c)} \tag{19.11}$$

For $f(s) = f_o$, we have

$$A(s) = \frac{a_o}{[1 + a_o f_o] + a_1 s + a_2 s^2 + a_3 s^3} \tag{19.12}$$

This function always has one real pole, but for large enough values of $a_o f_o$ the other two poles leave the real axis to form a complex pair. In addition, for sufficiently large values of $1 + a_o f_o$, this complex pair moves into the right half plane. Thus the amplifier becomes unstable, in the sense that the step response is dominated by growing exponential waveforms.

Typical loci of poles of $A(s)$ for Eq. 19.12 are shown in Fig. 19.5. The frequency response and step response of the amplifier can be envisioned to some extent from the Q of the complex pair of poles. However, the real-axis pole tends to smooth out both the hump in the frequency response and the ringing in the step response which would result from the complex pair alone. This will be discussed in more detail in Section 19.2.3.

It should be clear from these three simple examples that the amount of midband loop transmission $a_o f_o$ in a feedback amplifier can profoundly influence the location of the natural frequencies of $A(s)$, hence the stability, frequency response, and transient response of the feedback amplifier. An important problem in feedback amplifier design, then, is how to choose a basic amplifier and feedback network combination to obtain at the same time

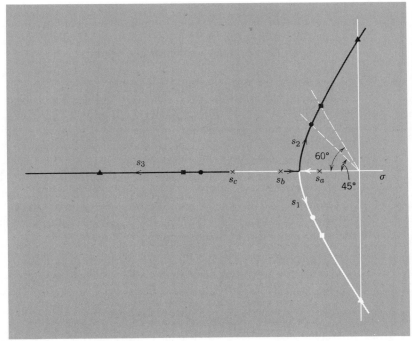

Figure 19.5 Loci of natural frequencies s_1, s_2, and s_3 of $A(s)$ as $a_o f_o$ is increased from zero. Also shown are locations of the poles for four specific values of $a_o f_o$.

both large loop transmission (hence good desensitivity) and acceptable frequency response and transient response. There are two principal methods of analysis which are helpful in attacking this problem. One method concentrates on the location of the natural frequencies of $A(s)$ in the complex plane—this is the *root-locus* method (essentially the same technique that we used in this section to introduce the stability problem). We discuss this method in more detail in the remainder of this chapter. A second method, based solely on the measured sinusoidal steady-state response $a(j\omega)$ of the transistor amplifier, will be discussed in Chapter 20.

19.2 Root-Locus Calculations

The essential idea of the root-locus method is to *trace out the path of the feedback amplifier natural frequencies, that is, the poles of $A(s)$, as a function of the midband loop transmission $a_o f_o$*. On the basis of this locus, we can determine the maximum allowed loop transmission without instability, or, more realistically, the maximum allowed loop transmission consistent with a "reasonable" frequency response or transient response. If this value of $a_o f_o$ does not provide enough midband desensitivity, *compensating networks* that alter the pole locations of *af* can be added either to the basic amplifier or to the feedback network in order to reshape the locus. With proper reshaping we can obtain both the desired desensitivity and the proper pole locations in $A(s)$ for good frequency and transient response.

19.2.1 Construction of Approximate Root Loci

As we saw in Chapter 15, it is a relatively simple matter to find the poles of an amplifier by using a digital computer. Thus we can readily calculate the poles of $A(s)$ for a given basic amplifier and several assumed values of the feedback function *f*. Unfortunately, such calculations often do not provide the insight necessary for intelligent design, especially when a compensating network must be added to obtain the desired performance. Thus it is important to develop a number of simple rules for sketching approximate root loci to facilitate the design process. Although there are many rules for forming approximation loci,[1] the following five rules will be found to be particularly useful for transistor feedback amplifiers.[2]

1. Start and end of locus: *for increasing amounts of midband feedback, the locus of each pole of $A(s)$ starts from a pole of af and terminates on a zero of af.*
   If we express the loop transmission as

$$af = a_o f_o g(s) \tag{19.13}$$

where $g(s)$ is a ratio of polynomials that is by definition equal to unity at midband, then

$$A(s) = \frac{a(s)}{1 + a_o f_o g(s)} \tag{19.14}$$

For finite, nonzero values of $a_o f_o$, the poles of $A(s)$ occur only where $a_o f_o \, g(s) = -1$. If $a_o f_o$ is very small, then at a pole of $A(s)$, the function $g(s)$ must be very much larger than one, that is, we must be close to a pole of $g(s)$, hence a pole of *af*. Conversely, if $a_o f_o$ is very large, then at a pole of $A(s)$, the function $g(s)$ must be much less than one, that is, we must be close to a zero of *af*. Thus we can say that for increasing amounts of midband feedback, that is, increasing $a_o f_o$, the locus of each pole of $A(s)$ starts from a pole of *af* and terminates on a zero of *af*. If *af* has more finite poles than finite zeros, some of the loci will terminate on the zeros at infinity. [Notice that the poles of $a(s)$ appear in $g(s)$ also, as shown by Eq. 19.13. Therefore, as stated above, as long as $0 < a_o f_o < \infty$, $A(s)$ does *not* have the poles of $a(s)$. However, when $f = 0$, $A(s)$ has poles only at the poles of $a(s)$. Moreover, for $f_o = \infty$, $A(s)$ has poles only at the zeros of $f(s)$].

As a simple example, consider the case shown in Fig. 19.6*a* where the basic amplifier has a zero at s_a and a pole at s_b, and the feedback network has a

---

[1] See, for example, Reference 19.1.

[2] If desired, the plausibility arguments following each of these rules can be omitted in an introductory course without loss of continuity.

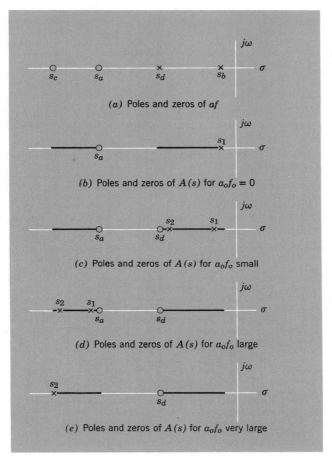

(a) Poles and zeros of af

(b) Poles and zeros of $A(s)$ for $a_o f_o = 0$

(c) Poles and zeros of $A(s)$ for $a_o f_o$ small

(d) Poles and zeros of $A(s)$ for $a_o f_o$ large

(e) Poles and zeros of $A(s)$ for $a_o f_o$ very large

Figure 19.6   Real-axis loci of s_1 and s_2, the poles of $A(s)$, for increasing amounts of midband feedback $a_o f_o$.

zero at s_c and a pole at s_d. For $f_o = 0$, it is clear from Eq. 19.14 that the poles and zeros of $A(s)$ will be the same as the poles and zeros of $a(s)$, as shown in Fig. 19.6b. For $a_o f_o$ finite, $A(s)$ is still zero when $a(s)$ is zero, as can be seen from Eq. 19.14. However, $A(s)$ no longer has the poles of $a(s)$. For $a_o f_o$ small, we know from the preceding discussion that the poles of $A(s)$ will be close to s_b and s_d, as shown in Fig. 19.6c. (Just why they are on the real axis between s_b and s_d is explained under Rule 2 below.) The poles and zeros of $A(s)$ for $a_o f_o$ large and $a_o f_o$ infinite are also shown in the figure.

2. *Location of loci on the real axis: the loci of the poles of $A(s)$ include all portions of the real axis to the left of odd numbers of left-half-plane poles and zeros of af.*

We can easily locate those portions of the loci of the poles of $A(s)$ that lie on the real axis. From Eq. 19.3,

$$A(s) = \frac{a(s)}{1 + a(s)f(s)} \qquad (19.15)$$

Thus at a pole of $A(s)$, $1 + af$ must be zero; hence at this point af is real and is equal to -1. On the real axis, s is real; hence $a(s)f(s)$ must also be real, because a polynomial with real coefficients and a real variable can have only real values. Furthermore, we are free to adjust $a_o f_o$ so that $|af|$ on the real axis is unity. Then the only remaining question is, which segments of the real axis correspond to $\angle af = \pi$?

Consider the example shown in Fig. 19.7. At a point A, the phase contributions of the real poles and real zeros of af are zero, as shown by the angle of the vectors from the poles and zeros to that point. (The phase contributions of the complex pair must cancel out everywhere on the real axis because af is real.) Thus the phase of af for this value of s is zero.

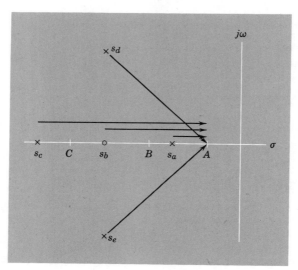

Figure 19.7   Calculation of locus on real axis from the poles and zeros of af.

For a point B, which lies between s_a and s_b, $\angle af = \pi$. For a point between s_b and s_c, $\angle af = 0$. We can generalize from this example, and the fact that the poles of $A(s)$ move continuously as $a_o f_o$ is increased, to obtain the rule: the loci of the poles of $A(s)$ include all of the segments of the real axis that lie to the left of odd numbers of left-half-plane poles and zeros of af.

Note that to simplify the rule we ignore right-half-plane zeros. To show why this simplification is possible, let us examine the case of negative resistive feedback applied to a three-stage direct-coupled common-emitter cascade.

With no feedback, such an amplifier will have six left-half-plane poles and three right-half-plane zeros, as shown in Fig. 19.8. If we apply *negative* feedback, then by definition $a_o f_o$ is *positive*. But for this amplifier, $a_o f_o$ is the response at $s = 0$, that is the dc response. It follows from Eq. 19.15 that for any allowed value of $a_o f_o$, $A(s)$ at $s = 0$ must be real and finite, that is, $A(s)$ *cannot have a pole at $s = 0$*. Thus the allowed real-axis loci for poles of $A(s)$ *does not include the origin* and therefore must be as shown in Fig. 19.8. This is the same result that we obtain if we apply Rule 2 to the left-half-plane singularities only. The procedure works because each right-half-plane zero of *af* changes the sign of $a_o f_o$, and Rule 2 already includes information about the sign of $a_o f_o$.

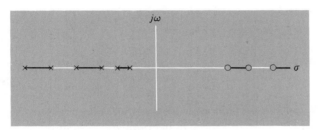

Figure 19.8 Real-axis loci for a three-stage feedback amplifier.

3. *Formation of a complex pole pair: all segments of loci that lie on the real axis between pairs of poles (or pairs of zeros) of af must at some internal "break-away point" branch out at right angles from the real axis to form conjugate pairs of loci.*

Figure 19.6 is an interesting illustration of Rule 2. For this case, Rule 2 says that the real-axis loci of the poles of $A(s)$ must lie only between s_a and s_c, and between s_b and s_d, as shown in Fig. 19.6c. But we know from Rule 1 that for $a_o f_o$ small, one of the poles of $A(s)$ is near s_b and the other near s_d. Similarly, when $a_o f_o$ becomes large, one pole of $A(s)$ approaches s_a and the other approaches s_c. In order to move continuously from s_b and s_d to s_a and s_c, and at the same time not violate the condition on real-axis loci, the poles of $A(s)$ must leave the real axis and form a complex pole pair, as stated above. The corresponding complex pair of loci are shown in Fig. 19.9.

4. *Average distance from the imaginary axis: for resistive feedback around multipole amplifiers, the average distance of the poles of $A(s)$ from the j axis will remain constant as $a_o f_o$ is increased.* Equation 19.12 illustrates this guide. Recall from Eq. 15.53 that

$$\frac{a_{n-1}}{a_n} = -\sum s_j \tag{19.16}$$

Because all complex poles occur in conjugate pairs, the imaginary part of any complex pole pair will cancel out in this summation, so that Eq. 19.16 can be

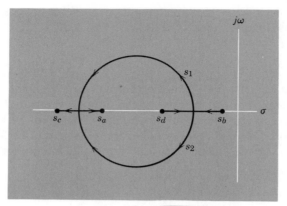

Figure 19.9   Complete root locus of $A(s)$ for af as given by Fig. 19.6a.

rewritten as

$$\frac{a_{n-1}}{a_n} = -\sum \text{Re}[s_j] \qquad (19.17)$$

We shall see that for multipole amplifiers employing resistive feedback, the two highest coefficients of the denominator polynomial of $A(s)$ are not functions of the midband loop transmission $a_o f_o$. Thus for these amplifiers the sum of the poles (or the sum of the real parts of the poles) of $A(s)$ will remain constant as $a_o f_o$ is changed. It is usually easier to visualize this constraint in terms of the average distance from the j axis. Hence we divide both sides of Eq. 19.17 by n, the number of poles in af:

$$\frac{a_{n-1}}{na_n} = \frac{-\sum \text{Re}[s_j]}{n} = \text{average distance of poles from } j \text{ axis} \qquad (19.18)$$

Thus if n, a_n, and a_{n-1} do not change, the average distance of the poles of $A(s)$ from the j axis (or, if you prefer, the "center of gravity" of the poles) will be constant. It follows from Rule 1 that this average distance must be the same as the average distance of the poles of af from the j axis.

5. *Invariance of the higher poles of $A(s)$ in a widely split set: if the natural frequencies of the mid- and high-frequency incremental af circuit are widely split, the higher poles of the correspondingly split natural frequencies of $A(s)$ will remain almost fixed for moderate amounts of feedback.*

Consider an $af(s)$ in which the poles are widely split and the zeros are much farther from the origin than the poles. Because in this case $|af|$ will fall off rapidly beyond the 0.707 frequency, $|af|$ will invariably be less than unity for values of s comparable in magnitude to the high-frequency pole values. Thus in the high frequency range the feedback has negligible effect on the dynamics of the system and $A(s)$ approaches $a(s)$. Consequently the far-out poles of $A(s)$ are close to the far-out poles of $a(s)$, regardless of the amount of midband feedback $a_o f_o$.

Let us illustrate by a numerical example. Assume that the transfer function of the mid- and high-frequency incremental a circuit has widely split poles. Specifically, assume that it has three identical poles at $s = 1$ and a fourth pole a thousand times farther out on the negative real axis, at $s = -1000$. Then

$$a(s) = \frac{1000a_o}{(s + 1)(s + 1)(s + 1)(s + 1000)}$$

$$= \frac{a_o}{0.001s^4 + 1.003s^3 + 3.003s^2 + 3.001s + 1}$$

For resistive feedback, $f = f_o$, so that

$$A(s) = \frac{a}{1 + af}$$

$$= \frac{a_o}{0.001s^4 + 1.003s^3 + 3.003s^2 + 3.001s + (1 + a_o f_o)}$$

The poles of $A(s)$ occur for those values of s that make the denominator (D) go to zero. Hence to find how far away from $s = -1$ and $s = -1000$ the poles of A have moved for $a_o f_o$ equal to, say, 100, we examine D for $s = -1$ and $s = -1000$.

For $s = -1$, the denominator is equal to

$$D = 0.001 - 1.003 + 3.003 - 3.001 + (1 + a_o f_o)$$

For $a_o f_o = 100$, $D = 100$ and a *major* change in s is required to make $D = 0$. Specifically, s must be changed to -5.65 or $1.32 \pm j4.0$ to make D again equal to zero. Hence the three low poles of $A(s)$ are a substantial distance away from $s = -1$, the low-frequency poles of a.

On the other hand, for $s = -1000$,

$$D = 10^9 - 1.003 \times 10^9 + 3.003 \times 10^6 - 3.001 \times 10^3 + (1 + a_o f_o)$$

For $a_o f_o = 100$, D again equals 100, but only a very minor change in s (one part in 10^6) is required to make D equal zero again, because the $a_o f_o$ term is not the dominant term in the equation in this frequency range. Thus $a_o f_o$ has negligible effect on the dynamics at these frequencies, and the high-frequency pole of A is still very close to $s = -1000$, the high-frequency pole of a.

For convenient reference, we repeat at this point the five basic root-locus rules developed above.

1. *Start and end of locus*: for increasing amounts of midband feedback, the locus of each pole of $A(s)$ starts from a pole of af and terminates on a zero of af.

2. *Location of loci on the real axis*: the loci of the poles of $A(s)$ include all portions of the real axis to the left of odd numbers of left-half-plane poles and zeros of af.

3. *Formation of a complex pole pair*: all segments of loci that lie on the real axis between pairs of poles (or pairs of zeros) of *af* must at some internal "break-away point" branch out at right angles from the real axis to form conjugate pairs of loci.

4. *Average distance from the imaginary axis*: for resistive feedback around multipole amplifiers, the average distance of the poles of $A(s)$ from the *j* axis will remain constant as $a_o f_o$ is increased.

5. *Invariance of the higher poles of $A(s)$ in a widely split set*: if the natural frequencies of the mid- and high-frequency incremental *af* circuit are widely split, the higher poles of the correspondingly split natural frequencies of $A(s)$ will remain almost fixed for moderate amounts of feedback.

19.2.2 Example of Root-Locus Calculations

To illustrate the concept of root-locus calculations, we examine the stability of a three-stage feedback amplifier employing node-node feedback, as shown in Fig. 19.10a. For simplicity, we use for the basic amplifier the circuit developed in Sections 16.1 and 18.3.3. We wish to design the feedback network so that it is possible to obtain at the same time both large loop transmission (hence large desensitivity) and an acceptable amplifier response.

It should be clear from previous discussions, particularly Section 14.1.1, that the high-frequency and low-frequency aspects of feedback amplifier analysis and design can be considered separately. Thus in the present discussion we shall concentrate only on the high-frequency stability problems. Of course, the low-frequency staoility problem in a feedback amplifier can be just as difficult as the high-frequency problem. Nevertheless, since the methods of analysis are identical, we discuss here only the latter.

On the basis of the discussion in Section 18.3, we can draw the mid- and high-frequency *a* circuit and *f* circuit for the amplifier in Fig. 19.10a. These circuits are shown in Fig. 19.10b and *c*. Recall from Section 18.3.3 that (ignoring stability problems) a desensitivity of 71 can be obtained by using a 5000-ohm feedback resistor. Because $R_s = 50$ ohms and $R_L = 100$ ohms, it is clear that for this amount of desensitivity (or any lesser amount) R_f can be neglected in Fig. 19.10b, compared to either R_s or R_L. If this assumption is made, the *a* circuit becomes identical to the 3-stage amplifier circuit in Section 16.1.2 (Fig. 16.2), hence has natural frequencies (in units of $nsec^{-1}$) at

$$s_a = -0.0251$$

$$s_b = -0.0943$$

$$s_c = -0.409$$

$$s_d = -9.55$$

$$s_e = -18.22$$

$$s_f = -28.56$$

The amplifier also has three zeros in the right half plane, but again, as in Chapter 16, these are so far out that they play no part in the present calculations.

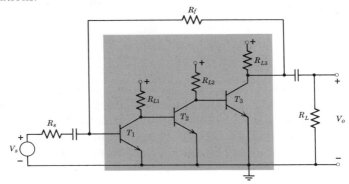

(a) Three-stage feedback amplifier (node–node)

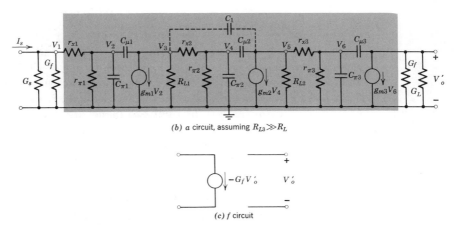

(b) a circuit, assuming $R_{L3} \gg R_L$

(c) f circuit

Figure 19.10 Three-stage feedback amplifier (from Sections 16.1 and 18.3.3). Element values are

Element	Units	T_1	T_2	T_3
r_x	kilohms	0.2	0.05	0.025
r_π	kilohms	2.5	0.5	0.25
g_m	millimhos	40	200	400
C_π	picofarads	9	45	90
C_μ	picofarads	2	2	2
R_L	kilohms	0.5	0.2	$\gg R_L$
$R_s = 50$	ohms			
$R_L = 100$	ohms			

We can now sketch out the root locus for this amplifier. We know from Section 19.2.1 that the loci of the poles of $A(s)$ start from the poles of $a(s)$ listed above. On the real axis, the loci can only lie between s_a and s_b, s_c and s_d, and s_e and s_f. Also, the average distance from the j axis of the poles of $A(s)$ will be according to Eq. 19.18,

$$\frac{\text{Re}[s_j]}{n} = -9.48 \text{ nsec}^{-1}$$

However, because the poles of $a(s)$ are so widely split, we know from Rule 5 and Rule 1 that for moderate feedback the three highest poles of $A(s)$ will remain close to the locations listed above for s_d, s_e, and s_f. Hence we can modify Rule 4 and Eq. 19.18 to state that in this case the average distance of the *three lowest* poles of $A(s)$ from the j axis will remain nearly constant, at a value of

$$\frac{s_a + s_b + s_c}{3} = \frac{-0.528}{3}$$

$$= -0.176 \text{ nsec}^{-1}$$

On this basis, the root-locus plot for the *three lowest poles of $A(s)$* must look much like Fig. 19.5. Pole s_3 starts from $s_c = -0.409$ and moves to the left, whereas s_1 and s_2 start at $s_a = -0.025$ and $s_b = -0.094$, respectively, and move toward each other. After s_1 and s_2 form a complex pair, they must move to the *right* to keep the average distance from the j axis equal to -0.176. Eventually, they move into the right half plane, and the amplifier becomes unstable.

We now wish to find the amount of desensitivity that can be obtained while still achieving acceptable frequency response. Working only with the three lowest poles, we find

$$a(s) \simeq \frac{a_o(0.0251)(0.0943)(0.409)}{(s + 0.0251)(s + 0.0943)(s + 0.409)} \tag{19.19a}$$

$$\simeq \frac{a_o(9.67 \times 10^{-4})}{s^3 + 0.528s^2 + 0.0516s + 9.67 \times 10^{-4}} \tag{19.19b}$$

Hence

$$A(s) = \frac{a}{1 + af}$$

$$= \frac{a_o(9.67 \times 10^{-4})}{s^3 + 0.528s^2 + 0.0516s + (9.67 \times 10^{-4})(1 + a_o f_o)} \tag{19.20}$$

Suppose that we are willing to accept a slightly humped frequency response. Then according to Figs. 19.3a and 19.4a, the complex pole pair can be located on the $\pm 60°$ radial lines through the origin ($Q = 1$). That is, $A(s)$ will have the general form

$$A(s) = \frac{k}{(s - \gamma)(s - \alpha - j\sqrt{3}\alpha)(s - \alpha + j\sqrt{3}\alpha)} \tag{19.21a}$$

$$= \frac{k}{s^3 - s^2(2\alpha + \gamma) + 2\alpha s(2\alpha + \gamma) - 4\alpha^2\gamma} \tag{19.21b}$$

We now have three unknowns: the pole locations α and γ, and the required midband loop transmission $a_o f_o$. These can be found by solving the equations relating the three coefficients in Eq. 19.20 to the corresponding coefficients in Eq. 19.21b:

$$-(2\alpha + \gamma) = 0.528 \tag{19.22}$$

$$2\alpha(2\alpha + \gamma) = 0.0516 \tag{19.23}$$

$$-4\alpha^2\gamma = (9.67 \times 10^{-4})(1 + a_o f_o) \tag{19.24}$$

Thus from Eqs. 19.22 and 19.23,

$$\alpha = -\frac{0.0516}{2(0.528)}$$

$$= -0.049 \text{ nsec}^{-1}$$

To find γ, we substitute this value into Eq. 19.22:

$$\gamma = -0.528 - 2(-0.049)$$

$$= -0.43 \text{ nsec}^{-1}$$

Now from Eq. 19.21a, the three lowest poles of $A(s)$ will be (in units of reciprocal nanoseconds)

$$s_1 = -0.049 + j0.085 \tag{19.25a}$$

$$s_2 = -0.049 - j0.085 \tag{19.25b}$$

$$s_3 = -0.43 \tag{19.25c}$$

Now the value of loop transmission $a_o f_o$ can be found. From Eq. 19.24,

$$9.67 \times 10^{-4}(1 + a_o f_o) = -4\alpha^2\gamma = -4(-0.049)^2(-0.43)$$

$$= 4.14 \times 10^{-3}$$

Hence

$$1 + a_o f_o = 4.3$$

$$a_o f_o = 3.3$$

The value of the feedback resistor can be found if we recall from Section 18.3.3 that $a_o = -354$ kohm.

$$G_f = -f_o = -\frac{3.3}{a_o} = -\frac{3.3}{-354}$$

$$= 0.93 \times 10^{-2} \text{ mmho}$$

$$R_f = 104 \text{ kohm}$$

The frequency response of the amplifier will be controlled primarily by the complex pole pair, so that the bandwidth can be estimated with the aid of Figs. 19.3 and 19.4. The normalizing constant ω_o is, in this case,

$$\omega_o = [(0.049)^2 + (0.085)^2]^{1/2}$$

$$= 0.098 \text{ nsec}^{-1}$$

and the Q is unity. Hence there will be a small hump in the response, and the upper 0.707 frequency will be a little larger than ω_o, that is, ω_h will be about 120 Mrad/sec.

We conclude that the maximum desensitivity obtainable with this amplifier using *resistive* feedback, while still maintaining reasonably flat frequency response, is only 4.3, a figure far below the desired desensitivity of 70. The reader can further verify that for any desensitivity greater than 28.2, the amplifier is unstable, that is, has right-half-plane poles. (See Problem P19.1.)

To verify the preceding results, the natural frequencies of the complete feedback amplifier (Fig. 19.10a) were calculated via a computer for values of G_f in the general range established by the approximate calculations above. The results are presented in Table 19.1 and Fig. 19.11. The agreement between the predicted pole locations for $G_f = 0.0093$ mmho (Eqs. 19.25) and the more accurate computer calculation for this value of G_f shown in the table is excellent, so that the various approximations made, particularly the neglect of the three highest poles, are (at least in this case) validated.

Table 19.1 Computer-Calculated Poles of $A(s)$ for Varying Amounts of Resistive Feedback Units are nsec^{-1}.

G_f (mmho)	s_1	s_2	s_3	s_4	s_5	s_6
0.001	-0.045	-0.071	-0.412	-9.55	-18.22	-28.56
0.0025	$-0.056 \pm j0.036$		-0.417	-9.55	-18.22	-28.56
0.005	$-0.052 \pm j0.061$		-0.424	-9.55	-18.22	-28.56
0.0093	$-0.047 \pm j0.087$		-0.435	-9.55	-18.22	-28.56
0.046	$-0.012 \pm j0.184$		-0.504	-9.55	-18.22	-28.56

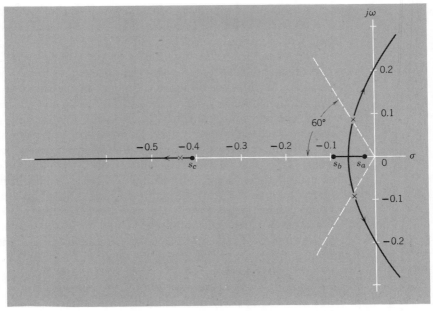

Figure 19.11 Root locus of the three lowest poles of $A(s)$ for amplifier in Fig. 19.10, obtained by computing the poles of $A(s)$ for various values of feedback resistor R_f. (See Table 19.1.) Indicated pole positions are for $G_f = 0.0093$ mmho. Units are for nsec^{-1}.

19.2.3 Criteria for Acceptable Response

It should be clear from the preceding example that the amount of midband feedback $a_o f_o$ we apply around an amplifier has a profound effect on the location of the poles of $A(s)$. See, for example, Fig. 19.11. Because we are now able to control to some extent the poles of $A(s)$, we are faced with two new problems: (1) what constitutes "satisfactory" frequency response or step response for an amplifier and (2) what are the restrictions on the locations of the poles of $A(s)$ to bring about this satisfactory response.

The criteria for "satisfactory" response depend principally on the application. For example, in an oscilloscope amplifier, a ringing step response is intolerable. On the other hand, for audio amplifiers, some small overshoot in the step response might be permitted. And for many servo amplifiers, substantial overshoot is permitted, and a peak in the frequency response as well, in order to obtain a fast rise time in the step response.

The pole (and zero) locations of an amplifier uniquely determine (within a constant) its frequency response and transient response. Unfortunately, the relationships between pole locations and response are often not simple. We do know, however, that if the amplifier has complex poles, it is likely that the transient response will be oscillatory and the frequency response peaked at the ringing frequency. Specifically, for a single pair of complex poles with a Q

greater than 0.5 (i.e., lying off the axis) there will be overshoot and ringing in the step response, and for a Q greater than 0.707 (45° radials) the frequency response will be peaked as well (see Fig. 19.4).

We shall see in the next section that by proper compensation, it is possible to move a real pole of $A(s)$ in to about the same radius from the origin as the complex pair. In this case both the overshoot in the step response and the peaking in the frequency response will be reduced. For one particular three-pole configuration, called the *Butterworth*[3] configuration, the peak in the frequency response disappears, and the response becomes "maximally flat." In general, the poles of a Butterworth filter are the values of the $2n$th roots of $(-1)^{n+1}$ that lie in the left half plane.[4,5] Thus the roots are equally spaced around the circumference of the unit circle, as shown in Fig. 19.12a for the two-pole and three-pole configurations. These two are of principal concern to us here, because feedback amplifiers can be designed quite readily to have either of these pole locations.

The normalized frequency responses of the two-pole and three-pole Butterworth filters are shown in Fig. 19.12b, together with the response of a single RC circuit (one-pole Butterworth!). In each case the poles are assumed to lie on the unit circle. Because the 0.707 frequency of any Butterworth filter is equal to the pole radius, all three filters have the same bandwidth in this normalization. But do not be misled. We shall shortly see that *major increases in both bandwidth and desensitivity result in a feedback amplifier*

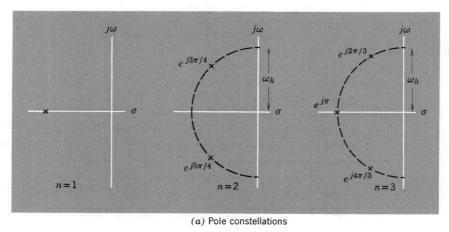

(*a*) Pole constellations

Figure 19.12   One-, two- and three-pole Butterworth filters.

[3] The two-pole Butterworth configuration has already been discussed briefly in Section 17.2.3.
[4] Reference 19.2, page 177.
[5] Reference 19.3, page 422.

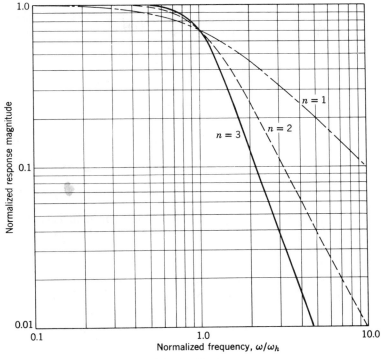

(b) Normalized frequency response

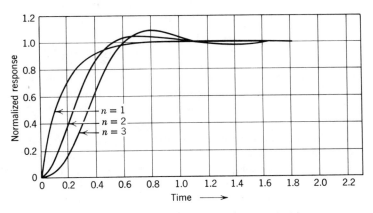

(c) Normalized step response, in units of $2.2/\omega_h$

Figure 19.12, continued

when the dominant pole configuration shifts from a one- to two- to three-pole Butterworth design.[6]

For completeness we also include in Fig. 19.12c the step response of the three Butterworth filters. The peak overshoots for the three cases are given in Table 19.2. Note in particular that the overshoot for the three-pole filter

Table 19.2 Overshoot in Step Response for Butterworth Filters

Number of Poles	Overshoot (%)
1	0
2	4.3
3	8.15

is only 8.15%, in spite of the complex pole pair with a Q of unity. Comparison with Fig. 19.4b indicates that with this complex pair alone, the overshoot would be about 11%.

Now that we have rough guidelines for acceptable response, we turn briefly to the problem of relating the desired pole locations to the parameters in the feedback amplifier. We have already seen in the preceding section an example of how this relationship can be established. Stated in general terms, we equate the coefficients in the $A(s)$ expression (three lowest poles only),

$$A(s) = \frac{k}{s^3 + b_2 s^2 + b_1 s + b_0} \tag{19.26}$$

to the corresponding coefficients (after expansion) in $A(s)$ expressed in terms of some particular pole configuration,

$$A(s) = \frac{k}{(s - \gamma)(s - \alpha + j\beta)(s - \alpha - j\beta)} \tag{19.27}$$

By equating coefficients, we obtain relations for b_2, b_1, and b_0 in terms of the desired pole locations. The appropriate interrelations for several frequently encountered pole locations, including the three-pole Butterworth, are given in Table 19.3.

In some cases it is possible to solve the b_2, b_1, and b_0 equations explicitly, to obtain relations for the pole locations α, β, and γ in terms of the polynomial coefficients. These relations are given in Table 19.4. Given any two of b_2, b_1, b_0, γ, and α (or appropriate interrelations), and either the Q or the angle of the poles, we can use Tables 19.3 and 19.4 to find the remaining parameters.

---

[6] A further improvement in bandwidth and desensitivity is possible if we are willing to tolerate peaking in the response curve. In this case the poles should be spaced around on an ellipse rather than a circle. The resulting pole configuration is that of a *Chebyshëv filter*. See Reference 19.4.

Table 19.3 Polynomial Coefficients in Terms of Pole Locations*

Q of Complex Pair	Angle from Real axis		b_2	b_1	b_0
0.5	0°	(two poles together)	$-(2\alpha + \gamma)$	$\alpha(\alpha + 2\gamma)$	$-\alpha^2\gamma$
0.707	±45		$-(2\alpha + \gamma)$	$2\alpha(\alpha + \gamma)$	$-2\alpha^2\gamma$
1	±60		$-(2\alpha + \gamma)$	$2\alpha(2\alpha + \gamma)$	$-4\alpha^2\gamma$
1	±60	(Butterworth)	-4α	$8\alpha^2$	$-8\alpha^3$
∞	±90		$-\gamma$	β^2	$-\gamma\beta^2$

* Symbols are defined in Eqs. 19.26 and 19.27

Table 19.4 Pole Locations in Terms of Polynomial Coefficients*

Q of Complex Pair	Angle from Real Axis		Complex Pole α	β	Real Pole γ
0.5	0°	(two poles together)	$(3\alpha^2 + 2b_2 + b_1 = 0)$	0	$-b_2 - 2\alpha$
0.707	±45°		$\left(\alpha^2 + b_2\alpha + \dfrac{b_1}{2} = 0\right)$	α	$-b_2 - 2\alpha$
1	±60°		$-\dfrac{b_1}{2b_2}$	$\sqrt{3}\alpha$	$-b_2 - 2\alpha$
1	±60°	(Butterworth)	$\dfrac{-b_2}{4}$	$\sqrt{3}\alpha$	2α
∞	±90°		0	$\sqrt{b_1}$	$-b_2$

* Symbols are defined in Eqs. 19.26 and 19.27

It is important to note that both tables were derived using the specific normalization of the denominator polynomial given in Eq. 19.26. Thus the tables are valid *only if s^3 coefficient in $A(s)$ has been normalized to unity.*

19.2.4 Compensation: Modification of the Feedback Network

Let us return now to the node-node feedback amplifier introduced in Section 19.2.2. Clearly, we need a substantially greater amount of feedback than $a_o f_o = 3.3$ if we wish to obtain a reasonable amount of amplifier desensitivity. In this and the following subsections we examine various ways of *compensating* the amplifier. That is, we add passive circuit components to either the basic amplifier or the feedback network to change the poles and zeros of *af*. By careful compensation, we can increase $a_o f_o$ while still keeping the Q of the complex pole pair less than unity. One way of accomplishing this is to add reactive elements to the feedback network. In this section we show that by adding one small capacitor C_f in parallel with G_f (Fig. 19.13a) we can bring about an extensive modification of the root locus and thus substantially improve the feedback amplifier performance characteristics.

The a circuit for this amplifier (Fig. 19.13b) is the same as that in Fig. 19.10b, except for the additional capacitive loading at input and output. There are now eight capacitors in the a circuit, but because of the capacitor loop at nodes V_6 and V_o', there are only seven independent energy storage elements. Thus there will be seven natural frequencies. As we shall shortly

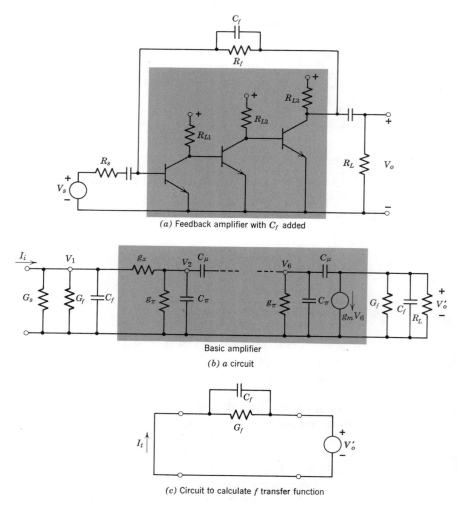

(a) Feedback amplifier with C_f added

Basic amplifier

(b) a circuit

(c) Circuit to calculate f transfer function

Figure 19.13   Feedback amplifier with C_f added.

see, the value of C_f required to compensate the amplifier is very small (fractions of a picofarad). Hence C_f will add one new pole to $a(s)$ at a very high frequency, but cause only a minor change in the other pole locations. Thus we base the remainder of the design on the assumption that *the three lowest poles of $a(s)$ are unchanged by the presence of C_f*. This assumption, although somewhat arbitrary at this point, will be verified by computer calculation at the conclusion of the design.

We can calculate the f transfer function by inspection of Fig. 19.13c:

$$f(s) = \frac{I_t}{V_o'} = -(G_f + sC_f) \tag{19.28}$$

If we again approximate $a(s)$ using only its three lowest poles, as in Eq. 19.19a, the loop transmission will be

$$af(s) = \frac{-a_o(9.67 \times 10^{-4})(G_f + sC_f)}{(s + 0.0251)(s + 0.0943)(s + 0.409)} \tag{19.29}$$

The loop transmission now has a finite zero at

$$s_f = -\frac{G_f}{C_f}$$

and it is this zero that can profoundly change the shape of the amplifier root locus.

Let us sketch the root locus of the poles of $A(s)$ for several assumed values of s_f. If we assume that $|s_f|$ is greater than $|s_c|$, we obtain the root locus shown in Fig. 19.14a.[7] It is clear from Section 19.2.1, Rule 2, that one real-axis locus will start from s_c and terminate on s_f. The other poles of $A(s)$ will come together as before and form a complex pair.

If we neglect the loading effect of C_f on the a circuit, the average distance of the poles of $A(s)$ from the j axis is unchanged by the feedback zero (see Problem P19.2). Thus, because pole s_3 moves only to s_f, the *asymptotes for the complex pair for large midband feedback must be parallel to the $j\omega$ axis* as shown in the figure. Therefore, these loci, for a proper choice of s_f, never cross into the right half plane. The feedback amplifier is then always stable (if only dominant effects are considered). (See Problem P19.3.)

A typical response curve $G_s V_o/I_i$ obtained experimentally using an amplifier[8] similar to that in Fig. 19.13a with $|s_f| > |s_c|$ is also shown in Fig. 19.14a. The response is peaked, indicating that the complex pole pair dominates the response. The corresponding pole locations are shown on the root locus.

---

[7] To formally calculate the loci in Fig. 19.14, both G_f and C_f must be changed so that the product $R_f C_f$ stays constant as $a_o f_o$ is changed. In this way we can vary the amount of midband feedback, yet keep the zero at s_f fixed.

[8] This amplifier can be used as the basis of a lecture demonstration on the general issue of compensation. See Section 19.4.

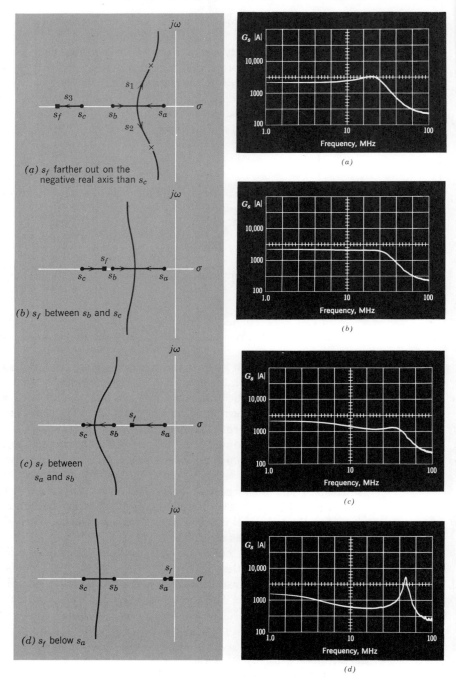

Figure 19.14   Root loci and measured response curves for several assumed values of s_f.

If we choose G_f/C_f such that s_f is between s_b and s_c, then we obtain the root locus shown in Fig. 19.14b. Because s_3 now moves *in* when the feedback is increased, the complex pole pair moves *away* from the j axis. This choice for s_f clearly results in pole locations that are better than those in Fig. 19.14a.

If we move s_f further in on the negative real axis, so that it is between s_a and s_b, we obtain the loci shown in Fig. 19.14c. In this case Rule 2 requires that the lowest pole stay on the real axis and the two higher poles split to form the complex pair. Unfortunately, the low real pole now dominates the frequency response, hence the bandwidth is considerably narrower than in the previous case. If enough feedback is applied to move the complex poles well off the real axis, a hump appears in the frequency response as shown in Fig. 19.14c. However, because this hump occurs beyond the 0.707 frequency, it does not improve the bandwidth of the amplifier.

Moving s_f below s_a merely causes the response to deteriorate further, as can be seen from either the root locus or the measured frequency response in Fig. 19.14d.

Clearly, there is an optimum location for s_f, somewhere between s_b and s_c. One excellent choice, which produces maximum bandwidth with no peaking, involves selecting s_f and $a_o f_o$ to place the three lowest poles of $A(s)$ in the *three-pole Butterworth filter configuration* discussed in the preceding section.

That is, we adjust s_f and $a_o f_o$ so that $A(s)$ is of the form

$$A(s) = \frac{K}{(s - 2\alpha)(s - \alpha + j\sqrt{3}\alpha)(s - \alpha - j\sqrt{3}\alpha)} \tag{19.30}$$

We know from Eqs. 19.19 and 19.29 that

$$A(s) = \frac{a_o(9.67 \times 10^{-4})}{(s + 0.0251)(s + 0.0943)(s + 0.409) - a_o(9.67 \times 10^{-4})(G_f + sC_f)}$$

$$= \frac{a_o(9.67 \times 10^{-4})}{s^3 + 0.528s^2 + s(0.0516 - 9.67 \times 10^{-4}a_oC_f) - 9.67 \times 10^{-4}(1 + a_oG_f)} \tag{19.31}$$

(Note in passing that the zero at s_f does *not* appear as a zero of the overall transfer function, even though it is present in the loop transmission). It is now possible to solve for the three unknowns C_f, G_f, and α by equating the corresponding coefficients in Eq. 19.30 (multiplied out) and Eq. 19.31. The required relations are given in Tables 19.3 and 19.4. Using Table 19.4, we find that

$$\alpha = -\frac{b_2}{4} = -\frac{0.528}{4} = -0.132 \text{ nsec}^{-1}$$

Hence the three lowest poles of $A(s)$ will be, in units of nsec^{-1}

$$s_1 = -0.132 + j0.228$$

$$s_2 = -0.132 - j0.228$$

$$s_3 = -0.264$$

From Table 19.3 we find that

$$b_0 = -8\alpha^3 = 18.4 \times 10^{-3}$$

Hence from Eq. 19.31, the midband loop transmission required to produce the Butterworth configuration is

$$a_o f_o = -a_o G_f = \frac{18.4 \times 10^{-3}}{9.67 \times 10^{-4}} - 1 = 18.2$$

For the Butterworth filter, $\omega_h = |s_3|$, so that the 0.707 frequency of the feedback amplifier is 264 Mrad/sec. Comparison with the results in Section 19.2.2 indicates that addition of C_f has brought about an increase in desensitivity from 4 to 20, an increase in bandwidth from 19 to 41 MHz. Also, the Butterworth response achieved here will have no peaking, whereas the amplifier in Section 19.2.2 will have a slightly peaked response.

To find G_f, recall that $a_o = -354$ kohm. Hence

$$G_f = \frac{18.2}{354} = 0.051 \text{ mmho}$$

To calculate C_f, we find from Table 19.3 that

$$b_1 = 8\alpha^2 = 0.139$$

Hence from Eq. 19.31,

$$C_f = \frac{0.139 - 0.0516}{354 \times 9.67 \times 10^{-4}} = 0.255 \text{ pf}$$

$$s_f = -G_f/C_f = -0.20 \text{ nsec}^{-1}$$

This capacitor value is impractically small, compared to the stray capacitance already present in the circuit. Thus it would be wise to redesign the feedback network. However, before we do that, we first check the present design on the computer.

To verify the design, the node equations for the complete feedback amplifier (Fig. 19.13a with s_f fixed at -0.20 nsec^{-1}) were solved on a computer for various values of midband loop transmission, including the design value of $a_o f_o = 18.2$. The results, summarized in Table 19.5 and plotted in Fig. 19.15, again are in substantial agreement with our approximate results, thereby validating, in this case at least, our initial assumptions that the design can be carried out in terms of the three lowest poles of $a(s)$ (see Problem P19.4) and that these poles are not changed by the presence of C_f (see Problem P19.5). Note the substantial improvement in loci, hence bandwidth—brought about by the compensation.

To obtain more practical element values in the feedback network, we combine the high-frequency feedback with the low-frequency feedback network required for bias stabilization, as shown in Fig. 19.16. Resistors R_2 and R_3 form a current divider, which attenuates the feedback signal and

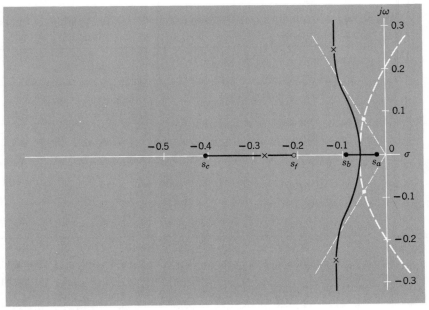

Figure 19.15 Root locus of three lowest poles of $A(s)$ for varying amounts of RC feedback (data in Table 19.5). Indicated pole positions are for $G_f = 0.051$ mmho, $C_f = 0.255$ pf. Dashed white curve is uncompensated locus from Fig. 9.11.

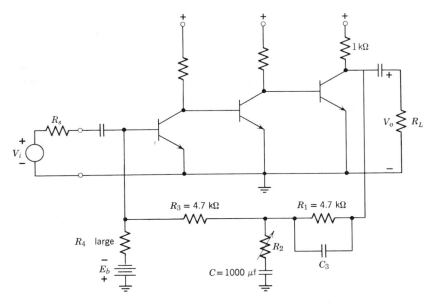

Figure 19.16 A node-node feedback network with more practical element values.

Table 19.5 Computer-Calculated Poles of $A(s)$ for Varying Amounts of RC Feedback. The Feedback Zero Is Held Constant at $s_f = -0.20\ \text{nsec}^{-1}$ (Units of Picofarads, Millimhos, and Nanoseconds)

Feedback Network	s_1	s_2	s_3	s_4	s_5	s_6	s_7
$C_f = 0$ $G_f = 0$	-0.025	-0.094	-0.409	-9.55	-18.22	-28.56	—
$C_f = 0.051$ $G_f = 0.0102$	$-0.075 \pm j0.082$		-0.374	-9.32	-18.22	-28.56	-503.5
$C_f = 0.255$ $G_f = 0.051$	$-0.121 \pm j0.240$		-0.260	-8.45	-18.18	-28.55	-112.3
$C_f = 0.51$ $G_f = 0.102$	$-0.123 \pm j0.382$		-0.225	-7.48	-18.14	-28.54	-64.3

thus permits a larger value for C_f. (See Problem P19.6 for calculations relating C_f to C_3.) A feedback amplifier of this type was used to obtain the measured response curves in Fig. 19.14. Note in particular the wide bandwidth and smooth response obtained in Fig. 19.14b for the optimum setting of R_2 and C_3. It should be emphasized that because of stray capacitance of circuit wiring and unpredictable transistor element values, it is necessary to make small adjustments in the calculated element values to achieve this desired smooth response.

19.2.5 Compensation: Adding Capacitance to the Basic Amplifier

A second way of compensating a feedback amplifier to permit more desensitivity is to add a capacitor to the basic amplifier to move the lowest pole of $a(s)$ much farther in on the negative real axis. It should be clear from the preceding root-locus discussion that if this can be accomplished, much larger values of loop transmission can be used before the lowest two poles of $A(s)$ come together and then split to form a complex pair (see Problem P19.7). One appropriate place to add such a capacitor is indicated in Fig. 19.17 (see

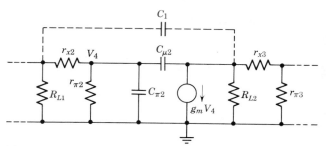

Figure 19.17 Addition of a compensating capacitor C_1 to the second stage of the amplifier.

Problem P19.8). Adding C_1 to the second stage as shown will alter to some extent the values of all the poles of $a(s)$, but if C_1 is much larger than $C_{\mu 2}$, then C_1 will provide in all probability the *dominant open-circuit time constant* in the a circuit. That is,

$$\sum \tau_{jo} \simeq -C_1 R_T \tag{19.32}$$

where R_T is the open-circuit resistance facing C_1 (see Section 15.2). Furthermore, we know from Eq. 15.43 that

$$\frac{1}{s_a} + \frac{1}{s_b} + \cdots + \frac{1}{s_f} = -\sum \tau_{jo} \tag{19.33}$$

If C_1 is large enough to produce one pole substantially lower than the others, this pole will dominate the sum in Eq. 19.32, and thus, combining Eqs. 19.32 and 19.33, we obtain

$$\frac{1}{s_{\text{low}}} \simeq -C_1 R_T \tag{19.34}$$

This equation is very useful for first-order design calculations.

   To check on the validity of Eq. 19.34, let us add a 50-pf capacitor (twenty-five times as big as $C_{\mu 2}$) from base to collector of transistor T_2 in Fig. 19.10. A straightforward calculation of the open-circuit resistance facing C_1, using Fig. 19.17 and the methods developed in Section 15.2, yields

$$R_T = 5900 \text{ ohms}$$

(see Problem P19.9). Hence from Eq. 19.34

$$s_{\text{low}} \simeq -\frac{1}{5.9 \times 50} = -0.0034 \text{ nsec}^{-1}$$

   This approximate result can now be checked by calculating the poles of $a(s)$ when C_1 is included in the a circuit. Such a calculation yields (in units of reciprocal nanoseconds)

$$s_a' = -0.003$$

$$s_b' = -0.192$$

$$s_c' = -0.402$$

$$s_d' = -1.71$$

$$s_e' = -9.58$$

$$s_f' = -22.3$$

We observe that our rough calculation of the lowest pole based on Eq. 19.34 agrees within about 10% with the value of s_a' found by the computer. (Note also that there are still only six poles in spite of the added capacitor, because C_1 forms a capacitor loop, as can be seen from Fig. 19.10b.)

   Comparison of the natural frequencies listed above with those for the unmodified a circuit (page 686) indicates that we have indeed succeeded in moving the lowest pole in on the real axis, in this case by a factor of 10. Thus we should be able to make $a_o f_o$ and the desensitivity substantially larger for a given Q of the complex pole pair of $A(s)$. This should be clear from the root locus in Fig. 19.5, because now the lowest pole of $A(s)$ must move a lot farther to the left on the real axis before it meets s_2 to form a conjugate pair.

There is a distinct advantage in adding C_1 in such a location as to lower the *lowest* pole, s_a, in the original amplifier, rather than s_b or s_c, because in this way we achieve maximum separation between the two lowest poles s_a' and s_b' in the compensated $a(s)$. (See Problem P19.10.) Thus the capacitor C_1 should if possible be added to the transistor stage most closely associated with s_a. Although the open-circuit time constants are not correlated on a one-to-one basis with the natural frequencies, it should be clear that the largest time constant in a given amplifier is most closely associated with the lowest pole. For example, in the limit of one dominant time constant and one dominant pole, we know from Eq. 19.34 that

$$-\frac{1}{s_{\text{low}}} = \tau_{\text{dominant}} \tag{19.35}$$

Thus it makes sense to add capacitor C_1 to the amplifier stage that has the largest open-circuit time constant. In the present amplifier this is clearly the second stage, because the source resistance driving T_1 and the load resistance on T_3 are small enough to make these stages fairly broadband (see Problem P19.11).

Standard root-locus calculations do not prove to be very helpful in selecting an appropriate value for C_1, because the poles of $a(s)$ change radically with the value of C_1, as we have seen. If on-line computational facilities are available, a trial-and-error solution is perhaps the quickest way of approaching the design problem. First calculate the natural frequencies of the feedback amplifier, using the desired amount of resistive feedback ($R_f = 5000$ ohms in the present example) and a value of C_1 one or two orders of magnitude larger than $C_{\mu 2}$. If the Q of the complex pole pair is still too high, then increase C_1. It may be helpful to plot the computer solutions in the form of a "root locus" in which R_f is fixed and C_1 is varied. Note, however, that these loci do *not* follow many of the standard root-locus rules listed in Section 19.2.1. (See Problem P19.12.)

Because it is considerably easier to carry out the detailed design of this type of compensation in terms of j-axis response rather than root locus, we postpone further discussion of this issue to Chapter 20. Note, however, that obtaining a large value of loop transmission by adding C_1 has an important disadvantage. The bandwidth of the a circuit has been greatly reduced, so that the desensitization properties of the feedback are effective over a much smaller passband. (See Problem P19.13.)

As mentioned in Section 19.1, designers of modern operational amplifiers often make use of compensation techniques similar to that in Fig. 19.17 to obtain circuits in which one pole is five or six orders of magnitude lower in magnitude than any others in the circuit.[9] This is accomplished by having a relatively low gain, and hence broadband, differential input stage, followed by a very high-gain stage which is made narrowband by adding a capacitor from output to input. This stage is followed by a broadband power amplifier.

If the operational amplifier has only one dominant pole as suggested above, then very large amounts of resistive feedback can be applied to the unit without causing instability. In fact, many units are stable even when the output is connected directly to the input, as suggested in Problem P18.25. Clearly if the amplifier is this stable, we can ignore altogether the stability problem, and design the feedback circuit by the simplified methods discussed in Chapter 18, specifically Eqs. 18.5 and 18.36.

19.2.6.   **Modification of both *a* and *f***

By using a parallel RC circuit in the feedback network, we were able in Section 19.2.4 to achieve a broad bandwidth and flat response. But the optimum loop transmission was 18.2, giving a desensitivity of only 19. To obtain a desensitivity of 70 as originally specified, it is necessary to combine the techniques discussed in Sections 19.2.4 and 19.2.5. First, we add a small capacitor C_1 from collector to base of transistor T_2 to split the poles, and then we add a small capacitor C_f across the feedback resistor to bend the root locus away from the j axis. The computer results for such a compensation scheme are summarized in Table 19.6.

Table 19.6   Computer-Calculated Poles of $A(s)$ when $G_f = 0.2$ and Compensation is Added to both the Feedback Network (C_f) and the Basic Amplifier (C_1) (Units of Picofarads, Millimhos, and Nanoseconds)

Compensation	s_1	s_2	Q of Lowest Two Poles	s_3	s_4	s_5	s_6	s_7
None ($C_f = 0, C_1 = 0$)	$+0.058 \pm j0.32$		—	-0.65	-9.64	-18.22	-28.56	—
$C_f = 0, C_1 = 50$	$-0.029 \pm j0.172$		3.1	-0.54	-1.71	-9.67	-22.31	—
$C_f = 0.5, C_1 = 50$	$-0.075 \pm j0.189$		1.34	-0.40	-1.71	-7.62	-22.18	-65.4
$C_f = 1, C_1 = 50$	$-0.147 \pm j0.239$		0.95	-0.207	-1.70	-6.12	-22.04	-41.9

With no compensation ($C_f = 0$, $C_1 = 0$) the feedback amplifier has right-half-plane poles, as expected (see Section 19.2.2). Adding a capacitor $C_1 = 50\,\text{pf}$ to transistor T_2 moves the poles into the left half plane, but the complex pole pair still has too high a Q. Thus we try compensating the

[9] See, for example, Reference 19.6.

feedback network by adding $C_f = 0.5$ pf in parallel with R_f. As expected, the complex pole pair moves away from the j axis when this is done. But Table 19.6 indicates that the Q is still too high. One further try, however, yields a satisfactory pole constellation. With $C_f = 1$ pf, the Q of the complex pair is less than unity, that is, the poles are below the 60° radials (see Problem P19.14), and we have achieved the desired desensitivity of 70.

19.2.7 Compensation by Adding Zeros to $a(s)$

Another technique for feedback amplifier compensation is to introduce zeros in the transfer function $a(s)$ of the basic amplifier. If additional capacitance has already been added to the amplifier as in Fig. 19.17, a zero can be added to $a(s)$ merely by adding a resistor in series with C_1, as shown in Fig. 19.18. This circuit produces a zero of $a(s)$ close to $s = -1/RC_1$, and also adds another pole to the system. The effect of the zero on the stability of the feedback amplifier is similar to that of a zero in the feedback network, as discussed in Section 19.2.4, except that the zero of $a(s)$ also appears as a zero of $A(s)$.

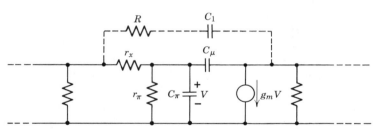

Figure 19.18 Technique for adding a zero to $a(s)$.

Complex zeros can be added to $a(s)$ by using a series RLC circuit as a shunt load between stages. The capacitor tends to move the lowest natural frequency of the basic amplifier nearer to the origin. The RLC circuit is then tuned to create a complex pair of zeros which can suppress the effect of high Q poles in the feedback amplifier response.

19.2.8 Summary

Before introducing further feedback examples, we summarize the procedure for designing a feedback amplifier to meet prescribed specifications on closed-loop gain A_o, desensitivity $1 + a_o f_o$, and so on. First, we decide on the general feedback topology required to meet some specified design objective, such as high input resistance or constant output current. Next we calculate the values of a_o and f_o required to meet the specifications on closed-loop gain and desensitivity,

$$a_o = A_o(1 + a_o f_o) \tag{19.36a}$$

and, if $a_o f_o$ is large,

$$f_o \simeq \frac{\text{desensitivity}}{a_o} \simeq \frac{1}{A_o} \tag{19.36b}$$

A first-cut midfrequency design of the a circuit (the basic amplifier augmented by the source resistor, the load resistor, and feedback loading) can now be made.

We next find out whether the proposed amplifier will have acceptable frequency response and transient response by computing the poles and zeros of the overall closed-loop transfer function $A(s)$ with resistive feedback. A reasonable criterion for acceptable transient response is that any complex poles lie below the 45° radial lines (Q less than 0.707). At worst, such an amplifier will have a 4.3% overshoot in the step response (see Fig. 19.4b), and the overshoot will be considerably smaller if there is a real-axis pole in the general vicinity of the complex pair. A reasonable criterion for acceptable frequency response is that all complex poles lie below the 60° radial lines, that is, have a Q less than unity. At worst, an amplifier with a pair of such complex poles will have a 6% hump in the response curve (see Fig. 19.4a), and this hump will also be reduced by an adjacent real-axis pole (see, for example, the Butterworth filter discussed in Section 19.2.3).

If the computed poles of $A(s)$ do not meet the appropriate criterion given above (and most amplifiers with three or more stages and resistive feedback will not), we compute the poles of $a(s)$, neglecting the feedback loading, sketch the root locus for the dominant poles, and compensate either $a(s)$ or $f(s)$, as described in the preceding four subsections. It would be nice, of course, to design the a circuit to have auspicious pole locations in the first place, but unfortunately the a circuit has highly intercoupled capacitors, so that such a design procedure is not easy to carry out.

It is important to recognize that two significant approximations are involved in root-locus sketches based on the dominant poles of $a(s)$. First, the nondominant poles of $a(s)$ do have some influence on the locus. Second, the poles of $a(s)$ are *not* constant, as we have assumed, but are themselves functions of the feedback resistor R_f, because loading effects of the feedback resistor are included in the a circuit. Both of these effects have been ignored in the preceding example for good reason: the high poles are more than a factor of 100 farther out than the lowest poles, and the feedback resistor is almost one hundred times as large as R_s and R_L. In other examples we may not be so fortunate; see, for instance, Section 19.3.2. It should be emphasized, however, that apart from a modest amount of frustration in the design process, these approximations have no lasting effect, because in all cases the final design is checked by *calculating the poles of $A(s)$ directly* on a computer.

19.3   Design Examples

To reinforce the preceding development of feedback amplifier stability calculations using root-locus concepts, we present in this section two further examples of feedback amplifier design. For simplicity, both are based on amplifiers already discussed (Chapter 18).

19.3.1 Loop-Loop Feedback

Let us complete the design of the loop-loop feedback amplifier in Fig. 19.19a, first introduced in Section 18.4.3. Recall from that section that the specification requires

$$R_s = 1000 \text{ ohms}$$

$$R_L = 50 \text{ ohms}$$

$$A_o = \frac{I_o}{V_s} = 2 \text{ mhos}$$

$$a_o f_o \simeq 50$$

It follows that

$$a_o = \frac{I'_o}{V_s} = 100 \text{ mhos}$$

$$f_o = \frac{V_t}{I'_o} = R_e = 0.5 \text{ ohm}$$

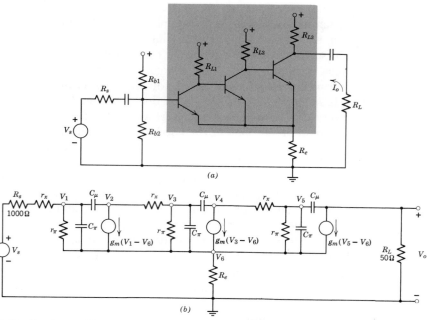

(a)

(b)

Figure 19.19 (a) Feedback amplifier employing loop-loop feedback. (b) Mid- and high-frequency model, assuming R_{L1}, R_{L2}, R_{L3}, R_{b1}, and R_{b2} large enough to be neglected.

One possible choice of transistor parameters to meet the specification is

$$\beta_o = 50$$

$$r_\pi = 250 \text{ ohms}$$

$$r_x = 25 \text{ ohms}$$

$$g_m = 0.2 \text{ mho}$$

Let us assume somewhat arbitrarily that $C_\pi = 50$ pf and $C_\mu = 5$ pf for all three transistors. The problem is to design the feedback network (R_e augmented by suitable compensating networks) so that the complete amplifier will have a flat frequency response and the desired desensitivity of 50. One approach to this problem is to calculate the poles of $a(s)$, sketch the root locus, and then use Tables 19.3 and 19.4 to design a compensating network to place the poles of $A(s)$ in the desired location. This method was employed in the preceding section. A minor variation of this is to calculate the value of R_e required to give the specified desensitivity and then compute the poles of $A(s)$ for this value of R_e. If the resulting pole configuration is unsatisfactory, suitable compensation can be found by enlightened trial and error. Let us use the latter approach in the present problem.

Computer calculations of the poles of $A(s)$, based on the incremental model of Fig. 19.19b, are summarized in Table 19.7 (see Problem P16.14). For $R_e = 0.5$ ohm, as required to meet the specifications on A_o and $a_o f_o$, $A(s)$ has a pair of complex poles very close to the j axis in the left half-plane, hence the amplifier is almost unstable. To obtain a reasonably flat frequency response without compensating a or f, it will be necessary to use a substantially smaller value of R_e, say one fifth of the present value. For $R_e = 0.1$ ohm, we see from Table 19.7 that the amplifier is indeed stable and that the response is now dominated by a complex pole pair with a Q of about 1.3. For $R_e = 0.05$ ohm, we obtain a complex pole pair with a Q slightly less than one. Hence we would expect a slightly humped closed-loop frequency

Table 19.7 Poles of $A(s)$ for Fig. 19.19 for Various Values of the Feedback Resistor R_e (Units Are Reciprocal Nanoseconds)

	$R_e = 0.5$ ohm ($a_o f_o = 50$)	$R_e = 0.1$ ohm ($a_o f_o = 10$)	$R_e = 0.05$ ohm ($a_o f_o = 5$)	$R_e = 0$ [Poles of $a(s)$]
s_1	$-0.005 + j0.116$	$-0.022 + j0.052$	$-0.024 + j0.035$	$s_a = -0.007$
s_2	$-0.005 - j0.116$	$-0.022 - j0.052$	$-0.024 - j0.035$	$s_b = -0.047$
s_3	-0.401	-0.368	-0.363	$s_c = -0.357$
s_4	-8.01	-8.04	-8.04	$s_d = -8.05$
s_5	-12.15	-12.15	-12.15	$s_e = -12.15$
s_6	-15.25	-15.25	-15.25	$s_f = -15.25$

response for this value of feedback resistor with a bandwidth of about

$$\omega_h \simeq 0.03 \text{ Grad/sec}$$

(see Problem P19.15).

It is now clear that we cannot obtain both flat response and the desired desensitivity of 50 using only resistive feedback. Thus to aid in subsequent calculations involving compensation, we also compute the natural frequencies for the circuit in Fig. 19.19 with $R_e = 0$ (by removing the row and column corresponding to V_6 from the determinant) to get the poles of $a(s)$. The results are included in Table 19.7. The root locus based on the data in Table 19.7 has been plotted in Fig. 19.20.

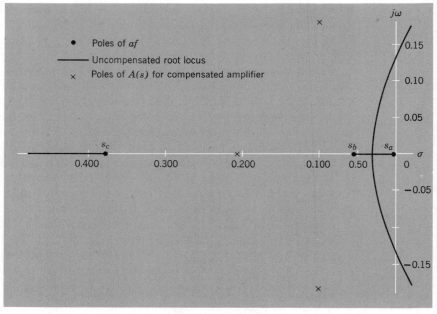

Figure 19.20 Root locus for loop-loop resistive feedback applied as shown in Fig. 19.19. Also shown are the poles of $A(s)$ which can be achieved by proper compensation. Units are nsec^{-1}.

A relatively simple way of compensating this amplifier is to add a zero to the feedback network, as discussed in Section 19.2.4 (see Problem P19.16). Recall from Section 18.4.3 that the f circuit for this configuration is a pure transimpedance:

$$f = z_{rf} = \frac{V_t}{I_o'} = R_e \qquad (19.37)$$

Thus to add a zero to z_{rf} we must add an inductor in series with R_e. We see from Fig. 19.21 that, for this compensated feedback network,

$$f = \frac{V_t}{I_o'} = R_e + sL \qquad (19.38)$$

Hence we have a zero at

$$s_f = \frac{-R_e}{L} \qquad (19.39)$$

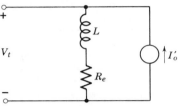

Figure 19.21   Circuit for calculating f transfer function.

From this point on, the design problem is identical in principle to that discussed in Section 19.2.4: we wish to place the zero between s_b and s_c, as shown by the root loci and response curves in Fig. 19.14. Specifically, for this amplifier we want s_f to be somewhere between -0.047 and -0.357 nsec^{-1}. A more exact location can be found by applying the appropriate relations from Tables 19.3 and 19.4, but often a first guess based on the "average distance" concept for the three lowest poles (Rule 4, modified) leads to rapidly converging results. We see from Table 19.7 that the average distance of the three lowest poles of $a(s)$ from the j axis is

$$\text{average distance} = \frac{-0.410}{3}$$

(see Problem P19.17). Thus for a three-pole Butterworth pole configuration, we want

$$s_1 = -0.102 - j0.175$$

$$s_2 = -0.102 + j0.175$$

$$s_3 = -0.205$$

(This calculation is obviously the same as that for finding α, β, and γ from Table 19.4.) Because in the root locus, s_3 moves from s_c toward s_f (see Fig. 19.14b), we now know that s_f must be between -0.047 and -0.205. Thus a reasonable first guess is $s_f = -0.1$ nsec^{-1}. From Eq. 19.39, the required value of L is (in kilohms, nanoseconds, and microhenries)

$$L = -\frac{R_e}{s_f} = \frac{0.5 \times 10^{-3}}{0.1} = 5 \times 10^{-3} \, \mu\text{h}$$

(which is the inductance of a short piece of wire).

A slightly different reduction routine must be used in the computer calculation because of the presence of the inductor in the circuit. The details are included in Appendix D. The results of the calculation are presented in Table 19.8. Clearly, the zero is too far in on the negative real axis, for s_3 has moved a little too far in on the axis, thereby forcing s_1 and s_2 too far out.

Table 19.8 Poles of $A(s)$ for Three Different Values of the Feedback Network Zero s_f (Units Are Reciprocal Nanoseconds)

	$s_f = -0.1$ $L = 0.005\ \mu h$	$s_f = -0.125$ $L = 0.004\ \mu h$	$s_f = -0.11$ $L = 0.0045\ \mu h$
s_1	$-0.114 + j0.144$	$-0.078 + j0.130$	$-0.097 + j0.135$
s_2	$-0.114 - j0.144$	$-0.078 - j0.130$	$-0.097 - j0.135$
s_3	-0.161	-0.238	-0.198
s_4	$-6.96 + j5.56$	$-8.20 + j5.71$	$-7.45 + j5.65$
s_5	$-6.96 - j5.56$	$-8.20 - j5.71$	$-7.45 - j5.65$
s_6	-11.9	-11.9	-11.9
s_7	-15.1	-15.1	-15.1

Note: these data do not form a conventional root locus.

A reasonable second guess is that $s_f = -0.125\ \text{nsec}^{-1}$, but this places s_3 too far out, as can be seen from the table. Interpolating between these two results, we choose $s_f = -0.11$ ($L = 4.5$ nh). For these values, we obtain results within 10 % of those predicted above. The three lowest poles for this design have been added to Fig. 19.20 to facilitate comparison with the uncompensated design. The closed-loop bandwidth of this amplifier is, because of the three-pole Butterworth configuration,

$$\omega_h = |\gamma| = |s_3| = 0.20\ \text{Grad/sec}$$

Thus we have obtained a sixfold improvement in bandwidth over that achieved with resistive feedback only, from 4.8 to 32 MHz, in addition to achieving the desired desensitivity of 50. Although these calculations on paper are relatively convincing, we hasten to add that in an actual circuit, stray inductance of the order of the compensating inductance calculated above will almost surely be present because of the finite lead lengths on the components. Thus a practical circuit of this type will probably already be compensated, or even overcompensated, by stray inductive effects.

Note in passing that the average distance of the three lowest poles from the j axis stays relatively constant in spite of the added inductor. On the other hand, the average distance of all seven poles does *not* stay constant as L is varied, because Rule 4 does not apply directly when a reactive network element is varied.

19.3.2   Feedback Amplifier with Loop Comparison and Node Sampling

Let us next try to design a feedback network for an amplifier employing loop comparison and node sampling. The midband characteristics of this circuit were discussed in Section 18.6, but it was pointed out that we should encounter some difficulty when we try to split the high-frequency model into *a* and *f* circuits.

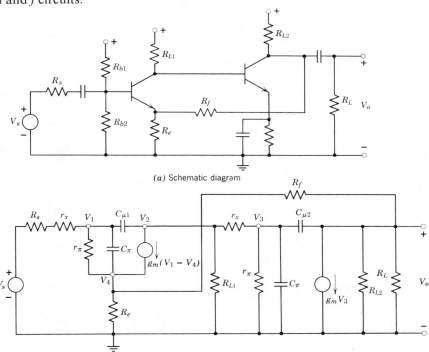

(a) Schematic diagram

(b) Mid- and high-frequency incremental model, assuming R_{b1}, $R_{b2} \gg R_s$

Figure 19.22   Loop-comparison, node-sampling feedback amplifier.

A simple two-stage amplifier of this type is shown in Fig. 19.22a, and the corresponding mid- and high-frequency incremental model is shown in Fig. 19.22b. Suppose that we are given transistors with the following parameters:

$$r_\pi = 250 \text{ ohms}$$

$$g_m = 0.4 \text{ mho}$$

$$r_x = 25 \text{ ohms}$$

$$C_\pi = 100 \text{ pf}$$

$$C_\mu = 10 \text{ pf}$$

Also, assume that $R_s = 100$ ohms, $R_{L1} = R_{L2} = 1$ kohm, $R_L = 250$ ohms, and $R_e = 10$ ohms. (See Problem P18.17 for comments on the choice of R_e.) We wish to design the feedback network to obtain the maximum amount of desensitivity without any ringing in the transient response.

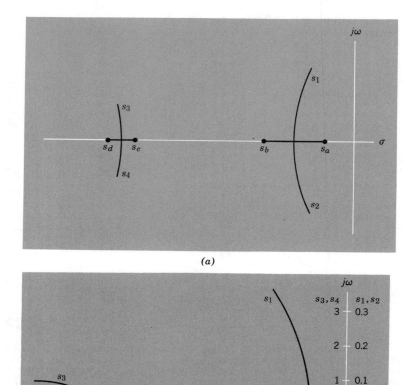

(a)

(b)

Figure 19.23 (a) Root locus for simple four-pole amplifier with resistive feedback in which $a(s)$ and f_o are assumed to be completely independent. (b) True root locus for amplifier in Fig. 19.22, for varying R_f. Units are nsec^{-1}. Note change of scale for s_3 and s_4.

We expect the incremental model in Fig. 19.22b to have two relatively low-frequency poles (call them s_1 and s_2) and two relatively high-frequency poles (s_3 and s_4). Because the response will be dominated by s_1 and s_2, the transient response specification requires that this pair of poles stay on the real axis. Given this constraint, we obtain maximum desensitivity when s_1 and s_2 are coincident and on the verge of breaking away from the real axis to form a complex pair.

Because neither the desensitivity nor the midband gain A_o has been specified in this design, we do not have an initial estimate for R_f. If rapid on-line computational facilities are available, a trial-and-error solution is quite possibly the most efficient approach to the problem. Assume a value for R_f, say 100 R_e or 1000 R_e, calculate the poles of $A(s)$, and then compare with the desired pole configuration. A quick root-locus sketch (Fig. 19.23a) will indicate which way to change R_f: if the two lowest poles are complex, reduce the feedback by increasing R_f; if they are real but not coincident, increase the feedback by reducing R_f.

A somewhat more "scientific" approach to this problem is to find the poles of $a(s)$ for infinite R_f and from this data estimate the value of R_f required to give coincident poles of $A(s)$. The a circuit, derived on the basis of the development in Section 18.6, is shown in Fig. 19.24a. Recall, however, that this is *not* strictly correct because of the presence of $C_{\mu 1}$. There is no longer a simple frequency-independent relationship between the source current, the a-circuit input current, and the f-circuit input current; hence we form an a circuit with some misgivings. Certainly some inaccuracy in root-locus calculations based on the poles of $a(s)$ must be expected.

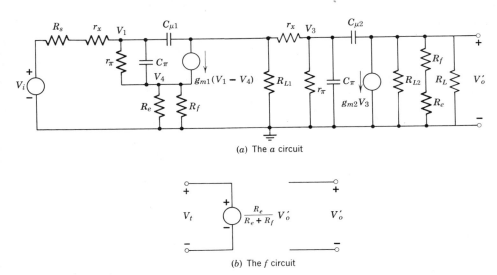

(a) The a circuit

(b) The f circuit

Figure 19.24 The a and f circuits for the amplifier in Fig. 19.22.

The natural frequencies for the a circuit in Fig. 19.24a, calculated by using $R_f = \infty$ and the remaining element values as specified above, are (in units of reciprocal nanoseconds)

$$s_a = -0.0049 \qquad s_c = -4.55$$

$$s_b = -0.182 \qquad s_d = -7.49$$

(see Problem P16.15). As expected, s_c and s_d are at a much higher frequency than s_a and s_b. Thus according to Rule 5, the two high poles of $A(s)$, s_3 and s_4, will stay relatively fixed while the low poles, s_1 and s_2, will come together and then form a complex pair. As a first approximation, therefore, we work only with the lower two poles. On this basis

$$a(s) \simeq \frac{a_o(0.00089)}{(s + 0.0049)(s + 0.182)}$$

and

$$A(s) \simeq \frac{a_o(0.00089)}{(s + 0.0049)(s + 0.182) + (0.00089)a_o f_o}$$

$$= \frac{a_o(0.00089)}{s^2 + 0.187s + (0.00089)(1 + a_o f_o)}$$

To obtain maximum desensitivity with no overshoot in the transient response, we want coincident poles in $A(s)$:

$$A(s) = \frac{k}{(s - \alpha)^2}$$

$$= \frac{k}{s^2 - 2\alpha s + \alpha^2}$$

Equating corresponding coefficients, we obtain

$$\alpha = -0.0935$$

$$a_o f_o = 8.82$$

The midband gain a_o, calculated from Fig. 19.24a assuming that R_f is infinite, is

$$a_o = \frac{V_o'}{V_i} = 1130$$

(see Problem P16.15). Thus from Fig. 19.24b

$$f_o = \frac{R_e}{R_e + R_f} = \frac{8.82}{1130} = 0.0078$$

Hence

$$R_f = 1270 \text{ ohms}$$

A computer computation of the poles of $A(s)$ for $R_f = 1270$ ohms yields

$$s_1 = -0.069 \qquad s_3 = -4.64$$

$$s_2 = -0.127 \qquad s_4 = -7.48$$

We have missed by a substantial margin our design objective of coincident poles, but a few iterations of the computer solution, starting by decreasing the value of R_f to obtain more feedback, will rapidly lead to the desired design. In fact, only a ten percent reduction in R_f will bring us close to the desired pole pattern, as can be seen from Table 19.9.

Table 19.9 Poles of $A(s)$ for increasing amounts of feedback for the amplifier in Fig. 19.22. See plot in Fig. 19.23b. Units are nsec^{-1}.

R_f (kilohms)	s_1	s_2	s_3	s_4
∞	-0.0049	-0.182	-4.55	-7.49
2	-0.038	-0.154	-4.61	-7.48
1.27	-0.069	-0.127	-4.64	-7.48
1.1	$-0.098 \pm j0.01$		-4.65	-7.48
0.5	$-0.105 \pm j0.096$		-4.77	-7.47
0.1	$-0.142 \pm j0.244$		-5.66	-7.35
0.05	$-0.174 \pm j0.313$		$-6.94 \pm j0.411$	

From Eq. 15.17, the resulting bandwidth will be

$$\omega_h \simeq \frac{0.098}{\sqrt{2}} = 0.069 \text{ Grads/sec}$$

or

$$f_h \simeq 11 \text{ MHz}$$

The desensitivity will be about 10.

As in previous examples, the bandwidth of this amplifier can be increased even more by allowing the poles of $A(s)$ to move off the axis to form a two-pole Butterworth pair. From Table 19.9, the value of R_f required to achieve this pole configuration is $R_f \simeq 500$ ohms. The bandwidth will be about 23 MHz. (See Problem P19.18.) A further increase in bandwidth can be realized by adding a small compensating capacitor (a few picofarads) in parallel with R_f.

Typical results for a two-stage amplifier[10] using inexpensive 2N3563 transistors in a circuit configuration similar to that in Fig. 19.22 are shown in Fig. 19.25. The response for $R_f = 0$, shown in Fig. 19.25a, indicates that the bandwidth without feedback is about 7 or 8 MHz. When R_f is adjusted to yield maximally flat response as in Fig. 19.25b, the bandwidth increases to about 60 MHz. When a small capacitor is added in parallel with R_f as in Fig. 19.25d, it is possible to achieve a flat response from low frequencies to above 100 MHz!

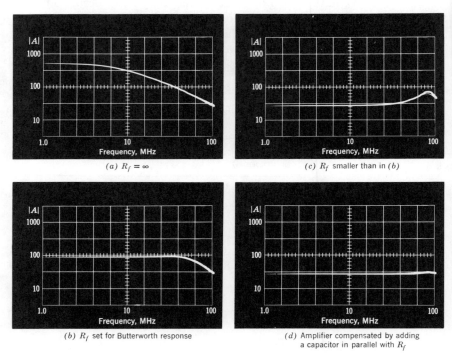

Figure 19.25 Oscilloscope photographs of the response of the amplifier in Fig. 19.22.

A root locus plot based on the computer calculations in Table 19.9 is shown in Fig. 19.23b. There is a marked disagreement between this plot and our original root locus sketch in Fig. 19.23a "predicted" from the poles of $a(s)$. Figure 19.23b shows the surprising fact that this amplifier is always stable (if parasitic effects are ignored), regardless of the amount of resistive feedback applied, because as R_f is reduced, the poles of $A(s)$ actually move *farther away from the j axis.*

Two independent factors contribute to the inaccuracy of our predicted root locus shown in Fig. 19.23a. First, as already mentioned, the basic concept

[10] See Section 19.4 for measurement details.

of breaking the circuit in Fig. 19.22b into the a and f circuits of Fig. 19.24 is open to question because of the presence of $C_{\mu 1}$. Second, the loading effect of R_f on the a circuit is not *negligible* in this circuit, so the poles of a do *not* stay fixed as the amount of resistive feedback is increased. Loading effects in two-stage feedback amplifiers are typically more serious than for amplifiers with three or more stages. With only two stages of gain, a_o is usually smaller, so that f_o must be correspondingly larger to achieve a given desensitivity. Larger f_0 always results in more loading on the output node. (See Problem P19.19.)

It is important to note that the root-locus design procedures outlined in this chapter *succeed in spite of the inaccuracies discussed above*, because the designs are all eventually based on direct calculation of the true poles of $A(s)$.

19.4 Lecture Demonstrations

Add to the feedback amplifier under test (the amplifier in Fig. 19.16, for example) a peak detector as shown in Fig. 19.26. Because the frequencies involved in this experiment may be as high as 100 MHz, the detector should be mounted on the same chassis as the amplifier. Connect up the remaining equipment as shown in Fig. 19.26. The logarithmic amplifiers[11] are required to produce log-log plots of the frequency response. With proper adjustment, the oscilloscope can have 10 db/division vertical sensitivity, and a horizontal scale with 1 MHz on the left, 10 MHz at center, and 100 MHz at the right.

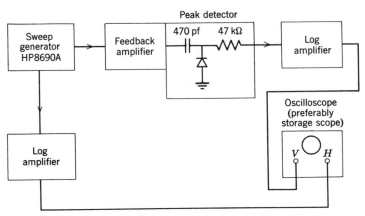

Figure 19.26 Block diagram of lecture demonstration.

Assuming that we are testing the amplifier in Fig. 19.16, set R_2 to zero to yield zero ac feedback and trace out the response curve. If a storage scope is used, store this image. Repeat for increasing amounts of resistive feedback, that is, increasing R_2 ($C_3 = 0$). Typical results, with several runs superimposed, are shown in Fig. 19.27a. Keep in mind the close tie between the

[11] See Reference 19.5, p. 150, for one possible design.

magnitude plots and the corresponding pole patterns derived in terms of root loci. Increase R_2 until the amplifier goes unstable.

Reset R_2 for slightly humped response, then increase C_3. Again, the storage scope is useful for presentation, although not essential. Typical results are shown in Figs. 19.27b and 19.14.

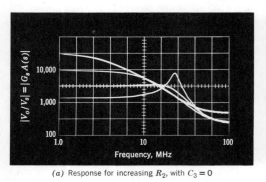

(*a*) Response for increasing R_2, with $C_3 = 0$

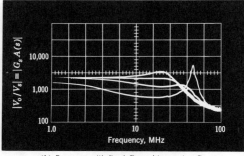

(*b*) Response with fixed R_2 and increasing C_3

Figure 19.27   Oscilloscope photographs from the lecture demonstration in Figs. 19.26 and 19.16.

REFERENCES

19.1   J. Truxal, *Control Engineers' Handbook*, McGraw-Hill, New York, 1958.

19.2   G. E. Valley and H. Wallman, *Vacuum Tube Amplifiers*, McGraw-Hill, New York, 1948.

19.3   S. J. Mason and H. J. Zimmermann, *Circuits, Signals and Systems*, Wiley, New York, 1960.

19.4   F. F. Kuo, *Network Analysis and Synthesis*, Wiley, New York, 1962.

19.5   J. N. Giles, *Linear Integrated Circuits Applications Handbook*, Fairchild Semiconductor, 1967.

19.6   R. J. Widler, *A New Monolithic Operational Amplifier Design*, National Semiconductor TP-2, August, 1968.

19.7   D. O. Pederson, *Electronic Circuits*, (prelim. ed.), McGraw-Hill, New York, 1965.

PROBLEMS

P19.1   Find for the feedback amplifier in Section 19.2.2 (Fig. 19.10) the midband loop transmission, the desensitivity, and the value of R_f required to make the amplifier on the verge of instability. (See page 691.)

P19.2   Compute the poles of $a(s)$ for the a circuit, Fig. 19.13b, *including* the loading effects of $C_f = 0.255$ pf, $G_f = 0.054$ mmho. Compare the average distance of the three lowest poles of $a(s)$ for this calculation to the corresponding number in Section 19.2.4, calculated by neglecting C_f. Comment on the loading effects of C_f. (See page 697.)

P19.3 Estimate the value of the zero s_f in the feedback loop, Fig. 19.13, which will insure that the amplifier is stable for all values of midband loop transmission. (See page 697.)

P19.4 Table 19.5 shows that when a compensating capacitor is added to a three-stage feedback amplifier as in Fig. 19.13, the amplifier has seven natural frequencies. Explain why. Check the average distance of the seven poles from the j axis as the feedback is varied. Is it constant? Repeat for the four lowest poles and the three lowest poles and comment. (See page 700.)

P19.5 Compute the poles of $a(s)$ for the a circuit in Fig. 19.13, including the effects of C_f and G_f. Use the values of C_f and G_f given in Table 19.5. Check to see how much the loading effects change the poles of $a(s)$. (See page 700.)

P19.6 For the resistor values given in Fig. 19.16, find the values of C_3 and R_2 that will have the same effect as $C_f = 0.255$ pf, $G_f = 0.054$ mmho in Fig. 19.13. (See page 702.)

P19.7 A certain feedback amplifier has resistive feedback, and has an a-circuit transfer function of the form

$$a(s) = \frac{10^5}{(s + 2)(s + 2)(s + 2)}$$

(a) How large can f_o be without producing instability?
(b) Move one of the poles of $a(s)$ down toward the j axis to $s_p = -1/50$. Now how large can f_o be without instability. Explain by sketching the root loci of $A(s)$ in each case. (See page 702.)

P19.8 Show that for a given capacitor size, the lowest pole of $a(s)$ in Fig. 19.10b is moved further down from the other poles if C_1 is connected as shown than if it is connected from base to *ground* on the second transistor. (See page 703.)

P19.9 Calculate the open-circuit resistance facing capacitor C_1 in Fig. 19.10. Substitute numerical values from Fig. 19.10, hence validate the calculation of R_T on page 703.

P19.10 Try adding a 50-pf capacitor from base to collector in the feedback amplifier in Fig. 19.10, first to T_1 and then to T_3. Calculate the poles of $a(s)$ in each case and sketch the resulting root loci. From the sketches, decide whether more or less desensitivity will result than achieved in Section 19.2.5. Verify your estimation by choosing R_f in the computer solution of the poles of $A(s)$ to achieve maximum desensitivity and flat frequency response. (See page 704.)

P19.11 There is an excellent reason for *not* adding compensating capacitance from base to collector in the output stage of a feedback amplifier, independent of the time-constant issue discussed in Section 19.2.5 and Problem P19.10. Explain. (See page 704.)

P19.12   Compute and plot the locus of the poles of $A(s)$ for varying amounts of C_1 in the amplifier in Fig. 19.10. Keep R_f fixed at 5000 ohms. Estimate the value of C_1 to produce a pair of poles of $A(s)$ with a Q of unity. (See page 704.)

P19.13   Estimate the bandwidth of the a circuit in Fig. 19.10, with and without the 50-pf compensating capacitor C_1. Comment on the effect of C_1 on desensitivity. (See page 704.)

P19.14   Table 19.6 indicates that "satisfactory" response (in this case, the Q of the complex poles less than 60°) can be achieved by adding a 50-pf capacitor C_1 between base and collector of transistor T_2 in Fig. 19.10, and also adding a 1-pf capacitor C_f in parallel with the feedback resistor R_f. This choice of C_1 and C_f is not necessarily optimum. Discuss the trade-off between C_1 and C_f. If possible, use a computer to find other combinations of C_1 and C_f that give the desired response. Which of these combinations is the best design, and why?

P19.15   For the amplifier in Section 19.3.1, (Fig. 19.19) calculate ω_h from the poles of $A(s)$ given in Table 19.7 for $R_e = 0.05$ ohm. Hence verify the result given on page 710.

P19.16   The amplifier in Section 19.3.1 (Fig. 19.19) can also be compensated by adding a capacitor to the basic amplifier as in Section 19.2.5. Of what size and where should a capacitor be added to meet the specifications stated at the start of Section 19.3.1. (See page 710.)

P19.17   Use the computer calculations in Table 19.8 to check the "average-distance from the j axis" concept for the feedback amplifier in Fig. 19.19 compensated by an inductance L in series with R_e. (See page 711.)

P19.18   Given the transfer function for $a(s)$ as in Section 19.3.2, design the feedback network in Fig. 19.22 to yield a two-pole Butterworth configuration for the closed-loop transfer function $A(s)$. Compare the bandwidth and desensitivity with the design in Section 19.3.2.

P19.19   Separate the two factors that lead to inaccurate root-locus predictions for the circuit of Fig. 19.22 by first assuming $g_m = 20$ mho for the second transistor to reduce the loading effect of R_f. Then make $C_{\mu 1} = 0$ in the first transistor to eliminate a-circuit inaccuracy. In each case compute the root locus and compare with the predicted locus, Fig. 19.23a. (See page 719.)

P19.20   Assuming ideal transistors ($C_\pi = C_\mu = 0$) in Fig. 18.29, sketch the root locus for this amplifier. Explain why the designer placed the RC network in the feedback path.

P19.21 If we try to solve Problem P18.25c by forming an *a* circuit and an *f* circuit, certain obvious contradictions arise. To show this, form the *a* and *f* circuits, assuming the operational amplifier has some finite output resistance R_o, and no internal dynamics, i.e., the output voltage of the amplifier *alone* is some constant a_o times the amplifier input current. Now find the *a* and *f* transfer functions, and hence find $A(s)$. How many poles does this function have? Find by inspection of the original circuit, Fig. 18.30a with R_2 replaced by a capacitor C_2, how many poles $A(s)$ really has. The first answer is wrong because this circuit does not meet some of the fundamental conditions required for forming the *a* and *f* circuits. Explain.

(See also Problems P20.17 and P20.18.)

CHAPTER TWENTY

Feedback Amplifier Design Based on j-Axis Response

20.1 Theory

We discussed in the preceding chapter methods of feedback amplifier design using root-locus plots. In this chapter we examine the problem from a somewhat different point of view, basing the design solely on the *measured* sinusoidal steady-state response of the *a* circuit. In essence, this method involves finding the steady-state loop transmission $af(j\omega)$ by measuring $a(j\omega)$ and either measuring or calculating $f(j\omega)$. From plots of the magnitude and phase of $af(j\omega)$, it is possible to estimate the steady-state response of the closed-loop amplifier, $A(j\omega)$. By direct analogy with the root-locus method, we then must decide if the design is satisfactory in terms of desensitivity and frequency or transient response. If the design is not satisfactory, we must again employ some form of compensation. An important advantage of this method of design is that it can be carried out *directly in terms of the measured frequency response* of the basic amplifier, without requiring any computer calculation of network natural frequencies.

20.1.1 Nyquist Criterion

It is essential to this method that we develop criteria for both stability and "satisfactory" transient response in terms of the steady-state response $af(j\omega)$ and $A(j\omega)$, just as we did in terms of poles and zeros in the root-locus method. We shall develop the criterion for stability in this section, and some criteria for satisfactory steady-state response and transient response in Section 20.1.2.

The basic stability criterion used in the root-locus discussion was that the natural frequencies of the feedback amplifier transfer function $A(s)$ had to be in the left half of the s plane for the feedback amplifier to be stable. The corresponding criterion in terms of the steady-state response is that the loop transmission $af(j\omega)$ must satisfy the so-called *Nyquist criterion* for amplifier stability. We shall develop the Nyquist test in terms of a plot of the log magnitude of $af(j\omega)$ versus the angle of $af(j\omega)$.

A plot of $\log|af(j\omega)|$ versus $\angle af(j\omega)$ for a typical amplifier is shown in Fig. 20.1a. The key idea of the Nyquist test is that *the $af(j\omega)$ locus plotted in Fig. 20.1a corresponds to the $j\omega$ axis in the s plane*, in the sense that a point moving up the $j\omega$ axis in Fig. 20.1b from minus infinity to plus infinity would move along the heavy contour in Fig. 20.1a in the indicated direction of increasing ω. The two plots are conformal: small squares in one plane appear as small squares in the other, and 90° turns in one plane appear as 90° turns in the other. Unfortunately, the conventional way of plotting $\log|af(j\omega)|$ versus $\angle af(j\omega)$, as shown in Fig. 20.1a, is *reversed* from that required for complete conformality, because positive angle is plotted to the right instead of the left. For this reason the angular relationships in the two plots are

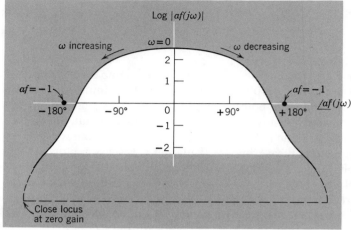

(a) Log magnitude versus phase for *af(jω)*

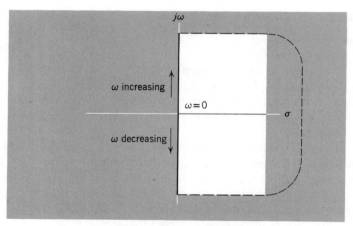

(b) *s*–plane, showing corresponding contour

Figure 20.1   Nyquist test.

reversed : +90° turns in one plane correspond with −90° turns in the other. For example, when we "walk" up the *jω* axis in the *s* plane in the direction of increasing *ω*, the right half plane always appears on our right. If we take a similar "walk" in the log magnitude versus angle plot in the direction of increasing *ω* along the corresponding path, that is, on the locus *af(jω)*, we must find the region corresponding to the right half of the *s* plane on our *left*. To emphasize the point, the two corresponding regions are shown in white in the figure. Thus the right half plane in the *s* plane corresponds to the portion of the Fig. 20.1*a inside the af(jω) locus.*

On the basis of our original definition,

$$A = \frac{a}{1 + af}$$

the poles of $A(s)$ occur where $af = -1$, as discussed in Section 19.2.1. Thus in terms of the log magnitude versus phase plots, the Nyquist criterion requires, to ensure the stability of $A(s)$, that the points $af = -1$ fall in that part of the plot which corresponds to the left half of the s plane. Specifically, *the points $af = -1$, that is, $|af| = -1$, $\angle af = \pm(2n + 1)\ 180°$, must lie outside of the $af(j\omega)$ locus.* On this basis, the plot in Fig. 20.1a shows that the amplifier in question is stable for the indicated value of midband loop transmission. (See Problem P20.1.)

We would expect from the root-locus discussion in Sections 19.1 and 19.2 that if $a_o f_o$ were increased, in all probability a pair of complex poles of $A(s)$ would be forced into the right half plane, and the amplifier would become unstable. Figure 20.1a indicates that such is indeed the case. Increasing $a_o f_o$ increases $|af(j\omega)|$ by a constant factor without changing $\angle af(j\omega)$, so that the locus in Fig. 20.1a under these circumstances is *transposed upward without change of shape,* because of the logarithmic coordinates. Clearly, such a transposition will cause the locus to encircle the points $af = -1$, indicating that the amplifier is now unstable.

For relatively simple situations, such as that in Fig. 20.1a in which the phase of $af(j\omega)$ is a monotonically decreasing function of ω, it can be seen from the figure that the Nyquist test reduces to the simple statement:

A feedback amplifier will be stable if the magnitude of $af(j\omega)$ is less than unity when the angle of $af(j\omega)$ is $\pm 180°$.

This simple test for stability can be applied directly to the usual plots of the magnitude and phase of $af(j\omega)$ versus ω (*Bode plots*) without ever forming log magnitude versus angle graphs as in Fig. 20.1a. To illustrate, the Bode plots for the same amplifier graphed in Fig. 20.1a are shown in Fig. 20.2. Because $|af(j\omega)|$ is less than 1 at $\omega = 56$, the frequency where $\angle af(j\omega) = -180°$, we conclude, as before, that the complete feedback amplifier will be stable.[1]

20.1.2 Criteria for Acceptable Response

In the root-locus discussion (Section 19.2.3) we pointed out that even though the poles and zeros of $A(s)$ uniquely determine (within a constant) the amplifier steady-state and transient response, it is necessary for ease of calculation to establish simpler criteria for acceptable response. Thus for acceptable transient response, we required that complex poles lie below the 45° radial lines (Q less than 0.707), and for acceptable frequency response we were willing to allow complex poles out to the 60° radial lines (Q of 1).

---

[1] Bode plots with nonmonotonic phase are discussed in Reference 20.1.

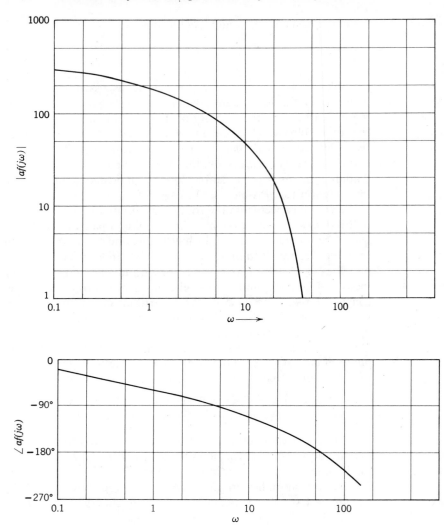

Figure 20.2   Bode plot for the amplifier graphed in Fig. 20.1a.

In the present discussion in terms of steady-state response, a similar situation pertains. The steady-state response $a(j\omega)$ and $f(j\omega)$ together uniquely determine the closed-loop steady-state frequency response $A(j\omega)$. A relatively simple graphical technique for finding the closed-loop frequency response $A(j\omega)$ is to plot the log magnitude versus phase of $af(j\omega)$, as in Fig. 20.1a, and then calculate $A(j\omega)$ by means of an overlay called a Nichols chart,[2] shown in simplified form in Fig. 20.3. This chart is formed by plotting

---

[2] The reader is referred to any standard text on feedback for more information.

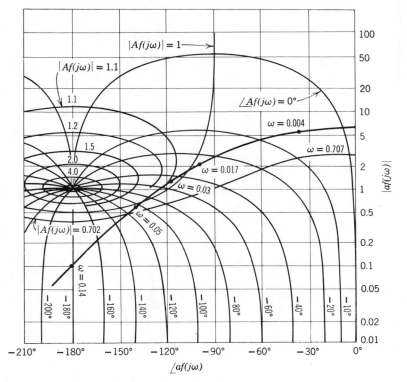

Figure 20.3 Nichols chart. Contour is for amplifier in Section 20.2.

the constant-magnitude and constant-phase contours of the function

$$Af(j\omega) = \frac{af(j\omega)}{1 + af(j\omega)}$$

on a rectangular grid whose coordinates are the magnitude and phase of $af(j\omega)$. Thus, knowing $af(j\omega)$, we can use the chart to find $Af(j\omega)$, and hence $A(j\omega)$.

Unfortunately, there is no simple way of determining the closed-loop *transient* response from $af(j\omega)$. Thus we are forced to use approximate criteria on $af(j\omega)$ to ensure both acceptable steady-state response and acceptable transient response. Two common criteria are *gain and phase margins* and *maximum amount of peaking of the steady-state response.*

The nearness of approach of the $af(j\omega)$ contour in Fig. 20.1a to the $af = -1$ points is clearly a measure of the degree of stability of the feedback amplifier. The "gain margin" and "phase margin," shown on both the log magnitude versus phase plot and the corresponding Bode plot in Fig. 20.4, are criteria commonly used to describe this nearness of approach. The gain margin is defined as $1/|af(j\omega)|$ calculated at the frequency where $\angle af(j\omega)$ is $\pm 180°$, hence

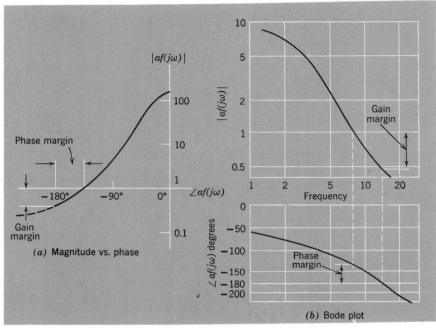

Figure 20.4 Gain and phase margins.

for this circuit the gain margin is 2. The phase margin is $180° - |\angle af(j\omega)|$, calculated at the frequency where $|af(j\omega)| = 1$, which for this locus is 45°.

For practical amplifiers, a frequently-encountered specification is that the gain margin be at least 4 and the phase margin be at least 60°. To some extent the size of these margins is indicative of the stability of the amplifier and the amount of overshoot in the step response.

Another criterion often used to ensure acceptable transient response is that the closed-loop amplifier response $|A(j\omega)|$ have only a small peak in it. From Figs. 19.3 and 19.4 it is clear that for a simple two-pole function, this criterion is identical to a specification on the pole locations. For more complicated functions, the relationship becomes correspondingly more complicated. Nonetheless, an often-used specification to ensure satisfactory transient response is that the peak of the frequency response $|A(j\omega)|$ be less than a factor of 1.1 above the midfrequency response. A factor such as this obviously depends to a great extent on the intended application. For example, in servo systems, factors as large as 1.3 or 1.5 are sometimes used.

20.2 Example of *j*-Axis Calculations
20.2.1 Initial Design

To illustrate feedback amplifier calculations in terms of *j*-axis response, let us examine the loop-loop feedback amplifier in Fig. 20.5a in these terms; we have chosen to reexamine the amplifier discussed in Section 19.3.1 to

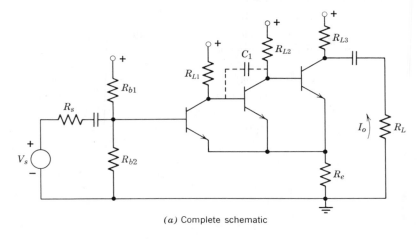

(a) Complete schematic

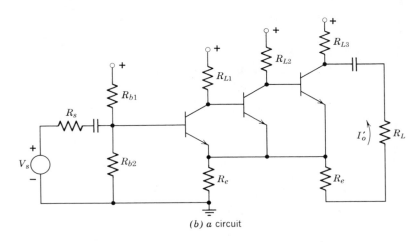

(b) a circuit

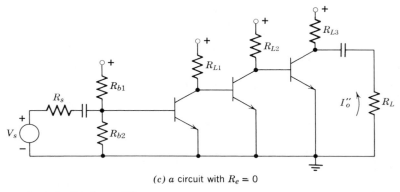

(c) a circuit with $R_e = 0$

Figure 20.5 Loop-loop feedback amplifier.

facilitate comparison between the root-locus and *j*-axis design methods. To be strictly correct, we should base the present design on the measured sinusoidal response $a(j\omega) = I'_o/V_s$ of the *a* circuit Fig. 20.5*b* (derived from Fig. 20.5*a* by the methods discussed in Section 18.4). Unfortunately, we do not as yet know the value of the feedback resistor R_e. Thus our only course of action is to assume that the value of R_e will be sufficiently small that the measured response I''_o/V_s of the basic amplifier, source, and load (Fig. 20.5*c*) will be almost identical to the *a*-circuit response. The response plot I''_o/V_s

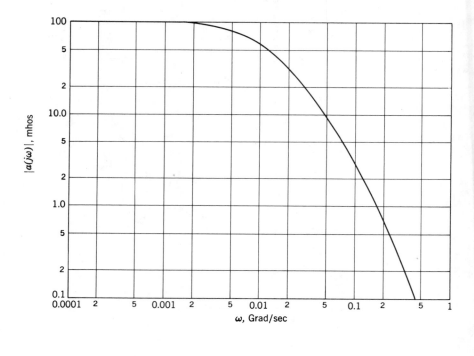

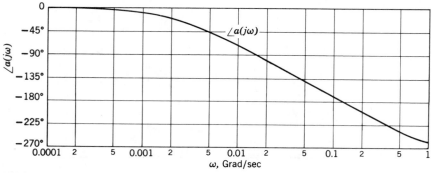

Figure 20.6   Measured response for the circuit in Fig. 20.5*c*.

(magnitude and phase versus frequency) is shown in Fig. 20.6.[3] The plots have been labeled as $|a(j\omega)|$ and $\angle a(j\omega)$, in accordance with the assumption above, in spite of the fact that we do not know the value of R_e.

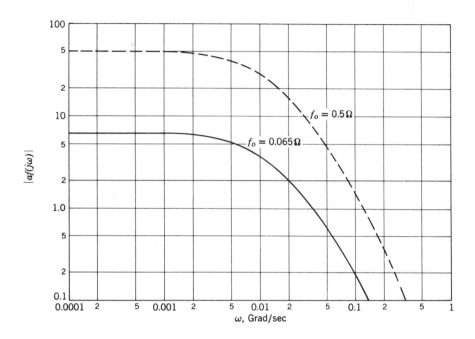

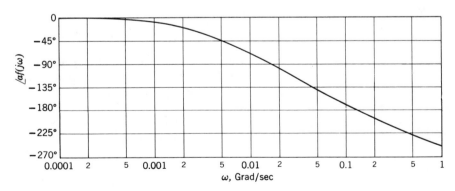

Figure 20.7   Bode plot of $af(j\omega)$ for the amplifier in Fig. 20.5.

[3] We cheated here. This is not a measured response as it should be; rather it was calculated from the poles of $A(s)$ for $R_e = 0$ (See Table 19.7), information that is "not available" according to our present ground rules. We take this liberty to facilitate comparison of the two solutions.

Let us first calculate the amount of midband feedback that can be applied while still meeting the following gain and phase margin specifications:

$$\text{gain margin} = 4$$

$$\text{phase margin} = 60°$$

To check for stability, gain margin, and so on, we need a plot of $af(j\omega)$. In this amplifier, $f(j\omega) = R_e$; hence $|af(j\omega)|$ is identical to $|a(j\omega)|$ except for a scale factor, and $\angle af(j\omega)$ is identical to $\angle a(j\omega)$. Thus in this simple case we could obtain $af(j\omega)$ without replotting; all we have to do is add a new vertical scale to the magnitude plot. However, to reduce confusion in this initial example, let us plot $af(j\omega)$ in a separate figure (Fig. 20.7).

The solid curve in Fig. 20.7 is the Bode plot drawn to yield a phase margin of 60°: at the frequency where $|af(j\omega)| = 1$, $\angle af(j\omega)$ is $-120°$. To generate the magnitude plot, we had to first plot the phase and then find the appropriate value of $a_o f_o$ to achieve the desired phase margin. From the phase curve in Fig. 20.7 we note that when $\angle af(j\omega)$ [here equal to $\angle a(j\omega)$] is $-120°$, $\omega = 0.035$ Grad/sec. Thus we must adjust $|af(j\omega)|$ to be unity at this frequency. From Fig. 20.6, at $\omega = 0.035$,

$$|a(j\omega)| = 15.5$$

To meet the phase margin specification,

$$15.5 f_o = 1$$

$$f_o = R_e = \frac{1}{15.5}$$

$$= 0.065 \text{ ohm}$$

and the midband loop transmission can be

$$a_o f_o = (100)(0.065) = 6.5$$

These figures were used as the basis for the magnitude plot in Fig. 20.7. A little thought will show that for this amplifier the phase margin is the controlling criterion; hence the corresponding design based on the gain margin will be left to the problems (see Problems P20.2 and P20.3).

Figure 20.8 shows the closed-loop response $A(j\omega)$, obtained either by a point-by-point calculation using Fig. 20.7 and the basic feedback relation

$$A(j\omega) = \frac{a(j\omega)}{1 + af(j\omega)} \tag{20.1}$$

or by plotting $af(j\omega)$ on a Nichols chart. To facilitate the latter computation, the $af(j\omega)$ contour has been added to the Nichols chart in Fig. 20.3. Note that the values read off the overlay correspond to $|Af(j\omega)|$ and thus must be

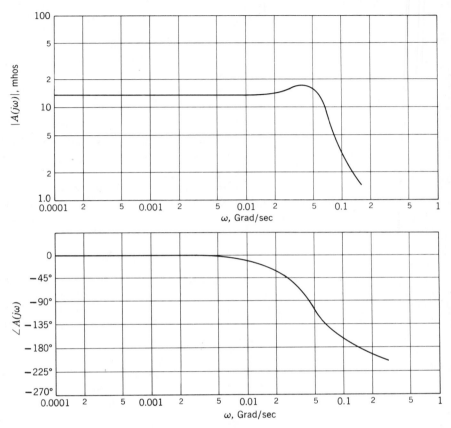

Figure 20.8 Closed-loop response $A(j\omega)$ for the amplifier in Fig. 20.5. $R_e = 0.065$ ohm.

divided by $R_e = 0.065$ ohm to obtain $|I_o/V_s|$. Because of the large phase margin, the overall response is quite flat. The plot of $A(j\omega)$ for $R_e = 0.065$ ohm compares favorably with the corresponding information in Section 19.3.1, Table 19.7.

A quick estimate of the closed-loop bandwidth can be made without actually plotting $A(j\omega)$. Note first that Eq. 20.1 can be rewritten as

$$A(j\omega) = \frac{1}{f(j\omega)}\left[\frac{af(j\omega)}{1 + af(j\omega)}\right]$$ (20.2)

At the phase margin frequency, we know that by definition for a 60° phase margin

$$af(j\omega) = 1\angle - 120°$$

Substituting into Eq. 20.2 and taking magnitudes, we obtain

$$|A(j\omega)| = \left| \frac{1}{f(j\omega)} \left(\frac{1\angle -120°}{1 + 1\angle -120°} \right) \right|$$

$$= \left| \frac{1}{f(j\omega)} \right| \tag{20.3}$$

Thus for frequency-independent feedback and a 60° phase margin, *the closed-loop gain* $|A(j\omega)|$ *is substantially constant out to the phase margin frequency.* In the present example, therefore, we know without plotting $A(j\omega)$ that the upper 0.707 frequency of the complete feedback amplifier is in excess of 0.035 Grad/sec, a factor of 5 broader than the basic amplifier.

Suppose now that we wish to increase the feedback by an order of magnitude to meet the original specification on desensitivity, namely $a_o f_o = 50$. Because $a_o = 100$ mhos, this requires that

$$R_e = f_o = 0.5 \text{ ohm}$$

Because we have only resistive feedback, increasing the midband loop transmission to 50 merely translates the amplitude curve vertically without changing its shape, as shown in Fig. 20.7. The Nyquist test on this new locus indicates that the amplifier is just barely stable, because $|af(j\omega)|$ is only slightly less than unity for $\angle af(j\omega) = -180°$ (this result again checks with the corresponding information in Table 19.7).

The plots of $af(j\omega)$ in Fig. 20.7 offer further proof that the very high poles of $af(s)$ do not materially influence the feedback calculations. These poles will influence the shape of $af(j\omega)$ at very high frequencies. However, in a multistage feedback amplifier the lower poles will be the dominant factors in the transfer function in the critical frequency range where $|af|$ is nearly unity and $\angle af$ is nearly 180°. The very high poles, on the other hand, will have little effect in this range. This fact is further justification for the neglect of the very high poles in the root-locus calculations in Chapter 19.

20.2.2   Compensation: Reducing High-Frequency Phase Shift

It is clear from Fig. 20.7 that if the amplifier in Fig. 20.5 has R_e equal to 0.5 ohm as required to meet the specification, the gain margin and phase margin will be very inadequate. (See Problem P20.4.) Thus we expect a large peak in the closed-loop response $A(j\omega)$ in the vicinity of the critical frequency where $|af| \simeq 1$ and $\angle af \simeq -180°$, that is, at $\omega = 0.14$ Grad/sec. (See Problems P20.5 and P20.6.) Hence to meet the specifications and still have a reasonably flat frequency response, we must somehow apply compensation to either the amplifier or the feedback network.

The essential idea of compensation, stated in terms of plots of $af(j\omega)$ versus ω, is to reshape the plots so that $|af|$ is appreciably less than unity when $\angle af = \pm 180°$. However, for simple *RLC* circuits the magnitude and phase functions are closely related, so that unfortunately we do not have independent control of $|af|$ and $\angle af$. To illustrate this problem, let us try to compensate the amplifier in Fig. 20.5a by reducing the phase shift of $af(j\omega)$ in the vicinity of the critical frequency $\omega \simeq 0.14$ Grad/sec, where the phase is presently $-180°$. One way of doing this is to add a small inductor in series with R_e, to introduce a *positive phase shift* angle in $f(j\omega)$.

Recall from Section 19.3.1. that with the added inductor, f becomes

$$f(j\omega) = \frac{V_t}{I'_o} = R_e + j\omega L \tag{20.4}$$

Thus $\angle f(j\omega)$ increases with frequency, eventually reaching $+90°$, as shown in Fig. 20.9, a normalized plot of Eq. 20.4. This positive phase shift will

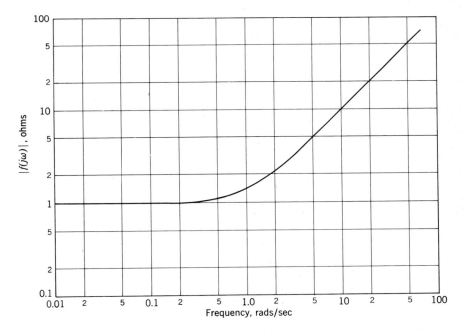

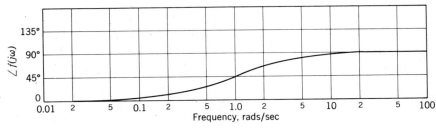

Figure 20.9   Normalized plot of $f(j\omega) = R_e + j\omega L$, assuming $R_e = 1$ ohm, $L = 1$ henry.

obviously have a beneficial effect on the Bode plot because now when we form $\angle af(j\omega)$ (by adding the angle plots in Figs. 20.6 and 20.9) we can *reduce* the phase shift in the vicinity of the critical frequency $\omega \simeq 0.14$ Grad/sec. However, the problem is not quite this simple. Note from Fig. 20.9 that the *magnitude of $f(j\omega)$ also increases* with frequency, and this is a distinct disadvantage. We already have too much gain at $\omega = 0.14$; if anything, we would like to *reduce* $|af(j\omega)|$ in this range. Thus simple compensating networks of the type being discussed here, because they do not provide independent control of amplitude and phase, tend to improve $\angle af(j\omega)$ while making $|af(j\omega)|$ worse, or vice versa. On this basis, too much compensation can be just as disastrous as too little, so that we must design compensating networks with some care.

One important property of simple *RL* and *RC* networks is very helpful in the design of compensating networks: as can be seen from the normalized plot in Fig. 20.9, the phase of this *RL* circuit changes by 45°, as ω increases from zero to one, while the amplitude changes only from 1 to 1.41. We can take advantage of this fact by choosing L such that the 45° phase shift occurs at $\omega = 0.14$ Grad/sec, so that the undesired increase in amplitude will be small in the vicinity of the critical frequency. From Eq. 20.4, this requires that

$$L = \frac{R_e}{\omega} = \frac{0.5}{0.14 \times 10^9}$$

$$= 3.6 \times 10^{-3} \, \mu\text{h}$$

A Bode plot for this value of L is shown in Fig. 20.10 (solid line). This can be derived directly from Figs. 20.6 and 20.9 by multiplying the frequency scale in Fig. 20.9 (i.e., translating the logarithmic scale) by a factor of 0.14 and then adding the logarithmic magnitudes of the two amplitude plots and the phases. (Note that we have tacitly assumed in so doing that the *a*-circuit response $a(j\omega)$ does not change significantly as a result of the series loading effect of L on the input and output.) As predicted above, the inductor has caused a minor increase in gain magnitude at the critical frequency, but has brought about a major reduction in phase shift. Specifically, the compensation has increased the phase margin from 6 to 45°.

With this phase margin, the closed loop response $|A(j\omega)|$ will have a small hump in it, and, on the basis of Eq. 20.3, the upper 0.707 frequency will be somewhat in excess of 0.14 Grad/sec, a factor of 5 improvement over the uncompensated design. These results are in substantial agreement with those of Section 19.3.1. (See Problem P20.7.)

20.2.3   Compensation: Adding a Capacitor to the Basic Amplifier

A second method of compensation is to add a large capacitor to the basic amplifier, as indicated by the dotted lines in Fig. 20.5a. Hopefully, such a modification will reduce $|af(j\omega)|$ in the vicinity of the critical frequency, $\omega = 0.14$ Grad/sec, without unduly increasing the phase shift.

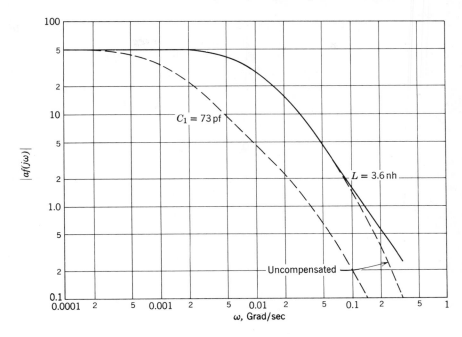

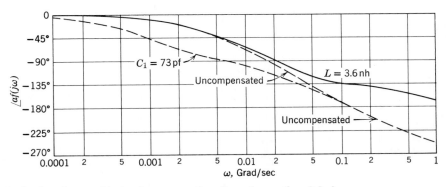

Figure 20.10 Bode plots for two kinds of compensation. In each case $f_o = 0.5$ ohm.

Let us initially oversimplify the problem by arbitrarily assuming that af is

$$af(s) = \frac{a_o f_o}{(s + 1)(s + 1)(s + 1)} \tag{20.5}$$

and that adding the capacitor C_1 changes the transfer function to

$$af(s) = \frac{a_o f_o}{(s + 1)(s + 1)(R_T C_1 s + 1)} \tag{20.6}$$

Specifically, we are assuming that adding C_1 moves one pole down in frequency but leaves the other two poles of our hypothetical a circuit unchanged. The Bode plot for Eq. 20.5, assuming that $a_o f_o = 10$, is shown by the solid curves in Fig. 20.11. For this value of midband loop transmission, the plot shows that the amplifier is unstable (see Problem P20.8).

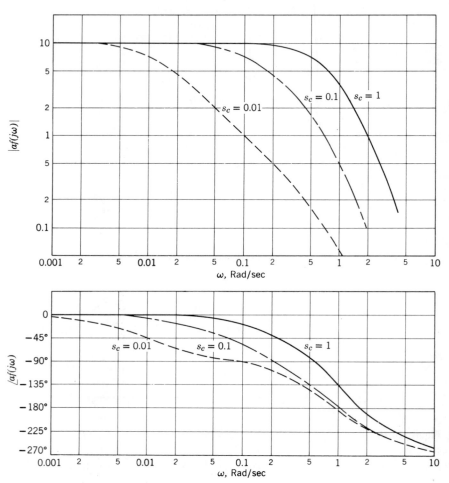

Figure 20.11   Bode plot for Eqs. 20.5 and 20.6.

To compensate the amplifier, we add capacitor C_1, thereby producing a *dominant pole* at $s_c = -1/R_T C_1$ according to Eq. 20.6. The Bode plots for two possible choices of C_1 are shown in Fig. 20.11 by dashed lines. For $s_c = -0.1$, the amplifier is stable and has a gain margin of 2.5. For $s_c = 0.01$, the gain margin has been increased to 20.

The selection of C_1 is straightforward in this simple case. Recall first that producing a dominant pole by adding a large capacitance to the a circuit has a distinct disadvantage. It narrows the bandwidth of the a circuit and thus reduces the bandwidth over which the desensitivity of the complete feedback amplifier is effective. Therefore, we want to *add as small a capacitor as possible*. Next we note that in many cases the phase shift contributed by the dominant pole at the critical frequency is $-90°$ because it is usually necessary to have the dominant pole at least in order of magnitude below the critical frequency. Suppose, then, that we want a gain margin of 4. The compensated $af(j\omega)$ will have $-180°$ phase shift at $\omega = 1$: $-90°$ from the dominant pole and $-45°$ from each of the other two poles, s_a and s_b. We see from the original Bode plot that (solid lines in Fig. 20.11) that $|af(j\omega)|$ for the two high poles only will equal 5 at $\omega = 1$, so that to achieve the gain margin of 4, we need to decrease the amplitude at $\omega = 1$ by a factor of 20. The asymptotic amplitude of a single-pole function falls off linearly with frequency; hence placing the dominant pole a factor of 20 below the critical frequency, that is, setting $s_c = -1/20$, or $R_T C_1 = 20$, will give the required gain margin. (See Problem P20.9.)

Now let us return to the actual transistor feedback amplifier (Fig. 20.5a). As suggested in Section 19.2.5, an appropriate place to add a capacitor to the a circuit is between collector and base of the second transistor (Fig. 20.5a) because again for this amplifier, the second transistor has the largest open-circuit time constants. (See Problem P20.10.) We also know from Section 19.2.5 that if C_1 is made large enough, it produces a dominant pole in $a(s)$, of value

$$s_{\text{low}} \simeq -\frac{1}{R_T C_1} \tag{20.7}$$

where R_T is the open-circuit resistance facing C_1. The problem now is that the other five poles of $a(s)$ will surely move when we add C_1, as we saw in Section 19.2.5. In terms of the j-axis response, this means that the Bode plot of $af(j\omega)$ will change in a more complicated manner than that produced by the motion of one pole alone. An experimental cut-and-try approach makes excellent sense in this case, but the Bode plots can be used to find a first-cut value for C_1.

To illustrate, let us find an approximate value for C_1, assuming that we again want a desensitivity of 50 ($R_e = 0.5$ ohm) and a phase margin of $45°$. We have added capacitance to the stage that already has the largest open-circuit time constants, to ensure that we move down the *lowest* pole of the uncompensated amplifier, as explained in Section 19.2.5. Thus to a first approximation we can *subtract out* the effect of the lowest pole in the uncompensated $a(j\omega)$ and then add it back in at a much lower frequency. To this end, we estimate the location of the lowest pole by finding the 0.707 frequency of the uncompensated $af(j\omega)$ locus. From Fig. 20.10 (or Fig. 20.7), ω_h is approximately 0.007 Grad/sec. Thus we assume that the lowest pole is at $s = -0.007 \text{ nsec}^{-1}$ and subtract from $af(j\omega)$ a single-pole function,

$$P(j\omega) = \frac{1}{1 + j\omega/0.007} \tag{20.8}$$

The resulting function $a'f(j\omega)$ is plotted in Fig. 20.12 (see Problem P20.11). Note that in forming $a'f(j\omega)$ we are making the *totally unjustified* approximation that the other five poles of $a(j\omega)$ do not move when C_1 is added.

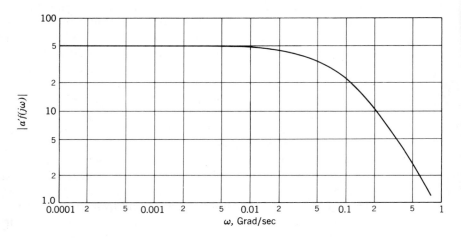

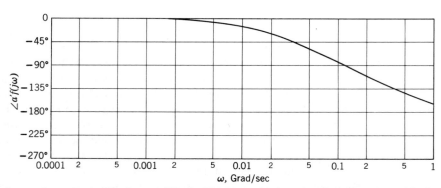

Figure 20.12   Approximate Bode plot for amplifier in Fig. 20.5, with lowest pole removed graphically.

For a 45° phase margin, the compensated amplifier must have $\angle af(j\omega)$ $= -135°$ when $|af(j\omega)|$ is unity. As explained above, we can expect a contribution of $-90°$ from the dominant pole. Thus the critical frequency is where the phase in Fig. 20.12 is $-45°$. This occurs at $\omega = 0.037$ Grad/sec. At this frequency, the magnitude in Fig. 20.12 is 39, so that C_1 must be chosen such that the dominant pole decreases $|af|$ by a factor of 39 at this point. Thus the dominant pole must be at

$$s_{low} = \frac{-0.037}{39} = -0.95 \times 10^{-3} \text{ nsec}^{-1}$$

For this amplifier, the resistance R_T facing capacitor C_1 in Fig. 20.5a turns out to be 14.3 kohms (see Problem P16.16). Hence, from Eq. 20.7,

$$C_1 = \frac{1}{R_T|s_{low}|}$$

$$= \frac{1}{14.3 \times 0.95 \times 10^{-3}}$$

$$= 73 \text{ pf}$$

The Bode plot of the compensated $af(j\omega)$ for this solution has been added to Fig. 20.10 to facilitate comparison of the two designs involving compensation. We have indeed achieved the required 45° phase margin by adding the 73-pf capacitor, but note that the bandwidth of the a circuit is substantially reduced by so doing. Thus the desensitivity will be effective over a smaller bandwidth than in the other designs.

The closed-loop response of the amplifier with C_1 added will be very similar to that of the uncompensated amplier with $R_e = 0.065$ ohm, as can be verified by comparing the Bode plots for these two designs (Figs. 20.10 and 20.7). In both cases we designed for $A_o = 2$ mhos, and in the vicinity of the critical frequency the plots are almost identical, so that we expect identical closed-loop responses. However, because $a_o f_o$ is much larger in the compensated amplifier, we obtain better midfrequency desensitivity in this case.

Pertinent parameters of the three designs discussed in this section are summarized in Table 20.1. Note in particular that for the design with C_1 added to the basic amplifier, the bandwidth of the compensated $af(j\omega)$ and the overall closed-loop bandwidth $A(j\omega)$ are substantially less than for the design involving adding a zero to the feedback network. (See Problem P20.12.)

Table 20.1 Comparison of the three amplifier designs discussed in Sec. 20.2

Design	Desensitivity	Upper Band Edge of $A(j\omega)$ (Closed-Loop Bandwidth)	Upper Band Edge of $af(j\omega)$
Uncompensated			
$R_e = 0.065$ ohm	6.5	0.058 Grad/sec	0.007 Grad/sec
Compensated			
$R_e = 0.5$ ohm, $L = 3.6$ nh	50	0.3	0.007
$R_e = 0.5$ ohm, $C_1 = 73$ pf	50	0.058	0.00095

20.3   Instability at Low Frequencies

As a final example of stability calculations, we examine the problem of low-frequency instability in a simple three-stage RC-coupled feedback amplifier (Fig. 20.13). (Recognize that the direct-coupled circuit of Fig. 19.16 is prefer-

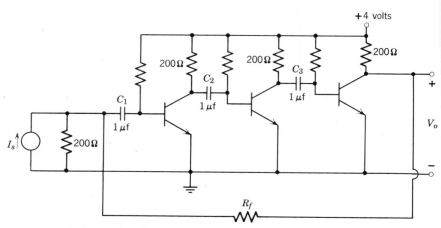

Figure 20.13   Three-stage amplifier with RC coupling (biasing oversimplified).

able to this circuit for many reasons). This simple circuit has three low-frequency poles, each of which depends on only one capacitor. It is entirely possible, therefore, for these three poles to be coincident, in which case the low-frequency a transfer function might be (in units of microfarads, kilohms, and milliseconds)

$$a(s) = \frac{V'_o}{I_s} = \frac{a_o s^3}{(s+1)(s+1)(s+1)} \tag{20.9}$$

(see Problem P20.13). The magnitude and phase of the transfer function $a(j\omega)$ (measured or calculated), assuming that $a_o = -1000$ kohm, is shown in Fig. 20.14. For this type of feedback, a_o is always negative; hence the plot shows $a(j\omega)$ approaching $-180°$ at midband.

Suppose that we wish to design the feedback amplifier to have a midband desensitivity of about 100. Then $a_o f_o = 100$, so

$$f_o = -\frac{1}{R_f} = \frac{100}{-1000} = -0.1 \text{ mmho}$$

$$R_f = 10 \text{ kohm}$$

Even if we do not encounter high-frequency stability problems with this much feedback, the Bode plot of $af(j\omega)$ at low frequencies (Fig. 20.15) shows that the amplifier is *completely unstable*[4] (see Problem P20.14).

---

[4] Note that regardless of minus or plus signs in a_o and f_o, and regardless of whether we are analyzing the high-frequency or the low-frequency circuit, the *midband* $a_o f_o$ must be *positive for negative feedback*, as we have defined it. Thus by definition, for negative feedback, $\angle a_o f_o = 0$.

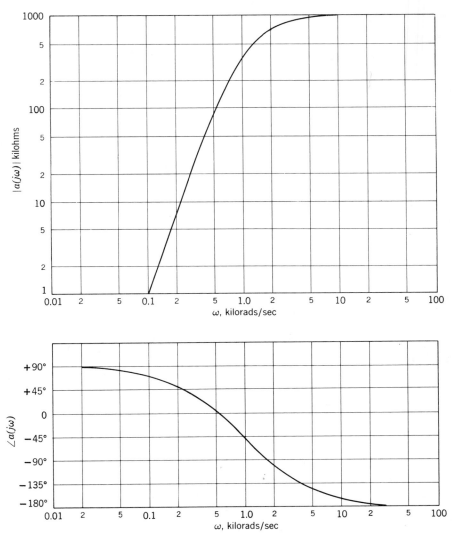

Figure 20.14   Low-frequency a-circuit response of the amplifier in Fig. 20.13.

Because the low-frequency incremental circuits for feedback amplifiers are so much simpler than the corresponding high-frequency circuits, and because we have direct access to the capacitors in the low-frequency circuit, it is usually most appropriate to "compensate" low-frequency circuits by directly changing capacitor sizes, rather than adding new compensating elements. In this case we compensate by increasing the size of two of the capacitors, thereby moving two of the poles lower down in frequency and leaving the third pole at $s = -1$ as the *dominant low-frequency pole*. An appropriately compensated Bode plot that gives a gain margin of 4 has been

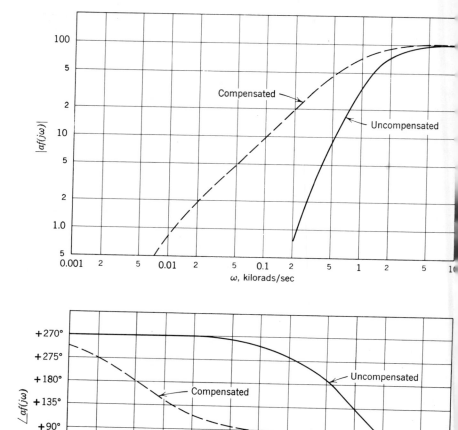

Figure 20.15   Bode plot for the amplifier in Fig. 20.13.

added to Fig. 20.15. The procedure for finding the capacitor values to give this plot is identical in principle to that discussed in the preceding section and will not be further elaborated here (see Problem P20.15).

Any of the three-stage direct-coupled feedback amplifiers discussed in this and the preceding chapters will also have low-frequency stability problems. The energy-storage elements involved are the input coupling capacitor, the bypass capacitor in the bias network (see, for example, Fig. 19.16), and any other coupling and bypass capacitors in the circuit. These stability problems can always be solved by changing the size of some of the capacitors (see Problem P20.16).

References

20.1   R. D. Thornton et al., *Multistage Transistor Circuits*, Wiley, New York, 1965.

Problems

P20.1   To illustrate the difference between Fig. 20.1 and the more conventional Nyquist test, draw the polar plot of $af(j\omega)$ to form a true Nyquist plot, obtaining values from Fig. 20.1 or Fig. 20.2. Indicate the region of the polar plot that corresponds to the right half plane. Is the amplifier stable?

P20.2   Rework the design example in Section 20.2.1 to find the value of midband loop transmission that can be used before the gain margin of 4 is exceeded. Solve the problem by forming a new Bode plot from Fig. 20.6. (See page 736.) Does the gain margin or the phase margin control the design?

P20.3   Find directly from Fig. 20.6, *without* replotting, the values of f_o and $a_o f_o$ for the amplifier in Section 20.2.1 which yield a gain margin of 4. (See page 736.)

P20.4   Calculate from Fig. 20.7 the gain and phase margins of the amplifier in Fig. 20.5a, assuming $R_e = 0.5$ ohm. (See page 738.)

P20.5   Plot the closed-loop response $A(j\omega)$ for the amplifier in Fig. 20.5a, assuming $R_e = 0.5$ ohm. Solve either by replotting $af(j\omega)$ from Fig. 20.7 on the Nichols chart (Fig. 20.3) or by using Eq. 20.1 and Fig. 20.7. (See page 738.)

P20.6   Compare the response $A(j\omega)$ for the amplifier in Fig. 20.5 with $R_e = 0.5$ ohm (Problem P20.5) to the corresponding natural-frequency information in Table 19.7 and comment. (See page 738.)

P20.7   Use the data in Fig. 20.10 for $af(j\omega)$ with inductive compensation (high-frequency zero in f) to find $A(j\omega)$. This can be done by direct computation using Eq. 20.1 or via a Nichols chart (Fig. 20.3). Compare the results with the corresponding natural-frequency information in Section 19.3.1. (See page 740.)

P20.8   Plot the log magnitude versus angle for the function $af(j\omega)$ in Eq. 20.5, assuming $a_o f_o = 10$. By comparing this plot to Fig. 20.1, decide whether the amplifier is stable. Explain. (See page 742.)

P20.9   Draw the Bode plot for Eq. 20.6, assuming $a_o f_o = 10$ and $R_T C_1 = 20$. That is, assume that the amplifier in Fig. 20.5a has been compensated by lowering one pole. Verify that the amplifier now has a gain margin of 4. (See page 743.)

P20.10   Check the base-to-collector open-circuit time constants for the three transistors in Fig. 20.5b, assuming $\beta_o = 50$, $r_\pi = 250$ ohms, $r_x = 25$

ohms, $R_s = 1000$ ohms, $R_L = 50$ ohms, and $R_e = 0.5$ ohm. Neglect all other resistors. Where is the best place to add a compensating capacitor C_1? (See page 743.)

P20.11 Graphically remove a pole at $s = -0.007$ nsec^{-1} from the Bode plot of $af(j\omega)$ in Fig. 20.10 (uncompensated). Compare your answer to Fig. 20.12. (See page 744.)

P20.12 Calculate the upper band-edge frequency ω_h for the loop transmission $af(j\omega)$ in the C_1-compensated amplifier, Fig. 20.5 and Section 20.2.3. Also calculate the upper band edge for $A(j\omega)$. Use Fig. 20.10. Check your results against Table 20.1.

P20.13 Calculate in literal form the low-frequency a circuit transfer function for the feedback amplifier in Fig. 20.13. Hence verify the *form* of Eq. 20.9. (See page 746.)

P20.14 What is the maximum value of midband loop transmission for the amplifier in Fig. 20.13 which will yield a low-frequency gain margin of 5. (See page 746.)

P20.15 Find appropriate new values for two of the coupling capacitors in Fig. 20.13 to meet the original specifications of $a_o f_o = 100$, with a phase margin of 60°. (See page 748.)

P20.16 Complete the design of the amplifier in Section 16.1, Fig. 16.6, by choosing values of coupling, bypass, and decoupling capacitors so that the low-frequency phase margin will be 60°. (See page 748.)

P20.17 Solve Problem P20.15 from the root-locus point of view, designing so that no low-frequency poles of $A(s)$ have a Q greater than unity.

P20.18 Solve Problem P20.16 from the root-locus point of view, designing so that no low-frequency poles of $A(s)$ have a Q greater than unity.

P20.19 The following data were taken on an amplifier:

f(MHz)	$|a|$	$\angle a$
0	1000	0°
0.1	800	45°
0.3	450	$-100°$
1.0	150	$-150°$
3.0	15	$-200°$
10.0	1	$-250°$

What is the maximum amount of resistive feedback f_o that can be applied around this amplifier (*a*) without instability and (*b*) while still retaining "reasonable" frequency response?

P20.20 Compensate the amplifier of Problem P20.19 in order to obtain a desensitivity of 100 and still have "acceptable" frequency response.

CHAPTER TWENTY-ONE

Operation of Bipolar Transistors outside the Active Region

21.1 Models for Arbitrary Junction Voltages

The models for bipolar transistors that we developed earlier are all limited in the sense that they describe transistors that are operating as control valves in the active region, that is, with forward-biased emitter and reverse-biased collector. This limitation applies not only to the incremental models of Chapter 11, but also to the total-signal models developed in Chapters 7 and 8. In all cases, our analysis of the internal physical behavior of the device has been based on the explicit conditions that the collector junction be reverse-biased and the emitter junction forward-biased. In some transistor applications (particularly those in which the transistor is used as a switch rather than a continuously-controllable power modulator), the collector junction is forward-biased at least part of the time. Although incremental behavior in this operating condition is of little practical interest, the relationships among the total terminal variables are important. To deal with such situations, we must extend the total-signal models of Sections 7.3 and 8.1 to permit arbitrary collector-to-base and emitter-to-base voltages. This extension is simple and straightforward for low-injection conditions. Once again, we base our analysis on a *pnp* structure and then extend our results to include *npn* transistors as well.

21.1.1 Charge Stores in the Neutral Base Region

In developing circuit models that apply with arbitrary junction voltages, we assume that the junction voltages are changing slowly enough so that the distribution of excess carriers in the neutral base region changes as a succession of static distributions. That is, we assume that the excess-carrier distribution changes slowly enough so that if a motion picture were made of the changing charge distribution, each frame in the sequence would be indistinguishable from a still picture of an appropriate *static* distribution. Furthermore, the particular static distribution to which a certain frame in the motion picture corresponds is that which would result if the emitter-to-base voltage were stationary at the instantaneous value that existed when the frame was exposed. Thus in evaluating the terminal currents we need consider only static distributions of excess charge.

This approximation is the same as that made in Section 8.1, where we developed a charge-control model that was valid only in the active region. Just as we found there, the assumption that the dynamic excess-carrier distribution is *quasi-static*, that is, changes as a succession of static distributions, is valid if the instantaneous base current is small compared with either the instantaneous emitter current or the instantaneous collector current. This condition on the currents is met in most circuit applications of bipolar transistors simply because the circuit usually must provide a reasonable current gain from base to emitter or collector.

The quasi-static distribution of excess charge in the base is governed by the two junction voltages. The excess-carrier concentration at the edge of each space-charge layer is related to the corresponding junction voltage by a Boltzmann relation. Thus the excess concentration at the emitter edge of the base ($x = 0$) in a *pnp* transistor is

$$p_b'(0) = p_{bo}(e^{qv_{EB}/kT} - 1) \tag{21.1a}$$

where p_{bo} denotes the equilibrium minority-carrier concentration in the uniform base region and v_{EB} the instantaneous emitter-to-base voltage. Similarly, the excess-carrier concentration at the collector edge of the base (at $x = W$) is

$$p_b'(W) = p_{bo}(e^{qv_{CB}/kT} - 1) \tag{21.1b}$$

where v_{CB} denotes the instantaneous collector-to-base voltage.

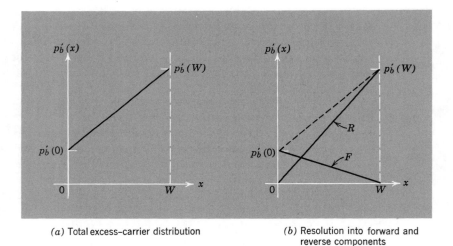

(a) Total excess–carrier distribution

(b) Resolution into forward and reverse components

Figure 21.1   Base-region excess-carrier distribution for forward bias on both junctions.

The quasi-static excess-carrier distribution in the base that obtains with forward bias on *both* emitter and collector junctions is shown in Fig. 21.1a. The positive excess-carrier concentration at the edge of each space-charge layer reflects the fact that each junction is forward-biased. The distribution is linear because minority carriers move longitudinally in the base solely by diffusion and because there is negligible recombination in the base. Consequently, the minority-carrier current density must be approximately independent of position in the base; this requires a constant concentration gradient which, in turn, implies a linear distribution.

The constant longitudinal minority-carrier diffusion current associated with the linear distribution in Fig. 21.1*a* flows from the collector to the emitter, which is opposite to the direction associated with active-region behavior. In circuit terms, i_E is negative and i_C is positive for the distribution illustrated. This current flows from collector to emitter because the forward bias on the collector junction exceeds the forward bias on the emitter junction, that is, $p_b'(W) > p_b'(0)$. If the emitter were more forward-biased than the collector, the distribution would tilt downward toward the collector and the minority-carrier current flow would be reversed.

21.1.2   Resolution into Forward and Reverse Components

The trapezoidal base-region excess-carrier distribution that obtains when both junctions are forward-biased can be resolved into a pair of additive component distributions, illustrated in Fig. 21.1*b* and labeled *F* and *R*. These components meet the following constraints:

1. Each component corresponds to a longitudinal minority-carrier diffusion current that is independent of position.
2. Each component is zero at one junction, that is, each component is *triangular*. In particular, the *forward* excess-carrier component (labeled *F*) is zero at $x = W$, whereas the *reverse* component (labeled *R*) is zero at $x = 0$.

The concentration at $x = 0$ depends directly on v_{EB}, and the concentration at $x = W$ depends directly on v_{CB}, in accordance with Eqs. 21.1. Consequently, the forward component of the excess-carrier distribution depends on v_{EB} but *not* on v_{CB}. Similarly, the reverse component depends on v_{CB} but *not* on v_{EB}. Although Fig. 21.1 illustrates the case with forward bias on each junction, the one-to-one correspondence between a component and a junction voltage holds true for *any* value (forward or reverse) of that voltage.

The excess-carrier distribution components shown in Fig. 21.1*b* obviously have the property that the area of the total distribution is equal to the sum of the areas of the component distributions and the slope of the total distribution is equal to the sum of the slopes of the component distributions. As we have seen in Sections 7.3 and 8.1, the terminal currents associated with a particular base-region excess-carrier distribution are linearly dependent on the slope and area of that distribution, for *both* static and dynamic situations. Consequently, each of the terminal currents that accompany the total distribution shown in Fig. 21.1*a* must be the sum of a pair of component currents, each of which is associated with one of the component distributions shown in Fig. 21.1*b*. For example, the emitter current can be regarded as the sum of two component currents. One component corresponds to the *forward* component of the base-region excess charge; the other component corresponds to the *reverse* charge component. The collector and base currents can be similarly resolved into forward and reverse components.

This resolution of the carrier distribution and the terminal currents into superposable components is useful because each charge component depends on only one junction voltage and because each component corresponds to the charge distribution on which we have based our analysis of active-region behavior. This approximate active-region distribution is shown by the dashed curve in Fig. 7.7, which we repeat here as Fig. 21.2. This approximate distribution is the basis of the active-region analysis of Chapters 7 and 8. Comparison of Figs. 21.1*b* and 21.2 shows that the distribution labeled *F* in Fig. 21.1*b* corresponds to the approximate active-region distribution on which we have based the analysis of Chapter 7, while the distribution labeled *R* also corresponds, except for interchange of the emitter and collector. *Consequently, the terminal currents associated with each component distribution can be expressed, without further analysis, simply by analogy with the active-region behavior developed earlier.* We first exploit this analogy to obtain a static model and then consider dynamic situations.

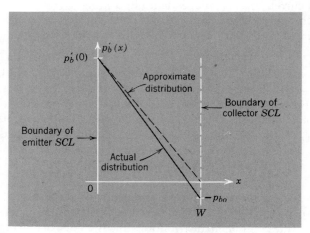

Figure 21.2   Excess-carrier distribution in the base for active-region operation.

21.2   Ebers–Moll Static Models
21.2.1   The Ebers–Moll Model for a *pnp* Transistor

We now proceed to develop a static circuit model for a *pnp* bipolar transistor. We regard each terminal current as comprised of the sum of a forward and reverse component. These components correspond to the component charge distributions shown in Fig. 21.1*b*. The *forward* component of the emitter current is, by analogy with the active-region result expressed by Eq. 7.9,

$$I_{EF} = I_{ES}(e^{qV_{EB}/kT} - 1) \qquad (21.2a)$$

The coefficient I_{ES} is the saturation current characteristic of the forward component of the charge distribution; it is analogous to the coefficient $(1 + \delta)I_1$, in Eq. 7.9. The forward component of the collector current is smaller than I_{EF} because some of the forward component of the emitter current results from the injection of electrons into the emitter and because not all of the holes injected into the base survive to reach the collector. We have used the symbol α_F to denote the ratio of the magnitude of the forward component of the collector current to the magnitude of the forward component of the emitter current. Thus the forward component of the collector current is

$$I_{CF} = -\alpha_F I_{EF} = -\alpha_F I_{ES}(e^{qV_{EB}/kT} - 1) \tag{21.2b}$$

The sign is negative here because the reference direction of I_C is into the collector, while the holes that comprise I_{CF} in a *pnp* transistor flow *out* at the collector. The forward component of base current, which supports injection into the emitter and the recombination of the small fraction of the injected carriers that die in the base, is

$$I_{BF} = -(I_{EF} + I_{CF})$$

Thus

$$I_{BF} = -(1 - \alpha_F)I_{ES}(e^{qV_{EB}/kT} - 1) \tag{21.2c}$$

The reverse components of the terminal currents are governed by similar relationships, except that the roles of collector and emitter are interchanged. Thus the reverse components of the currents, which are associated with the reverse component of the distribution, are

$$I_{ER} = -\alpha_R I_{CS}(e^{qV_{CB}/kT} - 1) \tag{21.3a}$$

$$I_{CR} = I_{CS}(e^{qV_{CB}/kT} - 1) \tag{21.3b}$$

$$I_{BR} = -(1 - \alpha_R)I_{CS}(e^{qV_{CB}/kT} - 1) \tag{21.3c}$$

where I_{CS} denotes the saturation current characteristic of the reverse component of the carrier distribution and α_R denotes the fraction of carriers that make it from collector to emitter.[1]

---

[1] In general α_R does not equal α_F and I_{CS} does not equal I_{ES}. In our simple physical model, forward and reverse parameters differ only because of different impurity concentrations, diffusion coefficients, or diffusion lengths in the emitter and collector. Actual bipolar transistor structures are not physically symmetric about the base, and the junctions have different areas. Consequently, the current-voltage relationships are different for forward and reverse components, and these differences are reflected by unequal values of α_F and α_R and of I_{ES} and I_{CS}.

The total currents are given by the superposition of the independent component currents. Thus:

$$I_E = I_{EF} + I_{ER} \tag{21.4a}$$
$$= I_{ES}(e^{qV_{EB}/kT} - 1) \qquad\qquad - \alpha_R I_{CS}(e^{qV_{CB}/kT} - 1)$$

$$I_C = I_{CF} + I_{CR} \tag{21.4b}$$
$$= -\alpha_F I_{ES}(e^{qV_{EB}/kT} - 1) \qquad\qquad + I_{CS}(e^{qV_{CB}/kT} - 1)$$

$$I_B = I_{BF} + I_{BR} \tag{21.4c}$$
$$= -(1 - \alpha_F)I_{ES}(e^{qV_{EB}/kT} - 1) - (1 - \alpha_R)I_{CS}(e^{qV_{CB}/kT} - 1)$$

These equations express the terminal currents as functions of the junction voltages for arbitrary values (forward and reverse) of those voltages. These equations, and the superposition principle on which they are based, are called the *Ebers-Moll relationships*.[2]

The Ebers-Moll equations can be interpreted in terms of circuit models that have the form of networks. One of these models is shown in Fig. 21.3a. This model, which is for a *pnp* transistor, is a physical superposition of two of the active-region models developed in Section 7.3 and illustrated in Fig. 7.8b. The equivalence of the network model to Eqs. 21.4 can be seen simply by summing the currents at each of the three terminals.

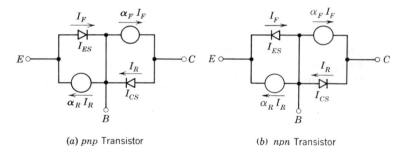

(a) *pnp* Transistor   (b) *npn* Transistor

Figure 21.3   Static models that are applicable for arbitrary junction voltages. The current sources depend on the currents in the exponential diodes.

21.2.2   Ebers–Moll Model for an *npn* Transistor

The corresponding model for an *npn* transistor is shown in Fig. 21.3b; it differs only in that the exponential diodes are reversed. The equations that this *npn* model represents are:

$$I_E = -I_{ES}(e^{-qV_{EB}/kT} - 1) \qquad\qquad + \alpha_R I_{CS}(e^{-qV_{CB}/kT} - 1) \tag{21.5a}$$
$$I_C = \alpha_F I_{ES}(e^{-qV_{EB}/kT} - 1) \qquad\qquad - I_{CS}(e^{-qV_{CB}/kT} - 1) \tag{21.5b}$$
$$I_B = (1 - \alpha_F)I_{ES}(e^{-qV_{EB}/kT} - 1) + (1 - \alpha_R)I_{CS}(e^{-qV_{CB}/kT} - 1) \tag{21.5c}$$

[2] They were first proposed by J. J. Ebers and J. L. Moll of the Bell Telephone Laboratories.

The coefficients α_F, α_R, I_{ES}, and I_{CS} are, in both cases, defined to be *positive* quantities.

The parameters α_F and α_R, which appear in these models, are the static short-circuit forward and reverse common-base current gains. The forward common-base gain α_F has been discussed previously; the corresponding reverse gain α_R has a similar interpretation. The coefficients I_{ES} and I_{CS} are called the emitter and collector *short-circuit saturation currents*. These descriptions follow from Eqs. 21.4 and 21.5, or from the models of Fig. 21.3, which show that I_{ES} and I_{CS} are the saturation currents of the emitter and collector junctions, respectively, *when the other junction is shorted.*

21.2.3   Models That Depend on Terminal Currents

The Ebers-Moll equations provide the basis for another set of models, which differ in that the current generators depend directly on the *terminal* currents rather than on the diode currents or, equivalently, the junction voltages. Specifically, Eqs. 21.4a and 21.4b, which are for *pnp* transistors, can be written in the following form:

$$I_C = -\alpha_F I_E + I_{CO}(e^{qV_{CB}/kT} - 1) \qquad (21.6a)$$

$$I_E = -\alpha_R I_C + I_{EO}(e^{qV_{EB}/kT} - 1) \qquad (21.6b)$$

where

$$I_{EO} = (1 - \alpha_F \alpha_R)I_{ES} \qquad (21.7a)$$

$$I_{CO} = (1 - \alpha_F \alpha_R)I_{CS} \qquad (21.7b)$$

This pair of equations can be expressed in terms of the model in Fig. 21.4a (see Problem P21.1).

The coefficients I_{EO} and I_{CO} are called the emitter and collector *open-circuit saturation currents*. As can be seen from Eqs. 21.6 or from Fig. 21.4, they are the saturation currents of the emitter and collector junctions, respectively, *when the opposite terminal is open-circuited.*

The models of Fig. 21.4 are fully equivalent to those of Fig. 21.3. Since the current sources in the models of Fig. 21.3 are directly dependent on the diode currents, and thus on the junction voltages, these models are generally most

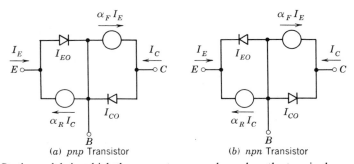

(a) *pnp* Transistor   (b) *npn* Transistor

Figure 21.4   Static models in which the current sources depend on the terminal currents.

appropriate in circuit situations where the junction voltages are either known or can be determined simply. On the other hand, the current sources in the models of Fig. 21.4 are directly dependent on the terminal currents. Thus these models are appropriate in situations where more is known about the terminal currents than about the junction voltages.

The models that we have developed in this section are characterized by *four* parameters: α_F, α_R, I_{ES}, and I_{CS} (or I_{EO} and I_{CO}). However, these parameters are not independent. Although we shall not develop a proof here, it can be shown that the parameters are related by[3]

$$\alpha_F I_{ES} = \alpha_R I_{CS} \qquad (21.8a)$$

or, equivalently, by

$$\alpha_F I_{EO} = \alpha_R I_{CO} \qquad (21.8b)$$

These *reciprocity conditions* show that three, and not four, measurements suffice to characterize the static *V–I* relationships of a transistor.

All of the models shown in Figs. 21.3 and 21.4 contain exponential diodes; therefore, they preserve the exponential nonlinearity that is characteristic of an idealized *pn* junction. These exponential diodes can, if we are satisfied with less accuracy, be replaced by ideal piecewise-linear diodes. The resulting models are less precise but easier to apply.

21.3   Dynamic Charge-Control Models
21.3.1   The Charge-Control Model for a *pnp* Transistor

We can use the same superposition principle that we discussed in Section 21.1.2 to formulate dynamic models for bipolar transistors if we recognize that the *total* excess charge in the base, which is associated with the distribution of Fig. 21.1*a*, can be resolved into additive components which are associated with the component distributions of Fig. 21.1*b*. Thus the total excess charge in the base q_B is

$$q_B = q_F + q_R \qquad (21.9)$$

where q_F is the forward component and q_R the reverse component. Each of these components depends on only one junction voltage. Thus, by analogy with Eq. 8.8 we have, for *pnp* transistors,

$$q_F = Q_{FO}(e^{qv_{EB}/kT} - 1) \qquad (pnp) \qquad (21.10a)$$

$$q_R = Q_{RO}(e^{qv_{CB}/kT} - 1) \qquad (pnp) \qquad (21.10b)$$

The coefficients Q_{FO} and Q_{RO} are equal in value for an idealized one-dimensional transistor structure in which the junctions have the same area; they then have the value $qAWp_{bo}/2$, as shown by Eq. 8.8. We introduce separate symbols for these two coefficients to allow for asymmetries in the

---

[3] See Section 9.1.3 of Reference 21.1.

transistor structure. Note that the charge components q_F and q_R are *positive* when the corresponding junctions are *forward-biased*, that is, when the corresponding junction voltages are *positive*.

The forward components of the instantaneous terminal currents depend only on q_F. The forward component of the collector current, which is proportional to the *slope* of the forward component of the base-region excess-carrier distribution, is thus proportional to q_F (which is governed by the *area* of the distribution). Consequently, by analogy with Eq. 8.6a, we have

$$i_{CF} = -\frac{q_F}{\tau_F} \tag{21.11a}$$

The forward component of the base current has two components. One is proportional to q_F; it feeds the recombination of excess carriers in the base and supports reverse injection into the emitter. The second component is proportional to dq_F/dt. This charge-changing component arises because excess majority carriers must be supplied at the base in order to neutralize the injected excess minority carriers. Thus, by analogy with Eq. 8.6b, we have a relationship that expresses conservation of charge in the base.

$$i_{BF} = -\frac{dq_F}{dt} - \frac{q_F}{\tau_{BF}} \tag{21.11b}$$

The forward component of the emitter current is constrained by Kirchhoff's current law to be $-(i_{CF} + i_{BF})$. Thus we have

$$i_{EF} = \frac{dq_F}{dt} + \frac{q_F}{\tau_{BF}} + \frac{q_F}{\tau_F} \tag{21.11c}$$

Similarly, the reverse components depend only on q_R. These components are obtained simply by analogy with Eqs. 21.11, but with the roles of emitter and collector interchanged. Thus

$$i_{CF} = \frac{dq_R}{dt} + \frac{q_R}{\tau_{BR}} + \frac{q_R}{\tau_R} \tag{21.12a}$$

$$i_{BR} = -\frac{dq_R}{dt} - \frac{q_R}{\tau_{BR}} \tag{21.12b}$$

$$i_{ER} = -\frac{q_R}{\tau_R} \tag{21.12c}$$

Finally, the total instantaneous terminal currents are obtained by super-position:

$$i_E = i_{EF} + i_{ER} = \frac{dq_F}{dt} + q_F\left(\frac{1}{\tau_F} + \frac{1}{\tau_{BF}}\right) - \frac{q_R}{\tau_R} \qquad (pnp) \qquad (21.13a)$$

$$i_C = i_{CF} + i_{CR} = -\frac{q_F}{\tau_F} + \frac{dq_R}{dt} + q_R\left(\frac{1}{\tau_R} + \frac{1}{\tau_{BR}}\right) \qquad (pnp) \qquad (21.13b)$$

$$i_B = i_{BF} + i_{BR} = -\frac{dq_F}{dt} - \frac{q_F}{\tau_{BF}} - \frac{dq_R}{dt} - \frac{q_R}{\tau_{BR}} \qquad (pnp) \qquad (21.13c)$$

21.3.2   Relationship between the Charge-Control and Ebers–Moll Parameters

Clearly, the charge-control model must reduce to the Ebers-Moll model for static situations. We can use this fact to relate some of the parameters in the charge-control model of Eqs. 21.13 to the Ebers-Moll parameters. Perhaps the simplest way of establishing the relation is to compare the two sets of equations under static conditions. Under these conditions the term in dq_F/dt in Eq. 21.13a is negligible and the charge-control equation for the emitter current reduces to

$$i_E = q_F\left(\frac{1}{\tau_F} + \frac{1}{\tau_{BF}}\right) - \frac{q_R}{\tau_R} \qquad (21.14)$$

This relationship can be expressed in terms of the junction voltages by making use of Eqs. 21.10, which express q_F and q_R in terms of v_{EB} and v_{CB} respectively. The result is

$$i_E = Q_{FO}\left(\frac{1}{\tau_F} + \frac{1}{\tau_{BF}}\right)(e^{qv_{EB}/kT} - 1) - \frac{Q_{RO}}{\tau_R}(e^{qv_{CB}/kT} - 1) \qquad (21.15)$$

The corresponding Ebers-Moll relationship is given by Eq. 21.4a, which is repeated here:

$$I_E = I_{ES}(e^{qV_{EB}/kT} - 1) - \alpha_R I_{CS}(e^{qV_{CB}/kT} - 1)$$

Obviously this relationship is equivalent to Eq. 21.15 if the charge-control and Ebers-Moll parameters are related in the following way

$$I_{ES} = Q_{FO}\left(\frac{1}{\tau_F} + \frac{1}{\tau_{BF}}\right) \qquad (21.16a)$$

$$\alpha_R I_{CS} = \frac{Q_{RO}}{\tau_R} \qquad (21.16b)$$

In the same manner the charge-control expression for i_C given by Eq. 21.13b reduces under static conditions to a form that is equivalent to the Ebers-Moll relationship of Eq. 21.4b if the parameters have the following relations:

$$I_{CS} = Q_{RO}\left(\frac{1}{\tau_R} + \frac{1}{\tau_{BR}}\right) \tag{21.17a}$$

$$\alpha_F I_{ES} = \frac{Q_{FO}}{\tau_F} \tag{21.17b}$$

The dependence of α_F (and β_F) on the charge-control parameters can be determined by eliminating I_{ES} and Q_{FO} between Eqs. 21.16a and 21.17b. The result is:

$$\alpha_F = \frac{\tau_{BF}}{\tau_{BF} + \tau_F} \tag{21.18a}$$

Thus, since $\beta_F = \alpha_F/(1 - \alpha_F)$

$$\beta_F = \frac{\tau_{BF}}{\tau_F} \tag{21.18b}$$

The corresponding expressions for the reverse parameters are:

$$\alpha_R = \frac{\tau_{BR}}{\tau_{BR} + \tau_R} \tag{21.18c}$$

$$\beta_R = \frac{\tau_{BR}}{\tau_R} \tag{21.18d}$$

Note that the reciprocity relationship of Eq. 21.8a requires

$$\frac{Q_{FO}}{Q_{RO}} = \frac{\tau_F}{\tau_R} \tag{21.19}$$

This correspondence between the charge-control and Ebers-Moll models makes possible the development of a circuit or network representation for the charge-control relationships, as shown in Fig. 21.5. This circuit model is fully equivalent to Eqs. 21.13. The dq_F/dt term in i_E is represented by the

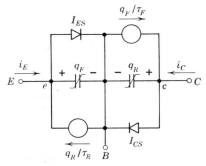

Figure 21.5 A dynamic model that is applicable for *pnp* transistors with arbitrary junction voltages.

nonlinear capacitance, the term in q_F is represented by the exponential diode having saturation current I_{ES}, and the term in q_R is represented by the dependent current generator. The interpretation on the collector side is similar.

21.3.3 A *pnp* Charge-Control Model That Includes Space-Charge-Layer Capacitances

The dynamic model of Fig. 21.5 accounts for the components of the terminal currents required to sustain and to change the excess-carrier charge stores in the neutral base region. As we have already seen for the junction diode and for the transistor in the active region, it is also necessary to account for components of the terminal currents that change the dipole layers of charge in the junction space-charge layers. These components of the terminal currents can be modeled by adding dq_V/dt terms to the basic charge-control equations given by Eqs. 21.13.

$$i_E = \frac{dq_F}{dt} + q_F\left(\frac{1}{\tau_F} + \frac{1}{\tau_{BF}}\right) - \frac{q_R}{\tau_R} + \frac{dq_{VE}}{dt} \qquad (pnp) \qquad (21.20a)$$

$$i_C = -\frac{q_F}{\tau_F} + \frac{dq_R}{dt} + q_R\left(\frac{1}{\tau_R} + \frac{1}{\tau_{BR}}\right) + \frac{dq_{VC}}{dt} \qquad (pnp) \qquad (21.20b)$$

$$i_B = -\frac{dq_F}{dt} - \frac{q_F}{\tau_{BF}} - \frac{dq_R}{dt} - \frac{q_R}{\tau_{BR}} - \frac{dq_{VE}}{dt} - \frac{dq_{VC}}{dt} \qquad (pnp)$$

$$(21.20c)$$

The term dq_{VE}/dt represents the current that charges the dipole layer at the emitter-base junction; it appears in both the emitter and base current expressions. The term dq_{VC}/dt has the same significance at the collector-base junction. The charge stores q_{VE} and q_{VC} are explicit functions of v_{EB} and v_{CB} respectively. This functional dependence is given by Eq. 4.36, which is repeated here:

$$q_V = K[(\psi_0)^n - (\psi_0 - v)^n] \qquad (21.21)$$

for an abrupt junction: $n = \frac{1}{2}$

for a linearly-graded junction: $n = \frac{2}{3}$

The contact potential is denoted by ψ_0, and K is a constant that depends on the junction area and the details of the impurity profile (see Section 4.4.1). The space-charge-layer charge store is, of course, directly related to the incremental space-charge-layer capacitance; we shall see in Section 22.5.1 that the constant K can easily be determined from information about this incremental capacitance.

These space-charge-layer charging currents can be represented in our network models for dynamic behavior by adding nonlinear capacitances across each junction, as shown in Fig. 21.6.

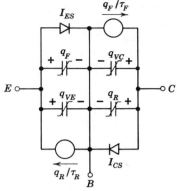

Figure 21.6   A dynamic model for *pnp* transistors that accounts for space-charge-layer charging currents.

21.3.4   Relation between Charge-Control Model and Hybrid-Pi Model

Just as the charge-control model must reduce to the Ebers-Moll model for static situations, so it must reduce to the hybrid-pi model for small-signal dynamic operation in the forward-active region. In this region the collector is reverse biased, so that q_R is fixed and equal to $-Q_{RO}$. Thus dq_R/dt is zero. Furthermore, we know from Eq. 21.19a that in this region

$$\frac{q_R}{\tau_R} = -\frac{Q_{RO}}{\tau_R} = -\alpha_R I_{CS}$$

Since I_{CS} is typically in the range from 10^{-8} to 10^{-10} ampere, the q_R term in Eq. 21.20b will be in the nanoampere range and thus can be neglected compared to the other currents. On this basis, Eq. 21.20b reduces to

$$i_C \simeq -\frac{q_F}{\tau_F} + \frac{dq_{VC}}{dt} \tag{21.22a}$$

and Eq. 21.20c becomes

$$i_B \simeq -\frac{q_F}{\tau_{BF}} - \frac{d}{dt}(q_F + q_{VE} + q_{VC}) \tag{21.22b}$$

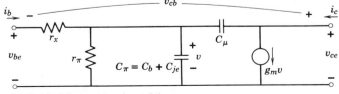

Figure 21.7   The hybrid-pi incremental model.

The corresponding small-signal time-domain equations for the hybrid-pi model (Fig. 21.7) are, if we assume that $r_x \simeq 0$,

$$i_b = g_\pi v_{be} + (C_b + C_{je})\frac{dv_{be}}{dt} - C_\mu \frac{dv_{cb}}{dt} \qquad (21.23a)$$

$$i_c = g_m v_{be} + C_\mu \frac{dv_{cb}}{dt} \qquad (21.23b)$$

If we denote the charge on C_b as Q_b and recall from Chapter 11 (Eq. 11.20d) that

$$C_b = \frac{W^2}{2D_b} g_m \qquad (21.24)$$

then

$$Q_b = C_b v_{be} = \frac{W^2}{2D_b} g_m v_{be} \qquad (21.25)$$

Substituting for $g_m v_{be}$ from Eq. 21.25 into Eq. 21.23b, we obtain

$$i_c = \frac{Q_b}{W^2/2D_b} + C_\mu \frac{dv_{cb}}{dt} \qquad (21.26)$$

Clearly, Eq. 21.26 is identical to Eq. 21.22a once we recognize that Q_b is the incremental component of $-q_F$ and linearize the space-charge-layer charge store,

$$\frac{dq_{VC}}{dt} = C_{jc}\frac{dv_{CB}}{dt} = C_\mu \frac{dv_{CB}}{dt} \qquad (21.27)$$

and recall from Chapter 8 that τ_F is defined as

$$\tau_F = \frac{W^2}{2D_b} \qquad (21.28)$$

It is important to note that we did *not* have to linearize the q_F charge store in the charge-control model, because of the *linear relationship between charge and current in this representation of the transistor.*

Similar manipulations can establish the fact that Eqs. 21.22b and 21.23a are also identical. (See Problem P21.4.)

Equations 21.24 and 21.28 serve to relate τ_F and ω_T. Specifically,

$$\tau_F = \frac{W^2}{2D_b} = \frac{C_b}{g_m} \qquad (21.29a)$$

Recall from Section 12.2.4 that

$$\omega_T = \frac{g_m}{C_\pi + C_\mu} = \frac{g_m}{C_b + C_{je} + C_{jc}} \qquad (21.29b)$$

Thus from Eq. 21.29a

$$\tau_F = \frac{1}{\omega_T} - \frac{C_{je} + C_{jc}}{g_m} \tag{21.29c}$$

If ω_T is measured in the 1 to 10 ma range so that C_b dominates the denominator of Eq. 21.29b then Eq. 21.29c reduces to

$$\tau_F \simeq \frac{1}{\omega_T} \tag{21.29d}$$

21.3.5 The Charge-Control Model for an *npn* Transistor

It is a simple matter to modify our charge-control models to apply to the *npn* transistor structure. For simplicity, we retain the convention that the *charge components q_F and q_R are positive when the corresponding junction voltages are positive.* Thus Eqs. 21.10 must be replaced by

$$q_F = Q_{FO}(e^{qv_{BE}/kT} - 1) \qquad (npn) \tag{21.30a}$$

$$q_R = Q_{RO}(e^{qv_{BC}/kT} - 1) \qquad (npn) \tag{21.30b}$$

Because the roles of holes and electrons are interchanged, the terminal currents in an *npn* transistor all have the opposite sign from the corresponding currents in a *pnp* transistor. Thus the *npn* equations analogous to Eqs. 21.13 are

$$i_E = -\frac{dq_F}{dt} - q_F\left(\frac{1}{\tau_F} + \frac{1}{\tau_{BF}}\right) + \frac{q_R}{\tau_R} \qquad (npn) \tag{21.31a}$$

$$i_C = \frac{q_F}{\tau_F} - \frac{dq_R}{dt} - q_R\left(\frac{1}{\tau_R} + \frac{1}{\tau_{BR}}\right) \qquad (npn) \tag{21.31b}$$

$$i_B = \frac{dq_F}{dt} + \frac{q_F}{\tau_{BF}} + \frac{dq_R}{dt} + \frac{q_R}{\tau_{BR}} \qquad (npn) \tag{21.31c}$$

The corresponding *npn* circuit model is shown in Fig. 21.8*a*. Note that the exponential diodes, the nonlinear charge stores, and the dependent generators are all reversed.

When space-charge-layer charging currents are accounted for, the expressions for the terminal currents become:

$$i_E = -\frac{dq_F}{dt} - q_F\left(\frac{1}{\tau_F} + \frac{1}{\tau_{BF}}\right) + \frac{q_R}{\tau_R} - \frac{dq_{VE}}{dt} \qquad (npn) \tag{21.32a}$$

$$i_C = \frac{q_F}{\tau_F} - \frac{dq_R}{dt} - q_R\left(\frac{1}{\tau_R} + \frac{1}{\tau_{BR}}\right) - \frac{dq_{VC}}{dt} \qquad (npn) \tag{21.32b}$$

$$i_B = \frac{dq_F}{dt} + \frac{q_F}{\tau_{BF}} + \frac{dq_R}{dt} + \frac{q_R}{\tau_{BR}} + \frac{dq_{VE}}{dt} + \frac{dq_{VC}}{dt} \qquad (npn) \tag{21.32c}$$

The corresponding *npn* circuit model is shown in Fig. 21.8*b*.

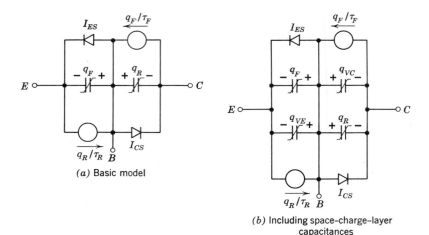

(a) Basic model

(b) Including space-charge-layer
capacitances

Figure 21.8   Charge-control models for *npn* transistors. These models should be compared with those of Figs. 21.5 and 21.6.

21.4   Regions of Operation

The general models developed in the preceding section apply for both forward and reverse voltages on either junction. Since the physical effect of a forward voltage is grossly different from the physical effect of a reverse voltage, these general models reduce to simple forms if the junction voltages are limited in range. Therefore, we now consider the simplified forms of these models that apply in the several domains or regions of operation that can be defined in terms of the forward or reverse nature of the junction voltages. Since each junction can have either a forward or a reverse voltage, there are just four regions of operation:

1. The *forward-active region* corresponds to forward bias on the emitter junction and reverse bias on the collector junction. It is the region of operation in which all of the total and incremental analyses of Chapters 7 through 20 apply.

2. The *reverse-active region* corresponds to forward bias on the collector junction and reverse bias on the emitter junction. It is a region in which the transistor behaves as a control valve, but the roles of emitter and collector are reversed.

3. The *cutoff region* corresponds to reverse bias on *both* junctions.

4. The *saturation region* corresponds to forward bias on *both* junctions.

21.4.1   Active-Region Behavior

When a transistor is operated in the *forward-active region*, the collector diodes in the static models of Figs. 21.3 and 21.4 are reverse-biased and can be replaced by current sources that have values equal to the saturation currents

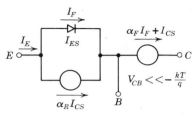

(a) Model for a *pnp* transistor

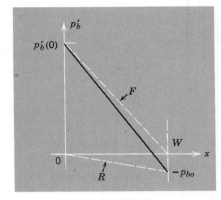

(b) Carrier distribution

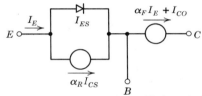

(c) Model for a *pnp* transistor with dependent
generator controlled by I_E

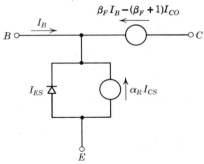

(d) Model for a *pnp* transistor with dependent
generator controlled by I_B

Figure 21.9   Models and carrier distribution for operation in the forward-active region.

of the corresponding collector diodes. Thus, the *pnp* model of Fig. 21.3a
reduces to the model of Fig. 21.9a for operation in the forward-active region.
The corresponding base-region carrier distribution is shown in Fig. 21.9b.
This model should be compared with the model of Fig. 7.9a, which was based

on analysis that, in fact, neglected the reverse component of the carrier distribution. The effect of the reverse component is to add the component $-I_{CS}$ to the collector current and the component $\alpha_R I_{CS}$ to the emitter current. Clearly, these components are of negligible effect if the transistor is well into the forward active region, in which case the current I_F is much larger than I_{CS}.

If we use Kirchhoff's current law to express I_F in the model of Fig. 21.9a in terms of the terminal current I_E, the model of Fig. 21.9c results (see Problem P21.5). This model should be compared with that of Fig. 7.11a, where the two *fixed* current generators were postulated to account for the small fixed value of q_R.

Of course, the static model of Fig. 21.9c can also be put in a form in which the dependent generator is controlled by the base current. We have

$$I_E = -(I_B + I_C)$$

Thus

$$I_C = -(\alpha_F I_E + I_{CO})$$
$$= +\alpha_F I_B + \alpha_F I_C - I_{CO}$$

or:

$$I_C = \beta_F I_B - (\beta_F + 1)I_{CO} \tag{21.33}$$

where $\beta_F = \alpha_F/(1 - \alpha_F)$. The resulting model, which is shown in Fig. 21.9d, is the same as that in Fig. 7.11b.

Similar approximate forward-active-region models can be developed for *npn* transistors. Note that the dependent portions of the collector current generators in the models of Figs. 21.9c and d are *not* reversed in the *npn* forms of these models, although the independent portions have the opposite sign and the diode and other generators are reversed. The dependent portions of the collector current generators stay the same because they depend on a *terminal* current, which has the same reference direction for *npn* and *pnp* transistors (see Problem P21.6).

The dynamic model of Fig. 21.6 can be simplified for application in the forward-active region by similar reductions. When the collector junction is reverse-biased by more than a few kT/q, the reverse charge q_R is fixed at $-Q_{RO}$ and is virtually zero. Specifically, if we assume that $\alpha_R = 0.2, I_{CS} = 10^{-10}$ amp, and $\tau_R = 1$ nsec, which are typically values for a low-power silicon transistor, we have

$$Q_{RO} = \alpha_R I_{CS} \tau_R$$
$$= 0.2 \times 10^{-19} \text{ coulomb}$$

which is less than the charge on a single electron. Consequently, Eqs. 21.20b and c reduce to

$$i_C = -\frac{q_F}{\tau_F} + \frac{dq_{VC}}{dt} \tag{21.34a}$$

$$i_B = -\frac{q_F}{\tau_{BF}} - \frac{d}{dt}(q_F + q_{VE} + q_{VC}) \tag{21.34b}$$

The corresponding active-region model is shown in Fig. 21.10. This model is, of course, equivalent to the charge-control model developed in Section 8.1.2 and shown in Fig. 8.5.

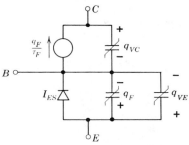

Figure 21.10   Active-region charge-control model.

In many cases for any forward bias on the emitter diode in excess of a few tenths of a volt, q_F will be much bigger than q_{VE}, so that we can also neglect the latter in Eq. 21.34b. These charges are compared in Fig. 8.7, which is repeated here as Fig. 21.11.

With most present-day transistors, it is reasonable to assume that in the active region, the collector current in Eq. 21.34a is dominated by the q_F/τ_F term, and the dq_{VC}/dt term can be neglected. That is,

$$i_C \simeq -q_F/\tau_F \tag{21.35a}$$

This approximation is analogous to the small-signal approximation of neglecting the loading of C_μ on the output of the hybrid-pi model, while retaining the loading effect of C_μ on the input circuit. Equations 21.34b and 21.35a can now be combined to yield

$$i_B = \frac{i_C}{\beta_F} + \tau_F \frac{di_C}{dt} - \frac{d(q_{VE} + q_{VC})}{dt} \tag{21.35b}$$

This equation can be used to determine $i_C(t)$ for a specified base drive current. The collector space-charge-layer charge q_{VC} is related to i_C through the parameters of the circuit in which the transistor is embedded. In general, this relationship is nonlinear.

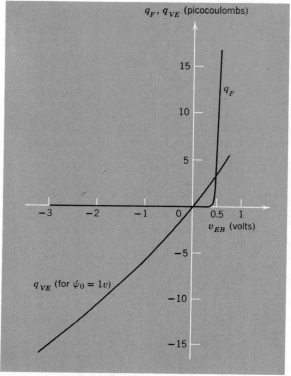

Figure 21.11   A comparison of the dependence of base-region charge q_F and emitter space-charge-layer charge q_{VE} on emitter base voltage v_{EB}.

If the transistor is driven with large base currents, almost all of the base current will go into changing the stored charge during the transient, and, relatively speaking, almost no current will be required to supply recombination. In this case Eqs. 21.34 can be further simplified by neglecting the q_F/τ_{BF} term in Eq. 21.34b.

Since the reverse-active region differs from the forward-active region only in that the collector and emitter are interchanged, no further discussion of models for this region of operation is necessary.

21.4.2   The Cutoff Region

The *cutoff region* of operation of a transistor can be modeled very simply because there is no injection of minority carriers into the base region. Thus the static model of Fig. 21.3 reduces to the form shown in Fig. 21.12a. In many cases, particularly with silicon transistors, the saturation currents are so small that they can be neglected completely, and the model can be represented as an open circuit as shown in Fig. 21.12b. That is, a transistor that is

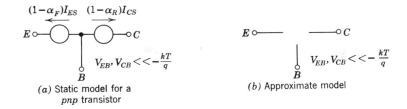

(a) Static model for a
pnp transistor

(b) Approximate model

$$E \circ\!\!-\!\!|\!\!|\!\!-\!\!\bullet\!\!-\!\!|\!\!|\!\!-\!\!\circ C$$
$$+ \quad q_{VE} \quad - \quad - \quad q_{VC} \quad +$$
$$B$$

(c) Dynamic model for the cutoff region

Figure 21.12   The cutoff region is characterized by small, constant terminal currents, and no coupling between emitter and collector.

operating in the cutoff region can be regarded, to first order in static situations, as providing no connections among the three terminals.

Similar simplifications take place in the charge-control model when operation is restricted to the cutoff region. As noted above, there is no injection of minority carriers, so that q_F and q_R must be substantially zero. This is shown graphically in Fig. 21.11, in which the space-charge-layer charge q_{VE} and the forward base charge q_F are plotted versus v_{EB}. For v_{EB} less than a few tenths of a volt positive, q_F is virtually zero. Clearly, q_{VE} is the only significant charge associated with the reverse-biased emitter diode. Similarly for the collector diode, q_R is zero but q_{VC} is important. On this basis all of the base current is available to change the charge in the space-charge layers. Thus for the cutoff region, Eqs. 21.20 simplify to

$$i_E = \frac{dq_{VE}}{dt} \tag{21.36a}$$

$$i_C = \frac{dq_{VC}}{dt} \tag{21.36b}$$

$$i_B = -\frac{d}{dt}(q_{VE} + q_{VC}) \tag{21.36c}$$

The cutoff region model corresponding to these equations is shown in Fig. 21.12c.

21.4.3   The Saturation Region

The *saturation region* of operation corresponds to forward bias on both junctions. If we wish to preserve the exponentially-nonlinear nature of the junctions, no simplification of the static models of Fig. 21.3 is possible. However, in many cases the small forward junction voltages can be neglected entirely, and the transistor can be modeled as shown in Fig. 21.13, that is, as a short circuit between all three terminals. This complete neglect of the forward junction voltages is equivalent to replacing the exponential diodes with ideal piecewise-linear diodes.

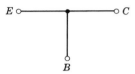

Figure 21.13 An approximate model for the saturation region.

The range of *static* terminal currents for which the approximate saturation-region model of Fig. 21.13 applies can be determined by inspection of the model of Fig. 21.4a. Both diodes in the model of a *pnp* transistor will be forward-biased if the following inequalities are *simultaneously* satisfied:

$$\alpha_F I_E > -I_C \tag{21.37a}$$

$$\alpha_R I_C > -I_E \tag{21.37b}$$

If we use Kirchhoff's current law ($I_B + I_E + I_C = 0$) to introduce I_B, these inequalities become

$$\alpha_F I_E > I_E + I_B \tag{21.38a}$$

$$\alpha_R I_C > I_C + I_B \tag{21.38b}$$

or, equivalently,

$$-I_B > (1 - \alpha_F)I_E \tag{21.39a}$$

$$-I_B > (1 - \alpha_R)I_C \tag{21.39b}$$

We now distinguish three possible modes of operation of a transistor in the saturation region. In the first mode the emitter is more forward-biased than the collector, so that current enters the base region at the emitter and leaves at the collector. In this mode, which is occasionally referred to as the *forward saturation region*, I_E is positive and I_C is negative. Thus the excess-carrier distribution in the base has the form shown in Fig. 21.14a; the gradient of the distribution is such that minority carriers diffuse from emitter to collector. In order for the inequality of Eq. 21.39a to be satisfied, I_B must be negative and *larger* in magnitude than $(1 - \alpha_F)I_E$. Since I_C is negative in this mode, the inequality of Eq. 21.39b is invariably satisfied. Thus the condition on the currents that must be satisfied for the transistor to be saturated and for the

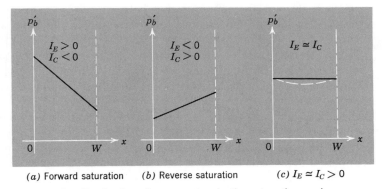

(a) Forward saturation   (b) Reverse saturation   (c) $I_E \simeq I_C > 0$

Figure 21.14 Excess-carrier distributions for operation in the saturation region.

model of Fig. 21.13 to apply when I_E is *positive* and I_C is *negative* is

$$-I_B > (1 - \alpha_F)I_E \qquad (21.40\text{a})$$

or, equivalently,

$$-I_B > -\frac{I_C}{\beta_F} \qquad (21.40\text{b})$$

where $\beta_F = \alpha_F/(1 - \alpha_F)$.

For operation in the second mode, called the *reverse saturation region*, the collector is more forward-biased than the emitter, so that current flows in at the collector and out at the emitter. In this mode, I_C is positive and I_E is negative. The excess-carrier distribution in the base is such that carriers diffuse from collector to emitter as shown in Fig. 21.14b. The condition on the currents can be written as

$$-I_B > (1 - \alpha_R)I_C \qquad (21.41\text{a})$$

or as

$$-I_B > -\frac{I_E}{\beta_R} \qquad (21.41\text{b})$$

where $\beta_R = \alpha_R/(1 - \alpha_R)$. Once again, I_B must be negative.

The third and last possibility for a *pnp* transistor that operates with forward voltage on both junctions is that current enters the base at *both* junctions. That is, both I_E and I_C are positive. This situation occurs if the junctions are forward-biased by about the same amount. In this mode, the right sides of both inqualities of Eq. 21.39 are positive. Thus I_B must again be negative and larger in magnitude than the larger of $(1 - \alpha_F)I_E$ and $(1 - \alpha_R)I_C$.

The excess-carrier distribution in this case has the form shown in Fig. 21.14c; there is no gradient in the base. This distribution appears to be inconsistent with the condition that both I_E and I_C be positive because we have neglected the influence of recombination in the base on the excess-carrier distribution (but not on the base current). In the situation illustrated in Fig. 21.14c there is no flow through the base from emitter to collector or vice versa; *all* of both I_E and I_C is consumed by recombination. Consequently, our neglect of recombination is, in this special case, unjustified and leads to an inconsistent distribution. If we account for recombination in evaluating the excess-carrier distribution, we obtain a distribution with a slight upward curvature, as shown by the dotted curve. Thus the slopes at $x = 0$ and $x = W$ have the proper sign to account for positive values of I_E and I_C and the apparent inconsistency is removed (see Problem P21.7).

The conditions on the currents that must hold for an *npn* transistor to be in the saturation region of operation are, from the model of Fig. 21.4b,

$$\alpha_F I_E < -I_C \tag{21.42a}$$

$$\alpha_R I_C < -I_E \tag{21.42b}$$

When the base current is introduced, the inequalities become

$$I_B > -(1 - \alpha_F)I_E \tag{21.43a}$$

$$I_B > -(1 - \alpha_R)I_C \tag{21.43b}$$

These inequalities show that the base current of a saturated *npn* transistor must be *positive*, regardless of the polarities of I_E and I_C.

The dynamics of a transistor in saturation are governed by the base-region excess charge. In the saturation region both v_{EB} and v_{CB} are nearly constant, so that changes in q_{VE} and q_{VC} can be ignored. Consequently, the behavior of the base-region excess charge in saturation is described, for a *pnp* transistor, by Eqs. 21.13; the collector and base current expressions are

$$i_C = -\frac{q_F}{\tau_F} + \frac{dq_R}{dt} + q_R\left(\frac{1}{\tau_R} + \frac{1}{\tau_{BR}}\right) \tag{21.44a}$$

$$i_B = -\frac{d}{dt}(q_F + q_R) - \frac{q_F}{\tau_{BF}} - \frac{q_R}{\tau_{BR}} \tag{21.44b}$$

An appropriate model is shown in Fig. 21.5. Equations 21.44 can be solved to yield the charge components $q_F(t)$ and $q_R(t)$ once the base and collector currents have been specified. The homogeneous solutions (i.e., the open-circuit natural modes) for $q_F(t)$ and $q_R(t)$ in saturation involve two exponential modes, the time constants or natural frequencies of which are widely separated for typical values of the charge-control parameters.[4] Detailed analysis shows that the fast mode represents a redistribution of charge between q_F and q_R, that is, the "slosh" of charge from one part of the base region to the other. On

---

[4] See, for example, Section 10.4.2 of Reference 21.1.

the other hand, the slow mode represents the simultaneous growth or decay of q_F and q_R, that is, the "fill" of the base with charge supplied by the base current. For most problems the fast-mode time constant is so short that the "slosh" can be assumed to take place instantaneously, and the transistor in saturation can be treated as a single-time-constant system, in which the dynamics are dominated by the "fill" mode.

Since in saturation there is one dominant mode, the slow or "fill" mode described above, it must be possible to approximate Eqs. 21.44 by a pair of equations that have only one independent charge variable and *one* natural frequency. We accomplish this simplification by imposing a relationship between q_F and q_R. First, we express $q_F(t)$ as the sum of two charge components:

$$q_F(t) = q_{BO} + q_{FS}(t) \tag{21.45a}$$

The charge q_{BO} is the base charge required by a transistor at the *edge* of saturation (no reverse component of base charge). That is,

$$q_{BO} = -\tau_F I_C(\text{sat}) \tag{21.45b}$$

The charge $q_{FS}(t)$ represents the portion of q_F above that required to take the transistor to the edge of saturation with a collector current $I_C(\text{sat})$.

In terms of these components of q_F, the total excess charge in the base $q_B(t)$ can be written as

$$q_B(t) = q_F(t) + q_R(t)$$
$$= q_{BO} + q_S(t) \tag{21.45c}$$

where

$$q_S = q_{FS}(t) + q_R(t) \tag{21.45d}$$

Clearly, $q_S(t)$ denotes the extra base charge in the saturation region. This resolution of q_B into q_{BO} and q_S is illustrated in Fig. 21.15.

When Eq. 21.45a is used to substitute for q_F in the charge-control equation for the collector current (Eq. 21.44a), we obtain

$$I_C(\text{sat}) = -\frac{q_{BO}}{\tau_F} - \frac{q_{FS}(t)}{\tau_F} + q_R(t)\left(\frac{1}{\tau_R} + \frac{1}{\tau_{BR}}\right) + \frac{dq_R}{dt} \tag{21.46}$$

or, using the defining equation for q_{BO} (Eq. 21.45b),

$$q_{FS}(t)\left(\frac{1}{\tau_F}\right) = q_R(t)\left(\frac{1}{\tau_R} + \frac{1}{\tau_{BR}}\right) + \frac{dq_R}{dt} \tag{21.47}$$

We now introduce an approximation that is tantamount to neglecting the fast or "slosh" mode discussed above. *We assume that $q_{FS}(t)$ and $q_R(t)$ are related under dynamic conditions in exactly the same way they are related statically.* Stated in another way, we neglect the dq_R/dt term in Eqs. 21.46

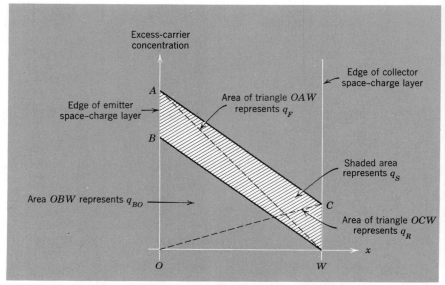

Figure 21.15 Components of the excess base charge in the saturation region. Although the triangular areas are proportional to the charge components as shown, the constants of proportionality are not identical.

and 21.47. This constraint between $q_{FS}(t)$ and $q_R(t)$ can be used together with the definition of $q_S(t)$ to express the charge-control equation for the base current (Eq. 21.44b) in terms of $q_S(t)$ alone. The result of this algebraic manipulation of the three linear relationships is a first-order differential equation (see Problem 21.9):

$$i_B(t) = -\frac{q_{BO}}{\tau_{BF}} - \frac{q_S(t)}{\tau_S} - \frac{dq_S(t)}{dt}$$ (21.48)

where τ_S is

$$\tau_S = \frac{\alpha_F(\tau_F + \alpha_R \tau_R)}{1 - \alpha_F \alpha_R}$$ (21.49a)

or, in terms of β_F and β_R,

$$\tau_S = \frac{\tau_{BF}(\beta_R + 1) + \tau_{BR}\beta_F}{\beta_F + \beta_R + 1}$$ (21.49b)

It is clear from Eq. 21.48 that the *saturation-region charge-control parameter* τ_S is the apparent lifetime that characterizes the recombination of q_S; it is a weighted average of τ_{BF} and τ_{BR} in which the weighting reflects the composition of q_S from q_{FS} and q_R. Equation 21.48 shows that τ_S is the time constant that governs the "fill" mode.

The first term on the right side of Eq. 21.48 can be expressed in terms of $I_C(\text{sat})$. Specifically,

$$-\frac{q_{BO}}{\tau_{BF}} = \frac{\tau_F}{\tau_{BF}} I_C(\text{sat}). \tag{21.50a}$$

or

$$-\frac{q_{BO}}{\tau_{BF}} = \frac{I_C(\text{sat}).}{\beta_F} = i_{BO} \tag{21.50b}$$

This term corresponds to the base current i_{BO} required by a transistor at the edge of saturation. Consequently, an alternate form of the linear saturation-region charge-control equation is

$$i_B(t) - i_{BO} = -\left(\frac{q_S}{\tau_S} + \frac{dq_S}{dt}\right) \tag{21.51}$$

In this form, the charge-control equation emphasizes that the *extra* base current above that required at the edge of saturation is coupled directly to the *extra* saturation base charge through the usual form of charge conservation relationship.

Although this analysis has been based on the equations for a *pnp* structure, the result of Eq. 21.51 applies as well to *npn* devices if the signs on the right side are changed.

21.5 Applications of Ebers–Moll Circuit Models

21.5.1 Parameter Evaluation

As we have seen in Section 21.2, the static behavior of a bipolar transistor can be represented by means of Ebers-Moll models such as those shown in Figs. 21.3 and 21.4. These models contain four parameters or coefficients— two saturation currents and two current gains—only three of which are independent. The coefficients must be determined before the models can be used in circuit analysis.

The key to evaluation of these parameters lies in the measurement of terminal *I-V* characteristics under appropriately chosen special conditions. For example, if a transistor is operated with the collector junction short-circuited, that is, with $V_{CB} = 0$, the models of Fig. 21.3 (or Eqs. 21.4 and 21.5) show that the current denoted by I_R (or I_{CR}) is zero. Thus I_{CS} and α_R do not appear in the models and we have

$$\alpha_F = -\frac{I_C}{I_E}\bigg|_{V_{CB}=0} \tag{21.52a}$$

or, equivalently,

$$\beta_F = \frac{I_C}{I_B}\bigg|_{V_{CB}=0} \tag{21.52b}$$

Also
$$I_E = I_{ES}(e^{qV_{EB}/kT} - 1)|_{V_{CB}=0} \tag{21.52c}$$

This equation is simply the I-V relationship of a junction diode (cf. Eq. 4.20). It shows that I_{ES} can be determined by plotting $ln\ I_E$ versus qV_{EB}/kT. On the other hand, the emitter junction could simply be reverse-biased in which case $I_{ES} \simeq -I_E$.

A word of caution is necessary here, however. The Ebers-Moll circuit model is based on an analysis in which terminal currents arise only from the flow and recombination of excess carriers in the neutral regions. This analysis neglects currents associated with generation and recombination in the junction space-charge layers. Although these space-charge-layer generation-recombination currents are negligible when a junction is forward-biased, they often are dominant when a junction is reverse-biased, particularly in silicon devices and at low temperatures. In such cases the measured reverse current of a junction will be substantially larger than either the saturation current predicted by our analysis or the value of I_{ES} measured by use of Eq. 21.52c under conditions of forward bias. Thus it is necessary to make the measurement of the parameter appropriate to the conditions under which the model will be used. If the model is to be used in the forward-active and saturation regions, where the emitter junction is forward-biased, I_{ES} should be measured with V_{EB} positive. On the other hand, if the model is to be used in the cutoff region, where the junctions are reverse-biased, I_{ES} should be measured with V_{EB} negative.

The reverse parameters I_{CS} and α_R can be measured in a manner similar to that used for I_{ES} and α_F simply by interchanging the emitter and collector leads.

We have described measurement of the saturation currents with the other junction short-circuited. These measurements yield I_{ES} and I_{CS} directly. The models of Fig. 21.4 show that if the measurements are made on one junction with the opposite terminal *open-circuited*, the measurements yield I_{EO} and I_{CO} directly.

In many cases we wish to determine typical values for the four Ebers-Moll parameters from manufacturers' data sheets, rather than by direct measurement. Unfortunately, sufficient data are not usually supplied, so that some judicious guesswork may be required.

Every data sheet will provide information for finding α_F. In most cases, a value of the dc current gain h_{FE} in the active region is given. By definition,

$$h_{FE} = \frac{I_C}{I_B}$$

that is, h_{FE} is the ratio of the *total* collector current to the *total* base current. We see from the model of Fig. 21.9*d* that if $I_{CO}(\beta_F + 1)$ is much smaller than I_C, as it will be for I_C in the milliampere range for silicon transistors,

$$h_{FE} \simeq \beta_F$$

Hence

$$\alpha_F = \frac{h_{FE}}{h_{FE} + 1}$$

In most cases data sheets also provide information about the collector saturation current. The parameters usually specified are either I_{CES}, which is equivalent to I_{CS}, or I_{CBO}, which we have denoted as I_{CO}. Frequently the data are presented in graphical form as reverse current versus bias voltage, as shown in Fig. 21.16.[5] In this event, either the low voltage or high voltage value should be chosen, depending on the intended application, as discussed above.

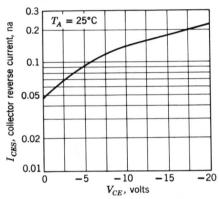

Figure 21.16   Collector-base reverse current versus reverse-bias voltage.

Unfortunately, manufacturers rarely supply information that can be used to determine either α_R or the emitter saturation current. However, we know that α_R is probably somewhere between 0.5 and 0.9, corresponding to β_R between 1 and about 10. Thus because α_F is always close to unity, we can estimate the emitter saturation current from Eqs. 21.8:

$$I_{ES} = \frac{\alpha_R}{\alpha_F} I_{CS} \simeq \frac{I_{CS}}{2}$$

or

$$I_{EO} \simeq \frac{I_{CO}}{2}$$

21.5.2   Amplifier Transfer Characteristics

The circuit of a common-emitter amplifier is shown in Fig. 21.17a. We use an Ebers-Moll circuit model to investigate the static transfer characteristics of

[5] The voltage dependence of the measured reverse currents reflect the fact that, particularly in silicon transistors at other than high temperatures, the currents are dominated by space-charge-layer-generation currents. These currents are proportional to the space-charge-layer volume, which increases as the reverse voltage, and thus the space-charge-layer width, increases.

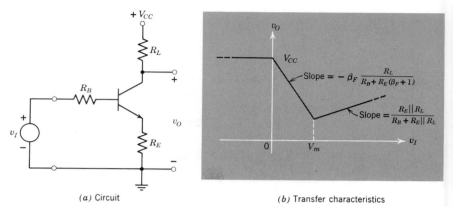

(a) Circuit   (b) Transfer characteristics

Figure 21.17   A common-emitter amplifier and its static transfer characteristics.

this amplifier for all values of the input voltage v_I, not just for the limited range of values in which the transistor operates in the active region.

We use the model of Fig. 21.4b to represent the *npn* transistor and replace the exponential diodes with ideal piecewise-linear diodes. This is equivalent to assuming that the exponential diodes have negligibly small values of saturation current and forward voltage drop.

We now consider the behavior of the circuit as the input voltage v_I changes from large negative values to large positive values. Since the base current of an *npn* transistor that has negligibly small saturation currents cannot be negative, the base-to-ground voltage cannot be more positive than v_I. Thus when v_I is negative, the base-to-ground voltage must be negative, the emitter junction must be reverse-biased, and the transistor must be cut off (the polarity of the collector supply voltage is such as to reverse-bias the collector junction). Consequently, when v_I is negative, the cutoff region model of Fig. 21.12b applies, and the circuit reduces to that shown in Fig. 21.18a. The output terminal is effectively disconnected from the input, and the output voltage is

$$v_O = +V_{CC} \qquad (21.53)$$

When v_I becomes positive, the emitter junction becomes forward-biased, and the transistor enters the forward-active region. Thus the model of Fig. 21.9d applies if we set I_{CS} and I_{CO} equal to zero (we are assuming that the saturation currents are negligibly small) and replace the emitter diode by a short. Thus, in this region of operation the circuit reduces to that shown in Fig. 21.18b. If we apply Kirchhoff's voltage law to the input loop, we obtain

$$v_I = R_B I_B + R_E(\beta_F + 1)I_B \qquad (21.54a)$$

In the output loop we have

$$v_O = V_{CC} - \beta_F R_L I_B \qquad (21.54b)$$

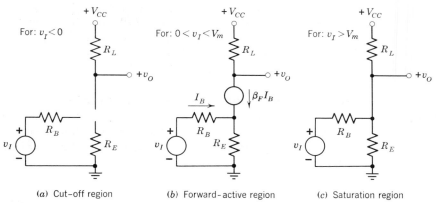

(a) Cut–off region   (b) Forward–active region   (c) Saturation region

Figure 21.18   Circuit models that apply in the three regions of operation of the circuit in Fig. 21.17.

Eliminating I_B between these equations yields

$$v_O = V_{CC} - \beta_F \frac{R_L}{R_B + R_E(\beta_F + 1)} v_I \tag{21.55}$$

Of course, this result applies only as long as the transistor remains in the forward-active region. Since v_O drops as v_I increases, and since the base-to-ground voltage increases, the collector-to-emitter voltage eventually falls to zero, the collector junction changes state, and the transistor leaves the active region. At the edge of saturation we have, since $I_C \simeq -I_E$,

$$I_C(R_L + R_E) = V_{CC} \tag{21.56a}$$

Thus the corresponding value of base current just at the edge of saturation is

$$I_B = \frac{I_C}{\beta_F}$$

$$= \frac{V_{CC}}{\beta_F(R_L + R_E)} \tag{21.56b}$$

The value of input voltage V_m at which the transistor leaves the active region thus is

$$V_m = [R_B + R_E(\beta_F + 1)] \frac{V_{CC}}{\beta_F(R_L + R_E)} \tag{21.56c}$$

For input voltages greater than V_m, the transistor is saturated, and the model of Fig. 21.13 applies. Thus the circuit reduces to that shown in Fig. 21.18c. The output voltage is, using superposition,

$$v_O = \frac{R_E \| R_B}{R_L + R_E \| R_B} V_{CC} + \frac{R_E \| R_L}{R_B + R_E \| R_L} v_I \tag{21.57}$$

We have now completed the task of evaluating the transfer characteristic of the amplifier. For v_I less than zero, v_O is given by Eq. 21.53; for v_I positive but less than V_m, v_O is given by Eq. 21.55; and for v_I greater than V_m, v_O is given by Eq. 21.57. Thus the transfer characteristic is piecewise-linear and has the form shown in Fig. 21.17*b*.

21.5.3   Static Characteristics of a Transistor Switch

As a second example of the use of the static models based on the Ebers-Moll equations, and of the concept of regions of operation, we consider the circuit of Fig. 21.19*a*, in which an *npn* transistor is used as a switch, as viewed at the terminals *aa′*.

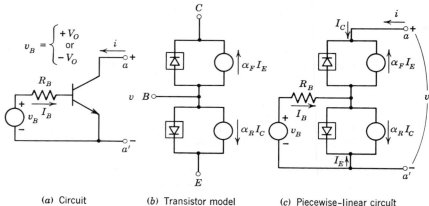

| (a) Circuit | (b) Transistor model | (c) Piecewise-linear circuit |

Figure 21.19   A transistor switch.

To explore the behavior of this circuit in detail, we characterize the *npn* transistor by the model shown in Fig. 21.19*b*. This is an Ebers-Moll model in which the exponential diodes have been replaced by ideal piecewise-linear diodes. The complete piecewise-linear model that results when the transistor is replaced by this model is shown in Fig. 21.19*c*. We now evaluate the driving-point characteristic seen at the terminals *aa′*.

The voltage source v_B, which is two-valued, controls the state of the transistor switch by means of the base current. When $v_B = -V_O$, the emitter-base junction is reverse-biased. If the range of v is limited appropriately, the collector junction is also reverse-biased and the transistor is cut off. In this condition the current i through the switch is small, and the transistor switch is considered to be *open*. If, on the other hand, $v_B = +V_O$, the emitter-base junction is forward-biased and base current flows. If the range of values of i is limited appropriately, the transistor is in saturation, the voltage v across the switch is small, and the switch is considered to be *closed*. Thus the state of the switch is controlled by v_B. This configuration is useful in circuits because the power required to operate the switch (the power delivered to R_B and the transistor by v_B) can be much less than the power that can be controlled at the terminals aa'.

We consider first the situation when $v_B = -V_O$, that is, when the switch is intended to be open, and evaluate the I-V relationship at the terminals aa'. This polarity of v_B reverse-biases the emitter junction. Furthermore, the collector junction will be reverse-biased ($V_{CB} > 0$) for all v such that

$$v > -V_O$$

If v satisfies this inequality, the transistor is in the cutoff region of operation, and the model of Fig. 21.12b applies. Clearly, i is zero for all v in this range. The corresponding portion of the off-state driving-point characteristic is shown in Fig. 21.20a.

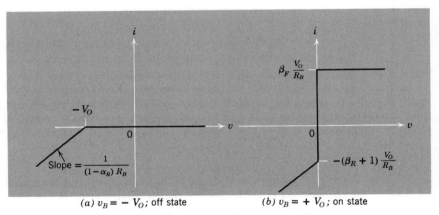

(a) $v_B = -V_O$; off state (b) $v_B = +V_O$; on state

Figure 21.20   Driving-point characteristics of the transistor switch shown in Fig. 21.19.

If v is less than $-V_O$, the collector junction becomes forward-biased, and i becomes negative. The drop across R_B produced by I_B tends to increase the reverse bias on the emitter junction, so that the transistor is in the reverse-active region. The voltage drop across the collector diode is zero. Hence

$$v = -V_O - I_B R_B \tag{21.58a}$$

and

$$I_B = -(1 - \alpha_R)I_C \tag{21.58b}$$

$$= -(1 - \alpha_R)i$$

If I_B is eliminated between these equations, we obtain

$$v = -V_O + (1 - \alpha_R)R_B i \tag{21.58c}$$

Thus this portion of the driving-point characteristic has a slope of $1/(1 - \alpha_R)R_B$, as indicated in Fig. 21.20a[6]. This characteristic shows that the circuit can be modeled as an open switch if $v > -V_O$.

When $v_B = +V_O$, the switch is intended to be closed. The base current is

$$I_B = \frac{V_O}{R_B} \tag{21.59a}$$

since v_B appears directly across R_B. The transistor will be in the saturation region of operation, where $v = 0$, if i is appropriately limited in range. When i is positive and not too large, the *npn* transistor is in forward saturation. Consequently, the upper limit on i is given by the *npn* form of Eq. 21.40b, which can be written as

$$i = I_C < \beta_F I_B$$

or, using Eq. 21.59a, as

$$i = I_C < \beta_F \frac{V_O}{R_B} \tag{21.59b}$$

When i is negative and not too large, the transistor is in reverse saturation. The corresponding lower limit on i is, from Eq. 21.43b,

$$i = I_C > -\left(\frac{1}{1 - \alpha_R}\right) I_B$$

or, using Eq. 21.59a and the definition of β_R,

$$i = I_C > -(\beta_R + 1)\frac{V_O}{R_B} \tag{21.59c}$$

Between the limits set by Eqs. 21.59b and 21.59c, the transistor is saturated, the model of Fig. 21.13 applies, and v is zero, as shown in Fig. 21.20b. If we try to increase i above the value set by Eq. 21.59b, the transistor leaves the saturation region and enters the *forward*-active region, that is, the collector junction becomes reverse-biased while the emitter junction remains forward-biased. Since the base current is fixed by V_O and R_B, the switch current i, which is just equal to I_C, remains constant while v increases, as shown in Fig. 21.20b. If we try to reduce i below the value set by Eq. 21.59c, the transistor enters the *reverse*-active region in which the collector junction is forward-biased while the emitter junction becomes reverse-biased. Thus Eqs. 21.58 apply if the sign of V_O is changed, and the driving-point characteristic once again has a slope of $1/(1 - \alpha_R)R_B$. The complete characteristic of Fig. 21.20b shows that the circuit can be modeled as a closed switch if i lies in the range

$$-(\beta_R + 1)\frac{V_O}{R_B} < i < \beta_F \frac{V_O}{R_B} \tag{21.60}$$

---

[6] The point of intersection of the straight-line segments is the breakpoint of the collector diode.

The transistor switch whose behavior we have just investigated can be used as a *chopper* or *modulator*, as shown in Fig. 21.21a. Here the transistor is driven by a square wave so that it spends equal times in the off and on states. The voltage v_O across the terminals aa' is approximately zero when the switch is on and is approximately equal to the input voltage v_I when the switch is off. Those familiar with modulation theory will recognize that if the output voltage v_O is filtered to remove the low-frequency component proportional to v_I, the resulting waveform represents the balanced modulation of v_B by v_I.

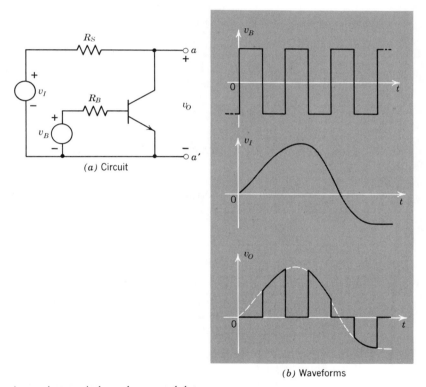

(a) Circuit

(b) Waveforms

Figure 21.21 A transistor switch used as a modulator.

REFERENCES

21.1 P. E. Gray et al., *Physical Electronics and Circuit Models of Transistors*, Wiley, New York, 1964.

21.2 C. L. Searle et al., *Elementary Circuit Properties of Transistors*, Wiley, New York, 1964.

21.3 J. N. Harris et al., *Digital Transistor Circuits*, Wiley, New York, 1966.

PROBLEMS

P21.1   Show that the static *pnp* model given by Eqs. 21.4 (Fig. 21.3*a*) is equivalent to the model given by Eqs. 21.6 (Fig. 21.4*a*) and verify Eqs. 21.7.

P21.2   The following questions should be answered by sketching a circuit that shows the connections of the transistor, a battery, and a dc ammeter. Be sure to show the polarity of the battery and the reference direction of the current. Assuming that the static behavior of these transistors is adequately described by the Ebers-Moll model:

(*a*) Specify a circuit arrangement that can be used to measure I_{ES} in an *npn* transistor.

(*b*) Specify a circuit arrangement that can be used to measure I_{CO} in a *pnp* transistor.

P21.3   Verify Eqs. 21.18 and Eq. 21.19e.

P21.4   This problem is concerned with the equivalence of the incremental form of Eq. 21.22b and the base current relationship for the hybrid-pi model, given by Eq. 21.23a.

(*a*) Show that Eq. 21.23a can be written as

$$i_b = \left(\frac{g_\pi}{g_m}\right)\frac{Q_b}{\tau_F} + \frac{dQ_b}{dt} + C_{je}\frac{dv_{be}}{dt} - C_\mu\frac{dv_{cb}}{dt}$$

where Q_b is the charge developed on C_b by v_{be}.

(*b*) Linearize Eq. 21.22b to obtain

$$i_b = \frac{Q_b}{\tau_{BF}} + \frac{dQ_b}{dt} + C_{je}\frac{dv_{be}}{dt} - C_\mu\frac{dv_{cb}}{dt}$$

Note that $-Q_b$ is the incremental component of q_F and that at some particular operating point $dq_{VE}/dt = C_{je}\,dv_{eb}/dt = -C_{je}\,dv_{be}/dt$, and pay particular attention to the signs in this equation. Since $g_\pi/g_m = \beta^{-1}$, these incremental relationships are equivalent. (See page 768.)

P21.5   This problem is concerned with models that apply in the forward region of operation. (See page 772.)

(*a*) Write the expressions for I_E and I_C that are implied by the model of Fig. 21.9*a*. Show that these expressions are equivalent to Eqs. 21.4a and b if $V_{CB} \ll -kT/q$.

(*b*) Show that the model of Fig. 21.9*c* can be developed from the model of Fig. 21.9*a* by using Kirchhoff's current law to express I_F in terms of I_E and $\alpha_R I_{CS}$.

(*c*) Write the expressions for I_E and I_C that are implied by the model of Fig. 21.9*c*. Show that these expressions are equivalent to Eqs. 21.4a and 21.6a if $V_{CB} \ll -kT/q$.

(d) Show that the model of Fig. 21.9d can be developed from the model of Fig. 21.9c by using Kirchhoff's current law to express I_E in terms of I_B and I_C.

P21.6 Sketch and label models for *npn* transistors that are analogous to the *pnp* forms shown in Figs. 21.9c and d. Recall that the coefficients α_F, α_R, I_{ES}, and I_{CS} are *positive* quantities in both *npn* and *pnp* devices and pay particular attention to polarities and reference directions.

P21.7 This problem is concerned with the saturation region behavior of a *pnp* transistor. Assume, for simplicity, that $\alpha_F = \alpha_R = \alpha$ (thus $I_{ES} = I_{CS} = I_S$). Assume also that the emitter current is *fixed* at the value I for all the conditions described below.

(a) Consider first the case in which the transistor is at the edge of saturation, that is, $v_{CB} = 0$. Evaluate the collector current I_C, the base current I_B, and the emitter-to-base voltage V_{EB} at the edge of saturation.

(b) Consider next the case in which the transistor is forced deep into saturation by making $I_C = I_E$; the corresponding base-region excess-carrier distribution is shown in Fig. 21.14c. Evaluate the base current I_B, and the emitter-to-base voltage V_{EB} under these conditions.

(c) Compare the value of total excess charge in the base q_B when $I_C = I_E$ with the corresponding value for $V_{CB} = 0$. Compare as well the corresponding values of V_{EB}.

(d) Explain, in terms of the internal physical behavior of the transistor, why q_B and V_{EB} are so much larger when $I_C = I_E$ than they are when $V_{CB} = 0$.

P21.8 The inequalities of Eqs. 21.40b and 21.41b apply to *pnp* transistors. Derive the corresponding inequalities for *npn* transistors.

P21.9 This problem is concerned with the approximate saturation-region dynamic analysis developed in Section 21.4.3.

(a) Verify Eq. 21.47.

(b) Assume that $q_{FS}(t)$ and $q_s(t)$ are related under dynamic conditions in the same way they are related statically, that is, neglect the dq_R/dt term in Eq. 21.47, and verify Eqs. 21.48 and 21.49.

P21.10 Consider an *npn* junction transistor in which $\beta_F \gg 1$ and $\tau_{BF} = 50$ nsec.

(a) Assume that the transistor is *symmetric* so that $\beta_R = \beta_F$ and $\tau_{BR} = \tau_{BF}$. What is the value of τ_S, the saturation-region charge-control parameter?

(b) The more common situation is one in which β_R is much smaller than β_F. Assume $\beta_R = \beta_F/10$ (but $\beta_R \gg 1$), and $\tau_{BR} = 100$ nsec, and evaluate τ_S.

P21.11 The dependence of the collector current I_C on the emitter-to-base voltage V_{EB} is shown for an *npn* transistor in Fig. 21.22. Note that this curve was determined for a reverse voltage on the collector junction, that is, for $V_{CB} \gg kT/q$. Assume that this transistor is adequately described by the Ebers-Moll model (Eqs. 21.5).

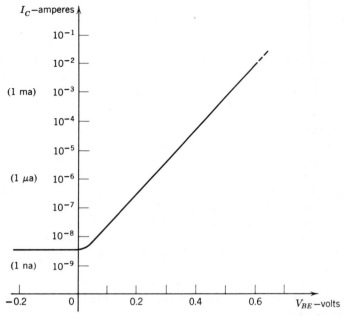

Figure 21.22   Dependence of collector current on base-to-emitter voltage for an *npn* transistor operating with reverse-biased collector. Note that the ordinate scale is logarithmic.

(a) What can you say about the relative sizes of I_{ES} and I_{CS}?

(b) Evaluate I_{CS}.

(c) Determine the value of kT/q for which these data apply (i.e., determine the temperatures at which the measurements were made).

(d) Evaluate I_{ES}.

CHAPTER TWENTY-TWO

Single-Stage Digital Circuits

22.1 Some Basic Properties of Digital Circuits

In most systems that process information in digital form, the electrical variables that represent information are nominally two-valued in nature. For example, information may be represented by a voltage or current that ideally takes on one or the other of two discrete values; or the representation may be in terms of a pulse of definite shape that is either present or absent at a specific time. Other forms of representation or scripts are obviously possible. Circuits that are employed in digital systems must respond to signals that are two-valued or binary in nature and must also produce appropriately quantized output signals. These requirements are in sharp contrast to those that apply to most systems that process information represented by continuous variables, where circuits must respond linearly over large dynamic ranges of the input and output variables.

Of course, variations caused by component and power-supply tolerances as well as by distortion and noise complicate the situation. Specifically, information that is, in principle, represented by discrete voltage levels must, in practice, be represented by ranges or bands of voltage as shown in Fig. 22.1. Similarly, systems in which information is conveyed by the presence or absence at a particular time of a pulse of nominally definite shape must distinguish between spurious signals and pulses that merely deviate from the ideal in shape or arrival time. Usually the main problem presented to the designer of digital circuits is that of ensuring that the circuits perform the proper logical function in spite of broad, nearly overlapping ranges of values

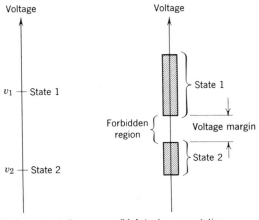

(a) Idealized representation   (b) Actual representation

Figure 22.1   Representation of a binary variable by means of voltage levels.

for the nominally two-valued variables. The important consideration is to be able to *distinguish* between the two states. In terms of the voltage-level representation of Fig. 22.1, a key parameter is the width of the forbidden region, called the *voltage margin*. The digital circuit designer must ensure that under no circumstances will the steady-state output of a circuit lie in the forbidden region. Also, the designer must choose a voltage margin large enough so that the circuit will respond unambiguously to inputs that lie within the permissible ranges on both sides of this forbidden zone, in spite of power-supply drift, noise, and similar factors.

Most of the circuits employed in digital systems either use highly non-linear devices, such as diodes, to set the levels of the variables that represent information, or operate the transistors in a nonlinear manner as the basis for establishing the two ranges of the output variables. In the latter case, it is the emitter and/or collector diodes that set the levels. Although it is certainly possible to design transistor circuits that accept and produce two-valued signals while operating as linear amplifiers, this is not usually done in digital systems. Circuits operated in a markedly nonlinear manner discriminate more accurately between the ranges of values of the input variable and produce outputs that are less sensitive to the parameters of the transistors and other components, hence better quantized. Use of such extreme non-linearity actually amounts to using the *on* and *off* states of a *pn* junction to represent the binary information, and as such really is a *state representation* rather than a representation in terms of a voltage or current level.

In one common form of state representation in transistor circuits, the transistor is cut off in one state and saturated in the other. The operating condition that lies in the *cutoff region* is usually referred to as the *off* state. In the *off* state the terminal currents, which result from the extraction of thermally-generated minority carriers, are very small and essentially in-dependent of the junction voltages. Furthermore, the minority-carrier concentration throughout the base region is negligible compared with its equilibrium value.

The operating state that lies in the *saturation region* is called the *on* state. In this state both the emitter and collector junctions are forward-biased, and thus all terminal-pair voltages are small and weakly dependent on the terminal currents. The minority-carrier concentration in the base is greater than the equilibrium concentration, so that the corresponding store of excess carriers is positive.

A transistor that is constrained by the circuit and input variables to operate in the *off* and *on* states described above can be regarded as a switch which is controlled by the *charge* in the base region. This charge appears in part as excess mobile charge throughout the neutral base region and in part as unneutralized impurity charge in the base sides of the junction space-charge layers. Inasmuch as majority carriers enter and leave the base region principally through the base terminal, both the excess charge in the neutral portion of the base and the space-charge-layer charge at the junctions are under the control of the base current. Consequently, a transistor can be switched from one state to the other by supplying or removing base charge at the base terminal.

We begin our analysis of transistor switches and digital circuits by examining the static and dynamic behavior of the simple inverter shown in Fig. 22.2a, which is similar to the circuit analyzed in Section 21.5.2 except here we have no emitter resistor. As we shall see, this common-emitter circuit can provide signal standardization, power gain, and other useful logical properties.

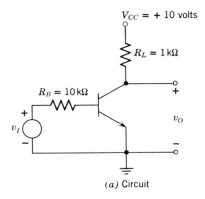

(a) Circuit

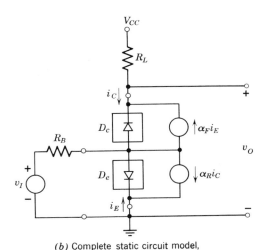

(b) Complete static circuit model,
with the transistor represented by
an ideal–diode model

Figure 22.2 A simple transistor pulse inverter (*npn*).

22.2 Static Properties of a Transistor Inverter
22.2.1 Transfer Characteristic

To establish the properties of the inverter circuit in Fig. 22.2a, we first calculate the static transfer characteristic of the circuit. We have chosen

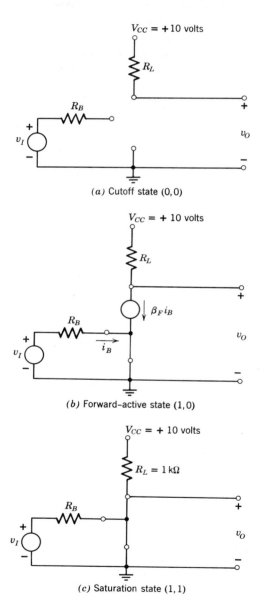

(a) Cutoff state (0,0)

(b) Forward–active state (1,0)

(c) Saturation state (1,1)

Figure 22.3 Limited-range circuit models.

in Fig. 22.2*b* to represent the transistor by the ideal-diode model, so that the analysis is quite simple: the characteristic will be made up of straight-line segments. There are four possible states for this circuit, corresponding to the four possible states of the diodes. However, a closer examination of Fig. 22.2*b* will show that there is no value of v_I that will force the collector diode *on* while leaving the emitter diode *off*. Hence the reverse-active state $(0,1)$ cannot be realized in this circuit. [It is often convenient to use the notation (A, B) to indicate the states of the emitter and collector diodes respectively.]

Circuit models appropriate for the cutoff state $(0, 0)$ the forward-active state $(1, 0)$, and the saturation state $(1, 1)$ are shown in Fig. 22.3. For the $(0, 0)$ state (Fig. 22.3*a*)

$$i_C = 0 \tag{22.1}$$

$$v_O = V_{CC} = 10 \text{ volts} \tag{22.2}$$

We see from Fig. 22.2*b* that any value of v_I less than zero will maintain the circuit in this state.

In the forward-active state (Fig. 22.3*b*) we find by inspection that

$$v_O = V_{CC} - \beta_F R_L i_B \tag{22.3a}$$

$$= V_{CC} - \beta_F R_L \frac{v_I}{R_B} \tag{22.3b}$$

Clearly, in this state the slope of the transfer characteristic v_O/v_I, that is, the incremental voltage gain, is just $-\beta_F R_L/R_B$.

For the saturation $(1, 1)$ state, it is clear from Fig. 22.3*c* that the output voltage and current are constant, independent of the input voltage:

$$v_O = 0 \tag{22.4}$$

$$i_C = I_C(\text{sat}) = \frac{V_{CC}}{R_L} = 10 \text{ ma} \tag{22.5}$$

The transition between the $(1, 0)$ state and the $(1, 1)$ state occurs for v_I such that $v_O = 0$ in Eq. 22.3. Thus at this point, from Eqs. 22.3a and 22.5,

$$i_B = \frac{V_{CC}}{\beta_F R_L} = \frac{I_C(\text{sat})}{\beta_F} \tag{22.6}$$

Also, from Eq. 22.3b, assuming that $\beta_F = 50$, $R_B = 10 \text{ kohm}$, $R_L = 1 \text{ kohm}$,

$$v_I = \frac{V_{CC} R_B}{\beta_F R_L} \tag{22.7}$$

$$= \frac{10 \times 10}{50 \times 1} = 2 \text{ volts}$$

The complete static transfer characteristic, based on the preceding calculations, is shown in Fig. 22.4.

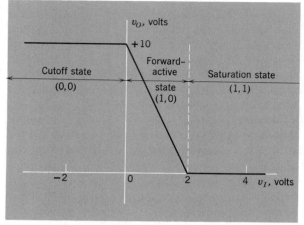

Figure 22.4   Static transfer characteristics for the transistor inverter circuit in Fig. 22.2.

22.2.2   Logical Properties

We see from the transfer characteristic in Fig. 22.4 that the inverter circuit in Fig. 22.2 will produce one or the other of two output values that are essentially independent of the characteristics of the transistor, if the input is constrained to take one or the other of two widely-separated ranges of values. More precisely, if v_I is negative, the transistor is cut off and v_O is approximately 10 volts (the collector supply voltage). If, on the other hand, v_I is more than about 2 volts, the transistor is saturated and v_O is approximately zero. These relationships are summarized in Table 22.1.

Table 22.1   Voltage Relationships

v_I(volts)	v_O(volts)
Less than 0	$\simeq +10$
More than 2	$\simeq 0$

In a digital system the voltages v_I and v_O correspond to *binary variables*[1] **a** and **b**. The relationship between the values of the binary variable and the ranges of the physical variable is an arbitrary one. For the purpose of this discussion we make the assignment shown in Table 22.2.

Table 22.2   Voltage Assignment

Range of Voltage	Value of Binary Variable
2.5 to 10 volts	**1**
−1 to 0 volt	**0**

[1] In this text, all binary numbers and variables are printed in boldface type to avoid confusion.

This assignment is called *positive representation* because the voltage range assigned to the **1** state is more positive than the range assigned to the **0** state. (The opposite assignment of voltages is obviously called *negative represent-ation*.) If the amplifier is driven with a voltage within the ranges listed above, we can describe the circuit operation very succinctly in terms of binary variables, as indicated in Table 22.3.

Table 22.3   Table of Combinations

Input	Output
0	**1**
1	**0**

This relationship is that of *complementation*: the output variable is the *complement* of the input variable. Thus the circuit is called an *inverter*.

The inverter circuit shown in Fig. 22.2 has other useful properties. Note first that the output variable is better quantized or standardized than the input variable. Any negative input voltage[2] produces an output voltage that is very nearly equal to 10 volts because the transistor is cut off. Similarly, any input voltage more positive than 2.5 volts (limited by the power dissipation in the input resistor) causes the transistor to be saturated and yields an output voltage of very nearly zero volts.

The inverter circuit provides power gain as well. When the input has a binary value **1**, the circuit can be characterized by an input resistance of about 10 kohm. When the output variable is **1**, the output resistance is 1 kohm. Consequently, the inverter can be loaded by as many as 30 other circuits like it (having an input resistance of 10 kohm) before the variable v_O

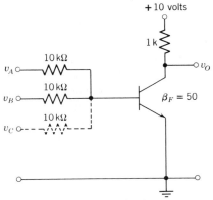

Figure 22.5   Transistor-resistor logic circuit.

[2] The lower limit on v_I is set by avalanche breakdown of the *emitter* junction.

corresponding to the output drops below the prescribed lower limit of its range, which is 2.5 volts. Because it is capable of driving 30 other circuits having the same input requirements as itself, the circuit is said to have a *fan-out ratio* of 30.

If one or more resistors are added at the base of the transistor, as shown in Fig. 22.5, our simple inverter becomes a logic gate. If we use the same positive representation as given in Table 22.2, the transistor will be saturated and the binary output will be **0** if one or more of the inputs is greater than 2.5 volts, that is, is a binary **1**. Thus the possible binary combinations for the circuit are as shown in Table 22.4 (assuming only two inputs).

Table 22.4   Table of Combinations

a	b	Binary Output
0	0	1
0	1	0
1	0	0
1	1	0

The output logical variable in this transistor gate is the *complement* of the corresponding output of the diode OR gate, Fig. 6.9a. Thus we call the gate in Fig. 22.5 a NOR gate meaning "Not Or", to indicate that both complementation and OR gating are involved. (See Problem P22.1.)

Although the transistor in the circuit in Fig. 22.5 is essentially an inverter and thus performs a certain logical function, its principal role is that of signal standardization. Note that the base current of the transistor varies over a range of nearly 3 to 1 depending on whether one, two, or three of the input variables is in the **1** state. However, the transistor is saturated for all such conditions, so the output voltage v_O is essentially independent of the base current.

22.2.3   Conditions on the Static States

The output voltage of a simple transistor switch will be reasonably well quantized only if the transistor is driven between cutoff and saturation. The circuit parameters, the input signal amplitude ranges, and the load that is driven by the circuit must be chosen so that under static conditions the *on* state lies in the saturation region and the *off* state lies in the cutoff region.

Saturation. Saturation of the transistor occurs, as we saw in Section 22.2.1, if

$$|I_B| \geqslant \frac{|I_C(\text{sat})|}{\beta_F} \tag{22.8}$$

There are several reasons why the static base current must be larger than the minimum value of $|I_C(\text{sat})/\beta_F|$. First, transistors of a particular type exhibit a rather broad range of values for β_F. Many transistor types show 2 to 1 ranges of variation in β_F at a particular operating point, and 10 to 1 variations are not uncommon. Clearly, a circuit that is to operate properly with *any* transistor of a certain type number must be designed so that adequate base current is provided for the units that have the *minimum* specified value of β_F. Consequently, units that have larger values of β_F will have more than enough base drive.

Second, the collector current in the *on* state depends on the load which the circuit drives, and this load generally is not constant. Inasmuch as Eq. 22.8 must be satisfied for the largest possible value of $|I_C(\text{sat})|$, the base current will be more than adequate for those operating conditions in which the collector current is less than maximum.

Third, normal variations of component values and power-supply voltages cause variations in the base drive and in the load current. The circuit designer must ensure that the base current is adequate for operation in the saturation region even with the most unfavorable combination of component and power-supply values. Therefore, the base current will be more than adequate under most conditions.

One of the processes by which the circuit designer ensures that the circuit will be in the proper state in spite of transistor variations from unit to unit, load and drive variations, and component and power-supply tolerances is called *worst-case design*. It involves determining the worst possible combination of circuit and device parameters, under the most unfavorable environmental conditions, and specifying the circuit so that it functions properly even in this worst-possible case. Such a design philosophy is extremely conservative, inasmuch as the worst case may be an exceedingly improbable event. Nevertheless, worst-case design guarantees proper circuit performance under all conditions short of component failure (see Problems P22.2 through P22.4).

Cutoff. The *off* state of a transistor switch corresponds to operation in the cutoff region with both junctions reverse-biased. The saturation currents I_{ES} and I_{CS} are so small in most silicon transistors that the collector current of a switch in the *off* state is substantially independent of the emitter junction voltage for junction voltages less than several tenths of a volt in the forward direction. This is illustrated in Fig. 22.6, which shows I_C versus V_{BE} for an *npn* silicon switching transistor. A switching circuit that uses this transistor and has an *on*-state collector current of several milliamperes is effectively in the *off* state if the emitter-base voltage is less than about 0.3 volt. Below this voltage, which is referred to as the *base-emitter threshold voltage* V_{BET}, the injection of minority carriers into the base by the emitter junction has an insignificant effect on the collector current. Threshold voltages are smaller in germanium transistors (about 0.1 volt at room temperature) because the saturation currents are larger. The threshold voltage reflects the exponential temperature dependence of the saturation currents and thus has a

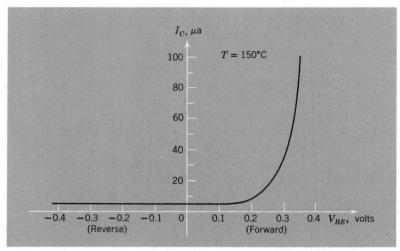

Figure 22.6   Dependence of collector current on base-emitter voltage in an *npn* silicon transistor at 150°C.

temperature coefficient of −2 to −3 mv/°C for both silicon and germanium. (See Section 4.3.3.)

In the design of a transistor switching circuit, the static *off* state must be examined under worst-case conditions to ensure satisfactory operation (see Problems P22.2 through P22.4). This usually implies consideration of the highest environmental temperature, for which the saturation currents are at their maximum values, and threshold voltages are at their minimum values.

22.3   Transitions between States

Now that we have explored the static properties of a transistor inverter, we turn to a detailed examination of the dynamics of the circuit. In digital applications we not only want voltages quantized into two discrete levels, corresponding to two distinct states of the transistor, but we also want to be able to change from one state to the other with the greatest possible speed. To change a transistor switch from the *off* state to the *on* state, we must supply charge to the base region. This charge is required to change the *off*-state space-charge-layer charges and to establish enough excess charge in the base region to support the *on*-state collector current. Conversely, to turn a transistor off, we must remove all the excess charge from the base region and must, in addition, change the space-charge-layer charges so that they can support the junction voltages demanded by the circuit with the transistor *off*. The times required to move these charges into and out of the transistor are of primary importance in digital circuit design, because they determine the maximum speed at which the switching circuit, hence the overall digital system, can be operated.

Clearly, the problem of switching between states involves operating the transistor in a nonlinear manner. Thus we are forced to represent the transistor by a large-signal dynamic model, that is, the charge-control model developed in Chapter 21. To be specific, we consider a silicon *npn* diffused transistor in the same inverter circuit that was discussed in Section 22.2. Obviously, the analysis of a *pnp* circuit poses no fundamental differences.

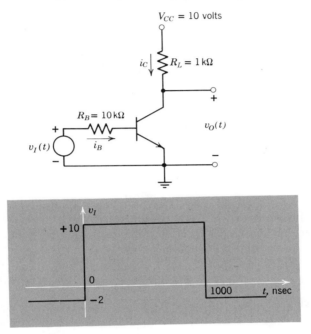

Figure 22.7 Transistor inverter.

The circuit for our simple inverter is repeated again in Fig. 22.7, along with a sketch of the voltage pulse that we assume is driving the input. For such a circuit we are usually interested in solving for $i_C(t)$, $v_O(t)$, or various transition times. With a voltage pulse drive as shown, the base current will, in general, depend on the junction voltages, which depend in a nonlinear fashion on the forward and reverse components of the base charge, which in turn depend on the history of the base current. This general situation can be described readily in terms of a set of simultaneous nonlinear differential equations. Specifically, we describe the circuit external to the transistor in Fig. 22.7 by the relations

$$v_I + v_{EB} = i_B R_B \qquad (22.9)$$

$$10 - v_O = i_C R_L \qquad (22.10)$$

$$v_O = v_{CB} - v_{EB} \qquad (22.11)$$

We describe the transistor by the charge-control relations developed in Section 21.3.5. Because we have to refer to these equations many times in this section, they are repeated below. The basic charge-control relations for this *npn* transistor are

$$i_B = \frac{q_F}{\tau_{BF}} + \frac{q_R}{\tau_{BR}} + \frac{d}{dt}(q_F + q_R + q_{VE} + q_{VC}) \tag{22.12a}$$

$$i_C = \frac{q_F}{\tau_F} - q_R\left(\frac{1}{\tau_R} + \frac{1}{\tau_{BR}}\right) - \frac{d}{dt}(q_R + q_{VC}) \tag{22.12b}$$

The base charge components q_F and q_R are related to the junction voltages by the expressions

$$q_F = Q_{FO}(e^{-q v_{EB}/kT} - 1) \tag{22.13a}$$

$$q_R = Q_{RO}(e^{-q v_{CB}/kT} - 1) \tag{22.13b}$$

where

$$Q_{FO} = \alpha_F I_{ES}\tau_F \tag{22.14a}$$

$$Q_{RO} = \alpha_R I_{CS}\tau_R \tag{22.14b}$$

Because this transistor is a graded-junction device, the space-charge-layer charges are related to the junction voltages by the expressions

$$q_{VE} = K_E[\psi_0{}^{\frac{2}{3}} - (\psi_0 + v_{EB})^{\frac{2}{3}}] \tag{22.15a}$$

$$q_{VC} = K_C[\psi_0{}^{\frac{2}{3}} - (\psi_0 + v_{CB})^{\frac{2}{3}}] \tag{22.15b}$$

We have nine equations and nine unknowns (three voltages, two currents, and four charges). Thus the equations can be solved, but in practice only by a digital computer. A complete computer-generated solution[3] is shown in Fig. 22.8, based on a silicon diffused-junction transistor with the following parameters:

$$\tau_F = 0.4 \text{ nsec} \qquad \tau_R = 10 \text{ nsec}$$

$$\beta_F = 75 \qquad \beta_R = 7$$

$$K_E = K_C = 5 \text{ pf(volt)}^{\frac{1}{3}}$$

$$\psi_0 = 0.9 \text{ volt}$$

$$Q_{FO} = 1 \times 10^{-10} \text{ pc} = 1 \times 10^{-22} \text{ coulombs}$$

$$Q_{RO} = 2.5 \times 10^{-9} \text{ pc}$$

Note from Fig. 22.8*b* that more than 40 nsec elapses before the transistor enters saturation and that it requires about 300 nsec to turn the transistor off once it is on. In fact, absolutely no change in the terminal voltages or

---

[3] The details of this solution, irrelevant at this point, are discussed in Section 22.6.

currents are observed for the first 75 nsec after the input voltage pulse is turned off! These delays are of central importance in digital circuit design because they represent the fundamental limit on the speed of operation of digital equipment.

Unfortunately, the computer solution shown in Fig. 22.8 provides little insight concerning how to reduce these undesirable delays in switching from one state to another. To gain this insight we must develop approximate methods of analysis which clearly pinpoint the sources of the time delays. Again we are willing to sacrifice accuracy for simplicity, because the performance of a final design can always be checked in detail on the computer.

Note first that in switching from cutoff to saturation and back to cutoff, the transistor will change state four times. To simplify the mathematics, we carry out the analysis state by state, representing the transistor in each state by one of the simple limited-range charge-control models developed in Section 21.4. We then piece together the solutions to form the entire transient solution.

To simplify the notation, we have defined in Figs. 22.8*a* and *c* the pertinent times in terms of the current and charge waveforms. All voltages, currents, and charges will be designated in terms of these times. The detailed shapes of the i_C and q_B waveforms in each region will be discussed in the following subsections.

22.3.1 Transitions through the Cutoff Region

We see from Fig. 22.7 that at the start of the transient, both v_{EB} and v_{CB} are positive. Specifically,

$$v_{EB}(t_0) = -v_I(t_0) = 2 \text{ volts} \tag{22.16}$$

$$v_{CB}(t_0) = V_{CC} - v_I(t_0) = 12 \text{ volts} \tag{22.17}$$

Thus the transistor starts out in the cutoff region, and we can model the circuit by using the simple cutoff region charge-control model, as shown in Fig. 22.9*a*. At $t = t_0$, the base current i_B becomes positive, corresponding to the flow of majority holes into the *p*-type base. It is clear from Fig. 22.9*a* that as a consequence of this base current, positive charge will be added to the space-charge-layer charges q_{VE} and q_{VC}, and the transistor will traverse the cutoff region. The transistor remains in the cutoff state until the emitter diode becomes sufficiently forward biased to bring the transistor into the active region, that is, until $v_{EB} \simeq -0.3$ volt for this silicon device. On the basis of this first-cut qualitative discussion, crude sketches can be made of the voltage, current, and charge waveforms of interest during the cutoff interval. These are shown in Figs. 22.9*b* through *g*. Obviously, the rough plots are not supposed to convey detailed information about the wave shapes. Rather, they help us to keep in mind the time intervals and the polarities of the variables in question.

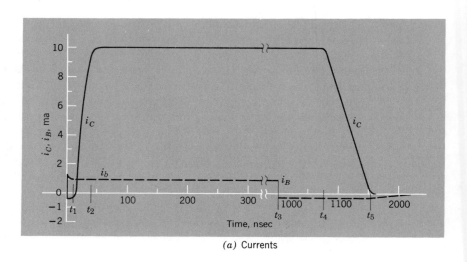

(a) Currents

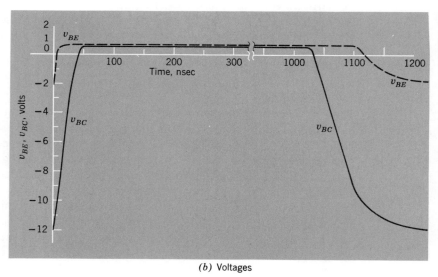

(b) Voltages

Figure 22.8 Computer-generated solution of the voltages, currents and charges for the inverter in Fig. 22.7.

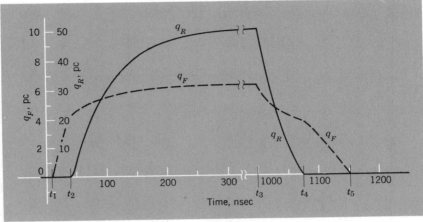

(c) Base charge

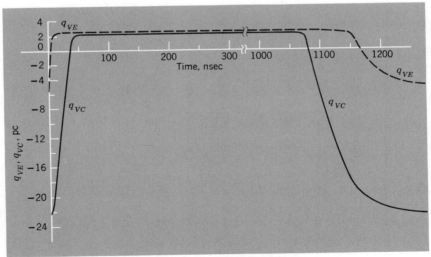

(d) Space–charge–layer charges

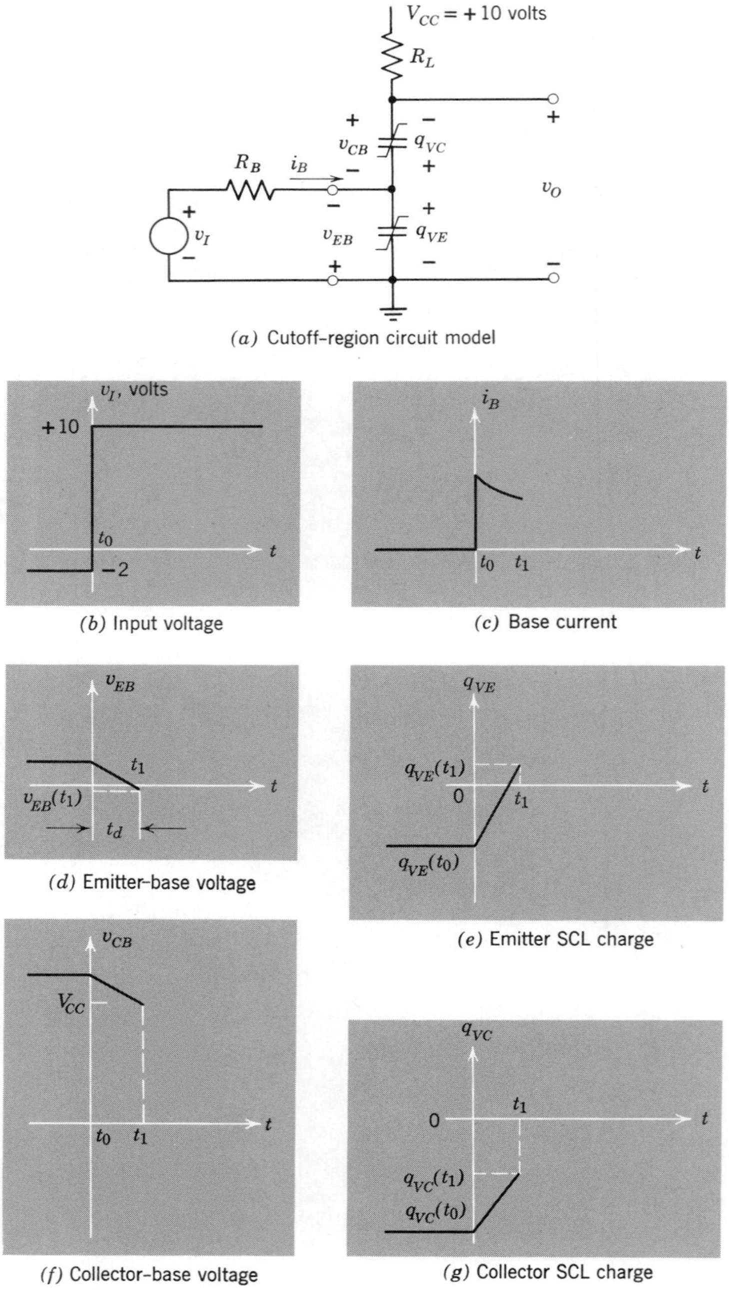

(a) Cutoff–region circuit model

(b) Input voltage

(c) Base current

(d) Emitter-base voltage

(e) Emitter SCL charge

(f) Collector-base voltage

(g) Collector SCL charge

Figure 22.9   Crude sketches of the transition through the cutoff region. The transistor enters the active region at $t = t_1$. For $t_0 < t < t_1$, the base-region excess charge is approximately zero.

The appropriate equations for the transistor in the cutoff region are, from Section 21.4.2,

$$i_B = \frac{d}{dt}(q_{VE} + q_{VC}) \tag{22.18a}$$

$$i_C = -\frac{dq_{VC}}{dt} \tag{22.18b}$$

If we can estimate $i_B(t)$ during the cutoff interval, we can integrate Eq. 22.18a and solve for the time interval required for the emitter-base junction to become forward-biased. Integration of Eq. 22.18a yields

$$\int_{t_0}^{t_1} i_B(t)\,dt = [q_{VE}(t_1) - q_{VE}(t_0)] + [q_{VC}(t_1) - q_{VC}(t_0)] \tag{22.19}$$

where, as stated above, the notation $q_{VE}(t_1)$ indicates the space-charge-layer charge at $t = t_1$. The four charge values in Eq. 22.19 can be readily calculated, so that if we can estimate i_B, the expression can be solved for the time interval $t_1 - t_0$, usually called the *delay time t_d*.

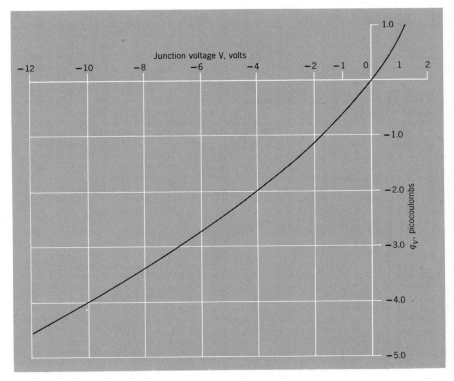

Figure 22.10 Space-charge-layer charge versus voltage for a graded junction with $K = 1$.

We can find $q_{VE}(t_0)$ and $q_{VC}(t_0)$ from Eqs. 22.15 using the voltage values specified in Eqs. 22.16 and 22.17. To facilitate this and subsequent calculations we show in Fig. 22.10 a normalized plot [$K = 1$ pf(volt)$^{1/3}$] of q_V versus voltage obtained using Eq. 22.15. From the graph, recalling that $K_E = K_C = 5$ pf(volt)$^{1/3}$ for this transistor, we obtain

$$q_{VE}(t_0) = -5.5 \text{ pc}$$

$$q_{VC}(t_0) = -22.9 \text{ pc}$$

At t_1, the end of the cutoff interval, the operating point moves from the cutoff region into the active region. For the silicon transistor the junction voltages at this instant will be approximately

$$v_{EB}(t_1) \simeq -0.3 \text{ volt}$$

$$v_{CB}(t_1) = V_{CC} - 0.3 = 9.7 \text{ volts}$$

(neglecting any collector current in R_L). Note that v_{EB} and v_{CB} change by the same amount between t_0 and t_1. The charges $q_{VE}(t_1)$ and $q_{VC}(t_1)$ can now be found from Eqs. 22.15 or Fig. 22.10:

$$q_{VE}(t_1) = +1.1 \text{ pc}$$

$$q_{VC}(t_1) = -19.2 \text{ pc}$$

We can often make a fairly good estimate of $i_B(t)$ when v_{EB} does not change by very much compared with v_I. In the present example v_{EB} changes by only 2 volts, whereas v_I is 10 volts. Thus the base current immediately following the input step will be

$$i_B(t_0) = \frac{v_I + v_{EB}}{R_B} = \frac{10 + 2}{10} = 1.2 \text{ ma}$$

and the final base current will be

$$i_b(t_1) = \frac{10 - 0.3}{10} = 0.97 \text{ ma}$$

On this basis we estimate an average base current of about 1.1 ma during the cutoff interval, and Eq. 22.19 becomes

$$\int_0^{t_d} (1.1)\, dt = (1.1 + 5.5) + (-19.2 + 22.9) = 10.3 \text{ pc}$$

Solving for the delay time t_d, we obtain

$$t_d = \frac{10.3}{1.1} = 9.4 \text{ nsec}$$

This value compares very favorably with the 10 nsec value obtained in the computer solution (see Fig. 22.8). (See also the lecture demonstrations in Section 22.7.)

The collector current is actually slightly negative during the delay time because majority carriers must be supplied to the collector half of the space-charge layer (see Eq. 22.18b). The division of the base current between the collector and emitter is determined by the relative rates of change of q_{VC} and q_{VE}. However, the collector current during this interval is usually negligible compared with the *on*-state collector current.

22.3.2 Transients in the Active Region

When the emitter junction becomes forward-biased, the transistor enters the active region. Thus we must change the circuit model to that shown in Fig. 22.11a. With the emitter forward-biased, excess charge q_F begins to accumulate in the base, and substantial collector current flows. The collector current increases until at time t_2 it reaches a saturation value defined by the external circuit parameters. Thus from Fig. 22.11a,

$$i_C(t_2) \equiv I_C(\text{sat}) \simeq \frac{V_{CC}}{R_L} = 10 \text{ ma} \qquad (22.20)$$

In the active region v_{EB} rises rapidly from -0.3 to -0.6 volt, then stays fixed at about -0.6 or -0.7 volt. Thus the base current will be about 0.94 ma. Rough sketches of the pertinent waveforms are shown in Fig. 22.11.

If we neglect the dq_{VC}/dt term in the collector current equation, in accordance with the discussion in Section 21.4, the charge-control equations in the active region become

$$i_B = \frac{q_F}{\tau_{BF}} + \frac{d}{dt}(q_F + q_{VE} + q_{VC}) \qquad (22.21a)$$

$$i_C \simeq \frac{q_F}{\tau_F} \qquad (22.21b)$$

The time required to traverse the active region can be found by integrating Eq. 22.21a:

$$\underbrace{\int_{t_1}^{t_2} i_B \, dt = \Delta q_F + \Delta q_{VE} + \Delta q_{VC}}_{\substack{\text{Change in} \\ \text{stored charge}}} + \underbrace{\frac{1}{\tau_{BF}} \int_{t_1}^{t_2} q_F \, dt}_{\substack{\text{Recombination} \\ \text{charge}}} \qquad (22.22)$$

Because β_F is 75,

$$\beta_F |I_B| \gg |I_C(\text{sat})| \qquad (22.23)$$

so that the transistor will eventually be driven deep into saturation. Thus we are assured of rapid traversal of the active region and can neglect the recombination term in Eq. 22.22. On this basis the equation can be solved for the *rise time* t_r, that is, the time interval between the particular instant when the emitter junction becomes forward-biased and the instant when the transistor enters saturation. Recall from the cutoff region calculations that $q_F(t_1) = 0$, $q_{VE}(t_1) = 1.1$ pc, and $q_{VC}(t_1) = -19.2$ pc. At t_2, when the

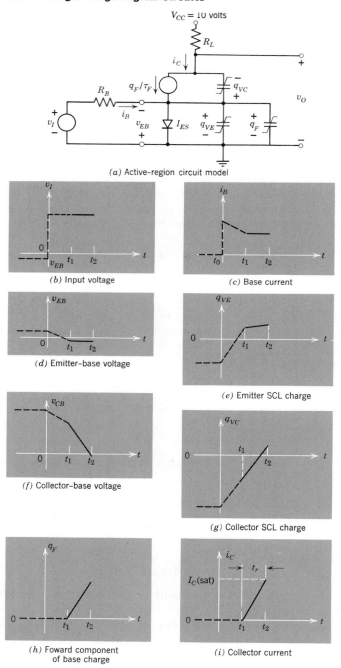

(a) Active-region circuit model

(b) Input voltage

(c) Base current

(d) Emitter–base voltage

(e) Emitter SCL charge

(f) Collector–base voltage

(g) Collector SCL charge

(h) Foward component of base charge

(i) Collector current

Figure 22.11 Rough sketches of the transition through the active region. The transistor enters the saturation region at $t = t_2$. For $t_0 < t < t_2$ the reverse component of the base-region excess charge is approximately zero.

transistor is at the edge of saturation, $v_{EB} = -0.7$ volt, and v_{CB} will be about -0.3 volt; hence from Fig. 22.10, $q_{VE}(t_2) = 2.7$ pc and $q_{VC}(t_2) = +1.1$ pc. We find $q_F(t_2)$ from Eqs. 22.21b and 22.20:

$$q_F(t_2) = I_C(\text{sat})\tau_F \tag{22.24}$$

$$= 10 \times 0.4 = 4 \text{ pc}$$

These results are summarized in Table 22.5.

Table 22.5   Charges in picocoulombs for circuit in Fig. 22.7

Time	q_{VE}	Δq_{VE}	q_{VC}	Δq_{VC}	q_F	Δq_F
t_0	-5.5		-22.9		0	
		$+6.6$		$+3.7$		0
t_1	1.1		-19.2		0	
		$+1.6$		$+20.3$		$+4$
t_2	2.7		$+1.1$		4	

As noted above, in the active region $i_B(t)$ is almost constant at 0.94 ma. Thus Eq. 22.22 reduces to

$$0.94 (t_2 - t_1) = 4 + 1.6 + 20.3$$

or the rise time is

$$t_r = t_2 - t_1 = \frac{25.9}{0.94} = 27.6 \text{ nsec}$$

The corresponding value obtained on the computer is, from Fig. 22.8,

$$t_r = 31 \text{ nsec}$$

We expect the approximate solution to yield a rise time smaller than is given by the computer solution because the recombination which we neglected will *slow down* the transient. Some of the base current must go into supplying this recombination, thereby reducing the current available for charging the capacitors (see Eq. 22.21a). We can estimate the amount of recombination by assuming a linear increase in q_F with time between t_1 and t_2. On this basis the charge lost in recombination is

$$q_{\text{lost}} = \frac{1}{\tau_{BF}} \int_{t_1}^{t_2} q_F \, dt$$

$$= \left(\frac{4}{0.4 \times 75}\right)\left(\frac{27.6}{2}\right) = 1.8 \text{ pc}$$

which is a 7% effect in our approximate calculations.

22.3.3   Saturation Region

Because the base current is more than adequate to drive the transistor into saturation, as we found in Section 22.3.2, the excess charge in the base, $q_B = q_F + q_R$, continues to build up for some time after time t_2 (when the transistor enters saturation). Specifically, q_F and q_R build up until the net rate of recombination is just equal to the base current. During this time, *all external variables, i_B, i_C, v_{EB}, and v_{CB} are almost constant.* Therefore, the exact wave shapes of the internal variables q_F and q_R are not too important. But we do need to know the sum $q_F + q_R$ at t_3, the instant of turn-off of the input pulse, because this directly influences the turn-off time of the circuit, as we shall see in the next section. Because the junction voltages are virtually constant, q_{VE} and q_{VC} do not change and therefore can be omitted from the model. Thus we can form the saturation-region circuit model shown in Fig. 22.12.

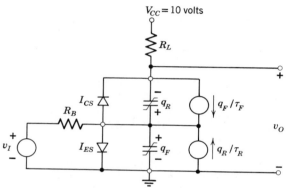

$V_{CC} = 10$ volts

Figure 22.12   Saturation-region charge-control circuit model.

Perhaps the simplest way of finding the total stored charge $q_F + q_R$ at time t_3 is to calculate the saturation charge q_S using Eq. 21.51:

$$i_B - \frac{I_C(\text{sat})}{\beta_F} = \frac{dq_S}{dt} + \frac{q_S}{\tau_S} \qquad (22.25)$$

Recall from Eq. 21.49b that the saturation time constant τ_S is

$$\tau_S = \frac{\tau_{BF}(\beta_R + 1) + \tau_{BR}\beta_F}{\beta_F + \beta_R + 1} \qquad (22.26)$$

$$= \frac{30(8) + (70)(75)}{75 + 7 + 1}$$

$$= 66 \text{ nsec}$$

Because the input voltage pulse is 1 μsec long and the delay and rise times sum to only 35.2 nsec, there is ample time for the transistor to reach steady-state saturation ($5\tau_S < 1000 - t_d - t_r$). Hence $q_S(t_3)$ is the steady-state q_S in Eq. 22.25:

$$q_S(t_3) = q_S \text{ (steady-state)} = \tau_S\left[I_B - \frac{I_C(\text{sat})}{\beta_F} \right]$$

$$= (66)\left(0.94 - \frac{10}{75}\right) = 53.5 \text{ pc}$$

Therefore, the charge in the base at time t_3 is

$$q_B(t_3) = q_F + q_R = q_S + q_{BO} = 53.5 + 4 = 58.5 \text{ pc}$$

These calculations are confirmed by the computer calculations in Fig. 22.8, which show the q_F and q_R transients substantially completed in 350 nsec, with a final base charge of $q_B(t_3) = 6.3 + 50.9 = 57.2$ pc.

22.3.4 Storage Delay

In the steady *on* state, the transistor switch has constant base current I_B and constant collector current $I_C(\text{sat})$. The transition to the *off* state is initiated by reversing the base current so that excess carriers are removed from the base, both through the base terminal and by recombination.

The turn-off transition can conveniently be divided into three intervals, as indicated on the roughly sketched waveforms in Fig. 22.13:

1. Because in this example the *on* state lies in the saturation region, there is an interval during which excess carriers are being removed from the base although there is no change in the collector current. This interval ends where q_R (and q_S) equal zero, at which time the collector junction comes out of forward bias and the transistor leaves the saturation region and enters the forward-active region. We designate the duration of this *storage-delay interval* as t_{sd}. Changes in the space-charge-layer charges are, of course, negligible during this interval, because the terminal voltages are nearly constant.

2. The continued removal of excess charge from the base causes i_C to decrease in magnitude as the transistor traverses the active region. The corresponding time interval, which ends when the transistor enters the cutoff region, is called the *fall time* t_f.

3. The turnoff base current continues to remove majority carriers from the space-charge layers, thereby increasing the magnitudes of the space-charge-layer charges q_{VC} and q_{VE}. The steady state is reached when the junction voltages reach the static values that correspond to the *off* state. The turn-off base current cannot of course, be sustained in the cutoff region. There-fore, the base current must drop almost to zero when the transition is complete.

In evaluating the storage-delay time, it is certainly possible to work in terms of the forward and reverse components of the base charge and to find

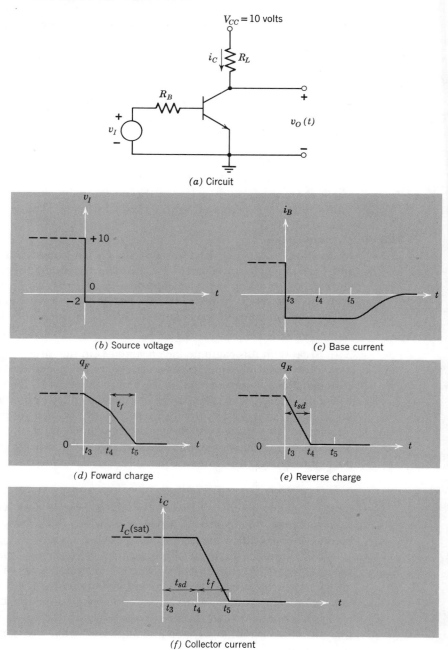

(a) Circuit

(b) Source voltage

(c) Base current

(d) Foward charge

(e) Reverse charge

(f) Collector current

Figure 22.13   Rough sketches showing the transition from *on* to *off*. When the base current reverses at $t = t_3$, q_S starts to drop. The transistor enters the active region at $t = t_4$ and the cutoff region at $t = t_5$.

the time required to reduce q_R to zero. However, it is again generally more convenient to work in terms of q_S and τ_S. The storage-delay time t_{sd} is obtained by solving Eq. 22.25 for $q_S(t)$, subject to the initial condition that $q_S(t_3) = 53.5$ pc, and calculating the time at which $q_S(t)$ goes to zero.

Since from t_3 on, v_I is negative, the base current abruptly reverses sign at t_3. It is clear from Fig. 22.12 that v_{EB} remains fixed at about -0.6 volt as long as q_F is positive. Thus

$$i_B = \frac{-2 - 0.6}{10} = -0.26 \text{ ma}$$

Substituting these values into Eq. 22.25, we obtain

$$-0.26 - \frac{10}{75} = \frac{q_S}{66} + \frac{dq_S}{dt} \tag{22.27}$$

Note that q_S is removed both by the negative base current and the recombination (see Problem P22.5). Thus applying a negative v_I during turn-off will appreciably shorten the turn-off interval.[4] Negative base current during turn-off is often referred to as *turn-off overdrive*. From the equation, we see that $q_S(t)$ is a decaying exponential, as shown in Fig. 22.14, with a final value (never reached because the transistor changes state) of

$$q_S(\text{final}) = -\left(0.26 + \frac{10}{75}\right)(66) = -26 \text{ pc}$$

As can be seen from Fig. 22.14, we can find the storage-delay time by solving for t_{sd} in the equation

$$26 = (53.5 + 26)e^{-t_{sd}/66}$$

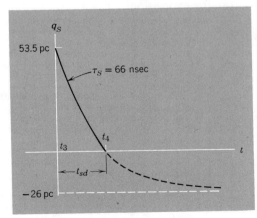

Figure 22.14   Decay of q_S, showing storage-delay time t_{sd}.

[4] This effect can be shown by the lecture demonstration discussed in Section 22.7.

Hence the storage-delay time is

$$t_{sd} = 66 \ln \frac{79.5}{26}$$

$$= 74 \text{ nsec}$$

From Fig. 22.8, the storage-delay time according to the computer solution is 76 nsec, which is in close agreement with our approximate solution.

It should be clear from the preceding calculation, and particularly from Fig. 22.14, that reducing $q_S(t_3)$ will reduce the storage-delay time. We can reduce $q_S(t_3)$ by reducing the input pulse amplitude, so that the transistor is not driven so hard into saturation, but then the turn-on time will increase. Also, recall from Section 22.2.3 that overdrive is required to ensure saturation under all circuit and environmental conditions.

The storage-delay time can also be reduced by increasing the turn-off overdrive. However, when this overdrive is produced by biasing the input pulse a few volts negative, as in the present example (see Fig. 22.7), the initial delay time t_d increases, because more space-charge-layer charge q_{VE} and q_{VC} must be supplied before the transistor enters the active region. (A better way of supplying overdrive is discussed in Section 22.4.) These methods of reducing storage-delay time, and the resulting interactions with the other switching times, can be shown most readily by the lecture demonstration discussed in Section 22.7.

22.3.5 Fall Time

Evaluation of the fall time is entirely analogous to the rise-time analysis in Section 22.3.2. If there is sufficient turn-off overdrive, we can frequently neglect the recombination component of base current. On this basis the fall time t_f can be found from the expression

$$\int_{t_4}^{t_5} i_B(t)\, dt \simeq [q_F(t_5) - q_F(t_4)] + [q_{VE}(t_5) - q_{VE}(t_4)]$$

$$+ [q_{VC}(t_5) - q_{VC}(t_4)]$$

where t_4 is the instant of entry into the active region and t_5 is the time when q_F drops to zero. A little thought will show that the Δq during the fall time will have the same magnitude as Δq during the rise time. Thus the integral equation reduces to

$$\int_{t_4}^{t_5} (-0.26)\, dt = -25.9$$

and the fall time t_f is

$$t_f = t_5 - t_4 = \frac{25.9}{0.26} = 99 \text{ nsec}$$

The computer solution indicates that the fall time is

$$t_f = 154 - 76 = 78 \text{ nsec}$$

The neglect of the recombination causes a significant (20%) error here because the active region is not traversed rapidly enough (see Problem P22.6). Note that recombination makes the transistor turn off *faster* than our crude calculations indicate.

If the turn-off transition is initiated by simply reducing the base current to zero, as it is in some switching circuits, the excess base charge decays solely by recombination. The fall time then is much longer than the value calculated above. (See Problem P22.7.)

22.3.6   Return to the Steady State

Although the collector current and the base charge components q_F and q_R are substantially zero at t_5, the end of the fall time, the circuit is not yet in the steady state. We still have to return the space-charge-layer charges to their initial values. The time required for the junction reverse voltages to reach their *off* state static values can be determined by computing the required changes in the space-charge-layer charges, as we did in evaluating the delay time in Section 22.3.1. Thus

$$\int_{t_5}^{t_6} i_B \, dt = \Delta q_V = -10.2 \tag{22.28}$$

During this interval, i_B will not be constant, but will be decreasing slowly from -0.26 ma to zero. If we arbitrarily assume a linear decrease, Eq. 22.28 becomes

$$\frac{-0.26}{2}(t_6 - t_5) = -10.2 \text{ pc}$$

$$t_6 - t_5 = 78.5 \text{ nsec}$$

The corresponding time interval in the computer solutions is about 100 nsec.

22.4   Speed-up Capacitor

Now that we have some insight into what causes turn-on and turn-off delays in transistor switches, let us try to modify the inverter circuit in order to reduce these delays. As we saw in the preceding section, one principal cause of distortion of the pulse shape and reduction in switching speed is the extra charge q_S stored in the base region in the *on*-state. This charge must be removed either by recombination or by a turn-off base drive, before the transistor can come out of saturation. The oscilloscope photograph in Fig. 22.15 of a typical transient response of an inverter circuit illustrates this phenomenon. In this case, for which the static *on*-state base current is considerably larger than the minimum value required for saturation, the

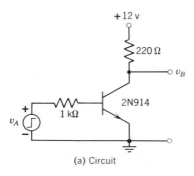

(a) Circuit

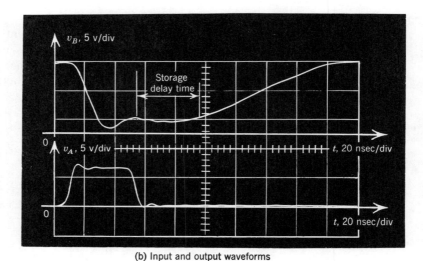

(b) Input and output waveforms

Figure 22.15   Storage-delay time in a saturating switching circuit.

storage-delay time is about 40 nsec. The fall time is about 80 nsec. These effects cause a gross distortion of the 40-nsec input pulse.

We saw in Section 22.3.4 that the storage-delay time can be reduced by providing a reverse base current (turn-off overdrive) that removes excess carriers from the base, thus augmenting the rate of decay of q_F and q_R (or q_S). In that example, the turn-off overdrive was provided by biasing the input voltage pulse as in Fig. 22.7. A better way of providing turn-off overdrive is to bridge the base resistor with a *speed-up capacitor* as discussed in Section 8.22 and shown in Fig. 22.16. In the *on*-state, the voltage across the capacitor is $I_B R$, so that the capacitor accumulates a charge of $I_B RC$. If C is adjusted so that the charge on the capacitor is equal to or greater than the *total* excess charge in the base in the *on*-state, the impulse-like current that results from the discharge of C when the input voltage drops, removes the excess

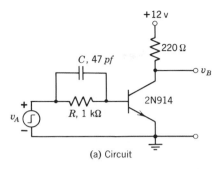

(a) Circuit

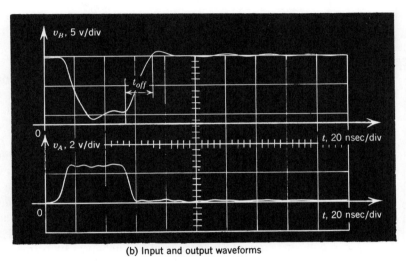

(b) Input and output waveforms

Figure 22.16   Reduction of storage-delay time by means of a speed-up capacitor. Note that the total turn-off time, t_{off}, is much less than without the speed-up capacitor.

base charge very rapidly, thereby reducing both the storage-delay time and the fall time. For the experiment illustrated in Fig. 22.16, the storage-delay time has been reduced to a few nanoseconds and the fall time is about 20 nsec.

The speed-up capacitor also provides an impulse-like turn-on current when the transistor is switched on, thereby reducing the delay time and the rise time. This latter effect was also discussed in Section 8.2.2.

The waveforms of Fig. 22.16 and the accompanying discussion are based on the tacit assumptions that the input pulse has rise and fall times that are negligibly small compared with the response times of the transistor, and that the pulse source can supply the peak current associated with the impulse-like components of the base drive. Neither of these conditions is satisfied in many practical switching circuits, particularly when the transistor in question is being driven by another transistor. In such cases the drive pulses have rise and fall times that are comparable to the response time of the transistor being driven, and peak drive currents are limited by the circuit. These matters will be discussed in Chapter 23.

22.5   Determination of the Charge-Control Parameters

We are now in a position to discuss methods of determining the eight charge-control parameters τ_F, τ_R, τ_{BF}, τ_{BR}, Q_{FO}, Q_{RO}, K_E, and K_C, both by direct measurement and by calculation from information supplied on manufacturers' data sheets. Because the charge-control model is by definition a large-signal model applicable from cutoff through saturation, the model parameters are assumed to be constant over the entire operating range and to be independent of voltage and current.

22.5.1   Parameter Determination by Direct Measurement

As pointed out in Chapter 12, there are many methods of measuring any given transistor parameter, but for simplicity and accuracy, the measurement should be made in such a way as to include an absolute minimum of parameters other than the desired one. This philosophy is followed as much as possible in the measurement procedures discussed below.

Measurement of τ_{BF} and τ_F. Clearly, parameters τ_{BF} and τ_F are associated with the forward injection of charge across the base, so that it is reasonable to determine these parameters by operating the transistor in the *forward-active region*. The key idea for the measurement of τ_{BF} is contained in Section 8.2.2 and Fig. 8.9. There it was shown that if a speed-up capacitor C was included in the circuit driving the base, as indicated in Fig. 22.17, a square wave collector current response could be achieved by proper adjustment of C and R_1. To minimize the influence of q_{VE}, we operate the transistor in the active region at all times ($|V_{EB}|$ greater than, say, 0.4 volt). Furthermore, we operate with the collector resistor R_2 very small (10 ohms or less) to minimize changes in v_{CB}, hence in q_{VC}. On this basis, the charge-control equations for an *npn* transistor reduce to

$$i_B \simeq \frac{q_F}{\tau_{BF}} + \frac{dq_F}{dt} \tag{22.29}$$

$$i_C \simeq \frac{q_F}{\tau_F} \tag{22.30}$$

If the step change in v_S is several volts, any small change in v_{EB} can be neglected. The step change in base current then is

$$\Delta i_B \simeq \frac{v_S(\text{final}) - v_S(\text{initial})}{R_1} = \frac{\Delta V}{R_1} \tag{22.31}$$

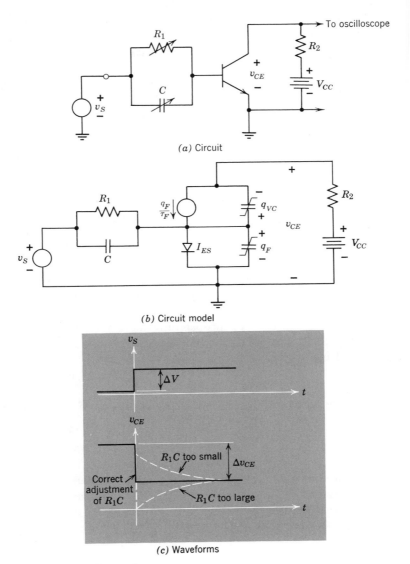

(a) Circuit

(b) Circuit model

(c) Waveforms

Figure 22.17   Measurement of τ_{BF} and τ_F.

and the charge delivered by C to the base of the transistor is

$$Q = C\,\Delta V \qquad (22.32)$$

Note that the symbol Δ is used to denote a change in a variable, that is, final value minus initial value, but in this context there is *no restriction on the size of the change*. In most cases the changes will be large. If R_1 and C

are appropriately adjusted, i_C and v_{CE} undergo step changes; otherwise, as indicated in the figure, growing or decaying response waveforms appear. At the condition of step i_C response, we know from Eq. 22.30 that q_F must also undergo a step change. As pointed out in Section 8.2.2, the capacitor C is inserting just enough charge into the base at $t = 0$ to bring about this step in q_F, and the resistor R_1 supplies just the right amount of base current to maintain this charge in the steady state in spite of recombination. Thus

$$C \, \Delta V = \Delta q_F \tag{22.33}$$

From Eq. 22.29, the step change in base current is related to Δq_F by

$$\Delta i_B = \frac{\Delta q_F}{\tau_{BF}} \tag{22.34}$$

Thus from Eqs. 22.31, 22.33, and 12.34 we have

$$\tau_{BF} = R_1 C \tag{22.35}$$

We conclude that τ_{BF} can be found by adjusting R_1 and v_S in Fig. 22.17, so that the transistor stays in the active region throughout the transient, and by adjusting C to give a step of output voltage. Under these conditions τ_{BF} is equal to the product $R_1 C$.

As noted above, for the proper adjustment of R_1 and C, both the collector voltage and collector current undergo a step change at $t = 0$. The step change in collector voltage will be

$$\Delta v_{CE} = -\Delta i_C R_2 \tag{22.36}$$

Thus from Eqs. 22.30, 22.36, and 22.33 we obtain a simple relation for finding τ_F:

$$\tau_F = -R_2 C \frac{\Delta V}{\Delta v_{CE}} \tag{22.37}$$

Note that if an oscilloscope with a current probe of sufficient sensitivity and bandwidth is available, then R_2 in Fig. 22.17 can be set to zero and the collector current measured directly. In this case the expression for determining τ_F becomes

$$\tau_F = \frac{C \, \Delta V}{\Delta i_C} \tag{22.38}$$

These measurement methods entail the adjustment of the resistor R_1 or capacitor C. To obtain the value of the charge-control parameter concerned, the resistance or capacitance values must be measured, unless the elements have been previously calibrated. It is often more convenient to modify the measurement technique as shown in Fig. 22.18. Now fixed values of R_1 and C can be used, but two synchronized pulse generators are required. The parameter determinations are then reduced to the measurement of v_1 and

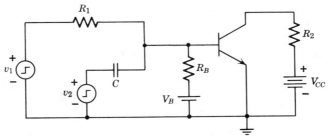

Figure 22.18   Modified circuit for measuring τ_{BF} and τ_F.

v_2 by oscilloscope display. When adjustment for correct base drive conditions has been made, we have, assuming $R_B \gg R_1$,

$$\tau_{BF} = R_1 C \frac{\Delta v_2}{\Delta v_1} \tag{22.39}$$

$$\tau_F = -R_2 C \frac{\Delta v_2}{\Delta v_{CE}} \tag{22.40}$$

$$\beta_F = \frac{\tau_{BF}}{\tau_F} = -\frac{R_1}{R_2} \frac{\Delta v_{CE}}{\Delta v_1} \tag{22.41}$$

Throughout our discussion, it has been assumed that a step source of voltage, of zero impedance, was available. It is important that these features of the base drive source be approached as closely as demanded by the transistor under test. The requirements are as follows:

1. The source voltage rise time should be small compared with τ_{BF}; preferably, the rise time should be no more than one-third of this parameter (recall that rise times of noninteracting circuits add quadratically).

2. The source resistance should be such that the source voltages are negligibly affected by the drive currents delivered. Also, the time constant of the v_2 source resistance and C should be no more than the rise time of the source voltages, preferably much less.

It is also necessary, as already discussed, that the source voltages be reasonably large compared with the voltage excursion of v_{BE}.

Measurement of τ_{BR} and τ_R. The charge control parameters τ_{BR} and τ_R, relating to *reverse* operation of the transistor, can be measured by the techniques described above simply by interchanging the collector and emitter leads of the transistor. Because β_R is usually one or two orders of magnitude smaller than β_F, a more sensitive oscilloscope display will be needed for the reverse parameters than for the forward parameters.

Measurement of Q_{FO}, Q_{RO}. The parameters Q_{FO} and Q_{RO}, the constants in the expressions for q_F and q_R (Eqs. 22.13) are directly related to parameters of the Ebers–Moll model by Eq. 22.14:

$$Q_{FO} = \alpha_F I_{ES} \tau_F \tag{22.42a}$$

$$Q_{RO} = \alpha_R I_{CS} \tau_R \tag{22.42b}$$

Thus measurement of the Ebers–Moll parameters as discussed in Section 21.5 together with the measurement of τ_F and τ_R as discussed above, will yield the desired values of Q_{FO} and Q_{RO}. Because q_F and q_R are of interest only in the active and saturation regions, the parameters I_{ES} and I_{CS} in Eq. 22.42 should be measured with the junctions *forward-biased*.

Measurement of K_E, K_C. Because q_{VE} and q_{VC} are of interest primarily under reverse-bias conditions, measurement of the associated constants K_E and K_C should be made with the appropriate diode reverse-biased. One particularly convenient technique is to measure the incremental junction capacitance at some particular reverse-bias voltage. The appropriate relations will now be developed.

We know from Eq. 4.40a that for a linearly-graded junction

$$q_V = K[\psi_0^{2/3} - (\psi_0 - v)^{2/3}] \tag{22.43}$$

where $\psi_0 \simeq 0.5$ volt in germanium and $\psi_0 \simeq 0.9$ volt in silicon. Because by definition the incremental junction capacitance at some fixed voltage V is $C_j(V) = dq/dt$, we find from Eq. 22.43 that

$$C_j(V) = \tfrac{2}{3} K[\psi_0 - V]^{-1/3} \tag{22.44}$$

Hence

$$K = \tfrac{3}{2} C_j(V)[\psi_0 - V]^{1/3} \tag{22.45}$$

The corresponding expression for an abrupt junction is

$$K = 2 C_j(V)(\psi_0 - V)^{1/2} \tag{22.46}$$

(see Problem P22.8.)

We conclude that K_E and K_C can be determined by measuring the appropriate incremental junction capacitances (which are, in fact, the common-base input and output capacitances C_{ibo} and C_{obo}), at some convenient dc voltage V, and substituting these values into Eq. 22.45. Because of inaccuracies inherent in the depletion approximation used in deriving Eq. 22.43 (and the corresponding expression for an abrupt junction), the determination of K will be more accurate if the measurement is made at a reverse voltage substantially larger in magnitude than ψ_0.

To illustrate, suppose that the junctions of the silicon diffused transistor used in Section 22.3 had been specified in terms of C_j rather than K as follows:

$$C_{je} = 1.7 \text{ pf at 6 volts reverse bias}$$

Then from Eq. 22.46

$$K_E = \tfrac{3}{2} \times 1.7(0.9 + 6)^{\frac{1}{3}}$$

$$= 5 \, \text{pf (volts)}^{\frac{1}{3}}$$

22.5.2 Determination of the Charge-Control Parameters from Data Sheets

Manufacturers' data sheets often specify transistor switching performance in terms of delay time, rise time, storage time, and fall time as a function of collector current and turn-on and turn-off base current. An abridged set of such data for a *pnp* diffused silicon transistor is shown in Fig. 22.19. Clearly, these measurements are made in terms of constant turn-on and turn-off base currents. If a particular transient problem conforms to these requirements, the graphs may be used directly to determine switching times without

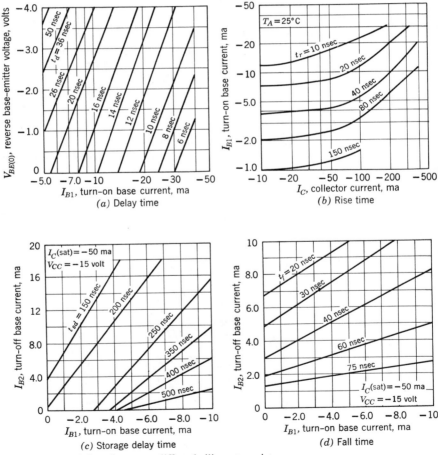

Figure 22.19 Switching speed data for a *pnp* diffused silicon transistor.

ever calculating τ_F, τ_{BF} and so on. However, in many switching circuits the base current is *not* constant, and in such cases it is necessary to abstract values of τ_F, and so forth, from the data in Fig. 22.19 and then calculate the switching response by the methods discussed in Section 22.3.

Calculation of τ_F. It is relatively easy to calculate τ_F from the rise time data in Fig. 22.19b, because the rise-time expression (Eq. 22.22) is quite simple if the base current is constant. Specifically, for $i_B(t)$ in Eq. 22.22 constant at a value I_{B1}, we can solve for $t_r = t_2 - t_1$ and substitute for $q_F(t_2)$ from Eq. 22.24 to obtain

$$t_r \simeq \frac{\tau_F|I_C(\text{sat})| + q_{VC}(t_2) - q_{VC}(t_1)}{|I_{B1}|} \tag{22.47}$$

For small values of collector current in saturation, Eq. 22.47 indicates that the rise time will be determined primarily by q_{VC} and not $\tau_F I_C(\text{sat})$ (i.e., q_F). On the other hand, for large values of $I_C(\text{sat})$, the changes in q_{VC} should become unimportant compared to q_F and the rise time should become linear in $I_C(\text{sat})$. Both of these features can be seen in Fig. 22.19b. Clearly, we should make the determination of τ_F in the high-current part of the graph, both for simplicity and accuracy. For example, if we choose I_{B1} = 20 ma, $I_C(\text{sat})$ = 200 ma, we obtain

$$\tau_F \simeq \frac{t_r|I_{B1}|}{|I_C(\text{sat})|} = \frac{20 \times 20}{200} = 2 \text{ nsec}$$

In the absence of other information on τ_F in a data sheet, recall from Section 21.3.4 that it is possible to obtain a rough estimate of τ_F from data on ω_T, because

$$\tau_F \simeq \frac{1}{\omega_T}$$

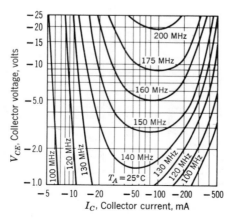

Figure 22.20   Contours of constant f_T for the same silicon transistor as in Fig. 22.19.

For this transistor, the f_T contours shown in Fig. 22.20 were included in the data sheet. Clearly, f_T lies somewhere between 100 and 200 MHz. Thus τ_F should lie somewhere between 0.8 and 1.6 nsec.

Calculation of τ_{BF}. Knowing τ_F, we can obtain a value for τ_{BF} by using the relation

$$\frac{\tau_{BF}}{\tau_F} = \beta_F = h_{FE}$$

For this transistor, h_{FE} is about 60 for collector currents between 1 and 100 ma, so that

$$\tau_{BF} \simeq 60 \times 2 = 120 \text{ nsec}$$

Calculation of τ_S. Because data on the reverse parameters τ_R, τ_{BR}, and β_R are not usually given on data sheets, it is probably advisable to work in terms of the saturation charge-control parameter τ_S, and not try to determine values for τ_R and τ_{BR}. The determination of τ_S from the storage-delay time data is again relatively simple because of the constant turn-off base current. Specifically, Eq. 22.25 will yield an exponentially decaying q_S, which will go to zero in the storage-delay time t_{sd}:

$$t_{sd} \simeq \tau_S \ln \left[\frac{|I_{B2}| - |I_{B1}|}{|I_{B2}| - |I_C(\text{sat})|/\beta_F} \right] \tag{22.48a}$$

(see Problem P22.9). If the turn-off base current is large enough, we can extrapolate the initial slope of the exponential in $q_S(t)$ (see Fig. 22.14) and find for the storage time:

$$t_{sd} \simeq \tau_S \left[\frac{|I_{B1}| - |I_C(\text{sat})|/\beta_F}{|I_{B1}| - |I_{B2}|} \right] \tag{22.48b}$$

Thus

$$\tau_S \simeq \frac{t_{sd}(|I_{B1}| - |I_{B2}|)}{|I_{B1}| - |I_C(\text{sat})|/\beta_F} \tag{22.49}$$

Values of τ_S ranging from 650 to 1500 nsec will be obtained from Fig. 22.19c using this equation.

Calculation of K_E *and* K_C. The parameters K_E and K_C in the space-charge-layer expressions can be found from the published values of incremental junction capacitances. For the particular *pnp* diffused silicon transistor discussed above, this capacitance information is presented graphically, as shown in Fig. 22.21. Ideally, values of C_{obo} and voltage taken anywhere along the C_{obo} curve in Fig. 22.21 should yield the same value for K_C. However, as already pointed out, a more accurate determination results if we choose V as large as possible. From Fig. 22.21, $C_{obo} = 12$ pf at $V = -10$ volts; thus from Eq. 22.45

$$K_C = \tfrac{3}{2}(12)(0.9 + 10)^{1/3} = 40 \text{ pf(volt)}^{1/3}$$

(See Problem P22.10.)

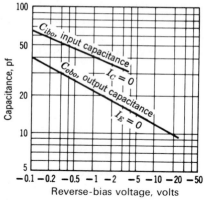

Figure 22.21   Incremental junction capacitances for a *pnp* diffused silicon transistor.

Calculation of Q_{FO} and Q_{RO}. For the approximate switching time calculations discussed in Section 22.3, we need only determine τ_F, τ_{BF}, τ_S, K_E, and K_C. However, for more exact calculations, we also need to know the constants Q_{FO} and Q_{RO} in the expressions for q_F and q_R versus voltage. As discussed in Section 22.5.1, these constants can be obtained from the Ebers-Moll parameters I_{ES}, I_{CS}, and α_F, using Eqs. 22.42. Unfortunately, these parameters are not always given in data sheets, so that some judicious estimating may be required. The details of the determination of the Ebers-Moll parameters from data sheets are given in Section 21.5.1.

22.6   Computer-Aided Solution of the Charge-Control Equations

It should be abundantly clear from the examples in Sections 8.2 and 22.3 that the basically nonlinear nature of the transistor dynamic switching problem forces us to resort to a digital computer for anything other than crude first-order calculations. The charge-control equations (Eqs. 21.20 or 22.12) are nonlinear first-order differential equations when expressed in terms of voltage. Thus we require some method of numerical integration to solve for the voltages, currents, and charges. Many such methods exist. The relative merits of the various integration methods, and questions of the stability and convergence of the solutions, are beyond the scope of this text.[5] Therefore, we describe briefly one method that can be used to solve charge-control problems, recognizing that other methods may be easier to use or faster, depending on the computational facilities available.

---

[5] See Reference 22.1 for discussion of these problems, plus an extensive bibliography on the subject.

22.6.1   The Runge-Kutta Method (Fourth-Order)

A simple first-order differential equation for a circuit can be written in the form

$$\dot{v} = \frac{dv}{dt} = f[v] \tag{22.50}$$

where $f[v]$ is some nonlinear relation involving the circuit parameters. One example of such a relation could be found by solving for dv_{CB}/dt from Eqs. 22.12b, 22.13b, and 22.15b. The basic idea of all numerical integration methods is to calculate the value of v at time t_1 based on the known value of v at time t_0. A crude approximation (Euler's method) can be obtained by a simple linear extrapolation of the slope at t_0, as shown in Fig. 22.22. The basic equation is

$$v(t_1) = v(t_0) + h\dot{v}(t_0) \tag{22.51}$$

where h is the time interval between t_0 and t_1. This expression is nothing more than the first two terms of the Taylor series expansion of $v(t)$.

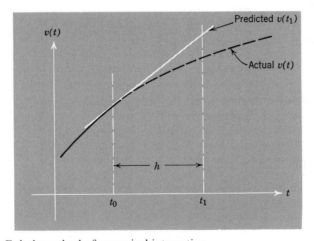

Figure 22.22   Euler's method of numerical integration.

The Runge-Kutta method is an extension of this method in that four values of the derivative are calculated (Fig. 22.23) and the *weighted average* of these slopes is used in Eq. 22.51 to find $v(t_1)$ from $v(t_0)$. First, we calculate the slope at time t_0 from the known initial voltage $v(t_0) = v_0$, using the circuit equation (Eq. 22.50):

$$\dot{v}(t_0) = f[v(t_0)] \tag{22.52}$$

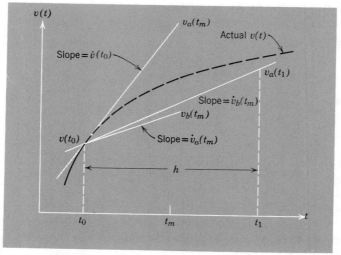

Figure 22.23 Runge-Kutta method.

This slope is used to obtain a first estimate of v at time t_m halfway between t_0 and t_1 (Fig. 22.23) using Euler's method:

$$v_a(t_m) = v_0 + \frac{h}{2}\dot{v}(t_0) \tag{22.53}$$

From this value we estimate the slope at t_m, again using the circuit equation:

$$\dot{v}_a(t_m) = f[v_a(t_m)] = f\left[v_0 + \frac{h}{2}\dot{v}(t_0)\right] \tag{22.54}$$

A second estimate of the voltage and slope at $t = t_m$ is then made by a modified Euler approximation:

$$v_b(t_m) = v_0 + \frac{h}{2}\dot{v}_a(t_m) \tag{22.55}$$

$$\dot{v}_b(t_m) = f\left[v_0 + \frac{h}{2}\dot{v}_a(t_m)\right] \tag{22.56}$$

This slope is used to find a first estimate of the voltage and slope at $t = t_1$:

$$v_a(t_1) = v_0 + h\dot{v}_b(t_m) \tag{22.57}$$

$$\dot{v}_a(t_1) = f[v_0 + h\dot{v}_b(t_1)] \tag{22.58}$$

Finally, the value of v at t_1 is recalculated based on the weighted averages of the four derivative values:

$$v(t_1) = v(t_0) + \frac{h}{6}[\dot{v}(t_0) + 2\dot{v}_a(t_m) + 2\dot{v}_b(t_m) + \dot{v}_a(t_1)] \tag{22.59}$$

The Runge-Kutta method is much more accurate than the Euler method, but requires much greater computation time because the network equation (Eq. 22.50) must be solved four times for each new point in the solution.

To illustrate these calculations, let us compute the output voltage of the simple linear RC circuit shown in Fig. 22.24 in response to a 1-volt input

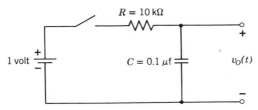

Figure 22.24 *RC* circuit with $\tau = 1$ msec. Switch closes at $t = 0$.

step. The basis first-order differential equation for the circuit, corresponding to Eq. 22.50, is

$$\frac{dv_O}{dt} = \frac{1}{CR}(1 - v_O) \tag{22.60}$$

The successive steps of a numerical calculation of $v_O(t)$ using the Euler method, Eq. 22.51, are shown in Table 22.6. The exact solution (easy to obtain in this linear example) is also tabulated. Notice that step sizes of the order of one time constant produce 30% errors in the solution, and a step size larger than two time constants yields an unstable solution.

The results of a solution based on the Runge-Kutta method are presented in Table 22.7. Note that in this case the numerical integration is within 1% for steps of one time constant. For steps of three time constants, the solution monotonically diverges. We conclude that to obtain a stable solution, we must take steps smaller than the smallest time constant, that is, smaller than τ_F.

22.6.2 Example: The Simple Inverter

For most numerical integration methods, including the Runge-Kutta method, we require equations in the form

$$\frac{dv_n}{dt} = f_n(v_1, v_2, \ldots, v_n) \tag{22.61}$$

It is certainly possible to rearrange the network equations for the simple inverter, (Eqs. 22.9 through 22.12) into this form. However, it is clearly more desirable to write the equations in the form of Eq. 22.61, the so-called *state-variable form*, in the first place. The state-variable formulation can be obtained by a simple extension of the node-variable method of writing network equations.

Table 22.6 Calculation of $v_O(t)$ in Fig. 22.24 by Euler's method (Units are milliseconds, volts)

Time	$v(t_0)$	$\dot{v}(t_0)$	$v_O(t_1)$ (Eq. 22.51)	$v_O(t_1)$ (exact)
Step size h = 0.5 msec				
0.5	0.000000	1.000000	0.500000	0.393469
1.0	0.500000	0.500000	0.750000	0.632121
1.5	0.750000	0.250000	0.875000	0.776870
2.0	0.875000	0.125000	0.937500	0.864665
2.5	0.937500	0.062500	0.968750	0.917915
3.0	0.968750	0.031250	0.984375	0.950213
3.5	0.984375	0.015625	0.992188	0.969803
4.0	0.992188	0.007813	0.996094	0.981684
4.5	0.996094	0.003906	0.998047	0.988891
5.0	0.998047	0.001953	0.999023	0.993262
Step size h = 1 msec				
1.0	0.000000	1.000000	1.000000	0.632121
2.0	1.000000	0.000000	1.000000	0.864665
Step size h = 1.5 msec				
1.5	0.000000	1.000000	1.500000	0.776870
3.0	1.500000	−0.500000	0.750000	0.950213
4.5	0.750000	0.250000	1.125000	0.988891
6.0	1.125000	−0.125000	0.937500	0.997521
7.5	0.937500	0.062500	1.031250	0.999447
9.0	1.031250	−0.031250	0.984375	0.999877
10.5	0.984375	0.015625	1.007813	0.999972
Step size h = 2 msec				
2.0	0.000000	1.000000	2.000000	0.864665
4.0	2.000000	−1.000000	0.000000	0.981684
6.0	0.000000	1.000000	2.000000	0.997521
8.0	2.000000	−1.000000	0.000000	0.999665
10.0	0.000000	1.000000	2.000000	0.999955
12.0	2.000000	−1.000000	0.000000	0.999994
Step size h = 3 msec				
3.0	0.000000	1.000000	3.000000	0.950213
6.0	3.000000	−2.000000	−3.000000	0.997521
9.0	−3.000000	4.000000	9.000000	0.999877
12.0	9.000000	−8.000000	−15.000000	0.999994
15.0	−15.000000	16.000000	33.000000	1.000000
18.0	33.000000	−32.000000	−63.000000	1.000000

The circuit for the simple inverter, and the corresponding circuit model using the complete charge-control model to represent the transistor, are shown in Figs. 22.25a and b. We choose as independent variables in the analysis the variables associated with the energy-storage elements; that is, the capacitor voltages (and inductor currents, if any). These are called the

Table 22.7 Calculation of $v_O(t)$ in Fig. 22.24 using the Runge-Kutta method (see text for definition of notation; units are milliseconds, volts)

Time	$v(t_0)$	$v_0(t_1)$ (Eq. 22.59)	$v_0(t_1)$ (exact)
Step size h = 1 msec			
1.0	0.000000	0.625000	0.632121
2.0	0.625000	0.859375	0.864665
3.0	0.859375	0.947266	0.950213
4.0	0.947266	0.980225	0.981684
5.0	0.980225	0.992584	0.993262
6.0	0.992584	0.997219	0.997521
7.0	0.997219	0.998957	0.999088
8.0	0.998957	0.999609	0.999665
Step size h = 2 msec			
2.0	0.000000	0.666667	0.864665
4.0	0.666667	0.888889	0.981684
6.0	0.888889	0.962963	0.997521
8.0	0.962963	0.987654	0.999665
10.0	0.987654	0.995885	0.999955
12.0	0.995885	0.998628	0.999994
14.0	0.998628	0.999543	0.999999
Step size h = 3 msec			
3.0	0.000000	-0.375000	0.950213
6.0	-0.375000	-0.890625	0.997521
9.0	-0.890625	-1.599609	0.999877
12.0	-1.599609	-2.574463	0.999994
15.0	-2.574463	-3.914886	1.000000
18.0	-3.914886	-5.757969	1.000000

state variables. We then write one first-order differential equation for each of these variables.

A simple method of checking that we have defined an appropriate set of variables is to draw the circuit in skeleton form (Fig. 22.25c) to show the *basic network topology.* Voltage sources and capacitors are indicated by solid lines and current sources, resistors, and inductors by dotted lines. If the tree formed by the solid lines touches all nodes, it is a so-called *proper tree*, and we have a complete set of independent voltage variables. If a node is not touched by the tree, an appropriate resistor voltage must be included as an independent variable, to tie this node to the tree. If a loop of three or more capacitor branches appears in the tree, this loop must be broken by introducing a small resistor in series with one of the elements. For the present circuit, the two capacitor voltages v_{BC} and v_{BE}, together with the two voltage sources v_I and V_{CC}, form a proper tree without modification, as can be seen from Fig. 22.25c.

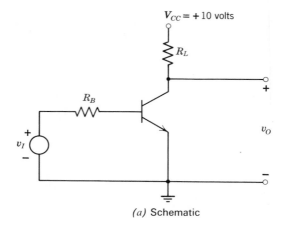

(a) Schematic

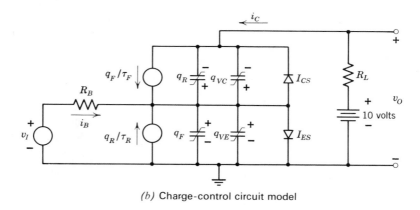

(b) Charge-control circuit model

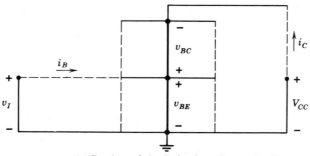

(c) Topology of circuit showing a "proper tree"
of voltage sources and capacitors

Figure 22.25   Transistor inverter.

The next step is to write a complete set of network equations in terms of the tree-branch voltages we have just defined. These are, in general, Kirchhoff-current-law equations, but they must have the special form given by Eq. 21.61, that is, a set of equations each of which contains only *one* derivative. At this point the systematic approach involves writing equations directly in terms of the variables defined in Fig. 22.25c (see Problem P22.11). However, there is a simpler approach which is adequate when no inductors are present, and simpler to handle by the computer. Note that Eqs. 21.20a and b, in effect the Kirchhoff-current-law equations for the emitter and collector nodes of the transistor, are already close to the desired state-variable form, Eq. 22.61, because in each case the derivative terms can be written in terms of one voltage only. Recasting these equations with the derivative terms on the left, we obtain

$$\frac{d(q_F + q_{VE})}{dt} = \frac{q_R}{\tau_R} - q_F\left(\frac{1}{\tau_F} + \frac{1}{\tau_{BF}}\right) - i_E \tag{22.62}$$

$$\frac{d(q_R + q_{VC})}{dt} = \frac{q_F}{\tau_F} - q_R\left(\frac{1}{\tau_R} + \frac{1}{\tau_{BR}}\right) - i_C \tag{22.63}$$

(If there are capacitors in the circuit, we write equations for these as well, following the format of Eqs. 22.62 and 22.63.)

To complete the formulation we must write each of the state-variable equations in terms of a single derivative, rather than the sum of two derivatives, as Eqs. 22.62 and 22.63 are now expressed. To do this, we express $q_F + q_{VE}$ in terms of the junction voltage v_{BE}. From Eqs. 22.13a and 22.15a this expression is

$$q_F + q_{VE} = Q_{FO}(e^{qv_{BE}/kT} - 1) + K_E[\psi_0^{2/3} - (\psi_0 - v_{BE})^{2/3}] \tag{22.64}$$

Hence we can define a nonlinear capacitor as

$$C(v_{BE}) = \frac{d(q_F + q_{VE})}{dv_{BE}} \tag{22.65}$$

$$= Q_{FO}\left(\frac{q}{kT}\right)(e^{qv_{BE}/kT}) + \frac{2}{3}K_E(\psi_0 - v_{BE})^{-1/3} \tag{22.66}$$

Eq. 22.65 can be rewritten as

$$\frac{dv_{BE}}{dt} = \frac{1}{C(v_{BE})}\frac{d(q_F + q_{VE})}{dt} \tag{22.67}$$

On substituting from Eqs. 22.62, 22.66, and 22.13, we obtain the desired relation in terms of a single voltage derivative. A similar manipulation can be used to convert Eq. 22.63 to the required form (see Problem 22.12). Note that Eqs. 22.62 through 22.67 are all formulated in terms of *transistor variables*, and are *completely independent of the network topology*. Thus, these relations can be used for any circuit, regardless of the specific circuit configuration.

Finally we must relate any currents used in the above equations to the tree-branch voltages. It is simplest to do this in two steps. First, we define currents for the links that are not directly in parallel with a tree branch, as shown in Fig. 22.25c, and write equations relating these currents to the tree-branch voltages. By inspection of Fig. 22.25b and c, these relations are

$$i_B = \frac{v_I - v_{BE}}{R_B} \tag{22.68}$$

$$i_C = \frac{10 - v_{BE} + v_{BC}}{R_L} \tag{22.69}$$

Now we must relate any currents used in the derivative equations, in this case, i_C and i_E in Eqs. 22.62 and 22.63, to the link currents defined by Eqs. 22.68 and 22.69, or directly to the voltages. Because i_C is already a link current, the only required relation is

$$i_E = -i_B - i_C \tag{22.70}$$

To apply the Runge Kutta method to this problem (on a computer, of course), we calculate i_B, i_C, q_F, q_R, and so on, from the known values of v_{BC} and v_{BE} at the start of the transient, $t = t_0$, and then find $\dot{v}_{BE}$ from Eqs. 22.66 *et al.* This process is repeated four times, as outlined in Section 22.6.1, until finally we arrive at values of v_{BE} (and v_{BC}) for $t = t_1$. The computation is then repeated for each successive step in the solution. Any available numerical integration program can also be used for this purpose. The computer solution to this particular problem has already been presented in Fig. 22.8.

22.7   Lecture Demonstrations

The lecture demonstrations described below are deceptively simple. Yet there is great strength in this simplicity. The apparatus is so minimal that there can be no confusion about the nature of the circuit. Thus the implications of the experiment are all the more forceful.

To verify the conclusions in Section 22.3, drive a simple pulse inverter such as that in Fig. 22.7 with a pulse generator that has versatile control of the output waveform. In particular, it is desirable to have direct control of the pulse amplitude, pulse width, and the dc offset voltage of the pulse, and be able to clamp either the base line or the peak of the pulse.

22.7.1   Introduction

Adjust the pulse generator so that the amplifier operates solely in the active region. Observe the symmetric exponential rise and fall of the output waveform. Increase the pulse height to derive the amplifier from cutoff into saturation. Observe the asymmetry in the rise and fall, plus the new problems of delay time at the start of the turn-on and storage delay at the start of the turn-off, which arise from nonlinear operation.

22.7.2 Turn-on Transient

Examine the turn-on transient in detail by adjusting the pulse length and the sweep speed on the oscilloscope so that only the turn-on transient is visible and the pulse appears to be a step. Now independently vary the initial and final values of the "step." Observe that (within limits) the delay time t_d is influenced by both the initial value of the step and its height, as predicted by the calculations in Section 22.3.1. On the other hand, the rise time t_r depends on the final amplitude of the step, and not the base-line value, as predicted in Section 22.3.2.

22.7.3 Turn-off Transient

Because the terminal voltages and currents are essentially constant, when the transistor is in saturation it is not possible to *directly* observe behavior in this region. However, it is a simple matter to make convincing indirect observations. Adjust the pulse length so that the turn-on transient [specifically, $q_S(t)$] goes to completion, and adjust the sweep speed on the oscilloscope to show the entire response waveform. Now make the base line of the pulse more negative while keeping the top of the pulse at some fixed positive voltage. This in effect increases the turn-off overdrive, and so reduces the storage-delay time t_{sd} and the fall time t_f. However, observe that the delay time t_d associated with turn-on *increases* because making the base line more negative means that more charge must be removed from the space-charge-layer capacitors before the transistor can enter the active region.

Now increase the pulse amplitude while keeping the base-line voltage fixed. Observe that the rise time decreases and the storage-delay time increases, whereas other pulse parameters will remain unchanged.

The most convincing experiment that indirectly shows the behavior of the circuit in saturation is to vary only the *length* of the input pulse. Observe that in such a case only the storage-delay time is changed. (To emphasize this, synchronize the oscilloscope on the trailing edge of the pulse, with enough delay in the pulse generator to allow the entire output pulse to be displayed.) When the input pulse is shortened, the q_S transient no longer has time to go to completion, so that the base charge at the start of turn-off is less. Consequently the storage-delay time is reduced.

22.7.4 Speed-up Capacitor

Add a small variable capacitor in parallel with R_B in Fig. 22.7. Observe the improvement in output pulse shape as the capacitor is adjusted to its optimum value.

REFERENCES

22.1 D. A. Calahan, *Computer-Aided Network Design*, (prelim. ed.), McGraw-Hill, New York, 1968.

22.2 J. Millman and H. Taub, *Pulse, Digital and Switching Waveforms*, McGraw-Hill, New York, 1965.

22.3 J. F. Gibbons, *Semiconductor Electronics*, McGraw-Hill, New York, 1966.

22.4 A. Ralston, *A First Course in Numerical Analysis*, McGraw-Hill, New York, 1965.

PROBLEMS

P22.1 What logical function does the circuit in Fig. 22.5 perform if we use negative representation? (See page 802.)

P22.2 Calculate with more accuracy than shown in Fig. 22.4 the transfer characteristic for the inverter shown in Fig. 22.2a. Assume that the transistor emitter junction has a threshold of conduction of 0.4 volt. (See page 803.)

P22.3 The parameter values of the inverter circuit shown in Fig. 22.2a are nominal ones. In reality all of them are subject to some variation. Assume that the resistors may have values within $\pm 20\%$ of their nominal values, the supply voltages may vary by $\pm 10\%$, and β_F may deviate by $\pm 20\%$ from its nominal value.

(a) Determine the minimum value of v_I for which $v_O \simeq 0$ for all possible actual parameter values. Base your analysis on the least favorable set of parameter values, that is, consider the worst case.

(b) Determine the maximum value of v_I for which v_O is approximately equal to the positive supply voltage for all possible actual parameter values. Assume that the transistor is at the threshold of forward conduction when $V_{BE} = 0.4$ volt. (See page 803.)

P22.4 Repeat Problem P22.2 for the inverter circuit in Fig. 22.2a, with a 90-kohm resistor added from the base of the transistor to a -10-volt supply. (See page 803.) Explain how the logical properties of the circuit are improved by this change.

P22.5 During the turn-off transient discussed in Section 22.3.4, the charge q_S is removed both by recombination and by negative base current. Identify in Eq. 22.25 which terms represent recombination and which terms represent base current. (See page 819.)

P22.6 In calculating the fall time in Section 22.3.5, we neglected recombination. Estimate the recombination effect, hence modify the calculated fall time accordingly. Compare this answer with the computer solution of $t_f = 78$ nsec. (See page 821.)

P22.7 Calculate the storage-delay time and the fall time of the inverter discussed in Section 22.3, assuming that the drive voltage v_I is set to zero at time t_3. (See page 821.)

P22.8   Derive Eq. 22.46, which expresses the constant K in terms of the incremental junction capacitance for an abrupt-junction diode. (See page 828.)

P22.9   Derive Eq. 22.48a. Figure 22.14 may be of some help.

P22.10   Find K_E for the transistor whose junction capacitance characteristics are shown in Fig. 22.21. (See page 831.)

P22.11   The circuit topology in Fig. 22.25c provides a convenient framework for formally writing a set of network equations involving only the variables defined in that figure. To do this, we draw a closed path through each of the trees branches defined by the capacitor voltages. Appropriate paths are shown Fig. 22.26. We now treat each of these closed paths as a "super-node" and write Kirchhoff's current law for the currents flowing into the "node," that is, across the closed path.

Write these equations by referring to Figs. 22.25b and 22.26. Note that these two equations together with the link current equations, Eqs. 22.68 and 22.69, are equivalent to the five network equations in Section 22.6.2.

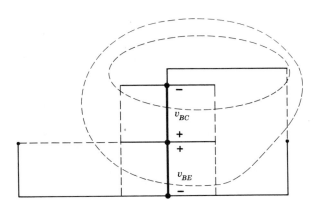

Figure 22.26   Super-nodes for the circuit in Fig. 22.25.

P22.12   Complete the state-variable formulation in the example in Section 22.6.2 by finding the equation for dv_{BC}/dt. (See page 839.)

P22.13   For the inverter circuit in Fig. 22.27, assume that we are using a *pnp* silicon transistor with the following parameters: $\tau_F = 1$ nsec, $\tau_R = 10$ nsec, $\tau_{BF} = 100$ nsec, $\tau_{BR} = 50$ nsec, $K_E = 10$, $K_C = 15$ (see Fig. 22.10).

(a) For $v_I = -6.6$ volt, find the value of the charges q_{VE}, q_{VC}, q_F, and q_R (or q_S and q_{BO}) in the steady state.

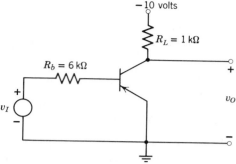

Figure 22.27   Inverter.

(b) At $t = 0$, v_I is changed abruptly to $+2.4$ volts. Estimate the length of time t_1 that will elapse before v_O begins to change.

(c) Estimate the value of the charges listed above at time t_1.

P22.14   (a) For $v_2 = v_3 = 0$ volts in the three-input RTL gate in Fig. 22.28, and v_1 a step of voltage from 0.2 to 10.6 volts, find the initial and final values of v_0. Use the transistor parameters given on page 808.

(b) Calculate the rise time of v_0. Make and state reasonable approximations. Sketch the approximate waveform of v_0 versus time.

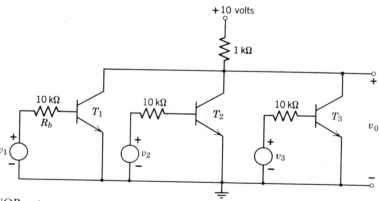

Figure 22.28   NOR gate.

P22.15   Write the state-variable equations for the circuit in Fig. 22.16. Assume that there is a 50-ohm source resistance associated with the source v_A. Leave the equations in a form similar to Eq. 22.62. (Note that the equations can be changed to voltage form by use of Eq. 22.66.)

P22.16   Redesign the inverter circuit discussed in Section 22.3 (Fig. 22.7) in order to decrease the rise and fall times. Specifically, add an appropriate size of speed-up capacitor across R_B, and readjust the driving waveform v_I.

P22.17 Check the circuit you designed in Problem P22.16 by using a digital computer, and the results of Problem P22.15.

P22.18 The silicon graded-junction transistor T_1 in Fig. 22.29 is supposed to discharge capacitor C_2 when a 10-volt positive step is applied at v_I.

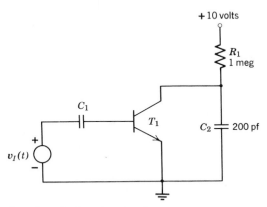

Figure 22.29 Capacitor-discharging circuit.

Assuming that $\tau_F = 1$ nsec, $\tau_R = 10$ nsec, $\beta_F = 50$, $\beta_R = 5$, and $K_E = K_C = 10$ (see Fig. 22.10):

(a) Determine the value of C_1 such that C_2 will be almost completely discharged in 10 nsec. Neglect recombination, current through R_1, and the effects of q_{VE} and q_{VC}.

(b) Refine your solution by taking into account the effects of recombination and q_{VE} and q_{VC}.

P22.19 (a) Repeat Problem 22.14a for $v_2 = v_3 = 10.6$ volts in Fig. 22.28.

(b) For the same conditions as in part (a), find (q_F, q_R) or (q_{BO}, q_S) for transistor T_1 at the beginning and end of the transient. Repeat for transistor T_2. Estimate the time required to complete the transient change in charge.

CHAPTER TWENTY-THREE

Multistage Digital Circuits: Nonregenerative

23.1 Classification of Digital Circuits

Transistors are used in digital systems in many ways. In some cases a transistor is used to realize a desired logical operation. Frequently transistors are employed to provide isolation, to produce power gain, or to restore and standardize the characteristics of a signal. Under ideal conditions the value of the output variable in such circuits depends at any time only on the value of the input variable (or variables) *at that time*. Any time delays that do occur result only from device limitations. Circuits of this type, referred to as *nonregenerative* switching circuits, are discussed in this chapter. Most of the important issues, such as voltage margin, fan-out, and switching speed, are discussed in the context of resistor-transistor logic in Section 23.2. Further examples of nonregenerative logic circuits are covered in Sections 23.3 and 23.4.

A second major class of digital circuits, called *regenerative* circuits, exhibit *memory*, in the sense that the output of the circuit depends intentionally on the past history of the input variable. Such circuits are used to generate pulses, either continuously or in response to another variable. Circuits of this type—called "regenerative" because they can usually be described in terms of a positive feedback mechanism— are discussed in Chapter 24.

Digital circuits can also be classified on the basis of the transistor operating conditions that correspond to the two states of the circuit. Three classes are used in practical systems:

1. In one state the transistor is in the *cutoff* region of operation with both junctions reverse-biased, but in the other state it operates in the *saturation region* with both junctions forward-biased. Such circuits, which are known as saturating switching circuits, usually do not employ diodes or other nonlinear elements for level establishment, because the transistor itself is operated in such a nonlinear manner.

2. One state corresponds to operation in the cutoff region, but the other state lies in the *forward-active region*, for which the emitter is forward biased and the collector is reversed-biased. Such *nonsaturating* circuits often use diodes to establish the output level corresponding to the state in which the transistor is in the active region.

3. Both states correspond to operation in the forward-active region; two markedly different operating points are used. These circuits, which are also nonsaturating, usually require diodes for level establishment in *both* states and thus are not so widely used as the other two classes.

All three classes fundamentally involve *state* representations; voltage or current levels are permitted to vary, but only to the extent that one band of levels is guaranteed to place a diode or transistor in one state, whereas another band of levels is guaranteed to produce a different state. Examples of circuits in the first two classes are given throughout this chapter.

In the past, limitations in logic circuit design arose from the fact that in using discrete components it was usually desirable to minimize the total number of components for reasons of economy and reliability. Also, the usual wide manufacturing tolerance on transistors and diodes made strict selection necessary in order to achieve high performance. In integrated logic circuits, these restrictions no longer apply. The cost of manufacturing an integrated circuit containing a dozen or more transistors and many passive components is often competitive with the cost of a single transistor. It has also been demonstrated that such an integrated circuit is no less reliable than a single transistor.

For integrated circuits, it is frequently easier to fabricate a transistor than to fabricate a resistor of close tolerance or high value. Because of these factors, new and sophisticated logic circuits are being designed that make use of many more transistors than do conventional circuits. In these circuits, transistors are often used to replace resistors, frequently as constant-current sources or as collector loads. In addition, advantage is taken of the greater uniformity of threshold voltages among transistors fabricated on a single integrated circuit chip. Throughout this chapter many examples of present-day digital integrated-circuit technology will be given. However, in most cases the particular logic function will first be introduced in terms of a simpler basic element, more reminiscent of a discrete-component circuit than an integrated-circuit realization.

Almost all transistor logic is now built with silicon transistors. The use of silicon devices in multistage digital circuits brings about major design simplifications, because direct coupling of cascaded transistors can be used successfully. Note, for example, that transistor T_2 in the direct-coupled gate shown in Fig. 23.1 contains no provision for reverse-biasing the emitter diode in the *off* state, but operates with v_{BE} slightly positive, by an amount

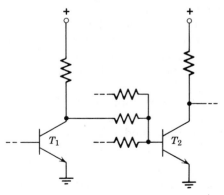

Figure 23.1 Cascaded logic circuits.

equal to the saturated collector-emitter voltage $V_{CE}(\text{sat})$ of transistor T_1. Because $V_{CE}(\text{sat})$ is the *difference* between the forward voltages of the two junctions in the transistor, it is always less than the threshold voltage V_{BET} of one diode alone, assuming comparable diode currents. Consequently, T_2 is *off* when T_1 is *on*. While it is possible to direct-couple germanium transistors in the same manner, in practice only silicon transistors operate satisfactorily in this circuit. The problem with germanium is that the difference between $V_{CE}(\text{sat})$ and V_{BET} (the *voltage margin* for this circuit) is too small for reliable operation. Therefore, we shall assume throughout the chapter that unless otherwise specified, silicon transistors are used in all circuits.

23.2   Direct-Coupled Resistor-Transistor Logic (DCTL, RTL)
23.2.1   RTL NOR Gates
The circuit shown in Fig. 23.2*a* is an example of what was originally referred to as direct-coupled transistor logic (DCTL), but now is more commonly called resistor-transistor logic (RTL). The gates normally require only a small number of components, which are arranged in a particularly simple manner. Thus RTL has special advantages for integrated circuits. Complete lines of integrated RTL are now available at very low cost per unit.[1] Such lines include buffers, gates, adders, and flip-flops. A photomicrograph of a chip containing four two-input RTL NOR gates is shown in Fig. 23.2*b*.

To determine the logical operation performed by the circuit in Fig. 23.2*a*, we first must specify the representation. We choose positive representation, with the **0** state represented nominally by the collector voltage of a *saturated* transistor,

$$v_0 \simeq V_{CE}(\text{sat}) \tag{23.1a}$$

and the **1** state represented nominally by the collector voltage with the transistor cut off,

$$v_1 = V_{CC} \tag{23.1b}$$

This is really a representation in terms of *transistor state* rather than a voltage representation, because the voltages could vary over a wide range without impairing circuit performance. What is important is the state, that is, cutoff or saturation, of the transistor.

On the basis of the representation defined by Eqs. 23.1, we see from Fig. 23.2*a* that for all inputs at $V_{CE}(\text{sat})$, the transistors will be cut off and

Table 23.1   Table of Combinations

A	B	Binary Output
0	0	1
0	1	0
1	0	0
1	1	0

[1] See, for example, Reference 23.3.

the output will be at V_{CC}. For all other combinations of input voltage, at least one transistor will be saturated. Thus the table of combinations for the circuit is as shown in Table 23.1 (for only two inputs). It is clear from the table that the circuit is a NOR gate.

In a digital system, the NOR gate in Fig. 23.2 would be used to drive other

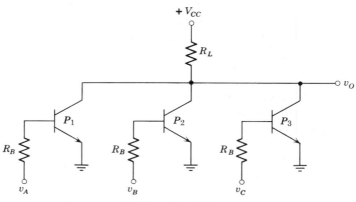

(a) Three-input NOR gate

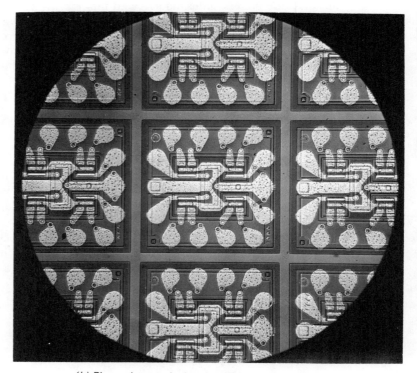

(b) Photomicrograph showing four two-input NOR gates

Figure 23.2   RTL (or DCTL) NOR gates.

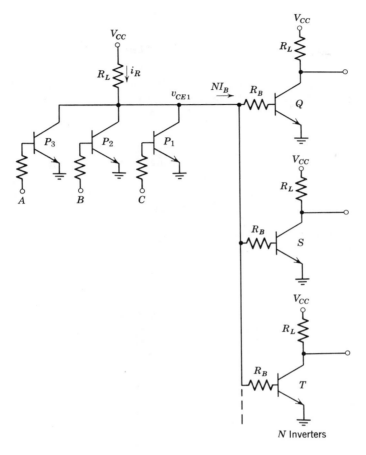

Figure 23.3 An RTL NOR gate driving other RTL circuits.

RTL circuits. An example of this is shown in Fig. 23.3 in which an RTL NOR gate, P_1, P_2, P_3, drives N transistors, each representing one stage of other gates. If the P gate is saturated, $v_{CE1} = V_{CE}(\text{sat})$ and transistors Q, S, T, and so on, will be *off*. If the P gate is *off*, the voltage V_{CE1} rises toward V_{CC} until the driven transistors Q, S, T, and so on, turn *on*. The base padding resistors R_B are included to equalize the base currents and thus reduce the variations in performance that are due to unequal input $I–V$ characteristics in the driven transistors.

The correct operation of RTL circuits is largely dependent on the following conditions:

1. Resistors R_L and R_B must be of appropriate value to ensure that when the P gate is *off*, transistors Q, S, T, and so on, will be *on*.

2. When the *P* gate is *on*, transistors *Q*, *S*, *T*, and so on, must be *off*. This requires that

$$V_{BET} > V_{CE}(\text{sat}) \tag{23.2}$$

where V_{BET} is the base-to-emitter threshold voltage, the voltage at which the transistor just begins to conduct. For silicon transistors, this condition is adequately satisfied at room temperature.

23.2.2   Voltage Margin

The *voltage-margin* Δ of a logic circuit was defined in Fig. 22.1 as the voltage between the maximum **0**-state voltage and the minimum **1**-state voltage (again assuming positive representation). An equivalent and somewhat more convenient definition is that Δ is the value that a noise voltage must exceed in order to cause a spurious transition from one state to another. We can find the voltage margin of an RTL gate on this basis by examining the basic RTL cascade shown in Fig. 23.4. The voltage margin limitation in RTL circuits arises when T_1 is saturated and v_{CE1} is equal to $V_{CE}(\text{sat})$. Under

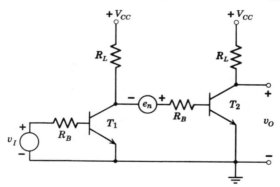

Figure 23.4   Calculation of voltage margin in an RTL circuit.

ideal circumstances this voltage is adequate to hold T_2 *off* as required, but if a noise voltage e_n is induced into the circuit at the point shown, then T_2 could possibly change state. Specifically, for

$$e_n + V_{CE}(\text{sat}) > V_{BET}(T_2) \tag{23.3}$$

transistor T_2 will start to conduct. Thus on the basis of the voltage margin definition given above, for RTL circuits

$$\Delta = V_{BET} - V_{CE}(\text{sat}) \tag{23.4}$$

As pointed out in Section 22.2.3, the threshold voltage V_{BET} has a temperature coefficient characteristic of an exponential diode. Specifically, the magnitude of V_{BET} decreases by 2 to 3 mv/°C for both germanium and silicon. The temperature coefficient of $V_{CE}(\text{sat})$ is somewhat more complicated because

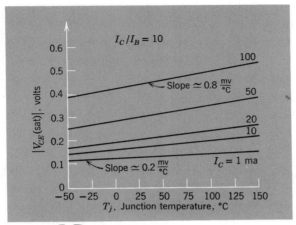

Figure 23.5   Temperature dependence of V_{CE} (sat).

voltage drops in the bulk regions of the unit and variation of both β_F and β_R with temperature are all contributing factors. Typical data are shown in Fig. 23.5.[2] The important point is that the magnitude of V_{CE}(sat) tends to *increase* with increasing temperature. Thus we see from Eq. 23.4 that the voltage margin is *reduced* when temperature increases. In fact, at high temperatures this margin can well be as low as 0.1 or 0.2 volt. Clearly, one of the principal disadvantages of RTL is the low voltage margin, hence the poor noise immunity.

It may seem somewhat surprising that the representation for this circuit as originally defined in Section 23.2.1 had adequate separation between the *off* and *on* states in terms of voltage, such as

$$V_0 = V_{CE}(\text{sat}) \simeq 0.2 \text{ volt}$$

$$V_1 = V_{CC} = 3 \text{ volts}$$

whereas we now state that the separation is only tenths of a volt. It is important to recall that the original representation was a *state* representation, and not a voltage representation. Thus the **1** and **0** logic states correspond to cutoff and saturation of the transistor, and not to some particular collector voltage. The collector current of the *off* and *on* state may differ by many orders of magnitude, but this large current difference (and definite description of the operating region of the transistor) can correspond to a relatively *large* or relatively *small* swing in collector voltage. The voltages quoted above are thus merely nominal values. This fact is emphasized in Fig. 23.6, in which the relationship between the nominal voltage values quoted above and V_{BET} and Δ is presented graphically.

[2] See Section 1.2.2 of Reference 23.2.

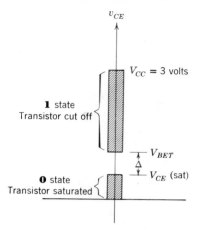

Figure 23.6 Collector voltages corresponding to the transistor state representation.

23.2.3 Fan-out

In Section 23.2.1 we stated that one condition for correct operation of the RTL NOR gate (Fig. 23.7) is that R_L and R_B must be such that when the P gate is *off*, transistors Q, S, T, and so on, must be *on*. This condition can be restated in a form that more clearly emphasizes the limitation on the maximum number of transistors that can be driven by an RTL gate, commonly referred to as the *fan-out* capability. Specifically, for a given gate design with given values of V_{CC}, R_L, and R_B, the maximum number of circuits that can be driven by the P gate is limited by the requirement that transistors Q, S, T must be *on* and saturated when the P gate is *off*. For identical transistors and resistors in all circuits, the saturation collector current in Q, S, T is

$$I_C(\text{sat}) \simeq \frac{V_{CC}}{R_L} \tag{23.5}$$

Thus the base current to Q must be

$$I_B \geqslant \frac{I_C(\text{sat})}{\beta_F} = \frac{V_{CC}}{\beta_F R_L} \tag{23.6}$$

If all transistors Q, S, T are *on*, they all require this base current; hence the total current that must be supplied by the P gate is $N I_B$. Because the transistors in the P gate are *off*, all of this current must come from the resistor R_L in the P gate. We can calculate this current I_R through R_L quite simply if we assume zero base-to-emitter drop in Q, S, and T:

$$I_R \simeq \frac{V_{CC}}{R_L + R_B/N} \tag{23.7}$$

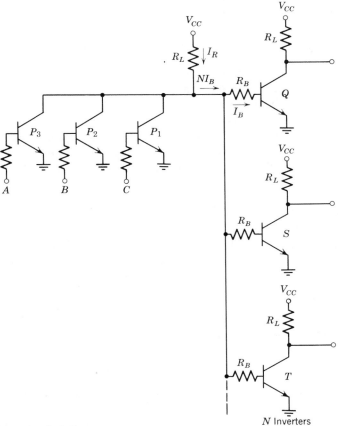

Figure 23.7   Fan-out calculation.

Thus from Eqs. 23.6 and 23.7

$$\frac{V_{CC}}{R_L + R_B/N} = NI_B \geqslant \frac{NV_{CC}}{\beta_F R_L} \qquad (23.8)$$

Solving Eq. 23.8 for the fan-out N, we obtain

$$N < \left(\beta_F - \frac{R_B}{R_L}\right) \qquad (23.9)$$

This condition will ensure that Q, S, T are at least at the *edge* of saturation. But as stated in Chapter 22, to ensure saturation in spite of variations in β_F, power-supply voltages, and similar factors, and to obtain fast response transitions between states, we usually *overdrive* the base of a transistor. That is, I_B is made many times larger than the minimum value specified by Eq. 23.6. But such base overdrive causes a proportional decrease in the maximum fan-out. Thus if I_B is five times that required for saturation, the fan-out limit becomes

$$N < \frac{\beta_F - R_B/R_L}{5} \tag{23.10}$$

In a given line of integrated digital circuits, the values of β_F, R_B, and R_L are known. Thus the fan-out can be stated in terms of simple *loading rules* that make such detailed calculations unnecessary. For example, according to the specification sheet for one RTL series of logic blocks, the 3-element NOR gate can drive 16 "unit loads", whereas each input of the NOR gate and most other logic blocks in the series represent 3 unit loads. Thus for this particular logic series, one NOR gate can drive five other NOR gates, that is, a fan-out of 5.

23.2.4   Buffer Stages

In many digital design problems it is necessary to drive more stages than permitted by the loading rules for the devices in question. For example, we may wish to use the NOR gate discussed above to drive more than the maximum number of transistors allowed by Eq. 23.10. In such cases we add a *buffer* stage to the circuit, whose main function is to increase the fan-out.

A simple buffer stage, an emitter-follower circuit, is shown in Fig. 23.8a. If the load consists of N other transistors, as in Fig. 23.7, then a little thought will show that the maximum *positive* output current, i_L, from the buffer, as defined in Fig. 23.8a, is

$$i_L(\max) \simeq \frac{V_C}{R_C/(\beta_F + 1) + R_B/N} \tag{23.11}$$

if we assume zero base-to-emitter drops (see Problem P23.1). Note, however, that this buffer can *absorb* almost no current. That is, if the load conditions are such that current is being forced *into* the emitter of B_1, so i_L is negative, then B_1 cuts off. Thus the circuit in Fig. 23.8a operates as a buffer and increases the fan-out *only* for i_L positive (see Problem P23.2).

A slightly more complicated buffer that overcomes this difficulty is shown in Fig. 23.8b. This circuit employs *complementary* pnp and npn emitter followers and thus can supply large currents of either polarity (see Problems P23.3 and P23.4).

A third buffer circuit is shown in Fig. 23.9a. If the buffer drive is in the **0** state, so that v_I is near zero, then B_1 and B_3 will be cut off. However, current flows through R_L and the diode D into the base of B_2, turning it on. Transistor B_2 is connected in the common-collector configuration, hence is capable of delivering a large positive current i_L to the load.

If now the input voltage is "high," transistors B_1 and B_3 will saturate. The voltage at the node K thus becomes

$$v_K = V_{BE3} + V_{CE1}(\text{sat}) \tag{23.12}$$

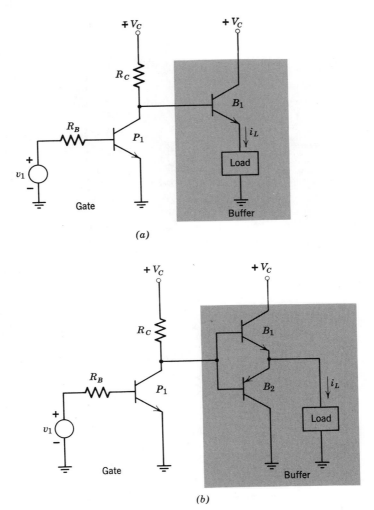

Figure 23.8   Buffer circuits.

and the output voltage becomes

$$v_O = V_{CE}(\text{sat}) \tag{23.13}$$

The purpose of the diode D can now be understood. If the diode were not present, B_2 in this state would be forward-biased by a voltage

$$v_K - v_O = V_{BE3}$$

and thus would draw substantial current. Inclusion of the diode introduces in effect a 0.6 volt offset, thereby reducing the input voltage of transistor B_2, thus producing a corresponding large reduction in the collector current

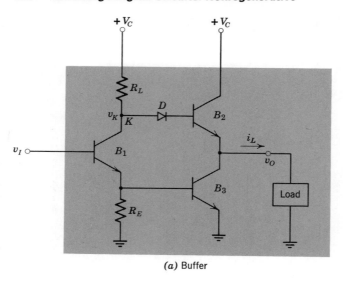

(a) Buffer

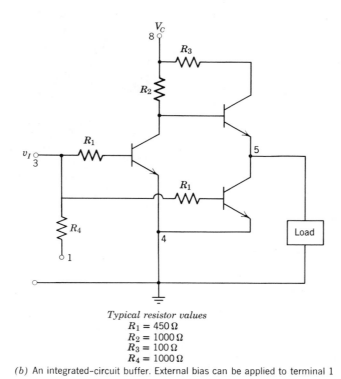

Typical resistor values
$R_1 = 450\,\Omega$
$R_2 = 1000\,\Omega$
$R_3 = 100\,\Omega$
$R_4 = 1000\,\Omega$

(b) An integrated–circuit buffer. External bias can be applied to terminal 1

Figure 23.9 Buffer circuits. In an integrated-circuit realization of (a), diode *D* might well be a diode-connected transistor.

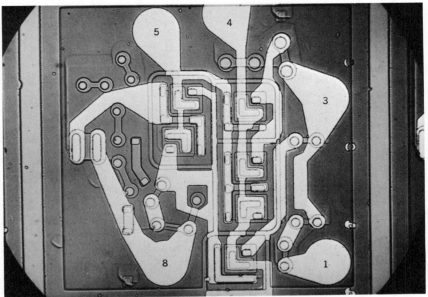

(c) Photomicrograph of the buffer in (b)

of B_2. Two diodes in series would raise the threshold voltage even further, hence give increased operating margin. Since B_3 is now saturated, the circuit can support substantial *negative* load current. Because large load current capability exists for both the "high" and "low" states, the fan-out capacity is very large.

A fourth buffer, this one available as one of a series of RTL integrated circuits,[3] is shown in Fig. 23.9b. Because of the many similarities to the buffer in Fig. 23.9a, circuit operation will not be discussed (see Problem P23.5). A photomicrograph of an integrated-circuit version of the buffer in Fig. 23.9b is shown in Fig. 23.9c. To facilitate identification, the pad numbers have been added to both figures.

23.2.5   Switching Speed

Obviously the calculation of the switching speed of a complete logic circuit, even one as simple as Fig. 23.7, is a formidable undertaking. However, we can obtain some feeling for the problem of switching speed in multistage digital circuits by examining two cascaded inverters, as shown in Fig. 23.10a.

First, let us trace out the overall static transfer characteristic v_O versus v_I of the circuit. For v_I low, that is, $v_I = V_{CE}(\text{sat})$, transistor T_1 will be cut off. Clearly, the second transistor T_2 is *on* under these conditions, so that its base current will be

$$i_{B2} = \frac{3 - 0.6}{0.6 + 0.4} = 2.4 \text{ ma}$$

[3] See Reference 23.3.

In the steady state, if we neglect $V_{CE}(\text{sat})$, we have

$$i_C(\text{sat}) = \frac{3}{0.6} = 5\,\text{ma}$$

It is clear that T_2 will be deep in saturation because the condition

$$i_{B2} > \frac{I_C(\text{sat})}{\beta_F} \qquad (23.14)$$

is generously fulfilled if we assume a typical β_F of 50.

If we now increase v_I, then for $v_I \simeq 0.4$ volt, T_1 begins to enter the active region. However, T_2 will remain saturated until there is substantial collector current in T_1. Thus v_I must rise to about 0.6 volt before T_2 comes out of saturation. With both transistors now in the active region, the transfer curve will rise steeply, with a slope equal to the cascaded incremental gain:

$$\frac{\Delta v_O}{\Delta v_I} = \frac{\beta_F{}^2 R_{L1}}{R_{L1} + R_{B2}} \times \frac{R_{L2}}{R_S + R_{B1}}$$

$$= 50^2 \times \frac{0.6}{1} \times \frac{0.6}{1}$$

$$= 900$$

These details are shown in the *static* transfer curve plotted in Fig. 23.10b (not to scale for obvious reasons).

If v_I is increased slowly, then T_2 cuts off when V_{CE1} drops to 0.4 volt, so that beyond this point the output voltage stays constant at V_{CC}. A further increase in v_I saturates T_1.

With the static behavior as background, we now turn to the main problem at hand, that of calculating the length of time it takes the two inverters to switch from one state to the other in response to a sudden step of voltage v_I. Let us assume that the input voltage v_I undergoes a step change at $t = 0$ from the **0** state of

$$v_I = V_0 = V_{CE}(\text{sat}) = 0.1\,\text{volt}$$

to the **1** state of

$$v_I = V_1 = V_{CC} = 3\,\text{volts}$$

Assume that the transistors are identical diffused silicon *npn* units, with charge-control parameters

$$\tau_F = 0.5\,\text{nsec} \qquad \tau_{BF} = 25\,\text{nsec}$$

$$\tau_R = 2\ \ \text{nsec} \qquad \tau_{BR} = 10\,\text{nsec}$$

$$Q_{FO} = 1 \times 10^{-10}\,\text{pc}$$

$$K_E = 7 \qquad K_C = 4$$

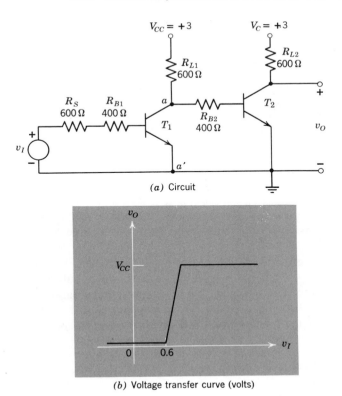

(a) Circuit

(b) Voltage transfer curve (volts)

Figure 23.10   Two cascaded RTL inverters.

We examine the details of the transition between states first by estimating performance using the method outlined in Section 22.3 and then check the results by a computer calculation.

We have already shown in the preceding static calculations that T_2 is initially deep in saturation. This fact somewhat simplifies the calculation, because it is reasonable to assume that excess base charge q_{S2} will hold T_2 in saturation for the entire turn-on interval of T_1. Thus the problem can be broken up into two almost independent single-stage transient problems.

Because T_2 is saturated throughout this interval, the base voltage of T_2 will remain fixed at about 0.6 volt positive. Thus we can account for the effects of T_2, as long as T_2 remains saturated, by forming the Thévenin equivalent of all of the network to the right of the points a, $á$:

$$R_T = R_{B2} \| R_{L1} = 0.6 \| 0.4 = 0.24 \, \text{kohm}$$

$$E_T = V_{CC} \frac{R_{B2}}{R_{B2} + R_{L1}} + 0.6 \frac{R_{L1}}{R_{L1} + R_{B2}}$$

$$= 1.6 \, \text{volts}$$

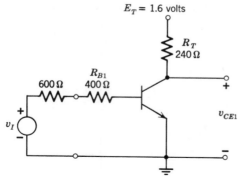

Figure 23.11   First stage with Thévenin equivalent load.

On this basis we obtain the equivalent single-stage circuit shown in Fig. 23.11.

Following the method outlined in Section 22.3.1, we find the changes in q_{VE} and q_{VC} which occur when T_1 is driven from cutoff to the edge of the active region. This charge is then equated to the integral of the base current. If we neglect the drop across R_T, and assume that the average base current is about 2.8 ma, we find that the delay time is (see Problem P23.6)

$$t_d \simeq 0.7 \text{ nsec}$$

Because of the substantial base overdrive, we are assured of rapid traversal of the active region. Thus to estimate the rise time of the circuit in Fig. 23.11 we neglect recombination, as discussed in Section 22.3.2, and integrate the base charge-control equation to yield

$$\int_0^{t_r} i_B \, dt \simeq \Delta q_{F1} + \Delta q_{VC} + \Delta q_{VE} \tag{23.15}$$

We have now reduced the first stage turn-on calculation to a form identical with that in Section 22.3.2, so that detailed calculations of the rise time will be left to the problems (see Problem P23.7). The result is that the rise time of the first stage is

$$t_r \simeq 3.8 \text{ nsec}$$

The collector voltage waveform V_{CE1} will be a ramp, as shown by the solid curve in Fig. 23.12b.

As already pointed out, transistor T_2 is initially deep in saturation. Thus it is reasonable to expect that the storage-delay time t_{sd} associated with removal of the excess charge q_{s2} will be considerably longer than t_r. On this basis we can approximate the voltage V_{CE1} driving T_2 as a step at $t \simeq 2.6$ ns rather than the ramp, as shown by the dashed curve in Fig. 23.12b. To estimate the storage-delay time and fall time of T_2, we note first that because the base resistors are small, there is substantial turn-off base current. Specifically,

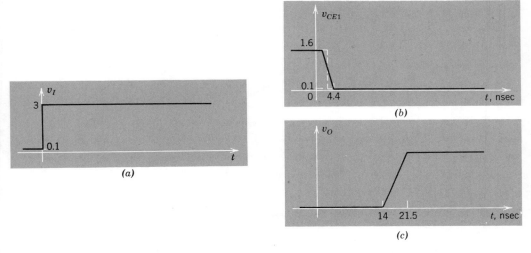

Figure 23.12 Collector voltage waveforms for the cascade of inverters in Fig. 23.10.

after T_1 is saturated and before T_2 comes out of saturation,

$$i_{B2} = -\frac{0.6 - 0.1}{400} = -1.25 \text{ ma}$$

The response of an inverter to a step turn-off pulse with turn-off overdrive was discussed in Section 22.3.4. Hence the detailed calculations for the present case have been relegated to the problems (see Problem P23.8). The results are that for the second transistor, the storage-delay time t_{sd} is about 11.4 nsec and the fall time is approximately 7.5 nsec. A rough sketch of the output voltage waveform is shown in Fig. 23.12c.

We conclude, therefore, that the total time required for the two cascaded inverters in Fig. 23.10a to change state from T_1 off, T_2 on to T_1 on, T_2 off is approximately

$$t \simeq 0.7 + 1.9 + 11.4 + 7.5 = 21.5 \text{ nsec}$$

Let us verify this result on the computer. Following the procedure outlined in Section 22.6, we first must write equations for the charge-control circuit model (Fig. 23.13b) in terms of the state variables, which in this case are the capacitor voltages v_{BE1}, v_{BC1}, v_{BE2}, and v_{BC2}. The sketch of the circuit topology shown in Fig. 23.13c indicates that these voltages, together with the voltage sources v_I and V_{CC}, form a "proper tree," so that we have defined an appropriate set of variables.

We have already derived in Section 22.6.2 the relations appropriate for a state-variable description of the transistor. Because we have two transistors in this problem, four equations are required. For the first transistor, these

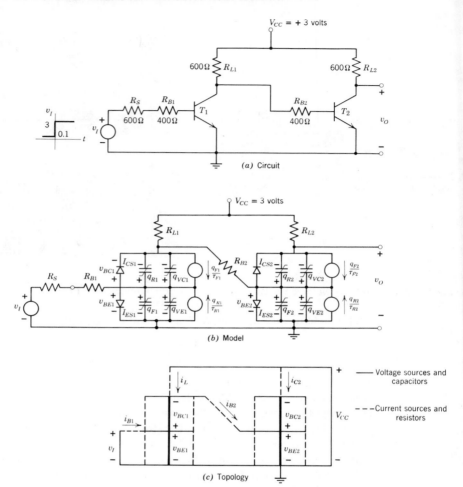

Figure 23.13   Charge-control analysis of two cascaded inverters.

are, from Eqs. 22.62 and 63,

$$\frac{d(q_{F1} + q_{VE1})}{dt} = \frac{q_{R1}}{\tau_R} - q_{F1}\left(\frac{1}{\tau_{BF}} + \frac{1}{\tau_F}\right) - i_{E1} \qquad (23.16)$$

$$\frac{d(q_{R1} + q_{VC1})}{dt} = \frac{q_{F1}}{\tau_F} - q_{R1}\left(\frac{1}{\tau_{BR}} + \frac{1}{\tau_R}\right) - i_{C1} \qquad (23.17)$$

For the second transistor,

$$\frac{d(q_{F2} + q_{VE2})}{dt} = \frac{q_{R2}}{\tau_R} - q_{F2}\left(\frac{1}{\tau_{BF}} + \frac{1}{\tau_F}\right) - i_{E2} \qquad (23.18)$$

$$\frac{d(q_{R2} + q_{VC2})}{dt} = \frac{q_{F2}}{\tau_F} - q_{R2}\left(\frac{1}{\tau_{BR}} + \frac{1}{\tau_R}\right) - i_{C2} \qquad (23.19)$$

Also needed are four relations similar to Eq. 22.67.

There are no external capacitors in the circuit, so no other derivative equations are required.

Next we must find expressions for the four link currents defined in Fig. 23.13c in terms of the state-variable voltages. These equations can be found by inspection from Figs. 23.13b and c:

$$i_{B1} = \frac{v_I - v_{BE1}}{R_{B1} + R_S} \tag{23.20a}$$

$$i_{B2} = \frac{v_{BE1} - v_{BC1} - v_{BE2}}{R_{B2}} \tag{23.20b}$$

$$i_L = \frac{V_{CC} - v_{BE1} + v_{BC1}}{R_{L1}} \tag{23.20c}$$

$$i_{C2} = \frac{V_{CC} - v_{BE2} + v_{BC2}}{R_{L2}} \tag{23.20d}$$

Finally we relate the currents used in formulating Eqs. 23.16 through 23.19 to the link currents. Because i_{C2} is already a link current, there are three such equations:

$$i_{E1} = i_{B2} - i_{B1} - i_L \tag{23.20e}$$

$$i_{C1} = i_L - i_{B2} \tag{23.21}$$

$$i_{E2} = -i_{B2} - i_{C2} \tag{23.22}$$

These equations, together with Eqs. 21.30 and 21.21 expressing q_F, q_R, q_{VE}, and q_{VC} in terms of the state variables, and the output voltage equation $v_O = -v_{BC2} + v_{BE2}$, can now be fed to the computer for analysis.

The computer results shown in Fig. 23.14 for a step turn-on of T_1 verify the intuitive solution given above. Transistor T_1 turns on in about 5 nsec, and the total time elapsed before T_2 is turned off is about 21 nsec.

23.3   Other Examples of Saturated Logic

23.3.1   Diode-Transistor Logic (DTL)

Diode-transistor logic is a natural extension of the diode logic circuits discussed in Chapter 6. As noted in Section 6.2.2, there is a shift in logic levels with diode logic caused by the 0.6-volt drop across the diode junctions in the *on* state. Furthermore, diode logic has no "gain" because there are no active elements, so that fan-out is severely limited. It is logical, therefore, to place a transistor amplifier at the output of each diode gate, thus simultaneously providing isolation, increased driving capabilities, and reconstituted logic levels. Generally, an inverting amplifier is used, as illustrated in Fig. 23.15.

For proper operation, when any input voltage is low, for example,

$$v_A = V_0 = V_{CE}(\text{sat})$$

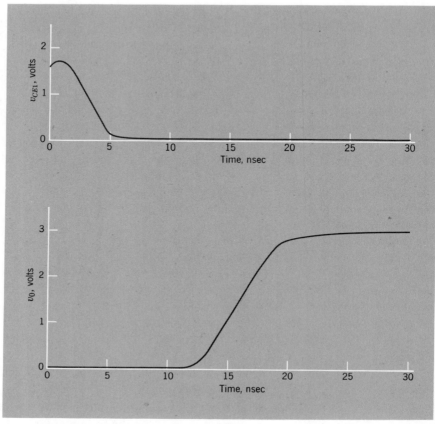

Figure 23.14   Computer-generated solution for the response of the cascaded inverter in Fig. 23.13*a* to a step input.

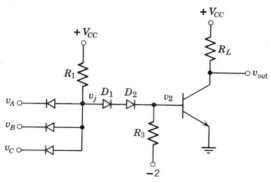

Figure 23.15   DTL NAND gate.

the transistor is supposed to be cut off. However, the voltage v_j at the diode gate output will be, for silicon,

$$v_j \simeq V_{CE}(\text{sat}) + 0.6$$

Thus diodes D_1 and D_2 and the negative supply voltage are added to shift this voltage to a value below the threshold voltage of the transistor. In this circuit there will be about a 0.6-volt drop across both diodes D_1 and D_2, so that the base voltage v_2 will be, for any input voltage low,

$$v_2 = v_j - 1.2 \simeq -0.5 \text{ volt}$$

Thus the transistor is amply cut off, ensuring a generous voltage margin.

Integrated circuit DTL gates, although basically the same as the gate in Fig. 23.15, usually contain somewhat more complicated transistor amplifiers, as can be seen from Fig. 23.16.[4] In these circuits the level shifting is provided by the emitter-to-base voltage drops of the intermediate amplifier stages, rather than by diodes. In addition, these transistors provide substantial current gain. A photomicrograph of a chip containing two of the gates in Fig. 23.16b, is shown in Fig. 23.16c. (See also Plate 3.) The resistor R_L is not on the chip; it is part of the external circuit.

23.3.2 Transistor-Transistor Logic (TTL, T²L)

Additional benefits can be realized if the gate diodes in Fig. 23.15 are replaced by the emitter diodes of transistors. The resulting circuit is shown in Fig. 23.17. For any input low, say

$$v_A = V_{CE}(\text{sat})$$

one of the gate transistors T_1, T_2, and T_3 will be saturated, so that the output inverter will be cut off. (Note that no level-shifting network is required here— a significant advantage over DTL.) If all inputs are high,

$$v_A = v_B = v_C = V_{CC}$$

all gate transistors will operate in the *reverse-active* region, because the collectors will be held at about $+0.6$ volt by the emitter-base diode of T_4. Thus T_4 will be saturated. Hence this gate performs the same NAND function as the corresponding DTL circuit (Fig. 23.15).

Because both the bases and the collectors of the gate transistors are tied together, it is possible to perform the same gating function in a single *multiple-emitter device*, as shown in Fig. 23.18a.[5] Such a configuration is easy to manufacture in integrated-circuit form. For this reason the multiple-emitter device is usually used in conjunction with one of the more sophisti-

---

[4] See References 23.3 and 23.4.
[5] See Reference 23.4.

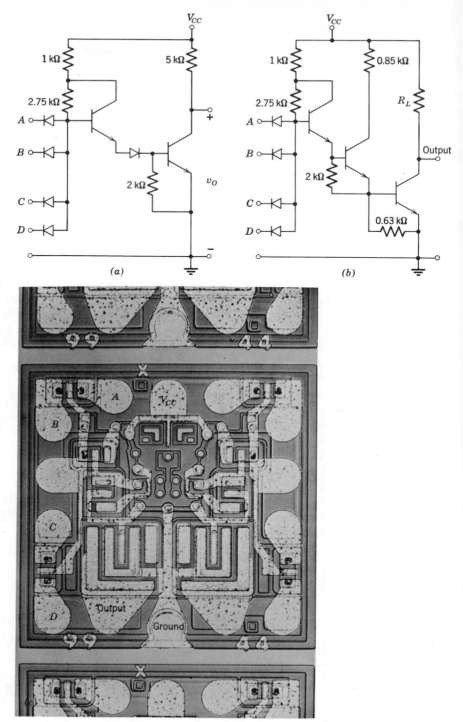

Figure 23.16 Integrated-circuit DTL NAND gates. (a) and (b) Circuits. (c) Photomicrograph of a chip containing two of the circuits in (b). See also Plate III.

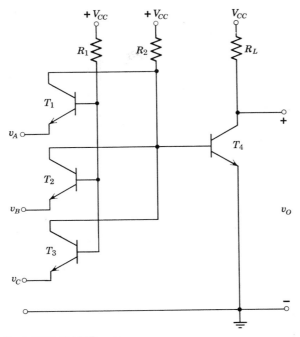

Figure 23.17   Basic TTL NAND gate.

cated buffer output stages discussed in Section 23.2.4. A typical example, which uses the buffer of Fig. 23.9a, is shown in Fig. 23.18b.

23.4   Nonsaturating Circuits

As indicated in Section 22.3.3, the stored excess charge that results when the *on* state of a transistor switch lies in the saturation region causes pulse distortion. Because this distortion appears as a widening of the pulse, it limits the maximum rate at which the switch may be operated. Although the unfortunate consequences of stored excess charge may be alleviated by using speed-up capacitors, as discussed in Section 22.4, storage delay cannot be completely eliminated in practical saturating switches because the peak turn-off current is circuit-limited.

Several circuit arrangements that prohibit saturation of the transistors have been developed. These circuits avoid saturation in one of two ways: either they use diode clamps to limit the collector-base voltage so that the collector junction cannot become forward-biased, or they control the *on*-state collector current at a value for which the drop across the load resistance is insufficient to saturate the transistor. We now consider the characteristics of two types of transistor switching circuits, in each of which the *on* state lies in the active region rather than in the saturation region.

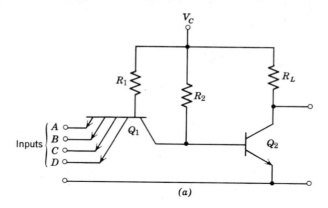

(a)

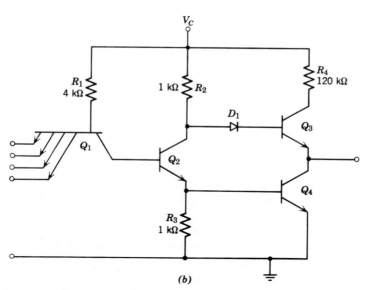

(b)

Figure 23.18   TTL gate in multiple-emitter integrated-circuit form.

23.4.1   Use of Clamping Diodes to Avoid Saturation

One obvious approach to prevent saturation of a transistor is to add a
clamping diode to the collector circuit, as shown in Fig. 23.19. The inverter
now has its *on* state in the active region, because the diode at the collector
terminal does not allow v_2 to drop below $V_S - V_D$, where V_D denotes the
forward drop across the diode. Thus for an appropriate choice of V_S, the
collector junction remains reverse-biased, regardless of how hard the base is
driven.

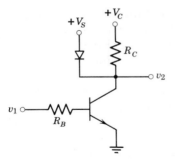

Figure 23.19 A clamping diode used to prevent saturation of the transistor.

However, this circuit has serious drawbacks. If we turn the transistor on by setting v_1 equal to V_{CC}, the collector current will be

$$i_C = \beta_F i_B = \beta_F \frac{V_C}{R_B} \tag{23.23}$$

This large collector current—much larger than V_C/R_L, the collector current for no diode clamp—means large stored charge, because in the steady state (active region, in this circuit),

$$q_F = I_B \tau_{BF} = \tau_{BF} \frac{V_C}{R_B} \tag{23.24}$$

Furthermore, there will be a large current through the diode, hence a large stored charge here as well. Because of these two effects, this nonsaturating circuit may well have a *slower* transient response than the corresponding

importance of q_F and q_{VC} (see Problem P23.9). The basic cause of waveform distortion in logic circuits is *not* saturation per se, but excessive base charge

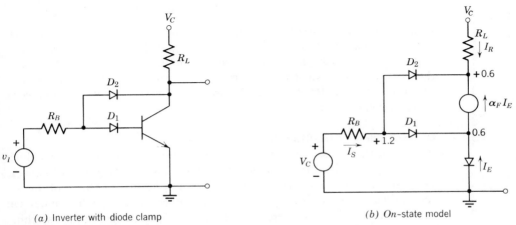

(a) Inverter with diode clamp   (b) On-state model

Figure 23.20 Nonsaturating inverter with fast response.

compared to that needed to support the desired collector current. Thus the trouble with the circuit in Fig. 23.19 is that the diode has insufficient influence over the important parameter, that is, base charge.

The circuit shown in Fig. 23.20a is a more practical way of avoiding saturation of the transistor. Diode D_1 becomes forward-biased as soon as v_I is greater than about a volt. Diode D_2 also becomes forward-biased after the collector voltage has dropped to about 0.6 volt, thus preventing the collector diode from closing. More important, however, is the fact that diode D_2 can now *divert* the input current directly to the collector circuit, thereby preventing the buildup of excessive base charge.

The model in Fig. 23.20b can be used to calculate the currents in the steady-state *on* condition. Because the *on* state is in the active region, we find by inspection that

$$I_S = \frac{V_C - 1.2}{R_B} \tag{23.25}$$

$$I_R = \frac{V_C - 0.6}{R_L} \tag{23.26}$$

$$I_C = -\alpha_F I_E = \alpha_F (I_S + I_R) \tag{23.27}$$

$$\simeq V_C \left(\frac{1}{R_B} + \frac{1}{R_L} \right) \tag{23.28}$$

Hence

$$q_F = \tau_F I_C = \tau_F V_C \left(\frac{1}{R_B} + \frac{1}{R_L} \right)$$

$$= \frac{\tau_{BF} V_C}{\beta_F} \left(\frac{1}{R_B} + \frac{1}{R_L} \right) \tag{23.29}$$

Comparison of this result with Eq. 23.24 indicates that in the present case the stored charge is more than a factor of β_F less than for the circuit in Fig. 23.19. The diode currents are also at least a factor of β_F smaller in this circuit than in Fig. 23.19, so that substantial improvement in transient response can be realized (see Problem P23.10) provided that q_F is the dominant charge component, and not q_{VC}.

23.4.2   Current-Mode Circuits (CML)

It is generally impossible to design nonsaturating switching circuits in which saturation is avoided by controlling the base current. The current gain β_F varies from unit to unit far too much to permit accurate control of the *on*-state collector current by this means. On the other hand, the collector current can be controlled, thereby preventing saturation, by designing the switching circuit so that the *emitter* current in the *on* state is carefully controlled and is essentially independent of the base drive. Circuits that use this design philosophy are called *current-mode* logic circuits (CML) or *emitter-coupled logic* (ECL). A simple form of a CML circuit is shown in Fig. 23.21a. Note that the circuit topology is identical to that of the difference amplifier discussed in Section 7.4.2.

The fixed current I_O provided by the current source divides between the two transistors in a manner determined by the input voltage v_I. If v_I is less than the reference potential V_R, transistor T_1 is cut off and essentially all of

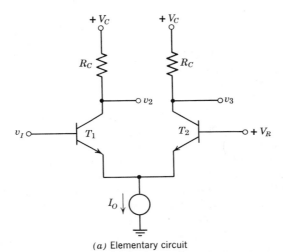

(a) Elementary circuit

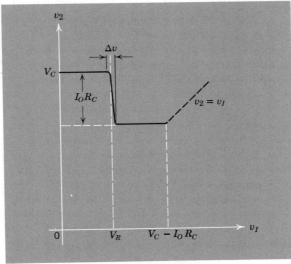

(b) Static transfer characteristic

Figure 23.21   A current-mode logic circuit.

I_O flows in transistor T_2. The circuit is in the *off* state, and the output voltage v_2 is equal to the collector supply voltage V_C. As the input voltage increases, T_1 begins to conduct, and the current I_O divides between the two transistors. When v_I exceeds the reference potential V_R by a small margin, the emitter diode of T_2 is reverse-biased, and all of I_O flows in T_1. This is the *on* state of the circuit, and it is characterized by an output voltage of $V_C - I_O R_C$. The fixed current I_O is "steered" to either transistor by the input voltage v_I. This behavior is summarized by the static transfer characteristic shown in Fig. 23.21*b*.

The range of input voltage over which the transition from *off* to *on* occurs, designated as Δv on the static transfer characteristic, is quite narrow. Voltage changes of only a few tenths of a volt suffice to steer the current from one transistor to the other.

The upward break in the characteristic at $v_I = V_C - I_O R_C$ occurs when the transistor saturates. Practical CML circuits are designed to operate below this point by restricting the range of the input voltage v_I. Note that the circuit has two *complementary* outputs v_2 and v_3 (and an additional input at the second base if desired). Consequently, this circuit, which is the basic building block of all current-mode logic circuits, can be used either as an inverter or as a noninverting amplifier (see Problem P23.11).

In practice, the current source in Fig. 23.21*a* is replaced by a resistor and a negative voltage source as illustrated in Fig. 23.22. This modification causes the static transfer characteristic to have a small negative slope in the region corresponding to the *on* state. The values shown for the output variables are approximate, and are based on the assumption that the current switched between transistors is constant at 10 ma. Actually the current in the emitter resistor is slightly different in one state than in the other (see Problem P23.12).

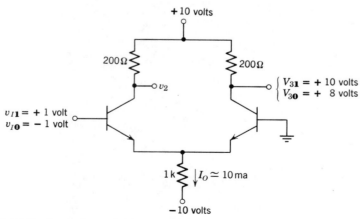

Figure 23.22   A CML circuit that provides complementary outputs.

The values of the input and output variables shown in Fig. 23.22 illustrate one inconvenient aspect of CML circuits: the voltage levels that correspond to the binary values of the *output* variable are shifted from the voltage levels at the *input*. Consequently, CML circuits cannot be directly cascaded.

23.4.3 Basic CML OR-NOR Gate

Figure 23.23 shows the basic structure of a current-mode logic gate. Initially assume that a *negative* signal is applied to the inputs v_A, v_B, v_C. Transistor Q_0, whose base is referenced to ground, will thus be *on* and have a collector current $I_C \simeq I_0$, whereas Q_1, Q_2, and Q_3 will be turned off. If now one or more of the inputs v_A, v_B, or v_C is *positive*, the corresponding transistor(s) is turned on. Thus output v_0 is a NOR function for positive representation. The OR function is also available by using the voltage v_Q as the output. The level shift between input and output voltages is obviously present in this circuit just as it was in the simple CML inverter discussed above.

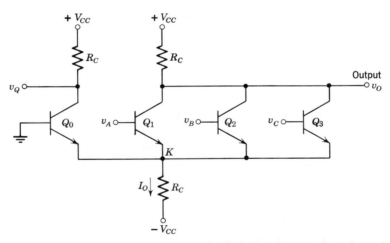

Figure 23.23 CML gate. Note that both the OR and the NOR logic functions are formed.

23.4.4 Coupling Methods for CML Circuits

One common way of eliminating the mismatch of dc levels referred to in the preceding section is illustrated in Fig. 23.24.[6] The outputs of the CML gate are fed to emitter-follower output stages, which shift the levels down by about 0.6 volt, in addition to providing increased output-current capability. Now by judicious choice of power supply voltages and signal voltage levels, the input and output levels can be made to match. For the power supply

---

[6] See Reference 23.4.

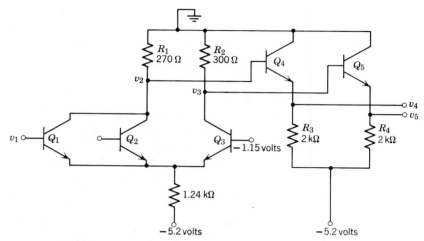

Figure 23.24   Emitter-coupled OR-NOR gate with consistent input and output logic levels.

voltages shown, logic levels of

$$V_0 = -1.6 \text{ volt}$$

$$V_1 = -0.75 \text{ volt}$$

will result in matching voltage levels for the input v_1 and the outputs v_4 and v_5 (see Problem P23.13).

A typical CML circuit in integrated form might include two complete four-input OR-NOR gates and a transistor regulator to supply the reference voltage to the base in the basic CML pair, as shown in Fig. 23.25.[7] A significant advantage of such an integrated circuit package is that changes in device temperature affect *both* the gate and the regulator. Thus by proper design it is possible to maintain the threshold point of the gate at the center of the transition region regardless of the temperature.

23.4.5   Transient Response of CML Circuits

Current-mode switching circuits are capable of much faster rates of operation than are saturating circuits constructed with the same transistors. This relative advantage arises principally because the storage-delay time (which inevitably accompanies an *on* state in the saturation region) is avoided. Furthermore, CML circuits generally operate with small voltage swings and high collector currents, so that the required changes in space-charge-layer charges can be accomplished more rapidly. Finally, these circuits are usually driven from relatively low-impedance sources, that is, the emitter-follower output stages of a previous gate (Fig. 23.24). Thus the peak base

---

[7] See Reference 23.5.

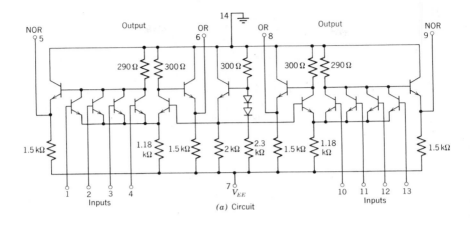

(a) Circuit

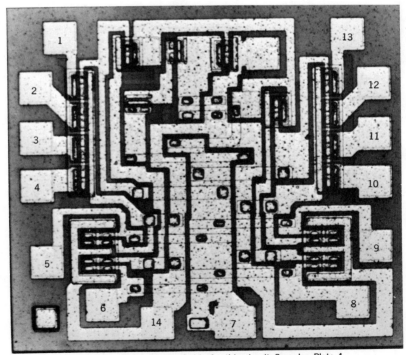

(b) Photomicrograph of chip for this circuit. See also Plate 4

Figure 23.25 An integrated-circuit, dual four-input OR-NOR gate.

current can be quite high during changes of state, thereby reducing the time required to change the excess charge in the base. These factors combine to make CML circuits five to ten times faster than saturating circuits that use comparable transistors. Of course, a price is paid in terms of increased power dissipation and greater circuit complexity. The latter factor is of diminishing importance in view of integrated-circuit technology.

The calculation of the transient response of a CML circuit is more complicated than the corresponding analysis of a saturating switch, simply because the current-mode circuit is driven from a low-voltage, low-impedance

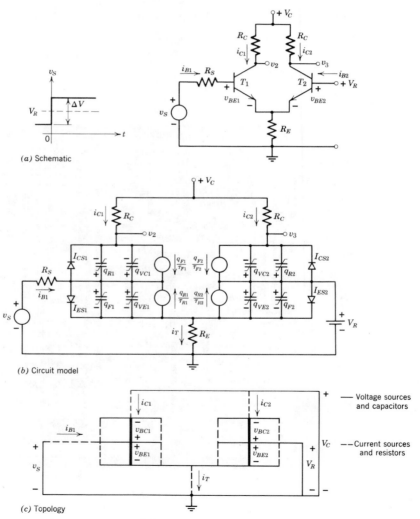

(a) Schematic

(b) Circuit model

(c) Topology

Figure 23.26   Switching transient calculation, CML.

source. Consequently, the base current is *not* determined solely by the parameters of the driving circuit and varies substantially during the traversal of the active region. For these reasons the approximate method of solution used in previous examples does not yield reasonable results. We are thus forced to rely solely on computer calculations.

We can illustrate the issues involved in transient analysis, and can obtain a feeling for the nature of the response times, by considering the two-transistor circuit shown in Fig. 23.26a. We assume that the Thévenin equivalent source voltage changes abruptly at $t = 0$ by an amount ΔV, as shown in the figure, thereby initiating a transient that concludes when the current i_T has switched from transistor 2 to transistor 1. We are interested in the time required for this change to occur; this time is the rise time of one collector current and the fall time of the other collector current. We assume that the transistors are identical to those used in the RTL discussion (Section 23.2.5).

The complete charge-control model for the circuit is shown in Fig. 23.26b. To check on the state variables, we sketch the circuit topology as in Fig. 23.26c, drawing the voltage sources and capacitors with solid lines and the current sources and resistors with dashed lines. Clearly, the voltage-source, capacitor tree is a proper tree, so we proceed.

The general charge-control equations written in terms of i_E and i_C, as formulated in Section 22.6.2, can be used to describe the transistors: two sets similar to Eqs. 22.62 and 22.63 are needed. Also required are four equations similar to Eqs. 22.67, and the relations between each of the eight charge variables and the corresponding state-variable junction voltage.

To complete the formulation, we relate the currents i_{E1}, i_{C1}, i_{E2}, and i_{C2} to the link currents defined in Fig. 23.26c. Because i_{C1} and i_{C2} are already link currents, the required relations are

$$i_{E1} = -i_{B1} - i_{C1} \qquad (23.30a)$$

$$i_{E2} = -i_T + i_{B1} + i_{C1} \qquad (23.30b)$$

Finally we need to express the four link currents in terms of the state-variable voltages. The relations are, from Fig. 23.26b and c,

$$i_{B1} = \frac{v_S - V_R + v_{BE2} - v_{BE1}}{R_S} \qquad (23.31a)$$

$$i_{C1} = \frac{V_C - V_R + v_{BE2} - v_{BE1} + v_{BC1}}{R_C} \qquad (23.31b)$$

$$i_{C2} = \frac{V_C - V_R + v_{BC2}}{R_C} \qquad (23.31c)$$

$$i_T = \frac{V_R - v_{BE2}}{R_E} \qquad (23.31d)$$

These relations, together with the relations between the output voltages and the state variables,

$$v_2 = V_R - v_{BE2} + v_{BE1} - v_{BC1} \qquad (23.32)$$

$$v_3 = V_R - v_{BC2} \qquad (23.33)$$

can now be fed to the computer for solution. The results for the particular parameter values given above, assuming an input step of 0.9 volt, are plotted in Fig. 23.27. As predicted, the rise time of this CML circuit is very fast.

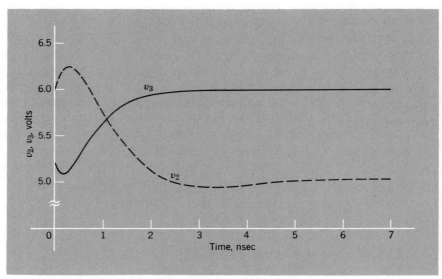

Figure 23.27   Computer-calculated response of the CML circuit in Fig. 23.26.

In fact, the entire transient is over in about 2.5 nsec, much faster than the RTL gate analysed in Section 23.2.5 (see Fig. 23.14).

23.5   Field-Effect Transistors as Switching Elements
23.5.1.   Switching Characteristics

Field-effect transistors of both the junction and insulated-gate or MOS variety can be used as switches in digital-circuit applications. Since conduction in the drain-to-source path is controlled by the gate-to-source voltage, as shown in Fig. 9.14 (which describes an n-channel enhancement-mode device), the current in the drain-to-source path can be switched between two values, one large and one quite small, by controlling the gate-to-source voltage.

This control function is illustrated in Fig. 23.28, in which an n-channel enhancement-mode device is operated with a resistive load. If we make the assignment of states shown in Table 23.2 (positive representation), it is clear

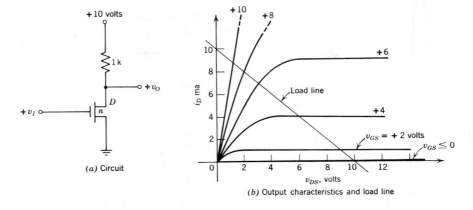

(a) Circuit

(b) Output characteristics and load line

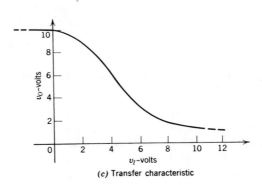

(c) Transfer characteristic

Figure 23.28 A field-effect transistor switch.

from the transfer characteristic of Fig. 23.28c that the MOS circuit functions as a logical *inverter*.

Table 23.2 State Assignments

State	Voltage Range
0	0 to 4 volts
1	6 to 10 volts

MOS, transistors that are used in digital circuits are often fabricated in integrated circuit form. In such cases it is as easy to fabricate another MOS transistor as it is to make a resistor for use as a load in an inverter circuit. Consequently, circuit configurations such as that shown in Fig. 23.29a are common. In this circuit the transistor labeled T_1, which operates with gate connected to drain, serves as a nonlinear load for transistor T_2; the corresponding load line construction is shown in Fig. 23.29b (See Problem P23.15.)

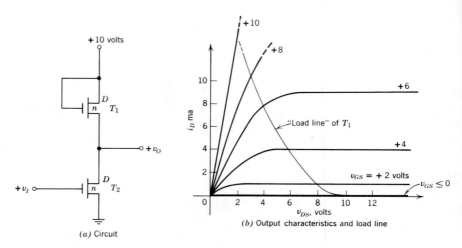

(a) Circuit

(b) Output characteristics and load line

Figure 23.29   A second MOS transistor can be used as a nonlinear load.

If both *n*-channel and *p*-channel devices are available, the properties of the basic transistor-loaded inverter can be greatly improved as shown in Fig. 23.30. When the input voltage v_I is $+10$ volts, the lower (*n*-channel) transistor conducts well, while the upper (*p*-channel) transistor is cut off. Thus the output terminal is connected to ground and $v_O \simeq 0$. Conversely, when $v_I = 0$, the lower transistor is cut off and the upper transistor conducts well. The output terminal is connected to the 10 volt supply, and $v_O \simeq 10$ volts. This circuit has the useful property that *no current is drawn from the*

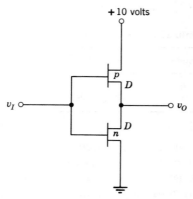

Figure 23.30   A complementary-symmetry MOS switch.

power supply except during transitions between states, when the associated capacitances must be charged and discharged.

The dynamics of switching in these MOS circuits are governed by the gate charge, which controls the current in the drain-to-source path. Unfortunately, useful charge-control models that describe this process are complex and nonlinear.

This discussion has emphasized MOS rather than junction field-effect transistors. There are two reasons for this emphasis. First, MOS devices can be operated in the enhancement mode, which facilitates direct coupling between logic stages. Second, MOS devices are easier to fabricate in integrated form. In fact, large arrays of MOS devices can be fabricated in integrated form with much less difficulty than arrays of bipolar transistors because MOS transistors are majority-carrier devices that do not require careful control of lifetime or of junction properties. For this reason, large-scale integrated digital arrays that contain many hundreds of active devices are, at present, dominated by MOS technology.

23.5.2   MOS Logic Gates

Two simple MOS transistor gates are shown in Fig. 23.31. In both cases all transistors are n-channel enhancement-mode devices. In the circuit of Fig. 23.31a the output voltage v_O is high if, and only if, neither v_A nor v_B nor v_C is high, i.e., if the three lower transistors are cut off. Thus the circuit is, for positive representation, a NOR gate. In the circuit of Fig. 23.31b the

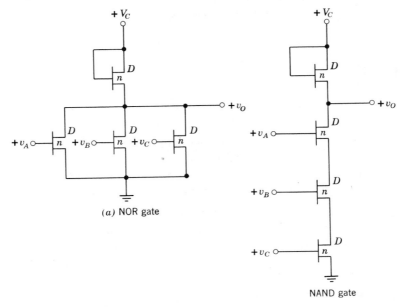

(a) NOR gate

NAND gate

Figure 23.31   MOS transistor logic gates.

output voltage is low if, and only if, v_A and v_B and v_C are high, i.e., if the three lower transistors are conducting. Thus, for positive representation this circuit is a NAND gate.

23.6 Lecture Demonstrations

Almost any of the circuits in this chapter can be used as lecture demonstrations. For example, an informative demonstration can be made by using the buffer circuits in Figs. 23.8 and 23.9 to drive a capacitive load. The relative speed of response of the simple inverter, the inverter with a diode clamp shown in Fig. 23.19, and the improved circuit in Fig. 23.20a can also be shown. Similarly, it is useful to demonstrate the relative response speeds of the various logic circuits, that is, the RTL gate, the DTL gate, and the CML gate.

REFERENCES

23.1   J. Millman and H. Taub, *Pulse, Digital, and Switching Waveforms*, McGraw-Hill, New York, 1965.

23.2   J. N. Harris et al., *Digital Transistor Circuits*, Wiley, New York, 1966.

23.3   *Fairchild Microcircuits*, Fairchild Semiconductor, 1968.

23.4   W. E. Wickes, *Logic Design with Integrated Circuits*, Wiley, New York, 1968.

23.5   *Motorola Digital Integrated Circuits : MECL*, Motorola Semiconductor Products, Pheonix, 1967.

23.6   V. A. Otero, *Simplified Transistor Models for Computer Aided Design*, S.M. Thesis, M.I.T., May 1968.

23.7   H. Camenzind, *Circuit Design for Integrated Circuits*, Addison-Wesley, Reading, Mass., 1968.

PROBLEMS

P23.1   Calculate the maximum positive load current i_L that can be drawn from the buffer stage in Fig. 23.8a, assuming that the load consists of N other transistors as in Fig. 23.7. Hence verify Eq. 23.11.

P23.2   Sketch the output waveform of the buffer circuit in Fig. 23.8a if the load is a 1-kohm resistor in parallel with a 1000-pf capacitor. Assume that the input waveform is a square pulse 1 μsec long, and large enough to saturate P_1. Ignore all transistor dynamics. (See page 858.)

P23.3   Calculate the maximum positive load current i_L for the buffer circuit in Fig. 23.8b, assuming that the load is a resistor R_L connected to ground. Also calculate the maximum negative current, assuming that the load is a resistor R_L connected to V_C. Compare with the performance of the simpler buffer in Fig. 23.8a.

P23.4   The buffers shown in Fig. 23.8b and Fig. 23.9 are particularly useful for driving capacitive loads, because they can supply large currents of either polarity. (For the same reason, these circuits can be adapted for use in audio amplifier output stages.) Repeat Problem P23.2 for these circuits, and compare the results with those obtained in Problem P23.2 for the simple buffer. (See page 858.)

P23.5 Explain why no diode is needed in the buffer circuit in Fig. 23.9*b*, whereas a diode *D* was needed in Fig. 23.9*a*. (See page 861.)

P23.6 Calculate the delay time for transistor T_1 in circuit discussed in Section 23.2.5, Fig. 23.10. (See page 864.)

P23.7 Complete the calculation of the rise time for T_1 in the cascaded RTL inverter circuit in Section 23.2.5, Fig. 23.10. Hence confirm the estimate of $t_r = 3.8$ nsec given in the text. (See page 864.)

P23.8 Complete the calculation of the response time of the circuit in Fig. 23.10 (Section 23.2.5) by calculating the storage-delay time and the fall time for transistor T_2. Compare with the results quoted in the text. (See page 865.)

P23.9 Calculate the stored base charge in the *on* state of the circuit in Fig. 23.19, assuming that the diode is not present. Compare with Eq. 23.24, and comment on the relative speed of the two circuits. (See page 873.)

P23.10 Compare the *on*-state stored-base charge in the circuit in Fig. 23.20 with that calculated in Eq. 23.24 and that calculated in Problem P23.9. Which circuit will respond fastest? Will space-charge capacitance effects influence your answer? Explain. (See page 874.)

P23.11 Find the static transfer curve v_3 versus v_I for the circuit in Fig. 23.21*a*. Plot the results along with the graph in Fig. 23.21*b*. (See page 876.)

P23.12 The circuit of Fig. 23.22 can be characterized by two static transfer characteristics that relate the two output voltages to the input voltage. Using the element values shown, compute, sketch, and dimension these transfer characteristics. Make reasonable assumptions concerning the static behavior of the transistors. (See page 876.)

P23.13 Derive the transfer curves v_4 versus v_1 and v_5 versus v_1 for the emitter-coupled circuit in Fig. 23.24, hence verify that it has compatible input and output logic levels. Assume that in the *on* state, $v_{BE} = 0.75$ volt. Use positive representation, with $V_0 = -1.6$ volt, $V_1 = -0.75$ volt. (See page 878.)

P23.14 Recalculate the voltage margin of the circuit in Fig. 23.4 assuming that resistors R_{B2} have been added from the transistor bases to a negative supply voltage V_R. Compare with Eq. 23.4 and comment.

P23.15 This problem is concerned with the circuit of Fig. 23.29.
(a) Note that when $v_{GS} = v_{DS}$, the drain current in an enhancement-mode

transistor for which the pinch-off voltage is zero can be written as

$$i_D = K v_{DS}^2$$

Estimate K for the circuit whose drain characteristics are shown in Fig. 23.29b.

(b) Using the relationship developed in (a), derive an expression for the nonlinear load line shown in Fig. 23.29b.

(c) Compute, sketch, and dimension the transfer characteristic that relates v_O to v_I.

CHAPTER TWENTY-FOUR

Multistage Switching Circuits: Regenerative

24.1 Bistable Regenerative Switching Circuits

The switching circuits we have considered up to this point all have in common the feature that the instantaneous state of the circuit, hence the instantaneous values of the output variables, are determined solely by the input variables at the same instant of time. That is, except for transient time delays associated with the dynamics of state changes, the output of a nonregenerative switching circuit is a single-valued function of the input or inputs at that time.

We now turn our attention to *regenerative* switching circuits, which are broadly characterized by having the signal at some point within the circuit determined, in part, by the output variables as well as by the input variables. That is, the output of the circuit is fed back and combined at some point with the input, so that in the signal-flow sense the circuit has a positive feedback path. This positive feedback may result from the external coupling of the output of an amplifier to its own input, or it may be produced by a feedback mechanism internal to the transistor, such as avalanche multiplication. In some cases it may be difficult to characterize the circuit in a manner that makes the feedback stand out. Nevertheless, the concept of positive feedback is the one feature that ties together essentially all regenerative switching circuits.

We shall see that these circuits generally have outputs which, as a consequence of the positive feedback, depend not only on the instantaneous values of the inputs but also on their past history. That is, regenerative switching circuits generally exhibit *memory*, and it is this characteristic that makes them useful.

The principal issues involved in the design of regenerative switching circuits, that is, circuit requirements to ensure regeneration, calculation of switching speed, and triggering requirements, are discussed in terms of *bistable* circuits in this section. Monostable and astable circuits are discussed in Sections 24.2 and 24.3.

24.1.1 Basic Bistable Circuit

We studied in Section 23.2.5 the static transfer characteristic of two cascaded inverters. The circuit and the general form of the characteristic are repeated for convenience in Figs. 24.1a and b. One interesting property of this circuit readily seen from the transfer curve is that the output voltage v_3 is the *same* as voltage v_1 at one point in each of the saturated states. This suggests an interesting experiment. What happens if we connect the output back to the input, and remove the input source? The circuit will now supply its own input and will maintain whatever state it was in at the time of the connection. That is, the circuit has *memory*.

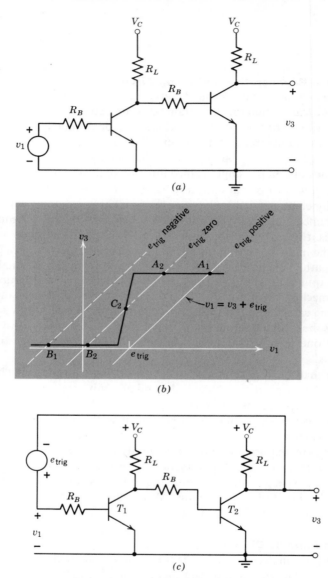

Figure 24.1   Development of bistable circuit from two cascaded inverters.

To examine this new property in more detail, we join the output of T_2 to the input of T_1 by a voltage source e_{trig}, as shown in Fig. 24.1c. To simplify the initial discussion, we suppress the loading issue by assuming that R_B is much larger in value than R_L. Thus the input resistor R_B is a negligible load on the output T_2. Essentially we have added to the circuit of Fig. 24.1a a *linear constraint*

$$v_1 = v_3 + e_{\text{trig}} \tag{24.1}$$

where e_{trig} is a triggering voltage that can be used to force the circuit to change state. This constraint has been superimposed on the transfer function in Fig. 24.1b, yielding an operating point A_1, with transistor T_2 cut off and T_1 saturated. If e_{trig} is now reduced to zero, the constraint indicated by the dash-dot line now intersects the transfer curve at the operating point A_2. Note that T_2 remains cut off, T_1 remains saturated, and $v_3 = V_C$. However, if e_{trig} is made negative enough, the constraint line $v_1 = v_3 + e_{\text{trig}}$ no longer intersects the transfer curve at $v_3 = V_C$, but intersects at $v_3 \simeq 0$. This condition is indicated by the dashed line. Thus the circuit abruptly changes to a new operating point B_1, with T_2 saturated and T_1 cut off. If e_{trig} is now returned to zero, the circuit *does not change state*, so that this time for e_{trig} equal to zero, the operating point is at B_2, and v_3 is almost zero. Thus in response to a negative "pulse" of trigger voltage, the circuit has changed state. We conclude that the circuit in Fig. 24.1c has two stable states and that it can be made to "flip" from one stable state to the other by applying a suitable trigger pulse; hence the names *bistable circuit, bistable multivibrator,* or *flip-flop*. The circuit has wide application in pulse and digital circuits.

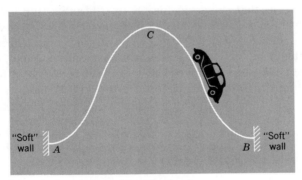

Figure 24.2 Mechanical analog of a bistable circuit.

A simple mechanical analogy may prove helpful at this point. Shown in Fig. 24.2 is a section of roller-coaster track terminated at each end by "soft" walls. Clearly, there are two points of stable equilibrium for the car, that is, points A and B. If the car is at point A, it can be made to "change state" to point B by applying a suitable trigger pulse with enough energy to push the car over the hill past point C.

24.1.2 Stability Considerations

The conditions for bistable behavior can best be explained with reference to the transfer curve in Fig. 24.1b. For e_{trig} equal to zero, there are *three* intersections of the transfer curve v_3 versus v_1 and the linear constraint $v_1 = v_3$. The three possible operating points have been designated as A_2, B_2, and C_2 in the figure. We showed above that operating points A_2 and B_2 are *stable*, in the sense that if the circuit is at one of these points, it will stay there indefinitely unless a trigger voltage is applied. These two operating points lie on the flat portions of the transfer characteristic, corresponding to operation with one or the other of the two transistors out of the active region. Consequently, in feedback terms the incremental loop transmission at either of these operating points is essentially zero, so there is no positive feedback.

Operating point C_2 in Fig. 24.1b corresponds to operation with both transistors active, hence in feedback terms the "basic amplifier" has substantial *positive* gain. Thus with node-node topology we have *positive feedback* with a loop transmission magnitude greater than unity. We know from Chapter 19 what these conditions imply. The circuit in this state has a pole in the right half plane, and the operating point is *unstable*. Therefore, any minute deviation from equilibrium at this operating point causes a transient that *grows* in amplitude with time, thus driving the system away from point C_2 in one direction or the other. Thus operating point C_2 in Fig. 24.1b is *unstable*, just as point C on the roller-coaster track in Fig. 24.2 is unstable, and the systems will never equilibrate at these points.

We conclude, therefore, that there are two methods of determining whether a circuit such as that shown in Fig. 24.1c is bistable, and for guiding the design of such circuits. First, we can look directly for the existence of *two* stable states, in each of which at least one transistor is out of the active region. If these states exist, the circuit will exhibit bistability. Second, we can treat the circuit as a two-stage positive-feedback amplifier, and check for bistability by calculating the loop transmission T with both transistors active, after proving that such an operating state exists. A value of $|T|$ in excess of unity

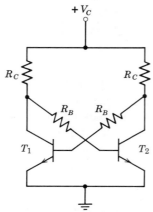

Figure 24.3   Symmetrical bistable circuit.

is a necessary condition for bistability. We illustrate these methods of ensuring bistability by applying both to the circuit of Fig. 24.3, the more conventional way of drawing the circuit in Fig. 24.1c.

24.1.3 Analysis of the Two Stable States

Inasmuch as the circuit in Fig. 24.3 is symmetric, and since we assume for simplicity that the transistors are identical, we need look for only *one* stable state; the other follows from symmetry. We first assume that transistor T_1 is *off* and then find the circuit conditions necessary to validate this assumption. For T_1 cut off, the base current of T_2 is

$$i_{B2} = \frac{V_C - v_{BE}}{R_C + R_B} \tag{24.2}$$

The collector current of T_2 is

$$i_{C2} = \frac{V_C - v_{CE}}{R_C} \tag{24.3}$$

The circuit configuration ensures that for silicon transistors, T_1 will be held *off*, in accordance with our original assumption, *if T_2 is saturated*, because v_{CE} in saturation is less than v_{BE} at the threshold of conduction. Saturation of T_2 is ensured if

$$i_{B2} > \frac{i_{C2}}{\beta_F}. \tag{24.4}$$

that is, if

$$\frac{V_C - v_{BE}}{R_C + R_B} > \frac{V_C - v_{CE}}{\beta_F R_C} \tag{24.5}$$

Often the supply voltage V_C is substantially greater than the saturation values of v_{BE} and v_{CE}. Under these conditions Eq. 24.5 reduces to

$$\beta_F > \frac{R_C + R_B}{R_C} \tag{24.6}$$

Thus if the condition in Eq. 24.6 is met, our original assumption of T_1 *off* is validated, and the existence of two stable states is assured. With germanium transistors, particularly at high temperatures, the difference between $V_{CE}(\text{sat})$ and v_{BE} at the threshold of conduction may be too small to ensure reliable operation. Therefore, in such circuits the base is often returned to a supply voltage (negative for *npn* transistors) which guarantees that the emitter junction of one transistor is reverse-biased when the other transistor is saturated.

24.1.4   Calculation of Incremental Loop Transmission

To check for bistability from the feedback point of view, we calculate the magnitude of the loop transmission from an incremental model of the circuit, shown in Fig. 24.4a. (Of course, we must first check the biasing in Fig. 24.3 to prove that operation with both transistors active is in fact possible.) Since we are not now investigating the speed of the regenerative switching action, we have used resistive g_m, r_π models to represent the

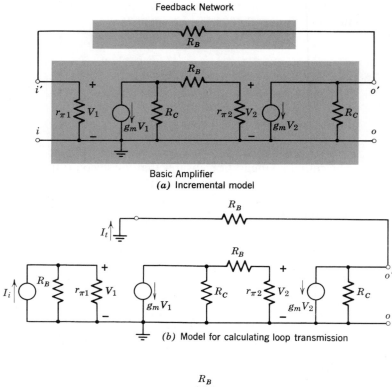

Feedback Network

Basic Amplifier
(a) Incremental model

(b) Model for calculating loop transmission

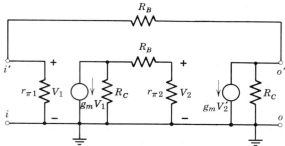

(c) Breaking the loop by making $g_m V_2'$ independent

Figure 24.4   Calculation of the incremental loop transmission for the circuit in Fig. 24.3.

transistors. The circuit can be considered as a node-node feedback amplifier in which the "output" appearing at terminals o–o' is coupled back to the "input" terminals i–i' by the feedback admittance $1/R_B$. To emphasize this point of view, we have indicated in Fig. 24.4a the "basic amplifier" and the "feedback network." Recognize, however, that because there is in fact no input source in the circuit, this assignment of feedback components is somewhat arbitrary.

The loop transmission can be calculated from Fig. 24.4a by the standard methods developed in Chapter 18. Specifically, we disconnect the feedback network at the input terminals, and account for the feedback network loading on the basic amplifier input terminals as shown in Fig. 24.4b. The loop transmission is now

$$T = \frac{I_t}{I_i} \tag{24.7}$$

If $|T|$ is greater than unity, the circuit is bistable.[1]

As already pointed out, our choice of "basic amplifier" and "feedback network" is somewhat arbitrary insofar as the input terminals $i - i'$ are concerned. Thus other choices of "input" are possible, leading to alternative calculations of the loop transmission. In fact, we can calculate the loop transmission by "breaking the loop" at any arbitrary point, without identifying input terminals at all. The voltage gain or current gain is then calculated, after a resistor has been added to the output terminals of the resulting amplifier to account for the loading present on these terminals when the loop was closed. Basically we are trying to find out whether the amplifier in Fig. 24.4a can deliver enough output power to supply its own input. Thus if loading effects are properly accounted for, we can check for instability by showing that *either* the voltage gain, *or* the current gain, *or* the power gain around the loop is greater than unity.

Clearly, a convenient procedure for calculating the loop transmission, based on the preceding discussion, is to break the loop at a point where the "output" resistance of the broken loop is either very high or very low, because then loading effects are minimized. For example, in Fig. 24.4c we have broken the feedback loop at the second dependent current source. To do this, we assume that $g_{m2}V'_2$ is an *independent* source, and calculate the magnitude of the loop transmission:

$$|T| = \frac{V_2}{V'_2} \tag{24.8}$$

No change in circuit loading is involved if the loop is broken in this manner. On the basis, the loop transmission becomes

$$|T| = \left| \frac{V_2}{V'_2} \right| = \left(\frac{g_{m2}R_C}{R_C + r_{\pi 1} + R_B} \right) r_{\pi 1} \left(\frac{g_{m1}R_C}{R_C + r_{\pi 2} + R_B} \right) r_{\pi 2} \tag{24.9a}$$

---

[1] In terms of the notation in Chapter 19, positive feedback at midfrequencies implies that $\angle T = 180°$. Thus the only further condition required for instability is $|T| > 1$.

(See Problems P24.1 and P24.2.) For r_π small compared to $R_C + R_B$ (a valid approximation for both transistors well into the active region, but *not* good when one transistor approaches cutoff), Eq. 24.9a reduces to

$$|T| = \frac{V_2}{V_2'} = \left(\frac{\beta_o R_C}{R_C + R_B}\right)^2 \qquad (24.9b)$$

The condition that the loop gain given by Eq. 24.9b be greater than unity is seen to be identical to the condition imposed by Eq. 24.6 for the existence of two stable states, assuming that β_o is approximately equal to β_F.

24.1.5 Summary of Conditions for Bistability

We are now in a position to summarize the necessary and sufficient conditions to assure bistable operation of a multivibrator.

1. A *necessary and sufficient condition* for bistable operation is the existence of two stable dc circuit states, in each of which at least one transistor is *not* in the active region.

2. An alternative necessary and sufficient condition for bistability is that the incremental loop transmission magnitude at dc with both transistors in the active region be greater than unity at one possible dc operating point. (This operating point will thus be unstable.)

It is important when applying condition 2 to check in addition that one or the other transistor is in fact saturated at points A_2 and B_2 in Fig. 24.1. If this condition is not met, regeneration may terminate before either device is driven out of the active region. Although such a circuit is bistable in the formal sense, the outputs are likely to be poorly quantized, and operation is likely to depend critically on the parameters of the transistors.

24.1.6 Switching Speed

The dynamics of the regenerative transitions between stable states are governed principally by the speed limitations of the transistors. Calculation of the switching interval, which begins when a trigger pulse moves the system into the active region of large loop transmission and terminates when one transistor is driven out of the active region, presents a problem of nonlinear analysis of sufficient complexity to require computer-aided numerical calculations if space-charge effects are included. We can, however, gain considerable insight into the parameters that influence the switching speed by analyzing the circuit of Fig. 24.5a using a simplified charge-control model that neglects space-charge capacitance effects, as shown in Fig. 24.5b.

Writing two loop equations for the circuit, we obtain

$$V_C = (i_{C1} + i_{B2})R_C + i_{B2}R_B - v_{EB2} \qquad (24.10a)$$

$$V_C = (i_{C2} + i_{B1})R_C + i_{B1}R_B - v_{EB1} \qquad (24.10b)$$

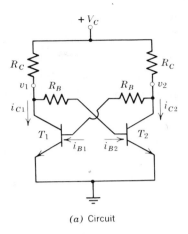

(a) Circuit

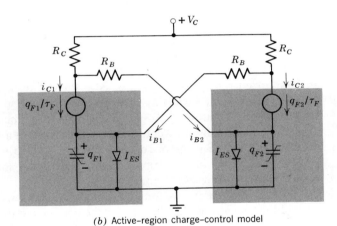

(b) Active–region charge-control model

Figure 24.5   Calculation of the response time of a regenerative circuit.

The charge-control relations for T_1, if we assume active-region operation and neglect q_{VE} and q_{VC}, are

$$i_{C1} = \frac{q_{F1}}{\tau_F} \tag{24.11a}$$

$$i_{B1} = \frac{q_{F1}}{\tau_{BF}} + \frac{dq_{F1}}{dt} \tag{24.11b}$$

On eliminating q_{F1} between the two equations, we obtain

$$i_{B1} = \frac{i_{C1}}{\beta_F} + \tau_F \frac{di_{C1}}{dt} \tag{24.12a}$$

Similarly, for T_2 we obtain

$$i_{B2} = \frac{i_{C2}}{\beta_F} + \tau_F \frac{di_{C2}}{dt} \tag{24.12b}$$

On substituting these relations into Eqs. 24.10 and assuming that v_{EB1} and v_{EB2} are nearly equal and nearly constant because both transistors are active, we obtain

$$Ai_{C1} + i_{C2} + \tau_{BF} \frac{di_{C2}}{dt} = I \tag{24.13a}$$

$$i_{C1} + Ai_{C2} + \tau_{BF} \frac{di_{C1}}{dt} = I \tag{24.13b}$$

where

$$A = \frac{\beta_F R_C}{R_C + R_B} \tag{24.14}$$

and

$$I = \beta_F \left(\frac{V_C + v_{EB}}{R_C + R_B} \right) \tag{24.15}$$

Clearly, A is the static current gain of each transistor stage. The expression in parentheses in Eq. 24.15 is just the steady-state base current of one transistor when the other transistor is cut off. Thus the constant I is the final value of the collector current if the transient went to completion without a change of state. In other words, I is the value of collector current toward which i_C is heading. Note that because of the approximations we have made, Eqs. 24.13 are *linear* first-order differential equations.

To find the natural frequencies, we assume that the currents are complex exponentials, yielding the following relations for the complex amplitudes:

$$AI_{c1} + I_{c2}(1 + s\tau_{BF}) = I \tag{24.16a}$$

$$I_{c1}(1 + s\tau_{BF}) + AI_{c2} = I \tag{24.16b}$$

The characteristic equation is found from the homogeneous equations that result when the right sides of Eqs. 24.16 are set equal to zero. On this basis the characteristic equation is

$$A^2 - (1 + s\tau_{BF})^2 = 0 \tag{24.17}$$

and the natural frequencies are

$$s_1 = \frac{-1 + A}{\tau_{BF}} \tag{24.18a}$$

$$s_2 = \frac{-1 - A}{\tau_{BF}} \tag{24.18b}$$

Natural frequency s_2 is always in the left half plane. But note that for the current gain A greater than unity (our original condition for bistability), s_1 is in *the right half plane*. We find by substituting the value of s_2 from Eq. 24.18b into either of Eqs. 24.16 with the right-hand side set to zero that the characteristic mode associated with the left-half-plane pole s_2 is described by

$$I_{c1} = I_{c2} \qquad (24.19a)$$

That is, the collector current components corresponding to this *symmetric* mode both decay exponentially with time. On the other hand, the mode associated with the right-half-plane pole s_1 is *antisymmetric* and is characterized by

$$I_{c1} = -I_{c2} \qquad (24.19b)$$

The collector current components corresponding to this mode behave in a "seesaw" manner and increase in magnitude exponentially with time. This corresponds to the physical situation in which one collector current is increasing at an exponentially growing rate toward saturation while the other collector current is decreasing at an exponentially growing rate toward cutoff. Thus the antisymmetric mode corresponds to the transition between states.

Assuming now that the loop transmission A is much greater than unity, we find from Eqs. 24.18 and 24.19 that the complete *homogeneous* solutions for the collector currents as a function of time are

$$i_{C1} = K_1 e^{At/\tau_{BF}} + K_2 e^{-At/\tau_{BF}} \qquad (24.20a)$$

$$i_{C2} = -K_1 e^{At/\tau_{BF}} + K_2 e^{-At/\tau_{BF}} \qquad (24.20b)$$

The first term in each equation invariably dominates every transition because it grows with time, whereas the second term decays to zero. Thus our first conclusion is that according to Eqs. 24.20, rapid switching requires that τ_{BF} be small and the loop gain A be large.

The switching speed of a bistable circuit can be increased by adding a speedup capacitor in parallel with each of the cross-coupling resistors. This has the effect of increasing the loop transmission for high rates of change, thereby making possible more rapid changes of the internal charge of the transistors.

24.1.7   Triggering Considerations

A bistable switching circuit can be made to change state by means of a trigger pulse that drives both transistors into the active region. By carrying the preceding analysis one step further, we can find just how far into the active region the transistors must be driven to ensure that the circuit changes state. First, we find the particular solution for Eqs. 24.16 by setting $s = 0$. The result is

$$I_{c1} = I_{c2} = \frac{I}{A + 1} = \frac{V_C + v_{EB}}{\beta_F R_C + R_C + R_B} \tag{24.21}$$

which clearly must be the point of *unstable* equilibrium of the circuit, that is, the active-region intersection C_2 in Fig. 24.1 (see Problem P24.3). Thus the complete time domain solution for the collector current is

$$i_{C1} = \frac{I}{A + 1} + K_1 e^{s_1 t} + K_2 e^{s_2 t} \tag{24.22a}$$

$$i_{C2} = \frac{I}{A + 1} - K_1 e^{s_1 t} + K_2 e^{s_2 t} \tag{24.22b}$$

The constants K_1 and K_2 in these equations are determined by the initial conditions on the collector currents. These initial values, which we denote by I_{C1i} and I_{C2i}, can be set independently by introducing suitable triggering signals to the bistable circuit. We can solve for the constants K_1 and K_2 by setting i_C equal to I_{Ci} in Eqs. 24.22, and setting t equal to zero corresponding to the instant that the trigger pulse has established the stated initial conditions. The results are

$$K_1 = \frac{I_{C1i} - I_{C2i}}{2} \tag{24.23a}$$

$$K_2 = \frac{I_{C1i} + I_{C2i}}{2} - \frac{I}{A + 1} \tag{24.23b}$$

The initial conditions on the collector currents to ensure that the circuit changes state can now be determined. Note first that regardless of the initial conditions, the growing exponential associated with s_1 will always dominate the solution. Thus we focus attention on the growing exponential terms only in Eqs. 24.22:

$$i_{C1}(\text{growing}) = \frac{I_{C1i} - I_{C2i}}{2} e^{s_1 t} \tag{24.24a}$$

$$i_{C2}(\text{growing}) = \frac{I_{C2i} - I_{C1i}}{2} e^{s_1 t} \tag{24.24b}$$

The equations show that for this symmetrical circuit configuration, if I_{C1i} is larger than I_{C2i}, then current i_{C1} has a *positive-going* exponentially-growing component, whereas i_{C2} has a negative-going exponential component. The converse is also true. Thus the *larger initial component grows exponentially larger.*

This means that if T_1 is initially cut off, we must trigger this symmetrical multivibrator in such a way that I_{C1i} is larger than I_{C2i}, to ensure switching to the other state. Otherwise there will be still a growing exponential response, but it will "grow" right back to the original state! (See Problems P24.4 and P24.5.) Because we have assumed that $i_C = q_F/\tau_F$, the condition for triggering can also be stated in terms of the base charges. Specifically, to ensure a transition of T_1 from cutoff to saturation, we must trigger in such a way that the initial q_{F1} is larger than the initial q_{F2}.

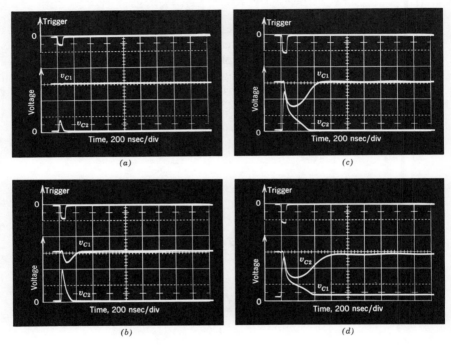

Figure 24.6   Oscilloscope photographs of the collector waveforms for a triggered bistable multivibrator. Successive photos show the effect of increasing trigger amplitude. (*a*) Only one transistor is driven out of saturation into the active region, no transition occurs; (*b*) and (*c*) both transistors driven into the active region, but no transition occurs; (*d*) Trigger large enough so that waveforms cross, so transition occurs.

These phenomena are illustrated very clearly in Fig. 24.6, which shows oscilloscope photographs of the waveforms of a triggered bistable multivibrator. (Details of the actual circuit are given in Section 24.4.) In each case the top trace is the trigger pulse, lasting about 75 nsec. The remaining two traces are the collector voltage waveforms. In Fig. 24.6*a*, only one transistor enters the active region; obviously no transition takes place. In Figs. 24.6*b*, *c*, and *d*, both transistors are driven into the active region. However, in Figs. 24.6*b* and *c*, no transition takes place because the requirement on initial conditions stated above has not been fulfilled: close examination of these two figures shows that the waveforms do not cross.

A careful examination of Fig. 24.6c reveals that the decaying exponential mode dominates the transient for about 75 nsec after the end of the trigger pulse, as evidenced by the fact that the two waveforms change together (see Eq. 24.19a). For the remainder of the transient, the growing exponential mode dominates, and the voltages diverge. However, because the triggering was insufficient, the waveforms grow *back* to their original state, and no transition occurs.

The oscilloscope traces in Fig. 24.6d show the case where the trigger pulse was strong enough to cause a transition. Note that the collector voltage waveforms *cross*, thus fulfilling the condition on I_{C1i} and I_{C2i}. The growing exponential transient again dominates after 100 nsec, but this time the waveforms grow *away* from the original state, and a regenerative transition occurs.

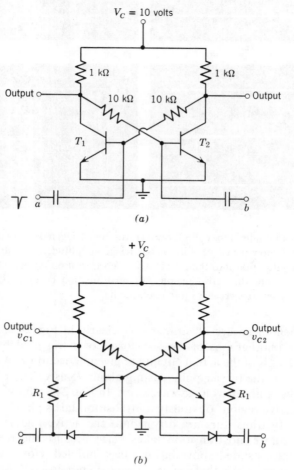

Figure 24.7   Triggering of bistable circuits.

Trigger pulses can be applied to the base or the collector of either transistor and be of such polarity as to drive an *on* transistor *off*, or drive an *off* transistor *on*. One example of base triggering is shown in Fig. 24.7a. If T_1 is *on*, the circuit can be triggered into the other stable state by applying a negative-going pulse at input *a*. This trigger pulse must satisfy several constraints. First, it must have an amplitude and duration such that the saturation charge q_S in T_1 (the *on* transistor) is removed and q_{F2} is made bigger than q_{F1}, as pointed out above. Second, the source impedance of the circuit supplying the trigger pulse must be large enough so that the loading it imposes does not reduce the loop transmission to less than unity. Although the circuit will change state under such conditions, it will not switch in the fast, definitive manner characteristic of regenerative switching.

A potentially ambiguous situation occurs if trigger pulses are applied to both bases of the bistable circuit simultaneously. This ambiguity can be eliminated by gating or "steering" the trigger inputs, as shown in Fig. 24.7b. Resistors R_1 sense the state of the circuit. Specifically, because of R_1, the *off* transistor reverse-biases the diode connected to its base, thereby inhibiting passage of a trigger pulse. On the other hand, the diode at the base of the *on* transistor is slightly forward-biased, so that a trigger pulse applied to that side of the circuit is unimpeded.

The arrangement of Fig. 24.7b can be used to realize a scale-of-two counter. The two trigger inputs are tied together so that each trigger pulse (in this case called a *clock pulse*) causes the circuit to change state or "toggle." Thus both output voltages pass through a full cycle *once* for every *two* clock pulses. A cascade of such circuits can be used to count pulses on the binary number scale.

24.1.8   Other Bistable Circuits

There are, of course, many other forms of two-transistor bistable circuits. One variation, which uses the complementary properties of *pnp* and *npn* transistors, is shown in Fig. 24.8a. One stable state of this circuit is characterized by having both transistors *on*; the other state has both transistors *off* (see Problem P24.6). The circuit is particularly useful if the application is such that the circuit spends much more time in the *off* state than in the *on* state. Under this condition the average power consumption can be made very low.

The *pnp–npn* transistor pair used in the circuit in Fig. 24.8a can be fabricated in a single structure. First, we note that the circuit will still exhibit bistable behavior with R_B equal to zero and R_C infinite, because these changes merely increase the loop transmission. The only problem is that to limit the current in the saturated state, we must add an external resistor, as shown in Fig. 24.8b.

Since the collector region of the *pnp* transistor and the base region of the *npn* transistor are of the same conductivity type and are now connected

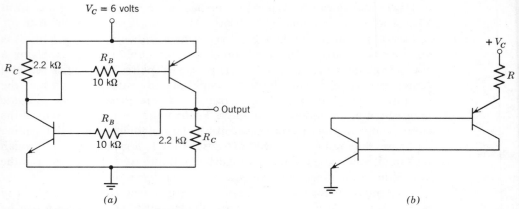

Figure 24.8 Complementary bistable circuit.

together, they can be fabricated as a single layer in the structure, as shown in Figs. 24.9. Similarly, the base region of the *pnp* transistor and the collector region of the *npn* transistor can be fabricated as a single layer. The resulting structure is known as a *four-layer diode* or, since it is usually made of silicon,

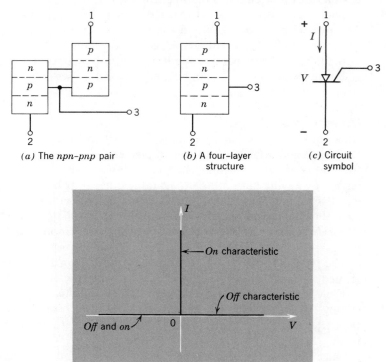

(d) Static V–I characteristics

Figure 24.9 The silicon-controlled rectifier.

as a *silicon controlled rectifier*. Its conventional circuit symbol is shown in Fig. 24.9.

The silicon controlled rectifier (SCR) is commonly used as a switch between the terminals marked 1 and 2, called the *anode* and *cathode* respectively, with the state of the switch controlled by a pulse that is applied between terminal 3, the *gate*, and the cathode. The driving-point characteristics seen between anode and cathode have the form shown in Fig. 24.9*d*. When V is negative and when the gate is open-circuited, there is no conduction and I is zero. In this region the back-to-back junctions of the *pnp* portion of the structure prevent current flow. When V is made positive, the SCR remains off or nonconducting until a brief positive pulse drives both the *pnp* and the *npn* transistors into saturation, and they stay saturated even after the pulse is removed. Thus the SCR changes from an open circuit to a short circuit and conducts as long as I is positive. This "controlled diode" behavior is useful in power supplies that must deliver a variable output voltage. (See Problem P24.7.)

A nonsaturating bistable circuit is shown in Fig. 24.10. This is basically a current-mode (emitter-coupled) circuit, in which the constant current through R_E is switched from one transistor to the other. Resistors R_1 and R_2 are adjusted so that each transistor alternates between the cutoff and active regions (see Problem P24.8). As with all CML circuits, this bistable circuit is capable of very fast switching between states.

As one might expect, the integrated-circuit bistable circuits now available commercially are considerably more complicated than the circuits we have discussed so far. This is because it is possible to add very useful circuit

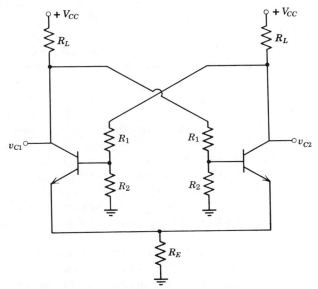

Figure 24.10 Nonsaturating bistable circuit (emitter-coupled or current-mode flip-flop).

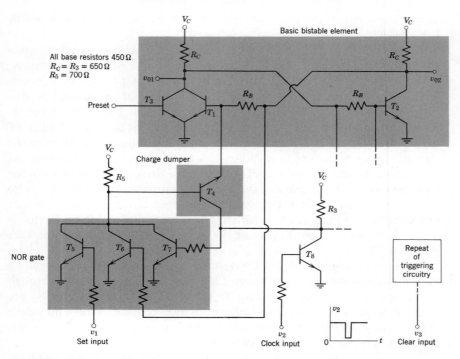

Figure 24.11 *J-K* flip-flop.

features to the basic two-transistor bistable circuit with little added cost. A typical example is the so-called *J–K flip-flop* shown in simplified form in Fig. 24.11. Transistors T_1 and T_2 form the basic bistable element in the circuit. All other transistors are associated with the triggering circuitry. The only function of T_3, for example, is to *preset* the flip-flop to a known state, that is, T_1 *on*, at any given time.

The heart of the trigger circuit is the *charge-dumper T_4*, which is controlled by the NOR gate T_5, T_6, and T_7. If all inputs to this gate are low, that is, $v_1 = V_{CE}(\text{sat})$, T_2 in the flip-flop *on*, and the clock input high ($v_2 = V_C$), the NOR gate will be cut off. Under these conditions, substantial base current will flow into T_4 via resistor R_5. The collector of T_4 is held at $V_{CE}(\text{sat})$ by the *on* clock pulse amplifier T_8. The emitter is also connected to the voltage $V_{CE}(\text{sat})$ but through resistor R_B. This situation is depicted in Fig. 24.12*a*. Clearly, the transistor is in saturation, with the current flowing *out* at both the emitter and the collector. The charge distribution in the base is sketched in Fig. 24.12*b*.

When a negative-going clock pulse is applied at v_2, T_8 cuts off and the collector of T_4 is *driven* positive by R_3 and V_C, as shown in Fig. 24.12*c*. The charge q_S "sloshes" virtually instantaneously to the distribution shown in

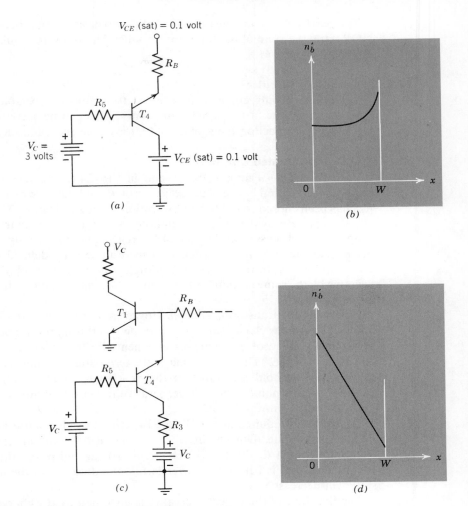

Figure 24.12 Operation of the charge-dumping transistor.

Fig. 24.12*d*, thus permitting a large current to flow out of the emitter of T_4 into the base of T_1, turning the latter *on*. This unique utilization of the "slosh" mode of the transistor permits rapid and precise triggering of the circuit.

The function of the two remaining transistors in the NOR gate, T_6 and T_7, can now be readily understood. Transistor T_6 performs the same function as the diodes in Fig. 24.7*b*—to sense the state of the bistable circuit, and gate the trigger input so that it is steered to the *off* transistor only. After the clock pulse turns T_8 *off*, transistor T_7 after a suitable delay time and rise time, turns the NOR gate *on*, thus ending the charge dump, independent of the clock-pulse length. (See Problem P24.9.)

The particular advantage of the J–K flip-flop design is that because of the NOR gate, the state of the flip-flop is predictable for every combination of inputs v_1, v_2, and v_3.[2]

24.2   Monostable Circuits

A bistable switching circuit can be made to exhibit monostable behavior if we suppress one of the equilibrium states. This can be accomplished by introducing a capacitor in one of the collector-to-base coupling circuits.

24.2.1   The Cross-Coupled Circuit

In the *cross-coupled* monostable circuit in Fig. 24.13, capacitive coupling has been introduced between the collector of T_1 and the base of T_2. Resistor R_{B2} has been chosen to hold T_2 in saturation in the stable state. The resistive cross-coupling provided by R_{B1} then holds T_1 *off*. If a suitable trigger pulse is applied, as discussed in Section 24.1.7, regenerative switching action will occur, and the circuit will switch to a metastable state defined by having T_2 *off* and T_1 *on*. In this initial transition at $t = 0$, the base of T_2 is driven negative by the same amount as the drop in V_{CE1}, as can be seen in the waveforms in Fig. 24.13b.

Following the transition, T_1 is *on*. However, T_1 cannot hold T_2 *off* indefinitely, because the charge on capacitor C decays through R_{B2}, and the base-to-ground voltage of T_2 increases exponentially toward V_{CC} with a time constant of $R_{B2}C$. The metastable state terminates at time t_1 when T_2 reaches the threshold of conduction, that is, when v_{B2} is a few tenths of a volt positive. At this point a second regenerative transition occurs, in which T_1 cuts off and T_2 saturates.

Some time is required after t_1 before the circuit reaches static equilibrium in the stable state. During this *recovery interval* the timing capacitor is charging through R_{C1} to V_{CC}. If the circuit is triggered before the recovery is complete, that is before t_2 in Fig. 24.13b, the duration of the metastable state will decrease.

The duration of the timed interval t_1 is governed by the charging of the capacitor C. Before the circuit is triggered, the voltage across C is

$$v_C \simeq V_{CC} \tag{24.25}$$

Consequently, the base-to-ground voltage v_{B2} of the second transistor drops to approximately $-V_{CC}$ when the circuit switches. Since v_{B2} is heading toward $+V_{CC}$ the metastable state ends at t_1, where

$$t_1 \simeq R_{B2}C \ln 2 \simeq 0.69 R_{B2}C \tag{24.26}$$

(See Problem P24.10.) Note that the time spent in the metastable state is controlled primarily by passive circuit elements. For this reason, monostable

[2] See Reference 24.1.

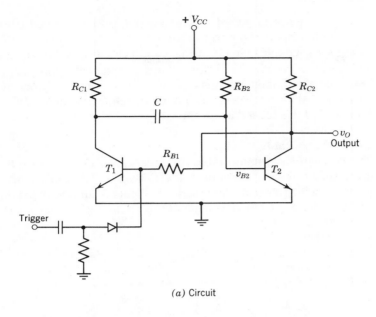

(a) Circuit

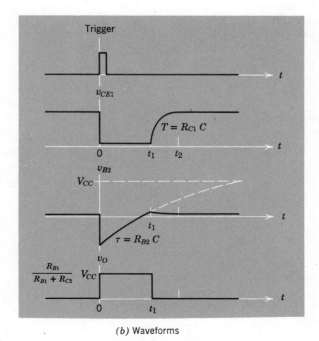

(b) Waveforms

Figure 24.13   A cross-coupled monostable multivibrator.

circuits are frequently used to generate pulses of prescribed amplitude and duration in response to a trigger pulse.

The cross-coupled circuit of Fig. 24.13a can also be biased so that in the stable state T_2 is *off*, by returning R_{B2} to a negative supply rather than V_{CC}. However, the timing intervals now depend more critically on the transistor parameters than in the original circuit. Therefore, the timing stability may be poorer with this second arrangement.

24.2.2   Other Monostable Circuits

An *emitter-coupled* monostable circuit is shown in Fig. 24.14. Because R_{B2} is returned to V_{CC}, in the stable state T_1 is *off* and T_2 is *on*. When the circuit is triggered into the metastable state, T_2 is cut off, and the timed interval ends when the base-to-emitter voltage of this transistor reaches the threshold of conduction.

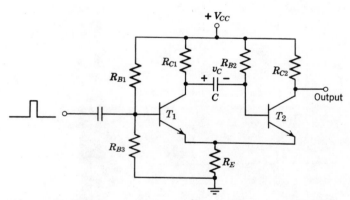

Figure 24.14   Emitter-coupled circuit.

The circuit for a *complementary pnp–npn* monostable multivibrator is shown in Fig. 24.15. Again the only change from the corresponding bistable

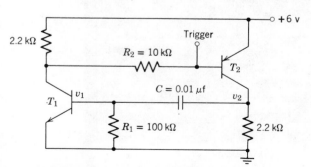

Figure 24.15   Complementary monostable multivibrator.

circuit is that one coupling resistor is replaced by a capacitor and a resistor is added from base to ground on the *npn* stage. To induce a transition to the metastable state, apply a negative trigger at the base of T_2. (See Problem P24.11.)

24.2.3 Conditions for Monostable Behavior

The only difference between monostable and bistable circuits is the substitution of a coupling capacitor for a resistor in one of the interstage coupling networks. This substitution will change the low-frequency behavior—that is, give only one stable state rather than two—but will not change the mid-frequency behavior. Thus the basic condition on loop transmission to ensure regenerative behavior, that is, $|T| > 1$, will still apply to the monostable circuit. This time, however, the condition applies at midfrequency, but must *not* apply at dc.

It follows that the conditions that *together* are necessary and sufficient for monostable behavior of a circuit are:

1. With the capacitor(s) removed, there must exist only one stable state. For circuits using identical transistors, one transistor should be cut off and the other active or saturated. For a complementary design, both should be cut off or both saturated.

2. The dc coupling network must be such that both transistors can be in the active region at the same time.

3. To ensure regenerative behavior in this active state, the magnitude of the incremental loop transmission at some frequency other than dc must be greater than unity and the feedback must be positive.

If these three conditions are met, the existence of a metastable state is ensured, and the circuit will exhibit monostable behavior.

It is generally a simple matter to check a circuit such as that in Fig. 24.13 for satisfaction of these requirements. The first requirement is concerned with the steady-state dc bias only and thus can be applied to the circuit with the capacitor C removed. The second condition as applied to this circuit requires that there be some dc voltage V_{B2} for which both T_1 and T_2 are in the active region. If this condition is met, a loop transmission calculation must be made using the incremental active-region model with capacitor C *shorted*, to verify that the feedback is positive and that the magnitude of the loop transmission is greater than unity. (See Problem P24.12.)

24.3 Astable Circuits
24.3.1 The Cross-Coupled Circuit

A regenerative switching circuit that has no stable state and thus continuously switches back and forth between two metastable states is called a *free-running* or *astable* multivibrator. Any circuit that is monostable can be made to exhibit astable behavior by adjusting the bias and dc coupling so that both transistors are in the active region when the energy storage element is removed. However, practical cross-coupled circuits are seldom built in this way, because it is difficult to guarantee that the requirement on active-region biasing is met for the worst-case variations of components and transistor parameters. For this reason most cross-coupled astable circuits employ two capacitors, as shown in Fig. 24.16, because now the bias conditions on the two transistors can be set independently. (Emitter-coupled monostable circuits can be operated satisfactorily with only one capacitor if independent emitter resistors are used, as we shall shortly see.)

Let us examine the operation of the cross-coupled circuit in Fig. 24.16a. With the capacitors removed, the biasing arrangement is such that the transistors are automatically biased in the active region regardless of resistor values or transistor parameters. When the timing capacitors are reconnected the positive feedback drives the circuit out of the quasi-linear region into one saturated state. However, this condition cannot persist because the capacitor charges change, letting the circuit relax toward the steady state in which both transistors are active. Thus the circuit eventually enters the active region and undergoes a regenerative transition through the quasi-linear region into the second saturated state, where it resides for a time in a second metastable state. (See Problem P24.13.)

Typical circuit waveforms are shown in Fig. 24.16c. Note that no trigger pulse is required to activate the circuit. It is in fact a nonlinear *oscillator*, hence is used for the generation of periodic waveforms and pulse trains.

A more conventional form of cross-coupled astable circuit is shown in Fig. 24.16b. When the capacitors are removed in this circuit, both transistors saturate. Nonetheless, the circuit will behave as an astable multivibrator, and oscillate as required *most of the time*, because it usually does not fall into the stable state with both transistors saturated at the same time. However, such a potentially stable circuit is unreliable. By momentarily shorting one collector to ground, we simultaneously kill the loop transmission and saturate both transistors. The circuit is then "hung up," and will not restart until triggered (by turning off the power supply, for example). For this reason we include as a condition for astable behavior a requirement on active-region biasing, thereby excluding circuits such as that shown in Fig. 24.16b.

24.3.2 The Emitter-Coupled Circuit

Typical emitter-coupled astable circuits are shown in Fig. 24.17. The circuit in (a) operates satisfactorily with only one capacitor because the independent emitter resistors assure stable active-region dc bias points. In this particular case the resistor values are chosen so that the transistors do not saturate at any time during the cycle, and, the collector voltage swings are small. Thus high-speed operation can be realized: 10-MHz repetition rates with 10-ns rise times.[3]

[3] See Reference 24.2.

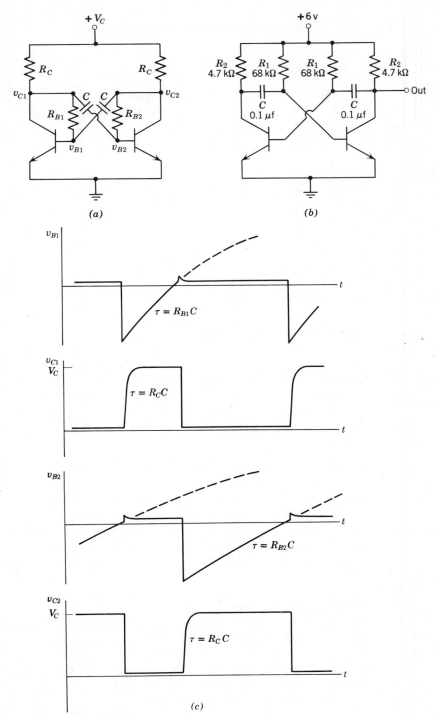

Figure 24.16 Cross-coupled astable multivibrators.

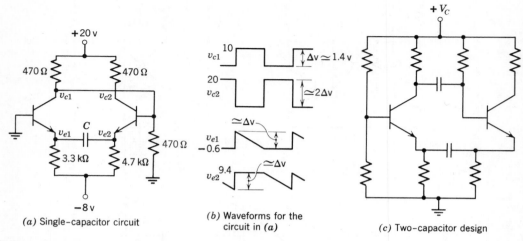

(a) Single-capacitor circuit

(b) Waveforms for the circuit in (a)

(c) Two-capacitor design

Figure 24.17 Emitter-coupled astable multivibrators.

24.3.3 Conditions for Astable Operation

The two conditions that *together* are necessary and sufficient to ensure astable operation of a circuit are:

1. The dc operating point of the circuit with the capacitors removed must be such that both transistors are in the active region.

2. In this active region the magnitude of loop transmission must be greater than unity at some nonzero frequency to ensure regenerative action and *less* than unity at dc to *prevent* bistable operation.

Application of these conditions to a specific circuit is again quite simple. For example, it is clear that with the capacitors removed in the circuit in Fig. 24.16a, the transistors will be biased in the active region. With the first condition satisfied, a calculation must be made on the active-region incremental model with the coupling capacitors shorted to ensure that the loop transmission is greater than unity. The loop transmission at dc for this circuit is clearly zero, so that the final condition is satisfied, thereby ensuring astable behavior.

24.4 Lecture Demonstrations

The waveforms of digital circuits, especially the switching transients of gates and the output waveforms of the multivibrators, are sufficiently photogenic so that no special circuits or equipment are needed to produce interesting and informative lecture demonstrations. In all cases a dual-trace or even a four-trace oscilloscope is invaluable.

Examples of possible demonstrations are:

1. The variation of pulse width as R_{B2} in Fig. 24.13 is varied.

2. A scale-of-two counter built by driving points *a* and *b* together in Fig. 24.7*b* from a pulse generator.

3. The same circuit viewed on a fast time scale using a high pulse-repetition frequency, to show the improvement in output waveforms that results when speed-up capacitors are added.

4. The "hang-up" problem in an astable multivibrator of the type shown in Fig. 24.16*b*.

The demonstration concerning the amplitude of triggering pulse required to achieve a regenerative transition in a bistable multivibrator (see Section 24.1.7) can be constructed using the circuit shown in Fig. 24.7*b*. The trigger pulse is fed to inputs *a* and *b* simultaneously. In this manner, a repetitive picture of the transition is assured whether or not the multivibrator changes state. Use transistors with a low f_T and low space-charge-layer capacitance to ensure that q_F and q_R will be the dominant charge components.

The same circuit can also be used to show the effects of trigger pulse *width*. Typical results are shown in Fig. 24.18. In Figs. 24.18*a* and *b*, the pulse is too narrow and too small to cause a transition. However, increasing the width of the trigger pulse without changing its amplitude causes a regenerative transition to occur, as shown in Fig. 24.18*c*.

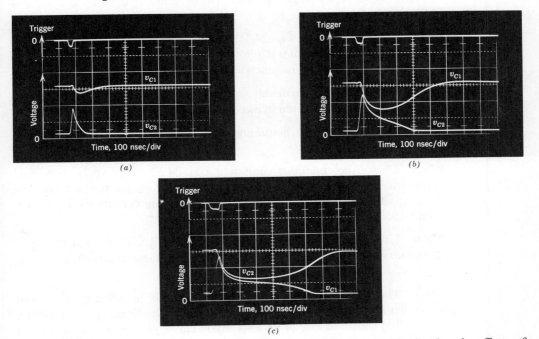

(a)

(b)

(c)

Figure 24.18 Oscilloscope waveforms of the bistable circuit in Fig. 24.7*b*, showing the effects of trigger-pulse length on triggering. (*a*) and (*b*) Trigger pulse too narrow and small to cause a transition; (*c*) A longer trigger pulse produces a transition.

REFERENCES

24.1 *Fan-out*, Number 116, Fairchild Semiconductor, February 1964.

24.2 P. J. Bénéteau and A. Evangelisti, An Improved Emitter-coupled Multivator, *Application App-59*, Fairchild Semiconductor, February, 1963.

24.3 M. Phister, Jr., *Logical Design of Digital Computers*, Wiley, New York, 1948.

24.4 J. Millman and H. Taub, *Pulse, Digital, and Switching Waveforms*, McGraw-Hill, New York, 1965.

24.5 R. Littauer, *Pulse Electronics*, McGraw-Hill, New York, 1965.

24.6 H. Camenzind, *Circuit Design for Integrated Circuits*, Addison-Wesley, Reading, Mass., 1968.

PROBLEMS

P24.1 (*a*) Draw the general *y*-parameter representation for two two-port networks connected in parallel (i.e., Fig. 18.11).

(*b*) Prove that, if the reverse transmission y_{ra} of the basic amplifier is negligible, a loop transmission

$$T = \frac{y_{rf} y_{fa}}{(Y_s + y_{ia} + y_{if})(y_{oa} + y_{of} + Y_L)}$$

can be found either by direct calculation or by breaking the loop as discussed in Section 24.1.4. (See page 898.)

P24.2 Calculate I_t/I_i, in Fig. 24.4*b*, and compare the result with Eq. 24.9a. Note that the feedback rules (Chapter 18) require that R_B be much greater than R_C to ensure that y_{ff} be much less than y_{fa}.

P24.3 Prove that the particular solution given by Eq. 24.21 is in fact the point of unstable equilibrium marked C_2 in Fig. 24.1*b*. (See page 902.)

P24.4 Solve Eqs. 24.22 assuming $I_{C1i} = I_{C2i} = I/(A + 1)$. Explain the result. (See page 903.)

P24.5 Derive the equations similar to Eqs. 24.22 which apply to an unsymmetric bistable multivibrator. Derive expressions for the constants in these equations, and from this derive the triggering conditions for such a circuit. (See Sections 24.1.6 and 24.1.7.)

P24.6 Using the conditions stated in Section 24.1.5, verify that the complementary circuit in Fig. 24.8*a* is indeed a bistable multivibrator. (See page 905.)

P24.7 The silicon controlled rectifier introduced in Section 24.1.8 and illustrated in Fig. 24.9 is frequently used in variable-voltage power supplies, such as that shown in Fig. 24.19. This circuit employs an SCR as a controlled half-wave rectifier (see Fig. 6.21*a* for the corresponding circuit with an ordinary junction diode). Full-wave circuits analogous to that shown in Fig. 6.24 can be made in a similar manner. The variable phase-shift network and transformer provide a control voltage whose phase measured with

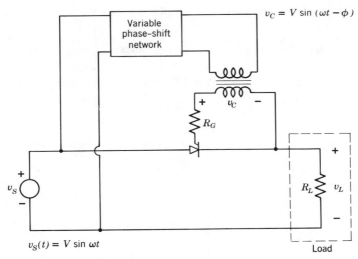

$v_C = V \sin (\omega t - \phi)$

v_C

R_G

$+$ v_S $-$

R_L v_L

$+$

$-$

$v_S(t) = V \sin \omega t$

Load

Figure 24.19 Variable-voltage power supply.

respect to the supply voltage v_s is variable. When v_c is *positive*, the SCR has the *on* anode characteristics shown in Fig. 24.9d; when v_c is *negative*, the *off* characteristic applies.

(*a*) Compute, sketch, and dimension the load voltage $v_L(t)$ for several values of phase angle ϕ in the range from 0° to 180°.

(*b*) Derive an expression for the *average* load voltage in terms of V and ϕ.

P24.8 Find values of R_1 and R_2 in the current-mode circuit of Fig. 24.10 to ensure bistable behavior. Assume that the dc level of the inputs is $V_{CC}/2$. (See page 907.)

P24.9 Draw the gating circuitry for the right-hand side of the *J-K* flip-flop in Fig. 24.11. Check the conditions of the right-hand NOR gate, assuming T_2 *on*, T_1 *off*, to see that the clock pulse is indeed inhibited on this side. (See page 909.)

P24.10 Derive Eq. 24.26 from Fig. 24.13. (See page 910.)

P24.11 What is the duration of the metastable state in the complementary multivibrator shown in Fig. 24.15. How does the accuracy of the timed interval compare with that of the more conventional circuit in Fig. 24.13? (See page 913.)

P24.12 Use the conditions stated in Section 24.2.3 to verify that the circuit in Fig. 24.14 is indeed a monostable multivibrator. (See page 913.)

P24.13 One of the triggering conditions for regenerative transitions in multivibrators is that the trigger must make the "smaller collector current larger" (See Section 24.1.7). The astable multivibrator is really self-triggering.

Explain how the circuit in Fig. 24.16a meets these conditions on triggering. (see page 914.)

P24.14 The circuit shown in Fig. 24.20 is often called a *Schmitt trigger circuit*. Sketch the static transfer curve v_O versus v_I. Prove that for a range of values of v_I in the vicinity of 2.2 volts, the device is bistable.

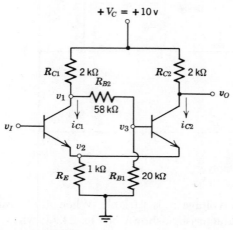

Figure 24.20   Schmitt trigger circuit.

APPENDIX A

Vacuum Tube Models and Circuits

A.1 Introduction

Historically, most of the applications of electronic circuits considered in this book first made use of vacuum tubes as the active devices. In recent years, vacuum tubes have been largely supplanted in these applications by various semiconductor active devices, which have the obvious advantages of smaller size, reduced power consumption, and much greater reliability. Although certain varieties of vacuum tubes are still used for some purposes, notably the generation and amplification of radio-frequency energy at very high power levels, such special applications are beyond the scope of this introductory book.

Appendix A contains a treatment of the physical electronics, modeling, and basic circuit properties of the class of simple vacuum tubes that have capabilities similar to those of the semiconductor active devices discussed in the book. Since the development here is similar in level and scope to that in Chapter 1, the appendix material can be used to supplement or replace Sections 1.2 through 1.4 whenever it is desirable to include vacuum tube active devices. In some respects this material provides a simpler introduction to active devices than do field-effect transistors.

A.2 Structure and Operation of Vacuum Diodes and Triodes
A.2.1 Physical Structure

The physical structure of a vacuum triode is shown in Fig. A.1. The device is comprised of essentially three elements, which are arranged coaxially in an evacuated enclosure. The innermost element is a metal sleeve called the *cathode*. Surrounding the cathode is an open spiral of wire called the *grid* which is, in turn, surrounded by a metal sleeve called the *anode* or *plate*. These three elements—the cathode, grid, and plate—are connected by means of the internal supporting structure to external pins or terminals.

Within the cathode is a twisted, insulated resistance wire, which is also connected at both ends to external pins. This wire, called the *heater*, is raised to temperatures ranging from 700 to 800°C by passing an electric current through it. In this sense it is not unlike the filament in an incandescent lamp. However, it is operated at much lower temperatures where its color is (at most) a dull red instead of the brilliant white that is characteristic of lamp filaments.

A.2.2 Thermionic Emission

The heater raises the temperature of the cathode sleeve to a level at which electrons are readily emitted from its surface. This process is called *thermionic emission*. Although any metal will emit electrons when its temperature is

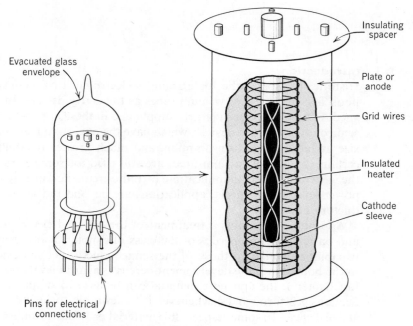

Figure A.1   The physical structure of a vacuum triode.

raised, some metals emit electrons more copiously than others. The cathode sleeve is coated with alkaline-earth oxides, which make it a particularly good source of thermionic electrons even at relatively low temperatures (about 700°C).

The vacuum inside the tube is good enough so that interactions between the emitted electrons and the residual gas molecules do not affect the physical behavior of the device. Some tubes are intentionally filled with a gas to achieve characteristics different from those discussed here, but we shall not investigate these more complex devices.

If the other elements—the grid and the plate—are not connected to anything, the electrons that are emitted by the heated cathode simply surround the cathode as a cloud of negative space charge. This cloud of charge does not disperse because the cathode becomes positively charged as a result of its loss of electrons to the cloud of negative space charge. Therefore, the electrons that comprise the cloud feel a coulomb force that attracts them to the metal and keeps them from moving too far away. When this system is in equilibrium at a fixed cathode temperature, electrons are continuously emitted from the oxide layer while other electrons from the cloud fall back into the cathode, thereby maintaining a state of dynamic equilibrium.

A.2.3   Behavior of a Two-Element Structure—The Diode

The equilibrium situation just described changes if the grid and plate are connected to circuits that place these elements at electrostatic potentials different from the potential of the cathode. For the moment, we focus on the role of the anode or plate and assume simply that the grid is absent from the structure.

If the potential of the plate is negative with respect to the cathode, the electrons in the cloud of space charge are repelled by the plate. As a result, the electrons crowd even more densely around the hot cathode, and no current flows in the plate-cathode circuit (Fig. A.2a).

On the other hand, if the plate is made positive with respect to the cathode, the electrons in the cloud of space charge around the cathode are attracted

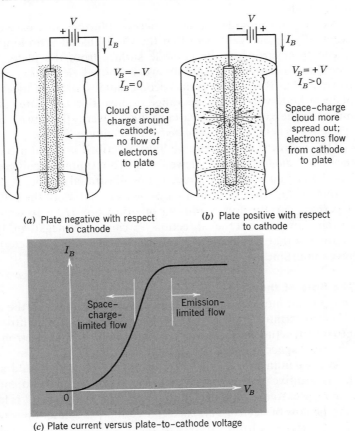

(a) Plate negative with respect to cathode

$V_B = -V$
$I_B = 0$

Cloud of space charge around cathode; no flow of electrons to plate

(b) Plate positive with respect to cathode

$V_B = +V$
$I_B > 0$

Space-charge cloud more spread out; electrons flow from cathode to plate

(c) Plate current versus plate-to-cathode voltage

Space-charge-limited flow

Emission-limited flow

Figure A.2   Current-voltage relationships in a two-element vacuum tube. Notice that the reference direction for current is such that *positive* charge carriers would flow in this direction for positive current. Consequently, a flow of electrons *out* of the tube at the plate corresponds to positive I_B.

to the plate, and move through the vacuum to the plate, where they enter the external plate-cathode circuit and give rise to a current (Fig. A.2b). The number of electrons per unit time that move across the interelectrode space to the plate depends on the plate-cathode voltage. As the voltage is increased, the quantity of space charge around the cathode is reduced, more electrons flow to the plate, and the plate current increases (Fig. A.2c).[1] In this range of voltages, the current is controlled by the amount of space charge and is described as *space-charge-limited*. This description emphasizes the role of the space charge in shielding the cathode from the attractive potential of the plate. Although the cathode emits electrons at a rate that far exceeds the rate at which electrons flow to the plate in this range of voltage, the electrons are shielded by the space charge, and most of them fall back into the cathode.

As the plate-cathode voltage is increased further, the space-charge density eventually becomes so small that the charge cloud is no longer effective in screening electrons at the cathode surface from the plate. When such a condition is reached, essentially every emitted electron is collected at the plate, so that the plate current becomes almost entirely independent of the plate-cathode voltage. In this range of operation the plate current is determined by the cathode temperature, which governs the rate of emission, and is spoken of as being *emission-limited* or *temperature-limited*.

The electronic device that we have described is called a *vacuum diode* or *thermionic diode*. It can be viewed as a two-terminal circuit component that has the current-voltage characteristics illustrated in Fig. A.2c. Clearly, its distinguishing feature is the highly *nonlinear* nature of the *I-V* relationship; it permits current flow readily in one direction ($I_B > 0$) while prohibiting current flow in the other direction (I_B cannot be negative). It is shown in Chapter 6 that electronic devices that exhibit this characteristic behavior have important uses in circuits.

A.2.4 The Role of the Grid

Our present interest, however, is in control valves, which the diode (having only two terminals) clearly is *not*. Therefore, we now reintroduce the *grid* into our structure and consider its effect on the flow of electrons through the evacuated space between the cathode and plate.

As a vacuum tube is normally operated, the grid is held at a potential that is negative with respect to the cathode, and the plate potential is positive with respect to the cathode. Furthermore, the plate current is low enough so that the flow of electrons is space-charge-limited. Under these conditions the flow of electrons from cathode to plate is strongly influenced by the grid.

---

[1] The convention for current in the circuit external to the tube is the common one; the current is visualized in terms of the flow of *positive* charge. Thus electron flow from cathode to plate within the tube is represented *outside* the tube in terms of current that flows *in* at the plate and *out* at the cathode. For the reference direction shown in Fig. A.2, I_B is positive.

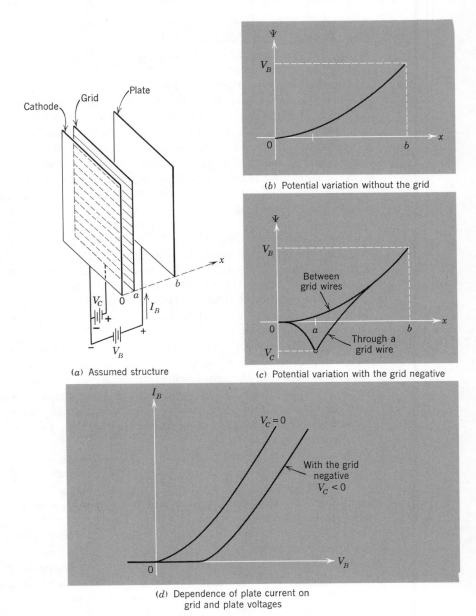

(a) Assumed structure

(b) Potential variation without the grid

(c) Potential variation with the grid negative

(d) Dependence of plate current on grid and plate voltages

Figure A.3   Illustration of the effect of the grid on the electrostatic potential distribution and on the plate current.

Specifically, the negative voltage on the grid (negative with respect to the cathode) lowers the electrostatic potential in the neighborhood of the grid. The potential at the grid wire is equal to the grid voltage. The potential at a point in the grid surface but between the grid wires is more positive than the grid voltage, but not so positive as it would be without the grid in the structure. This situation is illustrated in Fig. A.3, which shows the variation of potential in the region between cathode and plate. For simplicity we have assumed a plane-parallel structure instead of the more common arrangement in which the cathode is entirely enclosed by the grid and plate.

As a result of the negative grid potential, the average electrostatic potential in the plane of the grid is reduced. Consequently, the electric field in the region between the cathode and the grid is reduced, and the rate at which electrons flow to the plate decreases. Because the electrons near the cathode surface are partially shielded from the attractive influence of the plate by the negative grid, the current in the plate-cathode circuit is less, for any value of plate-to-cathode voltage, than it would be if the grid were either not present or less negative. This situation is illustrated in Fig. A.3d, where the plate current is shown as a function of the plate-to-cathode voltage for two fixed values of grid-to-cathode voltage. These curves show that for any value of plate-to-cathode voltage the plate current decreases as the grid-to-cathode voltage becomes more negative.

The curves shown in Fig. A.3d are two members of a family of parametric curves that express the dependence of plate current on both the plate-to-cathode voltage and the grid-to-cathode voltage of the triode. Figure A.4 shows a family of these curves in which the grid-to-cathode voltage changes by a fixed interval from curve to curve. This family, which is typical of triode behavior, is often called the *output characteristics* or the *plate characteristics* of the triode.

The triode output characteristics show that if the grid-to-cathode voltage is made sufficiently negative, the plate current is reduced to zero. This condition of no conduction is referred to as *cutoff*. Clearly, the value of grid-to-cathode voltage required to cut off the flow of plate current depends on the plate-to-cathode voltage.

The control of the plate current by means of the grid-to-cathode voltage, as summarized in Fig. A.4, is accomplished with the expenditure of very little power in the grid-cathode circuit. Since the grid is negative with respect to the cathode, it repels the negatively-charged electrons, and the grid current is exceedingly small, usually of the order of nanoamperes.[2]

The control of conditions in the plate-cathode circuit by the grid-to-cathode voltage, with negligible grid current required, is the basis of the con-

---

[2] This small grid current results from the collection of residual positive gas ions at the grid; it is usually of little importance in circuit applications. Nevertheless, we must keep in mind the existence of grid current, no matter how small, so that we are not tempted to operate the tube without a dc return path in the grid-cathode circuit.

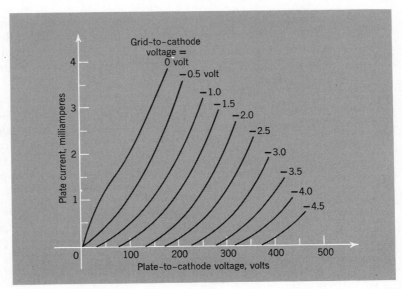

Figure A.4 Typical triode output characteristics. Only the first quadrant of the plate current, plate-to-cathode voltage plane is shown because the plate current is never negative, and is nonzero only when the plate is positive with respect to the cathode.

trol action of a vacuum triode; this behavior lies at the root of the usefulness of a triode as a control valve or power modulator.[3]

A.2.5 Diodes and Triodes as Circuit Components

The conventional circuit symbol for a vacuum diode is shown in Fig. A.5a. The heater, which raises the cathode temperature to the level necessary to provide sufficient thermionic emission, is not shown in this symbol, and the connections to the heater are omitted. If desired, the heater connections can be shown explicitly by modifying the symbol, as indicated in Fig. A.5b.

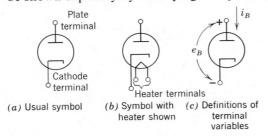

Figure A.5 Diode circuit symbols and reference directions.

[3] The description of vacuum-triode behavior given in this section is intended to be the minimum that is necessary for an understanding of the operation of simple circuits in which a triode is used as a control valve. For more detailed treatment of the physical electronics of vacuum tubes, see Appendix B.

The voltage and current reference directions shown in Fig. A.5c are widely accepted as standard. The plate current i_B is positive when it flows into the tube (thus corresponding to an internal flow of electrons from cathode to plate), and the plate voltage e_B is positive when the plate is positive with respect to the cathode.

The circuit symbol and reference directions for a triode are shown in Fig. A.6. These conventions are simply extensions of the diode situation.

The terminal variables defined in Fig. A.6b suffice for a complete description of the electrical behavior of the device. The cathode current and the grid-to-plate voltage (which are not defined on the symbol) can be expressed in terms of the two defined currents and the two defined terminal-pair voltages by applying Kirchhoff's laws.

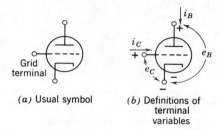

(a) Usual symbol   (b) Definitions of terminal variables

Figure A.6   Triode circuit symbols and reference directions.

A.3.   An Elementary Amplifier

We illustrate the principal performance features of circuits that contain vacuum triodes by studying the simple vacuum tube circuit shown in Fig. A.7. This circuit uses a vacuum triode to control the flow of power from a source (characterized here as a voltage source of value V_B) to a load (characterized by a resistance R_L). The characterization of the load by a resistance would

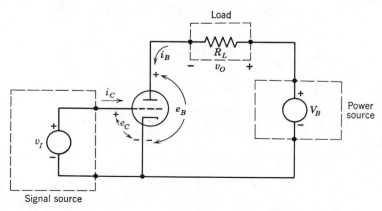

Figure A.7   A simple triode circuit.

be applicable, under appropriate limiting conditions, for a load such as a loudspeaker, an electromechanical actuator, or a transmission line. The input of the active device—the grid-to-cathode voltage—is set by a signal source (characterized here by the variable voltage source v_I). Our objective is to determine the dependence of the current i_B in the load (or, equivalently, the voltage v_O across the load) on the signal source voltage v_I.

From a network point of view this circuit contains two meshes or loops. The *input* mesh includes the grid-cathode path in the triode as well as the signal source. The *output* mesh includes the plate-cathode path in the triode, the power source, and the load.

The physical nature of the triode is such that there is negligible grid current. Furthermore, the grid-to-cathode voltage is directly constrained by the signal source. Thus for the input mesh we may write

$$i_C = 0 \tag{A.1a}$$

$$e_C = v_I \tag{A.1b}$$

Application of Kirchhoff's voltage law to the output mesh yields

$$V_B = v_O + e_B \tag{A.2}$$

or, equivalently,

$$V_B = i_B R_L + e_B \tag{A.3a}$$

The triode imposes a constraint on i_B and e_B which is of the form

$$i_B = i_B(e_C, e_B) \tag{A.3b}$$

This constraint can be expressed in graphical form by output characteristics such as those shown in Fig. A.4.

Since we wish to determine the dependence of the plate current i_B on the signal source voltage v_I, all that is required is to eliminate e_C and e_B from among Eqs. A.1b, A.3a, and A.3b. The problem, of course, is that Eq. A.3b is nonlinear. At this point in the discussion the only model we have available for the triode is a graphical one, such as Fig. A.4. Consequently, we turn to graphical methods for the solution of these equations.

A.3.1 Graphical Analysis

We assume for the purposes of this illustration that the vacuum triode used in the circuit of Fig. A.7 is described by the output characteristics of Fig. A.4. These curves present the *driving-point characteristics* of the triode at the output terminal pair. That is, they display the dependence of a current at a terminal pair on the voltage at that same terminal pair. Of course, these are parametric curves—the parameter is the voltage at the input terminal pair.

The constraint imposed by the power source and load (Eq. A.3a) constitutes a linear relationship between the current and voltage variables at the output terminal pair. That is, Eq. A.3a expresses a linear relationship between i_B and e_B. Consequently, this constraint can be plotted as *straight-line* on the driving-point characteristics at the output terminal pair, that is, on the output or plate characteristics of Fig. A.4. The straight line that corresponds to the constraint of Eq. A.3a is called the *load line*.

The intercepts of the load line are, from Eq. A.3a,

$$\text{when } e_B = 0, \qquad i_B = \frac{V_B}{R_L} \tag{A.4a}$$

$$\text{when } i_B = 0, \qquad e_B = V_B \tag{A.4b}$$

Thus the load line has a slope, on the i_B versus e_B coordinates:

$$\text{slope} = -\frac{1}{R_L} \tag{A.5}$$

The load-line construction is shown in Fig. A.8. The parameter values used in making this construction are

$$V_B = 300 \text{ volts}$$

$$R_L = 10^5 \text{ ohms} = 100 \text{ kohm}$$

The values of i_B and e_B at which the circuit operates for any particular value of $v_I (= e_C)$ correspond to the coordinates of the point of intersection of the load line and the output characteristic curve for that value of v_I.

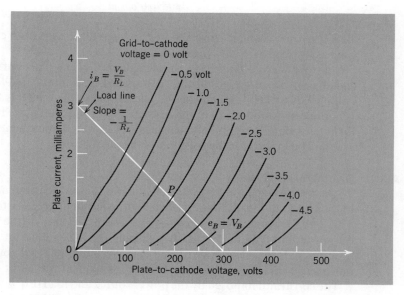

Figure A.8   Triode output characteristics with the load line imposed by the circuit of Fig. A.7.

For example, if $v_I = -1.5$ volts, the state of the circuit is defined by the point P.

The manner in which the input voltage v_I controls the load or output voltage v_O can be summarized graphically by means of the voltage *transfer characteristic* shown in Fig. A.9. The characteristic is generated by considering the set of intersections of the load line with the output characteristics for various *negative* values of v_I.[4] For any value of $v_I(= e_C)$, the output voltage v_O can be calculated from the value of i_B found from Fig. A.8 (1.05 ma for point P) and the relation

$$v_O = i_B R_L \tag{A.6}$$

Hence v_O at point P is $1.05 \times 100 = 105$ volts as shown by P' in Fig. A.9. Alternatively, we can determine v_O from Eq. A.2. We find e_B from Fig. A.8 (195 volts for point P) and subtract this from $V_B = 300$ volts to obtain 105 volts as before.

The transfer characteristic flattens for values of v_I more negative than about -3.5 volts because the triode does not conduct in this region. Thus there is no current in the load, and the plate current is said to be *cut off*.

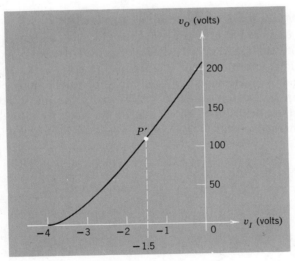

Figure A.9 Transfer characteristic for the circuit of Fig. A.7.

A.3.2 Energy Flow

The capability of a vacuum triode as a control valve or power modulator is evident from the transfer characteristics of Fig. A.9. As v_I increases above -3.5 volt, the voltage v_O, and thus the power delivered to the load, increase as well.

[4] We cannot consider positive values of v_I because we have not investigated the shape of the output characteristics when the grid-to-cathode voltage is positive.

The details of energy flow in this simple triode circuit are important because they illustrate a fundamental point. To investigate the power distribution in the output mesh (there is *no* power developed in the input mesh because we assume that i_C is zero), we multiply Eq. A.3a, which expresses Kirchhoff's voltage law in that mesh, by i_B, the current in that mesh. The result, slightly rearranged, is

$$i_B{}^2 R_L = V_B i_B - e_B i_B \tag{A.7}$$

This equation has a simple interpretation. The power delivered to the load is $i_B{}^2 R_L$; the power supplied by the source is $V_B i_B$; the power dissipated as heat in the tube is $e_B i_B$. Thus Eq. A.7 states that the power delivered to the load is equal to the power supplied by the energy source reduced by the power dissipated in the active device. Hence the active device, in this case the tube, controls the flow of energy from the source to the load and, in the process, consumes some power itself (unless e_B or i_B is zero).

The tube in this circuit is considered to have *power gain* because it can control more power than is required at its input terminals. Since the grid current is exceedingly small, the power gain is in this case very large.

A.3.3 Graphical Methods in More Complex Circuits

The load-line construction developed in the preceding section can be adapted to any circuit situation in which a device described in terms of a driving-point characteristic at a terminal pair is embedded in a network consisting solely of sources and linear elements. Any such situation can be analyzed by forming the Thévenin or Norton equivalent network of the linear portion of the circuit and then describing this equivalent network by a load line on the nonlinear characteristics.

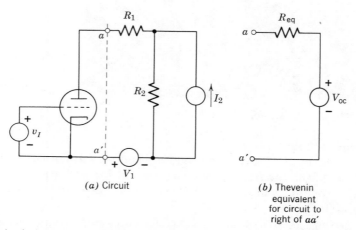

(a) Circuit

(b) Thévenin equivalent for circuit to right of aa'

Figure A.10   A triode circuit in which Thévenin's theorem can be used to determine a load line.

As a specific example of such a construction, consider the circuit of Fig. A.10a. The portion of the network to the right of the terminals labeled aa' can be replaced by a Thévenin equivalent network as shown in Fig. A.10b. The elements in this equivalent network are obtained by inspection of the original circuit. The equivalent source resistance R_{eq} is determined by disconnecting the independent current source I_2 and replacing the independent voltage source V_1 by a short circuit. Thus

$$R_{eq} = R_1 + R_2 \tag{A.8a}$$

The open-circuit voltage at the terminals aa' is obviously

$$V_{oc} = I_2 R_2 - V_1 \tag{A.8b}$$

Thus the short-circuit current at the terminals aa' is

$$I_{sc} = \frac{V_{oc}}{R_{eq}} = \frac{I_2 R_2 - V_1}{R_1 + R_2} \tag{A.8c}$$

Consequently, the intercepts of the load line on the output driving-point characteristics of the triode, which are plotted on the e_B-i_B plane, are:

$$\text{when } i_B = 0, \qquad e_B = V_{oc}$$
$$\text{when } e_B = 0, \qquad i_B = I_{sc}$$

The slope of the load line is, of course, $-1/R_{eq}$.

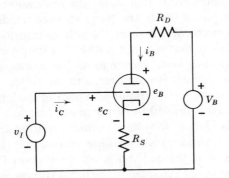

Figure A.11   A triode circuit in which the output and input meshes share a common resistor.

The circuit of Fig. A.11 provides another example of graphical analysis. Note that the input and output meshes are coupled by a resistance in the cathode lead. Thus the grid-to-cathode voltage is no longer equal to the input signal source voltage as it was in the previous examples.

Since the grid current is negligible, the current in the common cathode resistance is just equal to the plate current. Consequently, application of

Kirchhoff's voltage law to the two meshes yields

$$\text{input mesh:}\quad v_I = e_C + i_B R_S \tag{A.9a}$$

$$\text{output mesh:}\quad V_B = e_B + (R_D + R_S)i_B \tag{A.9b}$$

The second of these equations defines a load line on the output characteristics of the transistor. The intercepts are:

$$\text{for } i_B = 0,\qquad e_B = V_B$$

$$\text{for } e_B = 0,\qquad i_B = \frac{V_B}{R_D + R_S}$$

The load line can be used to generate a transfer characteristic that relates the plate current i_B to the grid-to-cathode voltage e_C. Once this relationship between i_B and e_C has been determined, Eq. A.9a can be used to relate the signal source voltage v_I to i_B. Thus the desired relationship that shows the dependence of i_B on v_I is obtained by working "in both directions" from e_C.

The analysis of the circuit of Fig. A.11 would, of course, be considerably more complicated if i_C were nonzero. In such a case the voltage across R_S would be $(i_B + i_C)R_S$, so that both of Eqs. A.9 would contain an additional term. The effect of this term would be to make it impossible to use a loadline construction in solving the equation of the output mesh.

A.3.4   Linear Amplification

As we have seen in Fig. 1.1, many applications of electronics present a requirement for linear amplification, that is, for the replication of a signal or waveform at a higher power level. The basic vacuum triode circuit of Fig. A.7 can meet this requirement. However, the voltage transfer characteristic of Fig. A.9 shows clearly that it is not possible to simply connect the input signal at the grid-to-cathode terminals if linear amplification is desired; the transfer characteristic is nonlinear, and the voltage across the load will in no sense be a scaled-up or amplified replica of the input voltage. If, however, the input signal is limited in its range of excursion, and if it is added to an appropriately-chosen dc voltage, a linear relationship between output and input can be obtained. This is possible because there is a portion of the transfer characteristic, in the neighborhood of the point P', in which the output voltage is responsive to changes in the input voltage *and* in which changes in these voltages are approximately linearly related. Thus linear operation can be achieved if the circuit is operated on the portion of the characteristic near P'.

A circuit that permits operation near P' is shown in Fig. A.12. Note that the plate power source is not shown explicitly; it is understood to be connected between the terminal labeled $+V_B$ and the "ground" or reference point symbolized by $\perp\!\!\!\perp$. This circuit differs from that shown in Fig. A.7 only in that the input voltage v_I, which appears between the grid and the cathode of the tube, consists of the sum of two component voltages. That is,

$$v_I = V_I + v_i \tag{A.10}$$

The dc voltage V_I is provided by a fixed voltage source, symbolized by the battery. The signal that is to be amplified is denoted by v_i.[5]

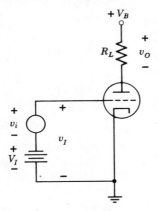

Figure A.12   A circuit in which the grid-to-cathode voltage is comprised of a dc component and a signal component.

The dc component of the input voltage (V_I) must be chosen so that the circuit operates on a linear portion of the transfer characteristic. We arbitrarily assume that the input signal (v_i) has equal positive and negative excursions, and choose V_I so that when the signal voltage is zero, the circuit operates in the middle of the linear region.[6] The point P' in Fig. A.9 is more or less in the middle of the linear portion of the characteristic. This point corresponds to $v_I = -1.5$ volt. Thus we set V_I at this value:

$$V_I = -1.5 \text{ volt}$$

The action of the circuit as a linear amplifier is shown in Fig. A.13. For the purposes of this illustration, the signal voltage v_i is assumed to be a sine wave of 1-volt amplitude. The instantaneous output voltage is determined by projecting the instantaneous input voltage onto the transfer characteristic to find the corresponding value of v_O. This construction is shown for a specific time t_1 by the dotted lines.

---

[5] The notation introduced here is standard for electronic circuits. Instantaneous total variables are set in lower case with uppercase subscripts (v_I). Fixed or dc components appear in upper case with uppercase subscripts (V_I). Instantaneous signal components appear in lower case with lowercase subscripts (v_i). We shall later use uppercase variables with lowercase subscripts to denote complex amplitudes. Although this notation may, at this point, seem cumbersome or unnecessary, some convention is absolutely essential to reduce confusion. This notation has the important advantage of displaying at a glance the type of variable under consideration.

[6] If v_i had unequal positive and negative swings, an operating point toward an extreme of the linear region would be a better choice.

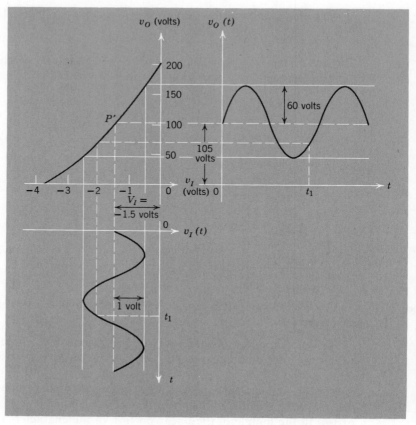

Figure A.13   A graphical method for evaluating $v_O(t)$ in the circuit of Fig. A.12.

The construction of Fig. A.13 shows clearly that the output voltage has a component that is an amplified replica of the signal component of the input voltage. This sine-wave component is superimposed on a dc component which corresponds, of course, to the value of v_O at the point P'. Thus the instantaneous output voltage v_O may be written as

$$v_O = V_O + v_o \tag{A.11}$$

where V_O is a dc component having a value of about $+105$ volts and v_o is the signal component; it is approximated by a sine wave having an amplitude of about 60 volts.

If we focus attention on the *signal component* v_i and v_o, we find that these are approximately linearly related, as desired. Specifically,

$$v_o(t) \simeq 60 v_i(t) \tag{A.12}$$

The *voltage amplification* or *voltage gain* of 60 corresponds to the slope of the transfer characteristic in the region of operation; a tangent to the curve of v_O versus v_I at the point P' has a slope of about 60.

This circuit has the property of *power amplification* or *power gain* as well. The average ac power dissipated in the 100 kohm load resistor is

$$P_{av} = \frac{1}{2} \frac{(60)^2}{10^5}$$

$$\simeq 18 \text{ mw}$$

while the power that must be supplied at the input terminals by the signal voltage source v_i might be as small as a few nanowatts. Thus the power gain can be as large as 10^5 or 10^6.

It is important to recognize that the property we call power gain, which, after all, is what distinguishes this active circuit from a passive transformer

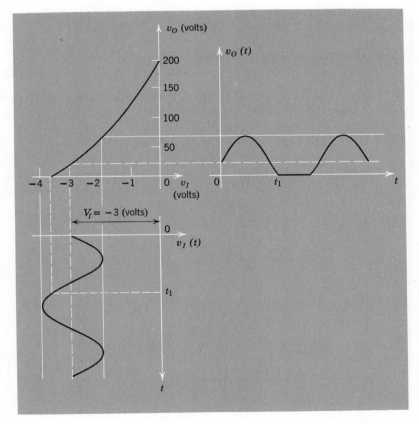

Figure A.14 The output signal is distorted if the operating point is improperly chosen or if the amplitude of the input signal is too large.

with voltage gain, is a manifestation of a controlled transfer of power from the plate power source (V_B) to the load. The tube simply controls the flow of power from the source to the load so that the desired replica of the input signal is obtained.

The construction of Fig. A.13 shows that two conditions must be met if the signal component of the output is to be linearly related to the signal component of the input. First, the dc component of the input voltage must be chosen so that the circuit operates in a linear portion of the transfer character-istic in which there is gain. That is, the *operating point* or *quiescent point* must be properly chosen. The battery that establishes the operating point is often called the *bias source*. Second, the excursion of the input signal must be limited appropriately. If the circuit is improperly biased, or if the input signal voltage is too large, *distortion* will occur as the relationship between the signal components becomes nonlinear, that is, as the instantaneous point of operation moves into a portion of the transfer characteristic where the curvature matters. The effect of distortion on the output signal is illustrated in Fig. A.14.

A.3.5 Coupling and Bias Circuits

As a practical amplifier, the circuit of Fig. A.12 has two disadvantages:

1. The input signal source v_i must be connected in series with the bias source V_1. Thus the dc characteristics of an actual signal source might disturb the operating point.

2. The output signal is superimposed on a dc component. In amplifier applications, both the input signal and the desired output signal are often referenced to ground. Also the input voltage should not influence the operating point and the output should not contain a dc component.

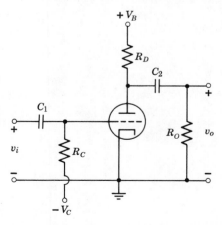

Figure A.15 An amplifier circuit in which capacitors are used to isolate the input and output terminals for dc.

An amplifier circuit in which the input and output terminals are referenced to ground and isolated from the dc power source (V_B) is shown in Fig. A.15. Since the capacitors block direct current, they isolate the portions of the circuit connected to the power source from the terminals. Thus the circuit that governs the operating point of the triode consists only of R_C, R_D, and the tube, as shown in Fig. A.16. The dc value of the grid-to-cathode voltage is approximately equal to $-V_C$, since the grid current is negligible. Thus if we take $V_B = 300$ volts, $R_D = 100$ kohm, and $V_C = 1.5$ volts, the dc grid-to-cathode voltage is -1.5 volt, and the operating point is the same as in the circuit of Fig. A.7; the graphical load-line construction is shown in Fig. A.8.

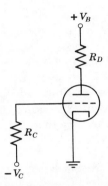

Figure A.16 A circuit having the same quiescent operating point as that of Fig. A.15.

Because of the capacitors in the circuit of Fig. A.15, the output voltage v_o is zero when the input voltage v_i is zero. The input capacitor C_1 charges up to a voltage of E_C while the output capacitor C_2 charges to a voltage of E_B, the dc plate-to-cathode voltage at the operating point.

The capacitors serve to couple ac input signal (v_i) to the grid and also to couple ac component of the plate-to-cathode voltage to the output terminals, that is, to v_o. If the capacitors are large enough in value so that the change in the voltages across them is negligible during the time intervals of interest, the *signal component* e_c of the grid-to-cathode voltage is equal to the input voltage v_i, and the output voltage v_o is equal to the *signal component* e_b of the plate-to-cathode voltage.[7] That is,

$$v_i = e_c \tag{A.13a}$$

$$v_o = e_b \tag{A.13b}$$

---

[7] The traditional terminology used with vacuum tubes denotes the signal component of the grid-to-cathode voltage by e_g, rather than e_c, while the signal component of the plate-to-cathode voltage is denoted by e_p, rather than e_b. In this book we use the notation e_c and e_b.

Note, however, that when nonzero values of v_i cause the instantaneous point of operation of the transistor to shift away from the quiescent point (P in Fig. A.8), the motion is *not* along the load line used in determining the operating point. Because the voltage across C_2 does not change, but remains fixed at the value it has when v_i is zero, a change in plate voltage appears across *both* R_D and R_O, and the corresponding change in the plate current is the sum of the changes in the currents in these two resistors. Consequently, the load line that governs ac or signal-produced changes from the operating point has a slope, not of $-1/R_D$, but of[8]

$$\text{slope} = -1/R_D \| R_O = -\frac{R_D + R_O}{R_D R_O} \tag{A.14}$$

The locus of operation, which is called the *ac load line*, has a slope greater than the *dc load line*, as shown in Fig. A.17, because the ac load resistance $R_D \| R_O$ is smaller than the dc load load resistance (the sketch is drawn for $R_O = R_D$). The darkened portion of the ac load line shows the excursion of the state of the circuit that accompanies an input signal excursion of ± 0.5 volt. The ac component of the plate-to-cathode voltage, which can be determined simply by projecting the operating point excursion along the ac load line onto the voltage axis, is equal to v_o. In this way an *ac transfer characteristic* can be constructed.

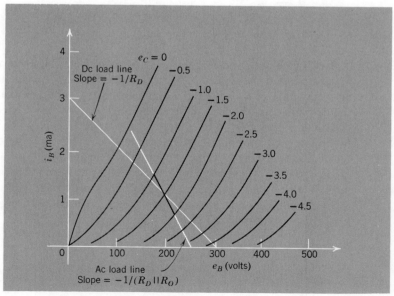

Figure A.17   The dc and ac load lines for the circuit of Fig. A.15.

[8] The notation $\|$ is used to denote the parallel combination of resistances.

An alternative circuit that uses a transformer to separate the output signal voltage from the dc component of the plate voltage and to isolate the load resistance R_L from the power source is shown in Fig. A.18a. The transformer does not, of course, transform the direct current. A model for the transformer that reflects this fact is shown in Fig. A.18b. The inductance L_m, which is called the magnetizing inductance, shorts out the ideal transformer for direct current. If L_m is large enough, the current through it does not change appreciably during the time intervals of interest when signals are present, and it can then be ignored.

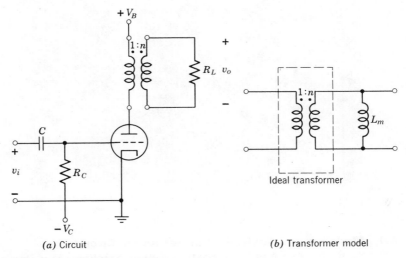

(a) Circuit   (b) Transformer model

Figure A.18 A transformer-coupled amplifier.

The ac and the dc load lines for this circuit are shown in Fig. A.19. The dc load line is vertical because there is no dc voltage drop across the transformer.[9] The quiescent operating point P is set by V_C which governs the dc grid-to-cathode voltage. The ac load line goes through the operating point with a slope of $-1/(R_L/n^2)$, since the transformed load resistance seen on the primary of the transformer is R_L/n^2. The ac component of the plate-to-cathode voltage is determined, as in Fig. A.17, by projecting the variation of the instantaneous operating point on the ac load line onto the voltage axis. This ac voltage is, of course, n times smaller than the ac output voltage v_o. Note that the instantaneous plate-to-cathode voltage may be larger than V_B in this circuit.

The capacitors used in the two amplifier circuits discussed in this section block dc currents and couple ac signals into (or out of) the amplifier. Thus

---

[9] A more realistic transformer model would allow for winding resistance. The dc load line would then be steep but not vertical.

they are known either as *coupling capacitors* or *blocking capacitors* and are selected so that the signal voltage drops across them are negligible (see Chapter 14).

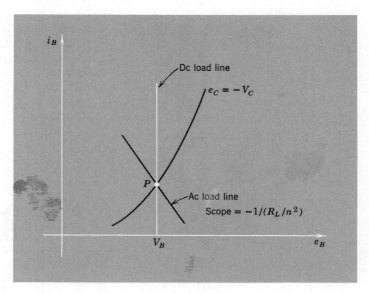

Figure A.19   Load lines for the circuit of Fig. A.18.

A.4   Modeling and Analysis of Linear Active Circuits

As we have seen in the preceding section, amplifiers that employ active devices are often operated in such a way that linear input-output relationships are obtained. This is accomplished by restricting the range of variation of the currents and voltages at the terminals of the active device sufficiently for the nonlinearities in its characteristics not to be perceived. When this is the case, the signal components of the variables, which measure the departures from a quiescent operating point, are approximately linearly related.

We can make use of the fact that the signal components of the variables are linearly related for small enough excursions to obtain an algebraic description of the behavior of the device. Such a description provides an alternative to the graphical models we have thus far considered and makes it possible to bring the powerful tools of linear circuit theory to bear on the analysis of active circuits. We once again employ a triode vacuum tube to illustrate this technique.

A.4.1   An Incremental Model

The physical nature of the triode is such that it is sensible to regard the terminal-pair voltages as independent variables and the terminal currents as dependent variables. Thus a formal description of the electrical behavior of the device has the following form:

$$i_B = i_B(e_B, e_C) \tag{A.15a}$$

$$i_C \simeq 0 \tag{A.15b}$$

We regard each of the terminal variables as comprised of a *quiescent* or dc component and a *signal* component. The quiescent components define the dc operating point; the signal components measure departures from that operating point. Thus the four instantaneous total variables that appear in Eqs. A.15 can be written as

$$e_B = E_B + e_b \tag{A.16a}$$

$$e_C = E_C + e_c \tag{A.16b}$$

$$i_B = I_B + i_b \tag{A.16c}$$

$$i_C = I_C + i_c. \tag{A.16d}$$

The notation is that introduced in Section A.3.4; the first terms on the right sides of these equations are the dc components, and the second terms are the signal components.

A formal representation of the relationship between the signal components can be obtained by expanding, in Taylor's series about the quiescent state, the functional relationships implied by Eqs. A.15. Expansion of Eq. A.15a yields

$$i_B = i_B|_Q$$

$$+ \frac{\partial i_B}{\partial e_B}\bigg|_Q e_b + \frac{\partial i_B}{\partial e_C}\bigg|_Q e_c \tag{A.17}$$

$$+ \frac{1}{2!}\frac{\partial^2 i_B}{\partial^2 e_B}\bigg|_Q e_b{}^2 + \frac{1}{2!}\frac{\partial^2 i_B}{\partial^2 e_C}\bigg|_Q e_c{}^2 + \frac{\partial^2 i_B}{\partial e_B \partial e_C}\bigg|_Q e_c e_b$$

$$+ \text{higher-order terms}$$

The notation $i_B|_Q$ or $\partial i_B/\partial e_B|_Q$ denotes that the indicated function or partial derivative is to be evaluated at the quiescent operating point, that is, the point $e_B = E_B, e_C = E_C$. Now if the signal variables are small enough so that the instantaneous plate current is approximately linear in these variables, the expansion can be approximated by the truncated series that is obtained when *all* terms that are second-order and higher are neglected. Thus

$$i_B \simeq i_B|_Q + \frac{\partial i_B}{\partial e_B}\bigg|_Q e_b + \frac{\partial i_B}{\partial e_C}\bigg|_Q e_c \tag{A.18a}$$

If we express the plate current in terms of its dc and signal components, using Eq. A.16c, Eq. A.18a becomes

$$I_B + i_b = i_B\big|_Q + \frac{\partial i_B}{\partial e_B}\bigg|_Q e_b + \frac{\partial i_B}{\partial e_C}\bigg|_Q e_c \tag{A.18b}$$

Since the incremental components are independent of the quiescent components, they may be set equal to zero without affecting the quiescent state of the device. In this case Eq. A.18b becomes

$$I_B = i_B\big|_Q \tag{A.19a}$$

Finally, if this quiescent relationship is subtracted from Eq. A.18b, we are left with a relationship among the incremental components:

$$i_b = \frac{\partial i_B}{\partial e_B}\bigg|_Q e_b + \frac{\partial i_B}{\partial e_C}\bigg|_Q e_c \tag{A.19b}$$

There is nothing new in Eq. A.19a. It states simply that the quiescent plate current is related to the quiescent terminal-pair voltages by the functional relationship of Eq. A.15a evaluated at the operating point. The second equation (Eq. A.19b) is a *linear* relationship among the *signal* components. The coefficients of this linear relationship are derivatives of the total-variable relationship evaluated at the quiescent operating point.

The fact that the grid current is approximately zero means that a formal expansion is not required. Rather, we have

$$i_C \simeq 0 \tag{A.20a}$$

$$i_c \simeq 0 \tag{A.20b}$$

Of course, a nonzero functional relationship for the total grid current could be expanded in precisely the same manner as illustrated for i_B.

The results of the plate current expansion, given by Eq. A.19b, constitute a model that relates the signal components and is linear in those components. This model is called a *small-signal model* or an *incremental model*. The signal variables it relates are often called *incremental variables*. These names emphasize that the model applies only for restricted ranges of variation of the signal or incremental variables.

The incremental model can be expressed in terms of an arrangement of idealized circuit elements. Toward this end we write Eq. A.19b as

$$i_b = g_p e_b + g_m e_c \tag{A.21a}$$

where

$$g_p = \frac{\partial i_B}{\partial e_B}\bigg|_Q \tag{A.21b}$$

is known as the *incremental output or plate conductance*, and

$$g_m = \left. \frac{\partial i_B}{\partial e_C} \right|_Q \tag{A.21c}$$

is called the *incremental forward transfer conductance* or simply the *incremental transconductance*. In terms of this notation, the incremental model can be represented as shown in Fig. A.20. This model is equivalent to the description of Eqs. A.20b and A.21a because the node equations of the circuit correspond exactly to the algebraic descriptions.

Of course, the incremental model of Fig. A.20 is only a formal representation of the relationships among the incremental variables; it is not complete until the coefficients g_p and g_m are determined. Analysis of the physical electronics of the vacuum triode would, of course, provide us with a specific algebraic relationship having the form of Eq. A.15a. This device description could then be used as a basis for specifying the incremental parameters directly, in accordance with Eqs. A.21b and A.21c. We shall illustrate this route in Appendix B, after we have analyzed the physics of vacuum triodes in quantitative detail. For the present, we evaluate the incremental coefficients by noting their relationship to a graphical description of the device.

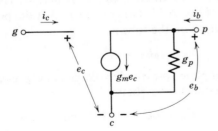

Figure A.20   An incremental model for a vacuum triode.

The incremental coefficients g_p and g_m are related to the slopes and spacings of the static output characteristics. The definition of Eq. A.21b shows that g_p can be written as

$$g_p \simeq \left. \frac{\Delta i_B}{\Delta e_B} \right|_{\Delta e_C = 0} \tag{A.22a}$$

In other words, the incremental output conductance is equal to the slope at the operating point of the curve of plate current versus plate-to-cathode voltage for fixed grid-to-cathode voltage. Similarly, the incremental transconductance can be written as

$$g_m \simeq \left. \frac{\Delta i_B}{\Delta e_C} \right|_{\Delta e_B = 0} \tag{A.22b}$$

This coefficient is equal to the per-unit spacing at the operating point of the curves of plate current. These relationships are shown in Fig. A.21.

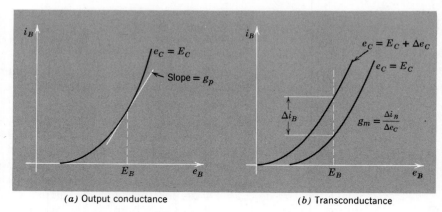

(*a*) Output conductance   (*b*) Transconductance

Figure A.21   Relationship of the incremental coefficients to the static plate characteristics.

A.4.2   Incremental Analysis of an Amplifier

To illustrate the application of incremental circuit models, we consider once again the simple amplifier of Fig. A.12. The constraint that the power source and the load resistance impose on the tube is

$$V_B = i_B R_L + e_B \tag{A.23a}$$

When the plate current and plate-to-cathode voltage are expressed in terms of their dc and signal components, we obtain

$$V_B = (I_B R_L + E_B) + (i_b R_L + e_b) \tag{A.23b}$$

Since the quiescent and incremental components are independent, this equation may be separated into two parts:

$$V_B = I_B R_L + e_B \tag{A.24a}$$

$$0 = i_b R_L + e_b \tag{A.24b}$$

Equation A.24a relates the dc components and has nothing new in it. Equation A.24b relates the incremental components. The left side is zero because the power source voltage is fixed in value and has no incremental component.

Equation A.24b is the constraint that the circuit imposes on the incremental variables at the plate-cathode terminals of the tube. Consequently, this constraint can be represented along with the incremental model of the device as shown in Fig. A.22. Note that the grid-cathode terminals are connected directly to v_i, the signal component of the input voltage; the corresponding dc component V_I (which sets the operating point) does not appear in this incremental network. In general, all dc sources must be suppressed when the incremental circuit is formed. That is, dc voltage sources must be replaced by short circuits (as in Fig. A.22), and dc current sources must be replaced by open circuits.

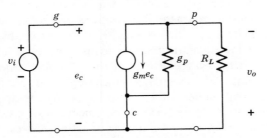

Figure A.22 An incremental model for the amplifier of Fig. A.12.

The circuit model of Fig. A.22 can be used to evaluate the dependence of v_o on v_i. Specifically, we have

$$v_o = (g_m e_c) R_L \left\| \left(\frac{1}{g_p} \right) \right.$$ (A.25a)

or, equivalently,

$$v_o = g_m \frac{R_L r_p}{R_L + r_p} e_c$$ (A.25b)

where r_p denotes the reciprocal of g_p. Finally, since $e_c = v_i$, we find that

$$\frac{v_o}{v_i} = g_m \frac{R_L r_p}{R_L + r_p}$$ (A.25c)

This ratio of incremental variables is the *forward incremental voltage transfer ratio* (which, of course, must be equal to the slope at the operating point of the voltage transfer characteristic shown in Fig. A.13).

To check, let us evaluate g_m and g_p from Fig. A.8 and calculate v_o/v_i. The operating point is shown on the output characteristics in Fig. A.8. In accordance with Eqs. A.22 we find for this operating point

$$g_p \simeq \frac{1}{80 \text{ kohm}}$$

$$g_m \simeq 1.5 \text{ mmho}$$

For $R_L = 100 \text{ kohm}$ we find $v_o/v_i \simeq 65$, which to the accuracy of these sketches, is the same as the slope of the transfer characteristic at this operating point.

In more complex circuits, linear incremental models such as that employed in this example offer important advantages when compared with graphical techniques of analysis. This is particularly apparent when the circuits of interest contain energy-storage elements and when the dynamics of the active devices must be considered. In such cases the use of linear incremental models permits us to employ all the analysis tools, viewpoints, and intuition developed in the study of the dynamics of linear passive circuits. For example, techniques that consider exponential excitations and focus on the natural frequencies of the system can often be employed very profitably.

Three aspects of incremental models and incremental analysis deserve special emphasis. First, the coefficients of these models depend explicitly on the operating point. Consequently, it is meaningless to specify the parameters of an incremental model without also specifying the operating point at which those parameters apply. Second, incremental analysis suppresses all evidence of the inherently nonlinear nature of active devices. Such models cannot be used to evaluate distortion in an amplifier; they do not even suggest the existence of distortion-producing nonlinearities. Thus it is necessary to bear in mind that incremental analysis is valid only for limited excursions of the variables and to make use of other points of view in determining the appropriate limits. Third, the incremental model applies *only* to the incremental or signal components of the variables and cannot be used to explore relationships among the quiescent components of the variables or among the total variables.

REFERENCES

A.1   H. J. Zimmermann and S. J. Mason, *Electronic Circuit Theory*, Wiley, New York, 1959.

A.2   T. S. Gray, *Applied Electronics*, The M.I.T. Press, Cambridge, Mass., 1954.

PROBLEMS

P.A.1   The vacuum triode whose output characteristics are shown in Fig. A.4 is connected in the circuit of Fig. A.7. The parameter values are

$$V_B = 250 \text{ volts}$$

$$R_L = 50 \text{ kohm}$$

(a) Sketch the load line on the coordinates of Fig. A.4.

(b) Determine the operating point (e_B, i_B) for

(1) $e_C = 0$ volt

(2) $e_C = -2$ volt

(c) What is the smallest value of e_C that will cut off the triode, that is, reduce i_B to zero?

P.A.2   Using the parameter values introduced in Problem P.A.1, determine, sketch, and dimension the static transfer characteristic, that is, v_O versus v_I for v_I in the range -4 volt $< v_I < 0$. Sketch the transfer characteristic on the coordinates of Fig. A.9.

P.A.3   This problem is concerned with the circuit shown in Fig. A.11. The tube is described by the output characteristics shown in Fig. A.4. Assume

$$V_B = 300 \text{ volts}$$
$$R_D = 80 \text{ kohm}$$
$$R_S = 500 \text{ ohms}$$

(a) Determine the operating point (e_B, i_B) when $v_I = 0$.

(b) Determine, sketch, and dimension the static transfer characteristic that relates the voltage v_D across R_D to the input voltage v_I, for v_I in the range $-4 \text{ volt} < v_I < 1 \text{ volt}$.

(c) With $V_B = 300 \text{ volts}$, $v_I = 0$, $R_D = 80 \text{ kohm}$, it is desired that the circuit operate with $i_B = 1.5 \text{ ma}$. What value of R_S will yield this operating point?

P.A.4   This problem is concerned with the amplifier circuit shown in Fig. A.15. Assume that the tube is described by the characteristics of Fig. A.4 and that

$$V_B = 300 \text{ volts}$$
$$R_D = R_O = 50 \text{ kohm}$$
$$V_C = -1.5 \text{ volt}$$

Find the static operating point (e_B, i_B).

P.A.5   Consider the transformer-coupled circuit shown in Fig. A.18a. If

$$V_B = 200 \text{ volts}$$
$$R_L = 2 \text{ kohm}$$

determine the value of V_C that will cause the circuit to operate with a quiescent plate current of 2 ma. Use the characteristic curves of Fig. A.4.

P.A.6   This problem is an extension of Problem P.A.3 and makes use of the parameter values introduced in that problem.

(a) At the operating point that occurs when $v_I = 0$ evaluate g_m and r_p.

(b) Derive an expression for the incremental voltage gain v_d/v_i, where v_d denotes the incremental component of the voltage across R_D.

(c) Evaluate the incremental voltage gain at the operating point that occurs when $v_I = 0$. Compare your result with the slope at the same point of the transfer characteristic determined in Problem P.A.3.

P.A.7   This problem is an extension of Problem P.A.4 and makes use of the parameter values introduced in that problem.

(a) Evaluate g_m and r_p at the dc operating point.

(b) Derive an expression for the incremental voltage gain v_o/v_i, and evaluate this expression at the operating point of the circuit.

APPENDIX B

Vacuum Tube Physical Electronics and Circuit Models

B.1. Physical Electronics of Vacuum Tubes
B.1.1 Static Diode Analysis and the Three-Halves Power Law

We now wish to explore, in quantitative terms, the dependence of the plate current on the plate-to-cathode voltage and to determine the form of the distributions of electrostatic potential and space charge in the diode. Although we could develop this analysis for the cylindrical structure shown in Fig. A.1, solutions of the differential equations that govern the distribution and flow of the electrons in the structure are easier to obtain if we focus on the plane-parallel structure shown in Fig. B.1. We assume that the electrodes, which are of area A, have dimensions that are large compared with the electrode spacing W. Thus we neglect fringing of the electric field and the current at the edges of the electrodes and assume that the field and the current are x-directed and are uniform over the entire area of the electrodes.

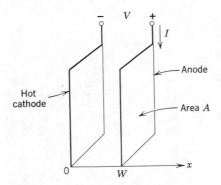

Figure B.1 Plane-parallel diode structure.

We now consider the consequences of increasing from zero the rate at which electrons are emitted from the cathode surface. This rate is determined by the cathode temperature. Thus the implicit variable in this discussion is the cathode temperature, which is controlled by the power supplied to the heater. We assume throughout this discussion that the plate-to-cathode voltage is fixed at the value V.

When the cathode is cold, there are essentially no electrons in the interelectrode space. Consequently, there is no space charge in this region, the potential varies linearly between the electrodes, the electric field is uniform, and there is no current. This situation, which is exactly analogous to that which exists in a parallel-plate capacitor of spacing W with voltage V applied, is illustrated by the curve labeled 0 in Fig. B.2. The uniform electric field originates on positive surface charge at the anode and terminates on an equal density of negative surface charge at the cathode.

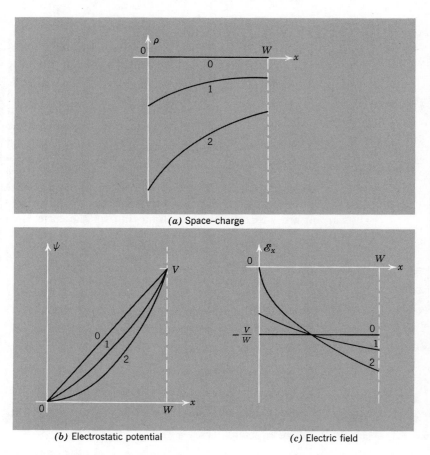

(a) Space–charge

(b) Electrostatic potential   (c) Electric field

Figure B.2   Dependence of space-charge, electrostatic potential, and electric field on position for the plane-parallel diode structure of Fig. B.1. The potential is arbitrarily assumed to be zero at the cathode surface ($x = 0$). The curves are shown for three values of electron emission rate: those labeled 0 correspond to no emission; those labeled 2 correspond to an emission rate many times larger than the rate of flow of electrons to the anode; those labeled 1 correspond to an emission rate for which all of the emitted electrons flow to the anode.

If the emission rate is increased, electrons enter the interelectrode space and flow toward the plate. Thus the space-charge density ρ becomes negative, as shown by the curve labeled 1 in Fig. B.2a. The space-charge density varies with position because the electrons are crowded together where their velocity is smallest, that is, near the cathode. Near the anode, their velocity is greater and thus their concentration must be less for the same current density. The potential distribution changes, and the electric field is no longer uniform because of the presence of space charge between the electrodes. Although the field still originates on positive surface charge at the anode, it now terminates, in part, on the negative space charge between the electrodes.

In the region of behavior illustrated by the curves labeled 1, the electron current that flows from cathode to anode is governed by the rate of electron emission at the cathode. Every emitted electron is collected at the anode. Thus the curve of anode current versus emission current is linear and has a slope of unity in this region of behavior, as illustrated in Fig. B.3 by the portion of the curve labeled "emission-limited flow."

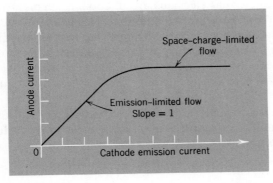

Figure B.3   Dependence of anode current on cathode emission current for fixed plate-to-cathode voltage.

As the rate of emission of electrons is increased still further, the space-charge density increases even more and the electric field at the cathode surface decreases further; more and more of the field lines terminate on the space charge between the electrodes. Eventually the field at the cathode surface drops to zero because the space charge between the electrodes suffices to terminate the field entirely. The condition of zero field at the cathode surface corresponds to complete shielding of the anode from the cathode by the negative space charge in between. Electrons emitted from the cathode are completely unaware of the presence of the positively-charged anode. The anode current is now governed not by the rate of emission of electrons but by the space charge in the interelectrode space. Most of the emitted electrons, which experience no field at the cathode surface, fall back into the cathode; only a small fraction of the emitted electrons contribute to plate current. This flow from cathode to anode is governed by the space charge; thus this region of behavior, in which the plate current is *independent* of emission current, is called the domain of space-charge-limited flow (Fig. B.3). Most thermionic vacuum tubes are operated in the space-charge-limited mode.

This discussion has a parallel in Section 4.2.3 where we considered the factors that govern the current in a forward-biased *pn* junction diode. The extreme cases in that situation are flow limited in the space-charge layer and flow limited in the neutral regions. Here the extreme cases are emission-limited flow, in which the current is governed not by the field distribution in the interelectrode space, but by the rate at which electrons are "boiled out" of the hot cathode, and space-charge limited flow, in which the cathode is in quasi equilibrium (most emitted electrons fall back into the cathode surface) and flow is governed by the field and charge distributions in the interelectrode space.

We now determine the dependence of the plate current on the plate-to-cathode voltage for space-charge-limited flow in the plane-parallel diode structure. We assume that electrons are in copious supply at the cathode surface and that they emerge from the cathode with negligibly small velocity.[1] We further assume that the concentration of electrons between the electrodes is small enough so that collisions between the electrons are of negligible effect. Thus the only force acting on an electron in its flight from cathode to anode is that produced by the electric field associated with the potential variation.

We denote the electrostatic potential at x by $\psi(x)$ and assume that $\psi(0) = 0$, that is, the potential is zero at the cathode surface. If we denote the x-directed velocity of an electron at x by $u(x)$, we have

$$\tfrac{1}{2}mu^2(x) = q\psi(x) \tag{B.1}$$

where m denotes the mass of the electron and q denotes the magnitude of the electronic charge. Equation B.1 is a statement of conservation of energy for an electron; the electron loses $q\psi(x)$ units of potential energy in falling through the potential increase of $\psi(x)$, and this decrease in potential shows up as an increase in kinetic energy. Since the electron is assumed to be at rest at the cathode surface, the change in kinetic energy is simply $mu^2(x)/2$.

The energy balance of Eq. B.1 can be solved for the electron velocity $u(x)$:

$$u(x) = \sqrt{\frac{2q}{m}\,\psi(x)} \tag{B.2}$$

Even as the electron motion is influenced by the potential distribution, the moving electronic charges also affect the potential distribution. The x-directed current density J, *which is independent of* x, can be expressed in

---

[1] Actually, the electrons are emitted with nonzero velocity. The average thermal energy of the electrons usually lies in the range from 0.1 to 2 eV. This initial velocity causes a dip in the potential distribution just beyond the cathode; the condition for space-charge-limited flow corresponds to a small retarding field at the cathode surface. This retarding field offsets the initial electron velocities and brings the electrons to rest at the location of the potential minimum. The errors associated with our neglect of initial velocities are unimportant except for plate-to-cathode voltages of the order of a few volts.

terms of the electron space-charge density $\rho(x)$ and the electron velocity $u(x)$:

$$J = \rho(x)u(x) \tag{B.3}$$

Thus the variation of charge density with position is governed by the velocity distribution:

$$\rho(x) = \frac{J}{u(x)} \tag{B.4}$$

This space charge influences the potential distribution through Gauss's law. For the one-dimensional case of the plane-parallel diode, Gauss's law can be written in differential form as

$$\frac{d\mathscr{E}_x}{dx} = \frac{\rho(x)}{\epsilon_0} \tag{B.5a}$$

where ϵ_0 denotes the permittivity of free space. Since

$$\mathscr{E}_x = -\frac{d\psi(x)}{dx} \tag{B.5b}$$

Gauss's law can be expressed in terms of the potential

$$\frac{d^2\psi(x)}{dx^2} = -\frac{\rho(x)}{\epsilon_0} \tag{B.6}$$

In this form it is known as *Poisson's equation* (in one dimension).

Now Eqs. B.2, B.4, and B.6 constitute a set of three simultaneous equations in the three variables $u(x)$, $\rho(x)$, and $\psi(x)$ (J is a parameter in their solution). In order to determine the form of the distributions of velocity, space charge, and potential, we reduce the three equations to a single equation in the potential. The result is

$$\frac{d^2\psi(x)}{dx^2} = -\frac{J}{\epsilon_0}\sqrt{\frac{m}{2q}}\,[\psi(x)]^{-\frac{1}{2}} \tag{B.7}$$

Although this differential equation is nonlinear, it can easily be integrated twice to obtain $\psi(x)$, which has as boundary conditions

$$\psi(W) = V \tag{B.8a}$$

$$\left.\frac{d\psi}{dx}\right|_{x=0} = 0 \tag{B.8b}$$

The result (see Problem P.B.1) is

$$\psi(x) = V\left(\frac{x}{W}\right)^{4/3} \tag{B.9}$$

The current density J that is associated with this potential distribution is

$$J = -\frac{4\epsilon_0}{9W^2}\sqrt{\frac{2q}{m}}\,V^{3/2} \tag{B.10}$$

The negative value of J corresponds to the flow of electrons from cathode to plate, that is, in the x direction. The total anode or plate current I (see Fig. B.1) is

$$I = -JA$$

Thus the I–V relationship of the space-charge-limited diode is

$$I = KV^{3/2} \tag{B.11a}$$

where

$$K = \frac{4\epsilon_0 A}{9W^2}\sqrt{\frac{2q}{m}} \tag{B.11b}$$

is called the *perveance* of the diode.

Although we have derived the I–V relationship of Eq. B.11a for the specific case of a plane-parallel diode structure, this *three-halves power law* is quite general and applies to all diode structures in which initial electron velocities are negligible and the flow is space-charge-limited. This general conclusion follows from the linear nature of the electrostatic situation. If we consider the consequences of multiplying the anode-to-cathode voltage of a space-charge-limited diode by a factor α, the potential and space-charge density must change at every point within the interelectrode space by the same factor α; this scaling is a consequence of the linear nature of Poisson's equation. However, the velocity distribution, which is governed by Eq. B.2 for *any* structural arrangement, scales by a factor of $\alpha^{1/2}$. Consequently, the current

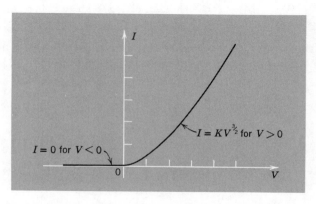

Figure B.4   *I*–*V* characteristic of a space-charge-limited thermionic diode.

density, which is given by Eq. B.3, must change by a factor of $\alpha(\alpha^{\frac{1}{2}}) = \alpha^{\frac{3}{2}}$. Hence the current I varies as the three-halves power of the voltage.

It should be clear that the analysis that yields the three-halves power law applies *only* when V is positive. As discussed earlier in this section, there is no flow of electrons when V is negative because the electric field, which is uniform throughout the interelectrode space, pushes electrons back toward the cathode surface. Thus the complete static I–V characteristic of a space-charge-limited thermionic diode has the form shown in Fig. B.4.

B.1.2 Dynamic Effects in Diodes

In the discussion of the preceding section we have tacitly assumed that the diode voltage and current are constant or static. We now consider the consequences of time-dependent voltage and current, and extend our understanding of the physical electronics of diodes to include the dynamic effects associated with large rates of change of the terminal variables.

There are two sources of dynamic effects in diodes:

1. A nonzero time is required for an electron to move from cathode to plate; this interval is called the *transit time*. If the plate-to-cathode voltage changes significantly during a transit time, inertial effects of the charge in transit become important, and the instantaneous anode current becomes a function of not only the instantaneous anode voltage but also of the past history of that voltage. Thus the I–V relationship of Eq. B.11a is no longer valid.

2. When the anode-to-cathode voltage changes rapidly, the changing space-charge distributions require displacement currents. These displacement currents must be accounted for at the terminals of the diode.

Although we do not develop the analysis of a thermionic diode in detail for rates of change of the terminal voltage that are large enough for transit time to be important, we do compute the transit time. This calculation provides a crude criterion for assessment of the importance of inertial effects in any practical situation.

The velocity of an electron is given by Eq. B.2. When Eq. B.9 is used to substitute for $\psi(x)$ in this relationship, we obtain

$$u(x) = \sqrt{\frac{2qV}{m}} \left(\frac{x}{W}\right)^{\frac{2}{3}} \tag{B.12}$$

The time required for an electron to move from x to $x + dx$ is

$$dt = \frac{dx}{u(x)} \tag{B.13}$$

Consequently, the transit time T is

$$T = \int_0^W \frac{dx}{u(x)}$$

$$= \sqrt{\frac{m}{2qV}} \int_0^W \left(\frac{x}{W}\right)^{-2/3} dx$$

Thus

$$T = 3W\sqrt{\frac{m}{2qV}} \tag{B.14}$$

The velocity of the electron upon impact with the anode is, from Eq. B.2,

$$u_m = \sqrt{\frac{2qV}{m}}$$

Hence the transit time may be written as

$$T = 3\frac{W}{u_m} \tag{B.15}$$

A diode with an interelectrode spacing of 1 mm and an anode voltage of 100 volts has an electron impact velocity of about 6×10^6 m/sec and a transit time of about 0.5 nsec (0.5×10^{-9} sec). Thus if the diode voltage changes relatively little on a time scale of nanoseconds, the motion of the electrons can be regarded as a succession of steady states, and the three-halves power law applies. A sinusoid of frequency 2 GHz (2×10^9 sec^{-1}) has a period equal to the transit time of this example. Thus we would expect the "static" analysis of Section B.1.1 to apply for ac components of the diode voltage with frequencies as large as several hundred megahertz.

We can determine the consequences of displacement currents by assuming that the diode voltage is changing slowly enough for the inertial effects to be unimportant and by using the static analysis of Section B.1.1 to evaluate the space charge (or the anode charge, which is equal to the space charge) associated with a particular voltage. Once again we consider a plane-parallel structure with space-charge-limited flow.

The electric field in the interelectrode space is, in accordance with Eq. B.9,

$$\mathscr{E} = -\frac{d\psi}{dx}$$

$$= -\left(\frac{4}{3}\right)\left(\frac{V}{W}\right)\left(\frac{x}{W}\right)^{1/3} \tag{B.16}$$

Thus the field at the anode surface is

$$\mathscr{E}(W) = -\frac{4}{3}\left(\frac{V}{W}\right) \tag{B.17a}$$

This field originates on positive surface charge on the anode. This surface-charge density is, in accordance with Gauss's law,

$$\sigma = -\mathscr{E}(W)\epsilon_0$$

$$= \tfrac{4}{3}\epsilon_0\left(\frac{V}{W}\right) \tag{B.17b}$$

Since the anode surface charge σ is proportional to the anode voltage V, this charge-voltage relationship can be expressed in terms of a plate-to-cathode capacitance C_{pk}:

$$C_{pk} = \frac{\sigma A}{V}$$

$$= \tfrac{4}{3}\epsilon_0\frac{A}{W} \tag{B.17c}$$

This capacitance, which is defined for space-charge-limited flow, differs from the capacitance that would be observed if there were no flow, that is, if the cathode were cold. In such cases the electric field would be uniform, as shown in Fig. B.2c, and the capacitance would be that of a parallel-plate capacitor of area A and spacing W: $\epsilon_0(A/W)$.

The capacitance defined by Eq. B.17c is occasionally identified incorrectly as the "hot capacitance" of a vacuum diode. In fact, the capacitance defined by Eq. B.17c is not the capacitance that one would measure between plate and cathode when there is plate current. The "hot capacitance" is inseparable from a space-charge distribution which produces a steady or dc anode current as well. Any measurement of the interelectrode capacitance requires some change in the anode voltage and thus produces a corresponding change in the steady conduction current, as well as a transient displacement current. Although the anode surface charge must indeed change by $C_{pk}\Delta v$, where C_{pk} is given by Eq. B.17c, some of the necessary charge change is accomplished by electron flow within the diode and need not be supplied as an external current. Consequently, the actual measured interelectrode capacitance is less than that given by Eq. B.17c. When both the conduction and displacement components of the anode current are properly accounted for, the "hot" capacitance is found to be slightly *less* than the "cold" capacitance. The actual numerical coefficient involved is not particularly important; the significant point is that a changing diode voltage must be accompanied by changes in the internal charge distribution, and the displacement currents that produce these charge changes must be accounted for in modeling the diode.

The displacement currents associated with changes in the space charge can be accounted for in circuit terms simply by adding a capacitance C_{pk} to the terminals of a static model. Thus the instantaneous anode current i associated with an anode voltage v is

$$i = C_{pk}\frac{dv}{dt} + Kv^{3/2} \tag{B.18}$$

where K is the perveance of the diode.[2]

B.1.3   Static Triode Analysis

The thermionic triode differs structurally from the diode discussed above in that it contains a third electrode—the grid—which is located between the cathode and the anode (or plate) as shown in Fig. A.1.

Triodes are invariably operated in the space-charge-limited mode; the plate current is governed not by the rate of electron emission from the cathode, but by the density of space charge in the interelectrode space. The space charge causes the electric field to vanish at the cathode surface so that emitted electrons feel no force, and the current is governed by the rate at which electrons can move through this cloud of screening charge toward the positively-charged plate.

Once again we focus our attention on a one-dimensional plane-parallel structure as shown in Fig. B.5. Also, we neglect fringing fields and their contribution to the current.

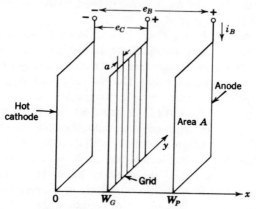

Figure B.5   Plane-parallel triode structure.

In an "ideal" thermionic triode the grid should meet two requirements:

1. It should control completely the space-charge distribution in the cathode-grid space, thereby exercising sole control over the electron current.

---

[2] Just as with semiconductor devices, lowercase symbols are used to represent the instantaneous values of time-dependent voltages and currents.

2. It should be "porous" to electrons so that the charge carriers pass right through the grid to be collected at the anode, which must of course be positively charged with respect to the grid.

If these conditions could be met, the vacuum triode would be a rather ideal control valve. The current in the plate-cathode circuit would be controlled solely by the grid-to-cathode voltage and would be independent of the plate-to-cathode voltage (because of the screening action of the grid, plate voltage changes would have no effect on the space charge in the cathode-grid space). Furthermore, the grid current would be zero (because the grid is porous to electrons and would not collect them), and the potential power gain would be extremely large.

In such an "ideal" structure the grid-to-cathode voltage would be positive (in order to attract electrons toward the grid through which they would pass to the plate), and Eq. B.11a, which was derived for the diode, would apply. Of course V, which denoted the diode plate voltage, would be replaced by e_C, the triode grid-to-cathode voltage, and the spacing W in the perveance would be changed to W_G, the cathode-grid spacing in the triode. Thus the static characteristics of this "ideal" triode would be:

$$i_B = K_G e_C^{3/2} \qquad \text{for all } e_B > e_C \text{ and for } e_C \geqslant 0 \qquad \text{(B.19a)}$$

$$i_G = 0 \qquad \qquad \text{(B.19b)}$$

$$K_G = \frac{4\epsilon_0 A}{9 W_G{}^2} \sqrt{\frac{2q}{m}} \qquad \qquad \text{(B.19c)}$$

In reality, the requirements above for the grid cannot be achieved, and the "ideal" triode that we have postulated cannot be realized. No practical grid structure can exercise total control over the distributions of electric field and space charge in the cathode-grid space without intercepting some, perhaps most, of the electron current that should go through to the anode.

In actual practice, the grid is an open mesh or coil of wire and is operated at a *negative* potential with respect to the cathode. Because it is an open structure, the field produced by the plate can penetrate through the grid and influence to some degree the space charge in the cathode-grid space. However, the grid potential also influences this space charge, which is the basis for the control action of actual triodes. Because the grid is much closer to the cathode than is the plate, it has a relatively larger influence on the space charge. Because it is negatively charged with respect to the cathode it does not collect electrons, and the grid current is negligible.[3]

The electrostatic potential distribution in the plane of the grid must have the general form shown in Fig. B.6. The potential is negative at the grid wires but positive at the center of the regions between the grid wires, where the positively charged plate is most influential. Of course, the bumps in the potential

---

[3] The grid does collect residual positive gas ions. Consequently, the grid current is not zero, but is typically very small.

distribution on the grid plane produce nonuniform current flow in the cathode-grid space. To avoid solving the difficult electrostatic problem implicit in this situation, we *assume* that the grid plane can be replaced by an *equipotential surface* whose potential is a weighted average of the grid and plate potentials. This approximation is justified if the cathode-grid separation (W_G in Fig. B.5) is large compared with the spacing of the grid wires (a in Fig. B.5).

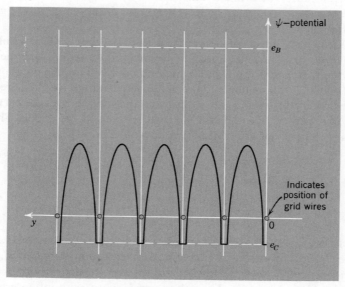

Figure B.6 Potential distribution on the grid plane. The transverse coordinate y is defined in Fig. B.5.

The average potential of the equivalent equipotential grid plane is *defined* to be

$$e_{eq} = e_C + \frac{e_B}{\mu_A} \tag{B.20}$$

where μ_A is a dimensionless parameter governed by the relative spacings of the grid and the plate and by the structure of the grid. This parameter, called the *amplification factor*, expresses the relative effectiveness of the grid, as compared with the plate, in controlling the potential of the equivalent grid plane. Since the grid is much closer to the cathode than is the plate, the grid has greater "leverage." Consequently, the amplification factor is usually much greater than unity; it is seldom smaller than 10 and may be as large as 200.

Since the equivalent grid plane governs the distribution of space charge in the cathode-grid space, the plate current of the triode is given by Eq. B.19a with e_C replaced by e_{eq}. That is,

$$i_B = K_G \left(e_C + \frac{e_B}{\mu_A} \right)^{3/2} \tag{B.21}$$

Of course, this equation, which expresses the current-voltage characteristic of the triode, applies only when the argument $e_C + e_B/\mu_A$ is positive (i.e., when the equivalent grid potential is positive) and when e_B is positive (the plate must be positive to attract electrons through the grid). When the argument is negative, the plate current is zero and the tube is said to be cut off. Thus the complete output or plate characteristics of the triode have the form

$$i_B = \begin{cases} K_G \left(e_C + \dfrac{e_B}{\mu_A} \right)^{3/2} & e_C + \dfrac{e_B}{\mu_A} > 0 \quad \text{and} \quad e_B > 0 \\[2ex] 0 & e_C + \dfrac{e_B}{\mu_A} \leqslant 0 \quad \text{or} \quad e_B \leqslant 0 \end{cases} \tag{B.22}$$

Throughout this analysis we have assumed that e_C is less than zero so that the grid does not collect electrons. If the grid becomes positive, it shares with the plate in collecting electrons, and the analysis is more complex.

The model that results from this analysis is shown in graphical form in Fig. B.7, where we have chosen to plot i_B versus e_B with e_C as a parameter.[4] These curves, which are called the *plate characteristics* of the triode, should be compared with the measured curves of Fig. A.4.

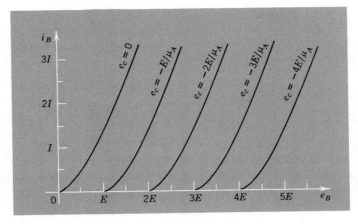

Figure B.7   Idealized triode characteristics—arbitrary scales.

[4] An equivalent graphical model can be obtained by plotting i_B versus e_C with e_B as a parameter.

B.1.4   Dynamic Effects in Triodes

The static analysis of triode behavior presented in the preceding section is subject to the same dynamic limitations that apply to vacuum diodes. Specifically, the current-voltage relationship we have derived applies only when the terminal voltages are changing slowly enough so that the fractional change that occurs in an electron transit time is negligible; in practical structures this condition becomes marginally valid when the tube is operated at frequencies in the range of several hundred megahertz. At higher frequencies the analysis must be modified to account for inertial effects. In addition, our model for the triode must be extended to account for the displacement currents that are associated with changes in the distribution of space charge and electrode charge. These currents become significant in comparison with the conduction current produced by the flow of electrons from cathode to plate when the terminal-pair voltages change rapidly. Just as for the diode, the displacement currents can be modeled by adding interelectrode capacitances to the static model. For the triode three of these capacitances are required, one for each terminal pair, as shown in Fig. B.8.

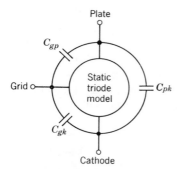

Figure B.8   Three interelectrode capacitances are required to model the displacement currents associated with changing internal charge distributions.

B.1.5   Multigrid Vacuum Tubes

The thermionic triode discussed in Section B.1.3 illustrates the fundamentals of all vacuum tube control valves: the flow of electrons between cathode and anode is controlled by the electrostatic potential on the intervening grid. As a circuit component, however, the triode has the disadvantage of direct capacitive coupling between grid and plate. This coupling is represented by the capacitance C_{gp} in the model of Fig. B.8. This capacitance severely limits the high-frequency or high-speed response of vacuum tube amplifiers by coupling currents proportional to the plate voltage back into the grid circuit.[5]

---

[5] This problem is discussed in terms of transistors in Section 14.5.

To reduce the capacitive coupling between plate and grid, other electrodes, which take the form of additional grids, are inserted into the structure. A structure that contains two grids (and thus has four electrodes exclusive of the heater) is called a *tetrode*. The grid closest to the cathode is called the control grid; the second grid is the *screen grid*. A structure with three grids is a *pentode*. The third grid, which is located between the screen grid and the plate, is called the *suppressor grid*. The physical structures of these multigrid tubes are suggested by the circuit symbols, which are shown in Fig. B.9.

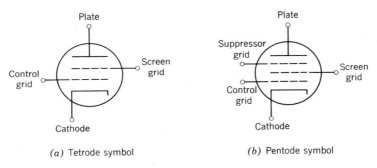

(a) Tetrode symbol   (b) Pentode symbol

Figure B.9   Circuit symbols for multigrid structures.

The screen grid in both tetrodes and pentodes is intended to serve as an electrostatic shield between plate and grid, thereby reducing the grid-to-plate capacitance. The screen is normally operated at a fixed potential that is positive with respect to the cathode. Although changes in plate voltage influence the charge on the screen, the same changes have little effect on the charge on the control grid. Consequently the plate-to-control-grid capacitance is much smaller than it would be in a triode of similar dimensions. Typical values of this capacitance lie in the range of 0.01 pf in tetrodes and pentodes compared with values in the range of a few picofarads in triodes.

Of course, the additional grids also influence the static characteristics of the tube. In both cases the plate current is relatively independent of the plate voltage. This lack of sensitivity of the plate current to the plate voltage results from the electrostatic shielding provided by the screen grid; while changes in the plate voltage influence the electric field between screen and plate, they do not affect the field near the cathode. Thus the space-charge distribution and the plate current do not vary appreciably with the plate voltage.

In effect, both the tetrode and pentode behave as if the cathode, control grid, and screen grid were a triode, a triode having a porous "plate." The electron flow through this "pseudotriode" is governed by the voltages on the control and screen grids, but is relatively independent of the voltage on the plate. Most of these electrons pass right through the screen, because of its open structure, and drift through the region between screen and plate. A small fraction of the electrons impact on the screen. Consequently, the plate current in a pentode or tetrode is somewhat less than the cathode current.

These multigrid tubes have plate characteristics that resemble the characteristics of the "ideal'" triode postulated in Section B.1.3 much more than do actual triodes. That is, the plate current is much less dependent on the plate-to-cathode voltage because the screen grid shields the space charge in the cathode-grid space from the plate.

The suppressor grid is necessary because each electron that impacts on the plate causes the secondary emission of several other electrons from the plate. If the plate is positive with respect to the screen grid, these secondary electrons will fall back into the plate, and the plate current will not reflect the secondary emission process that occurs at the plate (just as the static characteristics of a triode are not sensitive to the secondary emission that occurs there). If the plate is negative with respect to the screen, however, the secondary electrons will be attracted to the screen and will cause a sharp decrease in plate current.[6] The suppressor grid, which is operated at a fixed potential *lower than* the minimum plate potential, eliminates the effect of this secondary-electron emission by establishing a field in the space between the suppressor and plate that forces the secondary electrons back into the plate. Even though the suppressor slows down the primary electrons, it does not intercept many of them because of its open nature; most of the primary electrons pass right through the suppressor grid, beyond which they are accelerated into the plate.

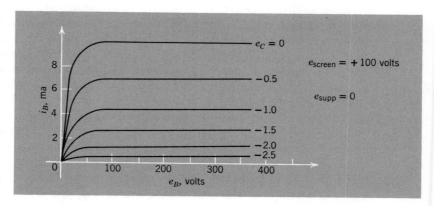

Figure B.10   Pentode static plate characteristics. All voltages are specified with respect to the cathode.

---

[6] Notice that the number of primary electrons that arrive from the cathode is not sensitive to the exact value of the plate voltage, even when the plate is less positive than the screen. Although these primary electrons will decelerate between screen and plate, they will arrive at the plate as long as the plate voltage is not too small (see Fig. B.10).

The general form of the static plate characteristics of a pentode is illustrated in Fig. B.10. These curves emphasize the fact that the plate current is essentially independent of the plate voltage as long as the plate voltage is sufficiently positive to collect all of the electrons in the flow developed by the pseudotriode comprised of the cathode, control grid, and screen grid.

B.2.   Circuit Models for Vacuum Tubes

The algebraic models developed in Section B.1 and the measured characteristic curves of vacuum devices provide adequate models of the behavior of these devices and can be used as the basis for understanding the performance of circuits that employ vacuum tubes. Nevertheless, it is often desirable to have alternative models for these control valves—models that are not graphical in nature. Since we would like to employ in the analysis of circuits using these devices the skills and intuition that are developed in the study of linear networks, we seek circuit models that are themselves networks comprised of idealized circuit elements. Thus we now consider the development of various piecewise-linear and linear incremental models for elementary vacuum tubes.

B.2.1   Piecewise-Linear Diode Models

A typical diode current-voltage characteristic curve is shown in Fig. B.11a. This behavior can be modeled by a piecewise-linear network having only one ideal piecewise-linear diode, as shown in Fig. B.11b. The model has the

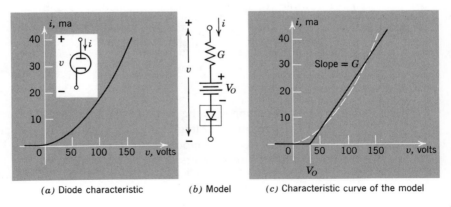

(a) Diode characteristic   (b) Model   (c) Characteristic curve of the model

Figure B.11   A diode can be modeled by a piecewise-linear network.

same form as that introduced in Section 6.1 as a characterization of a semiconductor junction diode. The characteristic curve of this model is shown as the solid line in Fig. B.11c. The parameter values for which the curve is drawn are

$$V_O = 30 \text{ volts}$$

$$G = 0.3 \text{ mmho}$$

These parameter values give a reasonable fit to the actual diode curve, which is dashed, for voltages in the range from negative values to about $+150$ volts. Of course, consideration of a more restricted range of voltages would require a different choice of parameter values in order to obtain a good fit.

The dependence of the parameters of the piecewise-linear model on the range of voltage over which the model must be used can be illustrated by considering the parameters of a piecewise-linear model that fits the current-voltage characteristics of an ideal vacuum diode. We consider an I–V characteristic of the form of Eq. B.11a:

$$i = Kv^{\frac{3}{2}} \tag{B.23}$$

and use the piecewise-linear model of Fig. B.11b. We arbitrarily assume that the characteristics of the ideal vacuum diode and the piecewise-linear model should be tangent at a current that we denote by I_T, as shown in Fig. B.12. The conductance G must be equal to the slope of the three-halves-power relationship at I_T. Thus from Eq. B.23

$$G = \tfrac{3}{2} Kv^{\frac{1}{2}}$$

$$= \frac{3I_T}{2V_T} \tag{B.24a}$$

The threshold voltage V_O is, from the geometry of Fig. B.12:

$$V_O = V_T - \frac{I_T}{G}$$

$$= \frac{V_T}{3} \tag{B.24b}$$

These equations emphasize the dependence of the model parameters on the choice of the current or voltage range over which the model is to apply. When the piecewise-linear model has the parameters given by Eqs. B.24, the model fits well for currents in the range near I_T and fits rather poorly for much smaller currents. If, however, we consider a current of $I_T/8$, which corresponds to a voltage of $V_T/4$, a much better fit can be obtained by reducing V_O by a factor of 4 and G by a factor of 2. The resulting model has the characteristic shown by the dashed line.

Of course, more accurate (and more complex) piecewise-linear models can be constructed by making use of more ideal piecewise-linear diodes. For example, a model that contains two piecewise-linear diodes produces a curve comprised of three line segments.

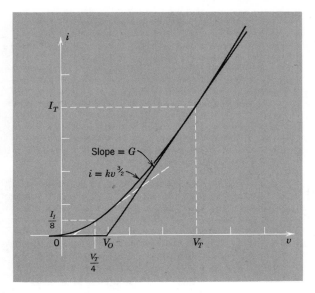

Figure B.12   The choice of model parameters depends on the range of current over which the model should apply.

B.2.2   Piecewise-Linear Triode Models

If we take the graphical characteristics of a triode (such as those shown in Fig. A.4) as a starting point, it is easy to derive networklike models that have similar behavior. For example, the plate current, plate-to-cathode voltage relationship that holds true for *zero* grid-to-cathode voltage can be approximated, at least in the first quadrant, by the current-voltage relationship of a resistance. A model that approximates, in the first quadrant, the i_B–e_B relationship for $e_C = 0$ is shown in Fig. B.13a.

We can devise a model that is valid for a fixed negative grid-to-cathode voltage if we recognize that the principal effect of a negative grid voltage is to shift the i_B–e_B relationship along the e_B axis, as shown in Fig. A.4. For example, the curve for $e_C = -1$ volt is similar in shape to the curve for $e_C = 0$, except that it is shifted to the right by a distance that corresponds to a change in e_B of about 100 volts. This shift can be accounted for in our model by adding a voltage source E_2 in the plate-cathode circuit, as shown in Fig. B.13b. The straight line in the i_B–e_B plane represents the relationship

$$e_B = E_2 + i_B R_P \tag{B.25a}$$

which is a statement of Kirchhoff's voltage law in the plate-cathode loop of the model. The physical fact of negligible grid current is represented by leaving the grid terminal disconnected within the model.

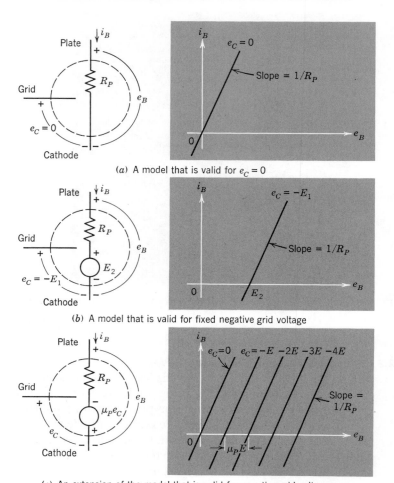

(a) A model that is valid for $e_C = 0$

(b) A model that is valid for fixed negative grid voltage

(c) An extension of the model that is valid for negative grid voltages

Figure B.13   Network models that approximate, in the first quadrant of the e_B–i_B plane, the static characteristics of a triode.

The model of Fig. B.13b can be extended to permit arbitrary negative values of grid-to-cathode voltage by making the value of the voltage source in the output loop dependent on the grid voltage so that, as e_C changes, the amount of the shift of the i_B–e_B relationship will change accordingly. Figure A.4 shows that the amount by which the i_B–e_B relationship is shifted is approximately proportional to the magnitude of the grid-to-cathode voltage. Hence the *dependent voltage source* in the output loop should be linearly dependent on e_C. Figure B.13c shows a model with a dependent voltage source. The constant of proportionality is denoted by μ_P. Thus the offset of the i_B–e_B line which corresponds to $e_C = -E_C$ is simply $\mu_P E_C$. The current-voltage relationship of this model is

$$e_B = -\mu_P e_C + i_B R_P \tag{B.25b}$$

This model is capable of representing the behavior of the triode for *all* negative values of e_C.

The principal defect of the model of Fig. B.13c is its failure to reflect the physical fact that the plate current can never be negative. This defect can be remedied by adding an ideal piecewise-linear diode in the plate-cathode circuit, as shown in Fig. B.14. The resulting model applies whenever the grid-to-cathode voltage is negative. In order to indicate the degree of approximation provided by this simple triode model, we show in Fig. B.15 the

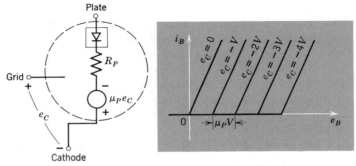

Figure B.14   A piecewise-linear model that is valid for negative grid voltages.

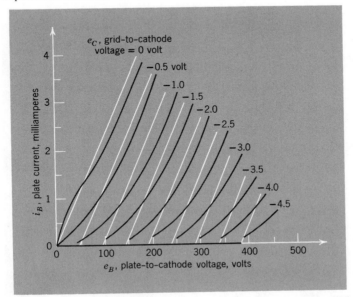

Figure B.15   Superposition of output characteristics of the network model of Fig. B.14 on a set of measured triode characteristics.

current-voltage characteristics of the network model superimposed on the measured triode characteristics of Fig. A.4. The values of the network model parameters used in this comparison are

$$R_P = 42 \text{ kohm}$$

$$\mu_P = 95$$

These values are not unique but are chosen to yield a reasonable overall fit; other choices would produce a better fit in limited regions of the characteristics.

The grid current is not negligible when the grid-to-cathode voltage is positive. The presence of grid current can be represented in our piecewise-linear model by adding a second ideal diode and a resistor (diode 2 and R_G in Fig. B.16a). The corresponding piecewise-linear grid characteristic is shown in Fig. B.16b. In order to make our model adequate for positive grid operation it is necessary to add a third diode (3 in Fig. B.16a), which prevents the plate voltage from becoming negative when the plate current is positive and the grid voltage is positive. Without the third diode the plate characteristics would follow the dotted line shown in Fig. B.16a for operation with $e_C = +V$. The piecewise-linear triode model shown in Fig. B.16 is adequate for most purposes. The parameters μ_P, R_P, and R_G must be chosen to yield a reasonable fit over the range of terminal variables that will be encountered in the application.

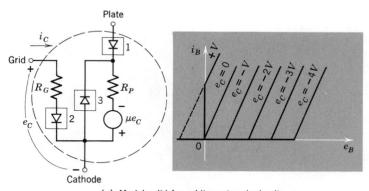

(a) Model valid for arbitrary terminal voltages

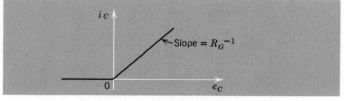

(b) Grid characteristics for the model of (a)

Figure B.16   A piecewise-linear triode model that applies for both polarities of grid voltage.

B.2.3   Incremental Triode Models

Incremental models for triode vacuum tubes can be obtained by the same process of linearization of the total-signal characteristics about an operating point that has been illustrated in Chapters 1 and 11. We shall start with a *static* characterization of the triode and extend the linear incremental model to include dynamic effects by adding interelectrode capacitances at the terminals. The *I–V* characteristics of a triode that operates with *negative* grid-to-cathode voltage can be represented, in general functional terms, as follows:

$$i_B = i_B(e_B, e_C) \qquad (B.26a)$$

$$i_C \simeq 0 \qquad (B.26b)$$

The variables that appear in these relationships are defined in Fig. A.6*b*. If we now regard each of these variables as the sum of a quiescent or dc variable (I_B, E_B, etc.) and an incremental or signal variable (i_b, e_b, etc.), expansion of the total-signal relationship in Taylor's series, exactly as in Section A.4.1, yields a set of linear relationships among the incremental variables[7]

$$i_b = g_p e_b + g_m e_c \qquad (B.27a)$$

$$i_c \simeq 0 \qquad (B.27b)$$

The coefficient g_p represents the *incremental output* or *plate conductance*

$$g_p = \left. \frac{\partial i_B}{\partial e_B} \right|_Q \qquad (B.28a)$$

while g_m represents the *incremental transconductance*

$$g_m = \left. \frac{\partial i_B}{\partial e_C} \right|_Q \qquad (B.28b)$$

A circuit model that represents the incremental behavior described by Eqs. B.27 is shown in Fig. B.17*a*. A dependent current generator represents the control action of the triode.

The model of Fig. B.17*a* can be transformed, by use of Thévenin's theorem, to the equivalent model shown in Fig. B.17*b*. The resistance r_p, which is

---

[7] The convention that we use in this book concerning identification of the nature of a variable by capitalizing or lowercasing the letters that indicate the variable and the subscript was adopted when semiconductor devices were first employed in active circuits. This notation is partially in conflict with that adopted several decades earlier for use with vacuum tubes. In the earlier notation incremental quantities at the plate are identified by the subscript p (while total quantities there carry the subscript B) and incremental quantities at the grid are identified by the subscript g (while total quantities there carry the subscript C). In this older notation, which we do *not* use, but which is employed in some other texts, Eq. B.27a would be written $i_p = g_p e_p + g_m e_g$.

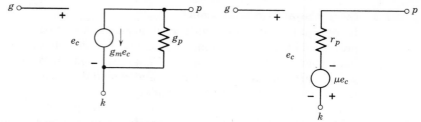

(*a*) Model with $g_m e_c$ generator   (*b*) Transformed model with μe_c generator

Figure B.17   Low-speed incremental models for triodes.

known as the *incremental plate resistance*, is given by

$$r_p = \frac{1}{g_p} = \left.\frac{\partial e_B}{\partial i_B}\right|_Q \tag{B.28c}$$

The coefficient μ, which is dimensionless, is called the *incremental amplification factor*. In order for the two networks of Fig. B.17 to be equivalent, μ must have the value

$$\mu = g_m r_p \tag{B.29a}$$

or, in terms of the partial derivatives,

$$\mu = \frac{\partial i_B / \partial e_C|_Q}{\partial i_B / \partial e_B|_Q}$$

$$= -\left.\frac{\partial e_B}{\partial e_C}\right|_Q \tag{B.29b}$$

These incremental coefficients can be evaluated either by making use of their relationships to the slopes and spacings of the static characteristic curves or by direct differentiation of an algebraic total signal model, such as that provided by Eq. B.22. The latter procedure yields:

$$g_p = \frac{1}{r_p} = \frac{3}{2}\frac{K_G}{\mu_A}\left(e_C + \frac{e_B}{\mu_A}\right)^{1/2}$$

$$= \frac{3}{2\mu_A} K_G{}^{2/3} i_B{}^{1/3} \tag{B.30a}$$

$$g_m = \frac{3}{2} K_G\left(e_C + \frac{e_B}{\mu_A}\right)^{1/2}$$

$$= \frac{3}{2} K_G{}^{2/3} i_B{}^{1/3} \tag{B.30b}$$

Consequently, the incremental amplification factor is, from Eq. B.29a,

$$\mu = g_m r_p = \frac{g_m}{g_p}$$

$$= \mu_A \qquad \qquad (B.30c)$$

Note that the amplification factor is independent of the operating point, since μ_A is a fixed coefficient that depends on the geometrical arrangement of the grid and plate. On the other hand, both the incremental transconductance and the incremental plate resistance depend on the choice of operating point, specifically on i_B. As the quiescent plate current increases, g_m increases (as $i_B^{1/3}$) while r_p decreases (it varies as $i_B^{-1/3}$).

The incremental consequences of displacement currents can be accounted for by adding interelectrode capacitances, as shown in Fig. B.18. Of course, these two models are equivalent descriptions of the triode.

The models of Fig. B.18 can be extended to be applicable for operation with positive grid-to-cathode voltage by adding a resistance in parallel with C_{gk}. This resistance, which is usually in the range of a few thousand ohms, accounts for the dependence of the incremental grid current on the incremental grid voltage.

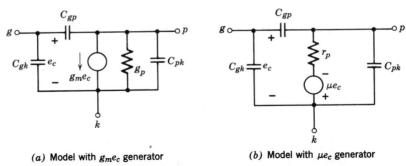

(a) Model with $g_m e_c$ generator   (b) Model with μe_c generator

Figure B.18 Incremental triode models that account for displacement currents.

B.2.4 Circuit Models for Pentodes

The pentode is normally operated with the screen and suppressor grid voltages fixed. Since there are only two electrodes on which signal voltages can appear, the pentode has the same form of incremental model as the triode. More precisely, either of the incremental models of Fig. B.18 is applicable. The model of Fig. B.18a, which contains a current source, is generally preferred because the incremental behavior of the device is essentially that of a controlled current source. In other words, the incremental plate resistance r_p is very large—often more than a megohm. The incremental transconductance g_m usually lies in the range from a few hundred to a few thousand micromhos.

Of course, the incremental model of a pentode differs significantly from that of a triode in that the grid-to-plate capacitance is one to two orders of magnitude smaller. This reduction was the motivation for insertion of the screen grid into the structure.

Piecewise-linear models that employ ideal diodes can be devised to represent the static characteristics of pentodes. The utility of these models is limited by the fact that pentode curves are frequently not uniformly spaced (Fig. B.10). Consequently, a linearly-dependent generator may not suffice to characterize the dependence of plate current on grid voltage.

REFERENCES

B.1   H. J. Zimmermann and S. J. Mason, *Electronic Circuit Theory*, Wiley, New York, 1959.

B.2   T. S. Gray, *Applied Electronics*, M.I.T. Press, Cambridge, Mass., 1954.

PROBLEMS

P.B.1   This problem is concerned with the analytical development of the three-halves power law for the space-charge-limited thermionic diode.

(a) Verify Eq. B.7.

(b) Show that this equation can be integrated once to yield

$$\left(\frac{d\psi}{dx}\right)^2 = -\frac{4J}{\epsilon_0}\sqrt{\frac{m}{2q}}\,\psi^{1/2} \tag{B.31}$$

Suggestion. Multiply both sides of Eq. B.7 by $d\psi/dx$ and recognize that

$$\frac{d\psi}{dx}\left(\frac{d^2\psi}{dx^2}\right) = \frac{1}{2}\frac{d}{dx}\left(\frac{d\psi}{dx}\right)^2$$

(c) Solve Eq. B.31 for $d\psi/dx$ and integrate to obtain $\psi(x)$. Show that Eq. B.9 follows from your result.

(d) Verify Eq. B.10.

P.B.2   Evaluate the transit time in a plane-parallel diode in which the flow is emission-limited and the charge in transit has no appreciable effect on the potential distribution. Compare your result with Eq. B.15, which is valid for space-charge-limited flow.

P.B.3   This problem is concerned with the specification of circuit models for a vacuum diode. Consider the diode characteristics shown in Fig. B.19a. Assume that the models are to be used with diode voltages in the range $-50 < v < 150$ volts.

(a) If this diode is modeled by the circuit of Fig. B.19b, what values of conductance G and voltage V_O should be used?

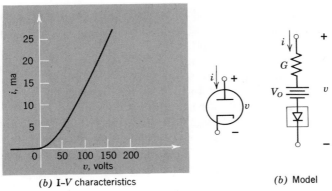

(b) I-V characteristics   (b) Model

Figure B.19 Diode characteristics and a piecewise-linear model.

(b) Do your answers to (a) depend significantly on the range of current or voltage over which the model is to be used? Specifically, how would the parameter values change if the models were to be used with voltages in the range $-50 < v < 50$ volts?

P.B.4 It is desired to fit a three-halves power law to the diode characteristics plotted in Fig. B.19a.

(a) On what set of coordinates will the three-halves-power law plot as a straight line?

(b) Replot the data of Fig. B.19a on the coordinates specified in (a) and determine the perveance of the diode.

Answer. $K \simeq 0.013$ ma/(volt)$^{3/2}$

P.B.5 Devise a piecewise-linear model for a pentode that represents the characteristics shown in Fig. B.10. Consider only negative values of grid-to-cathode voltage.

P.B.6 The incremental triode parameters defined in Eqs. B.28 are related to the slopes and spacings of the triode plate characteristics at the operating point.

(a) Illustrate, with labeled sketches, the relationships between g_m, μ, and r_p and the slope and spacings of the curves of constant e_C in the i_B-e_B plane.

(b) Evaluate g_m, μ, and r_p for the triode whose characteristics are shown in Fig. A.4 at each of the following operating points:

(1) $e_C = -1$ volt, $e_B = 200$ volts
(2) $e_C = -3$ volt, $e_B = 300$ volts

Answers. (b)(1) $\mu = 90$; $g_m = 2 \times 10^{-3}$ mho; $r_p = 45$ kohm; (b)(2) $\mu = 100$; $g_m = 1.1 \times 10^{-3}$ mho, $r_p = 91$ kohm.

P.B7 Evaluate the transconductance g_m and the plate resistance r_p of the pentode whose characteristics are shown in Fig. B.10 at an operating point of $e_B = 200$ volts, $e_C = -1$ volt.

P.B.8   This problem is based on the self-biased amplifier shown in Fig. B.20. Assume that the triode can be represented by a piecewise-linear model with $\mu_P = 30$, $R_P = 10$ kohm, and restrict operation to *negative* grid voltages. In both (*a*) and (*b*) assume that C_1 is large enough so that the voltage across it does not change appreciably when signals are applied.

(*a*) Assume that $C_B = 0$, and evaluate the transfer characteristics relating v_O and v_I. Sketch and dimension your results.

(*b*) Assume that C_B is large enough so that when signals are present the cathode-to-ground voltage does not change significantly from its quiescent value, and evaluate the transfer characteristic. Sketch and dimension your result on the same coordinates used in (*a*).

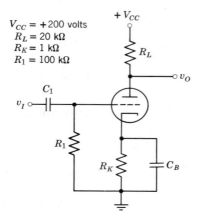

$V_{CC} = +200$ volts
$R_L = 20$ kΩ
$R_K = 1$ kΩ
$R_1 = 100$ kΩ

Figure B.20   A self-biased triode amplifier.

The slope of the transfer characteristic in the active gain region is less with an unbypassed cathode resistor because of degeneration introduced by R_K. More precisely, the signal component of the plate current develops a signal voltage across R_K which *opposes* the grid-to-ground voltage, thereby reducing the grid-to-cathode voltage. This degenerative mechanism can be used to make the slope of the transfer characteristic less sensitive to variations in the parameters of the active device.

P.B.9   The triode circuit shown in Fig. B.21 is a common-plate amplifier or *cathode follower*.

(*a*) What is the maximum value of v_I for which the triode operates in the negative-grid region? Use the triode characteristics of Fig. A.4 and assume $E = 250$ volts, $R_K = 20$ kohm.

(*b*) Use the piecewise-linear model of Fig. B.14 to determine the transfer characteristic relating v_O to v_I. Express your results in terms of E, R_P, R_K, and μ_P. Sketch and dimension your results on the rectangular coordinates v_I/E and v_O/E.

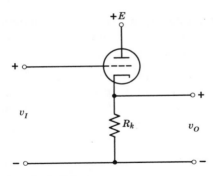

Figure B.21 A cathode follower.

P.B.10 The amplifier of Fig. B.22 is driven from a signal source whose Thévenin equivalent source voltage is v_S and whose internal resistance is $R'_G = 5$ kohm. Use the piecewise-linear model of Fig. B.14 (with $R_G = 2$ kohm, $R_P = 7.5$ kohm, $\mu_P = 20$) to determine the transfer characteristic relating v_O to the *source* voltage v_S. Sketch and dimension your results. *Suggestion.* Find the coordinates of the *three* breakpoints.

P.B.11 Use an incremental model to determine the incremental voltage gain of the amplifier shown in Fig. B.20. Assume that the coupling capacitor develops negligible signal voltage, and neglect the currents in the interelectrode capacitances. Consider two cases:

(1) The bypass capacitor C_B is large enough so that negligible signal voltage appears across it.

(2) $C_B = 0$, that is, the cathode resistor is unbypassed.

Express $A_v = v_o/v_i$ first in terms of the literal parameters of the circuit and triode. Then substitute the numerical values (assume $\mu = 30$, $r_p = 10$ kohm).

Answers. (1) $A_v \simeq -20$; (2) $A_v \simeq -10$.

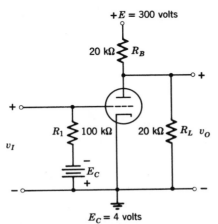

Figure B.22 A common-cathode amplifier.

P.B.12   Find the *incremental* voltage gain of the cathode-follower introduced in Problem P.B.9. Assume that the *quiescent* value of v_I is such that the triode operates in the negative grid region.

P.B.13   Use incremental models to evaluate, for the amplifier of Fig. B.22, the effect of noise in the plate power supply. Specifically, find the incremental output voltage v_o which appears in response to an ac component of the plate supply voltage E of value v_n. Then express v_o in terms of both v_n and the incremental input voltage v_i.

APPENDIX C

Fortran IV Program for Finding the Natural Frequencies of an RC Network

C.1 Instructions for Using the Program

1. Write the node equations for the network, putting the conductance in mmhos and the capacitance in pf. (Other sets of units can be used, but the user must then scale the computer solutions by an appropriate factor.)

2. Arrange the node equations in matrix form so that the first row of equations contains the input voltage on the left side. Have the last column in the matrix correspond to the node describing the output voltage. The right side of the node equations should now be a matrix containing N equations in N node voltages.

3. Punch this matrix on three sets of cards, with the first set consisting of one card containing the number of node equations and the conductance associated with the input voltage. The number of equations is punched as a two-digit number in columns 1 and 2, and the source conductance is punched in columns 11 through 20. The second set of cards consists of the real part of the node equations. These conductances are punched one row (equation) at a time, six values to a card, using as many cards as necessary to complete the row. Ten columns are allowed for each value, and each value should be punched completely within its assigned ten columns. If a value is zero, its corresponding ten columns may be left blank. Decimal points should always be included, even for integer values.

   After a row is completely entered on the cards, a new card should be fed and the next row punched in the same manner. After all the conductances are entered, go back to the first row and begin punching all the capacitance values in the same manner. This completes the third part of the data deck for that network.

   If more than one network is to be solved, punch the data deck for each additional network as described above, and place these decks behind the deck for the first network.

4. Place the data decks behind the source or object deck, and write the appropriate job control cards.

C.2 The Program

FORTRAN IV G LEVEL 0, MOD 0   MAIN   DATE = 68142   04/31/41

```
              C MAIN PROGRAM FOR FINDING THE NATURAL FREQUENCIES OF A NETWORK   100X100
0001            DIMENSION A(100,100),A1(100,100),S(100,100),S1(100,100),FR(100),
                1FI(100)
0002          3 CALL READ (A,A1,S,S1,N,G)
0003            WRITE (6,110)
0004            M=1
0005            N1=N-1
0006            IF (G.EQ.0) GO TO 6
0007            CALL GAIN (A,M,N,PROD)
0008         35 IF (M)  6,1,6
0009          6 CALL REDUCE (A,S,M,N)
0010            WRITE (6,111)
0011            IF (M)  2,1,2
0012          1 WRITE (6,100)
0013            GO TO 3
0014          2 CALL EIG5 (A,N,N,FR,FI,2.E35,0,0)
0015            WRITE (6,101)
0016            WRITE (6,106)
0017            DO 40  J=1,N
0018         40 WRITE (6,102) J,FR(J),J,FI(J)
              C CHECK IF THERE ARE RHP POLES
0019            DO 4  JB=1,N
0020            IF (FR(JB))  4,15,15
0021         15 G=0
0022            GO TO 11
0023          4 CONTINUE
0024            SUM=0
0025            SUM2=0
0026            CXSUM=0
0027            CXSUM2=0
              C CALCULATE THE SUM OF THE RECIPROCALS OF THE POLES
0028            DO 50  J=1,N
0029            IF (FI(J).NE.0) GO TO 51
0030            SUM=SUM-1/FR(J)
0031            GO TO 50
0032         51 VALUE=-FR(J)/(FR(J)**2+FI(J)**2)
0033            CXSUM=CXSUM+VALUE
0034         50 CONTINUE
0035            SUM=SUM+CXSUM
0036            WRITE (6,103) SUM
              C DETERMINE COMPLEXITY OF ROOTS
0037            DO 70  JJ=1,N
0038            L=N+1-JJ
0039            IF (ABS(FI(L)).GT..4*ABS(FR(L))) GO TO 71
0040            IF (ABS(FI(L)).GT..1*ABS(FR(L))) GO TO 72
0041         70 CONTINUE
              C ROOTS ARE EITHER REAL OR VERY SLIGHTLY COMPLEX - CALCULATE BANDWIDTH
0042            DO 5  J=1,N
0043            IF (FI(J))  7,21,7
0044         21 SUM2=SUM2+1./FR(J)**2
0045            GO TO 5
0046          7 VALUE2=(FR(J)**2-FI(J)**2)/((FR(J)**2+FI(J)**2)**2)
0047            CXSUM2=CXSUM2+VALUE2
0048          5 CONTINUE
0049            SUM2=SUM2+CXSUM2
0050            SUM2=1./SUM2
0051         75 W=SQRT (SUM2)
0052            F=1000.*W/6.2831853
0053            WRITE (6,104) F
0054            GO TO 10
0055         71 WRITE (6,107)
0056            GO TO 10
0057         72 DO 73  K=L,N
0058            IF (FR(L).LT.FR(K)) GO TO 23
0059         73 CONTINUE
              C COMPLEX PAIR ARE THE LOWEST ROOTS
              C CALCULATE BUTTERWORTH BANDWIDTH OF THIS PAIR
0060            SUM2=FR(L)**2+FI(L)**2
0061            GO TO 75
0062         23 WRITE (6,105)
              C CALCULATE ZEROS
0063         10 IF (G.EQ.0) GO TO 11
0064            CALL GAIN (A1,M,N1,PROD1)
0065            IF (M.EQ.0) G=0
0066         11 CALL REDUCE (A1,S1,M,N1)
0067            IF (M)  8,9,8
```

FORTRAN IV G LEVEL C, MOD C   MAIN   DATE = 68142   04/31/41

```
0068              9 WRITE (6,200)
0069                GO TO 3
0070              8 CALL EIG5 (A1,N1,N1,FR,FI,2.E35,0,0)
0071                IF (G)  48,49,48
      C CALCULATE VOLTAGE GAIN
0072             48 VGAIN=ABS(G*PROD1/PROD)
0073                WRITE (6,300) VGAIN
0074             49 WRITE (6,201)
0075                WRITE (6,106)
0076                DO 30  J=1,N1
0077             30 WRITE (6,102) J,FR(J),J,FI(J)
0078                GO TO 3
0079            100 FORMAT(48H0 MATRIX IS DEGENERATE -- CHECK INPUT PARAMETERS)
0080            102 FORMAT(1H0,10X,3HFR(,I2,2H)=,E15.7,10X,3HFI(,I2,2H)=,E15.7)
0081            110 FORMAT(23H1READ ROUTINE COMPLETED)
0082            111 FORMAT (25HCREDUCE ROUTINE COMPLETED)
0083            101 FORMAT (27HC THE POLES ARE - IN 1/NSEC)
0084            103 FORMAT (43HCTHE SUM OF THE RECIPROCALS OF THE POLES IS,F12.4,5H NS
                  1EC)
0085            104 FORMAT ('CTHE BANDWIDTH IS APPROXIMATELY',F12.4,' MEGAHERTZ')
0086            105 FORMAT (84HCYOUR COMPLEX POLES DOMINATE THE FREQUENCY RESPONSE - B
                  1ANDWIDTH CANNOT BE CALCULATED)
0087            106 FORMAT (1H0,19X,4HREAL,25X,9H1MAGINARY)
0088            107 FORMAT ('CYOUR COMPLEX POLES INDICATE THAT YOUR NETWORK HAS A Q GR
                  1EATER THAN 2 - BANDWIDTH CANNOT BE CALCULATED')
0089            200 FORMAT (51HC SUBMATRIX IS DEGENERATE -- CHECK INPJT PARAMETERS)
0090            201 FORMAT (26HCTHE ZEROS ARE - IN 1/NSEC)
0091            300 FORMAT (2CHCTHE VOLTAGE GAIN IS,F10.2)
0092                END
```

FORTRAN IV G LEVEL 0, MOD 0   READ   DATE = 68142   04/31/41

```
0001                SUBROUTINE READ (A,A1,S,S1,N,G)
      C DATA INPUT SUBROUTINE FOR A COMPLEX DETERMINANT UP TO 100X100
0002                DIMENSION A(100,100),S(100,100),A1(100,100),S1(100,100)
0003              3 READ (5,1100,END=100) N,G
0004                DO 8  I=1,N
0005              8 READ (5,1101) (A(I,J),J=1,N)
0006                DO 9  I=1,N
0007              9 READ (5,1101) (S(I,J),J=1,N)
0008                N1=N-1
0009                DO 12  J=1,N1
0010                DO 12  I=1,N1
0011                A1(I,J)=A(I+1,J)
0012             12 S1(I,J)=S(I+1,J)
0013                WRITE (6,1102)
0014                I1=1
0015                J1=1
0016                K=(N-1)/6
0017                IF (K) 10,10,11
0018             11 DO 70  L2=1,K
0019                J2=J1+5
0020                DO 69  L1=1,K
0021                I2=I1+5
0022                CALL PRINT (I1,I2,J1,J2,A,S)
0023             69 I1=I1+6
0024                I1=1
0025             70 J1=J1+6
0026                J2=N
0027                DO 71  L3=1,K
0028                I2=I1+5
0029                CALL PRINT (I1,I2,J1,J2,A,S)
0030             71 I1=I1+6
0031                I2=N
0032                CALL PRINT (I1,I2,J1,J2,A,S)
0033                J1=1
0034                DO 72  L4=1,K
0035                J2=J1+5
0036                CALL PRINT (I1,I2,J1,J2,A,S)
0037             72 J1=J1+6
0038                GO TO 80
0039             10 I2=N
0040                J2=N
0041                CALL PRINT (I1,I2,J1,J2,A,S)
0042             80 CONTINUE
0043                RETURN
0044            100 STOP
0045           1100 FORMAT (I2,8X,F10.4)
0046           1101 FORMAT (6F1C.4)
0047           1102 FORMAT (16H1INPUT MATRIX IS)
0048                END
```

```
0001            SUBROUTINE PRINT(I1,I2,J1,J2,A,S)
          C MATRIX PRINTOUT
0002            DIMENSION A(100,100),S(100,100)
0003            WRITE (6,1103) I1,I2,J1,J2
0004            DO 73 I=I1,I2
0005            WRITE (6,1104) (A(I,J),J=J1,J2)
0006         73 WRITE (6,1105) (S(I,J),J=J1,J2)
0007            RETURN
0008       1103 FORMAT(1H1,5CX,5HROWS ,I2,4H TO ,I2,1JH, COLUMNS ,I2,4H TO ,I2)
0009       1104 FORMAT(///////2X,6(F11.4,10X))
0010       1105 FORMAT(1H0,6(1H+,F11.4,1HS,8X))
0011            END
```

```
0001            SUBROUTINE GAIN (SS,M,N,PROD)
          C SUBROUTINE FOR TAKING THE DETERMINANT OF THE MATRIX S
0002            DIMENSION S(100,100),SS(100,100)
0003            DO 10  I=1,N
0004            DO 10  J=1,N
0005         10 S(I,J)=SS(I,J)
0006         25 DO 1  I=1,N
0007            IF (S(I,I)) 2,90,2
0008          2 DO 1  J=1,N
0009            IF (J-I) 3,1,3
0010          3 IF (S(I,J)) 4,1,4
0011          4 C=-S(I,J)/S(I,I)
0012            DO 8  K=1,N
0013            S(K,J)=C*S(K,I)+S(K,J)
0014          8 CONTINUE
0015          1 CONTINUE
0016            PROD=1
0017            DO 30  I=1,N
0018         30 PROD=PROD*S(I,I)
0019            M=1
0020            RETURN
          C SEE IF MATRIX IS DEGENERATE - SET M=0 AND RETURN IF IT IS
0021         90 M=0
0022            DO 21  J=I,N
0023            IF (S(I,J)) 91,21,91
0024         91 DO 20  K=1,N
0025            SK=S(K,I)
0026            S(K,I)=S(K,J)
0027         20 S(K,J)=SK
0028            J=N
0029            M=1
0030         21 CONTINUE
0031            IF (M)  25,31,25
0032         31 RETURN
0033            END
```

```
0001                   SUBROUTINE REDUCE(A,S,M,N)
             C SUBROUTINE FOR REDUCING THE NATURAL FREQUENCY PROBLEM  100X100
             C INTO A MATRIX EIGENVALUE PROBLEM
0002                   DIMENSION A(100,100),S(100,100)
0003              25 DO 1  I=1,N
0004                 IF (S(I,I)) 2,90,2
0005               2 DO 1  J=1,N
0006                 IF (J-I) 3,1,3
0007               3 IF (S(I,J)) 4,1,4
0008               4 C=-S(I,J)/S(I,I)
0009                 DO 8  K=1,N
0010                 A(K,J)=C*A(K,I)+A(K,J)
0011                 S(K,J)=C*S(K,I)+S(K,J)
0012               8 CONTINUE
0013               1 CONTINUE
             C NORMALIZE
0014              15 DO 10  J=1,N
0015                 C=-1./S(J,J)
0016                 DO 10  I=1,N
0017                 A(I,J)=C*A(I,J)
0018              10 S(I,J)=C*S(I,J)
0019                 M=1
0020                 RETURN
             C SEE IF MATRIX IS DEGENERATE - SET M=0 AND RETURN IF IT IS
0021              90 M=0
0022                 DO 21  J=I,N
0023                 IF (S(I,J)) 91,21,91
0024              91 DO 20  K=1,N
0025                 SK=S(K,I)
0026                 AK=A(K,I)
0027                 S(K,I)=S(K,J)
0028                 A(K,I)=A(K,J)
0029                 S(K,J)=SK
0030              20 A(K,J)=AK
0031                 J=N
0032                 M=1
0033              21 CONTINUE
0034                 IF (M)  25,30,25
0035              30 IF (I.LT.1) GO TO 69
             C CHECK FOR AN S TERM IN COLUMN I
0036              70 DO 71  J=I,N
0037                 IF (S(J,I))  72,71,72
0038              72 DO 73  K=1,N
0039                 AK=A(I,K)
0040                 SK=S(I,K)
0041                 A(I,K)=A(J,K)
0042                 S(I,K)=S(J,K)
0043                 A(J,K)=AK
0044              73 S(J,K)=SK
0045                 GO TO 25
0046              71 CONTINUE
             C PLACE ZERO ROWS + COLUMNS AT END OF MATRIX
0047                 J=N+1
0048                 DO 77  LL=I,N
0049                 J=J-1
0050                 IF (S(J,J).EQ.0) GO TO 74
0051              75 DO 76  K=1,N
0052                 AK=A(I,K)
0053                 SK=S(I,K)
0054                 A(I,K)=A(J,K)
0055                 S(I,K)=S(J,K)
0056                 A(J,K)=AK
0057              76 S(J,K)=SK
0058                 DO 78  K=1,N
0059                 AK=A(K,I)
0060                 SK=S(K,I)
0061                 A(K,I)=A(K,J)
0062                 S(K,I)=S(K,J)
0063                 A(K,J)=AK
0064              78 S(K,J)=SK
0065                 GO TO 25
             C CHECK FOR S TERMS IN COLUMN J.  IF ONE IS FOUND, PUT ON DIAGONAL
0066              74 DO 77  L=I,N
0067                 IF (S(L,J).EQ.0) GO TO 77
0068                 DO 79  K=1,N
0069                 AK=A(J,K)
0070                 SK=S(J,K)
0071                 A(J,K)=A(L,K)
```

FORTRAN IV G LEVEL 0, MOD C   REDUCE   DATE = 68142   04/31/41

```
0072                S(J,K)=S(L,K)
0073                A(L,K)=AK
0074             79 S(L,K)=SK
0075                GO TO 75
0076             77 CONTINUE
0077                II=I
          C SET NON-DIAGONAL S TERMS PAST ROW II TO ZERO
0078                DO 31  I=II,N
0079                DO 32  J=1,N
0080                IF (I-J) 31,31,34
0081             34 IF (S(I,J))  37,32,37
0082             37 C=-S(I,J)/S(J,J)
0083                DO 35  K=1,N
0084                S(I,K)=C*S(J,K)+S(I,K)
0085             35 A(I,K)=C*A(J,K)+A(I,K)
0086             32 CONTINUE
0087             31 CONTINUE
          C SET NON-DIAGONAL A TERMS OUTSIDE THE (II-1)X(II-1) MATRIX TO ZERO
0088                DO 39  I=II,N
0089                IF (A(I,I).EQ.0) GO TO 80
0090             39 CONTINUE
0091                DO 38  I=II,N
0092                DO 38  J=1,N
0093                IF (J-I)  40,38,40
0094             40 IF (A(I,J))  41,38,41
0095             41 C=-A(I,J)/A(I,I)
0096                DO 42  K=1,N
0097             42 A(K,J)=C*A(K,I)+A(K,J)
0098             38 CONTINUE
0099                IM1=II-1
0100                DO 43  J=II,N
0101                DO 43  I=1,IM1
0102                IF (A(I,J))  44,43,44
0103             44 C=-A(I,J)/A(J,J)
0104                DO 45  K=1,N
0105             45 A(I,K)=C*A(J,K)+A(I,K)
0106             43 CONTINUE
0107                N=II-1
0108                GO TO 15
0109             80 DO 81  J=I,N
0110                IF (A(I,J).EQ.0) GO TO 81
0111                DO 82  K=1,N
0112                AK=A(K,I)
0113                A(K,I)=A(K,J)
0114             82 A(K,J)=AK
0115                GO TO 39
0116             81 CONTINUE
0117             69 M=0
0118                RETURN
0119                END
```

```
0001              SUBROUTINE EIG5(A,M,N,RR,RI,STARTR,STARTI,PRINT)
           C THE NXN REAL MATRIX A IS REDUCED TO HESSENBERG FORM BY HESS. M EIGEN-
           C VALUES RR(J)&I*RI(J) ARE FOUND BY LAGUERRE'S METHOD USING THE HESSEN-
           C BERG FORM TO EVALUATE THE CHARACTERISTIC POLYNOMIAL AND DERIVATIVES.
           C IF PRINT=0. THERE WILL BE NO PRINT OUT.
           C SEE LAG FOR THE MEANING OF STARTR AND STARTI.
0002              DIMENSION A(100,100),RR(100),RI(100),GAMMA(100)
0003              CALL TRACE(A,N,PRINT)
0004              CALL HESS(A,N,SIZE,PRINT)
0005              CALL TRACE(A,N,PRINT)
0006              DO 10 I=2,N
0007          10 GAMMA(I-1)=A(I-1,I)
0008              GAMMA(N)=C.
           C IS MATRIX REDUCED. DISPENSE WITH LAG FOR 1X1 AND 2X2 MATRICES.
0009              NU=0
0010              NV=0
0011          15 IF(NV-N)20,75,75
0012          20 NV=NV+1
0013              NU=NV
0014          25 IF(GAMMA(NV)) 30,35,30
0015          30 NV=NV+1
0016              GO TO 25
0017          35 IF(NV-NU-1)60,46,40
0018          40 MM= MINO (NV,M)
0019              GAMMA(NV)=-1.0
           C     FIND THE TRACES OF THE SUBMATRIX AND ITS SQUARE
0020              NU1=NU+1
0021          41 SPUR1=A(NU,NU)
0022              SPUR2=SPUR1**2
0023              DO 42 J=NU1,NV
0024              T=A(J,J)
0025              SPUR1=SPUR1+T
0026          42 SPUR2=SPUR2+T**2+2.*A(J-1,J)*A(J,J-1)
0027          45 CALL LAG(A,GAMMA,RR,RI,NU,NV,MM,STARTR,STARTI,SPUR1,SPUR2,PRINT,
                 1SIZE)
0028              GO TO 15
0029          46 S=.5*(A(NU,NU)+A(NV,NV))
0030              DIS=(.5*(A(NU,NU)-A(NV,NV)))**2+A(NU,NV)*A(NV,NU)
0031              T=SQRT (ABS (DIS))
0032              IF(DIS)50,55,55
0033          50 RR(NU)=S
0034              RI(NU)=T
0035              RR(NV)=S
0036              RI(NV)=-T
0037              GO TO 65
0038          55 RR(NU)=S+SIGN (T,S)
0039              RI(NU)=0.
0040              RR(NV)=(S**2-DIS)/RR(NU)
0041              RI(NV)=0.
0042              GO TO 65
0043          60 RR(NU)=A(NU,NU)
0044              RI(NU)=0.
0045          65 IF(PRINT)70,15,70
0046          70 WRITE             (6,1)(RR(J),RI(J),J=NU,NV)
0047              GO TO 15
0048          75 S=0.
0049              DO 80 J=1,M
0050          80 S=S+RR(J)
0051              IF (PRINT) 85,90,85
0052          85 WRITE          (6,2)S
0053          90 RETURN
0054           1 FORMAT(11HOEIGENVALUE,12X,2E20.8)
0055           2 FORMAT(/,36X,20HSUM OF EIGENVALUES =E16.8)
0056              END
```

```
FORTRAN IV G LEVEL 0, MOD 0              HESS            DATE = 68142        04/31/41

0001                SUBROUTINE HESS(A,N,SB,PRINT)
           C        REDUCTION OF THE FULL NXN MATRIX A TO LOWER HESSENBERG FORM BY
           C        ELEMENTARY SIMILARITY TRANSFORMATIONS WITH INTERCHANGES. SB WILL
           C        BECOME THE ABSOLUTE VALUE OF THE GREATEST ELEMENT OF A.
0002                DIMENSION A(1CC,100)
0003                SB=ABS (A(N,N))
0004                N1=N-1
0005                N2=N-2
0006              8 DO 29 J=1,N1
0007                SA=0.
0008                DO 9 K=1,J
0009              9 SA=AMAX1(SA,ABS (A(J,K)))
0010                J1=J+1
0011                J2=J+2
0012                S=ABS (A(J,J1))
0013                L=J1
0014                NJ1=N-J1
0015                IF (NJ1) 10,10,11
0016             10 SB=AMAX1(S,SA,ABS (A(N,N-1)),SB)
0017                IF(S-1.E-8*SA) 2C,20,23
           C        FIND THE PIVOT IN ROW J
C018             11 DO 13 K=J2,N
0019                T=ABS (A(J,K))
0020                IF(T-S)13,13,12
0021             12 L=K
0022                S=T
0023             13 CONTINUE
0024                IF (L-J1)14,18,14
           C        INTERCHANGE ROWS AND COLUMNS J&1 AND L
0025             14 DO 15 K=1,N
0026                T=A(K,J+1)
0027                A(K,J+1)=A(K,L)
0028             15 A(K,L)=T
0029             16 DO 17 K=1,N
0030                T=A(J+1,K)
0031                A(J+1,K)=A(L,K)
0032             17 A(L,K)=T
0033             18 SB=AMAX1(S,SA,ABS (A(N,J)),SB)
           C        SEE IF MATRIX IS REDUCED,THEN FIND MULTIPLIERS AND UPDATE ROW J&1
0034                IF(S-1.E-8*SA)2C,20,21
0035             20 A(J,J+1)=0.
0036                NJ1=C
0037                GO TO 23
0038             21      IF (NJ1) 23,23,215
C039            215 T=A(J,J1)
0C40                DO 22 K=J2,N
0041             22 A(J,K)=A(J,K)/T
0042             23 DO 29 I=1,N
0043                M= MINC (J,I-2)
0044                S=C.
0045                IF(NJ1)26,26,24
0046             24 DO 25 K=J2,N
0C47             25 S=S+A(K,I)*A(J,K)
0048             26 IF(M)29,29,27
0049             27 DO 28 K=1,M
0C50             28 S=S-A(K,I)*A(J1,K+1)
0051             29 A(J1,I)=A(J1,I)+S
0052                IF(PRINT)31,32,31
0053             31 WRITE (6,1)
0054             32 RETURN
0055              1 FORMAT(1HC,48X,22HALMOST TRIANGULAR FORM)
0056                END




FORTRAN IV G LEVEL C, MOD C              TRACE           DATE = 68142        04/31/41

C001                SUBROUTINE TRACE(A,N,PRINT)
C002                DIMENSION A(1CC,100)
C0C3                IF(PRINT)10,30,10
0004             10 S=0.
C005                DO 2C J=1,N
C006             20 S=S+A(J,J)
0CC7                WRITE (6,1) S
C008             30 RETURN
00C9              1 FORMAT(1HC,48X,7HTRACE =E16.8)
0010                END
```

FORTRAN IV G LEVEL 0, MOD 0   LAG   DATE = 68142   04/31/41

```
0001            SUBROUTINE LAG(A,GA,RR,RI,NU,NV,MM,STR,STI,SP1,SP2,PR,SZ)
          C M EIGENVALUES RR(J)&I*RI(J) OF THE PRINCIPAL SUBMATRIX (NU,NU) THROUGH
          C (NV,NV) OF A ARE FOUND BY LAGUERRE'S METHOD. THE SEARCH BEGINS AT STR&
          C STI*I. HOWEVER IF STR IS GTR THAN 1.E35 THEN THE PROGRAM PROVIDES A
          C GUESS AT A ROOT OF MAXIMAL MODULUS.
0002            DIMENSION A(100,100),GA(100),RR(100),RI(100),P(6,101),B(6)
0003            IF(PR)3,4,3
0004          3 WRITE (6,2)
0005          4 SLOW=0.
0006            NUQ=NU-1
0007            ITS=0
0008            EGSUM1=0.
0009            EGSUM2=0.
0010            CUP=.25*SZ
0011            CAP=1.E-16*SZ**2
0012            ZZ=CAP
0013            RNEW=2.
0014            DO 5 J=2,6
0015          5 P(J,NU)=0.
          C
          C      STARTING VALUE,EITHER GIVEN OR THE ITERATE OF INFINITY
          C
0016            IF(STR-1.E+35)6,7,7
0017          6 X=STR
0018            Y=STI
0019            GO TO 14
0020          7 S1R=EGSUM1-SP1
0021            S2R=SP2-EGSUM2
0022            F1=NV-NUQ
0023            IF(ABS (S1R)+ABS (S2R)-1.E-8*ZZ)8,8,9
0024          8 X=CUP
0025            Y=0.
0026            GO TO 14
0027          9 DR=(F1-1.)*(F1*S2R-S1R**2)
0028            ER=SQRT (ABS (DR))
0029            IF(DR)10,11,11
0030         10 X=-S1R/F1
0031            Y=ER/F1
0032            GO TO 12
0033         11 X=-(S1R+SIGN (ER,S1R))/F1
0034            Y=0.
0035         12 IF(NUQ-NU+ITS)13,14,14
0036         13 X=1.75*X
0037            Y=1.75*Y
          C
          C      EVALUATE CHARACTERISTIC POLYNOMIAL AND DERIVATIVES
          C
0038         14 M=6
0039            P(1,NU)=1.0
0040            IO=0
0041            IF(ABS (Y)-1.E-5*ABS (X))15,19,19
0042         15 Y=0.
0043            M=3
0044            DO 18 J=4,6
0045         18 B(J)=0.
0046         19          DO 26 K=NU,NV
0047               DO 26 L=1,M
0048            IS=ISIGN (1,3-L)
0049            L1=L+3*IS
0050         20 R=-X*P(L,K)+Y*FLOAT (IS)*P(L1,K)-FLOAT ( MOD (L-1,3))*P(L-1,K)
0051            DO 21 J=NU,K
0052         21 R=R+P(L,J)*A(K,J)
0053            P(L,K+1)=-R/GA(K)
0054               IF (OVFL) 22,26,22
0055         22 OVFL=0.
0056            KP1=K+1
0057            IO=IO+1
0058               DO 24 I=NU,KP1
0059               DO 24 J=1,M
0060         24 P(J,I)=P(J,I)*1.E-20
0061            GO TO 20
0062         26 CONTINUE
0063         29 R=0.
0064            DO 30 J=1,M
0065            B(J)=P(J,NV+1)
```

```
0066              30 R=AMAX1(R,ABS (B(J)))
              C
              C     SCALE DOWN IF NECESSARY
              C
0067                 IF (R-1.E+18) 33,33,31
0068              31 DO 32 J=1,M
0069              32 B(J)=B(J)*1.E-22
0070              33 ITS=ITS+1
0071                 ABZZ=X**2+Y**2
0072                 ZZ=AMAX1(ABZZ,1.E-6*CAP)
0073                 G1=B(1)**2+B(4)**2
0074                 G2=B(2)**2+B(5)**2
0075                 G3=B(3)**2+B(6)**2
0076                 IF(PR)332,34,332
0077             332 WRITE           (6,96)X,Y,G1,G2,G3,IO
              C
              C     FIND THE CONTRIBUTIONS Q1,Q2 TO S1,S2 OF THE COMPUTED EIGENVALUES
              C
0078              34 Q1R=0.
0079                 Q1I=0.
0080                 Q2R=C.
0081                 Q2I=C.
0082                 VNEAR=C.
0083                 IF(NUQ-NU)40,35,35
0084              35 DO 38 J=NU,NUQ
0085                 DR=RR(J)-X
0086                 DI=RI(J)-Y
0087                 D2=DR**2+DI**2
0088                 IF(D2-1.E-14*ZZ)36,36,37
0089              36 VNEAR=1.
0090                 GO TO 41
0091              37 DR=DR/D2
0092                 DI=-DI/D2
0093                 Q1R=Q1R+DR
0094                 Q1I=Q1I+DI
0095                 Q2R=Q2R+DR**2-DI**2
0096              38 Q2I=Q2I+2.*DR*DI
0097              40 IF(G1-G2*ZZ*1.E-14)41,41,42
0098              41 MARK=1
0099                 GO TO 73
              C
              C     FIND S1 AND S2 THE LOGARITHMIC DERIVATIVES OF THE POLYNOMIAL
              C
0100              42 IF(Y)44,43,44
0101              43 T1R=B(2)/B(1)
0102                 T1I=C.
0103                 T2R=B(3)/B(1)
0104                 T2I=C.
0105                 GO TO 45
0106              44 T1R=(B(2)*B(1)+B(5)*B(4))/G1
0107                 T1I=(B(5)*B(1)-B(2)*B(4))/G1
0108                 T2R=(B(3)*B(1)+B(6)*B(4))/G1
0109                 T2I=(B(6)*B(1)-B(3)*B(4))/G1
0110              45 S1R=T1R+Q1R
0111                 S1I=T1I+Q1I
0112                 S2R=T1R**2-T1I**2-T2R-Q2R
0113                 S2I=2.*T1R*T1I-T2I-Q2I
              C
              C     FIND THE NEXT ITERATE USING LAGUERRE'S FORMULA
              C
0114                 MARK=2
0115              46 G=NV-NUQ
0116              47 IF(G-2.)53,53,48
0117              48 IF(ITS-1)51,51,49
0118              49 IF(Y-ABS (DELX)-ABS (DELY))51,51,50
0119              50 S1I=S1I+.5/Y
0120                 S2R=S2R+.25/Y**2
0121                 G=G-1.
0122              51 IF(SLOW)53,53,52
0123              52 H=.5*(G-2.)
0124                 GO TO 54
0125              53 H=G-1.
0126              54 DR=H*(G*S2R-S1R**2+S1I**2)
0127                 DI=H*(G*S2I-2.*S1R*S1I)
0128                 IF(DI)56,55,56
0129              55 T=SQRT (ABS (DR))
0130                 S=AMAX1(C.,SIGN (1.,DR))
```

FORTRAN IV G LEVEL 0, MOD 0   LAG   DATE = 68142   04/31/41

```
0131              ER=T*S
0132              EI=T*(1.-S)
0133              GO TO 57
0134         56 CALL CXSQRT(DR,DI,ER,EI)
0135         57  IF(S1R*ER+S1I*EI)58,59,59
0136         58 ER=-ER
0137              EI=-EI
0138         59 DR=S1R+ER
0139              DI=S1I+EI
0140              D2=DR**2+DI**2
0141              DELX=-G*DR/D2
0142              X=X+DELX
0143              DELY=G*DI/D2
0144              Y=Y+DELY
0145              DELNEW=DELX**2+DELY**2
0146              ABZ2=X**2+Y**2
0147              ZZ=AMAX1(ABZ2,1.E-6*CAP)
0148              IF(ITS-4)70,65,60
0149         60 IF(DELNEW-1.E-12*ZZ)70,70,61
        C
        C          TEST FOR A CYCLE
        C
0150         61 IF((OLDELX+DELX)**2+(OLDELY+DELY)**2-.11*DELOLD) 62,65,65
0151         62 IF(SLOW)63,63,65
0152         63 IF(ONCE)64,64,65
0153         64 ONCE=1.
0154              DELOLD=SZ*FLOAT (NV-NU)
0155              ROLD=SZ
0156              GO TO 7
        C
        C          TEST FOR LINEAR CONVERGENCE
        C
0157         65 RNEW=DELNEW/DELOLD
0158              IF(RNEW-.6*ROLD)70,66,66
0159         66 MARK=3
0160              IF(SLOW)67,67,69
0161         67 IF(G-3.)71,71,68
0162         68 X=X-DELX
0163              Y=Y-DELY
0164              SLOW=1.
0165              GO TO 47
0166         69 SLOW=0.
0167              GO TO 71
        C
        C          TEST FOR AN EIGENVALUE
        C
0168         70 IF(DELNEW-1.E-7*ZZ)73,73,71
0169         71 ONCE=0.
0170         72 DELOLD=DELNEW
0171              ROLD=RNEW
0172              OLDELX=DELX
0173              OLDELY=DELY
0174              IF(ITS-15)14,14,77
        C
        C          DO WE HAVE A COMPLEX APPROACH TO A REAL ZERO
        C
0175         73 SLOW=0.
0176              IF(Y)74,77,74
0177         74 IF(G2*Y**2-G1)75,77,77
0178         75 IF(ONCE)76,76,77
0179         76 ONCE=1.
0180              Y=0.
0181              GO TO 72
        C
        C          ACCEPT X&I*Y AS AN EIGENVALUE
        C
0182         77 NUQ=NUQ+1
0183              IF(ABZ2-1.E-12*CAP)78,79,79
0184         78 X=0
0185              Y=0
0186         79 RR(NUQ)=X
0187              IF(ABS (Y)-1.E-6*ABS (X))80,80,81
0188         80 Y=0
0189         81 IF(NUQ-NU)83,83,82
0190         82 IF(RI(NUQ-1))83,83,84
0191         83 Y=ABS (Y)
0192              GO TO 85
0193         84  IF ((X-RR(NUQ-1))**2+(ABS (Y)-RI(NUQ-1))**2-1.E-3*ZZ) 845,845,83
```

```
FORTRAN IV G LEVEL C, MOD 0                LAG              DATE = 68142           04/31/41
      0194              845 RR(NUQ-1)=X
      C195                  Y=-ABS (Y)
      0196                  RI(NUQ-1)=-Y
      0197               85 RI(NUQ)=Y
      0198                  IF(PR)86,87,86
      0199               86 WRITE                 (6,1)RR(NUQ),RI(NUQ),ITS,MARK
      02C0               87 ITS=C
      0201                  RNEW=2.
      0202                  CAP=AMAX1(ABZ2,CAP)
      0203                  EGSUM1=EGSUM1+X
      0204                  EGSUM2=EGSUM2+X**2-Y**2
      0205                  IF(NUQ-MM) 88,95,95
      0206               88 IF (Y) 9C,91,89
      0207               89 Y=-Y
      0208                  GO TO 14
      0209               90 RI(NUQ-1)=ABS (Y)
                       C
                       C   TAKE A NEWTON STEP FROM X&I*Y TO THE NEXT ROOT
                       C
      0210               91 ONCE=0.
      0211                  IF(NV-NUQ-3)7,7,92
      0212               92 IF(VNEAR) 925,925,7
      0213              925 IF((Q1R**2+Q1I**2)*ZZ-1.E+6)93,7,7
      0214               93 DR=B(3)+2.*(B(2)*Q1R-B(5)*Q1I)
      0215                  DI=B(6)+2.*(B(2)*Q1I+B(5)*Q1R)
      0216                  D2=DR**2+DI**2
      0217                  IF(D2)7,7,94
      0218               94 X=X-2.*(DR*B(2)+DI*B(5))/D2
      0219                  Y=ABS (Y-2.*(DR*B(5)-DI*B(2))/D2)
      0220                  IF(X**2+Y**2-4.*CAP)14,14,7
      0221               95 RETURN
      0222                1 FORMAT(11HOEIGENVALUE12X,2E20.8,12X,I3,17H ITERATIONS,TEST I1//)
      C223               96 FORMAT( 8HCITERATE20X,E15.8,5X,E15.8,8X,3E15.4,I4)
      0224                2 FORMAT(1HC50X,19HLAGUERRE ITERATIONS//31X,9HREAL PART10X,10HIMAG.
                         1PART19X,4HP**2,10X,5HP'**2,10X,6HP'**2,3X,4HOVFL)
      0225                  END


FORTRAN IV G LEVEL 0, MOD 0               CXSQRT            DATE = 68142           04/31/41
      0001                  SUBROUTINE CXSQRT(A,B,X,Y)
      0002                  F=AMAX1(ABS (A),ABS (B))
      0003                  F=F*SQRT ((A/F)**2+(B/F)**2)
      0004                  IF(A)1,1,2
      CCC5                1 Y=SQRT ((F-A)*.5)
      0006                  X=.5*B/Y
      0007                  IF(X)4,3,3
      0008                4 X=-X
      0009                  Y=-Y
      0010                  GO TO 3
      0011                2 X=SQRT ((F+A)*.5)
      0012                  Y=.5*B/X
      0013                3 RETURN
      C014                  END
```

References

C.1   W. H. Ohm, *Applications of Computer-Aided Circuit Design and Analysis*, SB Thesis, M.I.T., June, 1968.

APPENDIX D

APL Program for Finding the Natural Frequencies of a Network

D.1 Examples of Program Use

The following examples illustrate three ways in which input data can be supplied to this program. A reproduction of the computer console input and output material is given in each case. The determinant used for the first three examples is from Section 15.1.2.

In the first input method, applicable to RC networks, the user types NATFREQS $\iota 0$. The computer responds with instructions as shown. The symbol S11 means the capacitative part of the y_{11} in the determinant; R11 indicated the real part of y_{11}, i.e., the conductance. Thus the data is put into the computer as a series of numbers: the complex coefficients of the determinant, row by row, in each case entering first the capacitive part, then the conductance. When finished supplying input data, start a new line, and type 'E'. The computer will then calculate the natural frequencies.

The second method is essentially the same as the first, except by typing NATFREQS $\iota 1$, the computer goes directly to the input part of the previous program, without giving instructions.

In the third method of supplying data to the computer, the user structures the determinant himself. For RC networks, the data is formed into an array of two matrices. The first $n \times n$ matrix contains all of the capacitive terms in the determinant; the second $n \times n$ matrix contains all the conductive terms. To form this array, we use the ρ command in APL. The user first types in, in vector form, all of the capacitive parts of each term in the determinant, row by row, followed by all of the conductance terms. In the example shown below, this has been accomplished in two vectors. In larger networks, several vectors will be needed. These vectors are then structured into a two plane, n column, n row array by the ρ command, operating on the vectors defined above, catenated together. In the example, the array so formed was named VV. To check on the accuracy of the input procedure, the user requested a print-out of the array by typing VV. (The resulting array should be compared with the original determinant as given in Eqs. 15.7.) To find the natural frequencies, type NATFREQS VV.

For networks containing inductance as well as capacitance and resistance, it is necessary to follow a slightly different procedure. We form an array with *three* planes, rather than two, a capacitive $n \times n$ matrix, a conductive $n \times n$ matrix (as above) and a third $n \times n$ matrix containing all of the inductive terms (in units of reciprocal microhenries.) If we call this $3 \times n \times n$ array RLC, then the natural frequencies can be found by calling NATFREQS ONEOVERS RLC.

```
      ⍝ VECTOR INPUT WITH INSTRUCTIONS

      NATFREQS ⍳0
TYPE IN MATRIX AS A VECTOR S11 R11 S12 R12 S13 R13 ETC. YOU MAY CARRIAGE RETURN.
VECTOR WILL CATENATE.  WHEN FINISHED, CARRIAGE RETURN, TYPE 'E' AND CARRIAGE RETURN.
□:
      105 8.55 ‾5 0 0 0 0 0 ‾5 400 105 404 ‾100 ‾404 0 0
□:
      0 0 ‾100 ‾4 105 54 ‾5 0 0 0 0 ‾400 ‾5 400 5 5
□:
      'E'
REAL      IMAGINARY

 ‾0.08061157158     0
 ‾0.6435666794      0
 ‾4.04630002        0
 ‾16.45502173       0



      ⍝ VECTOR INPUT WITHOUT INSTRUCTIONS

      NATFREQS ⍳1
□:
      105 8.55 ‾5 0 0 0 0 0 ‾5 400 105 404 ‾100 ‾404 0 0
□:
      0 0 ‾100 ‾4 105 54 ‾5 0 0 0 0 ‾400 ‾5 400 5 5
□:
      'E'
REAL      IMAGINARY

 ‾0.08061157158     0
 ‾0.6435666794      0
 ‾4.04630002        0
 ‾16.45502173       0



      ⍝ DIRECT MATRIX INPUT

      V1←105 ‾5 0 0 ‾5 105 ‾100 0 0 ‾100 105 ‾5 0 0 ‾5 5

      V2←8.55 0 0 0 400 404 ‾404 0 0 ‾4 54 0 0 ‾400 400 5
      VV←2 4 4⍴V1,V2
      VV

 105           ‾5             0             0
  ‾5          105          ‾100             0
   0         ‾100          105            ‾5
   0            0            ‾5            5

 8.55           0             0             0
 400          404          ‾404            0
   0           ‾4           54             0
   0         ‾400          400             5
      NATFREQS VV
REAL        IMAGINARY

 ‾0.08061157158     0
 ‾0.6435666794      0
 ‾4.04630002        0
 ‾16.45502173       0



      ⍝ INPUT METHOD FOR RLC NETWORKS

      V←2 0 0 0  3 ‾2 ‾2 2  0 0 0 .5
      RLC←3 2 2⍴V
      RLC

 2             0
 0             0

  3            ‾2
 ‾2             2

 0             0
 0             0.5
      NATFREQS ONEOVERS RLC
REAL        IMAGINARY

 ‾0.375         ‾0.4841229183
 ‾0.375          0.4841229183
```

D.2   The Program

```
      ∇NATFREQS[[]]∇
    ∇ Z←NATFREQS M;MT;N;K;HFRS;I;GOTO
[1]    →(L10,L11,L9,L3)[1++/(+/ρM)≥ι3]
[2]    L9:M←TYPIN
[3]    →L3
[4]    L10:'TYPE IN MATRIX AS A VECTOR S11 R11 S12 R12 S13 R13 ETC. YOU MAY CARRIAGE RETURN.'
[5]    'VECTOR WILL CATENATE.  WHEN FINISHED, CARRIAGE RETURN, TYPE ''E'' AND CARRIAGE RETURN.'
[6]    L11:M←ι0
[7]    L6:MT←[]
[8]    →L5×ι+/MT='E'
[9]    M←M,MT
[10]   →L6
[11]   L5:N←⌈((⌈0.5×ρM)*0.5
[12]   MM←M← 2 3 1 ⍉(N,N,2)ρM
[13]   L3:GOTO←N+(ρM)[2]
[14]   K←1
[15]   REDUCE2
[16]   →L1×ι0=GOTO←M-HFRS←I
[17]   M←⍉⌽[2]⌽[3]M
[18]   K←2
[19] . REDUCE2
[20]   →L2×ιGOTO≠I
[21]   M←(⍉⌽[2]⌽[3]M)[;ιHFRS;ιHFRS]
[22]   →L3
[23]   L1:→L4×ιN=0
[24]   'REAL         IMAGINARY'
[25]   W←M
[26]   Z←LAG POLYNOMIAL←FRAME-M[2;;]
[27]   →0
[28]   L2:'MATRIX IS DEGENERATE'
[29]   L4:'NO NATURAL FREQUENCIES'
[30]   Z←ι0
    ∇
```

```
      ∇ R←LAG PP;P;N;OK;X;DS1;RS;CS;DS;B;D;NMIS;NUM1;T;H;PS;CT;CS1;DS2;J
[1]    CT←1E¯10
[2]    P←((2,ρPP)ρPP,0×PP)÷1
[3]    R←ι0
[4]    LAG6:NMIS←(-NMIS)+NUM1←N×NMIS←¯1+N←(ρP)[2]
[5]    →LAG8×ιN<2
[6]    OK←0
[7]    X←P[;2]
[8]    LAG3:DS1←RS←CS←DS← 0 0
[9]    R←ι0
[10]   T←CX X
[11]   J←1
[12]   →LAG2
[13]   LAG1:R←R,RS
[14]   LAG2:RS←P[;J]+T+.×PS
[15]   CS←RS+T+.×CS1←CS
[16]   DS2←DS1
[17]   DS←CS+T+.×DS1←DS
[18]   →LAG1×ιN≥J←J+1
[19]   B← 2 1 ⍉((N-1),2)ρR
[20]   →LAG5×ι1|OK
[21]   H←(NMIS×(CX CS1)+.×CS1)-NUM1×(PS←CX RS)+.×2×DS2
[22]   T←¯1+2×CS1[1]>0
[23]   D←CS1+T×SQRT H
[24]   D←N×PS+.× 1 ¯1 ×D÷+/D×D
[25]   X←X-D
[26]   →LAG3×ιCT≤+/D×D
[27]   OK←1
[28]   →LAG3
[29]   LAG5:R←R,X
[30]   P←R
[31]   →LAG6×ι0=|X[2]
[32]   →LAG7×ι0<OK←-OK
[33]   X← 1 ¯1 ×X
[34]   N←N-1
[35]   →LAG3
[36]   LAG7:P← 1 0 \[1]1 0 /[1]R
[37]   →LAG6
[38]   LAG8:R←((0.5×ρR),2)ρR
    ∇
```

```
      ∇ Z←SQRT H;C;T;E1
[1]     Z←(T*0.5)×(1,C÷|C←H[2])×(C×1E¯14<C←0.5×(1-C),1+C←-H[1]÷T←T×(+/E1×E1+H÷T←[/|H)*0.5)*0.5
      ∇

      ∇ZSRT[□]∇
      ∇ R←ZSRT X;I;J;K
[1]     R←(ρX)ρ0
[2]     J←1
[3]     I←X[;1]ₗ⌊/X[;1]
[4]     R[J;]←X[I;]
[5]     X←(I≠ₗ(ρX)[1])/[1]X
[6]     J←J+1
[7]     →(0≠(ρX)[1])/3
      ∇


      ∇ REDUCE2;MT;X;Y;SV;MAX;XMT
[1]     I←0
[2]     L8:MT←|M[K;I+ₗH-I;I+ₗGOTO-I]
[3]     →0×ₗ0=MAX←[/[/MT
[4]     X←I+XMT←([/[2]MT)ₗMAX
[5]     Y←I+MT[XMT;]ₗMAX
[6]     I←I+1
[7]     M[;I,X;]←M[;X,I;]
[8]     M[;I,Y]←M[;;Y,I]
[9]     M[;I;]←M[;I;]÷M[K;I;I]
[10]    SV←M
[11]    M←M-(2 3 1 ⍉(M[K;;I]×~I=ₗ(ρM)[2])∘.×(2 1 ⍉M[;I;]))
[12]    M[K;;I]←I=ₗ(ρM)[2]
[13]    M←M×(|H)>|SV×1E¯11
[14]    →L8×ₗI<GOTO
      ∇


      ∇CX[□]∇
      ∇ Z←CX R
[1]     Z← 2 2 ρ(1 ¯1 ×R),⌽R
      ∇

      ∇FRAME[□]∇
      ∇ R←FRAME A;I;J;K;N;TR
[1]     N←⌊/ρA
[2]     J←I+(ₗN)∘.=ₗH
[3]     R←K←1
[4]     J←J-I×TR←(+/ 1 1 ⍉J+A+.×J)÷K
[5]     R←R,-TR
[6]     →(N≥K←K+1)/4
      ∇



      ∇MODNATFREQS[□]∇
      ∇ Z←MODNATFREQS M;SUM;SUMSQS;V1;E1;E2;E3;E4
[1]     Z←NATFREQS M
[2]     Z
[3]     →0×ₗ0=+/ρZ
[4]     V1←+/Z×Z
[5]     ''
[6]     'SUM OF OPEN CIRCUIT TIME CONSTANTS'
[7]     □←SUM←-+/Z[;1]÷V1
[8]     ''
[9]     'ω(.707)~'
[10]    □←E1←(+/(-/Z×Z)÷V1×V1)*-0.5
[11]    ''
[12]    'F(.707)~'
[13]    E1÷6.283185307000004
[14]    Z←ₗ0
      ∇

      ∇ONEOVERS[□]∇
      ∇ Z←ONEOVERS M;U;MT;I1;J1;D;LI;JI;LJ;UI;UJ;IS;JS;IDENT;E1;E2;E3;E4
[1]     U←∨/[1]0≠M[3;;]
[2]     MT←U/[2]M[3;;]
[3]     I1←(ρM)[2]
[4]     J1←(ρM)[3]
[5]     D←+/U
[6]     LI←I1÷D
[7]     LJ←J1÷D
[8]     UI←(1+0×ₗI1),0×ₗD
[9]     UJ←(1+0×ₗJ1),0×ₗD
[10]    M←UJ\[3]UI\[2]M[1 2 ;;]
[11]    M[2;ₗI1;J1+ₗD]←MT
[12]    IDENT←(ₗD)∘.=ₗD
[13]    M[1;I1+ₗD;J1+ₗD]←-IDENT
[14]    M[2;I1+ₗD;ₗJ1]←U\IDENT
[15]    Z←M
      ∇
```

References

D.1   A. D. Falkoff and K. E. Iverson, *APL\360 User's Manual*, IBM, Thomas J. Watson Research Center, 1968.

D.2   P. Berry, *APL\360 Primer*, IBM Corporation, 1969.

INDEX